College Calculus with Analytic Geometry

This book is in the

ADDISON-WESLEY SERIES IN MATHEMATICS

Lynn H. Loomis
Consulting Editor

College Calculus with Analytic Geometry

by
MURRAY H. PROTTER
University of California
Berkeley, California

and

CHARLES B. MORREY, JR.
University of California
Berkeley, California

ADDISON-WESLEY PUBLISHING COMPANY
READING, MASSACHUSETTS · PALO ALTO · LONDON · DON MILLS, ONTARIO

Preface

At many colleges and universities it is customary to have two calculus courses. One course, planned for the majority of the students, treats topics in calculus and analytic geometry in the usual way, while the other, designed for honor students, is devoted to a rigorous and sophisticated development of the subject. While it is true that at the end of the third or fourth semester the honor students have covered all the material in the regular course (and indeed much more), it is usually the case that by the end of the first of these semesters the two courses have covered quite different selections of topics in calculus and analytic geometry. By the end of the first semester it invariably turns out that some students who are in the honor group more properly belong in the regular course; moreover, the best of the students who have been taking the standard material not only have the ability to master the more penetrating aspects of calculus but are often anxious to do so.

The task of shifting students from one course to the other after only one semester or less becomes rather difficult, and frequently the student who makes the transfer is penalized. Often even the talented beginner is reluctant to embark on the honors program: if he does not do well he discovers not only that his grade has suffered but also that his background is not adequate for him to transfer to the regular course. A shift in the opposite direction is a problem also. The student who has done well enough in the regular course to transfer to the honor section hesitates to do so because he has not studied the same material as those who have already been doing honors work for a full semester.

This text, together with *University Calculus*, by Charles B. Morrey, Jr.,* is designed to solve the problem described above. The topics taken up in this volume meet the needs of the majority of students taking the customary course (twelve semester hours) of calculus and analytic geometry at a college or university. This book leans heavily on the intuitive approach, gives many illustrative examples, emphasizes physical applications wherever suitable, and has a large selection of graded exercises. Definitions and theorems are stated with care and proofs of simple theorems are given in full. It is a companion to Morrey's *University Calculus*, which presents the same material (except for the last chapter) in the same order, but at a level suitable for the honor student. Morrey's text goes into the theory in much more detail, has complete proofs of many of the more difficult theorems, and in general gives a rigorous, soundly based treatment of calculus and analytic geometry. If both texts are used, one for the regular group and the other for the honors group, there should be little difficulty in shifting students back and forth depending on their ability to absorb rigorous mathematics.

---

* Reading, Mass.: Addison-Wesley Publishing Co., 1962.

At colleges where there are not enough students to form an honors group or where it is not the custom to do so, this text could be used, with Morrey's *University Calculus* recommended to those students who wish to do outside reading. Since both books use the same terminology and notation, the good student will be able to concentrate on mastering the theory. (When an unrelated book is used for outside reading the student may waste a great deal of time transposing the presentation into something he understands.)

Chapter 1 discusses inequalities, with emphasis on the solution of inequalities which contain the absolute-value symbol. Chapters 2 and 3 take up functions, functional notation, the elements of analytic geometry and, in particular, systems of linear inequalities in the plane.

Chapter 4, entitled "Preview of the Calculus," treats the fundamental notions of limit, differentiation, and integration in an informal way. This helps meet the need of many students of physics and engineering who are required to know as early as possible some of the elementary processes of calculus.

A rather thorough treatment of limits is given in Chapter 5. The definition of limit is illustrated geometrically, and the theorems on limits and continuity are stated and discussed.

Chapters 6 and 7 give a traditional development of the differentiation of algebraic functions and applications to problems of maxima and minima, related rates, and so forth.

The notion of area (Jordan content) is defined carefully in Chapter 8. This leads to the definition of integral and the Fundamental Theorem of Calculus. Applications are made to problems of liquid pressure, work, and so forth.

Chapters 9 and 10 resume the work on analytic geometry which was begun in Chapter 3. The methods of calculus are here used to great advantage. The amount of material on conics and related subjects is at least as great as that found in many texts devoted to analytic geometry alone.

The natural logarithm is defined by the integral and the exponential function is defined as its inverse. This approach is being used experimentally (and with apparent success) for students in eleventh-grade algebra and trigonometry classes under the SMSG program.

Vectors in the plane are the subject of Chapter 14 and vectors in space are treated in Chapter 18. Certain logical difficulties are avoided by defining a vector as an equivalence class of directed line segments. Furthermore, the discussion of equivalence classes puts this abstract concept in a natural setting. The material of these chapters is relatively independent of the rest of the book and could easily be omitted. On the other hand, for those who wish to introduce vectors early in calculus, much of Chapter 14 could be inserted after Chapter 6.

Chapter 17 is devoted to solid analytic geometry with coordinates used throughout. Once the student has mastered this material, the applications using vector terminology, which appear in Chapter 18, may be attacked with confidence.

The study of infinite series, taken up in Chapter 19, completes the customary elementary course in the calculus of functions of one variable. Chapters 20 and 21 are devoted to the initial topics in the calculus of functions of several variables.

Partial differentiation, line integrals and applications are taken up in Chapter 20. A definition of volume analogous to that given for area is discussed in Chapter 21. The elements of multiple integration with applications to area, volume, and mass are treated. In addition there are a number of physical applications to problems in center of gravity, moment of inertia, and so forth.

The last chapter is devoted to an elementary study of linear algebra. This chapter replaces the unit on differential equations in *University Calculus*. In recent years it has become evident that students in all the sciences have an urgent need for the elements of linear algebra. The presentation here is intended as a beginning study. Students who require or wish additional material would logically proceed to a course devoted entirely to linear algebra.

Although the subject of numerical analysis is not discussed, it is not entirely ignored. There are brief descriptions of the numerical implications of such topics as evaluation of integrals, computation of maxima and minima, solution of linear inequalities, etc. The purpose here is to make the student aware of the impact of digital computers on various branches of analysis. These remarks may be used as a springboard for a more detailed investigation of numerical analysis.

Berkeley, California   M.H.P.
November 1963   C.B.M., Jr.

Contents

Inequalities

1. INEQUALITIES

In elementary algebra and geometry we study equalities almost exclusively. The solution of linear and quadratic algebraic equations, the congruence of geometric figures, and relationships among various trigonometric functions are topics concerned with equality. As we progress in the development of mathematical ideas — especially in that branch of mathematics of which calculus is a part — we shall see that the study of inequalities is both interesting and useful. An inequality is involved when we are more concerned with the approximate size of a quantity than we are with its true value. Since the proofs of some of the most important theorems in calculus depend on certain approximations, it is essential that we develop a facility for working with inequalities.

We shall be concerned with inequalities among real numbers, and we begin by recalling some familiar relationships. Given that a and b are any two real numbers, the symbol

$$a < b$$

means that *a is less than b*. We may also write the same inequality in the *opposite direction*,

$$b > a,$$

which is read *b is greater than a*.

The rules for handling inequalities come from our knowledge of arithmetic and are only slightly more complicated than the ones we learned in algebra for equalities. However, the differences are so important that we state them as four Rules of Inequalities, and they must be learned carefully.

1. If $a < b$ and $b < c$, then $a < c$. In words: *if a is less than b and b is less than c, then a is less than c.*

2. If c is any number and $a < b$, then it is also true that $a + c < b + c$ and $a - c < b - c$. In words: *if the same number is added to or subtracted from each side of an inequality, the result is an inequality in the same direction.*

3. If $a < b$ and $c < d$ then $a + c < b + d$. That is, *inequalities in the same direction may be added.* It is important to note that in general inequalities may *not* be subtracted. For example, $2 < 5$ and $1 < 7$. We can say, by addition, that $3 < 12$, but note that subtraction would state the absurdity that 1 is less than -2.

4. If $a < b$ and c is any positive number,

then $$ac < bc,$$

while if c is a negative number,

then $$ac > bc.$$

In words: *multiplication of both sides of an inequality by the same positive number preserves the direction, while multiplication by a negative number reverses the direction of the inequality.*

Since dividing an inequality by a number d is the same as multiplying it by $1/d$, we see that Rule 4 applies for division as well as for multiplication.

| FIGURE 1–1 | FIGURE 1–2 | FIGURE 1–3 |

From the geometric point of view we associate a horizontal axis with the totality of real numbers. The origin may be selected at any convenient point, with positive numbers to the right and negative numbers to the left (Fig. 1–1). For every real number there will be a corresponding point on the line and, conversely, every point will represent a real number. Then the inequality $a < b$ could be read: *a is to the left of b.* This geometric way of looking at inequalities is frequently of help in solving problems. It is also helpful to introduce the notion of an *interval of numbers* or *points.* If a and b are numbers (as shown in Fig. 1–2), then the *open interval* from a to b is the collection of all numbers which are both larger than a and smaller than b. That is, an open interval consists of all numbers *between a and b.* A number x is between a and b if *both* inequalities $a < x$ and $x < b$ are true. A compact way of writing this is

$$a < x < b.$$

The *closed interval* from a to b consists of all the points between a and b, *including a and b* (Fig. 1–3). Suppose a number x is either equal to a or larger than a, but we don't know which. We write this conveniently as $x \geq a$, which is read: x *is greater than or equal to a.* Similarly, $x \leq b$ is read: x *is less than or equal to b,* and means that x may be either smaller than b or may be b itself. A compact way of designating a closed interval from a to b is to state that it consists of all points x such that

$$a \leq x \leq b.$$

An interval which contains the endpoint b but not a is said to be *half-open on the left.* That is, it consists of all points x such that

$$a < x \leq b.$$

Similarly, an interval containing a but not b is called *half-open on the right*, and we write

$$a \leq x < b.$$

Parentheses and brackets are used as symbols for intervals in the following way:

(a, b) for the open interval: $a < x < b$,
$[a, b]$ for the closed interval: $a \leq x \leq b$,
$(a, b]$ for the interval half-open on the left: $a < x \leq b$,
$[a, b)$ for the interval half-open on the right: $a \leq x < b$.

$$0 \qquad 7$$

FIGURE 1–4

We can extend the idea of an interval of points to cover some unusual cases. Suppose we wish to consider *all* numbers larger than 7. This may be thought of as an interval extending to infinity to the right. (See Fig. 1–4.) Of course, infinity is not a number, but we use the symbol $(7, \infty)$ to represent all numbers larger than 7. We could also write: all numbers x such that

$$7 < x < \infty.$$

In a similar way, the symbol $(-\infty, 12)$ will stand for all numbers less than 12. The double inequality

$$-\infty < x < 12$$

is an equivalent way of representing all numbers x less than 12.

The first-degree equation $3x + 7 = 19$ has a unique solution, $x = 4$. The quadratic equation $x^2 - x - 2 = 0$ has two solutions, $x = -1$ and $x = 2$. The trigonometric equation $\sin x = \frac{1}{2}$ has an infinite number of solutions: $x = 30°, 150°, 390°, 510°, \ldots$. *The solution of an inequality* involving a single unknown, say x, *is the collection of all numbers which make the inequality a true statement.* Sometimes this is called the *solution set*. For example, the inequality

$$3x - 7 < 8$$

has as its solution *all* numbers less than 5. To demonstrate this we argue in the following way. If x is a number which satisfies the above inequality we can, by Rule 2, add 7 to both sides of the inequality and obtain a true statement. That is, we have

$$3x - 7 + 7 < 8 + 7, \quad \text{or} \quad 3x < 15.$$

Now, dividing both sides by 3 (Rule 4), we obtain

$$x < 5,$$

and we observe that *if* x is a solution, *then* it is less than 5. Strictly speaking, however, we have not *proved* that every number which is less than 5 is a solution.

In an actual proof we would begin by supposing that x is any number less than 5; that is,

$$x < 5.$$

We multiply both sides by 3 (Rule 4) and then subtract 7 (Rule 2) to get

$$3x - 7 < 8,$$

the original inequality. Since the condition that x is less than 5 implies the original inequality, we have proved the result. The important thing to notice is that the proof consisted of *reversing* the steps of the original argument which led to the solution $x < 5$ in the first place. So long as each of the steps we take is *reversible*, the above procedure is completely satisfactory so far as obtaining solutions is concerned. The step going from $3x - 7 < 8$ to $3x < 15$ is reversible, since these two inequalities are equivalent. Similarly, the inequalities $3x < 15$ and $x < 5$ are equivalent. Finally, note that we can say that the solution set consists of all numbers in the interval $(-\infty, 5)$.

Methods for the solution of various types of simple algebraic inequalities are shown in the following examples, which should be studied carefully.

EXAMPLE 1. Solve for x:

$$-7 - 3x < 5x + 29.$$

Solution. Subtract $5x$ from both sides, getting

$$-7 - 8x < 29.$$

Multiply both sides by -1, reversing the direction of the inequality, to obtain

$$7 + 8x > -29.$$

Subtracting 7 from both sides yields $8x > -36$, and dividing by 8 gives the solution

$$x > -\tfrac{9}{2},$$

or stated in interval form: all x in the interval $(-\tfrac{9}{2}, \infty)$.

To verify the correctness of the result, it is necessary to perform the above steps in reverse order. However, the observation as we go along that each individual step is reversible is sufficient to check the validity of the answer.

EXAMPLE 2. Solve for x $(x \neq 0)$:

$$\frac{3}{x} < 5.$$

Solution. We have an immediate inclination to multiply both sides by x. However, since we don't know in advance whether x is positive or negative, we must proceed cautiously. We do this by considering two cases: (1) x is positive, and (2) x is negative.

Case 1. Suppose $x > 0$. Then multiplying by x preserves the direction of the inequality (Rule 4), and we get

$$3 < 5x.$$

Dividing by 5, we find that $x > \frac{3}{5}$. This means that we must find all numbers which satisfy both of the inequalities

$$x > 0 \qquad \text{and} \qquad x > \tfrac{3}{5}.$$

Clearly, any number greater than $\frac{3}{5}$ is also positive, and the solution in Case 1 consists of all x in the interval $(\frac{3}{5}, \infty)$.

Case 2. $x < 0$. Multiplying by x reverses the direction of the inequality. We have

$$3 > 5x,$$

and therefore $\frac{3}{5} > x$. We seek all numbers x, such that *both* of the inequalities

$$x < 0 \qquad \text{and} \qquad x < \tfrac{3}{5}$$

hold. The solution in Case 2 is the collection of all x in the interval $(-\infty, 0)$. A way of combining the answers in the two cases is to state that the solution consists of all numbers x *not* in the closed interval $[0, \frac{3}{5}]$. (See Fig. 1–5.)

EXAMPLE 3. Solve for x ($x \neq -2$):

$$\frac{2x - 3}{x + 2} < \frac{1}{3}.$$

Solution. As in Example 2, we must consider two cases, according to whether $x + 2$ is positive or negative.

Case 1. $x + 2 > 0$. We multiply by $3(x + 2)$, which is positive, getting

$$6x - 9 < x + 2.$$

Adding $9 - x$ to both sides, we have

$$5x < 11, \qquad \text{from which} \qquad x < \tfrac{11}{5}.$$

Since we have already assumed that $x + 2 > 0$, and since we must have $x < \frac{11}{5}$, we see that x must be larger than -2 and smaller than $\frac{11}{5}$. That is, the solution consists of all x in the interval $(-2, \frac{11}{5})$.

Case 2. $x + 2 < 0$. Again multiplying by $3(x + 2)$ and reversing the inequality, we obtain

$$6x - 9 > x + 2,$$

or $5x > 11$ and $x > \frac{11}{5}$. In this case, x must be less than -2 and greater than $\frac{11}{5}$, which is impossible. Combining the cases, we get as the solution all numbers in $(-2, \frac{11}{5})$. See Fig. 1–6.

0 $\frac{3}{5}$	-2 0 $\frac{11}{5}$
FIGURE 1–5	FIGURE 1–6

EXERCISES

Solve for x:

1. $3x - 2 < 5$

2. $-2x + \frac{7}{3} < 4 + x$

3. $\frac{8}{3}x + \dfrac{7 - x}{2} < -1$

4. $2x - 6 < \dfrac{3x + 8}{5}$

5. $2x + \dfrac{6 - 3x}{4} < 4$

6. $x - 8 < \dfrac{3x}{4} + \dfrac{2 - x}{5}$

7. $\dfrac{4}{x} < \dfrac{3}{5}$

8. $\dfrac{x - 1}{x} < 4$

9. $\dfrac{x + 3}{x - 2} < 5$

10. $\dfrac{2}{x} - 3 < \dfrac{4}{x} + 1$

11. $\dfrac{x + 3}{x - 4} < -2$

12. $\dfrac{2 - x}{x + 1} < \dfrac{3}{2}$

13. $\dfrac{x}{3 - x} < 2$

14. $\dfrac{x - 2}{x + 3} < \dfrac{x + 1}{x}$

In problems 15 through 21, find the values of x, if any, for which both inequalities hold.

15. $2x - 7 < 5 - x$ and $3 - 4x < \frac{5}{3}$

16. $3x - 8 < 5(2 - x)$ and $2(3x + 4) - 4x + 7 < 5 + x$

17. $\dfrac{2x + 6}{3} - \dfrac{x}{4} < 5$ and $15 - 3x < 4 + 2x$

18. $3 - 6x < 2(x + 5)$ and $7(2 - x) < 3x + 8$

19. $\dfrac{2}{x - 1} < 4$ and $\dfrac{3}{x - 2} < 7$ 20. $\dfrac{x - 2}{x + 1} < 3$ and $\dfrac{3 - x}{x - 2} < 5$

21. $\dfrac{3}{x} < 5$ and $x + 2 < 7 - 3x$

22. Show how Rule 3 for inequalities may be derived from Rules 1 and 2.

23. Multiplication of inequalities.

    (a) If a, b, c, d are all positive numbers, and if $a < b$ and $c < d$, then show that $ac < bd$.

    (b) State the most general circumstances in which the hypotheses $a < b$, $c < d$ imply $ac < bd$.

    (c) If $a < b$ and $c < d$, when is it true that $ac > bd$?

2. ABSOLUTE VALUE

If a is any positive number, the *absolute value* of a is defined to be a itself. If a is negative, the absolute value of a is defined to be $-a$. The absolute value of zero is zero. The symbol for the absolute value of a is $|a|$. In other words,

$$|a| = a \qquad \text{if} \quad a > 0,$$
$$|a| = -a \qquad \text{if} \quad a < 0,$$
$$|0| = 0.$$

For example,

$$|7| = 7, \qquad |-13| = 13, \qquad |2 - 5| = 3.$$

This rather simple idea has important consequences but, before we can consider them, we must discuss methods of solving equations and inequalities involving absolute values.

EXAMPLE 1. Solve for x: $|x - 7| = 3$.

Solution. This equation, according to the definition of absolute value, expresses the fact that $x - 7$ must be 3 or -3, since in either case the absolute value is 3. If $x - 7 = 3$, we have $x = 10$; and if $x - 7 = -3$, we have $x = 4$. We see that there are *two* values of x which solve the equation: $x = 4, 10$.

EXAMPLE 2. Solve for x: $|5 - 3x| = -2$.

This clearly has no solution, since the absolute value can never be negative.

EXAMPLE 3. Solve for x: $|2x - 6| = |4 - 5x|$.

Solution. The two possibilities are

$$2x - 6 = 4 - 5x$$

and

$$2x - 6 = -(4 - 5x).$$

Solving each of these for x, we obtain the two solutions

$$x = \tfrac{10}{7}, -\tfrac{2}{3}.$$

If x is any number which satisfies the condition that $|x| < 4$, we see that x could be any number in the interval extending from -4 to $+4$ (Fig. 1–7). Or, using the symbol for intervals, x must lie in the interval $(-4, 4)$. Sometimes a statement such as $|x| < 4$ is used to denote the interval $(-4, 4)$. In terms of inequalities without absolute value signs, the statement

$$-4 < x < 4$$

is equivalent to $|x| < 4$. In a similar way, the inequality $|x - 3| < 5$ means that $x - 3$ must lie in the interval $(-5, 5)$. We could also write

$$-5 < x - 3 < 5.$$

This consists of two inequalities, *both* of which x must satisfy. If we add 3 to each member of the double inequality above, we obtain

$$-2 < x < 8.$$

Therefore x must lie in the interval $(-2, 8)$. See Fig. 1–8.

FIGURE 1–7   FIGURE 1–8

EXAMPLE 4. Solve for x: $|3x - 4| \leq 7$.

Solution. We write the inequality in the equivalent form

$$-7 \leq 3x - 4 \leq 7.$$

Now we add 4 to each term:

$$-3 \leq 3x \leq 11,$$

and divide each term by 3:

$$-1 \leq x \leq \tfrac{11}{3}.$$

The solution consists of all numbers x in the *closed* interval $[-1, \tfrac{11}{3}]$. See Fig. 1–9.

$$-1 \quad 0 \qquad\qquad \tfrac{11}{3}$$

FIGURE 1–9

EXAMPLE 5. Solve for x: $|2 - 5x| < 3$.

Solution. Here we have

$$-3 < 2 - 5x < 3,$$

and subtracting 2 from each member yields

$$-5 < -5x < 1.$$

Dividing by -5 will reverse each of the inequalities, and we get

$$1 > x > -\tfrac{1}{5}.$$

The solution consists of those x in the open interval $(-\tfrac{1}{5}, 1)$. See Fig. 1–10.

$$-\tfrac{1}{5} \; 0 \qquad\qquad 1$$

FIGURE 1–10

EXAMPLE 6. Solve for x:

$$\left| \frac{2x - 5}{x - 6} \right| < 3.$$

Solution. Proceeding as before, we see that

$$-3 < \frac{2x - 5}{x - 6} < 3.$$

We would like to multiply by $x - 6$, and in order to do this we must distinguish two cases, depending on whether $x - 6$ is positive or negative.

Case 1. $x - 6 > 0$. In this case multiplication by $x - 6$ preserves the direction of the inequalities, and we have

$$-3(x - 6) < 2x - 5 < 3(x - 6).$$

Now the left inequality states that

$$-3x + 18 < 2x - 5,$$

or that

$$\tfrac{23}{5} < x.$$

The right inequality states that

$$2x - 5 < 3x - 18,$$

or that

$$13 < x.$$

We see that in Case 1 we must have $x - 6 > 0$ *and* $\tfrac{23}{5} < x$ *and* $13 < x$. If the third inequality holds, then the other two hold as a consequence. Hence the solution in Case 1 consists of all x in the interval $(13, \infty)$.

$$0 \quad \tfrac{23}{5} \quad 13$$

FIGURE 1–11

Case 2. $x - 6 < 0$. The inequalities reverse when we multiply by $x - 6$. We then get

$$-3(x - 6) > 2x - 5 > 3(x - 6).$$

The two inequalities now state that $\tfrac{23}{5} > x$ and $13 > x$. The three inequalities

$$x - 6 < 0 \quad and \quad \tfrac{23}{5} > x \quad and \quad 13 > x$$

all hold if $x < \tfrac{23}{5}$. In Case 2, the solution consists of all numbers in the interval $(-\infty, \tfrac{23}{5})$. We could also describe the solution by saying that it consists of all numbers not in the closed interval $[\tfrac{23}{5}, 13]$. See Fig. 1–11.

EXERCISES

Solve for x:

1. $|2x + 3| = 5$ 2. $|4x - 6| = 2$ 3. $|8 - 5x| = 3$

4. $|7 + 2x| = 7$ 5. $|3(x - 2) + 5| = 6$ 6. $|-5x - 8| = 12$

7. $|3x - 5| = |7x - 2|$ 8. $|2x + 1| = |3x|$ 9. $|x - 6| = |3 - 2x|$

10. $\left|\dfrac{x + 2}{2x - 5}\right| = 1$ 11. $\left|\dfrac{x + 2}{x + 5}\right| = 3$

Find the values of x, if any, for which the following inequalities hold. State answers in terms of intervals.

12. $|x - 3| < 2$ 13. $|2x + 5| < 3$ 14. $|3 - 7x| \leq 6$

15. $|12 + 5x| \leq 1$ 16. $\left|\dfrac{x + 1}{3x - 2}\right| < 5$ 17. $\left|\dfrac{3 - 2x}{2 + x}\right| < 4$

18. $|x + 3| \leq |2x - 6|$ 19. $|3 - 2x| \leq |x + 4|$ 20. $\left|\dfrac{x + 3}{6 - 5x}\right| \leq 2$

3. ABSOLUTE VALUE AND INEQUALITIES

If a and b are any two numbers, the reader can easily verify that

$$|ab| = |a| \cdot |b| \qquad \text{and} \qquad \left|\frac{a}{b}\right| = \frac{|a|}{|b|}.$$

In words, *the absolute value of a product is the product of the absolute values, and the absolute value of a quotient is the quotient of the absolute values.*

An interesting and useful inequality is stated in the following theorem, which we prove.

Theorem 1. *If a and b are any numbers, then*

$$|a + b| \leq |a| + |b|.$$

Proof.* We consider three cases.

Case 1. The numbers a and b are both positive. Then $|a| = a$, $|b| = b$, and $|a + b| = a + b$. The conclusion of the theorem is satisfied, since $|a + b| = |a| + |b|$.

Case 2. The numbers a and b are both negative. Then $|a| = -a$, $|b| = -b$, and $|a + b| = -(a + b)$. As in Case 1, we have $|a + b| = |a| + |b|$.

Case 3. One number, say a, is positive, and the other is negative. Then $|a| = a$, $|b| = -b$, and we have $|a + b|$ as either $a + b$ or $-(a + b)$, depending on whether $a + b$ is larger or smaller than zero. But we know that

$$a + b < a - b = |a| + |b|,$$

and

$$-(a + b) < a - b = |a| + |b|.$$

Therefore, we have shown that in all possible circumstances

$$|a + b| \leq |a| + |b|.$$

Corollary. *If a and b are any numbers, then*

$$|a - b| \leq |a| + |b|.$$

Proof. We write $a - b$ as $a + (-b)$, and apply Theorem 1 to obtain

$$|a - b| = |a + (-b)| \leq |a| + |-b| = |a| + |b|.$$

The final equality holds since, from the definition of absolute value, it is always true that $|-b| = |b|$.

---

* A shorter although less intuitive proof is given by the following argument. Since $|a| = a$ or $-a$, we may write $-|a| \leq a \leq |a|$, and similarly, $-|b| \leq b \leq |b|$. Adding these inequalities, we get $-(|a| + |b|) \leq a + b \leq |a| + |b|$. The conclusion of Theorem 1 is equivalent to this double inequality.

Theorem 1 and the Corollary are invaluable if we wish to estimate how large various expressions can get. We show how this is done by working a few examples.

EXAMPLE 1. Estimate how large the expression $x^3 - 2$ can become if x is restricted to the interval $[-4, 4]$.

Solution. From the Corollary, we have

$$|x^3 - 2| \leq |x^3| + |2|.$$

Since the absolute value of a product is the product of the absolute values, we have $|x^3| = |x \cdot x \cdot x| = |x| \cdot |x| \cdot |x| = |x|^3$. Therefore, we get

$$|x^3 - 2| \leq |x|^3 + 2.$$

By hypothesis we stated that $|x|$ is always less than 4, and we conclude that

$$|x^3 - 2| \leq 4^3 + 2 = 66$$

if x is any number in $[-4, 4]$.

EXAMPLE 2. Find a positive number M such that

$$|x^3 - 2x^2 + 3x - 4| \leq M$$

for all values of x in the interval $[-3, 2]$. From Theorem 1 and the Corollary we can write

$$|x^3 - 2x^2 + 3x - 4| \leq |x^3| + |2x^2| + |3x| + |4|,$$

and from our knowledge of the absolute value of products, we get

$$|x^3| + |2x^2| + |3x| + |4| \leq |x|^3 + 2|x|^2 + 3|x| + 4.$$

Since $|x|$ can never be larger than 3, we have

$$|x|^3 + 2|x|^2 + 3|x| + 4 \leq 27 + 2 \cdot 9 + 3 \cdot 3 + 4 = 58.$$

The positive number M we seek is 58.

Theorem 2. *If a, b, c, and d are all positive numbers and $a \geq b$, $c \leq d$, then*

$$\frac{a}{c} \geq \frac{b}{d}.$$

Proof. If c is less than or equal to d, we know that the reciprocal of c, $1/c$, is larger than or equal to the reciprocal of d. This follows from Rule 4 for inequalities, since dividing both sides of the inequality $c \leq d$ by the positive quantity cd gives

$$\frac{1}{c} \geq \frac{1}{d}.$$

Again from Rule 4, and from the fact that $a \geq b$, we have

$$a\left(\frac{1}{c}\right) \geq b\left(\frac{1}{c}\right) \geq b\left(\frac{1}{d}\right).$$

The first and last terms yield the result.

_____

EXAMPLE 3. Find a number M such that

$$\left|\frac{x+2}{x-2}\right| \leq M$$

if x is restricted to the interval $[\frac{1}{2}, \frac{3}{2}]$.

Solution. We know that

$$\left|\frac{x+2}{x-2}\right| = \frac{|x+2|}{|x-2|}.$$

If we can estimate the *smallest* possible value of the denominator and the *largest* possible value of the numerator then, by Theorem 2, we will have estimated the largest possible value of the entire expression. For the numerator we have

$$|x+2| \leq |x| + |2| \leq \tfrac{3}{2} + 2 = \tfrac{7}{2}.$$

For the denominator we note that the smallest value occurs when x is as close as possible to 2. This occurs when $x = \frac{3}{2}$, and so

$$|x - 2| \geq \tfrac{1}{2},$$

if x is in the interval $[\frac{1}{2}, \frac{3}{2}]$. We conclude finally that

$$\left|\frac{x+2}{x-2}\right| \leq \frac{\frac{7}{2}}{\frac{1}{2}} = 7.$$

EXAMPLE 4. What is the largest possible value of

$$\left|\frac{x^2+2}{x+3}\right|$$

if x is restricted to the interval $[-4, 4]$?

Solution. The numerator is simple to estimate, since

$$|x^2 + 2| \leq |x|^2 + 2 \leq 4^2 + 2 = 18.$$

However, we have to find a smallest value for $x + 3$ if x is in $[-4, 4]$. We see first of all that the expression is not defined for $x = -3$, since then the denominator would be zero, and division by zero is always excluded. Furthermore, if x is a number near -3, the denominator is near zero, the numerator has a value near 11, and the quotient will be a "large" number. In this problem there is no largest value of the given expression in $[-4, 4]$. Such questions are discussed further in Chapter 5.

EXAMPLE 5. Find a number M such that

$$\left| \frac{x + 2}{x} - 5 \right| \le M$$

if x is restricted to the interval $(1, 4)$.

Solution.

Method 1. Since, from elementary algebra,

$$\frac{x + 2}{x} - 5 = \frac{-4x + 2}{x},$$

we can write

$$\left| \frac{x + 2}{x} - 5 \right| = \frac{|-4x + 2|}{|x|} \le \frac{|4| \, |x| + |2|}{|x|}.$$

Since $|x| < 4$, we have $4|x| + 2 < 18$, while the denominator, $|x|$, can never be smaller than 1. We obtain

$$\left| \frac{x + 2}{x} - 5 \right| < 18.$$

Method 2. From the Corollary to Theorem 1 we see that

$$\left| \frac{x + 2}{x} - 5 \right| \le \left| \frac{x + 2}{x} \right| + |5| = \frac{|x + 2|}{|x|} + 5.$$

Now $|x| + 2 < 6$ and $|x| > 1$. Hence we obtain

$$\left| \frac{x + 2}{x} - 5 \right| < 11.$$

This example shows that some algebraic manipulations lead to better estimates than do others.

EXERCISES

In problems 1 through 10, find a positive number M, if there is one, such that the absolute value of the given expression is less than M if x is in the interval given.

1. $x^2 - 3x + 2$; x in $[-3, 3]$

2. $x^3 + 4x - 6$; x in $[-2, 4]$

3. $x^4 + 2x^3 - 6x^2 + 3x - 4$; x in $[-5, 1]$

4. $\dfrac{x + 3}{x - 2}$; x in $[4, 7]$ 5. $\dfrac{x^2 - 6x + 2}{x + 5}$; x in $(-4.5, 4)$

6. $\dfrac{x^3 - 6x + 5}{x^2 + 5}$; x in $(-2, 3)$ 7. $\dfrac{x + 7}{x^2 + 4x + 4}$; x in $(-1, 3)$

8. $\dfrac{x^3 - 2x + 1}{(x^2 - 2x - 3)}$; x in $[0, 5]$

9. $\dfrac{x - 3}{x(x^2 + 2x - 8)}$; x in $(-3, 1)$

10. $\dfrac{x^4 - 2x^3 - 3x + 1}{1 - x}$; x in $(0.7, 0.9)$

11. Prove for any numbers a and b that $|a| - |b| \leq |a - b|$.

12. Given that a and b are positive, c and d are negative, and $a > b$, $c > d$, show that

$$\frac{a}{c} < \frac{b}{d}.$$

CHAPTER 2

Relations, Functions, Graphs

1. FUNCTIONS

In mathematics and many of the physical sciences, simple formulas occur repeatedly. For example, if r is the radius of a circle and A its area, then

$$A = \pi r^2.$$

If b_1 and b_2 are the lengths of the bases of a trapezoid of height h, the area A is given by the formula

$$A = \tfrac{1}{2}h(b_1 + b_2).$$

If heat is added to an ideal gas in a container of fixed volume, the pressure p and the temperature T satisfy the relation

$$p = a + cT,$$

where a and c are fixed numbers with values depending on the properties of the gas, the units used, and so forth.

The relationships expressed by these formulas are simple examples of the concept of function. In order to give a general definition of function, we begin by fixing our attention on a portion of the number scale. We introduce a symbol, x, which may take any of the values in this portion of the number scale, and we employ the term *variable* for this symbol. The collection of numbers which the variable may assume is called the *domain of values*, or simply the *domain*, of the variable. In the first illustration above, the radius r is an example of a variable. The domain of r consists of all positive numbers; i.e., the domain is the interval $(0, \infty)$. Similarly, in the formula for the area of a trapezoid, h, b_1, and b_2 are examples of variables with domains consisting of all positive numbers. In the formula relating pressure and temperature, if the temperature T is measured in degrees celsius and if it is known that the lowest possible temperature attainable by any substance is -273 degrees, then the domain of the variable T is that portion of the real number scale above -273. It is easy to conceive of a variable which may have any portion of the number scale as its domain. If w stands for the weight of a parcel being mailed, then w is a variable with domain, according to postal regulations, between zero and seventy pounds.

15

Let C be the cost in cents of mailing a first-class letter of weight x, measured in ounces. We construct the following table:

TABLE 1

Weight x, ounces	Cost C, cents
0–1	5
1–2	10
2–3	15
3–4	20
4–5	25

The table presents certain ambiguities. For example, if a letter weighs *exactly* three ounces, is the charge 15 cents or 20 cents? We shall suppose that the postal clerk is generous and decides to charge the lesser amount whenever a letter weighs an exact number of ounces. Therefore a more accurate table would be:

TABLE 2

Weight x, ounces	Cost C, cents
$0 < x \leq 1$	5
$1 < x \leq 2$	10
$2 < x \leq 3$	15
$3 < x \leq 4$	20
$4 < x \leq 5$	25

We note that x and C are variables, and the domain of x consists of all positive numbers up to a specified maximum of 320 permitted by postal regulations. The possible values of C are the integers which are multiples of 5 up to a corresponding maximum of 1600.

Let x and y be two variables, and suppose that the domain of x is some portion of the number scale — the interval (a, b), to be specific. If with each value of x in the interval (a, b) *a single value* of y may be associated or determined in some manner or other, then we say that *y is a function of x*. The *function* is the association or correspondence that gives us the value of y when the value of x is assigned. We also say that the values of y *depend* on the values of x. For this reason, x is called the *independent variable* and y the *dependent variable*. The crucial thing to remember is that when the value of x is given, there is *exactly one value* of y. If two or more values of y correspond to a single value of x, then y is not a function of x.

In the formula for the area of a circle, r is the independent variable and A is the dependent variable. The quantity A is a function of r, since for each value of r in its domain (the positive numbers) there is exactly one value for the area A. In the example for the cost C of mailing a letter of weight x, Table 2 shows that C is a function of x, with x having the domain (0, 320]. Corresponding to any given weight, there is a single, precise value of the stamps which must be affixed. The variable x is the independent variable, while C is the dependent variable. It is important to notice that x is *not* a function of C, since to each possible value of C there corresponds a whole interval of values of x.

The tabular form of the "post-office function," as it is called, is useful for visualizing the concept of function. For any function, we may think of the values of the independent variable as occupying one column and those of the dependent variable an adjacent column. Then the function is the correspondence going from the column of the independent variable to the column of the dependent variable. The totality of possible values which the dependent variable may take on is called the *range of values* of the dependent variable, or simply the *range* of the function.

Here is a precise definition of the term "function."

DEFINITION. Consider a collection of ordered pairs of numbers (x, y), where x and y may have real values. If no two pairs in this collection have the same first member, we call the collection a *function*. We identify the totality of possible x-values with the *domain*, and the totality of possible y-values with the *range*.

Almost all of the functions we shall study in calculus will come from formulas — algebraic, trigonometric, logarithmic, and so forth. However, it is clear that functions occur in many instances where formulas relating the independent and dependent variables are unknown or do not exist. It is easy to think of examples in chemistry, biology, economics, and other disciplines.

2. FUNCTIONAL NOTATION

It is important to be able to discuss functions and their properties without actually specifying the particular ones we have in mind. For this purpose we introduce a symbol, a letter of the alphabet, to stand for a function. The letters customarily used are f, g, F, G, ϕ, Φ, and so forth. Sometimes, if a problem concerns many different functions, subscripts are employed, so that, for example, f_1, f_2, and f_3 would stand for three different functions. This device is much more than a concise and abbreviated notation. We have reduced to a single letter the rather complicated concept which required the entire previous section for explanation! In other words, whenever we start a discussion by saying, "Let f be a function," the reader should be in a position to recall and understand the content of Section 1. This same process occurs throughout the calculus. From time to time complex concepts will be introduced, described, discussed, and then replaced by a single symbol. The language of mathematics is compact, concise, and difficult, because a single statement may contain a number of symbols, each representing an intricate idea which evolved over many years. Therefore notation is important not only as a shorthand, but also as a means of expressing a number of ideas compactly and precisely, without becoming lost in a morass of involved and tortuous explanations.

Suppose that f is a function which associates values of the independent variable x with values of the dependent variable y. The symbol $f(x)$ (to be read f *of* x) stands for the particular value of y which corresponds to the value of x. For example, if f is the post-office function and the weight of a letter is $3\frac{1}{2}$ ounces then, from Table 2, $f(3\frac{1}{2}) = 20$. That is, the letter requires 20 cents postage.

When specifying a function we must give the domain of the independent variable, as well as the precise way of finding the value of the dependent variable corresponding to each value of the independent variable in this domain. For the most part, we shall give functions by means of formulas such as

$$f(x) = x^2 - x + 2.$$

Such a formula, by itself, does not give the domain of x; in such a case we shall take it for granted that any value of x may be inserted in the right side, so long as it makes sense. In the above illustration, when $x = 3$ we see that $3^2 - 3 + 2 = 8$, and we write $f(3) = 8$. When x is 3, the value of the function is 8.

EXAMPLE 1. Suppose that f is the function defined by the equation

$$f(x) = x^2 - 2x - 3.$$

Find $f(0), f(-1), f(-2), f(2), f(3), f(t),$ and $f(f(x))$.

Solution.

$$f(0) = 0^2 - 2 \cdot 0 - 3 = -3; \qquad f(-1) = (-1)^2 - 2(-1) - 3 = 0;$$
$$f(-2) = (-2)^2 - 2(-2) - 3 = 5; \qquad f(2) = 2^2 - 2 \cdot 2 - 3 = -3;$$
$$f(3) = 3^2 - 2 \cdot 3 - 3 = 0; \qquad f(t) = t^2 - 2t - 3.$$

The difficult part is finding $f(f(x))$, and here a clear understanding of the meaning of the symbolism is needed. The formula defining f means that whatever is in the parentheses in $f(\ )$ is substituted in the right side. That is, $f(f(x)) = (f(x))^2 - 2(f(x)) - 3$. However, the right side again has $f(x)$ in it, and we can substitute to get

$$f(f(x)) = (x^2 - 2x - 3)^2 - 2(x^2 - 2x - 3) - 3$$
$$= x^4 - 4x^3 - 4x^2 + 16x + 12.$$

Sometimes successions of parentheses become unwieldy, and we may use brackets or braces with the same meaning: $f[f(x)]$ is the same as $f(f(x))$. If we write

$$g(x) = x^3 + 2x - 6, \qquad -2 \le x \le 3,$$

this means that the function g is defined only for values of the independent variable in the domain -2 to 3. If, in the same formula, the portion $-2 \le x \le 3$ were omitted, we would have assumed that g is defined by the formula for *all* values of x. This opens up many possibilities. For example, we could write

$$F(x) = \begin{cases} x^2 + 3x - 2, & 1 \le x < 2, \\ x^3 - 2x + 4, & 2 \le x \le 5. \end{cases}$$

The function F is defined for x in the domain from 1 to 5, since to each value of x in this domain there corresponds exactly one value of the function.

Formulas defining functions may have obvious impossibilities. If these are not explicitly pointed out, the student should be in a position to find them. For example,

$$f_1(x) = \frac{1}{x - 3}$$

is a function defined for all values of x except $x = 3$, since division by zero is always excluded. If

$$f_2(x) = \sqrt{4 - x^2},$$

then it is clear that the domain of x cannot exceed the interval from -2 to $+2$, since complex numbers are excluded. Any value of x larger than 2 or less than -2 is impossible.

———————

EXAMPLE 2. Discuss the distinction between the functions

$$F(x) = \frac{x^2 - 4}{x - 2}$$

and

$$G(x) = x + 2.$$

Solution. Since the expression $x^2 - 4$ is factorable into $(x - 2)(x + 2)$, at first glance it appears that the functions are the same. However, the domain of G is the entire number scale. That is, x can have any value. For the function F, however, there is difficulty at $x = 2$. If this value is inserted for x, both numerator and denominator are zero. Therefore F and G are identical for all values of x *except* $x = 2$. For $x = 2$ we have $G(2) = 4$. For $x = 2$ the function F is *not defined*. We could define $F(2)$ to be 4 or any other quantity, at our pleasure. But we would have to specify that fact. If we write

$$F(x) = \frac{x^2 - 4}{x - 2} \quad \text{and} \quad F(2) = 4,$$

then this function is identical with G. This may seem to be a minor point, but we shall see later that it plays an important part in portions of the calculus.

EXAMPLE 3. Given that

$$f(x) = x^2,$$

show that

$$f(x^2 + y^2) = f[f(x)] + f[f(y)] + 2f(x)f(y).$$

Solution.
$$f(x^2 + y^2) = (x^2 + y^2)^2 = x^4 + 2x^2y^2 + y^4,$$
$$f[f(x)] = f[x^2] = (x^2)^2 = x^4,$$
$$f[f(y)] = f[y^2] = (y^2)^2 = y^4,$$
$$2f(x)f(y) = 2x^2y^2.$$

Adding the last three lines, we obtain

$$f[f(x)] + f[f(y)] + 2f(x)f(y) = x^4 + y^4 + 2x^2y^2,$$

which we have seen is just $f(x^2 + y^2)$.

EXERCISES

1. Given that $f(x) = x^2 + 2x + 3$, find $f(-3)$, $f(-2)$, $f(-1)$, $f(0)$, $f(1)$, $f(2)$, $f(3)$, $f(a - 1)$.

2. Given that $f(x) = \frac{1}{8}x^3 - x + 2$, find $f(-3)$, $f(-2)$, $f(-1)$, $f(0)$, $f(1)$, $f(2)$, $f(3)$, $f(a + 1)$.

3. Given that
$$f(x) = \frac{x + 2}{2x + 3},$$

   find $f(-4)$, $f(-3)$, $f(-2)$, $f(-1)$, $f(0)$, $f(1)$, $f(-1000)$, $f(1000)$, and $f[f(x)]$. What is the domain of f?

4. Given that
$$f(x) = \frac{x - 3}{3x - 1},$$

   find $f(x)$ for $x = -1000$; -3; -2; -1; 0; 1; 2; 3; 1000; and find $f[f(x)]$. Is $\frac{1}{3}$ in the domain of f?

5. Given that
$$f(x) = \frac{x}{x^2 + 1},$$

   find $f(x)$ for $x = -1000$; -3; -2; -1; 0; 1; 2; 3; 1000. Show that $f(-x) = -f(x)$ for all values of x.

6. Given that
$$f(x) = \sqrt{(x - 1)(x - 3)},$$

   what is the domain of f? What is the range of f?

7. Given that
$$f(x) = \sqrt{2 - 2x - x^2},$$

   find the domain of f.

8. Given the function
$$f(x) = \frac{x^2 + 2x - 3}{x + 3},$$

   find the domain of f. Give, by formula, a function defined for all values of x which coincides with f wherever f is defined.

9. Same as problem 8, for the function

$$f(x) = \frac{(x - 2)(x^2 - 6x - 16)(x + 6)}{(x + 2)(x^2 + 4x - 12)}.$$

In problems 10 through 17, find the value of

$$\frac{f(x + h) - f(x)}{h}.$$

10. $f(x) = 2x - 3$ 11. $f(x) = x^2$ 12. $f(x) = 2x^2 - 3x + 5$

13. $f(x) = x^3$ 14. $f(x) = \dfrac{1}{x}$ 15. $f(x) = \dfrac{1}{x^2}$

16. $f(x) = \sqrt{x}$ 17. $f(x) = \sqrt{x^2 + 3}$

3. COORDINATES

To introduce a *rectangular coordinate system* in the plane, we begin by constructing an arbitrary pair of perpendicular lines. We usually visualize one of them
as horizontal and the other as vertical, as shown in Fig. 2–1. The horizontal line
is called the *x-axis*, the vertical line the *y-axis*, and the point of intersection the
origin of the coordinate system. The axes together are called the *coordinate axes*.
A convenient unit of length is selected and, starting from the origin as zero, a
number scale is marked off on the x-axis, positive to the right and negative to the
left. Similarly, a scale is inserted along the y-axis, with positive numbers extending
upward and negative ones downward. It is not necessary that the units along the
horizontal axis have the same length as the units along the vertical axis.

A rectangular coordinate system is a method of associating with each point in
the plane a unique *ordered* pair of numbers. Conversely, to every ordered pair of
real numbers there corresponds a single point in the plane.

FIGURE 2–1

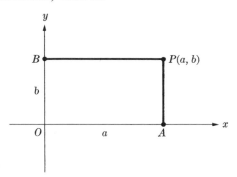

FIGURE 2–2

The numbers 1 and 6, for example, form a pair. If they appeared face up on two dice in a game of chance, then no distinction would be made between the pair 1 and 6 and the pair 6 and 1. On the other hand, an *ordered pair* of numbers consists of two numbers in which the order *is* taken into account. The ordered pair (6, 1) is different from the ordered pair (1, 6).

For a point *P* in the plane we associate an ordered pair in the following way. We construct perpendiculars from *P* to the coordinate axes, as shown in Fig. 2–2. The intersection with the *x*-axis is at the point *A*, and the intersection with the *y*-axis is at the point *B*. The distance from the origin to *A* (measured positive if *A* is to the right and negative if *A* is to the left) is denoted by *a*. Similarly, the distance *OB* is denoted by *b*. Then the ordered number pair associated with *P* is the pair (*a*, *b*). We say that *the coordinates of the point P* are the ordered pair (*a*, *b*). The number *a* is called the *x*-value of *P*, or the *abscissa*. The number *b* is the *y*-value, or *ordinate*.

Figure 2–3 shows the coordinates of a few points. The coordinate axes divide the plane into four parts called *quadrants*, numbered as shown in Fig. 2–4. If

FIGURE 2–3

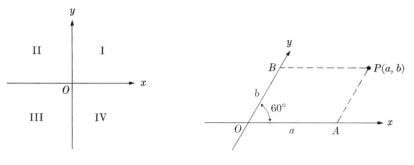

FIGURE 2–4   FIGURE 2–5

(c, d) is any ordered pair of real numbers, there is exactly one point in the plane corresponding to this pair. We merely start at the origin, go along the x-axis (to the right if c is positive, to the left if c is negative, of course) until we reach the point c units from the origin; then we go vertically d units (upward if d is positive or downward if d is negative). The point reached in this manner has coordinates (c, d). To each point in the plane there corresponds exactly one ordered pair and, conversely, to each ordered pair of real numbers there corresponds exactly one point. Such a correspondence between two collections of objects is called a *one-to-one correspondence*. Previously we used the symbol (a, b) to denote an open interval, but here we are using it for the coordinates of a point. We shall make the convention that unless we explicitly state that the symbol stands for an open interval it will always mean the coordinates of a point.

While the rectangular (also called *cartesian*) system of coordinates is one of the simplest and most useful in studying analytic geometry, it is not the only one. For example, we could use *oblique coordinates*, which are defined in the following way. Draw two lines in the plane which make a fixed angle (say 60°, to be specific), and call the point of intersection the *origin*. (See Fig. 2–5.) Designate one line as the *x-axis* and the other as the *y-axis*, and mark off number scales as in a rectangular system. From a point P draw parallels to the axes and call the points of intersection with the x-axis and the y-axis A and B, respectively. If OA has length a, and OB length b, the coordinates of P are (a, b). For some problems in geometry, oblique coordinates may be more convenient than rectangular coordinates. Later we shall study still other systems, such as polar coordinates.

Latitude and longitude form a coordinate system on the surface of the earth. However, there is not a one-to-one correspondence between all numbered pairs and the points on the earth. We know that no latitude exceeds 90° and, further, that the north pole has latitude exactly 90°, and for longitude we may insert any value between $-180°$ and 180°. This example indicates the care that must be taken in setting up coordinate systems.

4. EQUATIONS AND GRAPHS

A *solution* of an equation in x and y, such as

$$y = x^2 - 2x,$$

is a pair of numbers—one value for x and one value for y—which satisfies the

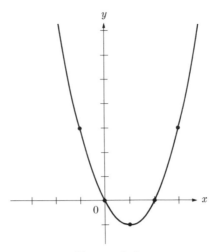

FIGURE 2–6

equation. The above equation has many solutions. If any value of x is inserted in the right side, that value of x and the corresponding value of y give a pair of numbers which form a solution. We see that solutions are: $x = 1$, $y = -1$; $x = 0$, $y = 0$; $x = 2$, $y = 0$; $x = -3$, $y = 15$. The totality of pairs of numbers which satisfy the equation is called the *solution set* of the equation. If we construct a rectangular coordinate system in the plane, each number pair of the solution set may be thought of as a point in the plane. The totality of all such points whose coordinates satisfy the equation is called the *locus* of the equation. In the particular equation we have, any value of x inserted in the right side will yield a value of y which satisfies the equation. We construct a table of values by letting x be a succession of convenient numbers, such as 0, 1, 2, 3, 4, -1, -2,

x	0	1	2	3	4	-1	-2	-3	-4
y	0	-1	0	3	8	3	8	15	24

-3, -4, ..., and by computing from the equation the corresponding values of y. These points are plotted in the usual way, and then the points are connected by a smooth curve (Fig. 2–6). The geometric representation of the locus is called the *graph* of the equation. It means that the coordinates of any point on the curve or graph satisfy the equation. But it also means—and sometimes this is important to realize—that the coordinates of every point *not* on the curve will *not* satisfy the equation. If, for example, the value 1.5 were taken for x, then the corresponding value of y is -0.75; if the curve were drawn carefully, the point (1.5, -0.75) would be on the curve. The point (2, 1) is not on the curve, and ($x = 2$, $y = 1$) does not satisfy the equation. We also notice that as x takes on larger and larger values, the corresponding values of y get larger. That is, the curve continues indefinitely to the right. The same is true for negative values of x. In other words, we are able to draw only a portion of the graph, and the actual drawing is merely suggestive of how the entire locus appears.

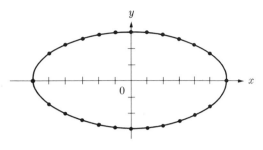

FIGURE 2–7

EXAMPLE 1. Sketch the graph of the equation

$$x^2 + 4y^2 = 36.$$

Solution. We set up a table of values by inserting a succession of values for x. The

x	0	0	1	1	2	2	3
y	3	-3	$\frac{1}{2}\sqrt{35}$	$-\frac{1}{2}\sqrt{35}$	$2\sqrt{2}$	$-2\sqrt{2}$	$\frac{3}{2}\sqrt{3}$

x	3	4	4	5	5	6	7
y	$-\frac{3}{2}\sqrt{3}$	$\sqrt{5}$	$-\sqrt{5}$	$\frac{1}{2}\sqrt{11}$	$-\frac{1}{2}\sqrt{11}$	0	–

important thing to see is that for some values of x there are *two* corresponding values of y. For others, there are no possible values for y. We also easily see that a negative value for x gives the same y-value as the corresponding positive value. Plotting the points and joining them with a smooth curve, we obtain the ellipse shown in Fig. 2–7. In contrast with the curve in Fig. 2–6, we are able to picture the entire locus of this equation.

EXAMPLE 2. Sketch the graph of the equation

$$y = |x - 1|.$$

Solution. From the definition of absolute value we know that

$$y = x - 1 \quad \text{if} \quad x - 1 \geq 0$$

and

$$y = -(x - 1) \quad \text{if} \quad x - 1 \leq 0.$$

We therefore get two tables of values:

For $x - 1 \geq 0$:

x	1	2	3	4
y	0	1	2	3

For $x - 1 \leq 0$:

x	1	0	-1	-2
y	0	1	2	3

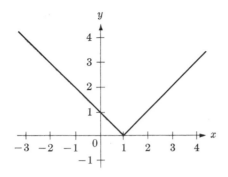

FIGURE 2–8   FIGURE 2–9

Each of these two tables represents points which lie on a straight line; the locus is shown in Fig. 2–8.

EXAMPLE 3. Sketch the graph of $y^2 = x$.

Solution. We construct a table by letting x have positive values. We note that for each

x	1	1	2	2	3	3	4	4	5	5
y	$+1$	-1	$+\sqrt{2}$	$-\sqrt{2}$	$+\sqrt{3}$	$-\sqrt{3}$	2	-2	$\sqrt{5}$	$-\sqrt{5}$

positive value of x there are two values of y, while for each negative value of x no value of y is possible. For $x = 0$ there is the single value $y = 0$. The graph extends only to the right of the origin (Fig. 2–9).

———————

When x and y satisfy an equation such as

$$y = x^2 - 2x \quad \text{or} \quad x^2 + 4y^2 = 36,$$

we say that we have a *relation* between the variables x and y or, simply, that the variables are *related. This is different from saying that one variable is a function of the other.* We recall that "y is a function of x" means that for each value of x (in the domain) there is *exactly one* value of y. Of the above equations, the first actually represents a function, since for each value of x there is one value of y. We could therefore write

$$y = f(x) = x^2 - 2x,$$

and the function is f. The symbols y and $f(x)$ are interchangeable. However, in the second equation,

$$x^2 + 4y^2 = 36,$$

for each value of x there are two possible values of y:

$$y = +\tfrac{1}{2}\sqrt{36 - x^2} \quad \text{and} \quad y = -\tfrac{1}{2}\sqrt{36 - x^2}.$$

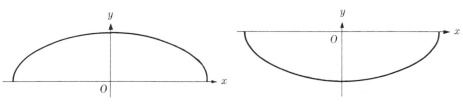

FIGURE 2–10   FIGURE 2–11

We see that the first equation has the graph shown in Fig. 2–10, while the second has the graph shown in Fig. 2–11. Together they give the ellipse shown in Fig. 2–7. In this case we have y as *two* functions of x, whose graphs together make up the locus of the equation of Example 1. In Example 3, the graph of $y^2 = x$ is drawn, and here again y is not a function of x. However, we note that for each value of y there is *exactly one* value of x, and this means that x *is a function of* y. We write

$$x = g(y) = y^2.$$

The process of interchanging the roles of independent and dependent variables in order to write a relation as a function is useful to remember. In Example 2, where $y = |x - 1|$ we have y as a function of x, but from the graph in Fig. 2–8 we observe that for each positive value of y there are two values of x. Therefore x is not a function of y.

EXERCISES

Sketch the graphs of the following equations, and in each case state whether or not y is a function of x.

1. $y - x = 0$
2. $x + 2y = 3$
3. $y - 3x = 2$
4. $3x - 2y = 5$
5. $y = |x|$
6. $y = |x + 1|$
7. $y = |x| + 1$
8. $x = 3$
9. $y = -2$
10. $x + y = 0$
11. $2x + 4y = 1$
12. $y = \frac{1}{3}x^2$
13. $x = 2y^2$
14. $y = x^2 - 4$
15. $x = y^2 - 1$
16. $y = x^2 + 2x - 3$
17. $y = x^2 - 2x + 3$
18. $x^2 + y^2 = 25$
19. $4x^2 + y^2 = 36$
20. $x^2 - y^2 = 4$
21. $2x^2 - y^2 = 9$
22. $x^2 - y^2 + 9 = 0$
23. $y = -2x^2$
24. $y = -x^2 + 2x + 3$
25. $y = \frac{1}{8}x^3$
26. $y = x^3 - 4x$
27. $y = x^3 - 3x + 2$
28. $y^2 = x^3$
29. $y = x^5$

In each of the following, show how y can be expressed as one or more functions of x, and sketch the curve.

30. $y^2 = 4x^3$
31. $y^2 - 2y + 1 = x$
32. $y^3 = x$
33. $y^4 = x^2$
34. $y^2 + 4y = x - 6$
35. $y^4 - 4y^2 = x^2 + 4x$

5.   INTERCEPTS, SYMMETRY, AND ASYMPTOTES

There are three steps to follow in the ordinary method for sketching the graph of an equation. First, a table of values is constructed. The points corresponding to the values in the table are then plotted on a graph. Finally, a smooth curve is drawn connecting these points. With the aid of additional information, however, the process of graphing can be facilitated. There are a few simple facts that can be obtained almost by inspection, so that a rough sketch of the graph can be drawn quickly. Later we shall see how the methods of calculus can be used to get additional information about a curve before it is drawn.

It is useful to know where a curve intersects the x-axis and the y-axis. A point at which any curve intersects the x-axis is called an x-*intercept;* a point where it intersects the y-axis is called a y-*intercept.* It may happen that a curve does not intersect either axis or, on the other hand, it may intersect both many times. To locate the intercepts, if any, we have the rule:

to find the x-intercepts, set $y = 0$ in the equation and solve for x;

to find the y-intercepts, set $x = 0$ in the equation and solve for y.

EXAMPLE 1.   Find the x- and y-intercepts of

$$x^2 - 3y^2 + 6x - 3y = 7.$$

Solution. Setting $y = 0$, we get

$$x^2 + 6x - 7 = 0 \qquad \text{or} \qquad x = -7, 1.$$

The x-intercepts are at the points $(-7, 0)$, $(1, 0)$.
Setting $x = 0$, we get

$$3y^2 + 3y + 7 = 0,$$

$$y = \frac{-3 \pm \sqrt{9 - 84}}{6} = \frac{-3 \pm \sqrt{-75}}{6}.$$

Since the solutions are complex numbers, there are no y-intercepts, and the curve does not intersect the y-axis.

In constructing the graphs of the curves discussed in Section 4 of this chapter, we see that some of them have certain kinds of symmetry. If we had known about these symmetries before drawing the graph, the actual sketching would have been much easier. We say that a curve is *symmetric with respect to the x-axis* if, whenever a point (a, b) is on the curve, the point $(a, -b)$ is also on the curve. The parabola shown in Fig. 2–9 is an example of such a curve. A curve is *symmetric with respect to the y-axis* if, whenever a point (a, b) is on the curve, the point $(-a, b)$ is also on the curve. The ellipse shown in Fig. 2–7 is an example of this, as are the curves in Figs. 2–10 and 2–11.

We also consider symmetry with respect to the origin. A *curve is symmetric with respect to the origin* if, whenever a point (a, b) is on the curve, the point $(-a, -b)$ is also on the curve. The ellipse in Fig. 2–7 is symmetric with respect to the origin. To test for various kinds of symmetry, we state the following rules.

1. *Replace y by −y in the equation for the curve; if the equation is unchanged, the curve is symmetric with respect to the x-axis.*

2. *Replace x by −x in the equation for the curve; if the equation is unchanged, the curve is symmetric with respect to the y-axis.*

3. *Replace x by −x and y by −y in the equation for the curve; if the equation is unchanged, the curve is symmetric with respect to the origin.*

The rules for symmetry reduce the work involved in sketching the graph of an equation. If a curve is symmetric with respect to the x-axis then, once the portion of the curve above the x-axis is drawn, the part below the axis is obtained as the mirror image of the part above. Similarly, if a curve is symmetric with respect to the y-axis, it is necessary only to plot points either to the right or to the left of this axis. Once the part of the curve on one side of the y-axis is drawn, the part on the other side may be sketched by inspection. The next examples illustrate the use of symmetry in sketching.

EXAMPLE 2. Given the curve with equation

$$9x^2 + 16y^2 = 144,$$

find the intercepts, test for symmetry, and sketch the graph.

Solution. To find the x-intercepts, set $y = 0$, getting $9x^2 = 144$ or $x^2 = 16$. The x-intercepts are at $(4, 0)$ and $(−4, 0)$. To get the y-intercepts, set $x = 0$, getting $y^2 = 9$; the y-intercepts are at $(0, 3)$ and $(0, −3)$.

To test for symmetry with respect to the x-axis, we replace y by $−y$ in the equation, which means that we have

$$9x^2 + 16(−y)^2 = 144.$$

However, $(−y)^2 = y^2$; therefore this equation is just

$$9x^2 + 16y^2 = 144,$$

which is identical with the original equation. We conclude that the curve is symmetric with respect to the x-axis.

To test for symmetry with respect to the y-axis, we replace x by $−x$ in the equation, and we get

$$9(−x)^2 + 16y^2 = 144,$$

which again is the same as the original. Therefore the curve is symmetric with respect to the y-axis.

If we replace x by $−x$ and y by $−y$, we again do not change the equation, and the curve is symmetric with respect to the origin. The curve (an ellipse) is sketched in Fig. 2–12.

EXAMPLE 3. Given the curve with equation

$$xy = 10,$$

find the intercepts, test for symmetry, and sketch the graph.

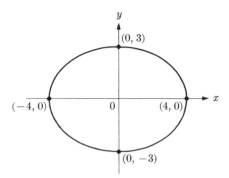

FIGURE 2–12

Solution. To find the *x*-intercepts, set $y = 0$, getting $0 = 10$. This is impossible, and the curve does not intersect the *x*-axis. Similarly, setting $x = 0$, we see that the curve does not intersect the *y*-axis.

To test for symmetry with respect to the *x*-axis, we replace *y* by $-y$, to find

$$x(-y) = 10 \quad \text{or} \quad xy = -10,$$

which is *not* the same equation. The curve is *not* symmetric with respect to the *x*-axis. Similarly, the curve is *not* symmetric with respect to the *y*-axis. To test for symmetry with respect to the origin, we simultaneously substitute $-x$ for *x* and $-y$ for *y*, getting

$$(-x)(-y) = 10 \quad \text{or} \quad xy = 10.$$

We conclude that the curve is symmetric with respect to the origin. Such symmetry means that if a line is drawn from any point on the curve through the origin, this line will intersect the curve at another point equidistant from the origin. The sketch shown in Fig. 2–13 illustrates the idea with both the points (5, 2) and (−5, −2) lying on the curve.

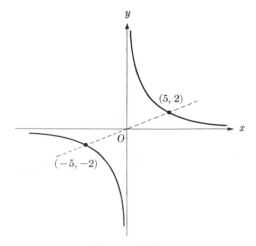

FIGURE 2–13

Knowledge of the symmetry cuts in half the work of sketching, since the portion of the graph in the third quadrant is obtained by reflection through the origin of the portion in the first quadrant.

If a curve is symmetric with respect to *both* the x-axis and the y-axis, it is clear that it is also symmetric with respect to the origin. The last example shows that it is possible for a curve to be symmetric with respect to the origin without being symmetric with respect to either axis.

EXAMPLE 4. Given the curve with equation

$$y(x^2 - 1) = 2,$$

find the intercepts, test for symmetry, and sketch the graph.

Solution. Setting $x = 0$, we get $y = -2$, which is the y-intercept; $y = 0$ yields the impossible statement $0 = 2$, and the curve has no x-intercept.

To test for symmetry with respect to the x-axis, we replace y by $-y$, getting

$$-y(x^2 - 1) = 2,$$

which means that the curve is not symmetric with respect to the x-axis. Replacing x by $-x$, we find

$$y[(-x)^2 - 1] = 2 \quad \text{or} \quad y(x^2 - 1) = 2,$$

which is the same as the original equation, and the curve is symmetric with respect to the y-axis. The curve is not symmetric with respect to the origin, since

$$(-y)[(-x)^2 - 1] = 2$$

is not the same as the original equation.

We make up a table of values for positive x:

x	0	1	2	3	4	5
y	-2	–	$\frac{2}{3}$	$\frac{1}{4}$	$\frac{2}{15}$	$\frac{1}{12}$

We see that as x increases, the values of y get closer and closer to zero. On the other hand, there is no value of y corresponding to $x = 1$. In order to get a closer look at what happens when x is near 1, we construct an auxiliary table of values for x near 1. We obtain the following set of values:

x	$\frac{1}{2}$	$\frac{3}{4}$	$\frac{7}{8}$	0.9	1.1	1.2	1.3	$1\frac{1}{2}$
y	$-\frac{8}{3}$	$-\frac{32}{7}$	$-\frac{128}{15}$	$-\frac{200}{19}$	$\frac{200}{21}$	$\frac{50}{11}$	$\frac{200}{69}$	$\frac{8}{5}$

As x moves closer to 1 from the left, the corresponding values of y become large negative numbers. As x approaches 1 from the right, the values of y become large positive num-

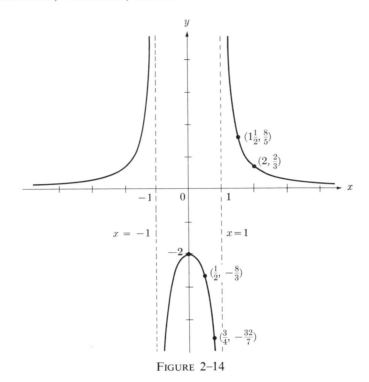

FIGURE 2–14

bers. The curve is sketched in Fig. 2–14. The portion to the left of the y-axis is sketched from our knowledge of the symmetry property; therefore a table of values for negative x is not needed.

In Example 4, the vertical line through the point $(1, 0)$ plays a special role. The curve to the right of the line gets closer and closer to this line as the curve becomes higher and higher. In fact, the distance between the curve and the line tends to zero as the curve continues upward beyond all bound. Such a line is called a *vertical asymptote* to the curve. Similarly, the x-axis is called a *horizontal asymptote*, since the distance between the curve and the x-axis tends to zero as x increases beyond all bound. A knowledge of the location of the vertical and horizontal asymptotes is of great help in sketching the curve. We now give a rule (which works in many cases) for finding the asymptotes.

RULE. *To locate the vertical asymptotes, solve the equation for y in terms of x. If the result is a quotient of two expressions involving x, find all those values of x for which the denominator vanishes and the numerator does not. If a is such a value, the vertical line through the point $(a, 0)$ will be a vertical asymptote. To locate the horizontal asymptotes, solve for x in terms of y, and find those values of y for which the denominator vanishes (and the numerator does not). If b is such a value, the horizontal line through the point $(0, b)$ is a horizontal asymptote.*

Two examples illustrate the technique.

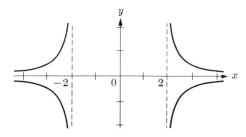

FIGURE 2–15

EXAMPLE 5. Find the intercepts, symmetries, and asymptotes, and sketch the graph of

$$y^2(x^2 - 4) = 1.$$

Solution. (a) *Intercepts:* when $y = 0$, we have none; when $x = 0$, $y^2 = -\frac{1}{4}$, and there are no y-intercepts.

(b) *Symmetry:* it is easy to see that the curve is symmetric with respect to both axes.

(c) *Asymptotes:* solving for y, we get

$$y = \pm\sqrt{1/(x^2 - 4)},$$

and we observe that when x has the values 2 and -2 the denominator is zero; since the numerator is not zero at these values, there are two vertical asymptotes through the points $(2, 0)$, $(-2, 0)$. To solve for x, we write

$$x^2 - 4 = \frac{1}{y^2} \quad \text{and} \quad x^2 = 4 + \frac{1}{y^2} = \frac{4y^2 + 1}{y^2}.$$

Therefore,

$$x = \pm\sqrt{(4y^2 + 1)/y^2}.$$

The value $y = 0$ gives the x-axis as a horizontal asymptote. Figure 2–15 exhibits the main features of the curve. Note that there are no points on the curve for x between -2 and 2. This follows from the relation

$$y = \pm\sqrt{1/(x^2 - 4)},$$

since values of x between -2 and $+2$ make y complex.

EXAMPLE 6. Find the intercepts, symmetries, and asymptotes, and sketch the graph of

$$yx^2 = (x - 3).$$

Solution. (a) *Intercepts:* when $y = 0$, $x = 3$, and the x-intercept is 3. Setting $x = 0$, we get no y-intercept.

(b) *Symmetry:* all symmetry tests fail.

(c) *Asymptotes:* solving for y, we have

$$y = \frac{x - 3}{x^2},$$

and $x = 0$ yields—according to our rule—the y-axis as a vertical asymptote. To solve for x in terms of y, we write the quadratic equation

$$yx^2 - x + 3 = 0,$$

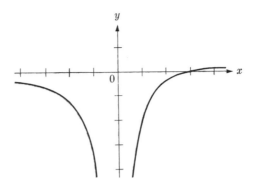

FIGURE 2–16

and solve for x by the formula

$$x = \frac{1 \pm \sqrt{1 - 12y}}{2y}.$$

The value $y = 0$ gives the x-axis as a horizontal asymptote. A table of values then gives

x	1	2	3	4	5	-1	-2	-3	-4
y	-2	$-\frac{1}{4}$	0	$\frac{1}{16}$	$\frac{2}{25}$	-4	$-\frac{5}{4}$	$-\frac{2}{3}$	$-\frac{7}{16}$

A sketch of the curve is shown in Fig. 2–16.

EXERCISES

In Exercises 1 through 30, discuss each problem with respect to intercepts, symmetry, and vertical and horizontal asymptotes; plot graphs of the equations.

1. $y = x^2$
2. $y^2 = x$
3. $y^2 = -2x$
4. $y^2 = 4x + 4$
5. $y = 2 - x^2$
6. $xy = 8$
7. $x^2y = 4$
8. $y^2 = x^2 - 1$
9. $y^2 = x^2 + 4$
10. $2x^2 + 3y^2 = 12$
11. $3x^2 + 2y^2 = 12$
12. $2x^2 - 3y^2 = 12$
13. $9x^2 - 4y^2 + 36 = 0$
14. $x^2 + xy + y^2 = 12$
15. $y^2 - xy = 2$
16. $y^2(x + 1) = 4$
17. $y^2(x^2 - 4) = 4$
18. $y^2(x^2 + 1) = 1$
19. $y^2(x - 2) + 2 = 0$
20. $y(x - 1)(x - 3) = 3$
21. $y^2(x - 1)(x - 3) = 4$
22. $x(y^2 - 4) = y$
23. $x^2(y^2 - 4) = y$
24. $y^2 + 2x - x^2y^2 = 0$
25. $y^4 = y^2 - x^2$
26. $x^2y^2 = 4$
27. $(x - 2)^2(y - 4)^2 = 4$
28. $x^2y^2 = (x - 2)$
29. $y^2(x^2 - 4) = x + 2$
30. $y^2 = \dfrac{x^2 - 1}{x^2 - 4}$

31. Show that if a curve is symmetric with respect to the x-axis and the origin, it must be symmetric with respect to the y-axis.
32. A curve may cross an asymptote, as demonstrated in Fig. 2–16, where it is seen that the curve crosses the x-axis. Construct an equation such that the curve crosses its asymptote twice.

6. INEQUALITIES IN TWO VARIABLES

The equation $x = 2$ means that the x-coordinate, or abscissa, of a point is 2. The points $(2, 7)$, $(2, 19)$, $(2, -3)$ all satisfy this equation. The line parallel to the y-axis and two units to the right of it contains all the points which satisfy the equation. We say that $x = 2$ is the equation of this line. Similarly, the equation $y = -1$ represents the line parallel to the x-axis and one unit below it (Fig. 2–17). More generally, $x = $ a constant will always represent a line parallel to the y-axis, and $y = $ a constant, a line parallel to the x-axis.

The inequality

$$1 < x < 3$$

means that the x-coordinate, or abscissa, of a point must be between 1 and 3. Nothing is said of the y-coordinate, which may have any value. The strip bounded by the lines $x = 1$ and $x = 3$ (shaded in Fig. 2–18) contains all points which satisfy the above inequality. A strip which extends indefinitely in both directions, such as the one shown in Fig. 2–18, is called an *infinite strip*. The inequality

$$1 < x < 3$$

may also be stated in a different way in terms of absolute values. If we write

$$|x - 2| < 1,$$

we are saying that $x - 2$ is between -1 and 1. That is,

$$-1 < x - 2 < 1.$$

Adding 2 to each term of this inequality, we have

$$1 < x < 3.$$

As a result, we see that the two inequalities

$$1 < x < 3 \qquad \text{and} \qquad |x - 2| < 1$$

are completely equivalent.

FIGURE 2–17   FIGURE 2–18

FIGURE 2–19   FIGURE 2–20

The inequality $2 < y < 5$ also represents an infinite strip (shaded region in Fig. 2–19). This inequality could also be written in the completely equivalent form

$$|y - 3\tfrac{1}{2}| < 1\tfrac{1}{2}.$$

We now raise the problem of finding all the points which satisfy *both* inequalities

$$1 < x < 3 \qquad \text{and} \qquad 2 < y < 5.$$

The only points which satisfy these two inequalities are the ones which are situated in *both* infinite strips. These are the points in the rectangle formed by the intersection of the strips (shaded region in Fig. 2–20). The corners of this rectangle are the points $(1, 2)$, $(3, 2)$, $(3, 5)$, and $(1, 5)$.

———————

EXAMPLE 1. Describe the region which satisfies both inequalities

$$2 \le x < 3 \qquad \text{and} \qquad |y - 2| < \tfrac{1}{2}.$$

Solution. The first inequality consists of an infinite strip between the lines $x = 2$ and $x = 3$. Note that the points *on* the line $x = 2$ are included, but the points on $x = 3$ are not. The second inequality may be written

$$-\tfrac{1}{2} < y - 2 < \tfrac{1}{2}$$

or, after adding 2 to each term, in the form

$$\tfrac{3}{2} < y < \tfrac{5}{2}.$$

This is an infinite strip which intersects the first one in a rectangle, with vertices at the points $(2, \tfrac{3}{2})$, $(3, \tfrac{3}{2})$, $(3, \tfrac{5}{2})$, and $(2, \tfrac{5}{2})$. This is actually a square, as shown in Fig. 2–21. We conclude that all the points inside this square satisfy both inequalities. However, in addition, the points on the boundary of the square along the line $x = 2$ (left boundary), except for the corners, also satisfy both inequalities.

FIGURE 2–21

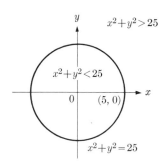

FIGURE 2–22

A single equation in two variables represents a curve in the plane. The equation

$$x^2 + y^2 = 25$$

represents a circle of radius 5 with center at the origin. We can readily see that all points inside this circle satisfy the inequality (Fig. 2–22)

$$x^2 + y^2 < 25,$$

while all points outside the circle satisfy the inequality $x^2 + y^2 > 25$.

As a general rule, the curve of an equation will divide the plane into several distinct regions. *In each of these regions an inequality will hold.* This inequality is obtained simply by replacing the equality symbol in the equation with an inequality sign. The only question that remains is whether a "greater than" sign or a "less than" sign should be inserted. The question is answered* by the following rule:

RULE. *Select **any** point in a region bounded by the curve of the equation. Substitute the coordinates of this point in the equation and see which way the **inequality** holds. Then the same inequality holds for all points of this region.*

The simplicity of the method will be shown in the following examples.

EXAMPLE 2. Graph the equation $y = x^2$, and describe what inequalities hold in the regions of the plane which this curve separates.

Solution. We first sketch the graph of the curve (Fig 2–23). We see that the curve divides the plane into two regions, one containing the positive half of the y-axis and the other containing all the rest. We select *any* point P, say $(1, 4)$, which we know is in the first region. The point $(1, 4)$ is in it, since it is above the point $(1, 1)$, which is on the curve. We have

$$4 > 1^2,$$

*At least for expressions of the type we have been considering, so long as the denominator is never zero.

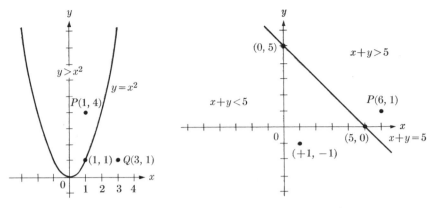

FIGURE 2–23   FIGURE 2–24

and so at P we know that $y > x^2$. According to the rule, we must have $y > x^2$ through-out this region. Now we select a point in the remaining region. For example, $Q(3, 1)$ is such a point. We see at once that

$$1 < 3^2,$$

and so at Q, $y < x^2$; therefore $y < x^2$ throughout the region containing Q.

EXAMPLE 3. Graph the equation $x + y = 5$ and describe what inequalities hold in the regions of the plane which this curve separates.

Solution. The graph of this equation is a straight line (Fig. 2–24) and the line divides the plane into two regions. Selecting the point $P(6, 1)$, we see that at P

$$6 + 1 > 5.$$

We conclude that $x + y > 5$ in the entire region on the same side of the line as P. Similarly, at $Q(1, -1)$, we have $1 + (-1) < 5$, and so $x + y < 5$ in the region con-taining Q. The portion of the plane on one side of any line is called a *half-plane*.

EXAMPLE 4. Graph the equation $x^2 - y^2 = 4$ and describe what inequalities hold in the regions of the plane which this curve separates.

Solution. The graph of this equation, shown in Fig. 2–25, was obtained by the methods of Section 5. The curve divides the plane into three regions, which we call R_1, R_2, and R_3. The region R_1 is the one containing the point A, the region R_2 is the one containing B, and R_3 the one containing C. At point A $(4, 1)$, we have $4^2 - 1^2 > 4$, and by the Rule we conclude that

$$x^2 - y^2 > 4 \quad \text{in } R_1.$$

Since $1^2 - 0^2 < 4$, we conclude that

$$x^2 - y^2 < 4 \quad \text{in } R_2.$$

Similarly, $(-4)^2 - 1^2 > 4$, and so

$$x^2 - y^2 > 4 \quad \text{in } R_3.$$

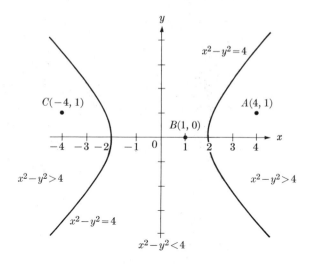

FIGURE 2–25

EXERCISES

In Exercises 1 through 12, describe the regions which satisfy the given inequalities:

1. $2 < x < 4$ and $-3 < y < 1$

2. $-4 < x < 8$ and $-10 < y < 5$

3. $|x - 3| < 2$ and $1 < y < 7$

4. $|x + 1| < 1$ and $-2 < y < 3$

5. $|x - 3| < 4$ and $5 < y < 5.5$

6. $1 < x < 1.2$ and $|y - 1| < \frac{1}{2}$

7. $1 < x \leq 3$ and $2 \leq y < 3$

8. $1 \leq x \leq 4$ and $2 \leq y \leq 6$

9. $|x - 3| < 1$ and $|y - 2| < 5$

10. $|x + 2| < 0.5$ and $|y - 1| < 0.1$

11. $|x + 3| < \frac{1}{4}$ and $|y + 2| \leq 0.5$

12. $|x + 2| \leq 1$ and $|y - 3| \leq 2$

In Exercises 13 through 16, we suppose that f is a function and that $y = f(x)$ has a certain graph. What can be said about where the graph of the function is situated in each of the following cases, if the given inequalities hold?

13. $|x - 2| < 1$ and $|f(x) - 3| < 4$

14. $|x + 1| < 0.05$ and $|f(x) - 2| < 0.35$

15. $|x + 6| < \frac{1}{2}$ and $|f(x) + 4| < 2$

16. $|x - 0.5| < 0.1$ and $|f(x) - 1| < 0.01$

In Exercises 17 through 30, the curve of the given equation divides the plane into a number of regions. Sketch the curve and state what inequality holds in each of the regions.

17. $x^2 = 4y$

18. $3x^2 + 2y^2 = 36$

19. $x^2 - 8y + 7 = 0$

20. $y^2 + 2x - 6 = 0$

21. $x^2 - 4y^2 + 4 = 0$

22. $x + 3y - 6 = 0$

23. $2x - 4y + 5 = 0$

24. $y^2 = x^3$

25. $y = x^3 + 6x - 5$

26. $y = \dfrac{1}{x^2 - 1}$

27. $y^2 = \dfrac{x^2}{1 - x}$

28. $x = \dfrac{1}{y - 1}$

29. $xy - 3 = 0$

30. $xy + x - 2y = 1$

CHAPTER 3

The Line. Linear Inequalities

1. DISTANCE FORMULA; DIRECTED DISTANCE; MIDPOINT FORMULA

We consider a rectangular coordinate system with the unit of measurement the same along both coordinate axes. The distance between any two points in the plane is the length of the line segment joining them. We shall derive a formula for this distance in terms of the coordinates of the two points.

Let P_1, with coordinates (x_1, y_1), and P_2, with coordinates (x_2, y_2), be two points, and let d denote the length of the segment between P_1 and P_2 (Fig. 3–1). Draw a line parallel to the y-axis through P_1, and do the same through P_2. These lines intersect the x-axis at the points $A(x_1, 0)$ and $B(x_2, 0)$. [The symbol $A(x_1, 0)$ is to be read "the point A with coordinates $(x_1, 0)$."] Now draw a line through P_1 parallel to the x-axis; this line intersects the vertical through P_2 and B at a point $C(x_2, y_1)$.

The length of the segment between P_1 and C (denoted $\overline{P_1C}$) is equal to the length $\overline{AB}$. If x_2 is to the right of x_1 (as shown in the figure), then the length of $\overline{AB}$ is $x_2 - x_1$. If x_2 were to the left of x_1, the distance would be $x_1 - x_2$. In either case, the length of $\overline{AB}$ is easily written by using absolute value notation: $\overline{AB} = |x_2 - x_1|$. Similarly, the length of $\overline{P_2C} = |y_2 - y_1|$. It is a good exercise for the reader to check the correctness of these facts when the points P_1 and P_2 are in various quadrants of the plane.

We note that triangle P_1P_2C is a right triangle, and we recall from plane geometry the Pythagorean theorem: "The sum of the squares of the legs of a right triangle is equal to the square of the hypotenuse." Applying the Pythagorean theorem to triangle P_1P_2C, we get

$$\overline{P_1P_2}^2 = \overline{P_1C}^2 + \overline{P_2C}^2 \qquad \text{or} \qquad d^2 = |x_2 - x_1|^2 + |y_2 - y_1|^2.$$

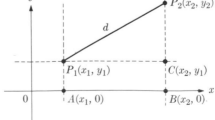

FIGURE 3–1

40

This may also be written

$$d^2 = (x_2 - x_1)^2 + (y_2 - y_1)^2$$

and, extracting the square root, we obtain the *distance formula:*

$$d = \sqrt{(x_2 - x_1)^2 + (y_2 - y_1)^2}.$$

The distance d between any two distinct points is always *positive* and, in keeping with this, we shall always use the square-root symbol without any plus or minus sign in front of it to mean the positive square root. If we wish to discuss the negative square root of some number, say 3, we will write $-\sqrt{3}$.

EXAMPLE 1. Find the distance between the points $P_1(3, 1)$ and $P_2(5, -2)$.

Solution. We substitute in the distance formula and get

$$d = \sqrt{(5 - 3)^2 + (-2 - 1)^2} = \sqrt{4 + 9} = \sqrt{13}$$

EXAMPLE 2. The point $P_1(5, -2)$ is 4 units away from a second point P_2, whose y-coordinate is 1. Locate the point P_2.

Solution. The point P_2 will have coordinates $(x_2, 1)$. From the distance formula we have the equation

$$4 = \sqrt{(x_2 - 5)^2 + (1 - (-2))^2} .$$

To solve for x_2, we square both sides and obtain

$$16 = (x_2 - 5)^2 + 9 \quad \text{or} \quad x_2 - 5 = \pm\sqrt{7}.$$

There are two possibilities for x_2:

$$x_2 = 5 + \sqrt{7}, \quad 5 - \sqrt{7}.$$

In other words, there are two points P_2, one at $(5 + \sqrt{7}, 1)$ and the other at $(5 - \sqrt{7}, 1)$, which have y-coordinate 1 and which are 4 units from P_1.

Let $A(x_1, 0)$ and $B(x_2, 0)$ be two points on the x-axis. We define the *directed distance from A to B* to be $x_2 - x_1$. If B is to the right of A, as shown in Fig. 3–2(a), the directed distance is positive. If B is to the left of A, as in Fig. 3–2(b), the directed distance is negative. If two points $C(0, y_1)$ and $D(0, y_2)$ are on the

(a)

(b)

FIGURE 3–2

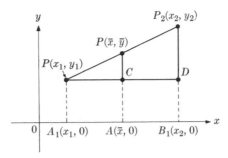

FIGURE 3–3

y-axis, the *directed distance from C to D* is similarly defined to be $y_2 - y_1$. Directed distances are defined only for pairs of points on a coordinate axis. While ordinary distance between any two points is always positive, note that directed distance may be positive or negative.

Let $P_1 (x_1, y_1)$ and $P_2(x_2, y_2)$ be any two points in the plane. We shall show how to find the coordinates of the midpoint of the line segment joining P_1 and P_2. Let P, with coordinates $(\bar{x}, \bar{y})$, be the midpoint. Through P_1, P, and P_2 draw parallels to the y-axis, and through P_1 a parallel to the x-axis, forming the triangles shown in Fig. 3–3. We recall from plane geometry the statement, "A line parallel to the base of a triangle which bisects one side also bisects the other side." Since PC is parallel to P_2D and P is the midpoint of P_1P_2, it follows that C is the midpoint of P_1D. We see at once that A is the midpoint of A_1B_1. The coordinates of A_1 are $(x_1, 0)$, the coordinates of A are $(\bar{x}, 0)$, and those of B_1 are $(x_2, 0)$. Therefore the directed distance A_1A must be equal to the directed distance AB_1. From the definition of directed distance we have

$$\bar{x} - x_1 = x_2 - \bar{x}$$

and, solving for $\bar{x}$,

$$\bar{x} = \frac{x_1 + x_2}{2}.$$

If we performed the same argument for the y-coordinates, the result by analogy is

$$\bar{y} = \frac{y_1 + y_2}{2}.$$

EXAMPLE 3. Locate the midpoint of the line segment joining the points $P(3, -2)$ and $Q(-4, 5)$.

Solution. From the above formula,

$$\bar{x} = \frac{3 - 4}{2} = -\frac{1}{2} \quad \text{and} \quad \bar{y} = \frac{-2 + 5}{2} = \frac{3}{2}.$$

EXAMPLE 4. Find the length of the line segment joining the point $A(7, -2)$ to the midpoint of the line segment between the points $B(4, 1)$ and $C(3, -5)$.

Solution. The midpoint of the line segment between B and C is at

$$\bar{x} = \frac{4 + 3}{2} = \frac{7}{2}, \qquad \bar{y} = \frac{1 - 5}{2} = -2.$$

From the distance formula applied to A and this midpoint we have

$$d = \sqrt{(7 - \tfrac{7}{2})^2 + (-2 - (-2))^2} = \tfrac{7}{2}$$

EXAMPLE 5. A line segment AB has its midpoint at $C(5, -1)$. Point A has coordinates $(2, 3)$; find the coordinates of B.

Solution. In the midpoint formula, we know that $\bar{x} = 5$, $\bar{y} = -1$, $x_1 = 2$, $y_1 = 3$, and we have to find x_2, y_2. Substituting these values in the midpoint formula, we get

$$5 = \frac{2 + x_2}{2}, \qquad -1 = \frac{3 + y_2}{2},$$

and

$$x_2 = 8, \qquad y_2 = -5.$$

EXERCISES

In problems 1 through 4, find the lengths of the sides of the triangles with the given points as vertices.

1. $A(3, 2)$, $B(7, -1)$, $C(-4, 5)$ 2. $A(-1, -2)$, $B(5, 0)$, $C(0, -6)$
3. $A(3, -4)$, $B(2, 1)$, $C(6, -2)$ 4. $A(0, 4)$, $B(0, 5)$, $C(12, 4)$

In problems 5 through 8, locate the midpoints of the line segments joining the given points.

5. $P_1(4, 8)$, $P_2(6, 3)$ 6. $P_1(-5, 4)$, $P_2(7, -2)$
7. $P_1(6, 0)$, $P_2(14, -3)$ 8. $P_1(12, 0)$, $P_2(0, 0)$

9. The midpoint of a line segment AB is at the point $P(-4, -3)$. The point A has coordinates $(8, -5)$. Find the coordinates of B.
10. The midpoint of a line segment AB is at the point $P(-7, 2)$. The x-coordinate of A is at 5, and the y-coordinate of B is at -9. Find the points A and B.
11. Find the lengths of the medians of the triangle with vertices at $A(4, 1)$, $B(-5, 2)$, $C(3, -7)$.
12. Same as problem 11, for $A(-3, 2)$, $B(4, 3)$, $C(-1, -4)$.
13. Show that the triangle with vertices at $A(1, -2)$, $B(-4, 2)$, $C(1, 6)$ is isosceles.
14. Same as 13, with $A(2, 3)$, $B(6, 2)$, $C(3, -1)$.
15. Show that the triangle with vertices at $A(0, 2)$, $B(3, 0)$, $C(4, 8)$ is a right triangle.
16. Same as 15, with $A(3, 2)$, $B(1, 1)$, $C(-1, 5)$.
17. Show that the quadrilateral with vertices at $(3, 2)$, $(0, 5)$, $(-3, 2)$, $(0, -1)$ is a square.
18. Show that the diagonals of the following quadrilateral bisect each other:

$$(-4, -2), \quad (2, -10), \quad (8, -5), \quad (2, 3).$$

19. Same as 18, for
$$(5, 3), \quad (2, -3), \quad (-2, 1), \quad (1, 7).$$

20. The four points $A(1, 1)$, $B(3, 2)$, $C(7, 3)$, $D(0, 9)$ form a quadrilateral. Show that the midpoints of the sides form the vertices of a parallelogram.

21. (a) Show how directed distances may be defined in a natural way for pairs of points on a line parallel to a coordinate axis. (b) Using this definition, carry through the proof of the midpoint formula, using directed distances along the line $P_1 D$ in Fig. 3–3.

2. SLOPE OF A LINE

A line L, not parallel to the x-axis, intersects it. Such a line and the x-axis form two angles which are supplementary. To be definite, we denote by α the angle formed by starting on the positive side of the x-axis and going counterclockwise until we reach the line L. The angle α will have a value between 0 and 180°. Two examples are shown in Fig. 3–4. The angle α is called the *inclination* of the line L. All lines parallel to the x-axis are said to make a zero angle with the x-axis and therefore have inclination zero. From plane geometry we recall the statement: "If, when two lines are cut by a transversal, corresponding angles are equal, the lines are parallel, and conversely." In Fig. 3–5, lines L_1 and L_2 each have inclination α. Applying the theorem of plane geometry, with the x-axis as the transversal, we conclude that L_1 and L_2 are parallel. More generally, we say that *all lines with the same inclination are parallel* and, conversely, *all parallel lines have the same inclination*.

The notion of inclination is a simple one which is easy to understand. However, for purposes of analytic geometry and calculus it is cumbersome and difficult to use. For this reason we introduce the notion of the *slope m of a line L* with inclination α. It is defined as
$$m = \tan \alpha.$$

Before discussing slope, we recall some of the properties of the tangent function. The tangent function is positive for angles in the first quadrant. It starts at zero for 0° and increases steadily, reaching 1 when $\alpha = 45°$. It continues to increase until, as the angle approaches 90°, the function increases without bound. The

(a)   (b)

FIGURE 3–4

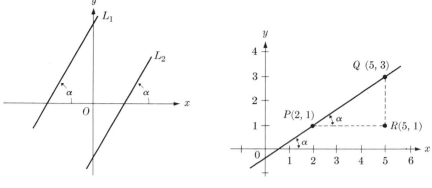

FIGURE 3-5   FIGURE 3-6

tangent of 90° is not defined. Loosely speaking, we sometimes say the tangent of
90° is infinite. In the second quadrant, the tangent function is negative, and its
values are obtained with the help of the relation

$$\tan(180° - \alpha) = -\tan \alpha.$$

That is, the tangent of an obtuse angle is the negative of that of the corresponding
acute supplementary angle.

From these facts about the tangent function, we see that any line parallel to the
x-axis has zero slope, while a line with an inclination between 0° and 90° has positive slope. A line parallel to the y-axis has no slope, strictly speaking, although we
sometimes say such a line has infinite slope. If the inclination is an obtuse angle,
the slope is negative. The line in Fig. 3–4(a) has positive slope, and the one in
Fig. 3–4(b) has negative slope.

Consider the line passing through the points $P(2, 1)$ and $Q(5, 3)$, as shown in
Fig. 3–6. To find the slope of this line, draw a parallel to the x-axis through P
and a parallel to the y-axis through Q, forming the right triangle PQR. The angle
α at P is equal to the inclination, by corresponding angles of parallel lines. The
definition of tangent function in a right triangle is "opposite over adjacent." The
slope is therefore given by

$$m = \tan \alpha = \frac{\overline{RQ}}{\overline{PR}}.$$

Since $\overline{RQ} = 3 - 1 = 2$ and $\overline{PR} = 5 - 2 = 3$, the slope m is $\frac{2}{3}$.

Suppose $P(x_1, y_1)$ and $Q(x_2, y_2)$ are any two points in the plane, and we wish
to find the slope m of the line passing through these two points. The procedure is
exactly the same as the one just described. In Fig. 3–7(a) we see that

$$m = \tan \alpha = \frac{y_2 - y_1}{x_2 - x_1},$$

and in Fig. 3–7(b)

$$m = \tan \alpha = -\tan(180 - \alpha) = -\frac{y_2 - y_1}{x_1 - x_2} = \frac{y_2 - y_1}{x_2 - x_1}.$$

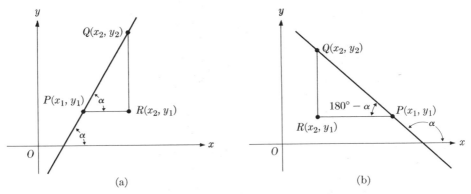

FIGURE 3–7

A difficulty may arise if the points P and Q are on a vertical line, since then $x_1 = x_2$ and the denominator is zero. However, we know that a vertical line has no slope, and we state that the formula holds for all cases except when $x_1 = x_2$. Note that there is no difficulty if P and Q lie on a horizontal line. In that case, $y_1 = y_2$ and the slope is zero, as it should be. We conclude: the *slope of a line through the points* $P(x_1, y_1)$ *and* $Q(x_2, y_2)$ *with* $x_1 \neq x_2$ *is given by the formula*

$$m = \frac{y_2 - y_1}{x_2 - x_1}.$$

EXAMPLE 1. Find the slope of the line through the points $(4, -2)$ and $(7, 3)$.

Solution. First we note that in the formula for slope it doesn't matter which point we label (x_1, y_1) [the other being labeled (x_2, y_2)]. Multiplication of numerator and denominator by -1 shows that

$$\frac{y_2 - y_1}{x_2 - x_1} = \frac{y_1 - y_2}{x_1 - x_2}.$$

We let $(4, -2)$ be (x_1, y_1) and $(7, 3)$ be (x_2, y_2). This gives

$$m = \frac{3 - (-2)}{7 - 4} = \frac{5}{3}.$$

FIGURE 3–8

EXAMPLE 2. Through the point $P(4, 1)$ construct a line which has slope equal to 3/2.

Solution. Starting at P, draw a parallel to the x-axis extending to the point R one unit to the right (Fig. 3–8). Now draw a parallel to the y-axis, stopping 3/2 units above R. The coordinates of this point Q are $(5, \frac{5}{2})$. The line through P and Q has slope 3/2.

3. PARALLEL AND PERPENDICULAR LINES

We have seen that parallel lines always have the same inclination. Therefore, *two parallel lines will always have the same slope.* Conversely, we show that *lines with the same slope must be parallel.* This fact is a result of a simple property of the tangent function: if this function has a given value, say b, there is exactly one angle between 0 and 180°, say β, such that $\tan \beta = b$. We conclude that if two lines have the same slope, their inclinations must also be the same, and the lines therefore are parallel. (This works even if the slopes are infinite, since then the lines are perpendicular to the x-axis and so parallel.)

When are two lines perpendicular? If a line is parallel to the x-axis, it has zero slope and is perpendicular to any line which has infinite slope. Suppose, however, that a line L_1 has slope m_1 which is not zero (Fig. 3–9). Its inclination will be α_1, also different from zero. Let L_2 be perpendicular to L_1 and have slope m_2 and inclination α_2, as shown. We recall from plane geometry: "An exterior angle of a triangle is equal to the sum of the remote interior angles." This means that

$$\alpha_2 = 90° + \alpha_1$$

and

$$\tan \alpha_2 = \tan(90° + \alpha_1).$$

We recall from trigonometry the formula

$$\tan(90° + A) = -\cot A,$$

from which we obtain

$$\tan \alpha_2 = -\cot \alpha_1 = -\frac{1}{\tan \alpha_1}.$$

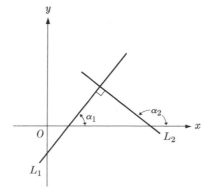

FIGURE 3–9

This last formula, in terms of slopes, states that

$$m_2 = -\frac{1}{m_1}$$

or, in words: *Two lines are perpendicular if their slopes are the negative reciprocals of each other, and conversely.*

———————————

EXAMPLE 1. Show that the line through $P_1(3, -4)$ and $Q_1(-2, 6)$ is parallel to the line through $P_2(-3, 6)$ and $Q_2(9, -18)$.

Solution. The slope of the line through P_1 and Q_1, according to the formula, is

$$m_1 = \frac{6 - (-4)}{-2 - 3} = \frac{10}{-5} = -2.$$

Similarly, the line through P_2 and Q_2 has slope

$$m_2 = \frac{-18 - 6}{9 + 3} = -2.$$

Since the slopes are the same, the lines must be parallel.

EXAMPLE 2. Determine whether or not the three points $P(-1, -5)$, $Q(1, 3)$, and $R(7, 12)$ lie on the same straight line.

Solution. The line through P and Q has slope

$$m_1 = \frac{3 - (-5)}{1 - (-1)} = 4.$$

If R were on this line, the line joining R and Q would have to be the very same line; therefore it would have the same slope. The slope of the line through R and Q is

$$m_2 = \frac{12 - 3}{7 - 1} = \frac{3}{2},$$

and this is different from m_1. Therefore, P, Q, and R do not lie on the same line.

EXAMPLE 3. Is the line through the points $P_1(5, -1)$ and $Q_1(-3, 2)$ perpendicular to the line through the points $P_2(-3, 1)$ and $Q_2(0, 9)$?

Solution. The line through P_1 and Q_1 has slope

$$m_1 = \frac{2 - (-1)}{-3 - 5} = -\frac{3}{8}.$$

The line through P_2 and Q_2 has slope

$$m_2 = \frac{9 - 1}{0 - (-3)} = \frac{8}{3}.$$

The slopes are the negative reciprocals of each other, and the lines are perpendicular.

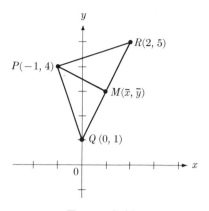

FIGURE 3–10

EXAMPLE 4. Given the isosceles triangle with vertices at the points $P(-1, 4)$, $Q(0, 1)$, and $R(2, 5)$, show that the median drawn from P is perpendicular to the base QR (Fig. 3–10).

Solution. Let M be the point where the median from P intersects the base QR. From the definition of median, M must be the midpoint of the segment QR. The coordinates of M, from the midpoint formula, are

$$\bar{x} = \frac{0 + 2}{2} = 1, \qquad \bar{y} = \frac{5 + 1}{2} = 3.$$

Now we check the slopes of PM and QR. The slope of PM is

$$m_1 = \frac{3 - 4}{1 - (-1)} = -\frac{1}{2}.$$

The slope of QR is

$$m_2 = \frac{5 - 1}{2 - 0} = 2.$$

Since

$$m_1 = -\frac{1}{m_2},$$

the median is perpendicular to the base.

EXERCISES

In problems 1 through 6, check to see whether the line through the pair of points P_1, Q_1 is parallel or perpendicular to the line through the pair of points P_2, Q_2.

1. $P_1(-5, 1)$, $Q_1(3, -2)$ and $P_2(3, 2)$, $Q_2(11, -1)$
2. $P_1(3, -1)$, $Q_1(-2, 5)$ and $P_2(5, 0)$, $Q_2(-1, -5)$
3. $P_1(4, 2)$, $Q_1(7, 2)$ and $P_2(8, 5)$, $Q_2(8, -3)$
4. $P_1(-6, 3)$, $Q_1(12, 0)$ and $P_2(4, -2)$, $Q_2(7, -6)$
5. $P_1(12, 8)$, $Q_1(4, 8)$ and $P_2(3, 1)$, $Q_2(-6, 1)$
6. $P_1(3, -5)$, $Q_1(6, -2)$ and $P_2(5, 1)$, $Q_2(6, 0)$

In problems 7 through 10, determine whether or not the three points all lie on the same straight line.

7. $P(3, 4)$, $Q(8, 5)$, $R(13, 6)$ 8. $P(2, -1)$, $Q(5, 3)$, $R(-7, 4)$

9. $P(7, 1)$, $Q(-7, 2)$, $R(4, -5)$ 10. $P(-3, 0)$, $Q(4, 1)$, $R(11, 2)$

11. Construct a line passing through the point $(5, -2)$ and having slope $3/4$.

12. Construct a line passing through the point $(-3, 1)$ and having slope $-2/3$.

In problems 13 through 23, the points P, Q, R, S are the vertices of a quadrilateral. In each case, determine whether the figure is a trapezoid, parallelogram, rhombus, rectangle, square, or none of these.

13. $P(1, 3)$, $Q(2, 5)$, $R(6, 17)$, $S(5, 15)$

14. $P(1, 3)$, $Q(3, 7)$, $R(3, 11)$, $S(1, 7)$

15. $P(2, 3)$, $Q(4, 1)$, $R(0, -8)$, $S(-5, -3)$

16. $P(5, 6)$, $Q(-8, -7)$, $R(-8, -10)$, $S(5, 3)$

17. $P(-1, 2)$, $Q(2, -2)$, $R(\frac{38}{13}, -\frac{8}{13})$, $S(-\frac{17}{13}, \frac{8}{13})$

18. $P(\frac{4}{3}, \frac{20}{3})$, $Q(4, 2)$, $R(1, -4)$, $S(5, 12)$ 19. $P(3, -1)$, $Q(2, -6)$, $R(1, 7)$, $S(0, -8)$

20. $P(5, 3)$, $Q(8, 3)$, $R(4, 4)$, $S(7, 4)$ 21. $P(3, 0)$, $Q(3, 5)$, $R(0, 9)$, $S(0, 4)$

22. $P(2, 1)$, $Q(7, 13)$, $R(-5, 18)$, $S(-10, 6)$

23. $P(6, 2)$, $Q(3, -1)$, $R(7, 5)$, $S(8, -4)$

24. The points $A(3, -2)$, $B(4, 1)$, and $C(-3, 5)$ are the vertices of a triangle. Show that the line through the midpoints of the sides AB and AC is parallel to the base BC of the triangle.

25. The points $A(0, 0)$, $B(a, 0)$, and $C(\frac{1}{2}a, b)$ are the vertices of a triangle. Show that the triangle is isosceles. Prove that the median from C is perpendicular to the base AB. How general is this proof?

26. The points $A(0, 0)$, $B(a, 0)$, $C(a + b, c)$, $D(b, c)$ form the vertices of a parallelogram. Prove that the diagonals bisect each other.

4. THE STRAIGHT LINE

We saw earlier that the equation $y = 4$ represented all points on a line parallel to the x-axis and four units above it. Similarly, the equation $x = -2$ represents all points on a line parallel to the y-axis and two units to the left. More generally, any line parallel to the y-axis has an equation of the form

$$x = a,$$

where a is the number denoting how far the line is to the right or left of the y-axis. The equation

$$y = b$$

describes a line parallel to the x-axis and b units from it. In this way we have obtained the equations of all lines with zero or infinite slope. A line which is not parallel to either axis has a slope m which is different from zero. Suppose also that

FIGURE 3–11

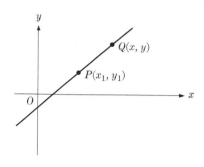

FIGURE 3–12

the line passes through a point $P(x_1, y_1)$. To be specific, we consider the slope m to be $-\frac{2}{3}$ and the point P to have coordinates $(4, -3)$. If a point $Q(x, y)$ is on this line, then the slope as calculated from P to Q must be $-\frac{2}{3}$, as shown in Fig. 3–11. That is,

$$\frac{y + 3}{x - 4} = -\tfrac{2}{3}, \quad \text{or} \quad y + 3 = -\tfrac{2}{3}(x - 4).$$

This is the equation of the line passing through the point $(4, -3)$ *with slope* $-\frac{2}{3}$. In the general case of a line with slope m passing through $P(x_1, y_1)$ the statement that $Q(x, y)$ is on the line is the same as the statement that the slope m as computed from P to Q (Fig. 3–12) is

$$\frac{y - y_1}{x - x_1} = m, \quad \text{or} \quad y - y_1 = m(x - x_1).$$

This last equation is called *the point-slope form for the equation of a line.* That is, if we are given the coordinates of a point and the numerical value of the slope, substitution in the above formula yields the equation of the line going through the point and having the given slope.

EXAMPLE 1. Find the equation of the line passing through the point $(-2, 5)$ and having slope 4/3.

Solution. Substitution in the above formula gives

$$y - 5 = \tfrac{4}{3}[x - (-2)], \quad \text{or} \quad 3y = 4x + 23.$$

We know that two points determine a line. The problem of finding the equation of the line passing through the points $(3, -5)$ and $(-7, 2)$ can be solved in two steps. First we employ the formula for the slope of a line, as given in Section 3, to obtain the slope of the line through the given points. We get

$$m = \frac{2 - (-5)}{-7 - 3} = -\frac{7}{10}.$$

Then, knowing the slope, we use *either* point, together with the slope, in the point-slope formula. This gives [using the point $(3, -5)$]

$$y - (-5) = -\tfrac{7}{10}(x - 3), \quad \text{or} \quad 10y = -7x - 29.$$

We verify quite easily that the same equation is obtained if the point $(-7, 2)$ is used instead of $(3, -5)$.

The above process may be transformed into a general formula by applying it to two points, $P_1(x_1, y_1)$ and $P_2(x_2, y_2)$. The slope of the line through these points is

$$m = \frac{y_2 - y_1}{x_2 - x_1}.$$

Substituting this value for the slope into the point-slope form, we get the *two-point form* for the equation of a line:

$$y - y_1 = \frac{y_2 - y_1}{x_2 - x_1}(x - x_1).$$

Note that this is really not a new formula, but merely the point-slope form with an expression for the slope substituted into it.

Another variation of the point-slope form is obtained by introducing a number called the *y*-intercept. Every line not parallel to the *y*-axis must intersect it; if we denote by $(0, b)$ the point of intersection, *the number b is called the y-intercept.** Suppose a line has slope m and *y*-intercept b. We substitute in the point-slope form to get

$$y - b = m(x - 0),$$

or

$$y = mx + b.$$

This is called the *slope-intercept form* for the equation of a straight line.

EXAMPLE 2. A line has slope 3 and *y*-intercept -4. Find its equation.

Solution. Substitution in the slope-intercept formula gives

$$y = 3x - 4.$$

If a line intersects the *x*-axis at a point $(a, 0)$, *the number a is called the x-intercept.*

Suppose a line has *x*-intercept a and *y*-intercept b (Fig. 3–13). This means the line must pass through the points $(a, 0)$ and $(0, b)$. Using the two-point form for the equation of a line, we have (assuming that $a \neq 0$)

$$y - 0 = \frac{b}{-a}(x - a), \quad \text{or} \quad bx + ay = ab.$$

---

*The point $(0, b)$ is also called the *y*-intercept.

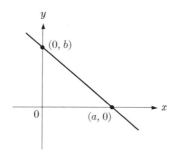

FIGURE 3–13

We divide through by ab (since if $a \neq 0$, b must also be different from zero) to get

$$\frac{x}{a} + \frac{y}{b} = 1,$$

which is called the *two-intercept form* for the equation of a line. It is valid whenever both the x- and y-intercepts are different from zero.

EXAMPLE 3. Find the equation of a line with x-intercept -3 and y-intercept 4.

Solution. Substitution in the above formula yields

$$\frac{x}{-3} + \frac{y}{4} = 1,$$

which is the desired result.

The important thing to notice is that the point-slope form is the basic one for the equation of a straight line. All other formulas were derived as simple variations or particular cases.

All three examples led to equations of lines which could be put in the form

$$Ax + By + C = 0,$$

where A, B, and C are any numbers. This equation is the most general equation of the first degree in x and y. We shall establish the theorem:

Theorem. *Every equation of the form*

$$Ax + By + C = 0,$$

so long as A and B are not both zero, is the equation of a straight line.

Proof. We consider two cases, according as $B = 0$ or $B \neq 0$. If $B = 0$, then we must have $A \neq 0$, and the above equation becomes

$$x = -\frac{C}{A},$$

which we know is the equation of a straight line parallel to the y-axis and $-C/A$ units from it.

If $B \neq 0$, we divide by B and solve for y, getting

$$y = -\frac{A}{B}x - \frac{C}{B}.$$

From the slope-intercept form for the equation of a line, we recognize this as the equation of a line with slope $-A/B$ and y-intercept $-C/B$.

In the statement of the theorem it is necessary to make the requirement that A and B are not both zero. If both of them vanish and C is zero, the linear equation reduces to the triviality $0 = 0$, which is satisfied by every point $P(x, y)$ in the plane. If $C \neq 0$, then no point $P(x, y)$ satisfies the equation $0 = C$.

EXAMPLE 4. Given the linear equation

$$3x + 2y + 6 = 0,$$

find the slope and y-intercept.

Solution. Solving for y, we have

$$y = -\tfrac{3}{2}x - 3.$$

From this we simply read off that $m = -\tfrac{3}{2}$ and $b = -3$.

EXAMPLE 5. Put the equation

$$2x - 5y + 7 = 0$$

in the two-intercept form.

Solution. We rewrite the equation in the form

$$2x - 5y = -7,$$

and divide by -7:

$$\frac{2x}{-7} - \frac{5y}{-7} = 1.$$

Now we again rewrite each term so that x and y appear alone in the numerator:

$$\frac{x}{-\frac{7}{2}} + \frac{y}{\frac{7}{5}} = 1.$$

The x- and y-intercepts are $-\tfrac{7}{2}$ and $\tfrac{7}{5}$, respectively. Note that if we merely wanted to find the intercepts we could set y equal to zero and solve for x to get the x-intercept, and set x equal to zero and solve for y to get the y-intercept. With this knowledge we could then write the answer to Example 5 by using the two-intercept formula.

An equation of the first degree in x and y is called a *linear equation*. When we solve for y in terms of x, as in the point-slope form, y becomes a function of x. Such a function is called a *linear function*. Any line not parallel to the y-axis may be thought of as a function of x. Similarly, the equation of any line not parallel to the x-axis may be solved for x in terms of y. Then x is a linear function of the variable y.

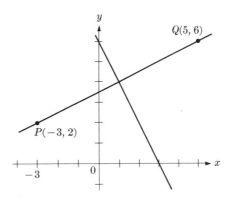

FIGURE 3–14

EXAMPLE 6. Find the equation of the line which is the perpendicular bisector of the line segment joining the points $P(-3, 2)$ and $Q(5, 6)$. (See Fig. 3–14.)

Solution. We give two methods. *Method* 1. We first find the slope m of the line through P and Q. It is

$$m = \frac{6 - 2}{5 + 3} = \frac{1}{2}.$$

The slope of the perpendicular bisector must be -2, the negative reciprocal. Next we get the coordinates of the midpoint of the line segment PQ. They are

$$\bar{x} = \frac{5 - 3}{2} = 1, \qquad \bar{y} = \frac{6 + 2}{2} = 4.$$

The equation of the line through $(1, 4)$ with slope -2 is

$$y - 4 = -2(x - 1), \qquad \text{or} \qquad 2x + y - 6 = 0,$$

which is the desired equation.

Method 2. We start by noting that any point on the perpendicular bisector must be equidistant from P and Q. Let $R(x, y)$ be any such point, and let d_1 denote the distance from R to P, and d_2 the distance from R to Q. From the formula for the distance between two points and the condition $d_1 = d_2$, we have

$$\sqrt{(x + 3)^2 + (y - 2)^2} = \sqrt{(x - 5)^2 + (y - 6)^2}$$

Squaring both sides and multiplying out, we obtain

$$x^2 + 6x + 9 + y^2 - 4y + 4 = x^2 - 10x + 25 + y^2 - 12y + 36.$$

The square terms cancel and the remaining terms combine to give

$$6x - 4y + 13 = -10x - 12y + 61,$$

or

$$16x + 8y - 48 = 0.$$

Dividing by 8, we obtain the same answer as in the first method:

$$2x + y - 6 = 0.$$

EXERCISES

In problems 1 through 20, find the equation of the line with the given requirements.

1. Slope 3 and passing through $(-2, 7)$
2. Slope -2 and passing through $(2, -6)$
3. Slope $-4/3$ and passing through $(-1, 7)$
4. Passing through the points $(5, 2)$ and $(-6, 1)$
5. Passing through the points $(-2, 6)$ and $(3, -5)$
6. Passing through the points $(0, 5)$ and $(3, 0)$
7. Slope 0 and passing through $(3, 8)$
8. Passing through the points $(5, 7)$ and $(5, -3)$
9. Passing through the points $(8, -2)$ and $(7, -2)$
10. Slope $-2/3$ and y-intercept 4
11. Slope 0 and y-intercept -5
12. Slope $4/5$ and y-intercept 8
13. Slope $1/3$ and x-intercept 3
14. Slope -4 and x-intercept 0
15. Slope -3 and y-intercept 0
16. x-intercept 3 and y-intercept -2
17. x-intercept -4 and y-intercept -3
18. x-intercept 5 and passing through the point $(-7, 2)$
19. y-intercept -7 and passing through the point $(3, 6)$
20. Parallel to the y-axis and passing through the point $(5, -2)$
21. Find the slope and y-intercept of the line $2x + 7y + 1 = 0$.
22. Find the slope and x-intercept of the line $x - 3y + 2 = 0$.
23. Find both intercepts of the line $2x + 5y + 8 = 0$.
24. Find both intercepts of the line $3x - 8y + 2 = 0$.
25. Find the equation of the line through the point $(1, -4)$ and parallel to the line $x + 5y - 3 = 0$.
26. Find the equation of the line through the point $(-2, -3)$ and parallel to the line $3x - 7y + 4 = 0$.
27. Find the equation of the line through the point $(3, -2)$ and perpendicular to the line $2x + 3y + 4 = 0$.
28. Find the equation of the line through the point $(1, 5)$ and perpendicular to the line $5x - 4y + 1 = 0$.
29. Find the equation of the line through the point $(-1, -3)$ and parallel to the line through the points $(3, 2)$ and $(-5, 7)$.
30. Find the equation of the line passing through $(4, -2)$ and parallel to the line through the points $(2, -1)$ and $(5, 7)$.
31. Find the equation of the line passing through $(-5, 3)$ and perpendicular to the line through the points $(7, 0)$ and $(-8, 1)$.

32. Find the equation of the line passing through $(2, -1)$ and perpendicular to the line through the points $(3, 1)$ and $(-2, 5)$.

33. Find the equation of the perpendicular bisector of the line segment joining $(6, 2)$ and $(-1, 3)$.

34. Find the equation of the perpendicular bisector of the line segment joining $(3, -1)$ and $(5, 2)$.

35. The points $P(0, 0)$, $Q(a, 0)$, $R(a, b)$, $S(0, b)$ are the vertices of a rectangle. Show that if the diagonals meet at right angles, then $a = \pm b$ and the rectangle must be a square.

36. Let P, Q, R, S be the vertices of a parallelogram. Show, by analytic geometry, that if the diagonals are equal the parallelogram must be a rectangle.

37. P, Q, R, S are the vertices of a parallelogram. Show, by analytic geometry, that if the diagonals are perpendicular the figure is a rhombus.

5.   INTERSECTION OF LINES; LINEAR INEQUALITIES

Any two nonparallel lines in the plane must intersect. The coordinates of the point of intersection satisfy *both* equations, since the point lies on both lines. Finding the point of intersection is a simple exercise in elementary algebra. If, for example, the equations of the lines are

$$2x - y - 7 = 0 \quad \text{and} \quad 4x + 3y - 9 = 0,$$

then solving simultaneously yields the values for x and y which satisfy both equations. These must be the coordinates of the point of intersection. A simple method of finding the solution is that of elimination: we multiply the first equation by 3 and add it to the second equation, to obtain

$$
\begin{array}{r}
6x - 3y - 21 = 0 \\
4x + 3y - 9 = 0 \\
\hline
10x - 30 = 0,
\end{array}
\quad \text{or} \quad x = 3.
$$

Now substitution of $x = 3$ in *either* of the two original equations gives $y = -1$. The point of intersection is $(3, -1)$. (See Fig. 3–15.)

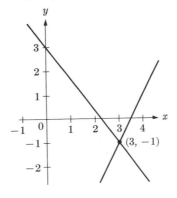

FIGURE 3–15

EXAMPLE 1. Find the equation of the line having slope -2 and passing through the intersection of the lines $3x - y + 2 = 0$ and $x + 2y - 5 = 0$.

Solution. We first solve the equations simultaneously to get the point of intersection. We find

$$
\begin{aligned}
6x - 2y + 4 &= 0 \\
\underline{x + 2y - 5} &= 0 \\
7x \qquad\quad - 1 &= 0, \qquad \text{or} \qquad x = \tfrac{1}{7}.
\end{aligned}
$$

Substitution of $x = \tfrac{1}{7}$ in the equation $x + 2y - 5 = 0$ gives $y = \tfrac{17}{7}$. Using the point-slope form for the equation of a line, we now obtain

$$ y - \tfrac{17}{7} = -2(x - \tfrac{1}{7}), \qquad \text{or} \qquad 14x + 7y - 19 = 0. $$

EXAMPLE 2. The points $P(0, 0)$, $Q(6, 0)$, and $R(4, 8)$ are the vertices of a triangle. Show that the medians intersect in a point.

Solution. We label the medians from P, Q, and R, respectively, L_1, L_2, and L_3, (Fig. 3–16). The line L_1 passes through the midpoint of the segment RQ; the coordinates of this midpoint are

$$ \bar{x} = \frac{4 + 6}{2} = 5, \qquad \bar{y} = \frac{8 + 0}{2} = 4. $$

Using the two-point form for a straight line, we get the equation for L_1:

$$ y - 0 = \frac{4 - 0}{5 - 0}(x - 0), \qquad \text{or} \qquad 5y = 4x. $$

Similarly, L_2 goes through $Q(6, 0)$ and the midpoint of RP. This midpoint has coordinates $(2, 4)$. The equation of L_2 is

$$ y - 0 = \frac{4 - 0}{2 - 6}(x - 6), \qquad \text{or} \qquad x + y = 6. $$

The equation of L_3 is found in the same way. It is

$$ 8x - y = 24. $$

FIGURE 3–16

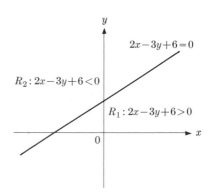

FIGURE 3–17

The point of intersection of L_1 and L_2 is found by elimination:

$$4x - 5y = 0$$
$$4x + 4y = 24$$

$$- 9y = -24, \quad \text{or} \quad y = \tfrac{8}{3}.$$

Substitution of $y = \tfrac{8}{3}$ in $x + y = 6$ gives $x = \tfrac{10}{3}$. Inserting $x = \tfrac{10}{3}$ and $y = \tfrac{8}{3}$ in the equation for L_3, $8x - y = 24$, we obtain

$$8(\tfrac{10}{3}) - \tfrac{8}{3} = 24,$$

which is a true statement. In other words, the point of intersection of L_1 and L_2 is on L_3. This is just another way of saying that the three medians intersect in a point.

In Chapter 2, Section 6, we made the important observation that equations give us information about points which do *not* satisfy them, as well as information about points which do. Every line divides the plane into two regions, one on each side of the line. All the points in one of these regions satisfy the same inequality, and all the points in the other satisfy the opposite inequality. For example, the equation

$$2x - 3y + 6 = 0$$

represents a straight line. As Fig. 3–17 shows, all the points in R_1 on one side of the line satisfy the inequality $2x - 3y + 6 > 0$, while all the points on the other side satisfy the inequality $2x - 3y + 6 < 0$.

Two intersecting lines divide the plane into four regions. Figure 3–18 shows how the lines

$$2x - y = 4 \quad \text{and} \quad 3x + y = 11$$

divide the plane into four regions, which we have labeled R_1, R_2, R_3, R_4. Each of

FIGURE 3–18

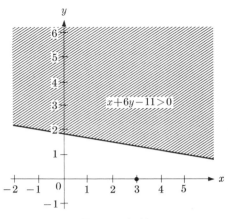

FIGURE 3–19

the regions is described by a *pair* of inequalities. That is, every point in R_1 satisfies both

$$2x - y - 4 > 0 \qquad \text{and} \qquad 3x + y - 11 > 0.$$

Similarly, the remaining regions satisfy the pairs of inequalities as shown in the figure. These relations, called *systems of linear inequalities*, are useful in describing regions bounded by straight lines. They all stem from the basic idea that a region of the plane bounded by a straight line satisfies a *linear inequality*. This inequality is obtained by taking the equation of the line and replacing the equality by a "greater than" or "less than" sign, according as the region is on one side or the other.

————————

EXAMPLE 3. Describe the region consisting of points which satisfy *all* three of the following inequalities:

$$x + 6y - 11 > 0, \quad 3x - 4y + 11 > 0, \quad -2x - y + 11 > 0.$$

Solution. We proceed step by step, first constructing the line with equation

$$x + 6y - 11 = 0$$

(Fig. 3–19). We select any point not on this line, say $(3, 0)$, and note that at $(3, 0)$ the inequality

$$3 + 6(0) - 11 < 0$$

holds. We conclude that this inequality holds for all points on the same side of the line as $(3, 0)$. The points on the other side (shown shaded in Fig. 3–19) all satisfy the inequality

$$x + 6y - 11 > 0.$$

Now we construct the line L_2: $3x - 4y + 11 = 0$, corresponding to the second in-

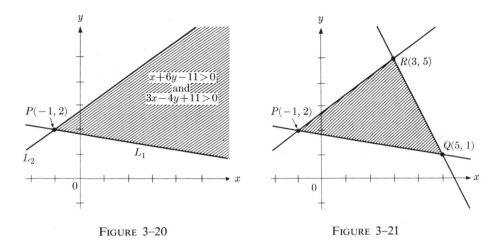

FIGURE 3–20   FIGURE 3–21

equality. We see that the shaded region (a sector) shown in Fig. 3–20 consists of all points which satisfy the first two inequalities. We now draw the third line L_3:

$$-2x - y + 11 = 0,$$

and the portion of the above sector which also satisfies the third inequality comprises the shaded triangle in Fig. 3–21. In other words, the three inequalities together describe all points inside the triangle with vertices at $P(-1, 2)$, $Q(5, 1)$, and $R(3, 5)$.

If, in Example 3, we had started with the inequalities

$$x + 6y - 11 \geq 0, \quad 3x - 4y + 11 > 0, \quad -2x - y - 11 > 0,$$

the solution would have consisted of all points inside the same triangle PQR and, in addition, all points on the line segment PQ (but excluding the endpoints P and Q).

A straight line may be thought of as the totality of points which satisfy a pair of inequalities. For example, all points which satisfy both

$$3x - 2y + 8 \geq 0 \quad \text{and} \quad 3x - 2y + 8 \leq 0$$

must be just those points on the line whose equation is

$$3x - 2y + 8 = 0.$$

EXERCISES

In problems 1 through 4, find the point of intersection of the lines.

1. $2x - 3y + 5 = 0$, $x - 6y + 7 = 0$ 2. $3x + 2y + 4 = 0$, $2x + 3y - 5 = 0$
3. $4x - 6y + 9 = 0$, $2x + 5y + 1 = 0$ 4. $x + 3y + 1 = 0$, $4x + 8y + 5 = 0$

In problems 5 through 10, determine whether or not the lines given are concurrent (i.e., whether they all intersect in the same point).

5. $3x - y + 8 = 0$, $2x + y - 3 = 0$, $4x - y + 9 = 0$
6. $2x + y - 1 = 0$, $5x - y - 7 = 0$, $4x + y - 5 = 0$
7. $3x + 2y - 1 = 0$, $8x - 4y + 9 = 0$, $2x + 6y - 5 = 0$
8. $x + 2y - 3 = 0$, $4x + 8y - 9 = 0$, $3x + 6y + 7 = 0$
9. $x - y + 1 = 0$, $2x - y + 11 = 0$, $x + y + 1 = 0$, $3x - y + 15 = 0$
10. $x - y - 4 = 0$, $x + y + 4 = 0$, $2x + y + 6 = 0$, $x + 3y + 8 = 0$
11. The points $A(3, 0)$, $B(9, 0)$, $C(7, 5)$ are the vertices of a triangle. Show that the altitudes from each vertex to the opposite side are concurrent.
12. The points $P(0, 0)$, $Q(a, 0)$, $R(b, c)$ are the vertices of a triangle. Show that the altitudes from each vertex to the opposite side are concurrent.

In problems 13 through 23, describe (by drawing a figure) the region of points (if any) which satisfy the system of linear inequalities.

13. $x + 3y - 6 > 0$ and $2x - y + 5 > 0$
14. $-x + 2y + 3 > 0$ and $3x - y + 4 > 0$
15. $2x + y - 3 \geq 0$ and $x - y + 2 > 0$
16. $x - 6y + 5 > 0$ and $3x + 4y - 7 > 0$
17. $x + 4y - 6 \geq 0$ and $2x - 6y + 7 \geq 0$
18. $2x - 6y + 5 \geq 0$ and $3x - 2y + 1 \geq 0$
19. $x - y > 0$, $-3x + 8y + 15 > 0$, and $-4x - y + 20 > 0$
20. $-x + 2y + 4 > 0$, $6x + y - 11 > 0$, and $-4x - 5y + 29 > 0$
21. $2x + y - 6 > 0$, and $-2x - y + 12 > 0$
22. $x > 0$, $y > 0$, $-2x - y + 10 > 0$, and $-y + 4 > 0$
23. $x - 2 \geq 0$, $y + 5 \geq 0$, $x - y \geq 0$, and $-2x - y + 20 > 0$
24. Can every trapezoid be described by a system of four linear inequalities? Prove your result.
25. What types of quadrilaterals can be described by four linear inequalities?
26. State a condition which guarantees that a polygon with n sides can be described by n linear inequalities.

6. SYSTEMS OF LINEAR INEQUALITIES; RELATION TO LINEAR PROGRAMMING

In Section 5 of this chapter we discussed regions in the plane bounded by straight lines which were defined by two or three linear inequalities. Suppose we have 10 such inequalities, or 1000. We may ask two questions: (1) Are there any points in the plane which satisfy all these inequalities? (2) If so, how would we go about finding them? To simplify the discussion, we shall consider a particular example and give some hints about the more general case.

Suppose we have the following five inequalities:

$$L_1: \qquad x + y - 4 \geq 0;$$
$$L_2: \qquad x + 3y - 8 \geq 0;$$
$$L_3: \qquad 8x + 7y - 27 \geq 0;$$
$$L_4: \quad -4x - y + 21 \geq 0;$$
$$L_5: \qquad 2x - 3y + 7 \geq 0.$$

To learn if there are any points which satisfy all the inequalities, we start by replacing the first two inequalities by the equations

$$x + y - 4 = 0 \qquad \text{and} \qquad x + 3y - 8 = 0$$

and solving them simultaneously. The solution of this system is the point $P_1(2, 2)$. We know that this point satisfies L_1 and L_2. We substitute in the remaining three inequalities, to obtain

$$8(2) + 7(2) - 27 \geq 0, \text{ yes;}$$
$$-4(2) - 2 + 21 \geq 0, \text{ yes;}$$
$$2(2) - 3(2) + 7 \geq 0, \text{ yes.}$$

We conclude that P_1 is a point which satisfies all the inequalities. Next we try two other inequalities, say L_1 and L_3. Solving the equations

$$x + y - 4 = 0 \qquad \text{and} \qquad 8x + 7y - 27 = 0$$

simultaneously, we get $P_2(-1, 5)$. We substitute this in the remaining three inequalities:

$$-1 + 3(5) - 8 \geq 0, \text{ yes;}$$
$$-4(-1) - 5 + 21 \geq 0, \text{ yes;}$$
$$2(-1) - 3(5) + 7 \geq 0, \text{ no!}$$

So P_2 is not a point which satisfies all the inequalities. Continuing in this way by solving all possible pairs of equations corresponding to L_1 through L_5, we find that of the ten points of intersection the four points

$$P_1(2, 2), \quad P_3(5, 1), \quad P_4(4, 5), \quad P_5(1, 3)$$

satisfy all the inequalities, while the other six do not. Figure 3–22 shows the four points. It can be shown that the shaded quadrilateral contains all the points which satisfy the system L_1 through L_5. The points P_1, P_3, P_4, P_5 are the vertices of this quadrilateral.

We now give the general procedure for determining the region of points satisfying an arbitrary number, say n, of linear inequalities. First, we find all possible points of intersection of the linear equations by pairs. To do so, we must solve $[n(n - 1)]/(1 \cdot 2)$ pairs of simultaneous equations. Second, each point of intersection is substituted in the remaining $n - 2$ inequalities, to see if all of them are

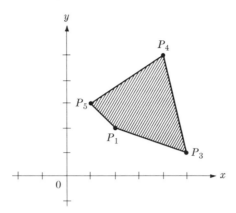

FIGURE 3–22

satisfied at this point. Third, we form the polygon having as vertices the points of intersection which satisfy all the inequalities. Fourth, if *no* points of intersection satisfy all the inequalities, we may conclude that there is no solution to the original system.

Clearly, if $n = 100$ the task is almost hopeless, and if $n = 1000$ or 10,000, the problem staggers the imagination. However, with modern electronic computers capable of performing thousands of additions, subtractions, multiplications, and divisions each second, problems of this type become feasible.

Systems of linear inequalities arise in many branches of engineering, physics, economics, statistics, and so forth. In fact, the problem usually doesn't end when the region satisfying the inequalities is obtained. Further questions may be asked. For example, what point in the region is closest to the x-axis? Does the region intersect a specific line? What point in the region is farthest from the origin? Computers can answer these and many other questions by modern programming methods.

In actual practice, the problems are much more complicated (usually involving many variables), and as a result the techniques developed for determining the region in question are much more sophisticated than the one outlined above.

EXERCISES

Find the region, if any, satisfied by each of the following systems of inequalities:

1. $x + y - 1 \geq 0$, $x + y - 3 \geq 0$, $x - 2 \geq 0$, $x + 2y - 1 \geq 0$, $-y + 2 \geq 0$, $-x + 6 \geq 0$

2. $x \geq 0$, $y \geq 0$, $x - y + 1 \geq 0$, $-x - y + 5 \geq 0$, $-3x - y + 8 \geq 0$

3. $-x \geq 0$, $y \geq 1$, $x - 2y + 4 \geq 0$, $x - 3y + 4 \geq 0$, $-x - y + 7 \geq 0$

4. $x + y + 3 \geq 0$, $2x - y + 6 \geq 0$, $-x + 7 \geq 0$, $-x - y + 12 \geq 0$, $-y + 8 \geq 0$, $x - 2y \geq 0$, $-x - 3y \geq 0$

5. Does the region in problem 1 intersect the x-axis?

6. In the region satisfying the conditions of problem 2, find the point which is closest to the line $x = -10$.

7. In the region satisfying the conditions of problem 3, find the point which is closest to the line $x - y = 30$.

8. Does the line $x - 2y = 7$ intersect the region satisfying the conditions of problem 4?

CHAPTER 4

Preview of the Calculus

1. LIMITS

The single most important idea in calculus is that of limit. The limit concept is at the foundation of almost all of mathematical analysis, and an understanding of it is absolutely essential. The reader should not be surprised to find the discussion rather complex and perhaps difficult. This should not prove discouraging, however, for once a precise understanding of the limit concept is achieved, the reward is a good grasp of the basic processes of calculus.

We shall begin with an intuitive discussion of limit and postpone a formal description to Chapter 5, Section 1. It may seem strange that it is possible to work with and apply an idea without defining it precisely, but historically the limit concept evolved in just this way. In the early development of calculus precise statements in the modern sense were seldom made. Yet progress was achieved because there was a certain degree of understanding. When imprecise ideas led to trouble, a later, more careful approach overcame the difficulty, and a more solid basis for calculus was attained. The same process continues today in mathematical research.

FIGURE 4–1   FIGURE 4–2

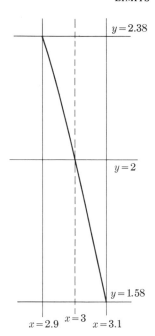

FIGURE 4–3   FIGURE 4–4

We begin by considering a function f with independent variable x and dependent variable y; that is, $y = f(x)$. We concentrate on a particular value of x, say $x = a$. For example, let the function be

$$y = f(x) = -2x^2 + 8x - 4,$$

and take the particular value $x = 3$. A graph of this function is shown in Fig. 4–1. We are interested in this function not only when $x = 3$ but also when x takes on values in various intervals containing 3.

Suppose that we select the interval from $x = 1$ to $x = 4$. A graph of the function in this region shows that the highest value is attained at $x = 2$ when y is 4, and the lowest value occurs at $x = 4$ when y is -4 (Fig. 4–2). In other words, the graph of the function lies in the rectangle bounded by the lines $x = 1$, $x = 4$ and $y = 4$, $y = -4$. The next step is to select a smaller interval about $x = 3$. Suppose we take the interval from $x = 2\frac{1}{2}$ to $x = 3\frac{1}{2}$ and draw the graph in this region (Fig. 4–3). The graph of the function is now in the rectangle bounded by the lines $x = 2\frac{1}{2}$, $x = 3\frac{1}{2}$; $y = -\frac{1}{2}$, $y = 3\frac{1}{2}$, as shown. Proceeding further, we take a still smaller interval about $x = 3$, say from $x = 2.9$ to $x = 3.1$. We draw the graph (enlarged) in this region, as shown in Fig. 4–4. The function values are now situated in the rectangle bounded by the lines $x = 2.9$, $x = 3.1$; $y = 1.58$, $y = 2.38$.

The main point we wish to emphasize concerns the height of these rectangles. As the widths of the rectangles become narrower, the heights also shrink in size. If we went further and took an x-interval from 2.99 to 3.01, the corresponding rectangle containing the graph of the function would be bounded by the lines

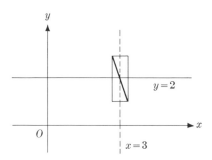

FIGURE 4–5

$x = 2.99$, $x = 3.01$; $y = 1.9598$, $y = 2.1398$. A width of 0.02 unit containing the value 3 leads to a rectangle of height only 0.18 unit. In addition to the heights becoming narrower and narrower as the widths squeeze in to the value $x = 3$, we observe that the heights cluster about the value $y = 2$. The reader may wonder what all this fuss is about, since the formula for the equation yields, by direct substitution, the result that $y = 2$ when $x = 3$. Note, however, that throughout the discussion we never made use of this fact (Fig. 4–5). Indeed, we carefully avoided any consideration at all of what happens when x is 3. We are concerned solely with the behavior of y when x is in some *interval* about the value 3.

For almost all functions we have studied up to this time, the behavior of a function at a point, say at $x = 3$, and its behavior in a sequence of shrinking intervals about this point were never distinguished. Now, however, a striking change occurs as we start to study functions whose behavior cannot be discovered by straight substitution. For example, the function

$$y = f(x) = \frac{\sin x}{x}$$

is defined for all values of x except $x = 0$. A straight substitution at $x = 0$ would tell us that

$$y = f(0) = \tfrac{0}{0},$$

which is completely meaningless. However, we shall see (Chapter 11, Section 1) that by studying a sequence of intervals about $x = 0$ which get smaller and smaller, we find that the corresponding rectangles containing the function get thinner and thinner, and the heights cluster about a particular value of y. Nothing is ever stated about the value of y when x *is* zero. We just study the value of y when x gets closer and closer to zero.

Returning to the first example of the function

$$f(x) = -2x^2 + 8x - 4,$$

we see that as x comes closer and closer to the value 3, $f(x)$ gets closer and closer to the value 2. We say, "$f(x)$ approaches 2 as x approaches 3." This sentence is abbreviated even further by the statement

$$\lim_{x \to 3} f(x) = 2.$$

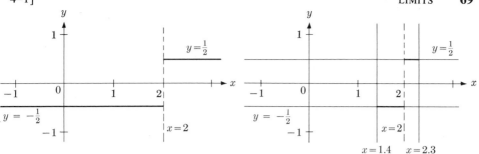

FIGURE 4–6   FIGURE 4–7

Here once again we have the shorthand typical of mathematics. A complex idea which takes several paragraphs to describe, even in a simple case, is boiled down to a brief symbolic expression. Furthermore, this symbolic expression contains a shorthand symbol for the notion of function, developed previously in Chapter 2, Section 2. As we proceed further, more concepts will be built on this symbolism.

If a function f is defined for values of x about the fixed number a, and if, as x tends toward a, the values of $f(x)$ get closer and closer to some specific number L, we write

$$\lim_{x \to a} f(x) = L,$$

and we read it, "The limit of $f(x)$ as x approaches a is L." Geometrically, this means that the series of rectangles which surround a and which have narrower and narrower widths become lower and lower in height and cluster about the point (a, L).

Of course all the above statements containing terms such as "closer," "nearer," "narrower," etc., are quite imprecise and are intended to give only an intuitive idea of what occurs. As mentioned, a precise definition of the expression

$$\lim_{x \to a} f(x) = L$$

is given in Chapter 5, Section 1.

Now let us take an example in which the result is quite different from that of the first example. We define the function

$$y = f(x) = \frac{x - 2}{2|x - 2|},$$

which is well determined for all values of x except $x = 2$. At $x = 2$ the function is not defined, since straight substitution yields $y = \frac{0}{0}$, a meaningless expression. The graph of the function, shown in Fig. 4–6, is quite simple. If x is larger than 2, then $|x - 2| = x - 2$ and the function has the value $+\frac{1}{2}$. If x is less than 2, then $|x - 2| = -(x - 2)$, and the function is equal to $-\frac{1}{2}$. We wish to study the behavior of the function as x tends to 2. We select an interval containing $x = 2$, say from $x = 1.4$ to $x = 2.3$. We see that the function is contained in the rectangle bounded by the lines $x = 1.4$, $x = 2.3$; $y = -\frac{1}{2}$, $y = +\frac{1}{2}$ (Fig. 4–7). In fact, no matter how narrow the interval about $x = 2$ becomes, the height of

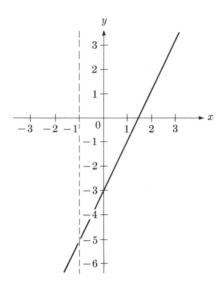

FIGURE 4–8

the rectangle will always be 1 unit. There is no limit as x approaches 2. We say that

$$\lim_{x \to 2} \frac{x - 2}{2|x - 2|} \quad \text{does not exist.}$$

We now examine a number of examples of functions, with a view toward discovering what happens in the neighborhood of a particular value when the function is not defined at that value by straight substitution.

EXAMPLE 1. The function

$$f(x) = \frac{2x^2 - x - 3}{x + 1}$$

is defined for all values of x except $x = -1$, since at $x = -1$ both numerator and denominator vanish. Does

$$\lim_{x \to -1} f(x)$$

exist and, if so, what is its value?

Solution. To get an idea of what is happening, we construct a table of values. Then we draw the graph, which appears to be a straight line with a "hole" at the point $(-1, -5)$ (Fig. 4–8). From the geometric discussion of rectangles given at the beginning of this section we see that

$$\lim_{x \to -1} f(x) = -5.$$

However, we would like a more systematic method of obtaining limits, without relying on pictorial representation and intuition. By means of factoring, we can write $f(x)$ in the form

$$f(x) = \frac{(2x - 3)(x + 1)}{x + 1}.$$

Now if $x \neq -1$, we are allowed to divide both the numerator and the denominator by $(x + 1)$. Then

$$f(x) = 2x - 3, \quad \text{if } x \neq -1.$$

This function tends to -5 as x tends to -1, since simple substitution now works. We conclude that

$$\lim_{x \to -1} f(x) = -5.$$

Note that we never substituted the value $x = -1$ in the original expression.

EXAMPLE 2. Find the limit of the function

$$f(x) = \frac{x - 4}{3(\sqrt{x} - 2)}, \quad x \neq 4,$$

as x tends to 4. (This function is defined for nonnegative values of x only.)

Solution. We note that straight substitution of $x = 4$ fails, since $f(4) = 0/0$, which is meaningless. We could proceed graphically, as in Example 1, but instead a useful algebraic trick is introduced. We rationalize the denominator by multiplying both numerator and denominator by $\sqrt{x} + 2$. So long as $x \neq 4$, we can write

$$\frac{x - 4}{3(\sqrt{x} - 2)} \frac{\sqrt{x} + 2}{\sqrt{x} + 2} = \frac{(x - 4)(\sqrt{x} + 2)}{3(x - 4)},$$

and furthermore the common factor can be cancelled if $x \neq 4$. We get

$$f(x) = \frac{\sqrt{x} + 2}{3}, \quad \text{if } x \neq 4.$$

The limit of this expression can be found by straight substitution of $x = 4$. We find

$$\lim_{x \to 4} f(x) = \frac{\sqrt{4} + 2}{3} = \frac{4}{3}.$$

EXAMPLE 3. Find the limit of the function

$$f(x) = \frac{\sqrt{2 + x} - 1}{x + 1}, \quad x \neq -1,$$

as x tends to -1. (This function is defined only for values of x larger than or equal to -2.)

Solution. Since straight substitution fails, we employ the device of "rationalizing the numerator." Multiplication of numerator and denominator by $\sqrt{2+x}+1$ yields

$$f(x) = \frac{(\sqrt{2+x}-1)(\sqrt{2+x}+1)}{(x+1)(\sqrt{2+x}+1)} = \frac{x+1}{(x+1)(\sqrt{2+x}+1)}, \qquad x \neq -1.$$

We now divide numerator and denominator by $x+1$ and find that

$$f(x) = \frac{1}{\sqrt{2+x}+1} \qquad \text{for } x \neq -1, \; x \geq -2.$$

As x tends to -1, $f(x)$ tends to

$$\frac{1}{\sqrt{2-1}+1} = \frac{1}{2}.$$

EXERCISES

In problems 1 through 12, find the limits approached by $f(x)$ as $x \to a$.

1. $f(x) = \dfrac{x^2 - 9}{x^2 - 5x + 6}$, $a = 3$ 2. $f(x) = \dfrac{x^3 + 8}{x^2 - 4}$, $a = -2$

3. $f(x) = \dfrac{x^4 - 2x - 3}{x + 1}$, $a = 3$ 4. $f(x) = \dfrac{x^2 - 3x + 2}{x^2 + x - 2}$, $a = 2$

5. $f(x) = \dfrac{5x^3 + 8x^2}{3x^4 - 16x^2}$, $a = 0$ 6. $f(x) = \dfrac{x^4 - 16}{x^2 - 4}$, $a = 2$

7. $f(x) = \dfrac{\sqrt{x+1} - 2}{x - 3}$, $a = 3, \; x \geq -1$

8. $f(x) = \dfrac{x^4 - 2x - 3}{x + 1}$, $a = -1$

9. $f(x) = \dfrac{\sqrt{2x+3} - x}{x - 3}$, $a = 3, \; x \geq -3/2$

10. $f(x) = \dfrac{\sqrt{x^2+3} - 2}{x + 1}$, $a = -1$

11. $f(x) = \dfrac{x - 9}{\sqrt{x} - 3}$, $a = 9, \; x \geq 0$

12. $f(x) = \dfrac{x + 3}{\sqrt{x^2+7} - 4}$, $a = -3$

Find the following limits:

13. $\lim\limits_{x \to 2} (x^2 + 5x - 7)$

14. $\lim\limits_{x \to -1} (2x^3 + 6x^2 - 3)$

15. $\lim\limits_{x \to 3} \dfrac{x^2 - 9}{x - 3}$

16. $\lim\limits_{x \to -2} \dfrac{\sqrt{4 - x^2}}{x + 2}$, $x \neq -2, \; |x| \leq 2$

17. $\lim\limits_{x \to 0} \dfrac{\sqrt{5+x} - \sqrt{5}}{2x}$

18. $\lim\limits_{h \to 0} \dfrac{\sqrt{9 + 2h} - 3}{h}$

19. $\lim\limits_{h \to 0} \dfrac{h^2}{\sqrt{4 + 3h^2} - 2}$

20. $\lim\limits_{h \to 0} \dfrac{\sqrt{3x + h} - \sqrt{3x}}{h}$

21. $\lim\limits_{h \to 1} \dfrac{\sqrt{b + 2(h - 1)} - \sqrt{b}}{h - 1}$

22. $\lim\limits_{x \to 2} \dfrac{\sqrt[3]{x} - \sqrt[3]{2}}{x - 2}$

23. $\lim\limits_{x \to -4} \dfrac{x^6 - 4096}{x + 4}$

2. LIMITS (continued)

In evaluating limits, functional notation plays a convenient and important part. Consider the function

$$f(x) = x^2 + 3,$$

and suppose that we wish to evaluate the limit

$$\lim_{x \to 0} \frac{f(5 + x) - f(5)}{x}, \qquad x \neq 0.$$

A straight substitution of $x = 0$ leads to the meaningless expression

$$[f(5) - f(5)]/0 = 0/0,$$

and we must penetrate a little deeper. We have $f(5) = 28$ and $f(5 + x) = (5 + x)^2 + 3 = x^2 + 10x + 28$. Therefore

$$\frac{f(5 + x) - f(5)}{x} = \frac{x^2 + 10x + 28 - 28}{x} = x + 10.$$

The cancellation of x from numerator and denominator is most fortunate, since now

$$\lim_{x \to 0} (x + 10)$$

may be found by direct substitution; the answer is 10.

EXAMPLE 1. Find the limit

$$\lim_{h \to 0} \frac{f(4 + h) - f(4)}{h}, \qquad h \neq 0,$$

where

$$f(x) = \frac{1}{(x + 1)^2}.$$

Solution. Direct substitution of $h = 0$ gives

$$\frac{f(4) - f(4)}{0} = \frac{0}{0},$$

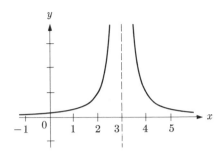

FIGURE 4–9

which again is meaningless. However,

$$f(4) = \frac{1}{25}, \qquad f(4+h) = \frac{1}{(4+h+1)^2} = \frac{1}{(5+h)^2}.$$

Therefore

$$\frac{f(4+h) - f(4)}{h} = \frac{\dfrac{1}{(5+h)^2} - \dfrac{1}{25}}{h}.$$

We might try direct substitution at this point, but again we would fail, since the result is again 0/0. We proceed by finding the lowest common denominator, getting

$$\frac{f(4+h) - f(4)}{h} = \frac{25 - (5+h)^2}{25h(5+h)^2} = \frac{-(10h + h^2)}{25h(5+h)^2}.$$

So long as $h \neq 0$, this factor may be cancelled in both numerator and denominator. Then

$$\lim_{h \to 0} \frac{-(10+h)}{25(5+h)^2}$$

may be obtained by direct substitution. The answer is $-2/125$.

EXAMPLE 2. Find the limit

$$\lim_{x \to 3} f(x),$$

where

$$f(x) = \frac{1}{(x-3)^2}, \qquad x \neq 3.$$

Solution. Sketching the graph of this function about $x = 3$, we see that it increases without bound as x tends to 3 (Fig. 4–9). According to the notion of limit as given in Section 1, we take an interval of x values about 3 and then see in what rectangle the function values are contained. From the figure it is clear that there is no such rectangle, regardless of how small an interval is chosen about $x = 3$. In such a case we say that

$$\lim_{x \to 3} f(x)$$

does not exist.

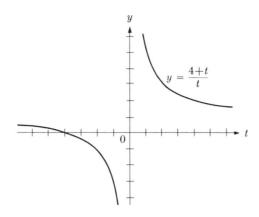

FIGURE 4–10

EXAMPLE 3. Find the limit

$$\lim_{t \to 0} \frac{f(2 + t) - f(2)}{t^2}$$

where $f(x) = x^2$.

Solution. Direct substitution of $t = 0$ fails, and we proceed as before to find that

$$f(2) = 4 \quad \text{and} \quad f(2 + t) = (2 + t)^2 = 4 + 4t + t^2.$$

Therefore

$$\frac{f(2 + t) - f(2)}{t^2} = \frac{4 + 4t + t^2 - 4}{t^2} = \frac{4 + t}{t}.$$

However, this function increases without bound as t tends to zero through positive values, and it decreases without bound as t tends to zero through negative values (Fig. 4–10). The limit does not exist.

EXAMPLE 4. Find the limit

$$\lim_{k \to 0} \frac{f(-1 + k) - f(-1)}{\sqrt{k}}, \qquad k > 0$$

where $f(x) = x^3$.

Solution. We have

$$f(-1) = -1, f(-1 + k) = (-1 + k)^3,$$

and

$$\frac{f(-1 + k) - f(-1)}{\sqrt{k}} = \frac{k^3 - 3k^2 + 3k - 1 - (-1)}{\sqrt{k}}$$

$$= \frac{k(k^2 - 3k + 3)}{\sqrt{k}} = \sqrt{k}(k^2 - 3k + 3).$$

As k tends to zero, this expression also tends to zero, and the answer is zero.

EXERCISES

Evaluate the following limits:

1. $\displaystyle\lim_{x\to 0}\frac{f(5+x)-f(5)}{x}$, $f(x)=2x^2+3$

2. $\displaystyle\lim_{h\to 0}\frac{f(-3+h)-f(-3)}{h}$, $f(x)=x^2-2$

3. $\displaystyle\lim_{t\to 0}\frac{f(2+t)-f(2)}{t}$, $f(x)=4x^3$

4. $\displaystyle\lim_{k\to 0}\frac{f(3+k)-f(3)}{k}$, $f(x)=\dfrac{1}{x}$, $x\neq 0$

5. $\displaystyle\lim_{h\to 0}\frac{f(a+h)-f(a)}{h}$, $f(x)=3x^2-1$

6. $\displaystyle\lim_{h\to 0}\frac{f(b+h)-f(b)}{h}$, $f(x)=-\dfrac{3}{x^2}$, $x\neq 0$

7. $\displaystyle\lim_{h\to 0}\frac{g(2+h)-g(2)}{h}$, $g(x)=12-x^2$

8. $\displaystyle\lim_{h\to 0}\frac{g(-4+h)-g(-4)}{h}$, $g(x)=\dfrac{1}{x^2+1}$

9. $\displaystyle\lim_{h\to 0}\frac{F(-2+h)-F(-2)}{h}$, $F(x)=\dfrac{1}{x-1}$, $x\neq 1$

10. $\displaystyle\lim_{h\to 0}\frac{F(a+h)-F(a)}{h}$, $F(x)=\dfrac{1}{\sqrt{x}}$, $x>0$, $a>0$

11. $\displaystyle\lim_{h\to 0}\frac{F(x+h)-F(x)}{h}$, $F(x)=-x^2+5$

12. $\displaystyle\lim_{k\to 0}\frac{G(b+k)-G(b)}{k}$, $G(x)=x^2-2x+3$

13. $\displaystyle\lim_{t\to 0}\frac{H(3+t)-H(3)}{t}$, $H(x)=x^3+2x+5$

14. $\displaystyle\lim_{h\to 0}\frac{F(4+h)-F(4)}{h}$, $F(x)=\dfrac{1}{x^2+4}$

15. $\displaystyle\lim_{h\to 0}\frac{F(2+h)-F(2)}{\sqrt{h}}$, $F(x)=x^4-2x+5$

16. $\displaystyle\lim_{h\to 0}\frac{L(3+h)-L(3)}{h^{3/2}}$, $L(x)=\dfrac{1}{x^2+2}-3$

17. $\displaystyle\lim_{h\to 0}\frac{f(x+h)-f(x)}{h}$, $f(x)=x^{3/2}$, $x>0$

18. $\displaystyle\lim_{h\to 0}\frac{F(t+h)-F(t)}{h}$, $F(x)=x^2-\dfrac{1}{x^2}$, $x\neq 0$

19. $\lim\limits_{h \to 0} \dfrac{g(c + h) - g(c)}{h}$, $g(x) = x^2 + 3x - c$

20. $\lim\limits_{h \to 0} \dfrac{g(x + 3h) - g(x)}{h}$, $g(x) = 3x^2 + 2x - 1$

3. THE DERIVATIVE

If f is a function of the independent variable x, *the derivative of the function f,* denoted by f' (read "f prime"), *is defined by the formula*

$$f'(x) = \lim_{h \to 0} \frac{f(x + h) - f(x)}{h}.$$

In this definition, x remains fixed, while h tends to zero. If the limit does not exist for a particular value of x, the function has no derivative for that value.

Looking back at the previous section, we see that many of the problems consisted of finding the derivative at a particular value of x. We now give a systematic procedure for obtaining derivatives, a method which we call the *five-step rule.* The technique is illustrated by some examples.

EXAMPLE 1. Given $f(x) = x^2$. Find the derivative, $f'(x)$, by the five-step rule.

Solution.

Step 1: Write the formula for the function at x: $f(x) = x^2$.

Step 2: Write the formula for the function at the value $x + h$: $f(x + h) = (x + h)^2$
$= x^2 + 2xh + h^2$.

Step 3: Subtract $f(x)$ from $f(x + h)$: $f(x + h) - f(x) = 2xh + h^2$.

Step 4: Divide by h. Since h is a common factor in numerator and denominator, we cancel it:

$$\frac{f(x + h) - f(x)}{h} = \frac{2xh + h^2}{h} = 2x + h.$$

Step 5: Take the limit as $h \to 0$:

$$\lim_{h \to 0} (2x + h) = 2x.$$

Answer: $f'(x) = 2x.$

In the five-step rule the first four steps are purely mechanical and are carried out in a routine manner. It is the fifth and last step which frequently requires ingenuity and algebraic manipulation.

EXAMPLE 2. Given $f(x) = \dfrac{1}{x}$. Find $f'(x)$ by the five-step rule.

Solution.

Step 1: $f(x) = \dfrac{1}{x}.$

Step 2: $f(x + h) = \dfrac{1}{x + h}.$

Step 3: $f(x + h) - f(x) = \dfrac{1}{x + h} - \dfrac{1}{x}.$

Step 4: $\dfrac{f(x + h) - f(x)}{h} = \dfrac{\dfrac{1}{x + h} - \dfrac{1}{x}}{h}.$

It is at this point that the difficulty arises, since letting h tend to zero yields $0/0$. Before applying the fifth step, we manipulate the expression by finding the lowest common denominator. We have

$$\frac{f(x + h) - f(x)}{h} = \frac{x - (x + h)}{hx(x + h)} = \frac{-1}{x(x + h)}.$$

Step 5: $\lim\limits_{h \to 0} \dfrac{-1}{x(x + h)} = -\dfrac{1}{x^2}.$

Answer: $f'(x) = -\dfrac{1}{x^2}.$

EXAMPLE 3. Given $f(x) = \sqrt{x}$, $x > 0$. Find $f'(x)$ by the five-step rule.

Solution.

Step 1: $f(x) = \sqrt{x}.$

Step 2: $f(x + h) = \sqrt{x + h}.$

Step 3: $f(x + h) - f(x) = \sqrt{x + h} - \sqrt{x}.$

Step 4: $\dfrac{f(x + h) - f(x)}{h} = \dfrac{\sqrt{x + h} - \sqrt{x}}{h}.$

Now we apply the trick of rationalizing the numerator, and find

$$\frac{\sqrt{x + h} - \sqrt{x}}{h} \cdot \frac{\sqrt{x + h} + \sqrt{x}}{\sqrt{x + h} + \sqrt{x}} = \frac{x + h - x}{h(\sqrt{x + h} + \sqrt{x})}.$$

The result of Step 4 becomes

$$\frac{f(x + h) - f(x)}{h} = \frac{1}{\sqrt{x + h} + \sqrt{x}}.$$

Now applying Step 5 we obtain

Step 5: $\lim\limits_{h \to 0} \dfrac{1}{\sqrt{x + h} + \sqrt{x}} = \dfrac{1}{2\sqrt{x}}.$

Answer: $f'(x) = \dfrac{1}{2\sqrt{x}}.$

EXERCISES

Find the derivatives of the following by the five-step rule.

1. $f(x) = 2x^2$ 2. $f(x) = -x^2 + 3$ 3. $f(x) = 3x^2 + 2x - 5$

4. $f(x) = x^3$ 5. $f(x) = x^4$ 6. $f(x) = 2x^3 + 3x$

7. $f(x) = \dfrac{1}{x - 1}$ 8. $f(x) = \dfrac{1}{x^2}$ 9. $f(x) = \dfrac{1}{x^3}$

10. $f(x) = \dfrac{2x + 3}{3x - 2}$ 11. $f(x) = \dfrac{x}{1 - x}$ 12. $f(x) = \dfrac{1}{x^2 + 1}$

13. $f(x) = \dfrac{x^2 - 1}{x^2 + 1}$ 14. $f(x) = \dfrac{x^2 - 2x}{2}$ 15. $f(x) = \dfrac{1}{\sqrt{x}}$

16. $f(x) = \dfrac{1}{\sqrt{x+3}}$ 17. $f(x) = x\sqrt{x}$ 18. $f(x) = x\sqrt{x+1}$

19. $f(x) = \dfrac{x}{\sqrt{x-1}}$ 20. $f(x) = \dfrac{\sqrt{x-1}}{x}$ 21. $f(x) = \sqrt{4-x^2}$

22. $f(x) = \dfrac{1}{\sqrt{4-x^2}}$

4. GEOMETRIC INTERPRETATION OF DERIVATIVE

It is easy to define a *tangent line* to a circle at a point P on the circle. A radius from the center O to P is drawn and then, at P, a line L perpendicular to this radius is constructed (Fig. 4–11). *The line L is called the tangent to the circle at the point P.* We next draw the curve given by the equation $y = x^2 + 1$, as shown in Fig. 4–12. How do we define a tangent line to this curve at a point P?

If the point P is $(0, 1)$, the lowest point on the curve, it seems natural to take the line $y = 1$, as shown, as the tangent line. However, at a point such as Q, it is not evident what line is tangent to the curve. Intuitively, the definition should state that a tangent line should "touch" the curve at one point only. But this "definition" is not good enough, since there may be several such lines and, in fact, a vertical line through Q has only one point in common with the curve. While the definition of tangent line to a circle is quite elementary, the definition for other kinds of curves requires the sophisticated notion of limit.

FIGURE 4–11

FIGURE 4–12

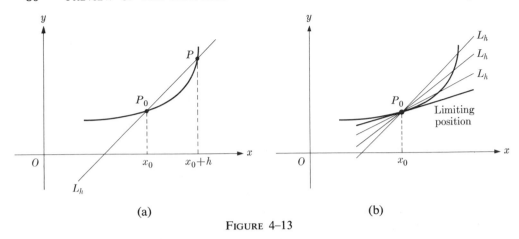

FIGURE 4–13

Let a curve be given by a function $y = f(x)$, a section of which is shown in Fig. 4–13(a). Draw a line L_h through P_0 and P, two points on the curve. Any line through two points on a curve is called a *secant line*. The line L_h is such a secant line. Suppose the coordinates of P_0 are (x_0, y_0). This means that $y_0 = f(x_0)$. The coordinates of P are taken to be $(x_0 + h, f(x_0 + h))$, where h is some positive or negative quantity. Figure 4–13 is drawn with h positive. If P were to the left of P_0, then h would be negative. The slope of the line L_h is obtained from the usual formula for slope when two points are known:

$$\text{slope of } L_h = \frac{f(x_0 + h) - f(x_0)}{(x_0 + h) - x_0} = \frac{f(x_0 + h) - f(x_0)}{h}.$$

As h tends to zero, we see geometrically that the point P tends to the point P_0. The secant line L_h rotates about P_0. Intuitively it seems that L_h approaches a limiting line as $h \to 0$, and this limiting line must be the tangent line to the curve at P_0. Figure 4–13(b) shows several positions for L_h and the limiting position as $h \to 0$. On the other hand, if the function f possesses a derivative, then

$$\lim_{h \to 0} \frac{f(x_0 + h) - f(x_0)}{h} = f'(x_0).$$

In other words, the slopes of the lines L_h tend to a limiting slope which is the derivative of the function f at P_0. Suppose we now construct, at P_0, the line passing through P_0 and having slope $f'(x_0)$. This can be done by the point-slope formula for the straight line.

DEFINITION. The *tangent* to the curve with equation $y = f(x)$ at $P_0(x_0, f(x_0))$ is the line through $P_0(x_0, f(x_0))$ with slope $f'(x_0)$.

We recall that the point-slope form for the equation of a straight line is

$$y - y_0 = m(x - x_0).$$

If in this formula we take $y_0 = f(x_0)$ and $m = f'(x_0)$, we obtain the equation of the line tangent to the curve at the point P_0.

EXAMPLE 1. Find the equation of the line which is tangent to the curve that has equation $y = x^2 + 1$ at the point on the curve where $x = 2$.

Solution. In this problem $f(x) = x^2 + 1$, $x_0 = 2$. Therefore $y_0 = f(x_0) = f(2) = 5$. To find $f'(x_0)$, we apply the 5-step rule to $f(x) = x^2 + 1$.

Step 1: $f(x) = x^2 + 1$.

Step 2: $f(x + h) = (x + h)^2 + 1$.

Step 3: $f(x + h) - f(x) = x^2 + 2xh + h^2 + 1 - x^2 - 1$.

Step 4: $\dfrac{f(x + h) - f(x)}{h} = \dfrac{2xh + h^2}{h} = 2x + h$.

Step 5: Taking the limit, we get $f'(x) = 2x$.

Then $f'(x_0) = f'(2) = 4$ and $m = 4$. The desired equation is

$$y - 5 = 4(x - 2).$$

DEFINITION. The *normal* to the curve with equation $y = f(x)$ at $P_0(x_0, f(x_0))$ is the line through P_0 which is perpendicular to the tangent line at P_0.

EXAMPLE 2. In the problem of Example 1, find the equation of the line normal to the curve at the point where $x = 3$.

Solution. Since $x_0 = 3$ and $f(x) = x^2 + 1$, we have $y_0 = f(x_0) = 10$. The tangent line at $x_0 = 3$ has slope $f'(x_0) = f'(3)$. We have already found that $f'(x) = 2x$ for any value of x. Therefore the tangent line at $x = 3$ has slope 6. The normal line must have a slope which is the negative reciprocal of the slope of the tangent line, namely $-1/6$. The equation of the normal line at $(3, 10)$ is

$$y - 10 = \frac{-1}{6}(x - 3).$$

We have just seen that the derivative is merely the slope of the tangent line. In fact, the tangent line is defined in this way. The intuitive notion of the nature of a line tangent to a curve is of great help in plotting graphs. If the derivative $f'(x)$ is positive, the slope is positive, showing that the curve must be rising as we go from left to right. Similarly, if $f'(x) < 0$, the curve must be falling as we go from left to right. The fact that $f'(x) = 0$ means that the tangent line is horizontal, and the curve *may* have either a low point or a high point at such a location. (However, other possibilities exist, as we shall see later in Chapter 7, Sections 3 and 4.)

EXAMPLE 3. Find the intervals in which the function $y = f(x) = x^3 - 3x + 2$ is increasing and those in which it is decreasing. Sketch the graph.

Solution. We first find the derivative by the 5-step rule.

Step 1: $f(x) = x^3 - 3x + 2$.

Step 2: $f(x + h) = (x + h)^3 - 3(x + h) + 2$.

Step 3: $f(x + h) - f(x) = x^3 + 3x^2h + 3xh^2 + h^3 - 3x - 3h + 2 - x^3 + 3x - 2$
$= 3x^2h + 3xh^2 + h^3 - 3h.$

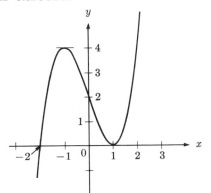

FIGURE 4–14

Step 4: $\dfrac{f(x + h) - f(x)}{h} = 3x^2 - 3 + 3xh + h^2.$

Step 5: Taking the limit as $h \to 0$, we get $f'(x) = 3x^2 - 3.$

We first find the places where $f'(x)$ is zero. That is, we solve $3x^2 - 3 = 0$ to get $x = 1, -1$. We construct the following table for $f'(x)$:

x	-2	-1	0	1	2
$f'(x)$	$+$	0	$-$	0	$+$

This table shows that, as x goes from left to right,

$$f(x) \text{ is increasing for } x < -1,$$
$$f(x) \text{ is decreasing for } -1 < x < 1,$$
$$f(x) \text{ is increasing for } x > 1.$$

A table of values for $f(x)$ gives the points

x	-2	-1	0	1	2
$f(x)$	0	4	2	0	4

The graph is sketched in Fig. 4–14.

The fact that the curve reached a low point at exactly $(1, 0)$ and a high point at exactly $(-1, 4)$ was discovered from studying the derivative. The location of high and low points could not easily be obtained merely from plotting points and sketching the graph, the process employed earlier in Chapter 2, Section 4. A low point such as $(1, 0)$ is a minimum point only if we restrict our attention to a small interval about this point. Such a point is called a *relative minimum*. It is clearly not the minimum point on the entire curve, since the curve falls below the x-axis as we go to the left beyond $x = -2$. Similarly, the point $(-1, 4)$ is called a *relative maximum*. At a relative maximum or minimum it is always true that if f has a derivative, then $f'(x) = 0$. (The converse is not necessarily true.)

EXERCISES

In problems 1 through 10, find the equation of the tangent and the normal at the point corresponding to the given value of x_0.

1. $y = x^2 - x + 1$, $x_0 = -1$

2. $y = x^2 - 2x$, $x_0 = 1$

3. $y = x^3 - 3x^2 + 2x$, $x_0 = 2$

4. $y = x^3 + x + 1$, $x_0 = -1$

5. $y = -x^3 + 3x + 1$, $x_0 = 2$

6. $y = \dfrac{x + 1}{x - 1}$, $x_0 = 2$

7. $y = \sqrt{2x}$, $x_0 = 2$

8. $y = \sqrt{3 - x}$, $x_0 = -1$

9. $y = \dfrac{1}{\sqrt{x - 2}}$, $x_0 = 6$

10. $y = 2x + 3\sqrt{x}$, $x_0 = 4$

In problems 11 through 18, find the intervals in which $f(x)$ is increasing and those in which it is decreasing, and plot the graph of $y = f(x)$. Note relative maxima and minima.

11. $f(x) = x^2 - 4x + 5$

12. $f(x) = 1 + 2x - x^2$

13. $f(x) = \frac{1}{3}x^3 - \frac{1}{2}x^2 - 2x$

14. $f(x) = \frac{1}{3}x^3 - x^2 - 3x + 2$

15. $f(x) = 1 + 3x^2 - x^3$

16. $f(x) = x^3 + 3x - 2$

17. $f(x) = 3x^4 - 8x^3 - 6x^2 + 24x + 2$

18. $f(x) = 3x^5 - 25x^3 + 60x + 10$

5. INSTANTANEOUS VELOCITY AND SPEED; ACCELERATION

If the needle of the speedometer in a car is pointing at 60, we say the car is traveling at 60 miles per hour. An analysis of this statement requires a definition of the phrase "60 miles per hour." As a start, we might say that if the car were to continue in exactly the same manner, then in one hour it would have traveled exactly 60 miles. But such a statement avoids the problem completely, since the needle pointing at 60 does so without any knowledge of the way the car behaved some minutes ago, or how it intends to behave in the future.

Before any further discussion of this question we introduce two simplifying assumptions.

(1) Motion will always be assumed to take place along a *straight line*, although the object in motion may go in either direction. One direction will arbitrarily be selected as positive, and the other direction will then be negative. (Motion along a curved path is discussed in Chapter 14.)

(2) The object in motion is idealized to be a point or particle. Such a simplification is necessary, since a mathematical treatment of the exact motion of every portion of a complicated object such as an automobile would defy analysis.

Suppose that the path of a particle is along a horizontal line L, with distance to the right designated as positive and that to the left as negative (Fig. 4–15). We let t denote time in some convenient unit such as seconds or minutes, and we measure the distance s of the object from the point O in units such as inches,

$$0 \qquad\qquad s_1 \qquad\qquad s_2 \qquad\quad L$$

FIGURE 4–15

feet, or miles. If the particle in motion is at the point s_1 at time t_1 and at the point s_2 at time t_2, then it took $t_2 - t_1$ units of time to travel the distance $s_2 - s_1$. We define the *average velocity* of the particle over this time interval to be

$$\frac{s_2 - s_1}{t_2 - t_1}.$$

If s is measured in feet and t in seconds, the units of this average velocity would be denoted as *feet per second* (ft/sec). If a car travels 40 miles in one hour, the average velocity of the car is 40 miles per hour (mi/hr). But we still know very little about how fast the car is traveling at various times during the hour. The needle of a speedometer pointing at 60 is an instantaneous event, and we need a notion of velocity at a given instant of time along the path. The development of this notion might proceed in the following way.

We mark off two points along a straight stretch of road, accurately measure the distance between them, and provide a timing device to indicate the exact moment the car passes each location. The average velocity is then computed. We feel that if the distance between the two points is small, the car's motion cannot change too radically as it travels from one point to the other; we therefore obtain a good indication of the velocity of the car at any time during this interval. For example, if the points are 100 yards apart and the average velocity is 60 mi/hr, the variation in the motion along such a short stretch of road is probably not too great. If we desire greater accuracy, we can shorten the interval to ten yards, improve the measurement of the distance, and increase the precision of the timing device. Now we again argue that, in such a short distance, the motion of the car varies so slightly that the average velocity closely approximates the velocity indicated on the speedometer. On the other hand, some variation may still be possible, and so we cut the interval again, this time to one foot, say. The continuation of this process shows that instantaneous velocity is the result of computing the average velocity over a sequence of smaller and smaller intervals.

To make the above discussion precise, we first note that the distance s traveled along the straight line is a function of the time t; that is, $s = f(t)$. Then the *average velocity* between the times t_1 and t_2 is simply expressed as

$$\frac{f(t_2) - f(t_1)}{t_2 - t_1} = \frac{\text{distance}}{\text{time}}.$$

The instantaneous velocity at time t_1 is defined to be

$$\lim_{t_2 \to t_1} \frac{f(t_2) - f(t_1)}{t_2 - t_1}.$$

That is, the instantaneous velocity is the limit of the average velocities as the time over which these averages is taken tends to zero. Since t_2 must be different from t_1, we can write $t_2 = t_1 + h$, where h may be positive or negative. The above expression for instantaneous velocity then becomes

$$\lim_{t_1 + h \to t_1} \frac{f(t_1 + h) - f(t_1)}{t_1 + h - t_1}, \qquad \text{or} \qquad \lim_{h \to 0} \frac{f(t_1 + h) - f(t_1)}{h}.$$

We note that this is precisely the derivative of $f(t)$ evaluated at t_1. In other words, *the instantaneous velocity of a particle moving in a straight line according to the law $s = f(t)$, describing the motion, is $f'(t)$*. The quantity $f'(t)$ may be positive or negative, according to whether the particle is moving along the line in the positive or negative direction. The *speed* of the particle is defined to be $|f'(t)|$. The speed is merely the magnitude of the velocity and is always positive or zero. It may seem strange to introduce a special term specifically for the absolute value of the velocity. However, the notion of speed is especially useful when studying motion along curved paths. The speed tells us how fast the particle is moving but gives no information about its direction.

EXAMPLE 1. A ball thrown directly upward with a speed of 96 ft/sec moves according to the law

$$y = 96t - 16t^2,$$

where y is the height in feet above the starting point, and t is the time in seconds after it is thrown. Find the velocity of the ball after 2 seconds. Is it still rising or is it falling? For how many seconds does it continue to rise? How high does the ball go?

Solution. It is assumed that the motion of the ball (particle) is in a straight vertical line. If we let $f(t) = 96t - 16t^2$, the velocity is given by $f'(t)$. Applying the five-step rule, we obtain

$$f'(t) = 96 - 32t.$$

Let v denote the velocity at any time t; then

$$v = f'(t) = 96 - 32t.$$

If $t = 2$, $v = 96 - 32(2) = 32$ ft/sec. Since v is positive, the ball is still rising. The velocity is zero when $96 - 32t = 0$, or $t = 3$. When t is larger than 3, the velocity is negative and the motion is downward, i.e., the ball is falling. When $t = 3$, we see that $f(3) = 96(3) - 16(9) = 144$ ft, and this is the highest point the ball reaches. See Fig. 4–16.

FIGURE 4–16

In motion along a straight line, whenever a particle changes direction the velocity goes from positive to negative or from negative to positive. *Therefore at the instant the particle reverses direction the velocity must be zero.*

EXAMPLE 2. A particle moves along a horizontal line (positive to the right) according to the law

$$s = t^3 - 3t^2 - 9t + 5.$$

During which intervals of time is the particle moving to the right, and during which is it moving to the left?

Solution. It is moving to the right whenever the velocity is positive and to the left when the velocity is negative. The velocity v is just the derivative of $f(t) = t^3 - 3t^2 - $

FIGURE 4–17

$9t + 5$. Applying the five-step rule, we have

$$v = f'(t) = 3t^2 - 6t - 9 = 3(t + 1)(t - 3).$$

If $t = -1, 3$ the velocity is zero. We make the following tabulation:

t	-2	-1	1	3	4
v	$+$	0	$-$	0	$+$

If $t < -1$, v is positive and the motion is to the right.
If $-1 < t < 3$, v is negative and the motion is to the left.
If $t > 3$, v is positive and the motion is to the right.

Motion to the left and motion to the right are separated by points of zero velocity, i.e., at $t = -1, 3$ (Fig. 4–17). Although the motion is along the line L, its schematic behavior is shown by the path above this line. Zero velocity occurs at points P, Q. The point P corresponds to $t = -1$, $s = 10$, $v = 0$; Q corresponds to $t = 3$, $s = -22$, $v = 0$.

Acceleration is a measure of the change in velocity. If a particle moves along a straight line with constant velocity, the acceleration is zero. In an automobile race, the cars pass the starting position traveling at a uniform velocity—say 30 mi/hr. Within ten seconds one of the cars is traveling at 120 mi/hr. The *average acceleration* of this car is

$$\frac{120 - 30}{10} = 9 \text{ (mi/hr)/sec.}$$

The units appear rather strange, since velocity is in miles per hour and the time in the denominator is in seconds. We can convert 120 mi/hr to 176 ft/sec if we multiply 120 by 5280/3600. Similarly, 30 mi/hr $= 44$ ft/sec. With this change the average acceleration is expressed as

$$\frac{176 - 44}{10} = 13.2 \text{ (ft/sec)/sec.}$$

If the velocity v of the particle is varying according to the law $v = F(t)$, where t is the time, then the *instantaneous acceleration a*, or simply the *acceleration*, is defined as the limit of the average acceleration:

$$a = \lim_{h \to 0} \frac{F(t + h) - F(t)}{h}.$$

In other words, $a = F'(t)$. This is in complete analogy with the definition of instantaneous velocity as the limit of the average velocity.

If a particle is moving (along a straight line) so that the distance s is given by $s = f(t)$, then the velocity v is found by taking the derivative $f'(t)$. The derivative f' is the law which describes the velocity. The derivative of this derivative is the acceleration. We call it the *second derivative* and use the notation $f''(t)$. That is, if $s = f(t)$, then

$$v = f'(t) \qquad \text{and} \qquad a = f''(t).$$

We could continue this process and take third derivatives, fourth derivatives, etc., and indeed we sometimes do. The notation for third derivative is $f'''(t)$ or $f^{(3)}(t)$. (Beyond the third derivative, primes become unwieldy, and a numeral in parentheses is used. For example, the seventh derivative is $f^{(7)}(t)$.) It should be mentioned that, from the point of view of physics, the first and second derivatives are the most important — especially in the study of the motion of objects. Derivatives higher than the second are of occasional interest only.

EXAMPLE 3.	A particle moves along a straight line according to the law

$$s = 132 + 108t - 16t^2 + 3t^3,$$

s being the distance in feet and t the time in seconds. Find the velocity and acceleration at any time t. What is the velocity when $t = 2$? What is the acceleration when $t = 1$ and when $t = 3$?

Solution. The velocity is found by taking the derivative, which we do according to the five-step rule. Then

$$v = 108 - 32t + 9t^2.$$

The acceleration is obtained by taking the derivative of this function, which we also do by the five-step rule. We have

$$a = -32 + 18t.$$

When $t = 2$, we substitute in the equation for v to get $v = 108 - 64 + 36 = 80$ ft/sec. When $t = 1$, we see that $a = -32 + 18 = -14$ (ft/sec)/sec, and when $t = 3$, $a = -32 + 54 = 22$ (ft/sec)/sec.

Since the acceleration is negative when $t = 1$, we conclude that the particle is slowing down, while a is positive when $t = 3$ and therefore the particle is speeding up.

EXERCISES

In problems 1 through 6, a particle is moving along a horizontal line (positive to the right), according to the stated law. Find whether the particle is moving to the right or to the left at the given time.

1. $s = t^2 - 3t + 5$, $t = 2$

2. $s = 6 + 2t - 16t^2$, $t = 3$

3. $s = t^3 - 3t^2 - 7t - 2$, $t = 1$

4. $s = t^3 - t^2 - 2t - 2$, $t = -2$

5. $s = t^3 - t^2 - t + 1$, $t = 1$

6. $s = t^3 - 2t^2 - 3t + 1$, $t = 2$

In problems 7 through 11, find the velocity and acceleration of the given laws of motion.

7. $s = t^2 - 4t + 2$

8. $s = 6 - 2t - 16t^2$

9. $s = \frac{1}{3}t^3 - 2t^2 + 3t - 5$

10. $s = t^3 + 2t^2 - t - 1$

11. $s = bt^2 + ct + d$ (b, c, d constants)

In problems 12 through 18, motion is along a horizontal line positive to the right. When is the particle moving to the right and when is it moving to the left? Discuss the acceleration.

12. $s = t^2 - 2t + 3$

13. $s = 8 - 4t + t^2$

14. $s = t^3 + 3t^2 - 9t + 4$

15. $s = 2t^3 - 3t^2 - 12t + 8$

16. $s = t^3 - 3t^2 + 3t$

17. $s = \dfrac{t}{1 + t^2}$

18. $s = \dfrac{1 + t}{4 + t^2}$

6. THE DEFINITE INTEGRAL AND ANTIDERIVATIVES

What is meant by the area enclosed in an irregularly shaped region, such as the one shown in Fig. 4–18? Area is a measure of the size of a region and, in developing this concept, we begin by determining the sizes of regions having simple shapes. Then we proceed step by step to define the areas of more complicated regions.

Almost all notions of area start with the idea that a rectangle of length l and width w has, *by definition*, area

$$A = lw.$$

From this formula we obtain immediately the formula for the area of a right triangle as half the area of a rectangle; then the usual formulas for the area of any triangle are developed as in elementary geometry. Any polygon may be decomposed into triangles, and therefore the area of a polygon is simply the sum of the areas of the triangles which comprise it.

Finding the area of a circle without the use of calculus is hard but not impossible. Sometimes a high-school course in elementary geometry will include the necessary steps. The method consists first of finding the area of inscribed and circumscribed regular polygons. Then, as the number of sides of the polygons increases without bound, the polygons approximate the circle more and more

FIGURE 4–18

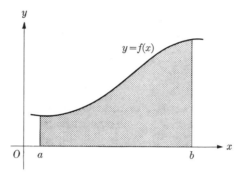

FIGURE 4–19

closely. Finally, we define the area of the circle as the limit of the areas of these polygons.

The area of an irregular region (as in Fig. 4–18) may be explained intuitively in the following way. Suppose the region were made of some uniform material of uniform thickness which could be weighed with great accuracy. We could then make a rectangular region from the same kind of material of the same thickness and having the same weight; we would like to be able to say that the two regions then have the same area. However, such a process could never be used as the basis of a mathematical definition. Not only is it impossible to reproduce the irregular region exactly, but also nonuniformities of all sorts appear in every material. Moreover, while physical processes have intuitive value, they can never yield mathematical definitions.

The concept of limit has as one of its most fruitful applications the development of the notion of area. The limiting process for area is different from that for derivative and, while precise statements will be postponed to Chapter 8, we shall give some introductory material here.

Suppose that $y = f(x)$ is a function of x which happens to lie above the x-axis, as shown in Fig. 4–19. At two points on the x-axis, a and b, vertical lines are drawn. We shall concern ourselves with the problem of calculating the area of the region bounded by the x-axis, the vertical lines through a and b, and the graph of the function f. The fact that three sides of the region are straight lines simplifies the problem. At this stage we assume that the only kind of region for which we can calculate the area is a rectangle. The problem seems fairly hopeless until we realize that we can get an *approximate* idea of how large the area is in the following way.

First, we take the interval $[a, b]$ on the x-axis and divide it into a number of subintervals (Fig. 4–20). We shall be astute and not say exactly how many at this time; we do so by letting n be the number of subintervals and by not saying exactly how large n shall be. We label the points of subdivision $x_1, x_2, x_3, \ldots,$ x_{n-1}, and we stipulate that $a = x_0$ and $b = x_n$. The subintervals do not have to

$$x_0 = a \quad x_1 \quad x_2 \quad \cdots \cdots \quad x_{n-1} \quad b = x_n$$

FIGURE 4–20

FIGURE 4–21

be of equal size. The first interval is $[x_0, x_1] = [a, x_1]$, and consists of all points x such that $x_0 \leq x \leq x_1$. The length of this interval is just $x_1 - x_0$. The length of the second interval is $x_2 - x_1$, and so on. In fact, if i is any number between 1 and n, then $x_i - x_{i-1}$ is the length of the ith subinterval. We introduce a special symbol for this:

$$\Delta_i x = \text{length of } i\text{th interval} = x_i - x_{i-1}.$$

Note that $\Delta_i x$ (read "delta sub i of x") does not mean Δ times x or any such thing. It is merely a complicated symbol used to represent a simple quantity.

In each of the intervals into which we divided the interval $[a, b]$ we now select a point. This may be done in any way we please. We designate these points $\xi_1, \xi_2, \ldots, \xi_n$, as shown in Fig. 4–21. At each of the points ξ_i we erect a vertical segment to the curve $y = f(x)$. In Fig. 4–22 this is shown for the case $n = 6$. The height of the dotted line through ξ_1 is $f(\xi_1)$, the height of the line through ξ_2 is $f(\xi_2)$, and so on. Now we calculate the areas of the rectangles formed by the subintervals and the heights $f(\xi_i)$. The first rectangle has area $f(\xi_1)(x_1 - x_0)$ or $f(\xi_1) \Delta_1 x$. The second has area $f(\xi_2)(x_2 - x_1) = f(\xi_2) \Delta_2 x$, and so on. If we add the areas of all these rectangles, we get

$$f(\xi_1) \Delta_1 x + f(\xi_2) \Delta_2 x + f(\xi_3) \Delta_3 x + \cdots + f(\xi_n) \Delta_n x,$$

which is the desired *approximation* to the area under the curve.

Figure 4–22 shows such an approximation for six intervals of subdivision. It is natural to expect that if we took 60 intervals of subdivision, each of them much narrower than the ones shown, the approximation to the area would be much better. And if we took 600 subintervals, it would be better still. Here the notion of limit appears. Suppose that these approximations approach a limiting value (call it L) as the number of subintervals tends to infinity, and suppose that the following statements are true:

(1) The value of L does not depend on how the subdivisions are selected, so long as the maximum length of any subinterval tends to zero as the number of such subintervals tends to infinity.

(2) The value of L does not depend on where in each subinterval the points ξ_i are chosen.

In these circumstances, we call this limit L the *definite integral of f from a to b* and denote it by

$$\int_a^b f(x)\, dx$$

(read "the integral from a to b of f of x, dx"). We must say a few words about this notation. The dx is just a juxtaposition of letters which are considered in-

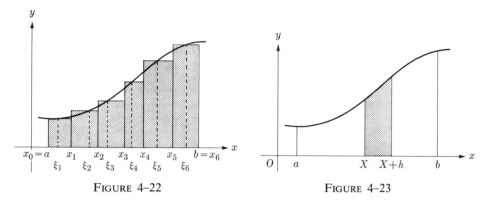

FIGURE 4–22   FIGURE 4–23

separable. From the way we defined "definite integral," the value of L depends only on f and a and b. Therefore the choice of the letter x has no particular meaning in the above notation; we could have used any symbol. For example, if we had the *same* function f but had used t as the independent variable, the expression

$$\int_a^b f(t)\, dt$$

would have exactly the same meaning and the value of L would be unchanged. The dt, in this case, merely identifies the variable being used in making evaluations of the function.

We shall show in Chapter 8 that the number L may be used, to define the area under the curve and, indeed, that this coincides with the usual definition of area for elementary regions.

The concepts of definite integral and area under a curve have an intimate connection with the idea of derivative. Consider the problem of finding the area under the curve $y = f(x)$ between the points a and X, where X is between a and b (Fig. 4–23). We would write this area as the definite integral

$$\int_a^X f(x)\, dx.$$

As X changes, this area assumes different values. If X is a, the value is zero. Let's call the area A and, since A is a function of X, we write

$$A = F(X).$$

We now select an $h > 0$ and compute $F(X + h)$. That is, we calculate the area under the curve between a and $X + h$. This is just the integral

$$\int_a^{X+h} f(x)\, dx.$$

The difference $F(X + h) - F(X)$ is the area of the shaded region shown in Fig. 4–23. If h is "small," the shaded region is almost a rectangle and, if we let Y

be some average value of the function $f(x)$ between X and $X + h$, we could say that

$$F(X + h) - F(X) = Y \cdot h,$$

or

$$Y = \frac{F(X + h) - F(X)}{h}.$$

If $h \to 0$, we know from our earlier experience that the limit approached is the derivative $F'(X)$. On the other hand, "geometrically" we see that as $h \to 0$, the average height Y must approach the height of the function f at the point X, namely $f(X)$. We conclude by this "argument" that

$$F'(X) = f(X),$$

which states that the function f is the derivative of the area function F. We also say that F is an *antiderivative* of f. In other words, the process of finding area and the process of differentiation are the inverse of each other.

A conscientious reader who has been applying the five-step rule up to this point must have made the following deductions for himself. If

$$f(x) = c \qquad (c = \text{const}),$$

then

$$f'(x) = 0.$$

If

$$f(x) = bx + c \qquad (b, c = \text{const}),$$

then

$$f'(x) = b.$$

If

$$f(x) = bx^2 + cx + d \qquad (b, c, d = \text{const}),$$

then

$$f'(x) = 2bx + c.$$

If

$$f(x) = bx^3 + cx^2 + dx + e \qquad (b, c, d, e = \text{const}),$$

then

$$f'(x) = 3bx^2 + 2cx + d.$$

In other words, when presented with the problem of finding the derivative of $f(x) = 5x^2 + 12x - 6$, we could write at once $f'(x) = 10x + 12$.

Now we pose the inverse problem. Suppose we know that the derivative of a function f is

$$f'(x) = 4x + 3.$$

What is the function? It's easy to guess an answer. One possibility is

$$f(x) = 2x^2 + 3x + 7.$$

Another is $f(x) = 2x^2 + 3x + 4$; still another is $f(x) = 2x^2 + 3x - 5$. We see that there is no single solution to the problem of finding the function if the derivative is given, i.e., to the problem of finding the antiderivative. A way out of this difficulty is to write

$$f(x) = 2x^2 + 3x + c$$

where c may have any value whatsoever. If, in addition, we are given one more fact which tells us the value of c, then the solution is determined precisely. In the above illustration, if we also know that $f(2) = 3$, we can write

$$f(2) = 3 = 2 \cdot 4 + 3 \cdot 2 + c$$

and conclude that $c = -11$. The function f is then

$$f(x) = 2x^2 + 3x - 11.$$

In problems of finding the area under a curve, i.e., in problems of finding the antiderivative of the function, we are given $F'(x)$ (that is, the equation of the curve) and wish to find $F(x)$. Use is made of the fact that $F(a) = 0$ to evaluate the constant in the antiderivative.

EXAMPLE 1. A ball is thrown upward, and we know that the acceleration is -32 (ft/sec)/sec. (a) What is the velocity at any instant of time if the ball was launched with a velocity of 96 ft/sec? (b) Find the height of the ball above the launching point at any time t.

Solution. Since the acceleration a is given, finding the velocity v is a problem in antiderivatives. We know that

$$a = -32,$$
$$v = -32t + c,$$

where t is the time (starting at $t = 0$ when the ball is thrown). We have $v = 96$ when $t = 0$, which means that $96 = -32 \cdot 0 + c$, or $c = 96$. We obtain the formula

$$v = -32t + 96.$$

To get the distance traveled, we again have a problem in antiderivatives. We find

$$s = -16t^2 + 96t + k.$$

To evaluate k, we note that at time $t = 0$ the distance traveled is also zero. This makes $k = 0$, and we have the formula

$$s = -16t^2 + 96t.$$

EXAMPLE 2. Approximate, by rectangles, the area under the curve $f(x) = x^3$ if $a = 0$, $b = 1$, the number of rectangles is 7, and the x_i and ξ_i are chosen according to the following table:

i	0	1	2	3	4	5	6	7
x_i	0	0.2	0.4	0.6	0.7	0.8	0.9	1.0
ξ_i		0.1	0.3	0.5	0.6	0.7	0.9	1.0

Sketch a graph and draw the rectangles with bases $\Delta_i x$ and altitudes $f(\xi_i)$.

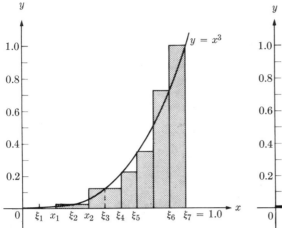

FIGURE 4-24   FIGURE 4-25

Solution. $\Delta_1 x = \Delta_2 x = \Delta_3 x = 0.2; \quad \Delta_4 x = \Delta_5 x = \Delta_6 x = \Delta_7 x = 0.1$ and

$$
\begin{aligned}
f(\xi_1)\,\Delta_1 x &= 0.0002 \\
f(\xi_2)\,\Delta_2 x &= 0.0054 \\
f(\xi_3)\,\Delta_3 x &= 0.0250 \\
f(\xi_4)\,\Delta_4 x &= 0.0216 \\
f(\xi_5)\,\Delta_5 x &= 0.0343 \\
f(\xi_6)\,\Delta_6 x &= 0.0729 \\
f(\xi_7)\,\Delta_7 x &= 0.1000 \\
\hline
\text{Sum} &= 0.2594
\end{aligned}
$$

The graph is shown in Fig. 4–24. It is clear from the figure that some rectangles are too large, others are too small, and some "strike a balance" by including some extra area and omitting some. The exact area is $\frac{1}{4}$.

EXAMPLE 3. Approximate, by rectangles, the area under the curve $f(x) = x^2$ if $a = 0$, $b = 1$, the number of rectangles is 5, the subintervals are all equal in size, and the ξ_i are all taken at the midpoints of the subintervals. Draw a graph. Compute the exact area by the antiderivative method.

Solution. Each $\Delta_i x = 0.2$, and $\xi_1 = 0.1$, $\xi_2 = 0.3$, $\xi_3 = 0.5$, $\xi_4 = 0.7$, $\xi_5 = 0.9$. We have (Fig. 4–25)

$$
\begin{aligned}
f(\xi_1)\,\Delta_1 x &= 0.002 \\
f(\xi_2)\,\Delta_2 x &= 0.018 \\
f(\xi_3)\,\Delta_3 x &= 0.050 \\
f(\xi_4)\,\Delta_4 x &= 0.098 \\
f(\xi_5)\,\Delta_5 x &= 0.162 \\
\hline
\text{Sum} &= 0.330
\end{aligned}
$$

Since $F'(x) = f(x) = x^2$, we see from our knowledge of antiderivatives that

$$
F(x) = \tfrac{1}{3}x^3 + c,
$$

which gives the area under the curve at any point x. We must, however, use the fact that we are starting at the point a. This is equivalent to the statement that $F(a) = 0$. In our case $a = 0$, and so $F(0) = 0$. Substituting in the above expression for $F(x)$, we get $c = 0$. The area we seek extends from $a = 0$ to $b = 1$; substituting $x = 1$ in the formula for $F(x) = \frac{1}{3}x^3$, we obtain

$$F(1) = \tfrac{1}{3} = \text{area under curve.}$$

EXERCISES

In problems 1 through 6, find the distance s traveled along a straight line by a particle if the velocity $v = v(t)$ follows the law given. The additional fact required for the result is also given.

1. $v = 2t + 3$ and $s = 3$ when $t = 1$
2. $v = \frac{3}{2}t^2 - 3t + 1$ and $s = 4$ when $t = 2$
3. $v = t^2 + t - 2$ and $s = 2$ when $t = -1$
4. $v = -t^2 + 2t + 1$ and $s = 0$ when $t = 2$
5. $v = 6 - 2t - 3t^2$ and $s = 0$ when $t = 0$
6. $v = 5 - 7t^2$ and $s = 5$ when $t = 0$
7. A ball is thrown upward from the ground with a launching velocity of 64 ft/sec. Its acceleration is constant and equal to -32 (ft/sec)/sec. How long does the ball continue to rise? How long does the ball stay in the air?
8. A man driving an automobile in a straight line at a speed of 80 ft/sec applies the brakes at a certain instant (which we take to be $t = 0$). If the brakes furnish a constant acceleration of -20 (ft/sec)/sec (actually a deceleration), how far will he go before he stops?

In problems 9 through 12, approximate by rectangles the area under the curve $y = f(x)$ from the data given. Then solve each problem accurately to three decimal places. Sketch a graph.

9. $f(x) = 2x + 3$, $n = 5$, $a = -1$, $b = 0$.

i	0	1	2	3	4	5
x_i	-1	-0.8	-0.6	-0.4	-0.2	0
ξ_i		-1.0	-0.8	-0.5	-0.2	0

(In this problem, compute the exact area.)

10. $f(x) = x^2$, $n = 5$, $a = -1$, $b = 0$

i	0	1	2	3	4	5
x_i	-1	-0.8	-0.6	-0.4	-0.2	0
ξ_i		-1.00	-0.75	-0.50	-0.25	0

11. $f(x) = x^2$, $n = 7$, $a = -2.0$, $b = 0$

i	0	1	2	3	4	5	6	7
x_i	-2	-1.8	-1.6	-1.4	-1.2	-0.8	-0.4	0
ξ_i		-2.0	-1.6	-1.5	-1.3	-1.0	-0.7	-0.1

12. $f(x) = 2x - x^2$, $n = 5$, $a = 0$, $b = 2$

i	0	1	2	3	4	5
x_i	0	0.4	0.8	1.2	1.6	2.0
ξ_i		0	0.5	1.0	1.5	2.0

In problems 13 through 19, find the exact area under the curve $y = f(x)$ from a to b by finding $F(x)$, the area function, and then $F(b)$.

13. $f(x) = x^2$, $a = -1$, $b = 0$ 14. $f(x) = x^2$, $a = -2$, $b = 0$
15. $f(x) = 2x - x^2$, $a = 0$, $b = 2$ 16. $f(x) = x^2 - 2x + 2$, $a = 1$, $b = 3$
17. $f(x) = 3x - x^2$, $a = 1$, $b = 2$ 18. $f(x) = x^2 + x + 1$, $a = -2$, $b = 1$
19. $f(x) = 6 + x - x^2$, $a = -2$, $b = -1$

In problems 20 through 23, approximate the area by rectangles with the number n given. Take the ξ_i at the midpoints.

20. $f(x) = x + 1$, $a = 1$, $b = 3$, $n = 1$
21. $f(x) = x^2$, $a = -2$, $b = -1$, $n = 5$
22. $f(x) = \dfrac{1}{1 + x}$, $a = 0$, $b = 1$, $n = 5$
23. $f(x) = \dfrac{1}{1 + x^2}$, $a = 0$, $b = 1$, $n = 5$

24. Compute the exact area in problems 20 and 21 by using the definite integral.

CHAPTER 5

Limits and Continuity

1. DEFINITION OF LIMIT

In Chapter 4 we introduced the notion of limit in an informal way. We spoke of intervals as being "small," numbers as being "close," quantities "approaching" zero, and so forth. However, these nonmathematical words vary widely in meaning from person to person and cannot be the basis for a mathematical structure. Therefore we give the following statement as a precise definition of limit:

DEFINITION. Given a function *f* and numbers *a* and *L*, we say that *the limit of* $f(x)$ *as x tends to a is L* if for each positive number ϵ there is a positive number δ such that $|f(x) - L| < \epsilon$ whenever $0 < |x - a| < \delta$.

The statement

$$\lim_{x \to a} f(x) = L$$

is a shorthand notation for the above definition. Another abbreviated notation having the identical meaning is

$$f(x) \to L \qquad \text{as} \qquad x \to a.$$

We now explain and elaborate on the meaning of the above definition. First of all, the definition itself implies that there can be at most one limit *L*. (This fact is proved at the beginning of the next section.) Next we recall that

$$|x - a| < \delta$$

is the same as the two inequalities

$$a - \delta < x < a + \delta.$$

FIGURE 5-1

This double inequality states that *x* must lie in an interval of length 2δ having *a* as its center (Fig. 5–1). The part of the inequality which states that $0 < |x - a|$ merely means that *x* is not allowed to be equal to *a* itself. This is done for convenience. The inequality

$$|f(x) - L| < \epsilon$$

is equivalent to

$$L - \epsilon < f(x) < L + \epsilon,$$

97

FIGURE 5-2

FIGURE 5-3

which asserts that the function f lies above the line $y = L - \epsilon$ and below the line $y = L + \epsilon$ (Fig. 5-2).

The definition itself may be interpreted as a test. If I am given any positive number whatsoever (call it ϵ), the test consists of finding a number δ such that $f(x)$ lies between the values $L - \epsilon$ and $L + \epsilon$ if x is in the interval $(a - \delta, a + \delta)$ and $x \neq a$. If such a δ can be found for *every* positive number ϵ, then we say that $f(x)$ has the limit L as x approaches a. Note that the value of δ will be different for different epsilons. Also the test must be performed for *every* positive epsilon, which means in general that it is an extremely difficult thing to check.

The geometric explanation, one similar to that given in Chapter 4, states that if an ϵ is given, a δ can be found such that the graph of the function f lies in the rectangle bounded by the lines $x = a - \delta, x = a + \delta, y = L - \epsilon, y = L + \epsilon$ (Fig. 5-3). Nothing at all is said about the value of f when x is a.

It is good to get some practice in finding the δ which corresponds to a given ϵ; the δ can actually be found in very simple cases. To consider an easy case, we let $f(x) = 3x - 2$ and take $a = 5$. We know intuitively from our earlier work that

$$\lim_{x \to 5} f(x) = 13.$$

We wish to show that, given an ϵ, we can find a δ such that

$$|3x - 2 - 13| < \epsilon \qquad \text{whenever} \qquad |x - 5| < \delta.$$

But $|3x - 15| = |3(x - 5)|$. If someone gives us an ϵ, we simply take $\delta = \epsilon/3$. Then, if $|x - 5| < \delta = \epsilon/3$, we find (by multiplying through by 3) that $3|x - 5| < \epsilon$, which is the same as $|3x - 15| < \epsilon$, as was required.

EXAMPLE 1. Draw a graph of the function

$$f(x) = \frac{1}{x + 1}, \qquad x \neq -1.$$

Find a δ so that $|f(x) - \tfrac{1}{2}| < 0.01$ if $|x - 1| < \delta$.

Solution. The graph is sketched in Fig. 5-4. In the definition of limit we have $L = \tfrac{1}{2}$ and $a = 1$. We must find an interval of the x-axis about $x = 1$ such that the graph lies in the proper rectangle. The function decreases steadily as we go to the right and therefore, when we erect vertical lines where the lines $y = 0.51, y = 0.49$ intersect the curve,

FIGURE 5–4   FIGURE 5–5

the largest possible interval on the x-axis is obtained. When we solve

$$\frac{1}{x+1} = 0.51$$

for x, we get $x = \frac{49}{51}$, and similarly, $1/(x+1) = 0.49$ gives $x = \frac{51}{49}$. In Fig. 5–4 these values are shown with units greatly exaggerated. Fortunately, once we find a δ, then any *smaller* δ will also be valid; for if the function lies in a rectangle, it certainly lies in a similar rectangle which is of the same height but narrower. So we take $\delta = 0.03$, since $\frac{49}{51} < 0.97$ and $\frac{51}{49} > 1.03$.

EXAMPLE 2. Draw a graph of

$$f(x) = \frac{2(x-4)}{\sqrt{x}-2}, \qquad x \geq 0, \quad x \neq 4,$$

and find a δ such that

$$|f(x) - 8| < 0.01 \qquad \text{whenever} \qquad 0 < |x-4| < \delta.$$

Solution. The function f is not defined at $x = 4$, but for $x \neq 4$ we can multiply numerator and denominator by $\sqrt{x} + 2$ to obtain

$$f(x) = \frac{2(x-4)(\sqrt{x}+2)}{(x-4)} = 2\sqrt{x} + 4 \qquad \text{for} \quad x \neq 4.$$

The graph of this function is shown in Fig. 5–5. We construct the lines $y = 7.99$ and $y = 8.01$, shown with greatly enlarged units in the figure. The intersections of these lines with the function are found by solving the equations

$$2\sqrt{x} + 4 = 7.99 \qquad \text{and} \qquad 2\sqrt{x} + 4 = 8.01.$$

We get $x = 3.980025$ and $x = 4.020025$. Since the function steadily increases to the right, an adequate selection for δ is 0.015. In other words, it is true that

$$|f(x) - 8| < 0.01 \qquad \text{whenever} \qquad 0 < |x-4| < 0.015.$$

Remark. To establish the existence of a limit we must find a δ for each positive ϵ. It is not necessary that we find the largest possible δ and, if work can be avoided by selecting a δ smaller than the largest possible one, we usually do so.

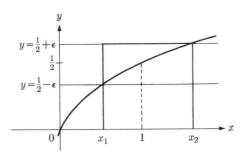

FIGURE 5-6

In Example 2 above, we obtained δ by solving the equations $2\sqrt{x} + 4 = 7.99$ and $2\sqrt{x} + 4 = 8.01$. Labor is avoided by noting that $2\sqrt{x} + 4 > 7.99$ for $x > 3.99$ and $2\sqrt{x} + 4 < 8.01$ for $x < 4.01$. That is, $\delta = 0.01$ works. If we try a value for δ and it does not satisfy the appropriate inequalities, we simply try a smaller one.

EXAMPLE 3. Show directly from the definition that

$$\lim_{x \to 1} \frac{x}{x + 1} = \frac{1}{2},$$

and draw the graph of the function $f(x) = x/(x + 1)$.

Solution. We have $L = \frac{1}{2}$ and $a = 1$. We must show that for every $\epsilon > 0$ we can find a $\delta > 0$ such that

$$\left| \frac{x}{x + 1} - \frac{1}{2} \right| < \epsilon \qquad \text{whenever} \qquad 0 < |x - 1| < \delta.$$

In order to get an idea of the appearance of the function we sketch the graph (Fig. 5-6). From the graph we see that the function is a steadily increasing one. We verify this fact by writing the identity

$$\frac{x}{x + 1} = 1 - \frac{1}{x + 1},$$

and noting that as x gets larger, $1/(x + 1)$ gets smaller and, therefore, $1 - [1/(x + 1)]$ increases.

Let us first suppose that $\epsilon < \frac{1}{2}$. Then $L + \epsilon < 1$ and $L - \epsilon > 0$, since $L = \frac{1}{2}$. Next, to see where the lines $y = \frac{1}{2} - \epsilon$ and $y = \frac{1}{2} + \epsilon$ intersect the curve, we solve the equations

$$\frac{x}{x + 1} = \frac{1}{2} - \epsilon \qquad \text{and} \qquad \frac{x}{x + 1} = \frac{1}{2} + \epsilon.$$

The first equation gives

$$x = (\tfrac{1}{2} - \epsilon)(x + 1) \qquad \text{or} \qquad (\tfrac{1}{2} + \epsilon)x = \tfrac{1}{2} - \epsilon \qquad \text{and} \qquad x = \frac{\tfrac{1}{2} - \epsilon}{\tfrac{1}{2} + \epsilon} \equiv x_1.$$

Similarly, the second equation yields

$$x = \frac{\tfrac{1}{2} + \epsilon}{\tfrac{1}{2} - \epsilon} \equiv x_2.$$

We select as δ the smaller of the distances between 1 and x_1 and between 1 and x_2. The student can check the fact that $1 - x_1$ is smaller than $x_2 - 1$. Therefore

$$\delta = 1 - x_1 = 1 - \frac{\frac{1}{2} - \epsilon}{\frac{1}{2} + \epsilon} = \frac{2\epsilon}{\frac{1}{2} + \epsilon} = \frac{4\epsilon}{1 + 2\epsilon}.$$

Remark. We restricted ϵ to a value smaller than $\frac{1}{2}$ and then found a δ for every positive $\epsilon < \frac{1}{2}$. While it is true that the basic definition states that a δ has to be found for *every* ϵ, in actuality this is not so. Once we have found a δ for a specific ϵ, we can use the same δ for *all* larger ϵ. Geometrically, this means that once the function is known to lie in a rectangle, clearly it lies in every rectangle which has the same sides but is taller.

EXERCISES

In problems 1 through 17, the numbers a, L, and ϵ are given. Determine a number δ so that $|f(x) - L| < \epsilon$ for all x such that $0 < |x - a| < \delta$. Draw a graph.

1. $f(x) = 2x + 3$, $a = 1$, $L = 5$, $\epsilon = 0.001$
2. $f(x) = 1 - 2x$, $a = -1$, $L = 3$, $\epsilon = 0.01$
3. $f(x) = (x^2 - 9)/(x + 3)$, $a = -3$, $L = -6$, $\epsilon = 0.005$
4. $f(x) = \sqrt{x}$, $a = 1$, $L = 1$, $\epsilon = 0.01$
5. $f(x) = \sqrt[3]{x}$, $a = 1$, $L = 1$, $\epsilon = 0.01$
6. $f(x) = \sqrt[3]{x}$, $a = 0$, $L = 0$, $\epsilon = 0.1$
7. $f(x) = \sqrt{2x}$, $a = 2$, $L = 2$, $\epsilon = 0.02$
8. $f(x) = 1/x$, $a = 2$, $L = \frac{1}{2}$, $\epsilon = 0.002$
9. $f(x) = 2/\sqrt{x}$, $a = 4$, $L = 1$, $\epsilon = 0.1$
10. $f(x) = 3/(x + 2)$, $a = 1$, $L = 1$, $\epsilon = 0.001$
11. $f(x) = 1/x$, $a = -1$, $L = -1$, $\epsilon = 0.01$
12. $f(x) = (x - 1)/(x + 1)$, $a = 0$, $L = -1$, $\epsilon = 0.01$
13. $f(x) = (\sqrt{x} - 1)/(x - 1)$, $a = 1$, $L = \frac{1}{2}$, $\epsilon = 0.01$
14. $f(x) = (\sqrt{2x} - 2)/(x - 2)$, $a = 2$, $L = \frac{1}{2}$, $\epsilon = 0.01$
15. $f(x) = x^2$, $a = 1$, $L = 1$, $\epsilon = 0.01$
16. $f(x) = x^3 - 6$, $a = 1$, $L = -5$, $\epsilon = 0.1$
17. $f(x) = x^3 + 3x$, $a = -1$, $L = -4$, $\epsilon = 0.5$

In problems 18 through 22, show that

$$\lim_{x \to a} f(x) = L$$

directly by finding the δ corresponding to every positive ϵ. (Use the method of Example 3.)

18. $f(x) = (x^2 - 4)/(x - 2)$, $a = 2$, $L = 4$
19. $f(x) = \sqrt{x}$, $a = 2$, $L = \sqrt{2}$ 20. $f(x) = \sqrt[3]{x}$, $a = 3$, $L = \sqrt[3]{3}$
21. $f(x) = 1/(x + 1)$, $a = 2$, $L = \frac{1}{3}$ 22. $f(x) = 1/(x + 2)$, $a = -3$, $L = -1$

2. THEOREMS ON LIMITS

In Chapter 4 we discussed limits without any attempt at rigorous or exact mathematical statements. In the process of doing this, we performed all sorts of algebraic manipulations. The skeptical student realizes that each of these needs justification, even though on the surface many appear obvious. The first step in such a justification requires the precise definition of limit which we have just given in Section 1. The next step should be the statements and proofs of the theorems which allow us to manipulate limits. However, with one exception we shall restrict ourselves to statements of the theorems only, since many of the proofs are beyond the scope of a course in elementary calculus. The statements themselves will help the student understand the kind of work that has to be done.

As an example of the kind of statement that should be proved even though it is completely obvious in character, we give the following theorem, which says that a function cannot approach two different limits at the same time.

Theorem 1. (Uniqueness of Limits.) *Suppose that $f(x) \to L_1$ as $x \to a$, and $f(x) \to L_2$ as $x \to a$. Then $L_1 = L_2$.*

This theorem is so simple that we can easily give a proof.

Proof. We shall suppose $L_1 \neq L_2$ and show it to be impossible. If $L_1 \neq L_2$, we let $\epsilon = \frac{1}{2}|L_1 - L_2|$ and ϵ will be *positive*. Since

$$\lim_{x \to a} f(x) = L_1,$$

we know from the definition of limit, that there is a δ such that

$$|f(x) - L_1| < \epsilon \quad \text{if} \quad 0 < |x - a| < \delta.$$

But if, in addition,

$$\lim_{x \to a} f(x) = L_2,$$

we also know from the definition that there is a δ' (perhaps different from the δ) such that

$$|f(x) - L_2| < \epsilon \quad \text{when} \quad 0 < |x - a| < \delta'.$$

Then either $\delta \leq \delta'$ or $\delta' \leq \delta$. For convenience, suppose that $\delta \leq \delta'$. We now use the trick of writing a simple expression in a complicated way:

$$L_1 - L_2 = L_1 - f(x) + f(x) - L_2.$$

Therefore,

$$|L_1 - L_2| = |(L_1 - f(x)) + (f(x) - L_2)| \leq |L_1 - f(x)| + |f(x) - L_2|,$$

the inequality arising from the fact — which we recall — that $|a + b| \leq |a| + |b|$. Let us now divide by 2 to obtain

$$\tfrac{1}{2}|L_1 - L_2| \leq \tfrac{1}{2}|L_1 - f(x)| + \tfrac{1}{2}|f(x) - L_2|.$$

But $|f(x) - L_2| < \epsilon$, and $|f(x) - L_1| < \epsilon$, and so

$$\tfrac{1}{2}|L_1 - L_2| < \tfrac{1}{2}\epsilon + \tfrac{1}{2}\epsilon = \epsilon.$$

However, we defined $\epsilon = \tfrac{1}{2}|L_1 - L_2|$, and we now have the absurd assertion that $\epsilon < \epsilon$. Therefore the assumption that $L_1 \neq L_2$ must be false.

Theorem 2. (Limit of a Constant.) *If c is a constant and f(x) = c for all values of x, then for any number a*

$$\lim_{x \to a} f(x) = c.$$

Theorem 2 is established by applying the definition of limit to the particular function $f(x) = c$. Geometrically the function $f(x) = c$ represents a line parallel to the x-axis and c units from it.

Theorem 3. (Obvious Limit.) *If m and b are constants and f(x) = mx + b for all values of x, then for any number a*

$$\lim_{x \to a} f(x) = ma + b.$$

Theorem 3 says that when the function represents a straight line, the limit is always obtained by direct substitution of the value a for x.

Theorem 4. (Limit of a Sum.) *If f and g are two functions with*

$$\lim_{x \to a} f(x) = L_1 \qquad and \qquad \lim_{x \to a} g(x) = L_2,$$

then

$$\lim_{x \to a} (f(x) + g(x)) = L_1 + L_2.$$

This hypothesis states that $|f(x) - L_1|$ can be made "small" if x is "close to" a; the same is true about $|g(x) - L_2|$. The conclusion asserts that $|f(x) + g(x) - L_1 - L_2|$ can be made "small" if x is "close to" a.

Once Theorem 4 is established, we can use it over and over to add the limits of any number of functions. For example, if

$$\lim_{x \to a} f(x) = L_1, \qquad \lim_{x \to a} g(x) = L_2, \qquad and \qquad \lim_{x \to a} h(x) = L_3,$$

then

$$\lim_{x \to a} (f(x) + g(x) + h(x)) = L_1 + L_2 + L_3.$$

To demonstrate this, we first apply Theorem 4 to f and g, designating $f(x) + g(x) = F(x)$. Then we apply Theorem 4 again to $F(x)$ and $h(x)$. This technique of combining and using the same theorem over and over occurs frequently in the study of limits. The limit of the sum of any (finite) number of functions is the sum of the limits of each of the functions.

Theorem 5. (Limit of a Product.) *If f and g are two functions with*

$$\lim_{x \to a} f(x) = L_1 \quad and \quad \lim_{x \to a} g(x) = L_2,$$

then

$$\lim_{x \to a} [f(x) \cdot g(x)] = L_1 \cdot L_2.$$

Here we note, as we did in Theorem 4, that the limit of the product of any number of functions is the product of the limits.

EXAMPLE 1. Given

$$\lim_{x \to a} f(x) = L_1, \quad \lim_{x \to a} g(x) = L_2, \quad and \quad \lim_{x \to a} h(x) = L_3,$$

find the value of

$$\lim_{x \to a} [f(x) \cdot g(x) + h(x)].$$

Solution. We define $F(x) = f(x) \cdot g(x)$. From Theorem 5 we know that

$$\lim_{x \to a} f(x) \cdot g(x) = L_1 \cdot L_2.$$

That is,

$$\lim_{x \to a} F(x) = L_1 \cdot L_2.$$

Applying Theorem 4 to $F(x) + h(x)$, we now find

$$\lim_{x \to a} \big(F(x) + h(x)\big) = L_1 \cdot L_2 + L_3.$$

Theorem 6. (Limit of a Quotient.) *If f and g are two functions with*

$$\lim_{x \to a} f(x) = L_1, \quad \lim_{x \to a} g(x) = L_2, \quad and \quad L_2 \neq 0,$$

then

$$\lim_{x \to a} \frac{f(x)}{g(x)} = \frac{L_1}{L_2}.$$

It is necessary to assume that $L_2 \neq 0$ if the expression L_1/L_2 is to have a meaning.

EXAMPLE 2. Given $F(x) = x^2$, show that

$$\lim_{x \to a} F(x) = a^2.$$

Solution. It is possible to obtain this result by appealing to the definition of limit. However, we can also prove the statement simply by correct application of the theorems on limits. Assuming that $m = 1$ and $b = 0$ in Theorem 3, we have

$$\lim_{x \to a} x = a.$$

Let $f(x) = x$ and $g(x) = x$. Then

$$\lim_{x \to a} f(x) = a \qquad \text{and} \qquad \lim_{x \to a} g(x) = a.$$

We can apply Theorem 5, with $L_1 = a$, $L_2 = a$, to get

$$\lim_{x \to a} f(x) \cdot g(x) = a \cdot a = a^2,$$

which says that

$$\lim_{x \to a} F(x) = a^2.$$

EXAMPLE 3. Given $F(x) = x^2/(3x - 2)$, show that

$$\lim_{x \to a} \frac{x^2}{3x - 2} = \frac{a^2}{3a - 2} \qquad \text{if} \quad a \neq \tfrac{2}{3}.$$

Solution. From Example 2 we know that

$$\lim_{x \to a} x^2 = a^2,$$

and from Theorem 3 with $m = 3$ and $b = -2$, we know that

$$\lim_{x \to a} (3x - 2) = 3a - 2.$$

An application of Theorem 6 with $f(x) = x^2$, $g(x) = 3x - 2$, $L_1 = a^2$, and $L_2 = 3a - 2$, shows that (since $L_2 \neq 0$ as $a \neq \tfrac{2}{3}$),

$$\lim_{x \to a} \frac{x^2}{3x - 2} = \frac{a^2}{3a - 2}.$$

Theorem 7. *If n is any positive integer and if f is such that*

$$\lim_{x \to a} f(x) = L,$$

then

$$\lim_{x \to a} \sqrt[n]{f(x)} = \sqrt[n]{L}.$$

If n is an even integer, we shall suppose that L is not negative; in this way we avoid problems with complex numbers.

EXAMPLE 4. Find the value of

$$\lim_{x \to 2} \frac{x^3 + 3}{2x^2 + 5}$$

and justify each step.

Solution. From Theorem 3 with $m = 1$ and $b = 0$, we know that

$$\lim_{x \to 2} x = 2.$$

Now let $f(x) = x$, $g(x) = x$, $h(x) = x$, and apply Theorem 5 (the limit of products) to the product of the three functions. The result is

$$\lim_{x \to 2} x^3 = 8.$$

Theorem 2 (limit of a constant) tells us that

$$\lim_{x \to 2} 3 = 3.$$

Letting $F(x) = x^3$ and $G(x) = 3$, and applying Theorem 4 (limit of a sum), we get

$$\lim_{x \to 2} (x^3 + 3) = 8 + 3 = 11,$$

which takes care of the numerator. As for the denominator, we have

$$\lim_{x \to 2} 2 = 2, \qquad \lim_{x \to 2} x^2 = 4$$

and an application of Theorem 5 gives

$$\lim_{x \to 2} 2x^2 = 8.$$

Theorem 4 (limit of a sum) yields

$$\lim_{x \to 2} (2x^2 + 5) = 8 + 5 = 13.$$

Finally, employing Theorem 6 (limit of a quotient) with $x^2 + 3$ as numerator and $2x^2 + 5$ as denominator, we conclude that

$$\lim_{x \to 2} \frac{x^3 + 3}{2x^2 + 5} = \frac{11}{13}.$$

EXAMPLE 5. Evaluate

$$\lim_{x \to 2} \sqrt{\frac{x^4 - 16}{x^3 - 8}}$$

and justify each step.

Solution. The problem here is a little more difficult than those above, since straight substitution shows that the function is undefined for $x = 2$. We factor numerator and denominator to get

$$\frac{x^4 - 16}{x^3 - 8} = \frac{(x - 2)(x + 2)(x^2 + 4)}{(x - 2)(x^2 + 2x + 4)} = \frac{x^3 + 2x^2 + 4x + 8}{x^2 + 2x + 4}, \qquad x \neq 2.$$

Step 1. We write

$$\lim_{x \to 2} x = 2, \qquad \lim_{x \to 2} x^2 = 4, \qquad \lim_{x \to 2} x^3 = 8,$$

the first limit coming from Theorem 3 with $m = 1$ and $b = 0$, and the next two from Theorem 5 (limit of a product).

Step 2. From Theorem 2,

$$\lim_{x \to 2} 2 = 2, \qquad \lim_{x \to 2} 4 = 4, \qquad \lim_{x \to 2} 8 = 8.$$

Step 3. From Theorem 5 (limit of a product) combined with the results in Steps 1 and 2, we find that

$$\lim_{x \to 2} 2x = 4, \qquad \lim_{x \to 2} 2x^2 = 8, \qquad \lim_{x \to 2} 4x = 8.$$

Step 4. Using Theorem 4 (limit of a sum) plus the limits in Steps 1, 2, and 3, we obtain

$$\lim_{x \to 2} (x^3 + 2x^2 + 4x + 8) = 32, \qquad \lim_{x \to 2} (x^2 + 2x + 4) = 12.$$

Step 5. Using Theorem 6 (limit of a quotient) we find that

$$\lim_{x \to 2} \frac{x^3 + 2x^2 + 4x + 8}{x^2 + 2x + 4} = \frac{8}{3}.$$

Step 6. Finally,

$$\lim_{x \to 2} \sqrt{\frac{x^4 - 16}{x^3 - 8}} = \sqrt{\frac{8}{3}},$$

which is derived from Theorem 7.

EXERCISES

In problems 1 through 18, evaluate the limits by following the methods given in Examples 4 and 5. Give the reason for each step by stating the appropriate theorem.

1. $\lim_{x \to 3} (x^2 - 3x + 5)$

2. $\lim_{x \to -2} (2x^3 - 6x^2 + 3x - 2)$

3. $\lim_{x \to 1} \dfrac{x + 3}{2x^2 - 6x + 5}$

4. $\lim_{x \to 4} \dfrac{2x^2 - 6}{x^3 + 5}$ 5. $\lim_{x \to 1} \dfrac{x^3 - 1}{x - 1}$ 6. $\lim_{x \to -1} \dfrac{x^3 + 1}{x + 1}$

7. $\lim_{x \to -2} \dfrac{x^2 + x - 2}{x^2 - 4}$ 8. $\lim_{x \to -2} \dfrac{x^2 - 4}{x^3 + 8}$ 9. $\lim_{t \to 2} \sqrt{\dfrac{2t + 5}{3t - 2}}$

10. $\lim_{r \to 1} \sqrt{\dfrac{2r^2 + 3r - 1}{r^2 + 1}}$ 11. $\lim_{y \to 2} \sqrt{\dfrac{y^2 - 4}{y^2 - 3y + 2}}$ 12. $\lim_{x \to 3} \sqrt{\dfrac{x^3 - 27}{x^2 + 2x + 1}}$

13. $\lim_{h \to 2} \sqrt{\dfrac{h^3 - 8}{h^2 - 4}}$ 14. $\lim_{h \to 0} \dfrac{\sqrt{1 + h} - 1}{h}$

15. $\lim_{h \to 0} \dfrac{\sqrt{x + h} - \sqrt{x}}{h}, \qquad x > 0$

16. $\lim_{h \to 0} \dfrac{1}{h} \left(\dfrac{1}{x + h} - \dfrac{1}{x} \right)$ 17. $\lim_{h \to 0} \dfrac{1}{h} \left(\dfrac{1}{\sqrt{1 + h}} - 1 \right)$ 18. $\lim_{h \to 0} \dfrac{(1 + h)^{3/2} - 1}{h}$

19. Prove Theorem 2 by employing the definition of limit.

20. Prove Theorem 3 by employing the definition of limit.

21. Given

$$\lim_{x \to a} f(x) = L_1, \quad \lim_{x \to a} g(x) = L_2, \quad \lim_{x \to a} h(x) = L_3, \quad \text{and} \quad \lim_{x \to a} p(x) = L_4,$$

state the theorems which justify the following statements:

(a) $\displaystyle \lim_{x \to a} \frac{f(x) + g(x)}{h(x)} = \frac{L_1 + L_2}{L_3}, \quad \text{if} \quad L_3 \neq 0.$

(b) $\displaystyle \lim_{x \to a} \frac{f(x)g(x) - h(x)}{g(x) + p(x)} = \frac{L_1 L_2 - L_3}{L_2 + L_4}, \quad \text{if} \quad L_2 + L_4 \neq 0.$

(c) $\displaystyle \lim_{x \to a} \left(\frac{f(x) - g(x) + h(x)p(x)}{g(x) + h(x)} \right)^{2/3} = \left(\frac{L_1 - L_2 + L_3 L_4}{L_2 + L_3} \right)^{2/3},$

$$\text{if} \quad L_2 + L_3 \neq 0.$$

3. CONTINUITY

In Section 1 we analyzed the meaning of

$$\lim_{x \to a} f(x) = L.$$

In doing so we made a point of ignoring the actual value of the function f when $x = a$. In fact, for many expressions the function was not even defined at $x = a$. Suppose we have a function f which is defined at $x = a$, and suppose the limit L, which f approaches when $x \to a$, is the value of f when x is a — just the quantity we call $f(a)$. When this happens, we say the function is *continuous* at $x = a$.

DEFINITION. *"The function f is continuous at the number a"* means that

(i) $f(a)$ is defined, and

(ii) $\displaystyle \lim_{x \to a} f(x) = f(a).$

When a function is not continuous, we say it is *discontinuous* at a. Most, but not all, of the functions we have been studying are continuous everywhere. For example, the functions

$$f(x) = 3x - 2, \quad g(x) = 5 - 2x + 4x^2, \quad \text{and} \quad h(x) = \frac{3x + 1}{2 + x^2}$$

are defined for all values of x and are continuous for all values of x. On the other hand, the function

$$G(x) = \begin{cases} \dfrac{3}{(x - 2)^2}, & x \neq 2 \\ 5, & x = 2 \end{cases}$$

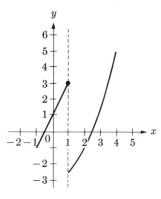

FIGURE 5–7   FIGURE 5–8

is discontinuous for one value of x. Note that it was necessary to give the value at $x = 2$ separately, since the expression $3/(x - 2)^2$ is meaningless when x is 2. The graph of this function (Fig. 5–7) shows that the value of $G(x)$ increases without bound as x tends to the value 2. Since $G(2) = 5$, it is evident that

$$\lim_{x \to 2} G(x) \neq G(2),$$

and the function is discontinuous at $x = 2$. We realize that no matter what value is assigned to the function G at $x = 2$, the function could never be continuous.

A second example of a discontinuous function is given by the following:

$$f(x) = \begin{cases} 2x + 1, & -1 < x \leq 1, \\ \tfrac{1}{2}x^2 - 3, & 1 < x < 4. \end{cases}$$

This function has a domain of values extending from -1 to 4 along the x-axis, as shown in the graph of the function in Fig. 5–8. The graph is perfectly smooth except for a "break" at $x = 1$. The way the function is defined, $f(1) = 2(1) + 1 = 3$, while the values immediately to the right of $x = 1$ cluster about -2.5. We see that as $x \to 1$ there is no limit, for if x is larger than 1 and tending to 1 the value approached is -2.5, while if x is smaller than 1 and tending to 1, the value approached is 3. There is no value that can be given to the function at $x = 1$ which will reconcile the difference. Since

$$\lim_{x \to 1} f(x)$$

does not exist, the function is discontinuous at $x = 1$.

The function

$$g(x) = \frac{x^2 - 9}{x + 3}$$

is defined for all values of x except $x = -3$. We can define $g(-3)$ in any way we like. From the methods given in Chapter 4, Sections 1 and 2, on limits, we can determine whether or not

$$\lim_{x \to -3} g(x)$$

exists. The technique of determining the limit employs factoring, and we find

$$\lim_{x \to -3} \frac{x^2 - 9}{x + 3} = \lim_{x \to -3} \frac{(x - 3)(x + 3)}{(x + 3)} = -6.$$

However, the function g is not continuous at $x = -3$, since it is not defined there. If we define $g(-3)$ to be -6, the function will be continuous at $x = -3$. If we define $g(-3)$ to have any other value, the function will be discontinuous.

_____

EXAMPLE 1. For what values of x is the function defined by

$$f(x) = \begin{cases} x^2 - 3, & -1 < x < 1 \\ 2x - 4, & 1 \le x < 2 \\ 5 - x^2, & 2 \le x < 3 \end{cases}$$

continuous? Sketch the graph.

Solution. The domain for this function is the interval $(-1, 3)$. The only questionable values are at $x = 1$ and $x = 2$. We have

$$f(1) = -2 \quad \text{and} \quad f(2) = 1.$$

If x is in the neighborhood of 1 and less than 1, the values cluster about $(1)^2 - 3 = -2$. Similarly, if x is near 1 and greater than 1, the values cluster about $2(1) - 4 = -2$. Since $f(1) = -2$, we see that

$$\lim_{x \to 1} f(x) = -2 = f(1),$$

and $f(x)$ is continuous at $x = 1$. On the other hand, if x is near 2 and smaller than 2, the values of f cluster about $2(2) - 4 = 0$, while if x is near 2 and larger than 2, the values of f are near $5 - (2)^2 = 1$. Therefore it is impossible that

$$\lim_{x \to 2} f(x)$$

should exist. The function is discontinuous at $x = 2$. Its graph is shown in Fig. 5–9.

EXAMPLE 2. For what values of x is the function

$$f(x) = \begin{cases} \dfrac{x + 3}{x^2 + x - 6}, & \text{for all } x \text{ except } x = -3, x = 2 \\ f(-3) = 2, & f(2) = 1 \end{cases}$$

continuous?

Solution. Note that the denominator of the above expression vanishes at $x = -3, 2$, and so has to be defined separately at these points. If $x \ne -3, 2$, by factoring we obtain

$$\frac{x + 3}{x^2 + x - 6} = \frac{x + 3}{(x + 3)(x - 2)} = \frac{1}{x - 2}.$$

FIGURE 5–9

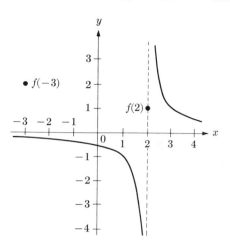

FIGURE 5–10

From this we get

$$\lim_{x \to -3} \frac{x+3}{x^2+x-6} = \lim_{x \to -3} \frac{1}{x-2} = -\frac{1}{5}.$$

Since $f(-3) = 2$, the function is not continuous at $x = -3$. Also, as $x \to 2$ from the right, $f(x)$ increases without bound, while as $x \to 2$ from the left, $f(x)$ decreases without bound. This means that

$$\lim_{x \to 2} \frac{x+3}{x^2+x-6}$$

does not exist. The function is discontinuous at $x = 2$. A graph of the function is given in Fig. 5–10.

In the above example, it is possible to redefine the value of f at $x = -3$ so that the function is continuous there. If we let $f(-3) = -\frac{1}{5}$, the function value and the limit coincide. On the other hand, no matter what we do at $x = 2$, the function can never be continuous there. We use the term *removable discontinuity* when a redefinition of the function at a point makes the function continuous at that point.

In a general way we see that discontinuities involve a "break" in the curve. The "post-office function,"

$$f(x) = \begin{cases} 5, & 0 < x \le 1 \\ 10, & 1 < x \le 2 \\ 15, & 2 < x \le 3 \\ \text{etc.} \dots \end{cases}$$

or, more compactly,

$$f(x) = 5n, \quad n-1 < x \le n, \quad n = 1, 2, 3, \dots,$$

has discontinuities at $1, 2, 3, \dots$. However, a function may have a "corner" and

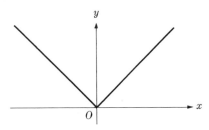

FIGURE 5–11

still be continuous. A simple example of this is the function

$$f(x) = |x|,$$

which has a corner at $x = 0$, as Fig. 5–11 shows. This function is continuous for all values of x.

Employing the notion of a continuous function we can complete our statements of theorems on limits given in Section 2; we do so with a theorem on composite functions.

Theorem 8. (Limit of a Composite Function.) *Suppose that f is continuous at a point b and, further, that g is a function such that*

$$\lim_{x \to a} g(x) = b.$$

Then

$$\lim_{x \to a} f[g(x)] = f(b).$$

To say that a function has a derivative at the value a means that a tangent to the curve can be drawn at the point $(a, f(a))$. In fact, the value of the derivative, defined as

$$\lim_{h \to 0} \frac{f(a + h) - f(a)}{h},$$

is simply the slope of this tangent line. A continuous function may have corners, and it is hard to imagine how a tangent to a curve can be constructed at a corner; in general, it cannot. Not every continuous function possesses a tangent at each point. If a function has a derivative, however, it is continuous, as we shall prove.

Theorem 9. *If the function f possesses a derivative at the value a, it is continuous at a.*

Proof. We recall that two things must be shown:

(i) $f(a)$ is defined,

and

(ii) $\lim_{x \to a} f(x) = f(a)$.

If a function has a derivative at a, then

$$\lim_{h \to 0} \frac{f(a + h) - f(a)}{h} = f'(a)$$

exists. This statement would have no meaning if $f(a)$ did not; therefore having a derivative at a means that $f(a)$ must have a meaning. As for (ii), we see that it has the same meaning as

$$\lim_{h \to 0} f(a + h) = f(a).$$

We can write

$$f(a + h) - f(a) = \left(\frac{f(a + h) - f(a)}{h} \right) \cdot h.$$

On the right, the term in parentheses approaches $f'(a)$, a finite number, as h tends to zero. The second part, namely h, tends to zero. Therefore, as h tends to zero, the right side—according to the theorem on the limit of a product—tends to zero. We conclude that $f(a + h) - f(a) \to 0$ as $h \to 0$, and (ii) is established; $f(x)$ is continuous at a.

EXERCISES

In each of the problems 1 through 20, a function is defined in a certain domain. State whether or not the function is continuous at all points in this domain. Sketch the graph.

1. $f(x) = \dfrac{1}{x^2 + 5}$ for $-7 < x < 5$

2. $f(x) = \begin{cases} \dfrac{1}{x + 7} & \text{for } -10 < x < -4, \quad x \neq -7 \\ f(-7) = 3 \end{cases}$

3. $f(x) = \dfrac{x + 2}{x^2 - 3x - 10}$ for $3 < x < 4$

4. $f(x) = \begin{cases} \dfrac{x - 6}{x^2 - 2x - 8} & \text{for } -1 < x < 6, \quad x \neq 4 \\ f(4) = -2 \end{cases}$

5. $f(x) = \begin{cases} \dfrac{x^2 - 9}{x^2 - 2x - 3} & \text{for } 0 < x < 5, \quad x \neq 3 \\ f(3) = \frac{3}{2} \end{cases}$

6. $f(x) = \begin{cases} \dfrac{x + 4}{x^2 - 16} & \text{for } -5 < x < 5, \quad x \neq 4, -4 \\ f(-4) = -\frac{1}{8}, \quad f(4) = 2 \end{cases}$

7. $f(x) = \begin{cases} \dfrac{x^3 - 1}{x^2 + x - 2} & \text{for } 0 < x < 2, \ x \neq 1 \\ f(1) = 1 \end{cases}$

8. $f(x) = \dfrac{x^2 - 4}{x^2 + 4}$ for all values of x

9. $f(x) = \begin{cases} x - 4 & \text{for } -1 < x \leq 2 \\ x^2 - 6 & \text{for } 2 < x < 5 \end{cases}$

10. $f(x) = \begin{cases} 3x - 2 & \text{for } 0 < x \leq 5 \\ x^2 + x + 1 & \text{for } 5 < x < 7 \end{cases}$

11. $f(x) = \begin{cases} x^2 - 6x + 1 & \text{for } -1 < x \leq 2 \\ 2x + 6 & \text{for } 2 < x \leq 3 \\ x^3 - 15 & \text{for } 3 < x < 5 \end{cases}$

12. $f(x) = \begin{cases} \dfrac{2x}{x^2 - 4} & \text{for } 0 < x < 2 \\ 3x - 5 & \text{for } 2 \leq x \leq 5 \\ x^2 + 6 & \text{for } 5 < x < 7 \end{cases}$

13. $f(x) = \begin{cases} \dfrac{x^2 - 1}{x^4 - 1} & \text{for } -1 < x < 2, \ x \neq 1 \\ x^2 + 3x - 2 & \text{for } 2 \leq x < 5 \\ f(1) = \frac{1}{2} \end{cases}$

14. $f(x) = \begin{cases} \dfrac{x}{3} & \text{for } -\infty < x < 2 \\ \frac{1}{6}x^2 & \text{for } 2 \leq x < \infty \end{cases}$

15. $f(x) = \begin{cases} x^2 - 6 & \text{for } -\infty < x < -1 \\ -5 & \text{for } -1 \leq x \leq 10 \\ x - 15 & \text{for } 10 < x < \infty \end{cases}$

16. $f(x) = |x + 3|$ for all values of x

17. $f(x) = \begin{cases} \dfrac{2x - 6}{|x - 4|} & \text{for all } x \text{ except } x = 4 \\ f(4) = -1 \end{cases}$

18. $f(x) = \begin{cases} \dfrac{x - 2}{|x - 2|} & \text{for all } x \text{ except } x = 2 \\ f(2) = 0 \end{cases}$

19. $f(x) = \dfrac{3 + |x - 2|}{x^2 + 1}$ for all values of x

20. $f(x) = \begin{cases} \dfrac{x^2 - x - 6}{x - 3} & \text{for all } x \text{ except } x = 3 \\ f(3) = 5 \end{cases}$

4. LIMITS AT INFINITY; INFINITE LIMITS

The graph of the function

$$f(x) = \frac{x^2}{1 + x^2}$$

is shown in Fig. 5–12. The values of this function are always less than 1; in particular, we note the following:

$$f(1) = \frac{1}{2}, \quad f(10) = \frac{100}{101}, \quad f(100) = \frac{10,000}{10,001}, \quad f(1000) = \frac{10^6}{10^6 + 1}, \dots.$$

As x gets larger and larger, the graph of f gets closer and closer to the line $y = 1$, as shown in Fig. 5–12. We use the term "x tends to infinity" when referring to values which increase without bound. If x is becoming larger through positive values only, we write $x \to +\infty$; if through negative values only, we write $x \to -\infty$. The symbol $x \to \infty$ means that $|x|$ increases without bound. In the above example, we would write

$$f(x) \to 1 \quad \text{as} \quad x \to \infty.$$

More generally, we formulate the following definition.

DEFINITION. *We say that $f(x) \to c$ as $x \to \infty$, if for each $\epsilon > 0$ there is a number $A > 0$, such that $|f(x) - c| < \epsilon$ for all x for which $|x| > A$.*
If we want to define

$$f(x) \to c \quad \text{as} \quad x \to +\infty$$

(i.e., $f(x)$ tends to c as x tends to infinity through positive values only), the only change in the definition would be to write $x > A$ instead of $|x| > A$. Further, the definition of

$$f(x) \to c \quad \text{as} \quad x \to -\infty$$

FIGURE 5–12

would require $x < -A$ instead of $|x| > A$.

The theorems on uniqueness of limit and on limit of a constant, sum, product, and quotient remain unchanged. In place of the theorem on limits of functions of the form $mx + b$, we have the following theorem on obvious limits.

Theorem 10. $\displaystyle\lim_{x \to \infty} \frac{1}{x} = 0,$ $\displaystyle\lim_{x \to +\infty} \frac{1}{x} = 0,$ $\displaystyle\lim_{x \to -\infty} \frac{1}{x} = 0.$

EXAMPLE 1. Evaluate

$$\lim_{x \to +\infty} \frac{3x - 2}{5x + 4},$$

giving the reason for each step.

Solution. We first divide each term in the numerator and denominator by x:

$$\frac{3x - 2}{5x + 4} = \frac{3 - (2/x)}{5 + (4/x)}.$$

For the numerator, we find that

$$\lim_{x \to +\infty} \left(3 - \frac{2}{x}\right) = \lim_{x \to +\infty} 3 + \lim_{x \to +\infty} \left(-\frac{2}{x}\right),$$

since the limit of a sum is the sum of the limits. We now reason that

$$\lim_{x \to +\infty} 3 = 3 \quad \text{(using limit of a constant)}$$

and

$$\lim_{x \to +\infty} \left(-\frac{2}{x}\right) = -2 \lim_{x \to +\infty} \frac{1}{x} = 0 \quad \text{(using limit of a product and Theorem 10).}$$

Therefore

$$\lim_{x \to +\infty} \left(3 - \frac{2}{x}\right) = 3.$$

In exactly the same way,

$$\lim_{x \to +\infty} \left(5 + \frac{4}{x}\right) = 5.$$

Now we can say that

$$\lim_{x \to +\infty} \frac{3 - (2/x)}{5 + (4/x)} = \frac{\displaystyle\lim_{x \to +\infty} (3 - (2/x))}{\displaystyle\lim_{x \to +\infty} (5 + (4/x))},$$

since the limit of a quotient is the quotient of the limits. We conclude that

$$\lim_{x \to +\infty} \frac{3x - 2}{5x + 4} = \frac{3}{5}.$$

EXAMPLE 2. Evaluate

$$\lim_{x \to +\infty} \frac{\sqrt{x^2 - 1}}{2x + 1},$$

giving a reason for each step.

Solution. We write

$$\frac{\sqrt{x^2 - 1}}{2x + 1} = \frac{\sqrt{1 - (1/x^2)}}{2 + (1/x)}.$$

Since

$$\frac{1}{x^2} = \frac{1}{x} \cdot \frac{1}{x},$$

we have

$$\lim_{x \to +\infty} \frac{1}{x^2} = \lim_{x \to +\infty} \frac{1}{x} \cdot \lim_{x \to +\infty} \frac{1}{x} = 0,$$

using the limit of a product theorem and Theorem 10. Then

$$\lim_{x \to +\infty} \left(1 - \frac{1}{x^2}\right) = \lim_{x \to +\infty} 1 - \lim_{x \to +\infty} \frac{1}{x^2} = 1 \quad \text{(using limit of a sum).}$$

Further, by using Theorem 7, we find that

$$\lim_{x \to +\infty} \sqrt{1 - \frac{1}{x^2}} = 1.$$

We now see that

$$\lim_{x \to +\infty} \left(2 + \frac{1}{x}\right) = 2,$$

as in Example 1, and when we apply the quotient rule, we have

$$\lim_{x \to +\infty} \frac{\sqrt{x^2 - 1}}{2x + 1} = \frac{1}{2}.$$

The graph of the function $f(x) = x/(x - 1)$ is shown in Fig. 5–13. We note the following values of this function.

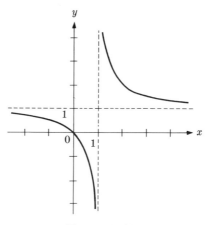

FIGURE 5–13

$$f(2) = 2, \quad f(\tfrac{3}{2}) = 3, \quad f(1.1) = 11, \quad f(1.01) = 101, \quad f(1.001) = 1,001, \ldots ;$$
$$f(0) = 0, \quad f(\tfrac{1}{2}) = -1, \quad f(0.9) = -9, \quad f(0.99) = -99, \quad f(0.999) = -999, \ldots .$$

This type of behavior implies that the function grows without bound as x gets closer and closer to 1. We use the expression

$$f(x) \to \infty \qquad \text{as} \qquad x \to 1,$$

which we define in the following way.

> DEFINITION. We say that $f(x)$ becomes infinite as $x \to a$, and write $f(x) \to \infty$ as $x \to a$, if for each number $A > 0$ there is a $\delta > 0$ such that $|f(x)| > A$, for all x for which $0 < |x - a| < \delta$.

This definition does not state whether the function goes off to infinity "upward" or "downward." Nor does it say how the values of x are tending to a — from the left or from the right. In the example we have given, we notice that as $x \to 1$ through values larger than 1, $f(x) \to +\infty$. On the other hand, as $x \to 1$ through values smaller than 1, $f(x) \to -\infty$. The symbol $x \to a^+$ means that x tends to a only through values to the right of a. This is called *the limit from the right, right-hand limit*, or *one-sided limit from the right*. The analogous symbol for limit from the left is

$$x \to a^-.$$

For the function shown in Fig. 5–13 we have

$$f(x) \to +\infty \quad \text{as} \quad x \to 1^+ \qquad \text{and} \qquad f(x) \to -\infty \quad \text{as} \quad x \to 1^-.$$

Some functions have limits from one side only. For example, the function

$$f(x) = \frac{1}{\sqrt{x - 2}}$$

is not defined for $x < 2$. We have

$$f(x) \to +\infty \qquad \text{as} \qquad x \to 2^+.$$

The rules for operating with limits are somewhat tricky when one of the quantities becomes infinite. We must remember that ∞ *is not a number* and cannot be treated as such. There are some simple facts about infinite limits which the reader will easily recognize. For example, in a case such as

$$f(x) \to +\infty \quad \text{as} \quad x \to a, \qquad g(x) \to c \quad \text{as} \quad x \to a,$$

where c is any number, then

$$f(x) + g(x) \to +\infty.$$

If $c \neq 0$, we have

$$f(x) \cdot g(x) \to +\infty \quad \text{when } c > 0, \qquad \text{and} \qquad f(x) \cdot g(x) \to -\infty \quad \text{when } c < 0.$$

On the other hand, if $c = 0$, further investigation is necessary. Similarly, when

$$f(x) \to +\infty \quad \text{as} \quad x \to a, \qquad \text{and} \qquad g(x) \to -\infty \quad \text{as} \quad x \to a,$$

nothing can be said about

$$f(x) + g(x)$$

without a closer examination of the particular functions.

EXERCISES

In problems 1 through 10, evaluate the limits, giving a reason for each step.

1. $\lim\limits_{x \to \infty} \dfrac{3x + 4}{2x + 3}$

2. $\lim\limits_{x \to \infty} \dfrac{2x^2 + 3x + 4}{x^2 - 2x - 3}$

3. $\lim\limits_{x \to \infty} \dfrac{x^2 - 2x + 3}{x^3 + 1}$

4. $\lim\limits_{x \to +\infty} \dfrac{\sqrt{x^2 + 1}}{x + 1}$

5. $\lim\limits_{x \to -\infty} \dfrac{\sqrt{x^2 + 1}}{x + 1}$

6. $\lim\limits_{x \to +\infty} (x - \sqrt{x^2 - a^2})$

7. $\lim\limits_{x \to 1^+} \dfrac{x - 1}{\sqrt{x^2 - 1}}$

8. $\lim\limits_{x \to 1^+} (x + \sqrt{x^2 - 1})$

9. $\lim\limits_{x \to 0^+} x \sqrt{1 + \dfrac{1}{x^2}}$

10. $\lim\limits_{x \to 0^-} x \sqrt{1 + \dfrac{1}{x^2}}$

In problems 11 through 19, either find the limit or state whether the function tends to $+\infty$, $-\infty$, or ∞ as the given value of x is approached.

11. $\lim\limits_{x \to 1} \dfrac{x^2}{1 - x^2}$

12. $\lim\limits_{x \to 2} \dfrac{x}{4 - x^2}$

13. $\lim\limits_{x \to 0} \dfrac{\sqrt{1 + x}}{x}$

14. $\lim\limits_{x \to \infty} \dfrac{x^2 + 1}{x}$

15. $\lim\limits_{x \to 2^+} \dfrac{\sqrt{x^2 - 4}}{x - 2}$

16. $\lim\limits_{x \to +\infty} (\sqrt{x^2 + 2x} - x)$

17. $\lim\limits_{x \to -\infty} (\sqrt{x^2 + 2x} - x)$

18. $\lim\limits_{x \to 2^-} \dfrac{\sqrt{4 - x^2}}{\sqrt{6 - 5x + x^2}}$

19. $\lim\limits_{x \to 0} \dfrac{x + 1}{|x|}$

20. Evaluate   (a) $\lim\limits_{x \to 0^+} \dfrac{x}{|x|}$ (b) $\lim\limits_{x \to 0^-} \dfrac{x}{|x|}$ Does $\lim\limits_{x \to 0} \dfrac{x}{|x|}$ exist?

5. LIMITS OF SEQUENCES

The numbers

$$3, \quad 8, \quad 17, \quad -12, \quad 15$$

form a sequence of numbers. Since this set contains both a first and a last element, the sequence is termed *finite*. The numbers

$$a_1, \quad a_2, \quad a_3, \ldots, \quad a_{25}, \quad a_{26}, \quad a_{27}$$

form a sequence with 27 elements. The subscripts used here to identify the location of each element are more than a convenience; they provide a way of associating a number with each of 27 positive integers. The process of determining one number when another is given reminds us of the idea of function. A *sequence* is a function the *domain* of which is a portion of, or all of, the positive integers. The *range* may be any part of the real number system. The subscripts form the domain and the members of the sequence make up the range.

A sequence such as

$$2, \quad 4, \quad 6, \quad 8, \ldots,$$

(here consisting of the even positive integers), where the dots indicate that it is nonterminating, is called an *infinite* sequence. In general, a finite sequence shows the last term, as in

$$a_1, \quad a_2, \ldots, \quad a_{56},$$

indicating that there are 56 terms. An infinite sequence is written

$$a_1, \quad a_2, \ldots, \quad a_n, \ldots,$$

where the final dots exhibit the never-ending character of the sequence. The domain of this sequence is the set of all positive integers.

A simple example of an infinite sequence is

$$1, \quad \frac{1}{2}, \quad \frac{1}{3}, \quad \frac{1}{4}, \quad \frac{1}{5}, \ldots, \quad \frac{1}{n}, \ldots$$

In this sequence

$$a_1 = 1, \quad a_2 = \frac{1}{2}, \quad a_3 = \frac{1}{3}, \ldots, \quad a_n = \frac{1}{n}, \ldots$$

When we draw a horizontal axis we see that the successive terms in the sequence come closer and closer to zero, and yet no term in the sequence actually is zero (Fig. 5–14). Intuitively, it appears that the further out one gets in this sequence, the more closely the terms approach zero.

A second example is the sequence

$$\frac{1}{2}, \frac{2}{3}, \frac{3}{4}, \frac{4}{5}, \frac{5}{6}, \ldots, \quad \frac{n}{n+1}, \ldots,$$

where

$$a_1 = \frac{1}{1+1}, \quad a_2 = \frac{2}{2+1}, \quad a_3 = \frac{3}{3+1}, \ldots, \quad a_n = \frac{n}{n+1}, \ldots.$$

FIGURE 5–14

FIGURE 5–15   FIGURE 5–16

Graphically it is readily seen that these terms approach 1 as n gets larger, although no individual element in the sequence actually has the value 1 (Fig. 5–15). We write $a_n \to 1$ as $n \to \infty$ in this case and say that the limit of the sequence is 1.

DEFINITION. Given the infinite sequence $a_1, a_2, \ldots, a_n, \ldots$, we say that $a_n \to c$ as $n \to \infty$ if for each $\epsilon > 0$ there is a positive integer N such that $|a_n - c| < \epsilon$ for all $n > N$.

We can visualize this definition by first marking off the quantity c on a number scale (taking $c = 0$ in the first example and $c = 1$ in the second), as in Fig. 5–16. The definition asserts that given any positive number ϵ, then, after a certain stage in the sequence is reached, all the terms lie in the interval $(c - \epsilon, c + \epsilon)$. That is,

$$c - \epsilon < a_n < c + \epsilon$$

for all n larger than some particular integer N. The first few (or few million) terms may be scattered anywhere. But if c is to be the limit, then eventually all the terms must be in this interval; the quantity ϵ may have any value. If ϵ is quite "small," then N, the place in the sequence where the terms must begin to be in the interval about c, may be required to be very "large."

Another interesting sequence is given by

$$1, \quad -\tfrac{1}{2}, \quad +\tfrac{1}{3}, \quad -\tfrac{1}{4}, \quad +\tfrac{1}{5}, \ldots,$$

where

$$a_1 = 1, \quad a_2 = -\frac{1}{2}, \quad a_3 = \frac{1}{3}, \quad a_4 = -\frac{1}{4}, \ldots, \quad a_n = \frac{(-1)^{n+1}}{n}, \ldots.$$

The "general term" is worth examining, since $(-1)^{n+1}$ is just equal to $+1$ when n is odd and to -1 when n is even. This comes out right, since all the terms with even denominators are negative and all the terms with odd denominators are positive. The sequence tends to zero, but the terms oscillate about the value zero, as shown in Fig. 5–17.

Suppose that we have a sequence of numbers in which each term in the sequence is larger than the preceding term. We usually think that there are only two possibilities: either (1) the terms increase without bound, i.e., they go off to $+\infty$ as

FIGURE 5–17

does, for example, the sequence of odd integers

$$1, \quad 3, \quad 5, \quad 7, \quad 9, \dots,$$

or (2) they cluster about a point which is a limit of the sequence as does, for example, the sequence

$$\tfrac{1}{2}, \quad \tfrac{3}{4}, \quad \tfrac{7}{8}, \quad \tfrac{15}{16}, \quad \tfrac{31}{32}, \dots,$$

in which the successive terms are

$$a_1 = \frac{1}{2}, \quad a_2 = \frac{2^2 - 1}{2^2}, \quad a_3 = \frac{2^3 - 1}{2^3}, \quad a_4 = \frac{2^4 - 1}{2^4}, \quad a_n = \frac{2^n - 1}{2^n}, \dots,$$

and the limit is 1. These facts cannot be proved on the basis of the number system as we know it. An additional axiom, the *Axiom of Continuity*, is required.

Axiom C. (Axiom of Continuity.) *Suppose that an infinite sequence* $a_1, a_2, \dots,$ $a_n, \dots$ *has the properties* (1) $a_{n+1} \geq a_n$ *for all n, and* (2) *there is a number M such that* $a_n \leq M$ *for all n. Then there is a number* $b \leq M$ *such that*

$$\lim_{n \to \infty} a_n = b \quad and \quad a_n \leq b$$

for all n.

FIGURE 5–18

Figure 5–18 shows the situation. The numbers a_n move steadily to the right, and yet they can never get beyond M. It is reasonable to have an axiom which assumes that there must be some number b (perhaps M itself) toward which the a_n cluster.

The evaluation of limits of sequences is quite similar to that of limits of functions. For example, we know that

$$\frac{1}{n} \to 0 \quad \text{as} \quad n \to \infty$$

in much the same way that

$$\frac{1}{x} \to 0 \quad \text{as} \quad x \to \infty.$$

EXAMPLE. Evaluate the limit

$$\lim_{n \to \infty} \frac{3n^2 - 2n + 1}{4n^2 + 1}.$$

Solution. When we divide both numerator and denominator by n^2, we have,

$$\frac{3n^2 - 2n + 1}{4n^2 + 1} = \frac{3 - (2/n) + (1/n^2)}{4 + (1/n^2)}.$$

The theorems on sums, products, quotients, etc., for limits apply equally well to sequences, and so we get

$$\lim_{n\to\infty} \frac{3 - (2/n) + (1/n^2)}{4 + (1/n^2)} = \frac{\lim\limits_{n\to\infty} [3 - (2/n) + (1/n^2)]}{\lim\limits_{n\to\infty} [4 + (1/n^2)]}$$

$$= \frac{\lim\limits_{n\to\infty} 3 - \lim\limits_{n\to\infty} (2/n) + \lim\limits_{n\to\infty} (1/n^2)}{\lim\limits_{n\to\infty} 4 + \lim\limits_{n\to\infty} (1/n^2)}.$$

We now see that

$$\lim_{n\to\infty} 3 = 3; \quad \lim_{n\to\infty} \frac{2}{n} = 2 \lim_{n\to\infty} \frac{1}{n} = 0; \quad \lim_{n\to\infty} \frac{1}{n^2} = \lim_{n\to\infty} \frac{1}{n} \cdot \lim_{n\to\infty} \frac{1}{n} = 0 \cdot 0 = 0,$$

and so on. This gives us

$$\lim_{n\to\infty} \frac{3n^2 - 2n + 1}{4n^2 + 1} = \frac{3}{4}.$$

What does it mean to say that a sequence does not approach a limit as n tends to infinity? The definition of the limit of a sequence contains a test for deciding when a limit is approached and when it is not. There are many ways in which a sequence may fail to approach a limit, some of which we illustrate with examples.

Perhaps the simplest type of sequence which does not tend to a limit is the *arithmetic progression*. Such a sequence has the property that the difference between successive terms always has the same value. That is, there is a number d, called the *common difference*, such that $a_{n+1} - a_n = d$ for all n. The sequence

$$1, \quad 4, \quad 7, \quad 10, \ldots, \quad 3n - 2, \ldots,$$

in which $d = 3$, is an example of an arithmetic progression. When d is positive, the nth term of such a sequence tends to $+\infty$, and when d is negative, it tends to $-\infty$.

A sequence such as

$$\tfrac{1}{2}, \quad \tfrac{3}{4}, \quad \tfrac{1}{4}, \quad \tfrac{7}{8}, \quad \tfrac{1}{8}, \quad \tfrac{15}{16}, \quad \tfrac{1}{16}, \quad \tfrac{31}{32}, \quad \tfrac{1}{32}, \cdots,$$

in which

$$a_1 = \tfrac{1}{2}, \quad a_2 = \tfrac{3}{4}, \quad a_3 = \tfrac{1}{4}, \quad a_4 = \tfrac{7}{8}, \quad a_5 = \tfrac{1}{8}, \ldots,$$

has as its formula for the general term,

$$a_{2n-1} = \frac{1}{2^n} \qquad \text{(for odd-numbered terms),}$$

and

$$a_{2n} = \frac{2^n - 1}{2^n} \qquad \text{(for even-numbered terms).}$$

FIGURE 5–19

This sequence does not tend to a limit since there are *two* numbers toward which the terms cluster (Fig. 5–19). In order for a sequence to approach a limit, there must be *exactly one number* about which the terms cluster.

A *geometric progression* is a sequence in which there is some number r, called the *common ratio*, with the property that

$$\frac{a_{n+1}}{a_n} = r \quad \text{for all } n.$$

Examples of geometric progressions are

$$\frac{3}{2}, \ \frac{3}{4}, \ \frac{3}{8}, \ \frac{3}{16}, \ \dots, \ \frac{3}{2^n}, \dots \qquad (r = \tfrac{1}{2});$$

and

$$6, \ 18, \ 54, \ 162, \ 486, \dots, \ 2 \cdot 3^n, \dots \qquad (r = 3).$$

If $-1 < r < 1$ in a geometric progression, the limit of the sequence is zero. If $r > 1$, the sequence does not tend to a limit. If $r = 1$, the terms are all identical and the limit is this common term. If $r = -1$, the sequence is of the form

$$a, \ -a, \ a, \ -a, \ a, \ -a, \dots,$$

which has no limit except in the trivial case where $a = 0$.

EXERCISES

Evaluate the limits of the following sequences:

1. $\displaystyle \lim_{n \to \infty} \frac{1}{\sqrt{n}}$

2. $\displaystyle \lim_{n \to \infty} \frac{3n - 2}{4n + 6}$

3. $\displaystyle \lim_{n \to \infty} \frac{2n + 1}{6 - 3n}$

4. $\displaystyle \lim_{n \to \infty} \frac{5n + 6}{n^2 + 2n}$

5. $\displaystyle \lim_{n \to \infty} \frac{3n^2 - 2n + 1}{n + 5}$

6. $\displaystyle \lim_{n \to \infty} \frac{2n^2 + 3n + 4}{n^2}$

7. $\displaystyle \lim_{n \to \infty} \frac{\sqrt[3]{n + 1}}{n}$

8. $\displaystyle \lim_{n \to \infty} \frac{1}{\sqrt[3]{n^2 + 2}}$

9. $\displaystyle \lim_{n \to \infty} \frac{2n^2 + n + 1}{n^2 + 1}$

10. $\displaystyle \lim_{n \to \infty} \frac{2n^2 + 3n + 4}{n^3}$

11. $\displaystyle \lim_{n \to \infty} \frac{n + 1}{n^2 + 3}$

12. $\displaystyle \lim_{n \to \infty} (\sqrt{2n + 1} - \sqrt{2n - 1})$

13. $\displaystyle \lim_{n \to \infty} (\sqrt{n^2 + 1} - n)$ 14. $\displaystyle \lim_{n \to \infty} (\sqrt{n^2 + n + 1} - n)$

15. Prove that an arithmetic progression with $d > 0$ cannot tend to a limit.

16. Prove that a geometric progression with $0 < r < 1$ must tend to the limit zero.

17. Show that

$$0 < \frac{n}{3^n} < \left(\tfrac{2}{3}\right)^n$$

for every $n \geq 1$ and, therefore, that

$$\lim_{n \to \infty} \frac{n}{3^n} = 0.$$

18. Show that

$$\lim_{n \to \infty} \frac{n}{2^n} = 0.$$

19. Does the sequence

$$\frac{1}{2}, \frac{3}{2}, \frac{2}{3}, \frac{4}{3}, \ldots, \frac{n-1}{n}, \frac{n+1}{n}, \ldots$$

tend to a limit?

20. Does the sequence

$$2, \frac{3}{2}, 2, \frac{7}{4}, 2, \frac{15}{8}, 2, \frac{31}{16}, \ldots, 2, \frac{2^{n+1}-1}{2^n}, \ldots$$

tend to a limit?

CHAPTER 6

Differentiation of Algebraic Functions

---

1. THEOREMS ON DIFFERENTIATION

The process of finding the derivative is called *differentiation*. The reader will recall that use of the five-step rule for differentiation, as shown in Chapter 4, Section 3, frequently involves a lengthy and complicated process. There are certain simple expressions and combinations of expressions which occur repeatedly; it pays to be able to differentiate these at sight. In this section we establish some theorems which help us in the process of differentiation so that we do not always have to bother with the five-step rule.

Theorem 1. *If $f(x) = c$, a constant, for all x, then $f'(x) = 0$ for all x.* (The derivative of a constant is zero.)

Proof. We prove this by the five-step rule.

Step 1: $f(x) = c$.

Step 2: $f(x + h) = c$.

Step 3: $f(x + h) - f(x) = c - c = 0$.

Step 4: $\dfrac{f(x + h) - f(x)}{h} = \dfrac{0}{h} = 0$.

Step 5: $\lim\limits_{h \to 0} 0 = 0$.

That is, $f'(x) = 0$.

Before going on to the next theorem, we introduce a new and useful symbol. The expression $f(x + h) - f(x)$ occurs so frequently that we abbreviate it and write

$$\Delta f = f(x + h) - f(x),$$

and read it "delta f." This does not mean "delta times f"; it is a single symbol which stands for $f(x + h) - f(x)$. If $g(x)$ is a second function and we write Δg, it means $g(x + h) - g(x)$.

Expressions such as

$$3x + 7, \qquad x^2 - 6x + 5, \qquad x^3 + 2x^2 - 7$$

are examples of polynomials in the variable x. In general, an expression of the form

$$a_n x^n + a_{n-1} x^{n-1} + a_{n-2} x^{n-2} + \cdots + a_1 x + a_0,$$

where n is a positive integer and the coefficients $a_n, a_{n-1}, a_{n-2}, \ldots, a_1, a_0$ are numbers, is called a polynomial in x. The *degree* of a polynomial is the highest exponent which appears. In the above examples the polynomials are of degree 1, 2, and 3, respectively.

Combinations of the form

$$\frac{2x - 6}{x^2 + 1}, \qquad \frac{3x^3 - 2x + 5}{7x - 6}, \qquad \frac{x^2 + 5x - 2}{x^5 - 3x^2 + 1}$$

are called *rational functions*. More generally, any function which can be written as the ratio of two polynomials is a *rational function*. That is, it must be expressible as

$$\frac{P(x)}{Q(x)}$$

where $P(x)$ and $Q(x)$ are polynomials.

Theorem 2. *If n is a positive integer and $f(x) = x^n$, then $f'(x) = nx^{n-1}$.*

Proof. We use the five-step rule.

Step 1: $f(x) = x^n$.
Step 2: $f(x + h) = (x + h)^n$.
Step 3: $\Delta f = (x + h)^n - x^n$.

At this point we make use of the binomial theorem and write

$$(x + h)^n = x^n + nx^{n-1}h + \frac{n(n - 1)}{2!} x^{n-2}h^2$$

$$+ \frac{n(n - 1)(n - 2)}{3!} x^{n-3}h^3 + \cdots + h^n,$$

and so we have

$$\Delta f = nx^{n-1}h + \frac{n(n - 1)}{2!} x^{n-2}h^2 + \frac{n(n - 1)(n - 2)}{3!} x^{n-3}h^3 + \cdots + h^n.$$

Note that every term on the right has h as a factor.

Step 4: $\dfrac{\Delta f}{h} = nx^{n-1} + \dfrac{n(n - 1)}{2!} x^{n-2}h + \dfrac{n(n - 1)(n - 2)}{3!} x^{n-3}h^2 + \cdots + h^{n-1}.$

Now we observe that every term on the right *except* the first has h in it. Since the limit of a sum is the sum of the limits, we take the limit of each of the terms on the right as $h \to 0$ and add the result. However, each term on the right, except the first, tends to zero. The term nx^{n-1} is completely unaffected as $h \to 0$, since it has no h in it at all.

Step 5: $f'(x) = \lim\limits_{h \to 0} \dfrac{\Delta f}{h} = nx^{n-1}$.

Theorem 2 asserts that whenever we see an expression such as x^8 or x^{17}, the derivative may be found by inspection. The derivative of x^8 is $8x^7$, and the derivative of x^{17} is $17x^{16}$.

Theorem 3. *If $f(x)$ has a derivative $f'(x)$, then the derivative $g'(x)$ of $g(x) = cf(x)$ is $cf'(x)$, where c is any constant.* (The derivative of a constant times a function is the constant times the derivative of the function.)

Proof. We use the five-step rule.

Step 1: $g(x) = cf(x)$.

Step 2: $g(x + h) = cf(x + h)$.

Step 3: $\Delta g = cf(x + h) - cf(x) = c \, \Delta f$.

Step 4: $\dfrac{\Delta g}{h} = c \, \dfrac{\Delta f}{h}$.

Step 5: $g'(x) = \lim\limits_{h \to 0} c \, \dfrac{\Delta f}{h} = c \lim\limits_{h \to 0} \dfrac{\Delta f}{h} = cf'(x)$.

The justification for Step 5 comes from the theorem that the limit of a product is the product of the limits.

Theorems 2 and 3 can be combined to find derivatives of expressions such as $4x^7$, $-2x^5$, etc. We know from Theorem 2 that x^7 has the derivative $7x^6$ and therefore, from Theorem 3, $4x^7$ has the derivative $4(7x^6) = 28x^6$. Similarly, the derivative of $-2x^5$ is $-10x^4$.

Theorem 4. *If $f(x)$ and $g(x)$ have derivatives and $F(x) = f(x) + g(x)$, then $F'(x) = f'(x) + g'(x)$.* (The derivative of the sum is the sum of the derivatives.)

Proof. We use the five-step rule.

Step 1: $F(x) = f(x) + g(x)$.

Step 2: $F(x + h) = f(x + h) + g(x + h)$.

Step 3: $\Delta F = \Delta f + \Delta g$.

Step 4: $\dfrac{\Delta F}{h} = \dfrac{\Delta f}{h} + \dfrac{\Delta g}{h}$.

Since the limit of a sum is the sum of the limits, we see that the right side tends to $f'(x) + g'(x)$. Therefore,

Step 5: $F'(x) = f'(x) + g'(x)$.

While Theorem 4 was proved for the sum of two functions, the same proof works for the sum of any (finite) number of functions. Theorems 2, 3, and 4 combine to enable us to differentiate any polynomial.

EXAMPLE 1. Find the derivative of

$$f(x) = 3x^5 + 2x^4 - 7x^2 + 2x + 5.$$

Solution. The quantity x^5 has the derivative $5x^4$, as we know from Theorem 2. Using this fact and Theorem 3, we find the derivative of $3x^5$ to be $15x^4$. Similarly, the derivative of

$$2x^4 \text{ is } 8x^3, \quad -7x^2 \text{ is } -14x, \quad 2x \text{ is } 2, \quad 5 \text{ is } 0.$$

Theorem 4 tells us that the derivative of the sum of these terms is the sum of the derivatives. We obtain

$$f'(x) = 15x^4 + 8x^3 - 14x + 2.$$

Theorem 5. *If $u(x)$ and $v(x)$ are any two functions which have a derivative and if $f(x) = u(x) \cdot v(x)$, then*

$$f'(x) = u(x) \cdot v'(x) + v(x) \cdot u'(x).$$

(The derivative of the product of two functions is the first times the derivative of the second plus the second times the derivative of the first.)

Proof. We use the five-step rule, as usual.

Step 1: $f(x) = u(x) \cdot v(x).$

Step 2: $f(x + h) = u(x + h) \cdot v(x + h).$

At this point we use a trick of a type we have used before. We write the right side in a more complicated way, as follows:

$$f(x + h) = [u(x) + u(x + h) - u(x)][v(x) + v(x + h) - v(x)].$$

With the delta symbols, this becomes

$$f(x + h) = (u + \Delta u)(v + \Delta v).$$

Step 3: $\Delta f = f(x + h) - f(x) = (u + \Delta u)(v + \Delta v) - uv.$

Multiplying the right side out, we obtain

$$\Delta f = u \, \Delta v + v \, \Delta u + \Delta u \cdot \Delta v.$$

Step 4: $\dfrac{\Delta f}{h} = u \dfrac{\Delta v}{h} + v \dfrac{\Delta u}{h} + \Delta u \cdot \dfrac{\Delta v}{h}.$

We now examine each term on the right as h tends to zero. The first term tends to $u(x)v'(x)$, since

$$\frac{\Delta v}{h} \rightarrow v'(x) \quad \text{as} \quad h \rightarrow 0.$$

The second term tends to $vu'(x)$. The last term has two parts, $\Delta v/h$ and Δu. The quantity $\Delta v/h$ tends to $v'(x)$. However, the function $u(x)$ is continuous (according to the theorem which says that if a function has a derivative it is continuous), and so $u(x + h) - u(x) = \Delta u \to 0$ as $h \to 0$. This means that the last term on the right tends to zero as $h \to 0$. We conclude

Step 5: $$f'(x) = \lim_{h \to 0} \frac{\Delta f}{h} = u(x)v'(x) + v(x)u'(x).$$

EXAMPLE 2. Find the derivative of

$$f(x) = (x^2 - 3x + 2)(x^3 + 2x^2 - 6x).$$

What is the value of $f'(3)$? the value of $f'(2)$?

Solution. One way to do this would be to multiply the two expressions in parentheses, thus obtaining a polynomial of the 5th degree, and then to find the derivative as in Example 1. However, Theorem 5 gives us an idea for a simpler way. We write

$$u(x) = x^2 - 3x + 2 \quad \text{and} \quad v(x) = x^3 + 2x^2 - 6x.$$

This means that $f(x) = u(x)v(x)$. We can now readily find $u'(x)$ and $v'(x)$, using the method in Example 1: $u'(x) = 2x - 3$ and $v'(x) = 3x^2 + 4x - 6$. Then

$$f'(x) = u(x)v'(x) + v(x)u'(x)$$
$$= (x^2 - 3x + 2)(3x^2 + 4x - 6) + (x^3 + 2x^2 - 6x)(2x - 3),$$
$$f'(3) = (9 - 9 + 2)(27 + 12 - 6) + (27 + 18 - 18)(6 - 3)$$
$$= 66 + 81 = 147,$$
$$f'(2) = (4 - 6 + 2)(12 + 8 - 6) + (8 + 8 - 12)(4 - 3)$$
$$= 0 + 4 = 4.$$

Theorem 6. *If $u(x)$ and $v(x)$ are any two functions which have a derivative and if*

$$f(x) = \frac{u(x)}{v(x)}$$

with $v(x) \neq 0$, then

$$f'(x) = \frac{v(x)u'(x) - u(x)v'(x)}{[v(x)]^2}.$$

(The derivative of a quotient of two functions is the denominator times the derivative of the numerator minus the numerator times the derivative of the denominator, all divided by the square of the denominator.)

Proof. We proceed by the five-step rule.

Step 1: $f(x) = \dfrac{u(x)}{v(x)}.$

Step 2: $f(x + h) = f + \Delta f = \dfrac{u(x + h)}{v(x + h)} = \dfrac{u + \Delta u}{v + \Delta v}.$

Step 3: $\Delta f = \dfrac{u + \Delta u}{v + \Delta v} - \dfrac{u}{v}$

$$= \frac{v(u + \Delta u) - u(v + \Delta v)}{v(v + \Delta v)}$$

$$= \frac{v\,\Delta u - u\,\Delta v}{v(v + \Delta v)}.$$

Step 4: $\dfrac{\Delta f}{h} = \dfrac{v\dfrac{\Delta u}{h} - u\dfrac{\Delta v}{h}}{v(v + \Delta v)}.$

Step 5: $\lim\limits_{h \to 0} \dfrac{\Delta f}{h} = f'(x) = \dfrac{vu'(x) - uv'(x)}{v^2}.$

EXAMPLE 3. Find the derivative of

$$f(x) = \frac{2x^2 - 3x}{x^2 + 3}.$$

Solution.　We set $u = 2x^2 - 3x$ and $v = x^2 + 3$.　Then $u'(x) = 4x - 3$ and $v'(x) = 2x$. Now, by Theorem 6,

$$f'(x) = \frac{(x^2 + 3)(4x - 3) - (2x^2 - 3x) \cdot 2x}{(x^2 + 3)^2}$$

$$= \frac{3x^2 + 12x - 9}{(x^2 + 3)^2}.$$

The last step was merely an algebraic simplification and, strictly speaking, not a part of the differentiation process.

Theorem 7.　*If n is a positive integer and* $f(x) = x^{-n}$*, then*

$$f'(x) = -nx^{-n-1}.$$

Proof.　A negative exponent simply means that we may write $f(x)$ in the form

$$f(x) = \frac{1}{x^n}.$$

We can apply Theorem 6: Let $u(x) = 1$ and $v(x) = x^n$. Then

$$f(x) = \frac{u(x)}{v(x)}.$$

From Theorem 1, $u'(x) = 0$ and, from Theorem 2, $v'(x) = nx^{n-1}$.　We substitute in the formula of Theorem 6 to get

$$f'(x) = \frac{x^n \cdot 0 - 1 \cdot nx^{n-1}}{(x^n)^2},$$

which gives us

$$f'(x) = \frac{-nx^{n-1}}{x^{2n}} = -nx^{-n-1}.$$

Combining Theorems 2 and 7, we see that *if k is any positive or negative integer and f(x) = x^k, then*

$$f'(x) = kx^{k-1}.$$

EXERCISES

In problems 1 through 30, differentiate the functions by the methods given in this section.

1. $x^2 - 3x + 2$

2. $2x^3 - 6x^2 + 7x - 5$

3. $x^{15} + 12x^2 - 8x + 2$

4. $x^7 + 2x^5 - 3x^4 + 9x - 7$

5. $x^{-3} + 4x^{-5} - 3x^{-8}$

6. $2x^{-1} + 4x^{-4} - 5x - 5$

7. $x^3 + 2x^2 - 3x + 5 - 2x^{-1} + 4x^{-2}$

8. $x^5 + 12x - 1 + 3x^{-4} - 5x^{-7}$

9. $x^2 + 2x - \dfrac{1}{x^2}$

10. $x^3 - 3x - \dfrac{2}{x^4}$

11. $\dfrac{3}{4x^7}$

12. $2x^4 - 3x + \dfrac{5}{8x^3}$

13. $(x^2 + 2x)(3x + 1)$

14. $(2x^3 + 6x)(7x - 5)$

15. $(x^3 + 6x^2 - 2x + 1)(x^2 + 3x - 5)$

16. $(x^4 + 2x - 3)(x^6 - 7x^5 + 8x^3 + 9x^2 + 1)$

17. $\dfrac{2x^2 - 3x + 4}{x}$

18. $\dfrac{x^3 - 3x + 5}{x^2}$

19. $\dfrac{2x^3 - 3x^2 + 4x - 2}{x^3}$

20. $\dfrac{x^3 - 4x^2 + 3x - 2}{x^4}$

21. $\dfrac{x - 1}{x + 1}$

22. $\dfrac{2x + 3}{3x - 2}$

23. $\dfrac{3x - 2}{2x + 3}$

24. $\dfrac{5x - 2}{4x + 3}$

25. $\dfrac{x}{x^2 + 1}$

26. $\dfrac{x^2 + 1}{x^2 - 1}$

27. $\dfrac{x + 1}{x^2 + 2x + 2}$

28. $\dfrac{2x^2 - 3x + 4}{x^2 - 2x + 3}$

29. $\dfrac{x + 1}{2x + 3}(2x - 5)$

30. $\dfrac{x^2 - x + 6}{x^2 + 1}(x^2 + x + 1)$

31. Using Theorem 5, find a formula for the derivative of $f(x) = [u(x)]^2$. Apply this to the functions

    (a) $(x^2 + 2x - 1)^2$,   (b) $(x^3 + 7x^2 - 8x - 6)^2$,   (c) $(x^7 - 2x + 3x^{-2})^2$.

32. Given that $f(x) = u(x) \cdot v(x) \cdot w(x)$, find a formula for $f'(x)$. (*Hint:* Apply Theorem 5 twice.) Using this formula, find the derivative of the following functions:

    (a) $(x^2 + 2x - 6)(3x - 2)(x^2 + 5)$,　(b) $(2x^2 + x^{-2})(x^2 - 3)(4x + 1)$,
    (c) $(2x + 3)^2(x^2 + 1)$,　　　　　　　(d) $(x^2 + x + 1)^3$.

33. Given that

$$f(x) = \frac{u(x)}{v(x)} w(x),$$

find a formula for $f'(x)$. (*Hint:* Apply Theorems 5 and 6.) Using this formula, find the derivative of the functions

(a) $\dfrac{x + 2}{3x + 1} (x - 6)$,　(b) $\dfrac{x^2 - 1}{2x + 6} (x^2 + 5)$,　(c) $\dfrac{x^3 + 1}{x^2 - 3} (x^4 - 2x^{-3} + 1)$.

2. THE CHAIN RULE. APPLICATIONS

The chain rule is one of the most important and most useful tools in differentiation. The proof of the theorem establishing this rule is somewhat difficult to follow but, if the reader studies it carefully, he will achieve a deeper understanding of differentiation which will make the effort well worth while. The examples should be gone over thoroughly as well, as a means of studying the applications of this rule.

Theorem 8. (Fundamental Lemma of Differentiation.) *Suppose that F has a derivative at a value u so that $F'(u)$ exists. Then*

$$\frac{F(u + h) - F(u)}{h} = F'(u) + [\text{a term which tends to zero as } h \text{ tends to zero}].$$

Proof. This statement follows from the definition of a derivative. We know that

$$\lim_{h \to 0} \frac{F(u + h) - F(u)}{h} = F'(u).$$

If we define, for $h \neq 0$,

$$G(h) = \frac{F(u + h) - F(u)}{h} - F'(u),$$

then $G(h)$ is the "term which tends to zero" in the statement of the theorem. From the definition of limit and the theorem on the limit of a sum, it follows that $G(h) \to 0$ as $h \to 0$.

Corollary 1. *If in Theorem 8 we define $G(0) = 0$, then $G(h)$ is continuous at $h = 0$.*

The corollary holds because the definition of continuous function in this case is simply

$$\lim_{h \to 0} G(h) = G(0).$$

Corollary 2. *If F and G are defined as in Theorem 8 and Corollary 1, then*

$$F(u + h) - F(u) = [F'(u) + G(h)]h.$$

Note that Corollary 2 holds even when $h = 0$.

Theorem 9.   (Chain Rule.)   *Suppose that f, g, and u are functions with* $f(x) = g[u(x)]$, *and suppose that g and u are differentiable. Then f is differentiable and the following formula holds:*

$$f'(x) = g'[u(x)]u'(x).$$

Proof: We use the five-step rule to find the derivative of f.

Step 1: $f(x) = g[u(x)]$.
Step 2: $f(x + h) = g[u(x + h)] = g[u(x) + u(x + h) - u(x)] = g(u + \Delta u)$.
Step 3: $\Delta f = g(u + \Delta u) - g(u)$.

We now apply Corollary 2 to the right-hand side, where g is used instead of F and Δu instead of h. Then Step 3 can be written

$$\Delta f = [g'(u) + G(\Delta u)]\Delta u.$$

Step 4: $\dfrac{\Delta f}{h} = [g'(u) + G(\Delta u)]\dfrac{\Delta u}{h}$.

Step 5: Since $\dfrac{\Delta u}{h} \to u'(x)$ as $h \to 0$ and $G(\Delta u) \to 0$ as $\Delta u \to 0$,

we conclude that

$$\lim_{h \to 0} \frac{\Delta f}{h} = f'(x) = g'(u)u'(x).$$

This is exactly the formula given in the statement of the theorem.
    Before illustrating the chain rule by examples, we establish one of the most important special cases.

Corollary. *If* $f(x) = [u(x)]^n$ *and n is an integer, then* $f'(x) = n[u(x)]^{n-1}u'(x)$.

Proof: In the chain rule we take $g(u) = u^n$. Then $f = g[u(x)]$ means that $f(x) = [u(x)]^n$. We obtain $f'(x) = g'(u)u'(x) = nu^{n-1}u'(x)$.
    We can also write schematically

$$f(x) = (\text{expression in } x)^n,$$
$$f'(x) = n (\text{expression in } x)^{n-1} (\text{derivative of expression in } x).$$

EXAMPLE 1. Find $f'(x)$, given that $f(x) = (x^2 + 3x - 2)^4$.

Solution. From the corollary, with $n = 4$ and the expression in x being $x^2 + 3x - 2$, we find

$$f'(x) = 4(x^2 + 3x - 2)^3 \cdot (2x + 3),$$

since the derivative of $x^2 + 3x - 2$ is $2x + 3$.

EXAMPLE 2. Find $f'(x)$, given that

$$f(x) = \frac{1}{x^3 + 3x^2 - 6x + 4}.$$

Solution. We write $f(x) = (x^3 + 3x^2 - 6x + 4)^{-1}$ and apply the corollary, with $n = -1$:

$$f'(x) = -1(x^3 + 3x^2 - 6x + 4)^{-2} \cdot (3x^2 + 6x - 6)$$

$$= \frac{-3(x^2 + 2x - 2)}{(x^3 + 3x^2 - 6x + 4)^2}.$$

We note that this example could also have been worked by using the formula for the derivative of a quotient.

EXAMPLE 3. Find $f'(x)$, given that

$$f(x) = \left(\frac{3x - 2}{2x + 1}\right)^7.$$

Solution. This requires a combination of formulas. First, from the corollary, we see that

$$f'(x) = 7\left(\frac{3x - 2}{2x + 1}\right)^6 \cdot \left(\text{derivative of } \frac{3x - 2}{2x + 1}\right).$$

To find the derivative of $(3x - 2)/(2x + 1)$ we apply the quotient formula to get

$$f'(x) = 7\left(\frac{3x - 2}{2x + 1}\right)^6 \frac{(2x + 1)(3) - (3x - 2)(2)}{(2x + 1)^2}$$

$$= \frac{49(3x - 2)^6}{(2x + 1)^8}.$$

EXAMPLE 4. Find $f'(x)$, given that

$$f(x) = (x^2 + 2x - 3)^{16}(2x + 5)^{13}.$$

Solution. We first observe that if we let $u(x) = (x^2 + 2x - 3)^{16}$ and $v(x) = (2x + 5)^{13}$, we may use Theorem 5, on the product of two functions:

$$f'(x) = u(x)v'(x) + v(x)u'(x).$$

To find $u'(x)$ we employ the chain rule:

$$u'(x) = 16(x^2 + 2x - 3)^{15}(2x + 2);$$

and similarly,

$$v'(x) = 13(2x + 5)^{12}(2).$$

Substituting in the formula for $f(x)$, we get

$$f'(x) = (x^2 + 2x - 3)^{16}26(2x + 5)^{12} + (2x + 5)^{13}32(x^2 + 2x - 3)^{15}(x + 1)$$
$$= (x^2 + 2x - 3)^{15}(2x + 5)^{12}[26(x^2 + 2x - 3) + 32(2x + 5)(x + 1)].$$

EXERCISES

In each of the following problems, find the derivative.

1. $(3x + 5)^{10}$

2. $(x^2 - 2x + 6)^5$

3. $(6 - 3x)^7$

4. $(x^3 + 2x^2 - 6x + 5)^4$

5. $(x + 5)^{-3}$

6. $(x^2 + 2x - 1)^{-4}$

7. $(x^3 + 2x - 3 + x^{-2})^4$

8. $(x^4 + 5x - 6x^{-1})^3$

9. $(x^2 + 2 - x^{-2})^{-1}$

10. $(3x^3 + 2x^2 - 6x^{-4})^{-4}$

11. $(x^2 + 1)^2(x^3 - 2x)^2$

12. $(x^3 + 2x - 6)^3(x^2 - 4x + 5)^7$

13. $(x^2 - x^{-1} + 1)(x^3 + 2x - 6)^7$

14. $\dfrac{(3x - 2)^2}{(2x - 6)^2}$

15. $\dfrac{(x^2 + 1)^3}{(x^2 + 2)^2}$

16. $\dfrac{(2x - 6)^4}{(x + 1)^7}$

17. $\dfrac{(x^2 + 2)^2}{(x^2 + x^{-1})^3}$

18. $\dfrac{(2x - 6)^{-1}}{(x^2 + 3)^{-2}}$

19. $\dfrac{(x^{-1} + x^2)^{-1}}{(x^3 - 2x^{-2})^{-2}}$

20. $\dfrac{(x^2 + 2x - 1)(x^3 + 3x - 4)^2}{(2x + 6)^2}$

21. $(x + 5)^2(3x - 6)^3(7x^2 + 1)^4$

22. $(2x^2 + 6x - 1)^3(x^2 + 5)^5(x^2 - 7)^6$

23. $\dfrac{(x^2 + 1)^5(3x - 7)^8}{(x^2 + 5x - 4)^6}$

24. $\dfrac{(x^2 + 2x - 1)^4}{(3x - 2x^{-1})^5} \cdot \dfrac{(x^2 + 1)^2}{(3x^2 - 6)^2}$

25. $\dfrac{(x^{-2} + 3x^{-4} + 7x^{-5})^{-8}}{(x^2 + x^{-2})^{-4}(x^{-1} + x^{-2})^{-3}}$

3. THE POWER FUNCTION

The function
$$f(x) = x^n,$$

where n is some number, is called the power function. That is, x is raised to an exponent called the *power*. If n is an *even positive integer*, the graph of the function appears as in Fig. 6–1. If n is an odd integer the curve is below the x-axis for negative values of x, as shown in Fig. 6–2.

For negative exponents, the y-axis is a vertical asymptote and the x-axis is a horizontal asymptote. The general behavior of these functions is shown in Fig. 6–3.

If n is of the form $1/q$ where q is a positive integer, the graph of the function has a completely different character. For example, the function

$$y = x^{1/2} = \sqrt{x}$$

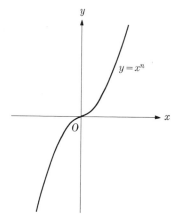

n, even positive integer

FIGURE 6–1

n, odd positive integer

FIGURE 6–2

is not even defined for negative values of x. In fact, if q is any even number, the function

$$y = x^{1/q} = \sqrt[q]{x}$$

is defined only for x positive or zero. On the other hand, if q is odd, we know that because the odd root of a negative number can be found (for example, $\sqrt[5]{-32} = -2$), the function is defined for all values of x. The graphs of $\sqrt[q]{x}$ are shown in Fig. 6–4.

We follow the same rule for the derivative of $x^{1/q}$ as for the derivative of the power function when the exponent is an integer. The following theorem establishes this fact.

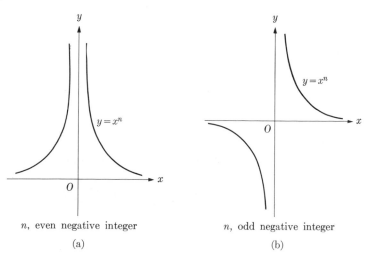

n, even negative integer

(a)

n, odd negative integer

(b)

FIGURE 6–3

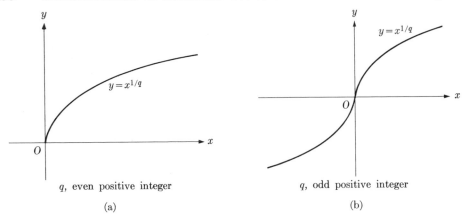

q, even positive integer

(a)

q, odd positive integer

(b)

FIGURE 6–4

Theorem 10. *If $f(x) = x^{1/q}$ and q is an integer, then*

$$f'(x) = \frac{1}{q} x^{\frac{1}{q}-1}.$$

Proof. The five-step rule is used.

Step 1: $f(x) = x^{1/q}$.

Step 2: $f(x + h) = f + \Delta f = (x + h)^{1/q}$.

Step 3: $\Delta f = (x + h)^{1/q} - x^{1/q}$.

Step 4: $\dfrac{\Delta f}{h} = \dfrac{(x + h)^{1/q} - x^{1/q}}{h}$.

Before proceeding to the limit, we have to "rationalize the numerator." When $q = 2$ this is easy, since we simply multiply both the numerator and the denominator by $\sqrt{x + h} + \sqrt{x}$. In the general case we use the following fact. If m is any positive integer, then

$$a^m - b^m = (a - b)(a^{m-1} + a^{m-2}b + a^{m-3}b^2 + \cdots + ab^{m-2} + b^{m-1}).$$

This formula can be checked by multiplying out the right side, and noting that all the terms cancel except a^m and $-b^m$. We now let

$$a = (x + h)^{1/q} \quad \text{and} \quad b = x^{1/q}, \quad m = q$$

in the above formula, and multiply both the numerator and the denominator in Step 4 by

$$a^{q-1} + a^{q-2}b + a^{q-3}b^2 + \cdots + ab^{q-2} + b^{q-1}.$$

The formula then becomes

$$\frac{\Delta f}{h} = \frac{(x + h)^{1/q} - x^{1/q}}{h} \left[\frac{(x + h)^{\frac{q-1}{q}} + (x + h)^{\frac{q-2}{q}} x^{1/q} + \cdots + x^{\frac{q-1}{q}}}{(x + h)^{\frac{q-1}{q}} + (x + h)^{\frac{q-2}{q}} x^{1/q} + \cdots + x^{\frac{q-1}{q}}} \right].$$

When we multiply out the numerator, we obtain $(x + h)^{q/q} - x^{q/q}$, or just h. Therefore*

$$\frac{\Delta f}{h} = \frac{1}{(x + h)^{\frac{q-1}{q}} + (x + h)^{\frac{q-2}{q}}x^{1/q} + \cdots + (x + h)^{1/q}x^{\frac{q-2}{q}} + x^{\frac{q-1}{q}}}.$$

Step 5: When we let $h \to 0$, each of the terms in the denominator tends to $x^{(q-1)/q}$, and there are exactly q such terms. We see that

$$\lim_{h \to 0} \frac{\Delta f}{h} = f'(x) = \frac{1}{qx^{\frac{q-1}{q}}} = \frac{1}{q}x^{\frac{1-q}{q}} = \frac{1}{q}x^{\frac{1}{q}-1}.$$

A *rational number* is one which can be written as one integer over another. "The number r is rational" means that $r = p/q$, where p and q are integers. Theorem 10 can be combined with the chain rule to give the general rule for differentiating the power function when the exponent is any rational number.

Corollary 1. *If $f(x) = x^r$ and r is any rational number, then $f'(x) = rx^{r-1}$.*

Proof. Since r is rational, we can write

$$f(x) = x^{p/q} = (x^{1/q})^p,$$

where p and q are integers. By the special case of the chain rule, we have

$$f'(x) = p(x^{1/q})^{p-1}(\text{derivative of } x^{1/q});$$

and so, by Theorem 10,

$$f'(x) = p(x^{1/q})^{p-1}\frac{1}{q}x^{\frac{1}{q}-1}$$

$$= \frac{p}{q}x^{\frac{p}{q}-\frac{1}{q}+\frac{1}{q}-1} = rx^{r-1}.$$

Corollary 2. *If $f(x) = [u(x)]^r$ and r is rational, then $f'(x) = r[u(x)]^{r-1}u'(x)$.*

Proof. This is an immediate consequence of combining Corollary 1 and the chain rule.

EXAMPLE 1. Given that $f(x) = 2\sqrt[5]{x^3}$, find $f'(x)$.

Solution. $f(x) = 2x^{3/5}$ and, by the rule for rational exponents,

$$f'(x) = 2(\tfrac{3}{5})x^{\frac{3}{5}-1} = \tfrac{6}{5}x^{-2/5}.$$

EXAMPLE 2. Given that $f(t) = \sqrt[3]{t^3 + 3t + 1}$, find $f'(t)$.

---

* The student who has difficulty following this will find it helpful to write out the complete proofs for the cases $q = 2, 3,$ and 4. The method of seeing how a proof goes in special cases is used by the experts when the going gets hard.

Solution. We write $f(t) = (t^3 + 3t + 1)^{1/3}$, and we use Corollary 2:

$$f'(t) = \tfrac{1}{3}(t^3 + 3t + 1)^{-2/3}(3t^2 + 3)$$

$$= \frac{t^2 + 1}{(t^3 + 3t + 1)^{2/3}}.$$

EXAMPLE 3. Given that $f(x) = (x + 1)^3(2x - 1)^{4/3}$, find $f'(x)$.

Solution. We use the rule for differentiating a product, setting $u(x) = (x + 1)^3$ and $v(x) = (2x - 1)^{4/3}$, so that $f(x) = u(x)v(x)$. Then

$$f'(x) = [(x + 1)^3]v'(x) + (2x - 1)^{4/3}u'(x).$$

By the chain rule for powers we have

$$u'(x) = 3(x + 1)^2 \cdot 1 \qquad \text{and} \qquad v'(x) = \tfrac{4}{3}(2x - 1)^{1/3} \cdot 2.$$

Therefore

$$f'(x) = \tfrac{8}{3}(x + 1)^3(2x - 1)^{1/3} + 3(2x - 1)^{4/3}(x + 1)^2$$
$$= (x + 1)^2(2x - 1)^{1/3}[\tfrac{8}{3}(x + 1) + 3(2x - 1)]$$
$$= \tfrac{1}{3}(x + 1)^2(2x - 1)^{1/3}(26x - 1).$$

EXAMPLE 4. Given that

$$f(s) = \frac{s}{\sqrt{s^2 - 1}},$$

find $f'(s)$.

Solution. We write

$$f(s) = \frac{s}{(s^2 - 1)^{1/2}},$$

and we use Theorem 6 for the derivative of a quotient:

$$f'(s) = \frac{(s^2 - 1)^{1/2} \cdot 1 - s\tfrac{1}{2}(s^2 - 1)^{-1/2}(2s)}{s^2 - 1}.$$

This expression may be simplified in several ways. One easy method is to multiply through both the numerator and the denominator by $(s^2 - 1)^{1/2}$. This gives

$$f'(s) = \frac{(s^2 - 1)^1 - s^2(s^2 - 1)^0}{(s^2 - 1)^{3/2}}.$$

Since $(s^2 - 1)^0 = 1$, we get

$$f'(s) = \frac{-1}{(s^2 - 1)^{3/2}}.$$

EXERCISES

In problems 1 through 28, find the derivative.

1. $x^{5/3} - 3x^{2/3} + 4x^{-1/3}$

2. $2x^{3/2} + 5x^{4/5} - 3x^{3/7}$

3. $x^{-2/3} - x^{-3/4} + 2x^{4/7}$

4. $3x^{1/3} - 4x^{-1/4} + \tfrac{3}{7}x^{7/3}$

5. $\tfrac{3}{2}x^{2/3} + 2x^{1/2} - x^{-1}$

6. $\tfrac{4}{7}x^{7/4} - \tfrac{1}{2}x^{-2} + 3x^{1/3}$

7. $\dfrac{x^{3/2} - 2x^{1/2} + 4x^{-1/2}}{5}$

8. $\dfrac{x^{5/2} - 3x^{3/2} + 2x^{1/2}}{x^2}$

9. $2x\sqrt{x} + 3\sqrt[3]{x^2} - 5x\sqrt[5]{x^2}$

10. $\frac{1}{4}x\sqrt[3]{x} - \frac{1}{7}x^2\sqrt[3]{x} + \frac{1}{10}x^3\sqrt[3]{x}$

11. $\dfrac{x^2 - 3x + 2}{2\sqrt{x}}$

12. $\dfrac{x^3 - 3x^2 - 5x + 2}{5x\sqrt[3]{x^2}}$

13. $(2x + 3)^{10/3}$

14. $(3x - 2)^{4/3}$

15. $(x^2 + 2x + 3)^{3/2}$

16. $(x^3 + 3x^2 + 6x + 5)^{2/3}$

17. $(2x^3 - 3x^2 + 3x - 1)^{-1/3}$

18. $(x^4 + 2x^2 + 1)^{-7/4}$

19. $\sqrt[3]{(x^3 + 3x + 2)^2}$

20. $\dfrac{1}{\sqrt[4]{x^2 + 2x + 3}}$

21. $\dfrac{(x^2 + x - 3)\sqrt{x^2 + x - 3}}{5}$

22. $\dfrac{1}{2(x^2 + 2x + 3)\sqrt[3]{(x^2 + 2x + 3)^2}}$

23. $(2x + 3)^4(3x - 2)^{7/3}$

24. $(3 - 2x)^{5/2}(2 - 3x)^{1/3}$

25. $(2x - 1)^{5/2}(7x - 3)^{3/7}$

26. $(2 - 3x)^{4/3}(5x + 2)^3$

27. $\sqrt[3]{(x + 1)^2}\sqrt{x - 1}$

28. $\sqrt{(1 - 2x)^3}\sqrt[3]{x^2 + 1}$

29. Find $g'(t)$, given that $g(t) = \dfrac{\sqrt[3]{2 + 6t}}{t}$

30. Find $\varphi'(s)$, given that $\varphi(s) = \dfrac{\sqrt{s^2 + 1}}{s}$

31. Find $f'(y)$, given that $f(y) = \dfrac{2y + 3}{\sqrt{y^2 + 3y + 4}}$

32. Find $\chi'(r)$, given that $\chi(r) = \dfrac{\sqrt{1 + 4r^2}}{r^2}$

33. Find $g'(s)$, given that $g(s) = \sqrt{2s} + \sqrt{2/s}$

34. Find $k'(t)$, given that $k(t) = \dfrac{2t}{\sqrt[3]{4t^2 + 3}}$

35. Find $F'(x)$, given that $F(x) = \dfrac{\sqrt{x - 2}}{\sqrt[3]{x + 2}}$

36. Find $G'(x)$, given that $G(x) = \dfrac{\sqrt{x^2 - 1}}{\sqrt[3]{x^2 + 1}}$

37. Find $f'(\tau)$, given that $f(\tau) = \sqrt{\dfrac{\tau - 1}{\tau + 1}}$

38. Find $K'(x)$, given that $K(x) = \sqrt{\dfrac{3x - 2}{2x + 3}}$

39. Find $\varphi'(t)$, given that $\varphi(t) = \sqrt[3]{\dfrac{3t + 4}{3t - 2}}$

40. Find $\psi'(y)$, given that $\psi(y) = \sqrt[3]{\dfrac{y^2 - 1}{y^2 + 1}}$

In problems 41 through 44, find the value of $f'(x)$ for the given value of x.

41. $f(x) = (x^2 + 2x + 3)^{2/3}$, $x = -1$

42. $f(x) = \dfrac{2x}{\sqrt{4x^2 + 1}}$, $x = 2$

43. $f(x) = (x^2 + 1)^3(2x + 4)^{1/3}$, $x = 2$

44. $f(x) = \sqrt[3]{5x + 12}(x^2 + 6)^2$, $x = 3$

In problems 45 through 50, find the equations of the tangent line and normal line to the curve $y = f(x)$, at the point having the given abscissa.

45. $f(x) = (2x - 3)^{5/2}$, $x = 2$ 46. $f(x) = \dfrac{1}{\sqrt[3]{2 - 3x}}$, $x = 1$

47. $f(x) = x\sqrt{25 - x^2}$, $x = 4$ 48. $f(x) = x\sqrt{2 - x}$, $x = 1$

49. $f(x) = \dfrac{\sqrt{5 + 2x}}{x}$, $x = 2$ 50. $f(x) = \dfrac{\sqrt{3 - x}}{x}$, $x = -1$

51. Find a formula for the derivative of

$$f(x) = [u(x)]^m[v(x)]^n$$

and apply it to the functions

(a) $f(x) = (2x + 1)^6(x^3 - 6)^{4/3}$,

(b) $f(x) = (x^2 + 2x - 1)^{3/2}(x^4 - 3)^3$.

52. Find a formula for the derivative of

$$f(x) = [u(x)]^r[v(x)]^s[w(x)]^t,$$

where r, s, and t are rational numbers. Apply it to the functions

(a) $f(x) = (x^2 + 1)^{3/2}(2x - 5)^{1/3}(x^2 + 4)^2$,

(b) $f(x) = \left(\dfrac{x - 1}{x + 1}\right)^3(3 - 2x)^2(x^2 - 5)^{4/3}$.

4. IMPLICIT DIFFERENTIATION

Before discussing implicit differentiation, we shall introduce additional symbolism which will be particularly helpful. Suppose that f is a function of x, such as

$$f(x) = x^4 - 2x^2 + 3.$$

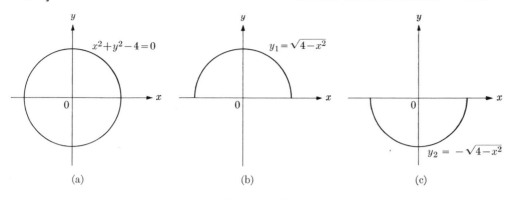

FIGURE 6-5

If y is chosen as the dependent variable, we can write

$$y = f(x) = x^4 - 2x^2 + 3.$$

Sometimes, instead of $f(x)$, it is useful to write $y(x)$, which means the same thing. The derivative of f is denoted by f', and, similarly, we may denote this derivative as y' or as $y'(x)$. Thus we could write

$$y = y(x) = x^4 - 2x^2 + 3, \quad \text{and} \quad y' = y'(x) = 4x^3 - 4x.$$

In Chapter 2, Section 4, we discussed relations between two variables. An equation such as

$$x^2 + y^2 - 4 = 0$$

is an example of such a relation. In this equation y is *not* a function of x nor is x a function of y. We have here *two* functions of x (also two functions of y, if y is considered to be the independent variable). The two functions are $y_1 = \sqrt{4 - x^2}$ and $y_2 = -\sqrt{4 - x^2}$; these two functions and the relation are sketched in Fig. 6-5. Other examples of relations which may or may not be functions are

$$x^2 - 2xy + 3y^2 - 7 = 0, \quad x^3y^2 - 4 = 0, \quad y^3 - x - 5 = 0.$$

Note that all these expressions are of the general form

$$f(x, y) = 0.$$

When this situation occurs we say that the functions, if any, are *defined implicitly*. We say "if any" because the relation may not define any function at all. For example, there are no values of x and y which satisfy an equation such as

$$x^2 + y^2 + 9 = 0.$$

We could easily compose other examples.

Returning to the equation

$$x^2 + y^2 - 4 = 0,$$

we see that this consists of two functions of x, each function defined for x in the interval $-2 \leq x \leq 2$. In this interval the functions possess derivatives which can readily be found by differentiating the expressions

$$\sqrt{4 - x^2} \quad \text{and} \quad -\sqrt{4 - x^2}.$$

However, it is possible to proceed directly, without solving for y in terms of x. In the equation

$$x^2 + y^2 - 4 = 0,$$

we first differentiate x^2; its derivative is simply $2x$. The derivative of y^2 is more complicated, since $y = y(x)$ and we must use the chain rule. The derivative of y^2 is $2yy'$. The derivative of -4 is zero. We have now found the derivative of the left side, and we know that the right side, being zero, has derivative zero. We conclude that

$$2x + 2yy' = 0.$$

This may be solved for y' to yield (when $y \neq 0$),

$$y' = -\frac{x}{y}.$$

We now ask ourselves which function of x has been differentiated. The answer is both. If y_1 is substituted for y in the right side of the expression for y', we have the derivative of y_1; if y_2 is substituted, we have the derivative of y_2. Further examples illustrate the method.

EXAMPLE 1. Assuming that y is a differentiable function of x defined implicitly by the equation

$$y^3 + 3xy + x^3 - 5 = 0,$$

find y' in terms of x and y.

Solution. The derivative of y^3 is $3y^2y'$. The term $3xy$ must be treated as a product. The derivative of $3xy$ is $3xy' + 3y$. The derivative of x^3 is $3x^2$. The derivative of -5 is 0. Therefore,

$$3y^2y' + 3xy' + 3y + 3x^2 = 0.$$

We can now solve for y':

$$y' = -\frac{y + x^2}{y^2 + x}.$$

Remark. If it turns out that the implicit relation defines several functions, then the answer gives the appropriate derivative according to which $y(x)$ is put into the right-hand side of the equation.

EXAMPLE 2. Find the derivative of

$$4x^2 + 9y^2 = 36$$

implicitly, and check the result by solving for y and differentiating explicitly.

Solution. The implicit method gives

$$8x + 18yy' = 0 \quad \text{and} \quad y' = -\frac{4x}{9y}, \quad y \neq 0.$$

On the other hand, using the explicit method, we find that

$$y_1 = +\tfrac{1}{3}\sqrt{36 - 4x^2}, \qquad y_2 = -\tfrac{1}{3}\sqrt{36 - 4x^2},$$

$$y_1'(x) = \tfrac{1}{3} \cdot \tfrac{1}{2}(36 - 4x^2)^{-1/2}(-8x) = -\frac{4x}{3\sqrt{36 - 4x^2}},$$

and $y_2'(x)$ is the same expression preceded by a plus sign.
From the implicit method,

$$y_1' = -\frac{4x}{9y_1} = -\frac{4x}{9 \cdot \tfrac{1}{3}\sqrt{36 - 4x^2}} = -\frac{4x}{3\sqrt{36 - 4x^2}},$$

which is identical with the explicit result; similar results are obtained for $y_2(x)$.

EXAMPLE 3. Assuming that y is a differentiable function of x, find the derivative when

$$y^5 + 3x^2y^3 - 7x^6 - 8 = 0.$$

Solution. In this problem we have no choice as to whether we shall use the explicit or the implicit method, since it is impossible to solve for one variable in terms of the other. We obtain

$$5y^4y' + 3x^2 \cdot 3y^2y' + 3y^3 \cdot 2x - 42x^5 = 0,$$

and it follows that

$$y' = \frac{42x^5 - 6xy^3}{5y^4 + 9x^2y^2}.$$

EXERCISES

In problems 1 through 12, find y' in terms of x and y by implicit differentiation, assuming that y is a differentiable function of x.

1. $x^2 - 3y^2 + 7 = 0$
2. $5x^2 + 12y^3 - 6 = 0$
3. $x^4 + 4y^4 - 2 = 0$
4. $x^3 + y^3 + 4 = 0$
5. $x^2 - 2xy + 2y^2 = 5$
6. $2x^2 - 3xy + y^2 + x + 2y - 8 = 0$
7. $x^3 + 6xy + 5y^3 = 3$
8. $x^3 + 2x^2y - xy^2 + 2y^3 = 4$
9. $2x^3 - 3x^2y + 2xy^2 - y^3 = 2$
10. $x^4 + 2x^2y^2 + xy^3 + 2y^4 = 6$
11. $x^6 + 2x^3y - xy^7 = 10$
12. $x^5 - 2x^3y^2 + 3xy^4 - y^5 = 5$

In problems 13 through 23, find y' in terms of x and y by implicit differentiation; then solve for y in terms of x, and show that each solution and its derivative satisfy the equation obtained.

13. $x^2 - 2xy = 3$ 14. $y^2 = 4x$

15. $xy - 4 = 0$ 16. $x^{1/2} + y^{1/2} = 1$

17. $x^{2/3} + y^{2/3} = a^{2/3}$, $a = \text{const}$ 18. $y^2 - 2x = 4$

19. $y^2 + 2x = 8$ 20. $2x^2 + 3y^2 = 5$

21. $2x^2 - y^2 = 1$ 22. $x^2 - xy + y^2 = 1$

23. $2x^2 - 3xy - 4y^2 = 5$

In problems 24 through 29, find y' by implicit differentiation; then solve for y in terms of x and select the particular function passing through the given point. Find the general form for y' for this function and evaluate y' at the given point.

24. $x^2 + y^2 = 25$ $(4, 3)$ 25. $y^2 = 2x$ $(2, -2)$

26. $xy = 3$ $(1, 3)$ 27. $x^2 + y^2 = 10$ $(3, -1)$

28. $3x^2 - 2xy - y^2 = 3$ $(1, 0)$ 29. $2x^2 - 3xy + 2y^2 = 2$ $(-1, -\tfrac{3}{2})$

CHAPTER 7

Applications of Differentiation. The Differential

1. TOOLS FOR APPLICATIONS OF THE DERIVATIVE

As we learned earlier, a *closed interval* along the x-axis is an interval which includes its endpoints, an *open* interval is one which excludes the endpoints, and a *half-open* interval contains one endpoint but not the other.

The basic theorem of this chapter is the *Extreme Value Theorem.*

Theorem 1. (Extreme Value Theorem.) *If f is a continuous function defined on the closed interval [a, b], there is (at least) one point in [a, b] (call it x_1) where f has a largest value, and there is (at least) one point (call it x_2) where f has a smallest value.*

This theorem is fairly clear intuitively if we think of a continuous function as one with no breaks or gaps. As we move along the curve from the point corresponding to $x = a$ to the point corresponding to $x = b$, there must be a place where the curve has a high point (called the *maximum* value) and there must also be a place where it has a low point (called the *minimum* value). In spite of the simplicity of the situation from the intuitive point of view, the proof of Theorem 1 is hard. Consequently we shall restrict ourselves to a discussion of the meaning of this theorem.

A good way to examine a theorem critically is to see what happens if some of the hypotheses are altered. In Theorem 1 there are two principal hypotheses: (1) the interval [a, b] is closed, and (2) the function f is continuous. We shall show by example that if we tamper with either hypothesis, the conclusion of the theorem may be false.

Suppose that the assumption of a closed interval is replaced by one assuming that the interval is open. The function $f(x) = 1/x$ is continuous on the open interval $0 < x < 1$ (Fig. 7-1), and it has no maximum value in this open interval. A more subtle example is given by the function $f(x) = x^2$ defined in the open interval $0 < x < 2$ (Fig. 7-2). This function has no maximum or minimum value

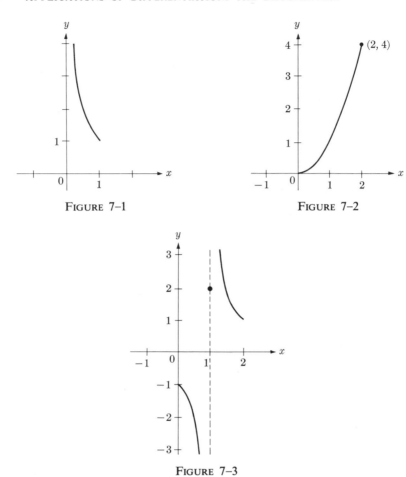

FIGURE 7–1   FIGURE 7–2

FIGURE 7–3

in the *open* interval but does have a maximum of 4 and a minimum of 0 in the *closed* interval. This situation comes about because $f(x) = x^2$ is continuous in the closed interval $0 \leq x \leq 2$. The first example of the function $1/x$ is continuous in $0 < x < 1$ but not in the closed interval $0 \leq x \leq 1$. Even making the interval half-open is not good enough. The first example of the function $1/x$ is continuous in the half-open interval $0 < x \leq 1$ and still has no maximum value there. The second example, $f(x) = x^2$, is continuous in the half-open interval $0 < x \leq 2$ and does not have a minimum in this half-open interval.

The second hypothesis, that of continuity, is also important. The function

$$f(x) = \begin{cases} \dfrac{1}{x-1}, & 0 \leq x \leq 2, \ x \neq 1 \\ f(1) = 2 \end{cases}$$

is continuous except at $x = 1$ (Fig. 7–3). As the graph clearly shows, the function has no maximum and no minimum in the closed interval $[0, 2]$. A second example

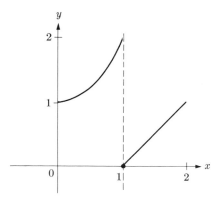

FIGURE 7–4

is the function

$$f(x) = \begin{cases} x^2 + 1, & 0 \le x < 1 \\ x - 1, & 1 \le x \le 2 \end{cases}$$

whose graph is shown in Fig. 7–4. This function is continuous except at $x = 1$, where its minimum occurs with the value zero. There is no point in the closed interval $[0, 2]$ where it has a maximum value. Note that the function gets close to the value 2 as $x \to 1$ from the left. But there is no point where it actually *has* the value 2.

If f is continuous in $[a, b]$, with its maximum value M at x_1 and its minimum value m at x_2, then Theorem 1 implies that

$$m \le f(x) \le M$$

for all x in $[a, b]$. We could equally well write $f(x_1)$ instead of M and $f(x_2)$ instead of m. In words, Theorem 1 states that *a function which is continuous on a closed interval takes on its maximum and minimum values there.*

We shall now prove a theorem concerning the value of the derivative at a maximum or minimum point.

Theorem 2. *Suppose that f is continuous on an interval and takes on its maximum (or minimum) at some point x_0 which is in the interior of the interval. If $f'(x_0)$ exists, then*

$$f'(x_0) = 0.$$

Proof. We prove the theorem for the case where $f(x_0)$ is a maximum. The proof for a minimum is similar. If $f(x_0)$ is the maximum value, then

$$f(x_0 + h) \le f(x_0)$$

for every possible h. The only restriction is that $x_0 + h$ must be in the interval in order for $f(x_0 + h)$ to have a meaning. We can also write (see Fig. 7–5)

$$f(x_0 + h) - f(x_0) \le 0.$$

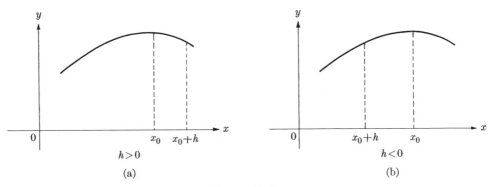

FIGURE 7–5

If h is positive we may divide by h to get

$$\frac{f(x_0 + h) - f(x_0)}{h} \leq 0, \qquad h > 0.$$

On the other hand, if h is negative, the inequality reverses when we divide by h, so that

$$\frac{f(x_0 + h) - f(x_0)}{h} \geq 0, \qquad h < 0.$$

No matter how h is selected, both of the above expressions must tend to $f'(x_0)$ as $h \to 0$. Since one of them is always nonpositive and the other always nonnegative, we conclude that the limit must actually be zero. That is, $f'(x_0) = 0$, which is what we wished to prove.

DISCUSSION. The important hypotheses in Theorem 2 are (1) that x_0 is an interior point, and (2) that f has a derivative at x_0. If the first hypothesis is neglected the theorem is false, as is shown by the example $f(x) = x^2$ in the interval $1 \leq x \leq 2$ (Fig. 7–6). The maximum occurs at $x = 2$ (not an interior point) and the minimum occurs at $x = 1$ (not an interior point). The derivative of $f(x) = x^2$ is $f'(x) = 2x$, and this is different from zero throughout the interval

FIGURE 7–6

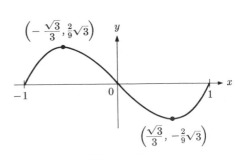

FIGURE 7–7

[1, 2]. The fact that x_0 is *interior* to the interval is important; whether the interval is open, closed, or half-open is irrelevant. The function

$$f(x) = x^3 - x, \qquad -1 < x < 1$$

has a maximum at the point

$$\left(-\frac{\sqrt{3}}{3}, \frac{2}{9}\sqrt{3} \right)$$

and a minimum at

$$\left(\frac{\sqrt{3}}{3}, -\frac{2}{9}\sqrt{3} \right)$$

(see Fig. 7–7). In finding these points we first get the derivative of f:

$$f'(x) = 3x^2 - 1.$$

Then, setting this equal to zero and solving for x, we find that $3x^2 - 1 = 0$, $x = \frac{1}{3}\sqrt{3}, -\frac{1}{3}\sqrt{3}$. Substitution of the x-values into the original expression yields the desired points.

The second hypothesis mentioned is also essential, as is shown by the following example. Let

$$f(x) = \begin{cases} -\frac{1}{3}x^2 + 2x - \frac{5}{3}, & 1 \le x \le 2 \\ -x^2 + 2x + 1, & 2 < x \le 3 \end{cases}$$

This function is continuous in the interval $1 \le x \le 3$, since both expressions approach the same value at $x = 2$. As Fig. 7–8 shows, however, there is a "corner" at $x = 2$, and the derivative does not exist at this point. Nevertheless, the point $P(2, 1)$ is exactly where the maximum occurs.

The derivative may not exist by virtue of being infinite at a maximum or minimum point. The relation $x^{2/3} + y^{2/3} = 1$, $-1 \le x \le 1$, has the graph shown in Fig. 7–9. The portion above the x-axis expresses y as a function of x. The maxi-

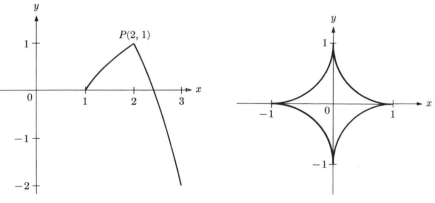

FIGURE 7–8　　　　　　　　　　　　　　FIGURE 7–9

mum occurs at $x = 0$. We can compute the derivative implicitly and obtain

$$\tfrac{2}{3}x^{-1/3} + \tfrac{2}{3}y^{-1/3}y' = 0 \quad \text{or} \quad y' = -\frac{y^{1/3}}{x^{1/3}},$$

and we see that this tends to infinity as x tends to zero. Therefore there is no derivative at the maximum point.

EXERCISES

1. Construct (by sketching) an example of a continuous function in the interval $[0, 3]$ which has its maximum value at 3 different points.
2. Construct (by sketching) an example of a continuous function in the interval $[-1, 4]$ which has its maximum at two different points and its minimum at four different points.
3. Construct (by sketching) an example of a continuous function in the interval $[1, 5]$ which has its maximum value at every point of the subinterval $[2\tfrac{1}{2}, 3\tfrac{1}{4}]$.
4. Give an example of a function which has a discontinuity at some point in the interval $[2, 5]$ and still takes on its maximum and minimum values in this interval.
5. A function f is continuous in the interval $(-2, 3)$, has a maximum at $x = -1$ and a minimum at $x = 2$. Is f necessarily continuous in $[-2, 3]$? Justify the answer.
6. A function f is continuous for all values of x from $-\infty$ to $+\infty$. The function never gets larger than 5 or smaller than -5. Give an example to show that it may not have a maximum or minimum value.
7. Given the function $f(x) = 3x^2 + 6x + 1$ in the interval $-2 \le x \le 0$, find the minimum point.
8. Given the function $f(x) = 3x^2 + 6x + 1$ in the interval $0 \le x \le 3$, find the minimum point.
9. Find the maximum value of

$$f(x) = \begin{cases} x + 1, & 0 \le x \le 1 \\ -x^2 + 3, & 1 < x \le 3 \end{cases}$$

in the interval $0 \le x \le 3$. Where is the minimum value?
10. Find the maximum point of $f(x) = \tfrac{1}{3}x^3 - x + 2$ in the interval $[-2, 2]$. What is the maximum point in the interval $[-3, 3]$?
11. Given the function

$$f(x) = \begin{cases} -x^2 + 4x - 2, & 1 \le x \le 2 \\ -\tfrac{1}{2}x^2 + 2x, & 2 < x \le 3, \end{cases}$$

find the maximum point. Does the function have a derivative at this point? If so, find the value of the derivative.
12. Examine the relation

$$x^{1/3} + y^{1/3} = 2, \quad -8 \le x \le 8$$

with regard to maximum and minimum points.

2. FURTHER TOOLS: ROLLE'S THEOREM; THEOREM OF THE MEAN

Theorems 1 and 2 of Section 1 are the basis for the following result, known as Rolle's Theorem.

Theorem 3. (Rolle's Theorem.) *Suppose that f is continuous for $a \leq x \leq b$ and that $f'(x)$ exists for each x between a and b. If*

$$f(a) = f(b) = 0,$$

then there must be (at least) one point, call it x_0, between a and b such that

$$f'(x_0) = 0.$$

Proof. There are three possibilities:

Case I (The trivial case). $f(x) = 0$ for all x between a and b; then $f'(x) = 0$ for all x, and x_0 can be chosen to be any value between a and b.

Case II. $f(x)$ is positive somewhere between a and b. Then the maximum of f is positive, and we choose x_0 (Theorem 1) to be a place where this maximum occurs. (See Fig. 7–10a.) According to Theorem 2 of the previous section, $f'(x_0) = 0$, since x_0 must be interior to the interval.

Case III. $f(x)$ is negative somewhere between a and b. Then the minimum of f is negative, and we choose x_0 to be a place where this minimum occurs. (See Fig. 7–10b.) According to Theorem 2 of the previous section, $f'(x_0) = 0$.

Since every function which is zero at a and b must fall into one of the three cases, the theorem is proved.

Figure 7–10(c) shows that a function may fall into both Case II and Case III, and Fig. 7–10(d) illustrates the possibility of several choices for x_0 even though it satisfies only Case II.

We can state Rolle's Theorem in a simple way: If a differentiable curve crosses the x-axis twice there must be a point between successive crossings where the tangent to the curve is parallel to the x-axis.

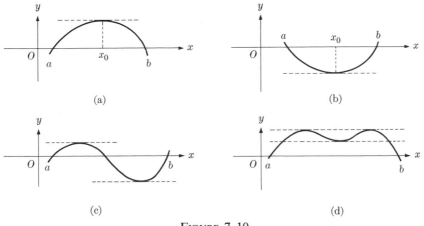

(a)   (b)

(c)   (d)

FIGURE 7–10

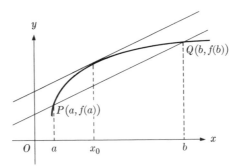

FIGURE 7–11

We have been building up to the proof of the theorem known as the *Theorem of the Mean*, one which is used over and over again throughout the branch of mathematics known as analysis. Every mathematician who works in analysis encounters it often, uses it, and feels at home with it. We shall see that, important though it is, it is merely a slight variation of Rolle's Theorem.

Theorem 4.   (Theorem of the Mean.)   *Suppose that f is continuous for $a \le x \le b$ and that $f'(x)$ exists for each x between a and b. Then there is an x_0 between a and b (that is, $a < x_0 < b$) such that*

$$f'(x_0) = \frac{f(b) - f(a)}{b - a}.$$

Before proving this theorem we shall discuss its meaning from a geometric standpoint. Figure 7–11 shows a typical function f between the points a and b. The point P has coordinates $(a, f(a))$ and Q has coordinates $(b, f(b))$. We construct the straight line through PQ and calculate its slope. We know that the slope is the difference of the y-values over the difference of the x-values, i.e.,

$$\frac{f(b) - f(a)}{b - a}.$$

This is exactly the same expression that occurs in the statement of the Theorem of the Mean. The theorem says that there is a point x_0 on the curve where the slope has such a value; that is, the tangent line at x_0 is parallel to the line through PQ. Glancing at the figure, we see that there must be such a point. In fact, by means of the following device, we can see that there must be one: We look at the figure and tilt it so that the line through PQ appears horizontally as the x-axis. Then the Theorem of the Mean resembles Rolle's Theorem.

Proof. The equation of the line through PQ (according to the two-point formula for the equation of a straight line) is

$$y - f(a) = \frac{f(b) - f(a)}{b - a} (x - a).$$

We construct the function

$$F(x) = f(x) - \frac{f(b) - f(a)}{b - a} (x - a) - f(a).$$

By straight substitution we find that

$$F(a) = f(a) - \frac{f(b) - f(a)}{b - a} (a - a) - f(a) = 0,$$

$$F(b) = f(b) - \frac{f(b) - f(a)}{b - a} (b - a) - f(a) = 0.$$

Therefore $F(x)$ satisfies all the hypotheses of Rolle's Theorem. There must be a value x_0 such that $F'(x_0) = 0$. But (by differentiation) we see that

$$F'(x) = f'(x) - \frac{f(b) - f(a)}{b - a}.$$

This implies that

$$f'(x_0) = \frac{f(b) - f(a)}{b - a},$$

which is what we wished to prove.

———————

EXAMPLE 1. Given that

$$f(x) = \frac{x + 2}{x + 1} \quad \text{and} \quad a = 1, b = 2,$$

find all values x_0 such that

$$f'(x_0) = \frac{f(b) - f(a)}{b - a}.$$

Solution.

$$f'(x) = \frac{(x + 1) \cdot 1 - (x + 2) \cdot 1}{(x + 1)^2} = \frac{-1}{(x + 1)^2},$$

$$f(1) = \frac{3}{2}, \quad f(2) = \frac{4}{3}, \quad \frac{f(b) - f(a)}{b - a} = -\frac{1}{6}.$$

We solve the equation $f'(x_0) = -\frac{1}{6}$, which yields

$$\frac{-1}{(x_0 + 1)^2} = -\frac{1}{6} \quad \text{or} \quad x_0^2 + 2x_0 - 5 = 0,$$

and

$$x_0 = \frac{-2 \pm \sqrt{24}}{2} = -1 \pm \sqrt{6}.$$

The value $x_0 = -1 + \sqrt{6}$ is in the interval [1, 2], while the value $x_0 = -1 - \sqrt{6}$ is rejected as being outside this interval.

EXAMPLE 2. Given that $f(x) = x^3 - 2x^2 + 3x - 2$ and $a = 0, b = 2$, find all possible values for x_0 such that

$$f'(x_0) = \frac{f(b) - f(a)}{b - a}.$$

Solution.

$$f'(x) = 3x^2 - 4x + 3, \qquad f(0) = -2, \qquad f(2) = 4,$$

so that

$$\frac{f(b) - f(a)}{b - a} = \frac{4 + 2}{2} = 3.$$

We must solve the equation

$$3x_0^2 - 4x_0 + 3 = 3,$$

which has two solutions: $x_0 = 0$ and $x_0 = \frac{4}{3}$. But $x_0 = 0$ is not *between* 0 and 2, and therefore the only answer is $x_0 = \frac{4}{3}$.

EXAMPLE 3. Given the function

$$f(x) = \frac{x^2 - 4x + 3}{x - 2} \qquad \text{and that} \qquad a = 1, b = 3,$$

discuss the validity of the Theorem of the Mean.

Solution. If we proceed formally, we see that $f(1) = 0$ and $f(3) = 0$, so we must find an x_0 in the interval $[1, 3]$ such that $f'(x_0) = 0$. Computing the derivative by the quotient rule, we write

$$f'(x) = \frac{(x - 2)(2x - 4) - (x^2 - 4x + 3)}{(x - 2)^2} = \frac{x^2 - 4x + 5}{(x - 2)^2}.$$

Setting this equal to zero, we obtain

$$x_0^2 - 4x_0 + 5 = 0, \qquad \text{and} \qquad x_0 = \frac{4 \pm \sqrt{16 - 20}}{2} = \frac{4 \pm \sqrt{-4}}{2},$$

which is impossible! We look once again at the function f and see that it becomes infinite at $x = 2$. Therefore the hypotheses of the Theorem of the Mean are not satisfied, and the theorem is not applicable. There is no value x_0.

EXERCISES

In problems 1 through 12, find all the numbers x_0 between a and b which satisfy the equation $(b - a)f'(x_0) = f(b) - f(a)$.

1. $f(x) = x^2 - 2x - 3$, $a = -1, b = 3$

2. $f(x) = x^3 - 6x^2 + 10x$, $a = 1, b = 4$

3. $f(x) = x^3 - 5x^2 - 3x$, $a = 1, b = 3$

4. $f(x) = x^3 + x^2 - x$, $a = -2, b = 1$

5. $f(x) = \dfrac{x - 1}{x + 1}$, $a = 0, b = 3$

6. $f(x) = \dfrac{2x + 3}{3x - 2}$, $a = 1, b = 4$

7. $f(x) = \sqrt{25 - x^2}$, $a = -3, b = 4$

8. $f(x) = \sqrt{x^2 + 81}$, $a = 12, b = 40$

9. $f(x) = x^4 - 2x^3 + x^2 - 2x$, $a = -1, b = 2$

10. $f(x) = x^4 + x^3 - 3x^2 + 2x$, $a = -2, b = -1$

11. $f(x) = \dfrac{x^2 - 3x - 4}{x + 5}$, $a = -1, b = 4$

12. $f(x) = \dfrac{x^2 + 6x + 5}{x - 6}$, $a = 1, b = 5$

13. Given that $f(x) = (2x + 3)/(3x + 2)$, $a = -1$, $b = 0$, show that there is no number x_0 between a and b which satisfies the Theorem of the Mean. Sketch the graph.

14. Given that $f(x) = 2x^{2/3}$, $a = -1$, $b = 1$, show that there is no number x_0 between a and b which satisfies the Theorem of the Mean. Sketch the graph.

15. Given that
$$f(x) = 1/(x - 1)^2, \ a = -1, \ b = 2.$$

Is there a number x_0 between a and b which satisfies the equation
$$(b - a)f'(x_0) = f(b) - f(a)?$$

Can the Theorem of the Mean be used?

16. Given that f is a quadratic function of x, and a and b are any numbers, show that $x_0 = \frac{1}{2}(a + b)$ is the value that satisfies the Theorem of the Mean. (*Hint:* Assume that $f(x) = cx^2 + dx + e$ where c, d, and e are any constants.)

3. APPLICATIONS TO GRAPHS OF FUNCTIONS

Knowing how the derivative of a function behaves helps us in obtaining an accurate idea of the graph of the function. In this and the following section we establish some rules (in the form of theorems) which are most useful for graphing functions; we also give some examples to illustrate the technique.

DEFINITION. A function f is said to be *increasing* on the interval (a, b) if $f(x_2) > f(x_1)$ whenever $x_2 > x_1$, so long as both x_1 and x_2 are in (a, b). It is *decreasing* if $f(x_2) < f(x_1)$ whenever $x_2 > x_1$ (Fig. 7–12).

DEFINITION. A function f is said to have a *relative maximum* at x_0 if there is some interval with x_0 as an interior point, such that $f(x_0)$ is the true maximum of f in this interval occurring at x_0. Similarly, it has a *relative minimum* at x_1 if there is some interval with x_1 as interior point, such that $f(x_1)$ is the true minimum of f in this interval.

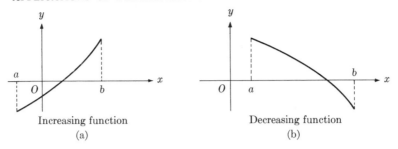

Increasing function   Decreasing function
(a)   (b)

FIGURE 7–12

FIGURE 7–13

The latter definition needs some explanation, as provided in Fig. 7–13, which shows a typical situation. The function f has its maximum in $[a, b]$ at x_0, a point which is a relative maximum. However, f has a relative maximum at x_2 although $f(x_2)$ is not the maximum of the function in $[a, b]$. The function f has a relative minimum at x_1. The true minimum in $[a, b]$ occurs at b. However, f does not have a relative minimum at b, since the definition for relative minimum is not satisfied there.

Theorem 5. *If $f'(x) > 0$ for each x in an interval (a, b), then f is increasing on (a, b).*

Proof. We apply the Theorem of the Mean to two points x_1, x_2 in (a, b). We find that

$$f(x_2) - f(x_1) = f'(x_0)(x_2 - x_1),$$

where x_0 is between x_1 and x_2. For $x_2 > x_1$ and f' positive, we obtain $f'(x_0)(x_2 - x_1) > 0$, and so $f(x_2) - f(x_1) > 0$. This means, by definition, that f is increasing.

Corollary. If $f'(x) < 0$ for each x in (a, b), then f is decreasing on (a, b).

It is apparent that Theorem 5 is useful for graphing; we can find out whether the graph of a function is rising or falling by observing whether the derivative is positive or negative. This theorem (together with Theorem 2 of Section 1, which says that at a relative maximum or minimum the derivative of a function is zero) helps us find the peaks and troughs.

There is a complication in using Theorem 2 because, although the derivative of a function is zero at a maximum or minimum point (assuming the derivative exists there), the converse may not hold true. For example, the function $f(x) = x^3$ (Fig. 7–14) has derivative $f'(x) = 3x^2$, which is zero at $x = 0$. But $(0, 0)$ is neither a maximum nor a minimum point of the function. Thus the knowledge that the derivative of a function vanishes at a certain point is not enough to guarantee that the function has a maximum or minimum there.

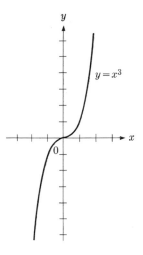

DEFINITION. A *critical point* of a function f is a value of x where $f'(x) = 0$.

A critical point occurs at any relative maximum or minimum point of a function which has a derivative at that point. However, the function $f(x) = x^3$ has a critical point at $x = 0$, but this point is neither a maximum nor a minimum of the function.

FIGURE 7–14

EXAMPLE 1. Study the derivative of the function $f(x) = \frac{1}{3}x^3 - x^2 - 3x + 3$, and use the resulting knowledge to help sketch the graph of the function in the interval $-3 \le x \le 5$.

Solution. The derivative is

$$f'(x) = x^2 - 2x - 3 = (x + 1)(x - 3).$$

The critical points are the solutions of

$$x^2 - 2x - 3 = 0.$$

That is, $x = -1, 3$.

Now we want to find out where the derivative is positive and where it is negative. This means that we have to study the inequalities

$$(x + 1)(x - 3) > 0 \quad \text{and} \quad (x + 1)(x - 3) < 0.$$

We can now profit from our study of inequalities in Chapter 1.

$$\left. \begin{array}{l} \text{If} \quad x + 1 > 0 \quad \text{and} \quad x - 3 > 0 \\ \text{or} \\ \quad\quad x + 1 < 0 \quad \text{and} \quad x - 3 < 0 \end{array} \right\} \quad \text{then} \quad f'(x) > 0.$$

$$\left. \begin{array}{l} \text{If} \quad x + 1 > 0 \quad \text{and} \quad x - 3 < 0 \\ \text{or} \\ \quad\quad x + 1 < 0 \quad \text{and} \quad x - 3 > 0 \end{array} \right\} \quad \text{then} \quad f'(x) < 0.$$

Consequently, if

$$x < -1 \quad \text{or} \quad x > 3, \quad \text{then } f' > 0,$$

while if

$$-1 < x < 3, \quad \text{we have } f' < 0.$$

After we have constructed a brief table of values, we are ready to graph the function (Fig. 7–15).

x	-3	-1	0	3	5
$f'(x)$	$+$	0	$-$	0	$+$
$f(x)$	-6	$4\frac{2}{3}$	3	-6	$4\frac{2}{3}$

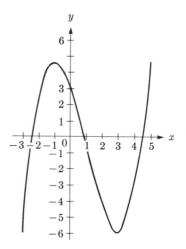

FIGURE 7–15

The critical value $x = -1$ corresponds to a relative maximum, and the critical value $x = 3$ corresponds to a relative minimum.

———————

The theorems and definitions presented in this section give us a method for finding relative maxima and minima. We state the method in the form of a test.

TEST I.   (Theorem 6). (a) *If f is increasing ($f' > 0$) in some interval to the left of x_0 with x_0 as endpoint of this interval, and if f is decreasing ($f' < 0$) in some interval to the right of x_0 (with x_0 as endpoint), then f has a relative maximum at x_0.*

(b) *If f is decreasing ($f' < 0$) in some interval to the left of x_0 with x_0 as endpoint of this interval, and if f is increasing ($f' > 0$) in some interval to the right of x_0 (with x_0 as endpoint), then f has a relative minimum at x_0.*

FIGURE 7–16

FIGURE 7–17

Remarks. Of course we assume that f is continuous at x_0. If f has a derivative there, then the derivative will be zero. However, we include the possibility that there may be a cusp or a corner. Figure 7–16 shows the various possibilities.

Proof of Theorem 6: To prove part (a), we denote by I' the interval to the left and by I'' the interval to the right of x_0, then we combine them into one interval and call this interval I (Fig. 7–17). Then x_0 is an interior point of I. Since f is increasing on I' and decreasing on I'' and both contain the point x_0, we must have $f(x_0) \geq f(x)$ for all x in I.
The proof of (b) is the same.

EXAMPLE 2. Discuss the function f defined by

$$f(x) = x^{5/3} + 5x^{2/3}$$

for relative maxima and minima, and determine the intervals in which f is increasing and those in which f is decreasing. Sketch the graph.
Solution. The derivative is

$$f'(x) = \tfrac{5}{3}x^{2/3} + \tfrac{10}{3}x^{-1/3} = \tfrac{5}{3}x^{-1/3}(x + 2).$$

The critical point is $x = -2$. The derivative is not defined at $x = 0$. We construct the following table:

x	-5	-2	-1	0	1
$f'(x)$	$+$	0	$-$	$*$	$+$
$f(x)$	0	$3(2)^{2/3}$	4	0	6

$* =$ undefined

We conclude that

$$f \text{ increases for } x < -2;$$
$$f \text{ decreases for } -2 < x < 0;$$
$$f \text{ increases for } x > 0.$$

We now apply Test I and conclude that there is a relative maximum at $x = -2$ and a relative minimum at $x = 0$. The graph is sketched in Fig. 7–18.

EXAMPLE 3. Discuss the function f defined by

$$f(x) = \frac{x^2 + x + 7}{\sqrt{2x + 1}}, \qquad x > -\frac{1}{2},$$

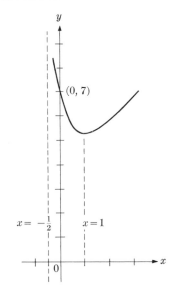

FIGURE 7–18   FIGURE 7–19

for relative maxima and minima, and determine where f is increasing and where it is decreasing. Sketch the graph.

Solution. The derivative is

$$f'(x) = \frac{(2x + 1)^{1/2}(2x + 1) - (x^2 + x + 7)\frac{1}{2}(2x + 1)^{-1/2}(2)}{(2x + 1)}.$$

We simplify by multiplying numerator and denominator through by $(2x + 1)^{1/2}$ and obtain

$$f'(x) = \frac{(2x + 1)^2 - (x^2 + x + 7)}{(2x + 1)^{3/2}} = \frac{3(x + 2)(x - 1)}{(2x + 1)^{3/2}}.$$

We set this equal to zero and find that $x = 1$ is a critical value. The apparent solution $x = -2$ is excluded, since the function is defined only for $x > -\frac{1}{2}$. We easily discover that

$$f(x) \text{ decreases for } -\tfrac{1}{2} < x < 1;$$
$$f(x) \text{ increases for } x > 1.$$

Test I now applies, and we find that the value $x = 1$ is a relative minimum. The graph is sketched in Fig. 7–19.

EXERCISES

In the following problems discuss each function for relative maxima and minima, and determine those intervals in which the function is increasing and those in which it is decreasing. Sketch the graphs.

1. $x^2 + 4x + 2$ 2. $x^2 + 3x - 8$
3. $-x^2 + 3x + 4$ 4. $-2x^2 + 5x - 6$

5. $\frac{1}{3}x^3 + x^2 - 2x$

6. $x^3 - 3x^2 - 9x + 10$

7. $x^3 + 2x^2 - 3x - 2$

8. $x^3 - 3x^2 + 6x - 3$

9. $x^3 + 6x^2 + 12x - 5$

10. $x^3 + 3x^2 + 6x - 3$

11. $-x^3 + 2x^2 - x + 1$

12. $-x^3 - 2x^2 + 3x - 6$

13. $x^4 - \frac{4}{3}x^3 - 4x^2 + \frac{2}{3}$

14. $x^4 + \frac{4}{3}x^3 - 12x^2$

15. $x^4 + 2x^3$

16. $x^4 + 4x^3 + 6x^2$

17. $x + \frac{1}{x}$

18. $\dfrac{2x}{x^2 + 1}$

19. $\dfrac{x - 1}{x + 1}$

20. $\dfrac{3x - 2}{2x + 3}$

21. $\dfrac{x^2}{\sqrt{x + 1}}, \, x > -1$

22. $3x^{1/2} - x^{3/2}$

23. $x^{2/3}(x + 3)^{1/3}$

24. $x/(x + 1)$

25. $x\sqrt{3 - x}, \; x \leq 3$

26. $x^2\sqrt{5 - x}, \; x \leq 5$

27. $x\sqrt{2 - x^2}, \; |x| \leq \sqrt{2}$

28. $\dfrac{x^2 - 2x + 1}{x + 1}$

29. $\dfrac{x^2 - 3x - 4}{x - 2}$

4. APPLICATIONS USING THE SECOND DERIVATIVE

The more information we have about a function the more accurately we can construct its graph. In Section 3 we saw that a knowledge of the first derivative helps us decide when the graph is increasing and when it is decreasing. Furthermore, we learned that Test I enables us to locate the relative maxima and minima. The second derivative yields additional facts which are helpful in determining the nature of the graph. The first of these facts consists of a test for relative maxima and minima which employs the second derivative.

DEFINITION. If, at each point of an interval, the locus of a function f always remains above the line tangent to the curve at this point, we say that the curve is *concave upward* on the interval (see Fig. 7–20). If the curve always remains below its tangent line, we say it is *concave downward* (see Fig. 7–21).

Before stating and proving the basic theorem of this section we recall the equation of the line tangent to a curve. At any value x_0 the function f has

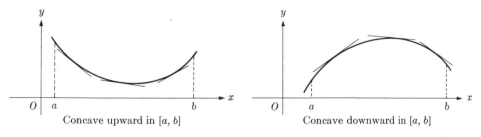

Concave upward in $[a, b]$ Concave downward in $[a, b]$

FIGURE 7–20   FIGURE 7–21

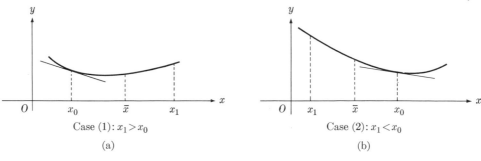

Case (1): $x_1 > x_0$ Case (2): $x_1 < x_0$

(a)   (b)

FIGURE 7–22

value $f(x_0)$ and the slope of the curve at this point is $f'(x_0)$. The equation of a line through the point $(x_0, f(x_0))$ with slope $f'(x_0)$ is, according to the point-slope formula,

$$y - f(x_0) = f'(x_0)(x - x_0) \qquad \text{or} \qquad y = f(x_0) + f'(x_0)(x - x_0).$$

This is the tangent line.

Theorem 7. *Assume that f has two derivatives in an interval I.*
(a) *If $f''(x) > 0$ for x interior to I, then the curve is concave upward on I.*
(b) *If $f''(x) < 0$ for x interior to I, then the curve is concave downward on I.*

Proof. To prove (a), we must show that the curve lies above the tangent line at any point. Let x_0 be any point in I (see Fig. 7–22). The tangent line at x_0 has equation

$$y = f(x_0) + f'(x_0)(x - x_0),$$

and we therefore have to establish (for all x in I) the inequality

$$f(x) \geq f(x_0) + f'(x_0)(x - x_0).$$

If $x = x_0$, this becomes $f(x_0) \geq f(x_0)$, which is true. If x is some other value, say x_1, then we can apply the Theorem of the Mean to the function f between the two points x_0 and x_1. This theorem says that there is a value $\bar{x}$ such that

$$f'(\bar{x}) = \frac{f(x_1) - f(x_0)}{x_1 - x_0},$$

where $\bar{x}$ is between x_0 and x_1. We have two possibilities: (i) $x_1 > x_0$, and (ii) $x_1 < x_0$. In case (i) we write the Theorem of the Mean in the form

$$f(x_1) = f(x_0) + f'(\bar{x})(x_1 - x_0). \tag{1}$$

Since $f'' > 0$ by hypothesis, we know from Theorem 5 that f' is increasing in I. If $x_1 > x_0$, then

$$f'(\bar{x}) > f'(x_0).$$

We multiply this last inequality through by the positive quantity $(x_1 - x_0)$ to get

$$f'(\bar{x})(x_1 - x_0) > f'(x_0)(x_1 - x_0),$$

and therefore, by substitution in Eq. (1), we obtain

$$f(x_1) > f(x_0) + f'(x_0)(x_1 - x_0),$$

which is what we wished to show.

In case (ii), since $x_0 > \bar{x}$, we must have $f'(x_0) > f'(\bar{x})$. But now we multiply through by the negative number $(x_1 - x_0)$, which reverses the inequality, giving

$$f'(\bar{x})(x_1 - x_0) > f'(x_0)(x_1 - x_0)$$

as before, and therefore

$$f(x_1) > f(x_0) + f'(x_0)(x_1 - x_0).$$

The proof of part (b) of Theorem 7 is similar.

Theorem 7 shows that knowledge of the second derivative gives us an even clearer picture of the appearance of the curve. In addition, it gives us the following useful test, known as the Second Derivative Test, for relative maxima and minima.

TEST II.   (Theorem 8). *Assume that f has two derivatives, f'' is continuous, and x_0 is a critical point $(f'(x_0) = 0)$. Then*

(a) *If $f''(x_0) > 0$, f has a relative minimum at x_0.*
(b) *If $f''(x_0) < 0$, f has a relative maximum at x_0.*
(c) *If $f''(x_0) = 0$, the test fails.*

Proof. To prove part (a), we see from Theorem 7 that the curve is concave upward and must lie above the tangent line at x_0. But this line is horizontal, since $f'(x_0) = 0$. Therefore $f(x_0)$ must be a minimum value. The proof of (b) is the same. Part (c) is added for the sake of completeness.

———

EXAMPLE 1. Discuss the function

$$f(x) = x^3 - \tfrac{21}{4}x^2 + 9x - 4$$

for relative maxima and minima. Sketch the graph.

Solution. The derivative is

$$f'(x) = 3x^2 - \tfrac{21}{2}x + 9 = 3(x^2 - \tfrac{7}{2}x + 3),$$

and the critical points are solutions of

$$x^2 - \tfrac{7}{2}x + 3 = 0 \quad \text{or} \quad x = \tfrac{3}{2}, 2.$$

We apply the Second Derivative Test.

$$f''(x) = 6x - \tfrac{21}{2}; \quad f''(\tfrac{3}{2}) = -\tfrac{3}{2} < 0, \quad f''(2) = \tfrac{3}{2} > 0.$$

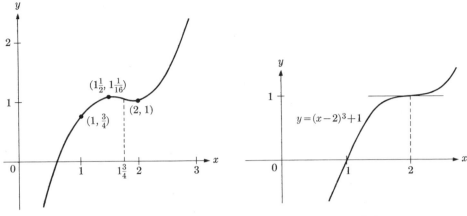

FIGURE 7–23   FIGURE 7–24

Therefore $x = \frac{3}{2}$ corresponds to a maximum, and $x = 2$ corresponds to a minimum. Also, the second derivative is positive if $x > \frac{7}{4}$ and negative if $x < \frac{7}{4}$. That is, the curve is concave upward for $x > \frac{7}{4}$ and concave downward for $x < \frac{7}{4}$. We construct the following table.

x	0	$\frac{3}{2}$	$\frac{7}{4}$	2	3
f	-4	$\frac{17}{16}$	$1\frac{1}{32}$	1	$\frac{11}{4}$
f'	$+$	0	$-$	0	$+$
f''	$-$	$-$	0	$+$	$+$

   This problem indicates the difficulty that may arise when a relative maximum and a relative minimum are close together. Without knowledge of the derivatives given in the table, we would normally plot the points at $x = 0, 1, 2, 3$, etc. This would miss the maximum at $x = \frac{3}{2}$ and give a misleading picture of the curve. We know that the curve is concave downward to the left of $x = \frac{7}{4}$ and concave upward to the right of $\frac{7}{4}$. These facts prevail indefinitely far to the left and right. The graph is sketched in Fig. 7–23. In this example the point $x = \frac{7}{4}$ is important, as it separates a concave downward region from a concave upward region.

   DEFINITION. A point on a curve is a *point of inflection* if $f''(x_0) = 0$ at this point and if the graph is concave upward on one side and concave downward on the other.

   We make two remarks which the reader should keep in mind: The first derivative may or may not vanish at a point of inflection. In Example 1 the value $x = \frac{7}{4}$ corresponds to a point of inflection, and $f'(\frac{7}{4}) = -\frac{3}{16}$. On the other hand, the function $f(x) = (x - 2)^3 + 1$ has a point of inflection (see Fig. 7–24) at $x = 2$, since $f''(x) = 6(x - 2)$ and $f''(2) = 0$. However, we notice that $f'(x) = 3(x - 2)^2$ and $f'(2) = 0$, also.
   The second remark: It is not enough to know that $f''(x_0) = 0$ to guarantee that x_0 is a point of inflection. We must also know that $f''(x) > 0$ on one side and that

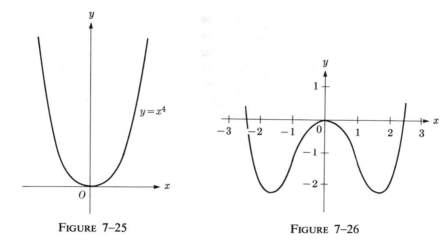

FIGURE 7–25   FIGURE 7–26

$f''(x) < 0$ on the other. An example which shows this difficulty is the function $f(x) = x^4$ (see Fig. 7–25). In this case, $f''(x) = 12x^2$ and $f''(0) = 0$. However, $f''(x)$ is always positive and, in fact, $x = 0$ is the value for a minimum. (Part (c) of Theorem 8 for the Second Derivative Test is the rule which holds here.) Test I, however, works to give a minimum.

EXAMPLE 2. Discuss the function

$$f(x) = \tfrac{1}{4}x^4 - \tfrac{3}{2}x^2$$

for relative maxima, relative minima, and points of inflection. Sketch the graph.

Solution. The derivatives are

$$f'(x) = x^3 - 3x \qquad \text{and} \qquad f''(x) = 3x^2 - 3.$$

The critical points are solutions of $x^3 - 3x = 0$, and so we get $x = 0, \sqrt{3}, -\sqrt{3}$. The Second Derivative Test tells us that

$$x = 0 \text{ is a relative maximum};$$
$$x = \sqrt{3}, -\sqrt{3} \text{ are relative minima.}$$

The possible points of inflection are solutions of $3x^2 - 3 = 0$; that is, $x = +1, -1$. Since $f''(x)$ is negative for $-1 < x < 1$ and positive for $|x| > 1$, both $x = 1$ and $x = -1$ are points of inflection. We construct the table:

x	-2	$-\sqrt{3}$	-1	0	1	$\sqrt{3}$	2
f	-2	$-\tfrac{9}{4}$	$-\tfrac{5}{4}$	0	$-\tfrac{5}{4}$	$-\tfrac{9}{4}$	-2
f'	$-$	0	$+$	0	$-$	0	$+$
f''	$+$	$+$	0	$-$	0	$+$	$+$

The graph is symmetric with respect to the y-axis (Fig. 7–26).

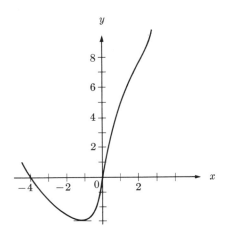

FIGURE 7-27

EXAMPLE 3. Discuss the function

$$f(x) = x^{4/3} + 4x^{1/3}$$

for relative maxima, relative minima, and points of inflection. Sketch the graph.

Solution. We have

$$f'(x) = \tfrac{4}{3}x^{1/3} + \tfrac{4}{3}x^{-2/3} = \tfrac{4}{3}x^{-2/3}(x + 1);$$
$$f''(x) = \tfrac{4}{9}x^{-2/3} - \tfrac{8}{9}x^{-5/3} = \tfrac{4}{9}x^{-5/3}(x - 2).$$

The first and second derivatives do not exist at $x = 0$. The value $x = -1$ is a critical value and $x = 2$ is a possible point of inflection. We construct the table:

x	-4	-1	$-\tfrac{1}{2}$	0	1	2	3
f	0	-3	$-\tfrac{7}{4}\sqrt[3]{4}$	0	5	$6\sqrt[3]{2}$	$7\sqrt[3]{3}$
f'	$-$	0	$+$	$*$	$+$	$+$	$+$
f''	$+$	$+$	$+$	$*$	$-$	0	$+$

From the table we see that $x = -1$ is a relative minimum and that $x = 2$ is a point of inflection. Furthermore, $x = 0$ is a point where the curve changes from concave upward to concave downward. The graph is shown in Fig. 7–27.

EXERCISES

In problems 1 through 27, discuss each of the functions for relative maxima and minima, concavity, and points of inflection. Sketch the graphs.

1. $f(x) = 2x^2 - 6x + 5$

2. $f(x) = -3x^2 + 2x - 1$

3. $f(x) = x^3 - 3x + 2$

4. $f(x) = x^3 + x^2 + 6x - 5$

5. $f(x) = x^4 + 2x^3$

6. $f(x) = x^4 + 2x^3 - 3x^2 - 4x$

7. $f(x) = x^2 + \dfrac{1}{x^2}$

8. $f(x) = 2x^2 - \dfrac{1}{x^2}$

9. $f(x) = \dfrac{2x}{x^2 + 1}$

10. $f(x) = x\sqrt{x + 3}$

11. $f(x) = x^3 - \frac{3}{2}x^2 - 6x + 2$

12. $f(x) = x^3 + x^2 - x - 1$

13. $f(x) = x^3 - 4x^2 + 4x - 1$

14. $f(x) = x^3 + 3x^2 - 3x - 5$

15. $f(x) = x^3 - x^2 + x - 1$

16. $f(x) = x^4 + \frac{4}{3}x^3 - 4x^2 - \frac{4}{3}$

17. $f(x) = (x + 2)(x - 2)^3$

18. $f(x) = x^4 - 3x^3 + 3x^2$

19. $f(x) = x^4 + 5x^3 + 6x^2$

20. $f(x) = x - 3 + \dfrac{2}{x + 1}$

21. $f(x) = \dfrac{4x}{x^2 + 4}$

22. $f(x) = 5x^{2/3} - x^{5/3}$

23. $f(x) = x\sqrt{8 - x^2}, \ |x| \le \sqrt{8}$

24. $f(x) = x^{2/3}(x + 2)^{-1}$

25. $f(x) = x^2\sqrt{5 + x}, \ x \ge -5$

26. $f(x) = x^2\sqrt{3 - x^2}, \ |x| \le \sqrt{3}$

27. $f(x) = x^{1/3}(x + 2)^{-2/3}$

28. Using the function $f(x) = x^4$ as a guide, devise a "Higher Derivative Test" for relative maxima and minima when both $f'(x_0) = 0$ and $f''(x_0) = 0$.

29. Devise a definition for points of inflection at places where the second derivative does not exist. Construct an example to which this definition is applicable.

5. THE MAXIMUM AND MINIMUM VALUES OF A FUNCTION ON AN INTERVAL

In the preceding sections we studied ways of finding relative maxima and minima of a function. One of these relative maxima may be the true maximum of the function, or it may not be. As Fig. 7–28 shows, the function exhibited has a relative maximum at P and a relative minimum at Q. As we go off to the right, however, the function gets larger than the value at P, and as we go off to the left, the function gets smaller than the value at Q. Suppose that we look at the above function only in some interval $[a, b]$, as shown. Then the maximum occurs at b and is $f(b)$, while the minimum occurs at a and is $f(a)$. If $[a, b']$ were the interval of interest, as shown, then the maximum of f in $[a, b']$ is at P, while the minimum is at a. Further, in the interval $[a', b']$ the maximum is at P, the minimum at Q.

To obtain the maximum and minimum of a continuous function in an interval $[a, b]$, we employ the following procedure:

RULE: (a) Find the relative maximum and minimum values of f.
(b) Find the value of the function at the endpoints.
The largest of the values of (a) and (b) is the maximum. The smallest value is the minimum.

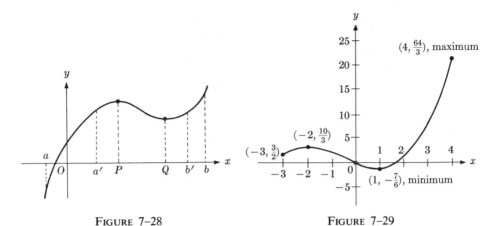

FIGURE 7–28   FIGURE 7–29

EXAMPLE. Given the function

$$f(x) = \tfrac{1}{3}x^3 + \tfrac{1}{2}x^2 - 2x,$$

find the maximum and minimum on the interval $[-3, 4]$.

Solution. We follow the Rule and find relative maxima and minima:

$$f'(x) = x^2 + x - 2,$$

and the critical points are at $x = -2, 1$. The Second Derivative Test gives us $f''(x) = 2x + 1$; $f''(-2) = -3$, making -2 a relative maximum, and $f''(1) = 3$, which makes 1 a relative minimum. That is, the point $(1, -\tfrac{7}{6})$ is a relative minimum, and $(-2, \tfrac{10}{3})$ is a relative maximum. Now we go on to part (b) of the Rule: $f(-3) = \tfrac{3}{2}$ and $f(4) = \tfrac{64}{3}$. Since $\tfrac{64}{3}$ is larger than $\tfrac{10}{3}$, the maximum of the function occurs at $x = 4$, the right endpoint. Since $-\tfrac{7}{6}$ is smaller than $\tfrac{3}{2}$, the minimum of the function is at $x = 1$, the relative minimum. Figure 7–29 shows the various points.

EXERCISES

In problems 1 through 10, find the maximum and minimum of the given function on the interval indicated.

1. $f(x) = x^2 - 2x + 5, \qquad -3 \le x \le 4$
2. $f(x) = -3x^2 + 2x - 1, \qquad 0 \le x \le 7$
3. $f(x) = x^3 + 2x - 4, \qquad -1 \le x \le 2$
4. $f(x) = -x^3 + 5x^2 - 6x, \qquad 0 \le x \le 4$
5. $f(x) = x^4 - 2x^2 + 1, \qquad -3 \le x \le 0$
6. $f(x) = x^4 - 2x^2 + 1, \qquad -2 \le x \le 1$
7. $f(x) = x^4 - 2x^2 + 1, \qquad 0 \le x \le 5$
8. $f(x) = x^4 - 2x^2 + 1, \qquad -5 \le x \le 5$

9. $f(x) = \dfrac{x}{x+1}$, $-\frac{1}{2} \leq x \leq 1$ 10. $f(x) = \dfrac{x+3}{x-2}$, $-3 \leq x \leq 1$

11. Show by an example that a function must be continuous in order for the Rule given in this section to work.

In the following problems, find the maxima and minima of the functions in the interval indicated, or show that there are none.

12. $f(x) = x^2$, $-2 \leq x < 1$

13. $f(x) = x^3 - 2x^2 + x - 1$, $-3 < x < 3$

14. $f(x) = \dfrac{x-1}{x+1}$, $-2 \leq x \leq 2$

15. $f(x) = \dfrac{x^2}{x-2}$, $1 \leq x \leq 3$

16. $f(x) = \dfrac{x^2+1}{x+2}$, $-2 < x \leq 0$

6. APPLICATIONS OF MAXIMA AND MINIMA

Until now we have encountered functions in the form of polynomials, rational functions, and so on. Once we knew these functions, we set out to find the various relative maxima and minima, maxima at endpoints, and such other properties as concavity and points of inflection.

Now we shall complicate matters by treating problems in which we must discover the function itself before we can discuss its properties. Having found the function, we then use the methods described in the previous sections of this chapter to determine the function's characteristics. In order to be equal to the task, the student should memorize the formulas for areas and volumes of simple geometric shapes, as listed below. In many of the problems these turn out to be likely candidates for functions.

(i)   Circle of radius r. Circumference $= 2\pi r$. Area $= \pi r^2$.
(ii) Circular sector. Area $= \frac{1}{2}r^2\alpha$, α being the central angle, measured in radians.
(iii) Trapezoid of height h and bases b and B. Area $= \frac{1}{2}h(b + B)$.
(iv) Right circular cylinder of height h, radius of base r. Volume $= \pi r^2 h$. Lateral surface $= 2\pi rh$.
(v)   Right circular cone of height h, radius of base r. Volume $= \frac{1}{3}\pi r^2 h$. Lateral surface $= \pi rL$, where $L = \sqrt{r^2 + h^2}$.
(vi) Sphere of radius r. Volume $= \frac{4}{3}\pi r^3$. Surface area $= 4\pi r^2$.

If a manufacturer wants to make a tin can at the lowest possible cost, he faces the problem of finding a *minimum*. Making the strongest possible bridge of a certain size, type and span presents a problem of finding a *maximum*. Whenever we use words such as largest, most, least, smallest, best, etc., we can easily translate them into mathematical language in terms of maxima and minima. If we have a specific formula for the function in question (a situation which is very often impossible in actual practice), then we may be able to use the methods of the calculus to find the required maximum or minimum.

We shall start by giving several examples of the operating technique and then outline the procedure by giving a set of rules consisting of five steps.

———

EXAMPLE 1.   A man has a stone wall alongside a field. He has 1200 ft of fencing material and he wishes to make a rectangular pen, using the wall as one side. What should the dimensions of the pen be in order to enclose the largest possible area?

Solution. Here we see that the problem is to find the largest area; clearly this is a maximum problem. If we can find the area as a function of something or other and then differentiate it, we may be able to find the maximum of this function and so get the answer. Let us then draw a figure (Fig. 7–30), and call the area of the pen by some letter, say A. The length and width of the pen are both unknown. However, if x is the width, then the length must be $1200 - 2x$, since there are 1200 ft of fencing to be used. Now we can get an expression for the area, namely, length times width or

$$A = A(x) = x(1200 - 2x) = 1200x - 2x^2.$$

We note that x must lie between 0 and 600.

The derivative gives us

$$A'(x) = 1200 - 4x,$$

and this vanishes when $x = 300$.

The Second Derivative Test tells us that

$$A'' = -4,$$

and so this must be a relative maximum. In fact, it is *the* maximum, since $A(x)$ is a quadratic function which is concave downward everywhere. In fact, $A = 0$ when $x = 0$ and $x = 600$, so the endpoints give a minimum. We conclude that the width of the pen must be 300 ft and the length $1200 - 600 = 600$ ft.

EXAMPLE 2.   A rectangular box with an open top is to be made in the following way. A piece of tin 10 in. by 16 in. has a small square cut from each corner (shaded portion in Fig. 7–31) and then the edges (dotted lines) are folded vertically. What should be the size of the squares cut out if the box is to have as large a volume as possible?

Solution. We see that if we cut out exceptionally small squares the box will have practically no height at all and so will have a small volume. Similarly, if the squares are

FIGURE 7–30

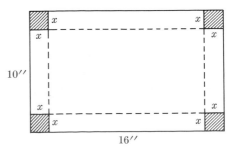

FIGURE 7–31

too large the base of the box will be tiny and again the volume will be small. We seek a formula for the volume. We let x be the edge of one of the squares cut out. Then

$$16 - 2x \text{ will be the length of the base of the box,}$$
$$10 - 2x \text{ will be the width of the base of the box,}$$

and

$$x \text{ will be the height of the box.}$$

The volume, of course, is length times width times height.
Therefore, calling the volume V, we have

$$V = V(x) = (16 - 2x)(10 - 2x)x, \quad \text{and} \quad V(x) = 4(40x - 13x^2 + x^3),$$

which gives volume as a function of x. Now we must note that there are restrictions on x. First of all, x must be positive in order to make any sense at all. Secondly, x must be less than 5. For, once it gets to 5, the width of the base is zero and we have no box at all. We write

$$0 < x < 5.$$

With this in mind we calculate the derivative:

$$V'(x) = 4(40 - 26x + 3x^2),$$

and by solving

$$40 - 26x + 3x^2 = 0,$$

we obtain

$$x = 2, 6\tfrac{2}{3}.$$

But $6\tfrac{2}{3}$ is outside the interval of interest and we reject it. We note that

$$V''(x) = (-26 + 6x) \quad \text{and} \quad V''(2) < 0,$$

which makes $x = 2$ a relative maximum. The endpoints of the interval $[0, 5]$ both give zero volume. Therefore $x = 2$ in. is the true maximum, and this is the answer. The volume of the box is 144 in^3.

EXAMPLE 3. The sum of one number and three times a second number is 60. Among the possible numbers which satisfy this condition, find the pair whose product is as large as possible.

Solution. We start by letting x be one of the numbers and y the other. We want to find the maximum of the product, which we shall call P. So we write

$$P = xy.$$

We have expressed P in terms not of one variable but of two. We can correct this diffi-culty by recalling that the first sentence of the problem asserts that

$$x + 3y = 60.$$

We can eliminate either x or y; if we eliminate y, we obtain

$$P = x\tfrac{1}{3}(60 - x) = 20x - \tfrac{1}{3}x^2.$$

Since P is a function of x, we can differentiate. We write

$$P' = P'(x) = 20 - \tfrac{2}{3}x.$$

Setting this equal to zero, we find that $x = 30$ and $y = 10$. It is easy to verify that this value of x gives the maximum value to P.

Using these three examples as a guide we now list the steps the student should take in attacking this type of problem in maxima and minima.

Step 1. Draw a figure when appropriate.

Step 2. Assign a letter to each of the quantities mentioned in the problem.

Step 3. Select the quantity which is to be made a maximum or minimum and express it as a function of the other quantities.

Step 4. Use the information in the problem to eliminate all quantities but one so as to have a function of one variable. Determine the possible domain of values of this variable.

Step 5. Use the methods of Sections 4 and 5 to get the maximum or minimum.

With this five-step procedure in mind, we now study more examples.

EXAMPLE 4. Find the dimensions of the right circular cylinder of maximum volume which can be inscribed in a sphere of radius 12.

Solution. When a cylinder is inscribed in a sphere it is necessary that the upper and lower bases of the cylinder have their bounding circles on the surface of the sphere. The axis of the cylinder is along a diameter of the sphere. We first draw a cross section of the inscribed cylinder, as in Fig. 7–32 (Step 1). The cylinder might be short and fat or tall and thin. We label the radius of the base r and the height of the cylinder h; the volume is denoted by V (Step 2). Then (Step 3),

$$V = \pi r^2 h.$$

We have now expressed the volume V in terms of two quantities, so we must eliminate one (Step 4). Referring to the figure, we use the Pythagorean Theorem to get

$$r^2 + \frac{h^2}{4} = 144.$$

This means that $h = 2\sqrt{144 - r^2}$, and

$$V = 2\pi r^2 \sqrt{144 - r^2}, \qquad 0 < r < 12.$$

By differentiating (Step 5), we obtain

$$V'(r) = 4\pi r\sqrt{144 - r^2} + 2\pi r^2 \cdot \tfrac{1}{2}(144 - r^2)^{-1/2}(-2r)$$

$$= 4\pi r\sqrt{144 - r^2} - \frac{2\pi r^3}{\sqrt{144 - r^2}}$$

$$= \frac{2\pi r[288 - 2r^2 - r^2]}{\sqrt{144 - r^2}}.$$

FIGURE 7–32

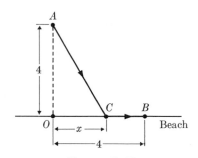

FIGURE 7–33

Setting this equal to zero, we find that

$$r = 0 \quad \text{or} \quad r = \pm 4\sqrt{6}.$$

We reject $r = 0$ and the negative value of r. Since the Second Derivative Test is rather messy, we reason as follows: when $r = 0$ and $r = 12$, we get $V = 0$. The volume is positive for r in this range. Therefore the critical value $r = 4\sqrt{6}$ must give the maximum. From the relation between r and h we find that $h = 8\sqrt{3}$.

EXAMPLE 5. A lighthouse is at point A, 4 mi offshore from the nearest point O of a straight beach; a store is at point B, 4 mi down the beach from O. If the lighthouse keeper can row 4 mi/hr and walk 5 mi/hr, how should he proceed in order to get from the lighthouse to the store in the least possible time?

Solution. Clearly he will row to some point on the beach between O (the nearest point) and the store at B and then walk the rest of the way. We draw a figure such as Fig. 7–33 (Step 1), where C is the spot on the beach where he lands and x is the distance from O to C. We denote by T the time of the trip from A to B (Step 2); T is the quantity we wish to make a minimum. To get a formula for T, we use the fact that rate times time equals distance. We then have

$$T = \text{time of trip along } AC + \text{time of trip along } CB$$
$$= \frac{\text{distance } AC}{4} + \frac{\text{distance } CB}{5}.$$

To express this in terms of one variable is not hard, since

$$CB = 4 - x,$$

and, using right triangle AOC,

$$AC = \sqrt{16 + x^2}.$$

Therefore (Step 3),

$$T(x) = \tfrac{1}{4}\sqrt{16 + x^2} + \tfrac{1}{5}(4 - x).$$

The only part of Step 4 we need is the determination of the domain of x. Since C is between O and B we have the restriction

$$0 \le x \le 4.$$

Taking the derivative (Step 5), we obtain

$$T'(x) = \tfrac{1}{8}(16 + x^2)^{-1/2}(2x) - \tfrac{1}{5}$$

and, setting this equal to zero, we find that

$$\frac{x}{4\sqrt{16 + x^2}} = \frac{1}{5} \quad \text{or} \quad x = \pm \frac{16}{3}.$$

But these are outside the interval. The conclusion is that there are no relative maxima or minima in the interval $0 \le x \le 4$. Therefore the minimum must occur at one of the endpoints. We have

$$T(0) = \tfrac{9}{5} \quad \text{and} \quad T(4) = \sqrt{2}.$$

Since $\sqrt{2} < \tfrac{9}{5}$, the fastest method for the lighthouse keeper is to row directly to the store B and do no walking.

EXERCISES

1. A rectangle has a perimeter of 120 ft. What length and width yield the maximum area? What is the result when the perimeter is L units?

2. Find the dimensions of the rectangle of maximum area that can be inscribed in a circle of radius 6. What is the result for a circle of radius R?

3. Find the dimensions of the right circular cylinder of maximum volume which can be inscribed in a sphere of radius R.

4. A horizontal gutter is to be made from a long piece of sheet iron 8 in. wide by turning up equal widths along the edges into vertical position. How many inches should be turned up at each side to yield the maximum carrying capacity?

5. The sum of twice one number and five times a second number is to be 70. What numbers should be selected so that the product of the numbers is as large as possible?

6. The difference between two numbers is 20. Select the numbers so that the product is as small as possible.

7. A box is to be made from a piece of sheet metal 12 in. square by cutting equal small squares from each corner and turning up the edges. Find the dimensions of the box of largest volume which can be made in this way.

8. A box with a square base is to have an open top. The area of the material in the box is to be 100 in². What should the dimensions be in order to make the volume as large as possible? What is the result for an area of S square inches?

9. A Norman window is in the shape of a rectangle surmounted by a semicircle. Find the dimensions when the perimeter is 12 ft and the area is as large as possible.

10. Find the radius and central angle (in radians) of the circular sector of maximum area having a perimeter of 16 in.

11. The top and bottom margins of a page are each $1\tfrac{1}{2}$ in. and the side margins are each 1 in. If the area of the printed material per page is fixed at 30 in², what are the dimensions of the page of least area?

12. At midnight, ship B was 90 mi due south of ship A. Ship A sailed east at 15 mi/hr and ship B sailed north at 20 mi/hr. At what time were they closest together?

13. Find the coordinates of the point or points on the curve $y = 2x^2$ which are closest to the point $(9, 0)$.

14. Find the coordinates of the point or points on the curve $x^2 - y^2 = 16$ which are nearest to the point $(0, 6)$.

15. Find the coordinates of the point or points on the curve $y^2 = x + 1$ which are nearest to the origin.

16. Find the coordinates of the point or points on the curve $y^2 = \frac{5}{2}(x + 1)$ which are nearest to the origin.

17. (a) A right triangle has hypotenuse of length 13 and one leg of length 5. Find the dimensions of the rectangle of largest area which has one side along the hypotenuse and the ends of the opposite side on the legs of this triangle. (b) What is the result for a hypotenuse of length H with an altitude to it of length h?

18. A trough is to be made from a long strip of sheet metal 12 in. wide by turning up strips 4 in. wide on each side so that they make the same angle with the bottom of the trough (trapezoidal cross section). Find the width across the top such that the trough will have maximum carrying capacity.

19. The sum of three positive numbers is 30. The first plus twice the second plus three times the third add up to 60. Select the numbers so that the product of all three is as large as possible.

20. The sum of three positive numbers is 40. The first plus three times the second plus four times the third add up to 80. Select the numbers so that the product of all three is as large as possible.

21. Suppose that in Example 5 of this section the lighthouse is 3 mi offshore, the lighthouse keeper can row only 3 mi/hr and walk 4 mi/hr, and the store is 5 mi down the beach. How far down the beach from O should he land?

22. Show that the value $x = \frac{16}{3}$ found in Example 5 yields the minimum of the function $T(x)$. Why does this value not yield the path requiring the shortest time?

23. Find the point on the x-axis the sum of whose distances from the points $(2, 0)$ and $(0, 3)$ is a minimum.

7. THE USE OF AUXILIARY VARIABLES

In outlining the procedure used in solving problems of maxima and minima, as given on page 174 of Section 6, we pointed out that the fourth step involved eliminating all the variables except one. However, there are some problems in which this step is difficult and occasionally not even possible. In this section an alternate method will be given in which the first three steps remain the same while Steps 4 and 5 are replaced by another process. We start with an example and then state the precise rule.

———————

EXAMPLE 1. Suppose that a closed right circular cylinder (i.e., top and bottom are included) has a surface area of 100 in². What should the radius and altitude be in order to provide the largest possible volume?

FIGURE 7–34

Solution. We draw Fig. 7–34, which shows a cylinder with radius of base r, altitude h, and volume V (Steps 1 and 2). The formula for the volume (Step 3) is

$$V = \pi r^2 h.$$

Normally, we would now come to Step 4, which involves employing the facts of the problem to eliminate r or h and so express V as a function of one variable. The lateral surface area of the cylinder is $2\pi rh$ and the top and bottom contribute $2\pi r^2$. Therefore,

$$2\pi rh + 2\pi r^2 = 100.$$

We could solve this for h in terms of r, substitute in the formula for V, and get V as a function of r alone. Instead we simply say to ourselves that V is a function of r and h is a function of r, and we take all derivatives *implicitly*. This means that

$$V' = V'(r) = 2\pi rh + \pi r^2 h'(r)$$

(derivative of a product). The derivative of the equation for surface area is

$$2\pi h + 2\pi rh'(r) + 4\pi r = 0,$$

or

$$h + rh'(r) + 2r = 0, \qquad h' = -2 - \frac{h}{r}.$$

Substituting this value for $h'(r)$ in the formula for $V'(r)$, we get

$$V' = 2\pi rh + \pi r^2 \left(-2 - \frac{h}{r}\right),$$

and setting this equal to zero yields

$$\pi rh - 2\pi r^2 = 0 \qquad \text{and} \qquad r = 0 \quad \text{or} \quad h = 2r.$$

The value $r = 0$ gives zero volume. The value $h = 2r$, when substituted in the formula for the area, gives

$$4\pi r^2 + 2\pi r^2 = 100, \qquad r^2 = \frac{50}{3\pi}.$$

The dimensions are $r = \sqrt{50/3\pi}$, $h = 2\sqrt{50/3\pi}$. It is easily verified that this is a relative maximum. Since r can never exceed $\sqrt{50/\pi}$ without h becoming negative, the relative maximum is a true maximum.

The process illustrated by the example above may be described in the following way:

Step 4'. After the quantity to be maximized (call it A) is expressed as a function of several variables, one variable is singled out. All other variables are taken to be functions of this one variable.

Step 5'. Derivatives are taken implicitly and these are substituted in the expression for A'. Then the methods of Sections 4 and 5 are used to find maxima and minima.

We give two more examples of this method.

EXAMPLE 2. A right circular cone has a volume of 120 in³. What shape should it be in order to have the smallest lateral surface area?

Solution. Figure 7–35 shows a cone with radius of base r, altitude h, and slant height L. We denote the volume by V and the lateral surface area by S (Steps 1 and 2). Then (Step 3)

$$S = \pi r L,$$

while

$$\tfrac{1}{3}\pi r^2 h = 120.$$

Further, we note from the figure the relation

$$r^2 + h^2 = L^2.$$

FIGURE 7–35

We regard everything as a function of r (Step 4'). That is, $S = S(r)$, $h = h(r)$, and $L = L(r)$. Taking derivatives (Step 5'), we get

$$S' = \pi r L' + \pi L,$$

and

$$\tfrac{1}{3}\pi r^2 h' + \tfrac{2}{3}\pi r h = 0, \qquad 2r + 2hh' = 2LL'.$$

We wish to set S' equal to zero, but first we substitute for L' from the last equation. We solve for h' and L', obtaining

$$h' = -\frac{2}{r}\,h \qquad \text{and} \qquad L' = \frac{r + hh'}{L} = \frac{r^2 - 2h^2}{rL}.$$

This yields

$$S' = \pi r\left(\frac{r^2 - 2h^2}{rL}\right) + \pi L = 0,$$

and

$$\frac{r^2 - 2h^2}{L} + L = 0 \qquad \text{or} \qquad r^2 - 2h^2 + L^2 = 0.$$

Since $L^2 = r^2 + h^2$, we arrive at the relation

$$h = \pm r\sqrt{2},$$

and we promptly reject the negative value. From the geometry of the problem we deduce that the positive value must give the minimum area.* Since the volume is 120 in³, we can now solve for r to get

$$\tfrac{1}{3}\pi r^3\sqrt{2} = 120, \qquad r = \left(\frac{360}{2^{1/2}\pi}\right)^{1/3}.$$

The altitude h is

$$\sqrt{2}\left(\frac{360}{2^{1/2}\pi}\right)^{1/3} = \left(\frac{720}{\pi}\right)^{1/3}.$$

The slant height L is

$$L = \sqrt{\left(\frac{360}{\sqrt{2}\,\pi}\right)^{2/3} + \left(\frac{720}{\pi}\right)^{2/3}}.$$

EXAMPLE 3. Two vertical poles 15 and 20 ft high are spaced 21 ft apart. The top of each pole is to be joined by a guy wire to a stake in the ground; the stake is located on a direct line between the poles. Where should the stake be placed in order to use the least amount of wire?

Solution. Figure 7–36 describes the setup, and we have already labeled all the possible variables. We denote by L the total length of wire (Steps 1 and 2). We wish to minimize L. We have the formulas (Step 3)

$$L = z + w, \qquad x + y = 21, \qquad x^2 + 225 = z^2, \qquad y^2 + 400 = w^2.$$

Now we think of L as a function of one of the variables; it doesn't matter much which one we choose. Let it be x (Step 4′). Then $L = L(x)$, $z = z(x)$, $w = w(x)$, and $y = y(x)$. We differentiate (Step 5′):

$$L' = z' + w',$$

and

$$1 + y' = 0, \qquad 2x = 2zz', \qquad 2yy' = 2ww'.$$

Substituting these in the formula for L' yields

$$L' = \frac{x}{z} - \frac{y}{w} = 0.$$

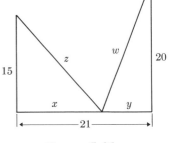

FIGURE 7–36

Since $y = 21 - x$, $z = \sqrt{x^2 + 225}$, and $w = \sqrt{y^2 + 400}$, we obtain

---

* To prove that the minimum occurs for the value of r which makes S' zero, we show that S' is negative for values less than this value of r and positive for values greater than this value. We find that

$$S' = \frac{\pi(r^2 - 2h^2)}{L} + \pi L = \frac{\pi(2r^2 - h^2)}{\sqrt{r^2 + h^2}}.$$

Since h decreases as r increases, we have $S' < 0$ for r less than the critical value and $S' > 0$ for r larger than the critical value.

$$\frac{x}{21-x} = \frac{\sqrt{x^2+225}}{\sqrt{y^2+400}} \quad \text{or} \quad \frac{x^2}{(21-x)^2} = \frac{x^2+225}{(21-x)^2+400}.$$

This yields

$$x = 9.$$

Since the interval of values for x is $[0, 21]$ we check the endpoints of this interval:

$$L(0) = 44, \quad L(21) = 20 + \sqrt{666} = 45.80^+,$$

while

$$L(9) = 7\sqrt{34} = 40.82.$$

The minimum is at $x = 9$.

EXERCISES

Employ the methods of either Section 6 or Section 7 to work the following problems.

1. (a) Find the dimensions of the right circular cylinder of maximum volume which can be inscribed in a right circular cone of altitude 10 and radius 12. (b) What is the result for a cone of altitude H and radius R?

2. Work Example 1 for a given surface area S.

3. Work Example 2 for a given volume V.

4. Find the dimensions of the rectangle of maximum area which can be inscribed in the ellipse $(x^2/16) + (y^2/9) = 1$.

5. Find the dimensions of the rectangle of maximum area which can be inscribed in the ellipse $(x^2/a^2) + (y^2/b^2) = 1$.

6. The stiffness of a given length of beam is proportional to the product of the width and the cube of the depth. Find the shape of the stiffest beam which can be cut from a cylindrical log (of the given length) with cross-sectional diameter of 4 ft.

7. (a) A manufacturer makes aluminum cups of a given volume (16 in^3) in the form of right circular cylinders open at the top. Find the dimensions which use the least material. (b) What is the result for a given volume V?

8. In problem 7, suppose that the material for the bottom is $1\frac{1}{2}$ times as expensive as the material for the sides. Find the dimensions which give the lowest cost.

9. Find the shortest segment with ends on the positive x- and y-axes which passes through the point $(1, 8)$.

10. One number plus the square of another number totals 50. Select the numbers so that their product is as large as possible.

11. The product of two numbers is 16. Determine them so that the square of one plus the cube of the other is as small as possible.

12. Find the dimensions of the cylinder of greatest lateral area which can be inscribed in a sphere of given radius R.

13. A piece of wire of length L is cut into two parts, one of which is bent into the shape of a square and the other into the shape of a circle. (a) How should the

wire be cut so that the sum of the enclosed areas is a minimum? (b) How should it be cut to get the maximum enclosed areas?

14. A piece of wire of length L is cut into two parts, one of which is bent into the shape of an equilateral triangle and the other into the shape of a circle. How should the wire be cut so that the sum of the enclosed areas is (a) a minimum? (b) a maximum?

15. Find the dimensions of the right circular cone of maximum volume which can be inscribed in a sphere of given radius R.

16. Find the dimensions of the right circular cone of minimum volume which can be circumscribed about a sphere of radius 12. Show that this minimum volume is twice that of the sphere. (*Hint:* Obtain a relation between r, the radius of the base of the cone and h, its altitude. Do not introduce the slant height as a variable.)

17. A fence $13\frac{1}{2}$ ft high is 4 ft from the side wall of a house. What is the length of the shortest ladder, one end of which will rest on the level ground outside the fence and the other on the side wall of the house?

18. A silo is to be built in the form of a right circular cylinder surmounted by a hemisphere. If the cost of the material per square foot is the same for floor, walls, and top, find the most economical proportions for a given capacity V.

19. Work problem 18, given that the floor costs twice as much per square foot as the sides and the hemispherical top costs three times as much per square foot as the sides.

20. A tank is to have a given volume V and is to be made in the form of a right circular cylinder with hemispheres attached at each end. The material for the ends costs twice as much per square foot as that for the sides. Find the most economical proportions.

21. Find the length of the longest rod which can be carried horizontally around a corner from a corridor 8 ft wide into one 4 ft wide. (*Hint:* Observe that this length is the minimum value of certain lengths.)

22. Suppose the velocity of light is V_1 in air and V_2 in water. A ray of light traveling from a point P_1 above the surface of the liquid to a point P_2 below the surface will travel by the path which requires the least time. Show that the ray will cross the surface at the point Q in the vertical plane through P_1 and P_2 so placed that

$$\frac{\sin \theta_1}{V_1} = \frac{\sin \theta_2}{V_2}$$

where θ_1 and θ_2 are the angles shown in Fig. 7–37.

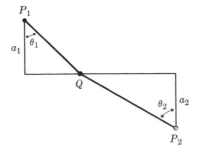

FIGURE 7–37

8. NUMERICAL TECHNIQUES FOR MAXIMA AND MINIMA

The methods for finding the maxima and minima of functions in an interval and the various applications given in Sections 5, 6, and 7 are valuable both as theoretical tools and as a means of helping the student to gain insight into the powerful methods of the calculus. However, for practical problems in determining the maximum and minimum of functions, such methods are fairly worthless and seldom used.

Many functions that appear in practice are so complicated that even calculating the derivative may be a formidable problem. Assuming that this can be done, we would still have the difficult task of finding the roots of the equation obtained by setting this derivative equal to zero. For example, the function

$$f(x) = x^6 - 3x^5 - 2x^4 + x^3 - x^2 + 4x + 1$$

has some relative maxima and minima in the interval $0 \le x \le 3$. However, solving the equation

$$f'(x) = 6x^5 - 15x^4 - 8x^3 + 3x^2 - 2x + 4 = 0$$

is very difficult.

Problems in elementary texts are usually carefully arranged so that the answers come out fairly neatly without too much complicated arithmetic. Such an arrangement is understandable, for the author wishes the reader to concentrate on the idea of the problem and not become distracted by lengthy and routine computations. However, problems that arise in industry and in technical applications frequently have numbers which are themselves the results of experiments. The equations and coefficients are messy, and the results are never expected to "come out even."

We shall now describe a reasonable procedure for finding the maximum or minimum of a function in an interval, one which uses the aid of an electronic computer.

Suppose that the interval is $0 \le x \le 5$ and the function $y = f(x)$ is the quotient of two polynomials, i.e., a rational function. Further, suppose that we wish to find the maximum value of $f(x)$ in this interval. As a first step we divide the interval [0, 5] into 50 equal parts, 0, 0.1, 0.2, 0.3, ..., 4.8, 4.9, 5. For each one of these values we compute $f(x)$. That is, we calculate $f(0)$, $f(0.1)$, $f(0.2)$, ..., $f(4.8)$, $f(4.9)$, $f(5)$. Since $f(x)$ is a rational function, computing the value at any point simply involves additions, subtractions, multiplications, and divisions. Assume that 100 such arithmetical operations are required to find f at any point. The whole process just described then requires (51)(100) arithmetical computations. A modern computer can do this in a few seconds at most. We have only to look at the answers and state that the largest figure is the maximum value of the function in the interval. If we like, we can arrange to have the machine tell us which is the largest and where it occurs. The answer may not be exact, but it will be pretty close. Also, if the function oscillates wildly in small intervals, we may be far off. If we are suspicious, we may divide the interval [0, 5] into 1000 parts and repeat the process. It would take a few more seconds of the machine's time, but the result would be more accurate than the former one. However, a law of diminishing returns sets in, since for many problems the equations and data with which we start have only a limited degree of accuracy, and if we carry our computations too far the result gains a spurious precision unwarranted by the original problem.

9. THE DIFFERENTIAL.   APPROXIMATION

A symbolic expression of the form

$$w = F(u, v),$$

where u and v are independent variables, means that the dependent variable w is a function of *both* the independent variables. Simple examples of such functions are

$$w = u^2 + 2v^2 + 3v^4, \qquad w = \frac{2\sqrt{u}}{3v + 1}, \qquad w = \frac{2u^2 - 3v^2}{2uv}.$$

We see that u and v together have a set of values which forms the *domain* of the independent variables. All possible values of w make up the *range* of the function. We use the same letters, f, ϕ, g, H, etc., to represent functions of two variables that we use for functions of one variable, a practice which at times may lead to some confusion. For example, if we have z as a function G of x and y, we write $z = G(x, y)$ instead of simply G, when there is a question about the number of independent variables.

A precise definition for a function of two variables follows the same pattern as the definition of a function of a single variable.

DEFINITION. Consider a collection of ordered pairs (A, w), where the elements A are themselves ordered pairs of real numbers and the elements w are real numbers. If no two members of the collection have the same item A as a first element—i.e., if it can never happen that there are two members (A_1, w_1) and (A_1, w_2) with $w_1 \neq w_2$—then we call this collection a *function of two variables*. The totality of possible ordered pairs A is called the *domain* of the function. The totality of possible values for w is called the *range* of the function.

We are now ready to define a quantity called the differential. Suppose that f is a function of x and we write $y = f(x)$. If h is an independent variable which can have any value (positive, zero, or negative), we define the *differential of y* as that function of the two variables x and h given by the equation

$$dy = f'(x) \cdot h.$$

The symbol dy is a new one and does not mean d times y. We could have used a single letter as the dependent variable, but traditionally the notation dy is used. The independent variables are x and h, and once a value is assigned to these quantities, the function is determined. That is, we could write $dy = F(x, h)$, with F being the particular function $f'(x) \cdot h$.

It is customary to use the symbol dx instead of the letter h in the formula for a differential, and so we write

$$dy = f'(x)\, dx.$$

There is some danger of confusion, since dx is the symbol for a differential. A mathematical justification for the use of dx instead of h will be given in the following section, but we may now argue intuitively in the following way. The function $f(x) = x$ has derivative 1. In this case, we get

$$dx = 1 \cdot h,$$

and h is a differential when the equation is $y = x$. Note that dx is an independent variable with values assigned as we wish; it is simply h. However, dy is a dependent variable with values determined by x and dx. Still another remark on customary notation is in order: the symbol dy is sometimes replaced by df, which means the same thing, and we can also write

$$df = f'(x) \cdot h \qquad \text{or} \qquad df = f'(x)\, dx.$$

EXAMPLE 1.　Given that $y = x^2(1 - x^2)^{1/2}$, find dy. Obtain the value of dy when $x = \frac{1}{2}$ and $dx = 3$.

Solution. By differentiation,

$$f'(x) = 2x(1 - x^2)^{1/2} - x^3(1 - x^2)^{-1/2}$$

Therefore

$$dy = x(1 - x^2)^{-1/2}[2(1 - x^2) - x^2]\, dx$$

$$= \frac{x(2 - 3x^2)}{(1 - x^2)^{1/2}}\, dx.$$

Substituting $x = \frac{1}{2}$ and $dx = 3$ in this expression, we obtain $dy = \frac{5}{4}\sqrt{3}$.

Earlier (in Chapter 6), we introduced the symbol Δf by defining

$$\Delta f = f(x + h) - f(x).$$

We did not say so at the time, but the reader can now see that Δf is a function of the two variables x and h. It will help in our understanding to compare the functions df and Δf. We can do this geometrically, as shown in Fig. 7–38, where P represents a point on the graph of $y = f(x)$. If h has any value, then the point $(x + h, f(x + h))$ is on the graph and is shown by Q. We see that

$$\Delta f = \text{height } SQ.$$

The tangent at P intersects the line QS at R, and we know that RS/SP is the slope of this line, or simply $f'(x)$. Since $PS = h$, we have

$$df = \text{height } SR.$$

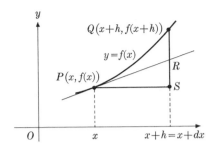

FIGURE 7–38

This tells us that the height RQ is just the difference between Δf and df. That is,

$$\Delta f - df = \text{height } RQ.$$

Also, we see from the graph that as h tends to zero (thus implying that the point Q slides along the curve to P), the difference between Δf and df tends to zero. In fact, we have

$$\lim_{h \to 0} \frac{\Delta f - df}{h} = 0.$$

The proof of this statement is easy. We know from the definition of derivative that

$$\frac{\Delta f}{h} \to f'(x) \qquad \text{as} \qquad h \to 0.$$

On the other hand, df/h is the derivative $f'(x)$. Therefore

$$\lim_{h \to 0} \frac{\Delta f - df}{h} = \lim_{h \to 0} \frac{\Delta f}{h} - \lim_{h \to 0} \frac{df}{h} = f'(x) - f'(x) = 0.$$

If h is small, Δf and df must be close together. The function Δf measures the *change* in f as we go from one point to another. The differential df can be used as a good approximation for Δf if the points are near each other.

EXAMPLE 2. Given that $f(x) = 1/x$, compute df and Δf when $x = 1$ and h (or dx) is 0.1, 0.01, 0.001. Do this to four significant figures.

Solution. $f(1) = 1; f'(x) = -1/x^2$ and $f'(1) = -1$. For $h = 0.1$,

$$f(1.1) = 0.909091 \qquad \text{and} \qquad \Delta f = 0.909091 - 1 = -0.09091$$

On the other hand, $df = f'(1) \cdot h = -1 \cdot (0.1) = -0.10000$. In this way we obtain the table:

h	df	Δf
0.1	-0.10000	-0.0901
0.01	-0.010000	-0.009901
0.001	-0.0010000	-0.0009990

The point of this example — as the student can readily see if he has worked along with it — is that the quantities df require practically no computing, while finding Δf is quite a bit of work. Since the error made in using df instead of Δf is small, the saving in computation time may make it worthwhile.

EXAMPLE 3. Use the differential to compute $\sqrt[5]{33}$ approximately.

Solution. To work this problem we need an idea; it is simply that we know $\sqrt[5]{32}$ *exactly* and 33 is "close to" 32. The function we are talking about is

$$y = \sqrt[5]{x} = x^{1/5}.$$

If we think of $x = 32$ and $h = 1$ and call the function f, then $f(33)$ is what we want to find. We know that

$$\Delta f = f(33) - f(32),$$

while

$$df = f'(32) \cdot (1).$$

The derivative is

$$f'(x) = \tfrac{1}{5}x^{-4/5},$$

and

$$f'(32) = \tfrac{1}{5} \cdot \tfrac{1}{16} = \tfrac{1}{80}, \qquad df = \tfrac{1}{80}.$$

Using the fact that df is almost the same as Δf, we write

$$f(33) = f(32) + \Delta f \approx f(32) + df.$$

(The symbol $\approx$ means "nearly equal.") Therefore,

$$\sqrt[5]{33} = f(33) = 2 + \tfrac{1}{80} = 2.0125,$$

approximately. The actual error in this computation is less than $\tfrac{1}{6400}$.

A measurement of a length of pipe is made, and it is found that there is an error of $\tfrac{1}{2}$ in. Is this error large or small? If the length of the pipe is about 8 in. we would say that the error is pretty large. If the total length measured were $\tfrac{1}{2}$ mi, we would consider the error extremely small. The error is the difference between the planned length and the actual length.

If a quantity is being measured and the planned value is a but there is an error of an amount h, we define the *proportional error* as

$$\frac{h}{a}$$

and the *percentage error* as

$$\frac{h}{a} \cdot 100\%.$$

In the above example of the $\tfrac{1}{2}$-in. error, when $a = 8$ in. and $h = \tfrac{1}{2}$, the proportional error is $\tfrac{1}{16}$, and the percentage error is $\tfrac{1}{16} \cdot 100 = 6\tfrac{1}{4}\%$. If $a = \tfrac{1}{2}$ mi and

$h = \frac{1}{2}$ in., then the proportional error is 1/63,360 and the percentage error is 0.0015%—less than two-thousandths of one percent.

Suppose that f is a function of a variable x, which is being measured. This measurement is not precise (measurements never are), and there is an error h in measuring the value a. That is, the function f may have the value $f(a + h)$ instead of $f(a)$. The error in the function is $\Delta f = f(a + h) - f(a)$ and the *proportional error* in the function is simply

$$\frac{\Delta f}{f} = \frac{f(a + h) - f(a)}{f}.$$

However, in such computations, we conveniently use the *approximation* to the proportional error:

$$\frac{df}{f} = \frac{f'(a) \cdot h}{f(a)}.$$

The percentage error is then found by multiplying by 100.

EXAMPLE 4. The radius of a sphere is found by measurement to be 3 in., but there is a possible error of ±0.03 in. in the measurement. Find the error and percentage error in the value of the surface area of the sphere that might occur because of the error in the radius.

Solution. The surface area S is given by the formula $S = 4\pi r^2$, and for $r = 3$ the area is 36π in². The error is approximated by $dS = S'(r) dr = 8\pi r \, dr$. The quantity $dr = \pm 0.03$, and so the error is $dS = 8\pi(3)(\pm 0.03) = \pm 0.72\pi$ in². The proportional error is

$$\frac{dS}{S} = \frac{\pm 0.72\pi}{36\pi} = \pm 0.02,$$

and the percentage error is 2%.

EXERCISES

In problems 1 through 6, find dy in terms of x and dx.

1. $y = x^3 - 2x^2 + 3x$

2. $y = \dfrac{x + 2}{x^2 + 5}$

3. $y = (x^2 + 2)\sqrt{x^2 + 8}$

4. $y = \dfrac{(x - 3)^{1/2}}{x^2 + 2x - 6}$

5. $y = (x^2 + 1)^{1/2}(2x - 5)^{1/3}$

6. $y = (x - 3)^{1/2}(x^2 + 2x - 1)^{1/3}$

In problems 7 through 14, find df and Δf and evaluate them for the quantities given.

7. $f(x) = x^2 + x - 1$, $x = 1$, $h = 0.01$

8. $f(x) = x^2 - 2x - 3$, $x = -1$, $h = -0.02$

9. $f(x) = x^3 + 3x^2 - 6x - 3$, $x = 2$, $h = 0.01$

10. $f(x) = x^3 - 2x^2 + 3x + 4$, $x = -1$, $h = 0.02$

11. $f(x) = 1/x$, $x = 2$, $h = 0.05$
12. $f(x) = x^{1/2}$, $x = 1$, $h = -0.1$
13. $f(x) = x^{-1/2}$, $x = 1$, $h = 0.1$
14. $f(x) = \dfrac{x}{1 + x}$, $x = 0$, $h = 0.1$

In problems 15 through 22, calculate (approximately) the given quantity by means of the differential.

15. $\sqrt{65}$ 16. $\sqrt[3]{124}$ 17. $(0.98)^{-1}$ 18. $\sqrt[4]{80}$

19. $(31)^{1/5}$ 20. $(17)^{-1/4}$ 21. $\sqrt{0.0024}$ 22. $\sqrt{82} + \sqrt[4]{82}$

23. The diameter of a sphere is to be measured and its volume computed. The diameter is 9 in., with a possible error of ±0.05 in. What is the maximum possible percentage error in the volume?

24. The radius of a sphere is to be measured and its volume computed. If the diameter can be accurately measured to within 0.1%, what is the maximum percentage error in the determination of the volume?

25. A coat of paint of thickness t in. is applied evenly to the faces of a cube of edge a in. Use differentials to find approximately the number of cubic inches of paint used. Compare this with the exact amount used by computing volumes before and after painting.

26. Work problem 25 with the cube replaced by a sphere of radius R.

10. DIFFERENTIAL NOTATION

Suppose that y is a function of the variable x but that x in turn depends on some other variable, t. Symbolically we can write

$$y = f(x) \quad \text{and} \quad x = g(t).$$

Since for each value of t there is a value of y, y is really a function of t. An example of this situation is given by

$$y = x^2 \quad \text{and} \quad x = 1 + t^2.$$

By substitution we can write y as a function of t:

$$y = (1 + t^2)^2.$$

For the general case the substitution is written as

$$y = f[g(t)].$$

To get the derivative of y with respect to t we use the chain rule, which yields

$$f'[g(t)] \cdot g'(t).$$

We now come to differentials. Since y is a function of t, the differential of y can be found; it is

$$dy = (\text{derivative of } y \text{ with respect to } t) \cdot h$$
$$= f'[g(t)] \cdot g'(t) \cdot h$$

The variable x also depends on t, and so we can obtain the differential of x. It is

$$dx = g'(t) \cdot h.$$

Substituting this in the expression for dy, we have

$$dy = f'[g(t)] \, dx,$$

and, since $g(t) = x$, we can write

$$dy = f'(x) \, dx.$$

We have just proved the following theorem.

Theorem 9. *If* $y = f(x)$ *then, whether or not* x *is an independent variable, it is always true that*

$$dy = f'(x) \, dx.$$

We can also write

$$\frac{dy}{dx} = f'(x)$$

whenever $dx \neq 0$.

Theorem 9 is particularly useful, for it gives us another symbol for the derivative. From now on we shall use both $f'(x)$ and dy/dx as symbols for the derivative.

It may seem mysterious that while dy is a function of two variables and dx is a function of two variables, the derivative, dy/dx, is a function of only one variable. This is not an accident; the definition of differential was carefully planned so that this would always happen.

With the symbol for derivative, we may write the chain rule for differentiation in the following way. Suppose that

$$y = f(u) \quad \text{and} \quad u = g(x).$$

The derivative of y with respect to x may be written

$$\frac{dy}{dx} \quad \text{if } dx \neq 0,$$

while by the chain rule,

$$\frac{dy}{dx} = f'(u) \cdot g'(x).$$

Since

$$f'(u) = \frac{dy}{du} \, (du \neq 0) \quad \text{and} \quad g'(x) = \frac{du}{dx} \, (dx \neq 0),$$

we get

$$\frac{dy}{dx} = \frac{dy}{du} \cdot \frac{du}{dx} \quad \text{if } du \neq 0 \text{ and } dx \neq 0.$$

Differentials may be multiplied, divided (whenever different from zero), added, and subtracted. One differential divided by another may be thought of as a derivative. We can now write all the elementary rules for derivatives as differentials. Since they become derivative formulas merely by division by dx, there is really not much new in them.

If c is a constant, $dc = 0$ and $d(cu) = c\,du$. Also,

$$d(u + v) = du + dv,$$
$$d(u \cdot v) = u\,dv + v\,du,$$
$$d\left(\frac{u}{v}\right) = \frac{v\,du - u\,dv}{v^2},$$
$$d(u^n) = nu^{n-1}\,du.$$

EXAMPLE 1. Given that $y = (x^2 + 2x + 1)^3$ and $x = 3t^2 + 2t - 1$, find dy/dt.

Solution. Here we have

$$\frac{dy}{dt} = \frac{dy}{dx} \cdot \frac{dx}{dt}$$

and

$$\frac{dy}{dx} = 3(x^2 + 2x + 1)^2 (2x + 2).$$

$$\frac{dx}{dt} = 6t + 2.$$

Therefore

$$\frac{dy}{dt} = 6(x + 1)(x^2 + 2x + 1)^2 \cdot 2(3t + 1).$$

EXAMPLE 2. Given that $y = \sqrt{x^2 + 1}/(2x - 3)$, find dy.

Solution. One way would be to find the derivative and multiply by dx. But we may also use the formula for the differential of a quotient, and we do it here for practice:

$$dy = \frac{(2x - 3)\,d(\sqrt{x^2 + 1}) - \sqrt{x^2 + 1} \cdot d(2x - 3)}{(2x - 3)^2}$$

We see now that $d(\sqrt{x^2 + 1}) = \frac{1}{2}(x^2 + 1)^{-1/2} 2x\,dx$ and $d(2x - 3) = 2\,dx$. We obtain

$$dy = \frac{x(2x - 3)(x^2 + 1)^{-1/2}\,dx - 2\sqrt{x^2 + 1}\,dx}{(2x - 3)^2}.$$

We now multiply both the numerator and the denominator by $\sqrt{x^2 + 1}$ to get

$$dy = \frac{-3x - 2}{\sqrt{x^2 + 1}(2x - 3)^2}\,dx.$$

The method of differentials is particularly helpful in implicit differentiation. If we have a relation among some variables, we do not need to know in advance which is the dependent and which the independent variable. We simply take differentials. (This is valid because of Theorem 9.) An example will illustrate the idea.

EXAMPLE 3. Suppose that u and v are functions of a variable, say t, which satisfy the relation

$$u^2 + 2uv^2 + v^3 - 6 = 0.$$

Find dv/du.

Solution. Take differentials:

$$2u\,du + 2u \cdot 2v\,dv + 2v^2\,du + 3v^2\,dv = 0.$$

Divide through by du and solve:

$$\frac{dv}{du} = -\frac{2(u + v^2)}{4uv + 3v^2},$$

if $du \neq 0$ and if $4uv + 3v^2 \neq 0$.

If $y = f(x)$, there are now two symbols for the derivative: $f'(x)$ and dy/dx. These are the most prevalent symbols, commonly used in texts and papers on various related subjects. Another symbol, not quite so common but nevertheless used often, is $D_x f$. The only notation we learned for the *second derivative* is $f''(x)$. The expression d^2y/dx^2 (read: d second y by dx second) is a classical one for the second derivative. The numerator, d^2y, and the denominator, dx^2, *have absolutely no meaning by themselves.* (In elementary calculus there is no such thing as the differential of a differential.) We just use d^2y/dx^2 as an equivalent for $f''(x)$. Similarly, third, fourth, and fifth derivatives are written

$$\frac{d^3y}{dx^3}, \quad \frac{d^4y}{dx^4}, \quad \frac{d^5y}{dx^5},$$

and so on. In each case, the expression is to be thought of not as a fraction dividing two quantities but as an inseparable symbol representing the appropriate derivative.

EXERCISES

In problems 1 through 23, find the derivative dy/dx by the method of differentials.

1. $y = (x^2 + 2x - 6)^7$

2. $y = \sqrt{2 + 3x}$

3. $y = \dfrac{1}{(3 - 2x)^3}$

4. $y = \dfrac{x}{2x + 1}$

5. $y = x\sqrt{2x - 1}$

6. $y = x\sqrt[3]{3x - 2}$

7. $y = (x + 1)^2(2x - 1)^3$ 8. $y = (x + 2)^{2/3}(x - 1)^{1/3}$

9. $y = \dfrac{2x}{x^2 + 1}$ 10. $y = \dfrac{x}{\sqrt{x^2 + 1}}$

11. $y = \dfrac{x^{2/3}}{(x + 1)^{2/3}}$ 12. $y = \dfrac{\sqrt{x^2 + 1}}{x}$

13. $y = \sqrt{\dfrac{x + 1}{x - 1}}$ 14. $y = \dfrac{x}{\sqrt{x^2 + x + 1}}$

15. $y = \dfrac{x^{2/3}}{x^2 + 1}$ 16. $y = \sqrt{2x + 3}\,\sqrt[3]{3x - 4}$

17. $y = \dfrac{\sqrt{2x + 3}}{\sqrt[3]{3x - 4}}$ 18. $x^2 - 2xy + 2y^2 = 0$

19. $2x^2 + xy - y^2 + 2x - 3y + 5 = 0$

20. $x^3 + x^2y - 2y^3 = 0$ 21. $\sqrt{x} + \sqrt{y} = 2$

22. $x^{2/3} + y^{2/3} = a^{2/3}$ 23. $2x^3 - xy^2 - y^3 + 2x - y = 0$

24. Find dy/dt, given that $y = (x^2 + 2x + 5)^{3/4}$ and $x = \sqrt{t^2 - 2t + 1}$

25. Find dz/dr, given that $z = (2u + 1)/(u^2 + u)$ and $u = (r^2 + 5)^4$

26. Find ds/dt, given that $s = x^2 + 3x - 6$, $x = r^3 - 8r + 5$, $r = \sqrt{t^3 + 5}$

27. Find dz/ds, given that

$$z = \frac{y + 1}{y - 1}, \qquad y = \frac{x^3 - 8x + 1}{\sqrt{x + 1}}, \qquad x = s^3 - 8s + 5$$

28. Find dy/dt, given that $x^3 + 2xy - y^3 + 8 = 0$ and $x = t^3 - 2t + 1$

11. RELATED RATES

In Chapter 4, Section 5, we discussed motion along a straight line and developed the ideas of velocity and speed. We learned that if a particle moves in a straight line so that the distance traveled, s, depends on the time t, according to some law $s = f(t)$, the velocity is obtained by finding the derivative $f'(t)$. In our new notation we can write

$$f'(t) = \frac{ds}{dt}.$$

The velocity may be thought of as the *rate of change* of distance with respect to time. If there are several particles, each moving in a straight line according to some law, then we can talk about the rate of change of each of the particles. Suppose the motion of these particles is related in some way. (One may go up as the other goes down, as in a lever, for example.) Then we say that we have a problem in *related rates*.

We are not limited to particles moving in a straight line. If a tank is being filled with water, the level of the surface is rising with time. We talk about the rate of change of the depth of the water. If the depth is denoted by h, then dh/dt is the rate of change of the depth. Similarly, the volume V is increasing; dV/dt measures the rate of this increase. Any quantity which grows or diminishes with time is a possible candidate for a problem in related rates.

In the problems we shall consider, it is important to remember that *time is always the independent variable.* All other quantities which change are functions of the single variable t. The derivative with respect to t is called the *rate of change.* Some examples are given first, and then the general rules of procedure are mapped out.

EXAMPLE 1. One airplane flew over an airport at the rate of 300 mi/hr. Ten minutes later another airplane flew over the airport at 240 mi/hr. If the first airplane was flying west and the second flying south (both at the same altitude), determine the rate at which they were separating 20 minutes after the second plane flew over the airport.

Solution. We give two methods for solving this problem.

METHOD I. Draw a diagram, as shown in Fig. 7–39. Let s represent the distance between the airplanes and let t be the time in minutes measured from the moment when the second plane passed over O. (*When* we start measuring time is a matter of convenience only.) The problem asks us to find ds/dt when $t = 20$. The plane going south travels 4 mi/min, and so its distance from O at any time t is $4t$ miles. The plane going west travels 5 mi/min. It has traveled 50 mi beyond O by the time the airplane going south reaches O, so its distance from O at time t min is $50 + 5t$. Then (referring to the figure),

$$s = \sqrt{16t^2 + (50 + 5t)^2} = \sqrt{41t^2 + 500t + 2500};$$

$$\frac{ds}{dt} = \frac{1}{2}\frac{82t + 500}{\sqrt{41t^2 + 500t + 2500}} = \frac{41(20) + 250}{\sqrt{41(400) + 10{,}000 + 2500}}$$

$$= \frac{107}{\sqrt{164 + 100 + 25}} = \frac{107}{17} \text{ mi/min.}$$

METHOD II. Draw a diagram, as shown in Fig. 7–40. Let s be the distance between the airplanes at time t, let x be the distance the westbound airplane has traveled at time t, and let y be the distance the southbound airplane has traveled at time t. We know that $dx/dt = 5$ mi/min, $dy/dt = 4$ mi/min. We wish to find ds/dt when $t = 20$ min, measured from the time the second airplane passes over O. We have the relation

$$s^2 = x^2 + y^2.$$

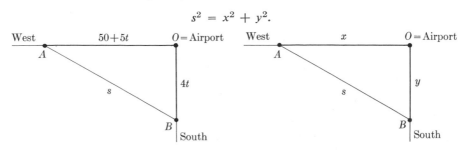

FIGURE 7–39   FIGURE 7–40

Take differentials:

$$2s\,ds = 2x\,dx + 2y\,dy.$$

Divide by dt:

$$s\frac{ds}{dt} = x\frac{dx}{dt} + y\frac{dy}{dt}.$$

When $t = 20$, then $y = 80$, $x = 150$, and $s = 170$, and substituting all these values we get

$$170 \cdot \frac{ds}{dt} = 150 \cdot 5 + 80 \cdot 4, \qquad \text{or} \qquad \frac{ds}{dt} = \frac{107}{17}\ \text{mi/min.}$$

In the first method, all quantities which change in the course of the problem are expressed in terms of the time t. The variable s is then differentiated with respect to t and the proper value of t substituted to give the answer. The part of this method which is difficult is the expression of the various distances in terms of t.

The second method starts with a simpler process. Every quantity which changes is denoted by a letter (x, y, and s in this example), and each of these represents a function of t. Some relation is found among the letters ($s^2 = x^2 + y^2$, as we saw), and differentials by implicit methods are used to get derivatives with respect to t. Then the numerical value for each quantity is substituted to obtain the answer. The difficult part of this method is the proper labeling of variables and the use of implicit methods.

EXAMPLE 2.   Water is flowing at the rate of 5 ft³/min into a tank (Fig. 7–41) in the form of a cone of altitude 20 ft and base radius 10 ft and with its vertex in the downward direction. How fast is the water level rising when the water is 8 ft deep?

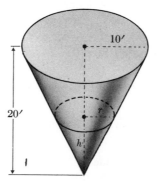

FIGURE 7–41

Solution. Let h be the depth, r the radius of the surface, and V the volume of the water at an arbitrary time t. We wish to find dh/dt. We know $dV/dt = 5$. The volume of water is given by

$$V = \tfrac{1}{3}\pi r^2 h,$$

where all quantities depend on t. By similar triangles,

$$\frac{r}{h} = \frac{10}{20} \qquad \text{or} \qquad r = \tfrac{1}{2}h,$$

and so

$$V = \tfrac{1}{3}\pi \frac{h^3}{4} = \tfrac{1}{12}\pi h^3.$$

We take differentials:

$$dV = \tfrac{1}{4}\pi h^2 \, dh,$$

and, dividing by dt:

$$\frac{dV}{dt} = \tfrac{1}{4}\pi h^2 \frac{dh}{dt}.$$

We want to find dh/dt when $h = 8$, and we obtain

$$\frac{dh}{dt} = \frac{5}{16\pi} \text{ ft/min.}$$

The major trap to avoid in this problem is the premature use of the fact that $h = 8$ at the instant we want to find dh/dt. The height h *changes* with time and must be denoted by a variable. If $h = 8$ is put in the diagram, it usually leads to disaster. *All* quantities which change with time must be denoted by letters.

The rules of procedure are outlined in the following steps. The numerals I and II indicate the steps to be used for Method I and Method II, respectively.

Step 1. (I and II) Draw a diagram. Label any numerical quantities which remain fixed throughout the problem (such as the dimensions of the cone in Example 2).

Step 2. (I) All quantities are expressed in terms of time. (II) All quantities which change with time are denoted by letters. A relation (or relations) is found among the quantities which vary; these relations must hold for all time.

Step 3. (I) Differentiate directly with respect to time. (II) Take differentials of the relation (or relations) found in Step 2. Divide by dt to obtain a relation among the derivatives.

Step 4. (I and II) Insert the special values of all quantities to get the numerical result.

We apply these rules in the following example.

EXAMPLE 3. An airplane at an altitude of 3000 ft, flying horizontally at 300 mi/hr, passes directly over an observer. Find the rate at which it is approaching the observer when it is 5000 ft away.

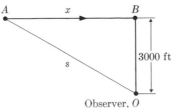

FIGURE 7–42

Solution. We draw Fig. 7–42. The airplane is at point A flying toward point B. The distance OB is labeled as 3000 ft (Step 1). Note that this distance does not change in the course of the problem. Let x be the distance of the airplane A from the point B directly over the observer, O, and s be the distance from the airplane to the observer. We want to find ds/dt when $s = 5000$. We are given $dx/dt = -300$ mi/hr. The negative sign is used because x is decreasing. A change of units gives us $dx/dt = -440$ ft/sec.

We have (Step 2, II)

$$s^2 = x^2 + (3000)^2,$$

and, applying differentials (Step 3, II),

$$2s\,ds = 2x\,dx.$$

Dividing by dt, we get

$$s\,\frac{ds}{dt} = x\,\frac{dx}{dt}.$$

We now insert the values (Step 4), noting that $x = 4000$ when $s = 5000$:

$$5000\,\frac{ds}{dt} = 4000(-440), \qquad \text{or} \qquad \frac{ds}{dt} = -352 \text{ ft/sec} = -240 \text{ mi/hr}.$$

EXERCISES

1. Two automobiles start from a point A at the same time. One travels west at 80 mi/hr and the other travels north at 45 mi/hr. How fast is the distance between them increasing 3 hr later?

2. At noon of a certain day, ship A is 60 mi due north of ship B. If A sails east at 15 mi/hr and B sails north at 12 mi/hr, determine how rapidly the distance between them is changing 2 hr later. Is it increasing or decreasing?

3. At a given instant the legs of a right triangle are 8 in. and 6 in., respectively. The first leg decreases at 1 in/min and the second increases at 2 in/min. At what rate is the area increasing after 2 min?

4. At a certain instant a small balloon is released (from ground level) at a point 75 ft away from an observer (on ground level). If the balloon goes straight up at a rate of $2\frac{1}{2}$ ft/sec, how rapidly will it be receding from the observer 40 sec later?

5. An arc light is 15 ft above a sidewalk. A man 6 ft tall walks away from the point under the light at the rate of 5 ft/sec. How fast is his shadow lengthening when he is 20 ft away from the point under the light?

6. A balloon is being inflated at the rate of 15 ft^3/min. At what rate is the diameter increasing after 5 min? Assume that the diameter is zero at time zero.

7. A baseball diamond is 90 ft on a side. (It is really a square.) A man runs from first base to second base at 25 ft/sec. At what rate is his distance from third base decreasing when he is 30 ft from first base? At what rate is his distance from home plate increasing at the same instant?

8. A man starts walking eastward at 5 ft/sec from a point A. Ten minutes later a second man starts walking west at the rate of 5 ft/sec from a point B, 3000 ft north of A. How fast are they separating 10 min after the second man starts?

9. A point moves along the curve $y = \sqrt{x^2 + 1}$ in such a way that $dx/dt = 4$. Find dy/dt when $x = 3$.

10. A point moves along the upper half of the curve $y^2 = 2x + 1$ in such a way that $dx/dt = \sqrt{2x + 1}$. Find dy/dt when $x = 4$

11. The variables x, y, and z are all functions of t and satisfy the relation $x^3 - 2xy + y^2 + 2xz - 2xz^2 + 3 = 0$. Find dz/dt when $x = 1$, $y = 2$, if $dx/dt = 3$ and $dy/dt = 4$ for all times t.

12. A ladder 15 ft tall leans against a vertical wall of a house. If the bottom of the ladder is pulled horizontally away from the house at 4 ft/sec, how fast is the top of the ladder sliding down when the bottom is 9 ft from the wall?

13. A light is on the ground 40 ft from a building. A man 6 ft tall walks from the light toward the building at 6 ft/sec. How rapidly is his shadow on the building growing shorter when he is 20 ft from the building?

14. A trough is 10 ft long and its ends are isosceles triangles with altitude 2 ft and base 2 ft, their vertices being at the bottom. If water is let into the trough at the rate of 3 ft³/min, how fast is the water level rising when it is 1 ft deep?

15. A trough 10 ft long has as its ends isosceles trapezoids, altitude 2 ft, lower base 2 ft, upper base 3 ft. If water is let in at the rate of 3 ft³/min, how fast is the water level rising when the water is 1 ft deep?

16. A swimming pool is 25 ft wide, 40 ft long, 3 ft deep at the shallow end, and 9 ft deep at the deep end, the bottom being an inclined plane. If water is pumped into the pool at the rate of 10 ft³/min, how fast is the water level rising when it is 4 ft deep at the deep end?

17. Sand is issuing from a spout at the rate of 3 ft³/min and falling on a conical pile whose diameter at the base is always three times the altitude. At what rate is the altitude increasing when the altitude is 4 ft?

18. Water is leaking out of a conical tank (vertex down) at the rate of 0.5 ft³/min. The tank is 30 ft across at the top and 10 ft deep. If the water level is rising at the rate of $1\frac{1}{2}$ ft/min, at what rate is water being poured into the tank from the top?

19. In Example 2, find the rate at which the uncovered surface of the conical tank is decreasing at the instant in question.

20. A boat is anchored in such a way that its deck is 25 ft above the level of the anchor. If the boat drifts directly away from the point above the anchor at the rate of 5 ft/min, how fast does the anchor rope slip over the edge of the deck when there are 65 ft of rope out? (Assume that the rope forms a straight line from deck to anchor.)

21. Water is flowing into a cylindrical tank of radius 2 ft at the rate of 8 ft³/min. How fast is the water level rising?

22. A launch whose deck is 7 ft below the level of a windlass on a wharf is being pulled toward the wharf by a rope attached to a ring on the deck. If the windlass pulls in the rope at the rate of 15 ft/min, how fast is the launch moving through the water when there are 25 ft of rope out?

23. A man lifts a bucket of cement to a scaffold 30 ft above his head by means of a rope which passes over a pulley on the scaffold. The rope is 60 ft long. If he keeps his end of the rope horizontal and walks away from beneath the pulley at 4 ft/sec, how fast is the bucket rising when he is $22\frac{1}{2}$ ft away?

24. Water is flowing into a tank in the form of a hemisphere of radius 10 ft with flat side up (Fig. 7–43) at the rate of 4 ft³/min. At any instant let h denote the depth of

FIGURE 7–43

the water, r the radius of the surface, and V the volume of the water. Assuming $dV = \pi r^2 \, dh$, find how fast the water level is rising when $h = 5$ ft.

25. A bridge is 30 ft above a canal. A motorboat going 10 ft/sec passes under the center of the bridge at the same instant that a man walking 5 ft/sec reaches that point. How rapidly are they separating 3 sec later?

26. If in problem 25 the man reaches the center of the bridge 5 sec before the boat passes under it, find the rate at which the distance between them is changing 4 sec after the man crosses.

CHAPTER 8

The Definite Integral

---

1. AREA

In Chapter 4, Section 6, the notion of the area of a region in the plane was discussed in an informal way. Now we shall go into more detail and treat the topic in a precise manner. The area of a region is a measure of its size. A rectangle of length l and width w has area $A = l \cdot w$. The area of a triangle of base b and altitude h is just $\frac{1}{2}bh$. Similarly, we may obtain the area of a polygon simply by decomposing it into triangles and adding the areas of the component parts. Moreover, we can readily see that the area of a polygon is independent of the way in which the polygon is cut up into triangles.

Suppose we have an irregularly shaped region in the plane, such as the one shown in Fig. 8–1. How do we go about defining its area? The process is rather complicated and depends intrinsically on the idea of limit, which we have previously learned. In this section the procedure for defining area will be given, although the proofs of some of the statements will be omitted.

FIGURE 8–1

We shall start with the notion of a *square grid*. The entire plane is divided into squares by constructing equally spaced lines parallel to the coordinate axes. Figure 8–2 shows a square grid with squares $\frac{1}{2}$ unit on each side, and Fig. 8–3 shows a square grid with squares $\frac{1}{4}$ unit on each side. We always select the coordinate axes themselves as lines of the grid, and then the size of the squares determines the location of all other grid lines. We may have a grid with squares of any size, but for convenience we consider only grids of size $\frac{1}{2}$, $\frac{1}{4}$, $\frac{1}{8}$, $\frac{1}{16}$, ..., $1/2^n$, ..., where n is any positive integer. We obtain a sequence of grids with the property that the lines of any grid in the sequence are also lines in all the grids further along in the sequence.

We want to *define* the area of an irregularly shaped region R, such as the one shown in Fig. 8–4. We begin by constructing a square grid (one of our sequence of grids) in the plane. All the squares of this grid can be divided into three types: (1) squares which are completely inside the region R; (2) squares which have some

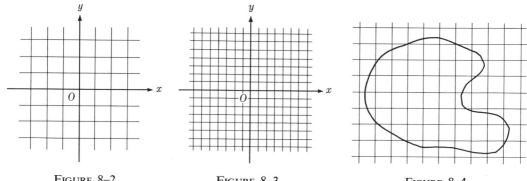

points in the region and some points not in the region; (3) squares which are completely outside the region.

If the grid we select is the 5th in the sequence ($n = 5$), then the length of the side of each square is $1/2^5 = 1/32$ and the area of each square is $\frac{1}{32} \cdot \frac{1}{32} = \frac{1}{1024}$ square units. We define for the square grid with $n = 5$:

$$A_5^L = \text{sum of the areas of all squares of type (1)},$$
$$A_5^U = \text{sum of the areas of all squares of type (1) plus type (2)}.$$

(The L stands for *lower* and the U stands for *upper*.) According to the way we have defined these quantities, if the region we started with is to have something we call "area," then we would expect that A_5^L would be less than this area, while A_5^U would be greater. We have the inequality

$$A_5^L \leq A_5^U,$$

which comes from the very definition. The expression A_5^U contains everything in A_5^L and more.

We have described a typical step in a process which consists of a sequence of steps. The next step consists of constructing a grid with $n = 6$. Each square is of side $\frac{1}{64}$, the area being $\frac{1}{64} \cdot \frac{1}{64} = \frac{1}{4096}$ square units. Each square of the $n = 5$ grid is divided into exactly 4 subsquares to form the $n = 6$ grid. We now define the quantities:

$$A_6^L = \text{sum of areas of all squares of type (1) of the } n = 6 \text{ grid};$$
$$A_6^U = \text{sum of areas of all squares of type (1) plus type (2) of the } n = 6 \text{ grid}.$$

As before, the definition tells us that

$$A_6^L \leq A_6^U.$$

But now we can see that there is a relation between A_5^L and A_6^L. Any square in A_5^L is the same as 4 squares of A_6^L, with the same total area. However, A_6^L may have some squares of type (1) near the boundary which are part of type (2) regions for the $n = 5$ grid. Figure 8–5 shows that the lower left corner is of type (1) for

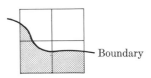

Figure 8–5

Figure 8–6

$n = 6$, while the large square is of type (2) for $n = 5$. It can be proved (although our discussion has not done so) that for any region, we have

$$A_5^L \leq A_6^L.$$

Similarly, A_5^U may have a type (2) region (see Fig. 8–6) which, when considered in the $n = 6$ grid, gives three type (2) regions and one type (3) region. This means that for such a square the contribution to A_6^U (three smaller squares) is less than the corresponding contribution to A_5^U (the larger square). *It can be shown in a general way that*

$$A_6^U \leq A_5^U.$$

The inequalities may also be combined to give

$$A_5^L \leq A_6^L \leq A_6^U \leq A_5^U.$$

When the above process is performed for $n = 1, 2, 3, \ldots$ we get a sequence of numbers

$$A_1^L \leq A_2^L \leq A_3^L \leq A_4^L \leq \cdots \leq A_n^L \leq \cdots$$

and a corresponding sequence

$$A_1^U \geq A_2^U \geq A_3^U \geq A_4^U \geq \cdots \geq A_n^U \geq \cdots$$

By Axiom C (of Chapter 5, Section 5) we know that the A_n^L tend to a limit, since the sequence is bounded (by A_1^U — in fact by all A_n^U) and is steadily increasing (or at least nondecreasing). The limit of A_n^L is denoted by A^- and is called the *inner area* of the region. Since the region is designated by R, we also write $A^-(R)$. In the same way it can be shown that the A_n^U tend to a limit which we denote by A^+, and this number is called the *outer area* of the region. We also write $A^+(R)$.

It is always true that

$$A^-(R) \leq A^+(R),$$

but it is not always true that these numbers are equal. However, the sets R for which they are unequal are weird, and for the kinds of regions we shall be concerned with it can be shown that

$$A^-(R) = A^+(R).$$

*This common value is then **defined** to be the area of the region, and we denote it $A(R)$.*

Note that the above discussion did not *prove* the validity of the inequalities for A_n^L and A_n^U. The arguments may or may not have appeared convincing, but arguing "pictorially" is not a proof. The material given here is intended only to establish the reasonableness of the results. Proofs of the statements made are given in Morrey, *University Calculus*, Section 8–2.

The fundamental unit for determining areas is the square. A completely analogous development could be made with rectangles instead of squares. A sequence of *rectangular grids* is then used, the lengths and widths of the sides of the rectangles tending to zero as the nth term in the sequence tends to infinity. We would naturally expect, and it can be proved, that both the rectangular and the square grids yield the same number for the area of R. Finally, if a region R is formed as the sum of two nonoverlapping regions R_1 and R_2, we can easily prove the expected fact that $A(R) = A(R_1) + A(R_2)$.

2. CALCULATION OF AREAS BY SUMS

The sum of seven terms,

$$a_1 + a_2 + a_3 + a_4 + a_5 + a_6 + a_7,$$

can be written in abbreviated form using a symbol which we shall now introduce. The Greek letter sigma and certain subscripts are combined in the following way:

$$\sum_{i=1}^{7} a_i \quad \text{means} \quad a_1 + a_2 + a_3 + a_4 + a_5 + a_6 + a_7.$$

It is read "the sum from 1 to 7 of a sub i." The lower number (1 in this case) indicates where the sum starts, and the upper number (7 in this case) indicates where it ends. The expression

$$\sum_{i=3}^{8} b_i \quad \text{means} \quad b_3 + b_4 + b_5 + b_6 + b_7 + b_8.$$

The symbol i is a "dummy" symbol (called the *index of summation*), since

$$\sum_{k=3}^{8} b_k \quad \text{means} \quad b_3 + b_4 + b_5 + b_6 + b_7 + b_8,$$

which is exactly the same thing.

Carrying the process one step further, we have

$$\sum_{i=1}^{5} (2i + 1) = (2 \cdot 1 + 1) + (2 \cdot 2 + 1) + (2 \cdot 3 + 1) + (2 \cdot 4 + 1)$$

$$+ (2 \cdot 5 + 1) = 3 + 5 + 7 + 9 + 11,$$

and

$$\sum_{k=2}^{5} [(k + 1)^3 - k^3] = [(2 + 1)^3 - 2^3] + [(3 + 1)^3 - 3^3] + [(4 + 1)^3 - 4^3]$$

$$+ [(5 + 1)^3 - 5^3] = -2^3 + 6^3.$$

The *summation notation*, as it is called, is of great help in manipulating sums. As an example, consider

$$\sum_{i=1}^{6} 2i = 2 \cdot 1 + 2 \cdot 2 + 2 \cdot 3 + 2 \cdot 4 + 2 \cdot 5 + 2 \cdot 6$$

$$= 2(1 + 2 + 3 + 4 + 5 + 6)$$

$$= 2 \sum_{i=1}^{6} i.$$

More generally, we have the rule that for any sum

$$\sum_{k=1}^{n} ca_k = c \sum_{k=1}^{n} a_k, \qquad c = \text{const},$$

where the symbol means that the sum starts with a_1 and ends with a_n. The number at the bottom is called the *lower limit* of the sum and the number at the top the *upper limit*. We also have

$$\sum_{k=1}^{n} (a_k + b_k) = \sum_{k=1}^{n} a_k + \sum_{k=1}^{n} b_k.$$

We introduce another convention which is quite useful. The symbol

$$\sum_{i=1}^{8} 1 \quad \text{means} \quad 1 + 1 + 1 + 1 + 1 + 1 + 1 + 1 = 8,$$

and, in general,

$$\sum_{i=1}^{n} 1 = n, \qquad \sum_{i=1}^{n} c = c \sum_{i=1}^{n} 1 = cn, \qquad c = \text{const}.$$

Consider the sum of the integers from 1 to 50. Finding this is easy but tedious. Letting s denote the sum, we write

$$s = 1 + 2 + 3 + \cdots + 49 + 50.$$

We can also reverse the order of summing and write

$$s = 50 + 49 + 48 + \cdots + 2 + 1.$$

Let us add these expressions term by term:

$$2s = (1 + 50) + (2 + 49) + (3 + 48) + \cdots + (49 + 2) + (50 + 1).$$

Each of the terms in the parentheses on the right adds up to 51, and there are exactly 50 such terms. We get

$$2s = 50 \cdot 51, \qquad s = \tfrac{1}{2} 50 \cdot 51.$$

Using the summation notation, we obtain the result in the following way:

$$s = \sum_{k=1}^{50} k$$

$$s = \sum_{k=1}^{50} (51 - k) \quad \text{(the sum in reverse order).}$$

Adding, we find that

$$2s = \sum_{k=1}^{50} k + \sum_{k=1}^{50} (51 - k) = \sum_{k=1}^{50} (k + 51 - k) = \sum_{k=1}^{50} 51,$$

$$2s = 51 \sum_{k=1}^{50} 1 = 51 \cdot 50,$$

$$s = \tfrac{1}{2} 51 \cdot 50.$$

Employing the same idea, we can obtain a general formula for the sum of any number of consecutive integers:

$$s = \sum_{k=1}^{n} k = \tfrac{1}{2} n(n + 1).$$

If $n = 50$ we get the above result. If $n = 80$ we see that

$$1 + 2 + \cdots + 80 = \tfrac{1}{2} 80(81) = 3240.$$

The formula for the sum of consecutive integers is just one of a whole collection of formulas which we shall find useful. The next one in the collection considers sums of squares, such as

$$1^2 + 2^2 + 3^2 + 4^2 + 5^2 = \sum_{k=1}^{5} k^2.$$

It is possible to arrive at a simple formula for adding such sums. We shall write down the answer and then show how we obtained it:

$$\sum_{k=1}^{n} k^2 = \tfrac{1}{6} n(n + 1)(2n + 1).$$

The trick in this case is to start with the formula

$$(k + 1)^3 - k^3 = k^3 + 3k^2 + 3k + 1 - k^3,$$

or

$$(k + 1)^3 - k^3 = 3k^2 + 3k + 1.$$

Now we use the summation notation and write

$$\sum_{k=1}^{n} (k + 1)^3 - k^3 = \sum_{k=1}^{n} (3k^2 + 3k + 1).$$

The left side is

$$(1 + 1)^3 - 1^3 + (2 + 1)^3 - 2^3 + (3 + 1)^3 - 3^3 + \cdots + (n + 1)^3 - n^3.$$

Observe that all the terms telescope, in such a way that the only remaining quantity is $-1^3 + (n + 1)^3$. Everything else cancels, and we obtain

$$-1 + (n + 1)^3 = 3 \sum_{k=1}^{n} k^2 + 3 \sum_{k=1}^{n} k + \sum_{k=1}^{n} 1.$$

Upon multiplying out the left side, we get $-1 + n^3 + 3n^2 + 3n + 1$. As for the right side, we know that

$$\sum_{k=1}^{n} 1 = n,$$

and we have already shown that

$$\sum_{k=1}^{n} k = \tfrac{1}{2}n(n + 1).$$

So we see that

$$n^3 + 3n^2 + 3n = 3 \sum_{k=1}^{n} k^2 + 3 \cdot \tfrac{1}{2}n(n + 1) + n.$$

Dividing by three and rearranging the terms, we can write

$$\sum_{k=1}^{n} k^2 = \tfrac{1}{3}(n^3 + 3n^2 + 3n - \tfrac{3}{2}n^2 - \tfrac{3}{2}n - n).$$

Combining and factoring yields the result

$$\sum_{k=1}^{n} k^2 = \frac{n}{6} (n + 1)(2n + 1).$$

The next formula in the collection is

$$\sum_{k=1}^{n} k^3 = \frac{n^2(n + 1)^2}{4}.$$

We shall not prove it but shall only remark that the starting point is $(k + 1)^4 - k^4$, and that the procedure is the same as the one just followed. In fact, this method can be used to get

$$\sum_{k=1}^{n} k^4, \quad \sum_{k=1}^{n} k^5,$$

and so forth.

We shall now use these formulas to calculate areas. We construct the right triangle formed by the x-axis, the line $x = 1$, and the line $y = x$ (Fig. 8–7). The area of this triangle is obviously $\tfrac{1}{2}$, but as an exercise in the use of a new

FIGURE 8–7

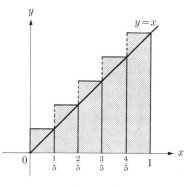

FIGURE 8–8

method for computing areas we shall calculate its area. First we divide the x-axis from zero to 1 into n equal parts. Figure 8–7 shows this subdivision with $n = 5$. The points of subdivision are at $x = 0, 1/n, 2/n, 3/n, \ldots, (n-1)/n, n/n = 1$. The function $y = x$ has a maximum and a minimum value in the first subinterval $[0, 1/n]$. The minimum value is at $x = 0$, the maximum value at $x = 1/n$. The function has a maximum value in the interval $[1/n, 2/n]$ at $x = 2/n$ and a minimum value at $x = 1/n$, and so on for each of the subintervals. At the minimum value of the function on each of the subintervals, we erect a rectangle with height of this minimum value and width equal to the size of the subinterval. Figure 8–7 shows the construction, with the rectangles shaded. The first rectangle has zero height, since the minimum value of the function in $[0, 1/n]$ is 0. In Figure 8–8 the corresponding set of rectangles is constructed with the height selected as the *maximum* value of the function on each subinterval. It is clear that in Fig. 8–7 the area of the rectangles is less than the area of the triangle, while in Fig. 8–8 the area of the rectangles is larger than the area of the triangle.

We first add the areas of the rectangles formed with the minimum ordinates. Since the width of each rectangle is $1/n$ and the heights are successively $0, 1/n, 2/n, \ldots, (n-1)/n$, we obtain for the total (which we call B_n^-)

$$B_n^- = 0 \cdot \frac{1}{n} + \frac{1}{n} \cdot \frac{1}{n} + \frac{2}{n} \cdot \frac{1}{n} + \cdots + \frac{n-1}{n} \cdot \frac{1}{n}.$$

This yields

$$B_n^- = \frac{1}{n^2}(1 + 2 + 3 + \cdots + n - 1) = \frac{1}{n^2} \cdot \frac{1}{2}(n-1) \cdot n,$$

a calculation in which we used the formula

$$\sum_{k=1}^{n-1} k = \tfrac{1}{2}(n-1)n.$$

That is,

$$B_n^- = \frac{1}{2}\frac{n-1}{n}.$$

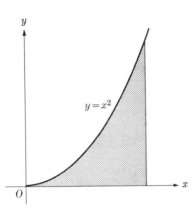

FIGURE 8–9   FIGURE 8–10

For the sum of the areas of the rectangles with maximum ordinates (which we call B_n^+), we get

$$B_n^+ = \frac{1}{n} \cdot \frac{1}{n} + \frac{2}{n} \cdot \frac{1}{n} + \cdots + \frac{n-1}{n} \cdot \frac{1}{n} + \frac{n}{n} \cdot \frac{1}{n}$$

$$= \frac{1}{n^2} (1 + 2 + \cdots + n) = \frac{1}{n^2} \cdot \frac{1}{2} n(n+1),$$

or

$$B_n^+ = \frac{1}{2} \frac{n+1}{n}.$$

For every n, B_n^- is smaller than the area of the triangle and B_n^+ is larger. We know that

$$B_n^- \le B_n^+.$$

As n tends to infinity,

$$B_n^- \to \tfrac{1}{2} \quad \text{and} \quad B_n^+ \to \tfrac{1}{2}.$$

The area is $\tfrac{1}{2}$.

We shall now use exactly the same method (Fig. 8–9) to find the area bounded by the curve $y = x^2$, the x-axis, and the line $x = 1$. Although our method will be the same as the one we just used to find the area of a triangle, the answer in this case is not obtainable by elementary methods. Again we divide the interval on the x-axis from 0 to 1 into n parts. Figure 8–10 shows the subdivision for $n = 6$. The points of subdivision are 0, $1/n$, $2/n$, ..., $(n-1)/n$, $n/n = 1$. The minimum of the function in each subinterval occurs at the left end and the maximum at the right end.

In $\left[0, \dfrac{1}{n}\right]$ the minimum value of $y = x^2$ occurs at $x = 0$ and is zero;

the maximum value of $y = x^2$ occurs at $\dfrac{1}{n}$ and is $\dfrac{1}{n^2}$.

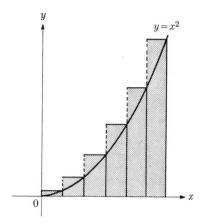

$$y = x^2$$

FIGURE 8–11

In $\left[\dfrac{1}{n}, \dfrac{2}{n}\right]$ the minimum value occurs at $x = \dfrac{1}{n}$ and is $\dfrac{1}{n^2}$;

the maximum value occurs at $x = \dfrac{2}{n}$ and is $\dfrac{4}{n^2}$.

In $\left[\dfrac{2}{n}, \dfrac{3}{n}\right]$ the minimum value occurs at $x = \dfrac{2}{n}$ and is $\dfrac{4}{n^2}$;

the maximum value occurs at $x = \dfrac{3}{n}$ and is $\dfrac{9}{n^2}$,

and so on.

We construct the rectangles with minimum heights, as shown in Fig. 8–10, and the rectangles of maximum heights, as shown in Fig. 8–11. We then calculate their areas to get

$$B_n^- = 0 \cdot \frac{1}{n} + \frac{1}{n^2} \cdot \frac{1}{n} + \frac{2^2}{n^2} \cdot \frac{1}{n} + \cdots + \frac{(n-1)^2}{n^2} \cdot \frac{1}{n} ;$$

$$B_n^+ = \frac{1}{n^2} \cdot \frac{1}{n} + \frac{2^2}{n^2} \cdot \frac{1}{n} + \frac{3^2}{n^2} \cdot \frac{1}{n} + \cdots + \frac{(n-1)^2}{n^2} \cdot \frac{1}{n} + \frac{n^2}{n^2} \cdot \frac{1}{n} .$$

Using the summation notation, we can write

$$B_n^- = \frac{1}{n^3} \sum_{k=1}^{n-1} k^2, \qquad B_n^+ = \frac{1}{n^3} \sum_{k=1}^{n} k^2,$$

knowing that B_n^- is always smaller than the area we wish to find and B_n^+ is always larger. We know that $B_n^- \le B_n^+$. We can now make use of the formula for the sum of squares of successive integers:

$$B_n^- = \frac{1}{n^3} \cdot \frac{n-1}{6} \cdot n(2(n-1)+1) = \frac{(n-1)(2n-1)}{6n^2} ;$$

$$B_n^+ = \frac{1}{n^3} \cdot \frac{n}{6} (n+1)(2n+1) = \frac{(n+1)(2n+1)}{6n^2} .$$

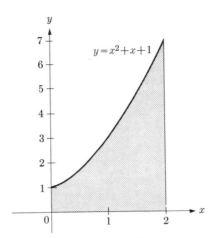

FIGURE 8–12

To calculate the limit of B_n^- and B_n^+ as $n \to \infty$ we divide both the numerator and the denominator by n^2, obtaining

$$B_n^- = \frac{\left(1 - \frac{1}{n}\right)\left(2 - \frac{1}{n}\right)}{6}, \qquad B_n^+ = \frac{\left(1 + \frac{1}{n}\right)\left(2 + \frac{1}{n}\right)}{6}.$$

As n tends to infinity,

$$B_n^- \to \frac{1 \cdot 2}{6} = \frac{1}{3}, \qquad B_n^+ \to \frac{1 \cdot 2}{6} = \frac{1}{3}.$$

The area is $\frac{1}{3}$.

EXAMPLE. Using the methods of this section, find the area bounded by the curve $y = x^2 + x + 1$, the line $x = 2$, the x-axis, and the y-axis.

Solution. Figure 8–12 shows the desired area. Divide the interval $[0, 2]$ into n parts. The points of division are at

$$2 \cdot 0, \quad 2 \cdot \frac{1}{n}, \quad 2 \cdot \frac{2}{n}, \quad 2 \cdot \frac{3}{n}, \quad 2 \cdot \frac{4}{n}, \quad \ldots, \quad 2 \cdot \frac{n-1}{n}, \quad 2 \cdot \frac{n}{n} = 2.$$

The function is an increasing one (as we can check by using our knowledge of derivatives); therefore in each subinterval the minimum value occurs at the left endpoint, the maximum value at the right endpoint.

In $\left[0, \dfrac{2}{n}\right]$ the minimum value is at 0 and $y = 0 + 0 + 1 = 1$;

the maximum value is at $\dfrac{2}{n}$ and $y = \dfrac{4}{n^2} + \dfrac{2}{n} + 1.$

In $\left[\dfrac{2}{n}, \dfrac{4}{n}\right]$ the minimum value is at $\dfrac{2}{n}$ and $y = \dfrac{4}{n^2} + \dfrac{2}{n} + 1$;

the maximum value is at $\dfrac{4}{n}$ and $y = \dfrac{4^2}{n^2} + \dfrac{4}{n} + 1,$

and so on. To compute the value of B_n^- and B_n^+ we simply find the areas of the rectangles and add:

$$B_n^- = 1 \cdot \frac{2}{n} + \left(\frac{2^2 \cdot 1}{n^2} + \frac{2}{n} + 1 \right) \frac{2}{n} + \left(\frac{2^2 \cdot 2^2}{n^2} + \frac{2 \cdot 2}{n} + 1 \right) \frac{2}{n}$$

$$+ \left(\frac{2^2 \cdot 3^2}{n^2} + \frac{2 \cdot 3}{n} + 1 \right) \frac{2}{n} + \cdots + \left(\frac{2^2 \cdot (n-1)^2}{n^2} + \frac{2(n-1)}{n} + 1 \right) \frac{2}{n};$$

$$B_n^+ = \left(\frac{2^2 \cdot 1^2}{n^2} + \frac{2}{n} + 1 \right) \frac{2}{n} + \left(\frac{2^2 \cdot 2^2}{n^2} + \frac{2 \cdot 2}{n} + 1 \right) \frac{2}{n} + \left(\frac{2^2 \cdot 3^2}{n^2} + \frac{2 \cdot 3}{n} + 1 \right) \frac{2}{n}$$

$$+ \cdots + \left(\frac{2^2(n-1)^2}{n^2} + \frac{2(n-1)}{n} + 1 \right) \frac{2}{n} + \left(\frac{2^2 \cdot n^2}{n^2} + \frac{2n}{n} + 1 \right) \frac{2}{n}.$$

Factoring and using summation notation, we obtain

$$B_n^- = \frac{2}{n} \sum_{k=0}^{n-1} \left(\frac{2^2 \cdot k^2}{n^2} + \frac{2k}{n} + 1 \right); \qquad B_n^+ = \frac{2}{n} \sum_{k=1}^{n} \left(\frac{2^2 \cdot k^2}{n^2} + \frac{2k}{n} + 1 \right).$$

The rules for this notation give us

$$B_n^- = \frac{8}{n^3} \sum_{k=0}^{n-1} k^2 + \frac{4}{n^2} \sum_{k=0}^{n-1} k + \frac{2}{n} \sum_{k=0}^{n-1} 1,$$

and

$$B_n^+ = \frac{8}{n^3} \sum_{k=1}^{n} k^2 + \frac{4}{n^2} \sum_{k=1}^{n} k + \frac{2}{n} \sum_{k=1}^{n} 1.$$

Two things are worth noting: first,

$$\sum_{k=0}^{n-1} k^2 = \sum_{k=1}^{n-1} k^2,$$

since the $k = 0$ term makes no contribution; second,

$$\sum_{k=0}^{n-1} 1 = n,$$

since the *number* of terms determines the result. We conclude that

$$B_n^- = \frac{8}{n^3} \cdot \frac{(n-1)}{6} \cdot n(2n-1) + \frac{4}{n^2} \cdot \frac{1}{2} (n-1) \cdot n + 2;$$

$$B_n^+ = \frac{8}{n^3} \cdot \frac{n}{6} (n+1)(2n+1) + \frac{4}{n^2} \cdot \frac{1}{2} n(n+1) + 2.$$

Some juggling yields

$$B_n^- = \tfrac{4}{3} \left(1 - \frac{1}{n} \right) \left(2 - \frac{1}{n} \right) + 2 \left(1 - \frac{1}{n} \right) + 2;$$

$$B_n^+ = \tfrac{4}{3} \left(1 + \frac{1}{n} \right) \left(2 + \frac{1}{n} \right) + 2 \left(1 + \frac{1}{n} \right) + 2.$$

As $n \to \infty$, $B_n^- \to \frac{20}{3}$, $B_n^+ \to \frac{20}{3}$, which is the area we were seeking.

EXERCISES

In problems 1 through 6, find the value of the given sums.

1. $\displaystyle\sum_{i=1}^{10} i$

2. $\displaystyle\sum_{i=2}^{5} (3i + 2)$

3. $\displaystyle\sum_{i=-2}^{5} (i + 1)$

4. $\displaystyle\sum_{k=4}^{8} a_k,$ given that $a_i = 2^i$ for every i.

5. $\displaystyle\sum_{i=1}^{4} \frac{1}{i}$

6. $\displaystyle\sum_{k=-1}^{2} \frac{1}{1 + k^2}$

7. Show that $\displaystyle\sum_{k=1}^{8} (3k + 2) = \sum_{k=0}^{7} (3k + 5)$

8. Find the value of $\displaystyle\sum_{k=1}^{6} (a_{k+1} - a_k),$ given that $a_k = 10^k$

9. Find the value of $\displaystyle\sum_{k=2}^{7} (a_k - a_{k+1}),$ given that $a_k = \dfrac{1}{k}$

In problems 10 through 17, find the areas of the regions by the methods of this section.

10. The region bounded by $y = 2x$, the line $x = 2$ and the x-axis.
11. The region bounded by $y = \frac{1}{2}x$, the line $x = 1$, the line $x = 3$, and the x-axis.
12. The region bounded by $y = x^2$, the line $x = 3$, and the x-axis.
13. The region bounded by $y = x^2$, the line $x = 1$, the line $x = 2$, and the x-axis.
14. The region bounded by $y = 2x + 1$, the y-axis, the x-axis, and the line $x = 2$.
15. The region bounded by $y = 2 + x^2$, the y-axis, the x-axis, and the line $x = 1$.
16. The region bounded by $y = 2x^2 + \frac{1}{2}x + 1$, the y-axis, the x-axis, and the line $x = 1$.
17. The region bounded by $y = x - x^2$ and the x-axis.

18. Show that $\displaystyle\sum_{k=1}^{n} k^3 = \frac{n^2(n + 1)^2}{4}.$

[*Hint:* Start with $(k + 1)^4 - k^4 = 4k^3 + 6k^2 + 4k + 1$, which is obtained by multiplying out $(k + 1)^4$.]

19. Starting with an expression for $(k + 1)^5 - k^5$, prove that

$$\sum_{k=1}^{n} k^4 = \frac{n}{30} (n + 1)(6n^3 + 9n^2 + n - 1).$$

20. Using the result of problem 18, find the area of the region bounded by $y = x^3$, the x-axis, and the line $x = 1$.

21. Using the result of problem 19, find the area of the region bounded by $y = x^4$, the x-axis, and the line $x = 1$.

22. Find the area of the region bounded by $y = 1 + x^2 + 2x^4$, the y-axis, the x-axis, and the line $x = 1$.

23. Find the area bounded by the curve $y = x^2 - x^4, 0 \le x \le 1$, and the x-axis.

3. THE DEFINITE INTEGRAL

In Chapter 4, Section 6, we introduced the definite integral and discussed its relationship to the notion of antiderivative. We are now in a position to make the treatment more precise and to develop a rigorous definition of the definite integral.

FIGURE 8–13

Suppose that f is a function defined on an interval $[a, b]$. We make a *subdivision* of this interval by introducing $n - 1$ intermediate points; call them $x_1, x_2, x_3, \ldots,$ x_{n-1} (Fig. 8–13). These points are not necessarily equally spaced. Letting $x_0 = a$ and $x_n = b$, we see that there are exactly n subintervals. Since it is convenient to have a symbol for such a subdivision, we shall use the Greek letter Δ for this purpose. That is, Δ stands for the process of introducing $n - 1$ points between a and b. The subdivision can be made in an infinite variety of ways for each value of n and can also be made for every positive integer n. However, we will simply use the symbol Δ to indicate such a subdivision without attempting to indicate the way in which it was made. An important symbol which we introduced in Chapter 4 is

$$\Delta_i x = x_i - x_{i-1} = \text{length of } i\text{th subinterval in the subdivision } \Delta.$$

There are exactly n subintervals, and among them there is always one which is largest. (Of course there may be several of equal size.) We introduce

$$\|\Delta\| = \text{length of largest subinterval in subdivision } \Delta.$$

This quantity, $\|\Delta\|$, is called the *norm* of the subdivision. The word norm is commonly used in mathematics, and in each context it is a measure of size. In our case, we want to know how "fine" the subdivision is, and the norm $\|\Delta\|$, the maximum distance between points, is a measure of this "fineness." For example, if $a = 2$, $b = 5$, and $\|\Delta\| = 0.05$, we know that n has to be at least 60. This reasoning holds because it takes 60 intervals of length 0.05 to add up to $b - a = 3$. Of course, $\|\Delta\|$ could be 0.05 and $n = 100$, with many points quite close together and only one or two intervals actually of length 0.05.

In each of the subintervals of a subdivision Δ we select a point. *Such a selection may be made in any way whatsoever.* Let ξ_1 be the point selected in $[x_0, x_1]$; let ξ_2 be the point in $[x_1, x_2]$, and, in general, let ξ_k be the point in $[x_{k-1}, x_k]$. We now form the sum

$$f(\xi_1)(x_1 - x_0) + f(\xi_2)(x_2 - x_1) + \cdots$$
$$+ f(\xi_k)(x_k - x_{k-1}) + \cdots + f(\xi_n)(x_n - x_{n-1}).$$

We can abbreviate this to

$$f(\xi_1)\,\Delta_1 x + f(\xi_2)\,\Delta_2 x + \cdots + f(\xi_k)\,\Delta_k x + \cdots + f(\xi_n)\,\Delta_n x,$$

and even further, by using the summation notation, to

$$\sum_{k=1}^{n} f(\xi_k) \, \Delta_k x.$$

DEFINITION. *A function f is said to be integrable on the interval* [a, b] *if there is a number A with the following property: for each* $\epsilon > 0$ *there is a* $\delta > 0$ *such that*

$$\left| \sum_{k=1}^{n} f(\xi_k) \, \Delta_k x - A \right| < \epsilon,$$

for every subdivision Δ with $\|\Delta\| < \delta$ and for any choices of the ξ_k in $[x_{k-1}, x_k]$.

A simpler but less precise way of writing the above definition nevertheless gives the idea of what is happening:

$$\lim_{\|\Delta\| \to 0} \sum_{k=1}^{n} f(\xi_k) \, \Delta_k x = A.$$

The lack of precision comes about because, for any given value of the norm, $\|\Delta\|$, the $\Delta_k x$ can vary greatly and the ξ_k can wander throughout the subinterval. This process is not quite the same kind of limiting process as the one we studied earlier.

It is natural to ask if there are several possible values for the number A in any particular case. *It can be shown that if there is a number A which satisfies the definition, then it is unique.* There cannot be two different values. The proof of this fact follows the same outline as does the proof of uniqueness of limits (see Chapter 5, Section 2) and can be found in Morrey, *University Calculus*, Section 8–5.

DEFINITIONS. The number A in the above definition is called *the definite integral of f from a to b* and is denoted by

$$\int_a^b f(x) \, dx.$$

The function f is the *integrand*, and the numbers a and b are the *lower* and *upper* limits of integration, respectively. The letter x is the *variable of integration*. This is a "dummy" variable and may be replaced by any other letter (although to prevent confusion we would avoid using a, b, d, or f for the variable of integration).

When does a function f satisfy the conditions of the definition? To find out in any particular case, we would have to investigate all possible subdivisions with all possible choices for the ξ_i and be sure that the same number A is approached in every instance. The task is a hopeless one. It is imperative that we have some theorems which tell us when a function is integrable. We have seen that not all functions possess derivatives. If a function has a "corner" or a discontinuity at a point, it has no tangent and therefore is not differentiable at that point. Similarly, we wish to know which of the various types of functions are integrable. Is a function with a corner integrable? Does a function with a "jump" discontinuity satisfy the definition of integrability?

In order to gain further insight into the process of integration we use a method of selecting special sums of the type which appear in the definition of integral. This method is closely related to the one we used in Section 2. Suppose that f is a continuous function on a closed interval $[a, b]$. The first theorem in Chapter 7 states that there is a place in $[a, b]$ where f has a largest value and another place where f has a smallest value (Extreme Value Theorem). Starting with this fact, we make a subdivision Δ of the interval $[a, b]$. That is,

$$\Delta \text{ is: } \{a = x_0 < x_1 < x_2 < \cdots < x_{n-1} < x_n = b\}.$$

Since f is continuous in $[x_0, x_1]$, there is a point, call it ξ_1', where f has a minimum value and a point, call it ξ_1'', where f has a maximum value. In $[x_1, x_2]$ f is continuous. Let ξ_2' and ξ_2'' be the places where f has minimum and maximum values, respectively. Continue this process. The values ξ_k', ξ_k'' are respectively the places where f has minimum and maximum values in the interval $[x_{k-1}, x_k]$. In this way corresponding to the subdivision Δ we get *two* sums:

$$\sum_{k=1}^{n} f(\xi_k') \Delta_k x \quad \text{and} \quad \sum_{k=1}^{n} f(\xi_k'') \Delta_k x.$$

We abbreviate this even further by writing

$$\underline{S}(\Delta) = \sum_{k=1}^{n} f(\xi_k') \Delta_k x, \quad \overline{S}(\Delta) = \sum_{k=1}^{n} f(\xi_k'') \Delta_k x.$$

From our method of selection we know that $\underline{S}(\Delta) \leq \overline{S}(\Delta)$, always. But we know even more: since in each subinterval the function f is always between its minimum and maximum, then for *any* choice ξ_i in a particular subdivision Δ we always have

$$\underline{S}(\Delta) \leq \sum_{k=1}^{n} f(\xi_k) \Delta_k x \leq \overline{S}(\Delta). \tag{1}$$

The purpose of our study of the material in Section 2 now becomes clear. The computations we made then, B_n^- and B_n^+, were just particular cases of $\underline{S}(\Delta)$ and $\overline{S}(\Delta)$ in which the points of subdivision were equally spaced. In Section 2 we always divided the interval into n *equal* parts. So if we can show that $\underline{S}(\Delta)$ and $\overline{S}(\Delta)$ tend to the same limit, A, for all possible Δ, with $\|\Delta\| \to 0$, then the same will be true for every possible choice of the ξ_i and therefore for all subdivisions. The function f will satisfy the definition of integrability.

––––––––––––

EXAMPLE. Given that $f(x) = x^2$ and given the subdivision

$$\Delta: \{a = x_0 = -1, \ x_1 = -0.6, \ x_2 = -0.2, \ x_3 = 0.3, \ x_4 = 0.7, \ x_5 = b = 1.\}$$

Find $\underline{S}(\Delta)$ and $\overline{S}(\Delta)$.

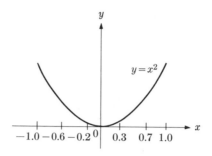

FIGURE 8-14

Solution. We construct the graph shown in Fig. 8-14, and the corresponding table:

	i	1	2	3	4	5
$\Delta_i x = x_i - x_{i-1}$	$\Delta_i x$	0.4	0.4	0.5	0.4	0.3
Place where minimum occurs	ξ_i'	-0.6	-0.2	0	0.3	0.7
Minimum value	$f(\xi_i')$	0.36	0.04	0	0.09	0.49
Place where maximum occurs	ξ_i''	-1	-0.6	0.3	0.7	1
Maximum value	$f(\xi_i'')$	1	0.36	0.09	0.49	1

Then we can obtain

$$\underline{S}(\Delta) = \sum_{i=1}^{5} f(\xi_i')\Delta_i x = 0.36(0.4) + 0.04(0.4) + 0(0.5) + 0.09(0.4) + 0.49(0.3)$$

$$= 0.343;$$

$$\overline{S}(\Delta) = \sum_{i=1}^{5} f(\xi_i'')\Delta_i x = 1(0.4) + 0.36(0.4) + 0.09(0.5) + (0.49)(0.4) + 1(0.3)$$

$$= 1.085.$$

We can now prove a theorem which indicates when certain functions are integrable.

Theorem 1. *If $f(x)$ is defined and increasing (or at least nondecreasing) in the closed interval $a \leq x \leq b$, then it is integrable there.*

Proof. Let Δ be any subdivision. In each subinterval $[x_{i-1}, x_i]$ the minimum must occur at the left endpoint and the maximum must occur at the right endpoint. That is, $\xi_i' = x_{i-1}$ and $\xi_i'' = x_i$. We construct the sums

$$\underline{S}(\Delta) = \sum_{i=1}^{n} f(x_{i-1})\,\Delta_i x, \qquad \overline{S}(\Delta) = \sum_{i=1}^{n} f(x_i)\,\Delta_i x.$$

We know that $\underline{S}(\Delta) \leq \overline{S}(\Delta)$. We now subtract:

$$\overline{S}(\Delta) - \underline{S}(\Delta) = \sum_{i=1}^{n} [f(x_i) - f(x_{i-1})]\,\Delta_i x.$$

Each $\Delta_i x$ is positive and the quantities $f(x_i) - f(x_{i-1})$ are all positive (or at least nonnegative). If we replace each $\Delta_i x$ by its largest possible value, the right side is larger, and we get the inequality

$$\overline{S}(\Delta) - \underline{S}(\Delta) \leq \sum_{i=1}^{n} [f(x_i) - f(x_{i-1})]\,\|\Delta\|.$$

The quantity $\|\Delta\|$, by definition, stands for the largest $\Delta_i x$. We now note that the terms on the right all telescope, and we have:

$$\overline{S}(\Delta) - \underline{S}(\Delta) \leq [f(x_n) - f(x_0)]\,\|\Delta\| = [f(b) - f(a)]\,\|\Delta\|.$$

Then, given any $\epsilon > 0$, if we select a subdivision with

$$\|\Delta\| < \frac{\epsilon}{f(b) - f(a)}, \qquad \text{we have} \qquad \overline{S}(\Delta) - \underline{S}(\Delta) < \epsilon.$$

From the definition of area as given in Section 1 and the inequality (1) on p. 215, it is possible to show that there is a limit A to which both $\overline{S}(\Delta)$ and $\underline{S}(\Delta)$ tend. (For additional details concerning this point, see Morrey, *University Calculus.*) Furthermore, every intermediate sum also tends to A. The function f is integrable.

Theorem 1 illustrates how careful we must be in stating the hypotheses of a theorem. To make the sloppy statement that an increasing function in an interval is integrable is to make a false statement. Consider the function

$$f(x) = \frac{1}{2 - x}$$

in the interval $0 \leq x < 2$. (See Fig. 8–15.) This function is increasing every-

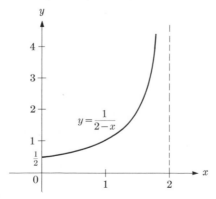

$$y = \frac{1}{2-x}$$

FIGURE 8–15

where from 0 to 2, and it tends to infinity as $x \rightarrow 2$. Since ∞ is not a number, there is no value we can give to f at 2 which will make it increasing in the *closed interval* $0 \leq x \leq 2$. In fact, this function is not integrable in [0, 2]. On the other hand, Theorem 1 tells us that the function is integrable in any interval [0, c] if $c < 2$.

In Theorem 1, the hypothesis that f is increasing is a fairly restrictive one. Actually functions are integrable under much more general hypotheses. The following theorem, which we state without proof, is an example of the type of result which establishes the integrability of a large class of functions — namely, those which are continuous on a closed interval.

Theorem 2. *If f is continuous on* [a, b], *then it is integrable on* [a, b].

The proof of this theorem depends on the notion of *uniform continuity*, a concept usually taken up in more advanced courses in analysis. However, the idea behind the proof can be discussed here. As in the discussion of the preceding theorem, we consider

$$\overline{S}(\Delta) - \underline{S}(\Delta) = \sum_{i=1}^{n} [f(\xi_i'') - f(\xi_i')] \, \Delta_i x.$$

We apply the "triangle inequality" for absolute values and, since $|\Delta_i x| = \Delta_i x$, we can write

$$\overline{S}(\Delta) - \underline{S}(\Delta) \leq \sum_{i=1}^{n} |f(\xi_i'') - f(\xi_i')| \cdot \Delta_i x.$$

Uniform continuity in an interval [a, b] means that, given any $\epsilon > 0$, there is a δ such that

$$|f(x') - f(x'')| < \epsilon$$

for any two points in [a, b] such that $|x' - x''| < \delta$. This concept is used to establish the inequality

$$\overline{S}(\Delta) - \underline{S}(\Delta) \leq \sum_{i=1}^{n} \epsilon \, \Delta_i x = \epsilon \sum_{i=1}^{n} \Delta_i x = \epsilon(b - a),$$

from which it follows that f is integrable. (A complete proof is given in Morrey, *University Calculus*.)

EXERCISES

In problems 1 through 10, a function f and a subdivision are given. Sketch the graph of the function and find the value of $\underline{S}(\Delta)$ and $\overline{S}(\Delta)$. Use knowledge of $f'(x)$ when necessary.

1. $f(x) = x^2 + 1$; Δ: $a = x_0 = 1$, $x_1 = 1.2$, $x_2 = 1.5$, $x_3 = 1.6$, $x_4 = 2$, $x_5 = 2.5$, $x_6 = b = 3$.

2. $f(x) = 1/(1 + x)$; Δ: $a = x_0 = 0$, $x_1 = 0.2$, $x_2 = 0.4$, $x_3 = 0.6$, $x_4 = 0.8$, $x_5 = b = 1$.

3. $f(x) = x^2 - x + 1; \Delta: a = x_0 = 0, x_1 = 0.1, x_2 = 0.3, x_3 = 0.5, x_4 = 0.7,$
$x_5 = 0.8, x_6 = 0.9, x_7 = b = 1.$

4. $f(x) = 1/(1 + x^2); \Delta: a = x_0 = -1, x_1 = -0.9, x_2 = -0.5, x_3 = -0.2,$
$x_4 = 0, x_5 = 0.2, x_6 = 0.3, x_7 = 0.7, x_8 = b = 1$

5. $f(x) = x^3 + x; \quad a = x_0 = 0, \quad x_1 = 0.1, \quad x_2 = 0.2, \quad x_3 = 0.3, \quad x_4 = 0.5,$
$x_5 = b = 0.6$

6. $f(x) = x^2 + 2x - 1; \Delta: a = x_0 = -2, x_1 = -1.8, x_2 = -1.6, x_3 = -1.4,$
$x_4 = -1.2, x_5 = b = -1$

7. $f(x) = (x^2 - 2)/(x + 1); \quad \Delta: \quad a = x_0 = 0, \quad x_1 = 0.5, \quad x_2 = 1, \quad x_3 = 1.5,$
$x_4 = 2, x_5 = 2.5, x_6 = 3, x_7 = b = 3.5$

8. $f(x) = x/(x^2 + 1); \Delta: a = x_0 = 0, x_1 = 1, x_2 = 2, x_3 = 3, x_4 = 4, x_5 = 4.5,$
$x_6 = 5, x_7 = b = 6.$

9. $f(x) = x^3 - 3x + 1; \Delta: a = x_0 = -2, x_1 = -1.5, x_2 = -1, x_3 = -0.5,$
$x_4 = 0, x_5 = 0.5, x_6 = 1, x_7 = 1.5, x_8 = b = 2.$

10. $f(x) = x^3/(x^3 + 1); \Delta: a = x_0 = 0, x_1 = 1, x_2 = 2, x_3 = 3, x_4 = b = 4$

11. Prove that if a function f is decreasing (or nonincreasing) on a closed interval it is integrable.

12. Why is the "post-office" function (see Chapter 2, Section 1) integrable even though it is not continuous? Find the value of the integral from $x = 0$ to $x = 4$.

13. Suppose that f and f' are continuous in $[a, b]$ and that $|f'(x)| \leq M$ in $[a, b]$. Use the Theorem of the Mean to show that for any subdivision Δ,

$$\overline{S}(\Delta) - \underline{S}(\Delta) \leq M(b - a) \cdot \|\Delta\|.$$

14. In what intervals is the function $f(x) = -1/x$ integrable?

15. Let Δ be a subdivision of the interval $[0, 1]$ into n equal parts. Compute $\underline{S}(\Delta)$ for $f(x) = 1/x^2$. What happens to $\underline{S}(\Delta)$ as $n \to \infty$? What can be said about $\overline{S}(\Delta)$ and therefore about the integrability of f?

4. PROPERTIES OF THE DEFINITE INTEGRAL

Later we shall develop techniques for evaluating integrals without recourse to the definition. This is analogous to what we did for derivatives: first we showed how to find the derivative directly from the definition, and then we developed methods for differentiation which bypassed the definition entirely. The properties we shall now discuss will be useful in learning methods for integrating various kinds of functions.

The simplest properties are given in the two following theorems.

Theorem 3. *If c is any number and f is integrable in $[a, b]$, then the function $cf(x)$ is integrable in $[a, b]$ and*

$$\int_a^b cf(x)\, dx = c \int_a^b f(x)\, dx.$$

Theorem 4. *If $f(x)$ and $g(x)$ are integrable in $[a, b]$, then $f(x) + g(x)$ is integrable in $[a, b]$ and*

$$\int_a^b [f(x) + g(x)]\, dx = \int_a^b f(x)\, dx + \int_a^b g(x)\, dx.$$

We shall prove Theorem 4.

Proof. If M and N are any numbers, we know that $|M + N| \le |M| + |N|$. Let Δ be any subdivision and take

$$M = \sum_{i=1}^{n} f(\xi_i) \, \Delta_i x - \int_a^b f(x) \, dx, \qquad N = \sum_{i=1}^{n} g(\xi_i) \, \Delta_i x - \int_a^b g(x) \, dx.$$

From the definition of integrability, we have $|M| < \epsilon$ and $|N| < \epsilon$ if $\|\Delta\|$ is sufficiently small. But

$$M + N = \sum_{i=1}^{n} [f(\xi_i) + g(\xi_i)] \, \Delta_i x - \left[\int_a^b f(x) \, dx + \int_a^b g(x) \, dx \right].$$

We conclude that $|M + N| < 2\epsilon$. This means that $M + N$ tends to zero as $\|\Delta\|$ tends to zero and, therefore, the function $f + g$ is integrable and equal to the sum of the integrals of f and g.

The proof of Theorem 3 is similar.

Theorem 5. *If $f(x)$ is integrable in an interval $[a, b]$, then f is bounded there.*

This theorem is proved in more advanced courses in mathematics. The theorem means that if a function is integrable there must be two numbers m and M (m may be negative and M may be very large, positive) such that for all values x in $[a, b]$, $f(x)$ lies between m and M. That is,

$$m \le f(x) \le M.$$

Theorem 5 is of considerable importance in developing the theory of integration.

Theorem 6. *If $f(x)$ is integrable in an interval $[a, b]$ and m and M are numbers such that*

$$m \le f(x) \le M \qquad for \qquad a \le x \le b,$$

then

$$m(b - a) \le \int_a^b f(x) \, dx \le M(b - a).$$

Proof. Let Δ be a subdivision of $[a, b]$. We know that

$$\sum_{i=1}^{n} f(\xi_i) \, \Delta_i x$$

tends to the integral if $x_{i-1} \le \xi_i \le x_i$ and if $\|\Delta\| \to 0$ as $n \to \infty$. By hypothesis, $m \le f(\xi_i) \le M$ for each i. Multiplying through by $\Delta_i x$ yields

$$m \, \Delta_i x \le f(\xi_i) \, \Delta_i x \le M \, \Delta_i x.$$

Summing from 1 to n, we now write

$$\sum_{i=1}^{n} m \, \Delta_i x \le \sum_{i=1}^{n} f(\xi_i) \, \Delta_i x \le \sum_{i=1}^{n} M \, \Delta_i x.$$

On the left and the right we can factor out the m and M, respectively, to find

$$m \sum_{i=1}^{n} \Delta_i x \leq \sum_{i=1}^{n} f(\xi_i) \Delta_i x \leq M \sum_{i=1}^{n} \Delta_i x.$$

But

$$\sum_{i=1}^{n} \Delta_i x$$

telescopes to give $b - a$. Therefore

$$m(b - a) \leq \sum_{i=1}^{n} f(\xi_i) \Delta_i x \leq M(b - a).$$

The term in the middle tends to the integral and, since the inequalities hold in the limit, the result follows.

Theorem 7. *If f and g are integrable in the interval* $[a, b]$ *and* $f(x) \leq g(x)$ *for each x in* $[a, b]$ *then*

$$\int_a^b f(x) \, dx \leq \int_a^b g(x) \, dx.$$

Proof. The proof furnishes an excellent illustration of the way in which mathematics is composed of building blocks. We can show how earlier theorems form the blocks which produce the result. We define $F(x) = g(x) - f(x)$. Then by hypothesis $F(x) \geq 0$ in $[a, b]$. By Theorem 3, if $f(x)$ is integrable, so is $-f(x)$, $(c = -1)$. According to Theorem 4, if $g(x)$ and $-f(x)$ are integrable, so is $g(x) + (-f(x)) = F(x)$. We recall that Theorem 6 tells us that

$$m(b - a) \leq \int_a^b F(x) \, dx$$

and we can select $m = 0$, since $F(x) \geq 0$ in $[a, b]$. Therefore

$$\int_a^b [g(x) - f(x)] \, dx \geq 0,$$

or

$$\int_a^b g(x) \, dx - \int_a^b f(x) \, dx \geq 0 \qquad \text{(by Theorem 4)},$$

or

$$\int_a^b g(x) \, dx \geq \int_a^b f(x) \, dx,$$

which is what we wanted to prove.

Theorem 8. *If f(x) is continuous in the interval* $[a, b]$ *and c is any number in* $[a, b]$, *then*

$$\int_a^b f(x) \, dx = \int_a^c f(x) \, dx + \int_c^b f(x) \, dx.$$

Proof. Consider a subdivision Δ of the interval $[a, b]$. This subdivision may or may not contain c as one of its points x_i. If it does not, we insert c into it and obtain a new subdivision Δ', with one more point and one more interval. The new subdivision has a norm $\|\Delta'\|$ which is smaller or the same as the norm $\|\Delta\|$; at least it is not larger. Then the part of the subdivision of Δ' from a to c gives a sum of the form

$$\sum_{i=1}^{n'} f(\xi_i)\, \Delta_i x,$$

where n' is the number of subintervals in $[a, c]$; similarly, if n'' is the number of subintervals from c to b there will be a sum of the form

$$\sum_{i=1}^{n''} f(\xi_i)\, \Delta_i x$$

for this range. The first sum tends to $\int_a^c f(x)\, dx$, the second sum tends to $\int_c^b f(x)\, dx$, and the two added together tend to $\int_a^b f(x)\, dx$. This is exactly the statement of the result of the theorem.

Two useful definitions,

$$\int_a^a f(x)\, dx = 0 \qquad \text{and} \qquad \int_a^b f(x)\, dx = -\int_b^a f(x)\, dx,$$

imply that the relation

$$\int_a^b f(x)\, dx = \int_a^c f(x)\, dx + \int_c^b f(x)\, dx$$

holds for any value of c whether or not it is between a and b. If $c = b$ the result is clear, while if $c > b$ or $c < a$, the appropriate reversal of sign reduces the result to the one stated in Theorem 8.

EXERCISES

1. Prove Theorem 3.

In problems 2 through 13, study the functions in the given intervals and apply Theorem 6 to find the largest and smallest values the stated integrals can possibly have.

2. $\displaystyle\int_1^3 \tfrac{1}{2}x\, dx$
    3. $\displaystyle\int_{-1}^2 x^2\, dx$
    4. $\displaystyle\int_{-1}^1 x^3\, dx$

5. $\displaystyle\int_1^4 \frac{1}{1+x}\, dx$
    6. $\displaystyle\int_{-2}^2 \frac{1}{1+x^2}\, dx$
    7. $\displaystyle\int_0^4 \frac{x^2}{1+x^2}\, dx$

8. $\displaystyle\int_{-3}^{-1} \frac{1}{1-x}\, dx$
    9. $\displaystyle\int_2^5 \sqrt{1+x}\, dx$
    10. $\displaystyle\int_0^3 \sqrt{x^2+1}\, dx$

11. $\displaystyle\int_0^4 \frac{2\sqrt{x}}{1+x}\, dx$
    12. $\displaystyle\int_1^2 \frac{1-x^2}{1+x^2}\, dx$
    13. $\displaystyle\int_{-2}^3 \frac{2+x}{\sqrt{1+x^2}}\, dx$

14. Given that
$$f(x) = \begin{cases} x, & -1 \le x \le 0, \\ x^2 - x + 1, & 0 < x \le 1, \end{cases}$$

show, by combining theorems of Sections 3 and 4, that $f(x)$ is integrable in the interval $[-1, 1]$.

15. Write out the details of the proof that

$$\int_a^b f(x)\, dx = \int_a^c f(x)\, dx + \int_c^b f(x)\, dx$$

when c is not between a and b.

5. EVALUATION OF DEFINITE INTEGRALS

It is apparent from the early work in Chapter 4, Section 6, and the methods developed in Section 2 of this chapter, that the definite integral is intimately connected with area. In fact, *if* $f(x) \ge 0$ *in an interval* $[a, b]$ *and if it is integrable there, then*

$$\int_a^b f(x)\, dx$$

is the area bounded by the lines $x = a$, $x = b$, *the x-axis, and the curve of* $y = f(x)$ (shaded region in Fig. 8–16). This is certainly not startling in the light of all our discussions of area as an interpretation of integral. If $f(x)$ is entirely *below* the x-axis, then the sums

$$\sum_{i=1}^n f(\xi_i)\, \Delta_i x$$

are always *negative*. If f is integrable in $[a, b]$, this integral will have a *negative value*. The value of

$$\int_a^b f(x)\, dx$$

will be *the negative of the area* bounded by the lines $x = a$, $x = b$, the x-axis, and the curve of $y = f(x)$ (shaded region in Fig. 8–17). If a function f is partly positive and partly negative in $[a, b]$ so that there is a point c where it crosses the x-axis (see Fig. 8–18), the value of

$$\int_a^b f(x)\, dx$$

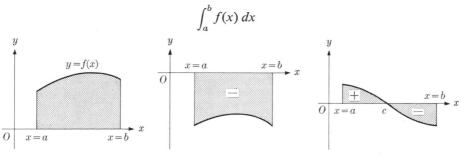

FIGURE 8–16   FIGURE 8–17   FIGURE 8–18

is the difference between the area above the x-axis and the area below it. To obtain the true area of a region such as the shaded one shown in Fig. 8–18, one must first find the point c and compute

$$\int_a^c f(x)\, dx \qquad \text{and} \qquad \int_c^b f(x)\, dx$$

separately. The value of the first integral is positive and that of the second negative. We add the absolute value of the second integral to the value of the first, and the resulting quantity is the total area.

The next theorem we shall establish, known as the Fundamental Theorem of the Calculus, is useful for actually finding the value of a definite integral. In Chapter 4, Section 6, we saw in an intuitive way the relationship between derivative and integral. The integral was interpreted as an area (we considered positive functions only) and the derivative of the integral turned out to be the integrand. Now we establish the relation between derivative and integral purely on the basis of the material in this chapter.

Theorem 9. (Fundamental Theorem of the Calculus, first form.) *Suppose that F is continuous and that F' is integrable on the interval* $[a, b]$. *Then*

$$\int_a^b F'(x)\, dx = F(b) - F(a).$$

Proof. We make a subdivision $\Delta \colon \{a = x_0 < x_1 < x_2 < \cdots < x_{n-1} < x_n = b\}$ of the interval $[a, b]$. We assemble the following facts:

(1) $$F(b) - F(a) = \sum_{i=1}^{n} [F(x_i) - F(x_{i-1})].$$

This comes about from telescoping.

(2) From the Theorem of the Mean (Chapter 7, Theorem 4) we know that for any two points $\bar{x}$, $\bar{\bar{x}}$, we have $F(\bar{\bar{x}}) - F(\bar{x}) = F'(\xi)(\bar{\bar{x}} - \bar{x})$, where ξ is some number between $\bar{x}$ and $\bar{\bar{x}}$.

(3) From the definition of integral, if ϵ is any positive number, then there is a number $\delta > 0$ such that if the norm of the subdivision, $\|\Delta\|$, is less than δ, then

$$\left| \sum_{i=1}^{n} F'(\xi_i)\, \Delta_i x - \int_a^b F'(x)\, dx \right| < \epsilon.$$

We apply the Theorem of the Mean to $F(x_i) - F(x_{i-1})$, calling the intermediate point ξ_i, to obtain

$$F(x_i) - F(x_{i-1}) = F'(\xi_i)(x_i - x_{i-1}).$$

We use fact (1) and the abbreviation $\Delta_i x = x_i - x_{i-1}$, to write

$$F(b) - F(a) = \sum_{i=1}^{n} F'(\xi_i)\, \Delta_i x.$$

Fact (3) allows us to substitute $F(b) - F(a)$ for the sum and so obtain

$$\left| F(b) - F(a) - \int_a^b F'(x)\,dx \right| < \epsilon.$$

We now make use of a typical mathematical argument which seems to give us something for nothing. Since the above inequality must hold for *every possible* $\epsilon > 0$, the part within the absolute-value sign must be *equal* to zero. (If it were not, we would simply choose an ϵ smaller than that value to get a contradiction.)

The above argument works because the quantity within the absolute-value sign *has nothing to do with* ϵ. If it did the reasoning would be false.

The Fundamental Theorem states that if we are given any integrable function f we can compute the definite integral over $[a, b]$ by finding *any* antiderivative of f and then evaluating this antiderivative at b, evaluating it at a, and then subtracting. A function f may have more than one antiderivative; in fact it has infinitely many of them. However, as the following corollary shows, any two antiderivatives differ by a constant.

Corollary. *If $F_1(x)$ and $F_2(x)$ are antiderivatives of the same function f on the interval $[a, b]$, then $F_1(x) = F_2(x) + \text{const on } [a, b]$.*

Proof: Since $F_1(x)$ and $F_2(x)$ are antiderivatives of the same function, the function $F(x) = F_1(x) - F_2(x)$ has a derivative which is identically zero. It follows from the Theorem of the Mean that $F(x)$ must be constant.

To get antiderivatives of functions we simply work backward from our knowledge of derivatives. If

$$f(x) = x^n, \qquad n \text{ rational}, \neq -1,$$

then

$$\text{antiderivative of } f = \frac{x^{n+1}}{n+1} + \text{const},$$

since the derivative of

$$\frac{x^{n+1}}{n+1}$$

is exactly x^n. We shall illustrate the procedure with some examples.

EXAMPLE 1. Evaluate $\int_1^2 x^2\,dx$.

Solution. The antiderivative of x^2 is

$$\frac{x^3}{3} + \text{const}.$$

We evaluate this at $x = 2$ and at $x = 1$ and then subtract:

$$\frac{x^3}{3} + \text{const at } x = 2 \quad \text{is} \quad \tfrac{8}{3} + \text{const};$$

$$\frac{x^3}{3} + \text{const at } x = 1 \quad \text{is} \quad \tfrac{1}{3} + \text{const}.$$

Difference $= \tfrac{8}{3} - \tfrac{1}{3} = \tfrac{7}{3}$. Then $\int_1^2 x^2\,dx = \tfrac{7}{3}$, which is the desired evaluation.

Observe that the constant in the antiderivative cancelled. *This is always the case when we evaluate definite integrals; therefore, from now on, the constant of integration will be omitted in evaluating definite integrals.*

EXAMPLE 2. Evaluate $\int_0^4 (x^3 - 2)\,dx$.

Solution. The antiderivative of $x^3 - 2$ is $\frac{1}{4}x^4 - 2x$.

$$\frac{1}{4}x^4 - 2x \quad \text{at} \quad x = 4 \quad \text{is} \quad 64 - 8 = 56;$$
$$\frac{1}{4}x^4 - 2x \quad \text{at} \quad x = 0 \quad \text{is} \quad 0.$$

Therefore

$$\int_0^4 (x^3 - 2)\,dx = 56.$$

There is a convenient and simple notation which reduces the work of evaluating integrals. We write

$$F(x)]_a^b \quad \text{or} \quad [F(x)]_a^b \quad \text{for} \quad F(b) - F(a).$$

The way in which the notation works is exhibited in the following example.

EXAMPLE 3. Evaluate $\int_{-1}^2 (2x^3 - 3x^2 + x - 1)\,dx$.

Solution.

$$\int_{-1}^2 (2x^3 - 3x^2 + x - 1)\,dx = \left[\frac{x^4}{2} - x^3 + \frac{x^2}{2} - x\right]_{-1}^2$$
$$= (8 - 8 + 2 - 2) - (\tfrac{1}{2} + 1 + \tfrac{1}{2} + 1) = -3.$$

If the integrand is a complicated function, it may be difficult or even impossible to get an expression for the antiderivative. In such cases we may be interested in obtaining an *approximate value* for the definite integral. The very definition of a definite integral yields useful methods for finding an approximate value. One such process, which we shall describe, is called the *midpoint rule*. We first subdivide the interval of integration into n *equal* parts so that each subinterval has length $(b - a)/n$. Then we obtain the value $f(\xi_i)$, where ξ_i is the *midpoint* of the ith subinterval. The quantity

$$\sum_{i=1}^n f(\xi_i)\,\frac{b-a}{n}$$

is an approximation of $\int_a^b f(x)\,dx$.

EXAMPLE 4. Using the midpoint rule, compute

$$\int_1^2 \frac{1}{x}\,dx$$

approximately, with $n = 5$.

Solution. Each $\Delta_i x = 0.2$, since there are five subintervals from 1 to 2. Then $x_0 = 1.0$, $x_1 = 1.2$, $x_2 = 1.4$, $x_3 = 1.6$, $x_4 = 1.8$, $x_5 = 2.0$. Using midpoints, we find that $\xi_1 = 1.1$, $\xi_2 = 1.3$, $\xi_3 = 1.5$, $\xi_4 = 1.7$, $\xi_5 = 1.9$. We obtain

$$f(\xi_1)\,\Delta_1 x = \frac{1}{1.1}\,(0.2) = 0.18182,$$

$$f(\xi_2)\,\Delta_2 x = \frac{1}{1.3}\,(0.2) = 0.15385,$$

$$f(\xi_3)\,\Delta_3 x = \frac{1}{1.5}\,(0.2) = 0.13333,$$

$$f(\xi_4)\,\Delta_4 x = \frac{1}{1.7}\,(0.2) = 0.11765,$$

$$f(\xi_5)\,\Delta_5 x = \frac{1}{1.9}\,(0.2) = 0.10503,$$

$$\sum_{i=1}^{5} f(\xi_i)\,\Delta_i x = 0.69168.$$

The true value of the integral, correct to three decimal places, is 0.693^+

EXERCISES

In problems 1 through 14, evaluate the given definite integrals.

1. $\displaystyle\int_{1}^{3} (x^2 - 3x + 2)\,dx$

2. $\displaystyle\int_{1}^{4} (x^{3/2} + 2x + x^{-1/2})\,dx$

3. $\displaystyle\int_{-1}^{2} (3x^2 + 2x + 1)\,dx$

4. $\displaystyle\int_{-3}^{-1} (4x^3 - 3x^2 + 2)\,dx$

5. $\displaystyle\int_{1}^{4} \left(\sqrt{x} + \frac{1}{\sqrt{x}}\right)dx$

6. $\displaystyle\int_{-1}^{1} \sqrt[3]{x^2}\,dx$

7. $\displaystyle\int_{1}^{9} \frac{x^2 + x + 1}{\sqrt{x}}\,dx$

8. $\displaystyle\int_{1}^{2} (2t + 1)^2\,dt$

9. $\displaystyle\int_{0}^{2} (x + 1)(2x + 6)\,dx$

10. $\displaystyle\int_{1}^{2} (2x + 1)^2 (x - 6)^2\,dx$

11. $\displaystyle\int_{-1}^{1} \frac{(x^2 + 6x - 2)^2}{9}\,dx$

12. $\displaystyle\int_{1}^{3} \frac{t^2 + 2t - 1}{\sqrt[3]{t}}\,dt$

13. $\displaystyle\int_{0}^{x} t^2\,dt$

14. $\displaystyle\int_{1}^{x} \frac{1}{\sqrt{t}}\,dt$

In problems 15 through 24, compute the integrals approximately, using the midpoint rule. Compute each term $f(\xi_i)\,\Delta_i x$ to four decimals and round off the result to three decimal places. *Also* compute the exact value of each term by the rule for integrating.

15. $\displaystyle\int_{-2}^{-1} x^2\,dx, \quad n = 5$ 16. $\displaystyle\int_{0}^{1} x^3\,dx, \quad n = 5$

17. $\displaystyle\int_{1}^{2} \frac{1}{x^2}\,dx, \quad n = 5$ 18. $\displaystyle\int_{0.5}^{1} \frac{1}{x^3}\,dx, \quad n = 5$

19. $\displaystyle\int_{1}^{3} (2x + 1)\,dx, \quad n = 1$ 20. $\displaystyle\int_{-1}^{0} (2 - 3y)\,dy, \quad n = 1$

21. $\displaystyle\int_{a}^{b} (At + B)\,dt, \quad n = 1$ 22. $\displaystyle\int_{1}^{4} \sqrt{u}\,du, \quad n = 6$

23. $\displaystyle\int_{1}^{2} (x + 1)(2x + 1)\,dx, \quad n = 4$ 24. $\displaystyle\int_{1}^{3} \frac{x^2 + 2}{x^2}\,dx, \quad n = 2$

In problems 25 through 28, use the midpoint rule to compute the integrals approximately. The answers given are the exact values rounded off to the number of decimals indicated. They are *not* necessarily the answers which the student should obtain by following the procedure given.

25. $\displaystyle\int_{0}^{1} \frac{dx}{x + 1}, \quad n = 5;$ answer, 0.693^{+}

26. $\displaystyle\int_{0}^{1} \frac{dx}{x^2 + 1}, \quad n = 5;$ answer, $\dfrac{\pi}{4} = 0.7854^{-}$

27. $\displaystyle\int_{0}^{1} \sqrt{1 - x^2}\,dx, \quad n = 5;$ answer, $\dfrac{\pi}{4} = 0.7854^{-}$

28. $\displaystyle\int_{0}^{0.5} \frac{dx}{\sqrt{1 - x^2}}, \quad n = 5;$ answer, $\dfrac{\pi}{6} = 0.5236^{-}$

6. THEOREM OF THE MEAN FOR INTEGRALS

In Chapter 7 we took up the Extreme Value Theorem (Theorem 1), which said that *a function which is continuous on a closed interval takes on its maximum and minimum values there.* A companion to this theorem is the Intermediate Value Theorem given below.

Theorem 10. (Intermediate Value Theorem.) *Suppose that f is continuous on an interval $[a, b]$ and that $f(a) = A, f(b) = B$. If C is any number between A and B, there is a number c between a and b such that $f(c) = C$.*

This theorem is usually proved in more advanced courses. However, we shall discuss the plausibility of the result. Figure 8–19 shows a typical function defined on $[a, b]$ with $f(a) = A$, $f(b) = B$. We give a geometrical interpretation of Theorem 10: If C is any point on the y-axis between A and B and we draw the line $y = C$, then this line must intersect the curve representing $y = f(x)$. Further-

FIGURE 8–19

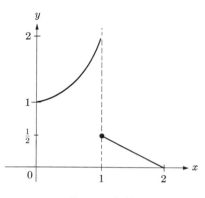

FIGURE 8–20

more, the x-value of the point of intersection is in (a, b). Figure 8–19 shows the intersection which occurs when $x = c$. That is, we have $f(c) = C$. Intuitively, the theorem asserts that if the function is continuous and if it extends from a point below the line $y = C$ to a point above the line $y = C$, it must cross this line. Note that for some values of C (say C', as shown in Fig. 8–19) there may be several possible values of c. The theorem says that there is always *at least one*.

If the function is not continuous the theorem is false, as the following example shows. Define

$$f(x) = \begin{cases} x^2 + 1, & 0 \le x < 1, \\ \tfrac{1}{2}(2 - x), & 1 \le x \le 2. \end{cases}$$

The graph of this function is shown in Fig. 8–20. If we select $a = 0, b = 2$, then $f(0) = 1$, $f(2) = 0$, and $A = 1, B = 0$. We see that if C is chosen so that $\tfrac{1}{2} < C < 1$, there is no value of c such that $f(c) = C$. The function never assumes any value between $\tfrac{1}{2}$ and 1. The discontinuity at $x = 1$ causes the trouble.

Another example in which Theorem 10 fails is given by the function

$$f(x) = \frac{1}{x - 3},$$

which is not continuous at $x = 3$ (no matter what value we assign to f at $x = 3$). Any interval $[a, b]$ which contains 3 will have values C for which we cannot find numbers c such that $f(c) = C$. If $a = 1, b = 4$, then $f(1) = -\tfrac{1}{2}, f(4) = 1$, and a value of $C = \tfrac{1}{2}$ which is between $A = -\tfrac{1}{2}, B = 1$ is taken on only when

$$\frac{1}{x - 3} = \frac{1}{2}, \quad \text{or} \quad x = 5.$$

Then $f(5) = \tfrac{1}{2}$, but 5 is not in the interval $[1, 4]$, and the theorem fails.

EXAMPLE 1. Given the function $f(x) = (x - 1)/(x^2 + 1)$, $a = 0, b = 2$. Select a value of C between the A and B of the Intermediate Value Theorem and verify the validity of the result.

Solution. $f(0) = -1$, $f(2) = \frac{1}{5}$. We select C between -1 and $\frac{1}{5}$, say $-\frac{1}{2}$. Then we solve for x:

$$\frac{x-1}{x^2+1} = -\frac{1}{2}.$$

This yields

$$x = -1 \pm \sqrt{2}.$$

The value $-1 + \sqrt{2}$ is in the interval $[0, 2]$ and is the value for which

$$f(-1 + \sqrt{2}) = -\tfrac{1}{2}.$$

The number $-1 - \sqrt{2}$ is rejected, since it falls outside $[0, 2]$.

———————

The Intermediate Value Theorem is used in establishing the Theorem of the Mean for Integrals.

Theorem 11. (Theorem of the Mean for Integrals.) *If f is continuous on a closed interval with endpoints a and b, there is a number ξ between a and b such that*

$$\int_a^b f(x)\,dx = f(\xi)(b - a).$$

We shall first prove this theorem and then discuss it geometrically.

Proof. We know by the Extreme Value Theorem (Chapter 7, Theorem 1) that there are two numbers m and M such that $m \leq f(x) \leq M$ for all x in $[a, b]$. Furthermore, in Theorem 6 of this chapter we showed that

$$m(b - a) \leq \int_a^b f(x)\,dx \leq M(b - a).$$

Since the integral is between two numbers, there must be some number which gives the exact value. That is, there is a number D between m and M such that

$$\int_a^b f(x)\,dx = D(b - a).$$

By the Extreme Value Theorem, we know that there are values x_0 and x_1 such that $f(x_0) = m$ and $f(x_1) = M$ with x_0 and x_1 in $[a, b]$. Now we bring into play the Intermediate Value Theorem, which states that there is a number ξ between x_0 and x_1 such that $f(\xi) = D$. In other words,

$$\int_a^b f(x)\,dx = f(\xi)(b - a).$$

In Fig. 8–21 we exhibit a geometric interpretation for a nonnegative function $f(x)$. Then $\int_a^b f(x)\,dx$ is the area bounded by the lines $x = a$, $x = b$, the x-axis, and the curve of $y = f(x)$.

In effect, Theorem 11 states that there is a point ξ (between a and b) such that the area determined by the integral is equal to that of the rectangle of height $f(\xi)$

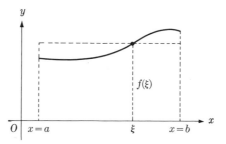

FIGURE 8–21

and width $b - a: f(\xi)(b - a)$. If $f(x)$ is considered to be made of rubber and if the low parts are pushed up and the high parts are pushed down, always keeping the area under the curve the same, the result would be a rectangle of height $f(\xi)$ and width $b - a$.

Finding the number ξ is usually very difficult. However, Theorem 11 proves its worth (particularly in the development of mathematical theory) by demonstrating that such a value ξ does exist. It may seem strange that a use can be found for the knowledge of the existence of something without knowledge of its value or even of how to obtain its value. But that is exactly the state of affairs, as is shown in the proof of Theorem 12, which follows. It may be compared to the situation in which we know there is a buried treasure but have no idea where it is or how to find it.

In some cases the value of ξ can be determined, and the following example shows one way to do it.

EXAMPLE 2. Find the value of ξ such that

$$\int_1^3 f(x)\, dx = f(\xi)(3 - 1),$$

where $f(x) = x^2 - 2x + 1$.

Solution. We find the value of the integral

$$\int_1^3 (x^2 - 2x + 1)\, dx = \tfrac{1}{3}x^3 - x^2 + x]_1^3 = (9 - 9 + 3) - (\tfrac{1}{3} - 1 + 1) = \tfrac{8}{3}.$$

Therefore $f(\xi) \cdot (2) = \tfrac{8}{3}$ and $f(\xi) = \tfrac{4}{3}$. We solve for ξ:

$$\xi^2 - 2\xi + 1 = \tfrac{4}{3},$$

and the result is

$$\xi = 1 \pm \tfrac{2}{3}\sqrt{3}.$$

Of these numbers, the value $1 + \tfrac{2}{3}\sqrt{3}$ is in the interval $[1, 3]$. We conclude that

$$\int_1^3 f(x)\, dx = f(1 + \tfrac{2}{3}\sqrt{3})(3 - 1).$$

Theorem 12. (Fundamental Theorem of Calculus, second form.) *Suppose that f is continuous on an interval [a, b] and c is some number in this interval. Define the function F by*

$$F(x) = \int_c^x f(t)\, dt$$

for each x in the interval (a, b). Then

$$F'(x) = f(x).$$

Proof. We know by Theorem 8 that

$$\int_c^{x+h} f(t)\, dt = \int_c^x f(t)\, dt + \int_x^{x+h} f(t)\, dt,$$

so long as h is a number sufficiently small that $x + h$ does not fall outside the interval. The way in which we defined F tells us that this relationship is nothing but

$$F(x + h) = F(x) + \int_x^{x+h} f(t)\, dt.$$

We apply the Theorem of the Mean for Integrals to the integral $\int_x^{x+h} f(t)\, dt$, getting

$$\int_x^{x+h} f(t)\, dt = f(\xi) \cdot h,$$

where ξ is some value between x and $x + h$. We now have

$$\frac{F(x + h) - F(x)}{h} = f(\xi).$$

The hypothesis that f is continuous states (by the definition of continuity) that given $\epsilon > 0$ there is a $\delta > 0$ such that

$$|f(\xi) - f(x)| < \epsilon$$

whenever $|\xi - x| < \delta$. Note that as $h \to 0$, $\xi \to x$, since ξ is always between x and $x + h$. Therefore, if h is sufficiently close to zero, we may write

$$\left| \frac{F(x + h) - F(x)}{h} - f(x) \right| < \epsilon.$$

Since, by definition,

$$\frac{F(x + h) - F(x)}{h} \to F'(x) \quad \text{as} \quad h \to 0,$$

we conclude that

$$F'(x) = f(x).$$

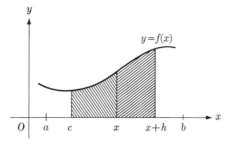

FIGURE 8–22

In the proof of Theorem 12, we employed the Theorem of the Mean for Integrals (Theorem 11) without ever finding the value of ξ which occurs. This is a common practice in the proof of mathematical theorems.

A geometric interpretation of the above result for nonnegative functions f was given in Chapter 4, Section 6. We shall repeat it here. From Fig. 8–22, where $F(x)$ is the shaded area on the left, $F(x + h)$ is the sum of the shaded areas, and $F(x + h) - F(x)$ is the shaded area on the right, we find that

$$\frac{F(x + h) - F(x)}{h}$$

is the *average* height of $f(x)$ in the right-hand area. As $h \to 0$ this average height tends to the height at x, namely $f(x)$. On the other hand, as $h \to 0$, the expression above tends to $F'(x)$.

The real meaning of the Fundamental Theorem of Calculus is that *differentiation and integration are inverse processes*. This is meant in the same sense that addition and subtraction are inverse processes, as are multiplication and division (excluding division by zero). What about squaring and taking the square root? These are inverse to each other if an additional condition is tacked on: only positive numbers are allowed. The same situation prevails for derivatives and integrals; they are inverse if some additional condition is added (such as continuity of f in Theorem 12). In more advanced courses theorems similar to Theorem 9 and Theorem 12 are established, which show under much less restrictive hypotheses that differentiation and integration are inverse processes.

EXERCISES

In problems 1 through 8, a function f and numbers a, b, and C are given. Verify the Intermediate Value Theorem, or show that this theorem does not apply.

1. $f(x) = x^2 + 2x - 1$, $a = -1, b = 2, C = 5$
2. $f(x) = (x + 3)/(x^2 + 2)$, $a = 0, b = 3, C = 1$
3. $f(x) = 3 - 2x + x^2$, $a = 2, b = 4, C = 6$
4. $f(x) = (x^2 + 1)/(x - 1)$, $a = 3, b = 5, C = 6$
5. $f(x) = 3x^2 + x - 6$, $a = 0, b = 2, C = 10$
6. $f(x) = (x - 1)/(x + 1)$, $a = -2, b = 1, C = \frac{1}{2}$

7. $f(x) = \begin{cases} 2x, & -1 \le x < 1 \\ 3 - x, & 1 \le x < 5 \end{cases}$ $a = 0, b = 2, C = \frac{1}{2}$

8. $f(x) = \begin{cases} 1 - x^2, & -10 \le x < 0 \\ x - 3, & 0 \le x < 5 \end{cases}$ $a = -1, b = 2, C = -\frac{1}{2}$

In problems 9 through 15, verify the Theorem of the Mean for Integrals by finding appropriate values of ξ. Sketch graphs.

9. $\displaystyle\int_2^5 f(x)\, dx$,   with $f(x) = 3x - 2$

10. $\displaystyle\int_{-1}^2 f(x)\, dx$,   with $f(x) = 2 + 4x$

11. $\displaystyle\int_2^7 f(x)\, dx$,   with $f(x) = x^2 - 2x + 1$

12. $\displaystyle\int_0^1 f(x)\, dx$,   with $f(x) = (x + 1)^2$

13. $\displaystyle\int_{-1}^1 f(x)\, dx$,   with $f(x) = 3 - 2x + 4x^2$

14. $\displaystyle\int_0^2 f(x)\, dx$,   with $f(x) = 4x^3 - 3x^2 - 4x$

15. $\displaystyle\int_{-2}^2 f(x)\, dx$,   with $f(x) = x^5 - 4x^3 + 3x$

16. Given that $f(x) = (x^2 + 2)^3$, verify that $f'(x) = 6x(x^2 + 2)^2$. Use the Fundamental Theorem of Calculus to evaluate $\int_0^2 6x(x^2 + 2)^2\, dx$.

17. Given that $f(x) = (x^2 + 5)^{1/2}$, verify that $f'(x) = x(x^2 + 5)^{-1/2}$. Use the Fundamental Theorem of Calculus to evaluate

$$\int_1^3 \frac{x\, dx}{\sqrt{x^2 + 5}}.$$

18. Given that $f(x) = 6(x + 2)^{3/2}(x^2 + 1)^{4/3}$, verify that

$$f'(x) = (x + 2)^{1/2}(x^2 + 1)^{1/3}(25x^2 + 32x + 9).$$

Evaluate

$$\int_0^2 (x + 2)^{1/2}(x^2 + 1)^{1/3}(25x^2 + 32x + 9)\, dx.$$

19. Given that $f(x) = (x + 3)/(x - 2)$, verify that $f'(x) = -5/(x - 2)^2$. Evaluate

$$\int_{-1}^1 \frac{dx}{(x - 2)^2}.$$

20. If a function is odd, that is, if $f(-x) = -f(x)$ for all x, what can be said about $\int_{-b}^b f(x)\, dx$?   (*Hint*: Draw a sketch.)

21. If a function is even, that is, if $f(-x) = f(x)$ for all x, what can be said about the relation between $\int_{-b}^b f(x)\, dx$ and $\int_0^b f(x)\, dx$?

7. INDEFINITE INTEGRALS. CHANGE OF VARIABLE

To evaluate the definite integral of a function, we must first obtain an anti-derivative of the function and then substitute the appropriate limits of integration into this antiderivative. Every function has an infinite number of antiderivatives, since a constant of arbitrary magnitude may be added to one antiderivative to yield another. A common notation used for all the antiderivatives of a function f is

$$\int f(x)\,dx,$$

in which there are no upper and lower limits. This is called the *indefinite integral* of f. For example, the formula for the antiderivative of x^n, n rational, $\neq -1$, is written

$$\int x^n\,dx = \frac{x^{n+1}}{n+1} + C, \qquad n \neq -1,$$

where the constant C is the *constant of integration*.

The following seemingly trivial variation of the above formula has many useful consequences. We write

$$\int u^n\,du = \frac{u^{n+1}}{n+1} + C, \qquad n \neq -1.$$

True, this *is* the same formula. However, according to the chain rule, we know that

$$d\left(\frac{u^{n+1}}{n+1}\right) = u^n\,du$$

holds if u is *any function* of x. Schematically we write

$$\int (\text{expression in } x)^n\, d(\textit{same expression in } x) = \frac{(\text{expression in } x)^{n+1}}{n+1} + C.$$

We shall illustrate the significance of this formula with some examples.

EXAMPLE 1. Find $\int (3x + 2)^7\,dx$.

Solution. The integrand could be multiplied out and then each term could be evaluated separately. Instead, we observe that $3x + 2$ is an expression in x raised to the 7th power. So we write

$$u = 3x + 2, \qquad du = 3\,dx \quad \text{or} \quad dx = \tfrac{1}{3}\,du.$$

Substituting, we get

$$\int (3x + 2)^7\,dx = \int u^7 \cdot \tfrac{1}{3}\,du.$$

A constant (*and only a constant*) may be moved in and out of integrals at will. We obtain

$$\int u^7 \tfrac{1}{3}\,du = \tfrac{1}{3}\int u^7\,du = \tfrac{1}{3}\left(\frac{u^8}{8} + C\right).$$

Since C represents *any* constant, so does $\frac{1}{3}C$, and we write, after substituting the value of u in terms of x,

$$\int (3x + 2)^7 \, dx = \tfrac{1}{24}(3x + 2)^8 + C.$$

EXAMPLE 2. Find $\int (x^2 + 1)^{5/2} x \, dx$.

Solution. Let $u = x^2 + 1$. Then $du = 2x \, dx$ and, after substitution, we obtain

$$\int (x^2 + 1)^{5/2} x \, dx = \int u^{5/2} \tfrac{1}{2} \, du = \tfrac{1}{2} \int u^{5/2} \, du$$

$$= \tfrac{1}{2}\left(\frac{2u^{7/2}}{7} + C \right) = \tfrac{1}{7}(x^2 + 1)^{7/2} + C,$$

which is our answer.

Remark. Example 2 was rigged so that the result was readily obtainable by the method we are learning. The integral $\int (x^2 + 1)^{5/2} \, dx$ cannot be evaluated by this method. For, if we let $u = x^2 + 1$, then $du = 2x \, dx$ and, substituting, we get

$$\int (x^2 + 1)^{5/2} \, dx = \int u^{5/2} \frac{1}{2x} \, du.$$

There is no way to get rid of the x in the denominator. Later we shall study other methods which will enable us to perform this type of integration.

The technique of *change of variable* may be used for evaluating definite integrals as well. However, *great care* must be exercised in evaluating the limits. There are two possible methods of procedure, and we illustrate each with an example.

EXAMPLE 3. Evaluate $\int_1^2 (x + 1)(x^2 + 2x + 2)^{1/3} \, dx$.

Solution. Let $u = x^2 + 2x + 2$. Then $du = (2x + 2) \, dx = 2(x + 1) \, dx$. Substituting, we find for the *indefinite integral*

$$\int (x + 1)(x^2 + 2x + 2)^{1/3} \, dx = \int u^{1/3} \tfrac{1}{2} \, du = \tfrac{1}{2} \tfrac{3}{4} u^{4/3} + C.$$

Method I involves substituting back for u in terms of x, thereby obtaining for the *definite integral*

$$\int_1^2 (x + 1)(x^2 + 2x + 2)^{1/3} \, dx = \tfrac{3}{8}(x^2 + 2x + 2)^{4/3} \big]_1^2$$

$$= \tfrac{3}{8}(10^{4/3} - 5^{4/3}).$$

The next example will be done by the second method.

EXAMPLE 4. Evaluate

$$\int_{-2}^{0} x\sqrt{2x^2 + 1} \, dx.$$

Solution. Let $u = 2x^2 + 1$, $du = 4x \, dx$.

Method II involves changing the limits of the definite integral to values of u instead of values of x. Since $u = 2x^2 + 1$, we easily see that when $x = -2$, $u = 9$, and when $x = 0$, $u = 1$. Therefore we can write

$$\int_{-2}^{0} x\sqrt{2x^2 + 1}\, dx = \int_{9}^{1} u^{1/2} \cdot \frac{1}{4}\, du = \frac{1}{4} \cdot \frac{2u^{3/2}}{3}\Big]_{9}^{1}$$

$$= \tfrac{1}{6}[1^{3/2} - 9^{3/2}] = -\tfrac{13}{3}$$

Most of the time Method II is simpler and shorter.* Occasionally there are problems in which it pays to go back to the original variables before evaluating the limits of integration.

EXERCISES

Find the following indefinite integrals and check your results by differentiation.

1. $\displaystyle\int (2x + 3)^6\, dx$

2. $\displaystyle\int (7x + 6)^{-5}\, dx$

3. $\displaystyle\int (2t + 1)^{1/3}\, dt$

4. $\displaystyle\int \frac{du}{(2u + 1)^2}$

5. $\displaystyle\int \frac{dy}{\sqrt[3]{(3y + 1)^2}}$

6. $\displaystyle\int (x^2 - 4)^7 x\, dx$

7. $\displaystyle\int (2x^2 + 3)^{7/3} x\, dx$

8. $\displaystyle\int (4 - x^2)^3 x\, dx$

9. $\displaystyle\int (3 - 2x^2)^{-2/3} x\, dx$

10. $\displaystyle\int \frac{x\, dx}{\sqrt{x^2 - 1}}$

11. $\displaystyle\int \frac{x\, dx}{(3x^2 + 2)^2}$

12. $\displaystyle\int x\sqrt{2x^2 - 1}\, dx$

13. $\displaystyle\int x^2\sqrt{x^3 + 1}\, dx$

14. $\displaystyle\int u^3\sqrt{u^4 + 1}\, du$

15. $\displaystyle\int \frac{(x^2 + 2x)\, dx}{\sqrt[3]{x^3 + 3x^2 + 1}}$

16. $\displaystyle\int \left(1 + \frac{1}{t}\right)^2 \frac{dt}{t^2}$

17. $\displaystyle\int (x^2 + 1)^3 x^3\, dx$

18. $\displaystyle\int (2x^2 - 3)^{4/3} x^3\, dx$

19. $\displaystyle\int (x^3 + 1)^{7/5} x^5\, dx$

20. $\displaystyle\int (x^2 - 2x + 1)^{4/3}\, dx$

---

* The justification for Method II depends on the proof of the formula

$$\int_{a}^{b} f[u(x)]u'(x)\, dx = \int_{u(a)}^{u(b)} f(u)\, du,$$

which is valid under appropriate hypotheses on the functions involved.

Evaluate the following definite integrals by Method I.

21. $\displaystyle\int_0^3 \sqrt[3]{(3t - 1)^2}\, dt$

22. $\displaystyle\int_{-2}^1 \sqrt{2 - x}\, dx$

23. $\displaystyle\int_{-3}^{-1} \frac{dx}{(x - 1)^2}$

24. $\displaystyle\int_0^1 x\sqrt{x^2 + 1}\, dx$

Evaluate the following definite integrals by Method II.

25. $\displaystyle\int_0^2 \frac{(x^2 + 1)\, dx}{\sqrt{x^3 + 3x + 1}}$

26. $\displaystyle\int_1^2 (2x + 1)\sqrt{x^2 + x + 1}\, dx$

27. $\displaystyle\int_1^2 \frac{(x^{1/3} + 2)^4\, dx}{\sqrt[3]{x^2}}$

28. $\displaystyle\int_1^3 \left(x + \frac{1}{x}\right)^{3/2}\left(\frac{x^2 - 1}{x^2}\right) dx$

8. AREA BETWEEN CURVES

Suppose that $f(x)$ and $g(x)$ are two continuous functions defined for x in the interval $[a, b]$ and, furthermore, suppose that

$$f(x) \geq g(x), \qquad a \leq x \leq b.$$

Figure 8–23 shows a typical situation. Let R denote the region bounded by the lines $x = a$, $x = b$, and the two curves. The area A of the region R is given by

$$A = \int_a^b f(x)\, dx - \int_a^b g(x)\, dx = \int_a^b [f(x) - g(x)]\, dx.$$

The interesting point about this formula is that *it holds whether the curves are above or below the x-axis.* Figures 8–24 and 8–25 show other possible situations. A moment's thought about Fig. 8–24 discloses the fact that $\int_a^b f(x)\, dx$ is the area below $f(x)$ and above the x-axis. Also, $-\int_a^b g(x)\, dx$ is the area be-

FIGURE 8–23

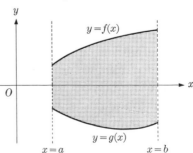

FIGURE 8–24

tween the x-axis and $g(x)$. Adding these, we get for the total area A between the curves

$$A = \int_a^b [f(x) - g(x)]\, dx.$$

Figure 8–25 appears slightly more complicated, but the student can easily satisfy himself that the same formula holds.

When we apply the formula for the area between two curves, the main problem lies in verifying the fact that $f(x)$ is larger than $g(x)$ *throughout the interval*. Once this verification is made, we perform the integration in the usual way.

EXAMPLE 1.   Find the area of the region R bounded by the lines $x = 1$, $x = 2$, $y = 3x$, and the curve $y = x^2$.

Solution. We draw a sketch, as shown in Fig. 8–26, which makes it obvious that $y = 3x$ is above $y = x^2$ in the interval $[1, 2]$. This can be shown analytically first by finding where the curves intersect and then by noting that between intersection points one curve must *always remain above* the other; $y = 3x$ and $y = x^2$ meet when $3x = x^2$ or $x = 0, 3$. Between $x = 0$ and $x = 3$, say at $x = 1$, we know that $3x > x^2$, since $3 > 1$. This means that $y = 3x$ is above $y = x^2$ throughout the interval $[0, 3]$.

The area is given by

$$A = \int_1^2 (3x - x^2)\, dx = \tfrac{3}{2}x^2 - \tfrac{1}{3}x^3\big]_1^2$$

$$= (6 - \tfrac{8}{3}) - (\tfrac{3}{2} - \tfrac{1}{3}) = \tfrac{13}{6}.$$

A similar situation, but one with a slight complication, is exhibited next.

EXAMPLE 2.   Find the area bounded by the curves $y = x$ and $y = x^3$.

Solution. To determine the nature of the region bounded by the curves, we begin by finding the points of intersection of the two curves. Solving the equation $x = x^3$, we get $x = 0, 1, -1$; therefore the curves intersect at $(0, 0)$, $(1, 1)$, and $(-1, -1)$. After plotting a few points, we easily see that the graph appears as in Fig. 8–27. There are two

FIGURE 8–25

FIGURE 8–26

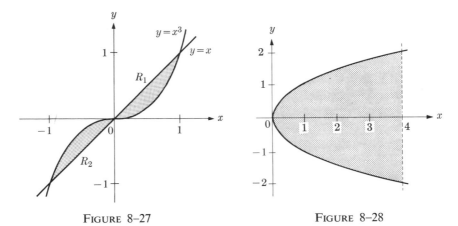

FIGURE 8-27   FIGURE 8-28

regions, one in the first quadrant (denoted R_1) and one in the third (denoted R_2). We label their areas A_1 and A_2, respectively. For R_1 the line $y = x$ is above the curve $y = x^3$, since for $x = \frac{1}{2}$ (a typical value between 0 and 1) $\frac{1}{2} > (\frac{1}{2})^3$. We obtain

$$A_1 = \int_0^1 (x - x^3)\, dx = \tfrac{1}{2}x^2 - \tfrac{1}{4}x^4 \big]_0^1 = (\tfrac{1}{2} - \tfrac{1}{4}) - 0 = \tfrac{1}{4}.$$

To find A_2 we note that $y = x^3$ is above $y = x$ for R_2 $\left(\text{since } (-\tfrac{1}{2})^3 > -\tfrac{1}{2}\right)$, and so

$$A_2 = \int_{-1}^0 (x^3 - x)\, dx = \tfrac{1}{4}x^4 - \tfrac{1}{2}x^2 \big]_{-1}^0 = 0 - (\tfrac{1}{4} - \tfrac{1}{2}) = \tfrac{1}{4}.$$

The total area between the curves is $A_1 + A_2 = \tfrac{1}{2}$.

Remark. We could have observed that since the function $h(x) = x - x^3$ is an *odd function*, that is, $h(-x) = -h(x)$, the areas A_1 and A_2 must be equal. Such knowledge should be exploited whenever possible.

The next example will be worked by two methods and, in the process, a number of ideas will be developed which will show how the scope of the method for finding the area between curves may be expanded considerably.

EXAMPLE 3. Find the area bounded by the curve $y^2 = x$ and the line $x = 4$.

Solution. A sketch of the region R is shown in Fig. 8-28. The first difficulty is that the relation $y^2 = x$ expresses y not as one but as *two* functions of x. The upper boundary of R is given by $y = \sqrt{x}$ and the lower boundary by $y = -\sqrt{x}$. Applying the method used in the previous examples, we obtain

$$A = \int_0^4 [\sqrt{x} - (-\sqrt{x})]\, dx = \int_0^4 (\sqrt{x} + \sqrt{x})\, dx$$

$$= 2\int_0^4 x^{1/2}\, dx = \tfrac{4}{3}x^{3/2} \big]_0^4 = \tfrac{32}{3}.$$

In the second method of solving this problem, we change our point of view. We now consider y as the *independent* variable and x as the *dependent* variable, and we integrate

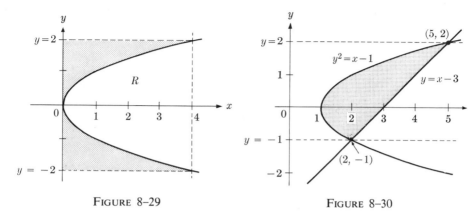

FIGURE 8–29   FIGURE 8–30

along the y-axis. The region bounded by the curve $x = y^2$, the line $y = -2$, the line $y = 2$, and the y-axis is shown as the shaded region in Fig. 8–29. Its area is

$$\int_{-2}^{2} y^2 \, dy = \tfrac{1}{3}y^3]_{-2}^{2} = \tfrac{8}{3} - (-\tfrac{8}{3}) = \tfrac{16}{3}.$$

The area of the rectangle bounded by the four lines $y = -2$, $y = 2$, $x = 0$, and $x = 4$ is 16. The area of the region R is obtained by subtraction:

$$A = 16 - \tfrac{16}{3} = \tfrac{32}{3}.$$

We could have performed the integration of this second method in one step by finding the area between the curves $x = 4$ and $x = y^2$. Integration along the y-axis then yields

$$\int_{-2}^{2} (4 - y^2) \, dy = 4y - \tfrac{1}{3}y^3]_{-2}^{2} = (8 - \tfrac{8}{3}) - (-8 + \tfrac{8}{3}) = \tfrac{32}{3}.$$

The technique of looking at the same problem from several points of view is a favorite trick of mathematicians. One way of looking at a problem often yields an insight which other ways miss. If in Example 3 we note that the region is symmetric with respect to the x-axis, the problem becomes simpler. In that case we integrate

$$\int_{0}^{4} \sqrt{x} \, dx,$$

double it, and get the answer.

EXAMPLE 4. Find the area bounded by $y^2 = x - 1$ and $y = x - 3$.

Solution. The curves are sketched in Fig. 8–30. They intersect where

$$y^2 + 1 = y + 3,$$

or $y = -1, 2$. The corresponding values of x are 2, 5.

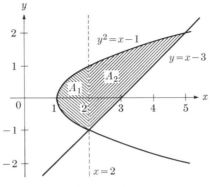

FIGURE 8–31

There are two ways of proceeding. The first considers y as the independent variable and x as a function of y. Then the equations are

$$x = y^2 + 1 \quad \text{and} \quad x = y + 3.$$

The area between the curves is obtained by integrating along the y-axis from $y = -1$ to $y = 2$. We get

$$A = \int_{-1}^{2} [(y + 3) - (y^2 + 1)]\, dy = \int_{-1}^{2} (-y^2 + y + 2)\, dy$$

$$= -\tfrac{1}{3}y^3 + \tfrac{1}{2}y^2 + 2y]_{-1}^{2} = (-\tfrac{8}{3} + 2 + 4) - (\tfrac{1}{3} + \tfrac{1}{2} - 2) = 4\tfrac{1}{2}.$$

The second method considers x as the independent variable. From the figure, we see that the upper portion of the region is bounded by

$$y = \sqrt{x - 1}.$$

The lower boundary is made up of two parts:

$$y = -\sqrt{x - 1} \quad \text{if } x \text{ is between 1 and 2;}$$
$$y = x - 3 \quad \text{if } x \text{ is between 2 and 5.}$$

Figure 8–31 shows how we solve the problem in two stages. The area A is divided into two parts A_1 and A_2, as shown.

$$A_1 = \int_{1}^{2} [\sqrt{x - 1} - (-\sqrt{x - 1})]\, dx = 2\int_{1}^{2} \sqrt{x - 1}\, dx;$$

$$A_2 = \int_{2}^{5} [\sqrt{x - 1} - (x - 3)]\, dx.$$

These integrations can be performed to yield $A_1 + A_2 = 4\tfrac{1}{2}$.

It is easy to imagine complicated regions in which the only way to find the area is to decompose it into a number of simpler subregions.

EXERCISES

In problems 1 through 25, sketch the regions bounded by the given curves and find their areas.

1. $x = 1$, $x = 3$, $y = x^2$, $y = -x$
2. $x = 1$, $x = -1$, $y = x^2$, $y = 8 - x^2$
3. $x = 0$, $x = 2$, $y = x^2$, $y = 9x$
4. $y = 0$, $y = \frac{1}{2}$, $x = y^2$, $x = y$
5. $x = -2$, $x = 0$, $y = x^3$, $y = -x$
6. $x = 0$, $x = 3$, $y = \sqrt{x + 1}$, $y = \frac{1}{2}x$
7. $x = 1$, $x = 2$, $x^2y = 2$, $x + y = 4$
8. $x = 0$, $x = \frac{1}{2}$, $y = x^2$, $y = x^4$
9. $y = x^2$, $y = x^4$
10. $x = 0$, $x = 3$, $y = 0$, $y = 1/\sqrt{x + 1}$
11. $x = 1$, $x = 2$, $y^2 = x$
12. $y = 0$, $y = 2$, $x = 0$, $x = y^2$
13. $y = -1$, $y = 1$, $x - y + 1 = 0$, $x = 1 - y^2$
14. $y = 1$, $x = y$, $xy^2 = 4$
15. $x = y^2$, $x = 18 - y^2$
16. $y = x^2$, $y^2 = x$
17. $y = \sqrt{x}$, $y = x^3$
18. $y^2 = 4x + 1$, $x + y = 1$
19. $y = x^2 + 4x + 2$, $2x - y + 5 = 0$
20. $y = 1$, $y = 2$, $x = 0$, $x = y/\sqrt{9 - y^2}$
21. $y^2 = 2 - x$, $y = 2x + 2$
22. $y = x^2$, $y = 3x$, $y = 1$, $y = 2$
23. $y = 2x$, $4y = x$, $y = 2/x^2$, $x > 0$
24. $x = 1$, $x = 2$, $x^2y = 1$, $y = 0$
25. $x = 1$, $x = 2$, $y = \frac{1}{2}x$, $x^2y = 1$. (Find area of all bounded regions.)

In problems 26 through 28, find the areas of the triangles having the given vertices, using the method of this section.

26. $(0, 0)$, $(4, 1)$, $(2, 4)$
27. $(-2, -1)$, $(2, 2)$, $(3, -2)$
28. $(2, 1)$, $(6, -1)$, $(4, 2)$
29. Find the area enclosed by the curves

$$y = x^2 - x, \qquad y = x - x^2.$$

30. A trapezoid connects the four points $(0, 0)$, $(B, 0)$, (a, h), $(a + b, h)$. Use the methods of this section to obtain the formula for the area

$$A = \tfrac{1}{2}h(B + b).$$

9. WORK

We shall consider only *the motion of objects along a straight line in one direction.* It is convenient to suppose that the motion is along the x-axis or the y-axis in the positive direction. The restriction to motions along a line is essential, since the study of motion along curved paths requires types of derivatives and integrals of a nature more complicated than those we have taken up so far.

The term *work* is a technical one which requires for its definition the notion of *force*. From Newton's Law we know that force = mass × acceleration.* Force is measured in units of pounds, tons, grams, etc. To take the simplest possible case, suppose that an object (assumed to occupy a single point) is moving along the x-axis (to the right) and suppose that this object is subject to a *constant force* (to the right) of B pounds. Let d be the distance it moves, measured in feet. We define the *work* done, W, as

$$W = B \cdot d.$$

The units of W are measured in foot-pounds. If the force were in tons and the distance in inches, the work would be measured in inch-tons. The definition above is fine so long as the force exerted is constant, but what is to be the definition when the force is variable (the most common situation)? As a start toward the definition we state the following principle:

PRINCIPLE 1. *If a body is moved from position A_0 to position A_1, then from A_1 to A_2, then from A_2 to A_3, etc., and finally from A_{n-1} to A_n, the total work done in moving the body from A_0 to A_n is the sum of the amounts of work done in moving the body from one position to the next.*

If the force exerted in moving a body from one position to another is constant, the work is known; otherwise it is not defined as yet. If the positions are sufficiently close together, the force is *almost constant*. Suppose that the body is moving along the x-axis from a to b ($b > a$) and suppose that there is a law $F(x)$ which gives the amount of force (exerted to the right) at point x. According to Principle 1, if we subdivide the interval $[a, b]$ into n parts: $\{a = x_0 < x_1 < \cdots < x_n = b\}$, and if we *assume that the force is constant* in each subinterval, an expression of the form

$$\sum_{i=1}^{n} F(\xi_i) \, \Delta_i x, \qquad x_{i-1} \leq \xi_i \leq x_i,$$

will give the *total work done*. This expression is suggestive of the way we defined integral and leads to the following definition of work.

DEFINITION. *The total work W done in moving an object along the x-axis from a to b, if the force exerted at point x obeys the law $F = F(x)$, is*

$$W = \int_a^b F(x) \, dx.$$

---

* Mass, distance, and time are undefined terms.

EXAMPLE 1. Suppose that an object is moved along the x-axis from $x = 2$ to $x = 5$ (units in inches), and suppose that the force exerted obeys the law $F(x) = x^2 + x$ lb. Find the total work done.

Solution.

$$W = \int_2^5 (x^2 + x)\, dx = \tfrac{1}{3}x^3 + \tfrac{1}{2}x^2]_2^5$$

$$= 49\tfrac{1}{2} \text{ in.-lb.}$$

EXAMPLE 2. A spring has a natural length of 12 in. When it is stretched x in. it pulls back with a force kx, by Hooke's Law. The constant k depends on the material, thickness of the wire, etc. If 10 lb of force are required to hold it stretched $\tfrac{1}{2}$ in., how much work is done in stretching it from its natural length to a length of 16 in.?

FIGURE 8–32

Solution. We locate the spring along the x-axis and place the origin at the position where we start stretching (Fig. 8–32). The fact that the force is 10 lb when $x = \tfrac{1}{2}$ is used to find k. We have $10 = k \cdot \tfrac{1}{2}$ or $k = 20$. From the force law, $F = 20x$. From the definition of work,

$$W = \int_0^4 20x\, dx = 10x^2]_0^4 = 160 \text{ in.-lb.}$$

Another type of work problem requires a somewhat different principle. Figure 8–33 represents a substance which occupies a large region R. Suppose the material in this region (sand, water, etc.) is to be moved horizontally to some location L. The following principle tells how to find the work done in moving this mass. It is supposed that each particle in R moves horizontally until it reaches the vertical line L.

R

L

FIGURE 8–33

PRINCIPLE 2. *If a mass M is moved to a position L, the total work done may be obtained by subdividing the mass into smaller masses $M_1 + M_2 + \cdots + M_n = M$, by finding the work done in moving each of the smaller masses to the position L, and by adding the results.*

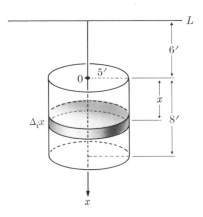

FIGURE 8–34

Principle 2 is used as a guide for setting up an integral in the same way that Principle 1 served as a guide for defining work. We illustrate the method in the following example.

EXAMPLE 3. A tank having the shape of a right circular cylinder of altitude 8 ft and radius of base 5 ft is full of water. Find the amount of work done in pumping all the water in the tank up to a level 6 ft above the top of the tank.

Solution. Figure 8–34 shows the tank. Since the motion is in a vertical direction we set up the x-axis so that it is vertically downward, as shown. According to Principle 2, we divide the tank into n portions, in the form of slabs or discs. That is, we divide the x-axis into n parts, $0 = x_0 < x_1 < x_2 < \cdots < x_n = 8$, and consider the ith disc to be of thickness $\Delta_i x = x_i - x_{i-1}$. Then the total work done is the work required to move each disc up to line L, 6 ft above the top. The only force exerted on the water is that due to gravity. By definition, the weight of any object is the measure of this force. Since water has a density of 62.4 lb/ft³, raising one cubic foot of water requires a force of 62.4 lb.

The volume of the disc of width $\Delta_i x$ is $\pi \cdot 5^2 \cdot \Delta_i x = 25\pi \Delta_i x$. The force required to raise this volume is its weight: $(62.4)(25\pi \Delta_i x)$. Since the force is *constant*, the work done is merely the product of the force and the distance that it moves. Here is the real crux of the problem: each disc moves a distance which is different from that of any other disc. In fact, even within one disc different particles are raised different distances.

A disc with midpoint at location x ft below the top of the tank moves approximately $(6 + x)$ ft. Since x is between x_{i-1} and x_i, the work done in moving one disc is approximately $(62.4)(25\pi \Delta_i x)(6 + x)$. We now recall that Principle 2 says that we may add the work done in moving each of these discs to find the total work, and so (approximately)

$$W = \sum_{i=1}^{n} (62.4)(25\pi \Delta_i x)(6 + x), \qquad x \text{ between } x_{i-1} \text{ and } x_i.$$

When we proceed to the limit, this formula suggests the integral

$$W = \int_0^8 (62.4)(25\pi)(6 + x)\, dx = 1560\pi \left[6x + \tfrac{1}{2}x^2 \right]_0^8 = 124{,}800\pi \text{ ft-lb.}$$

Such an integral is used to define the work done in moving a large mass. Its evaluation yields the total work performed.

The ideas about work follow the outline:

(1) A physical law is given in the simplest case. (Work is defined when the force is constant and the object occupies a single point.)

(2) A principle is stated which says that a complicated situation may be decomposed into a large number of simple ones; each of these may be solved by the simple physical law (1), and then the results may be added.

(3) The sum obtained in (2) is of the form used in defining an integral.

(4) We proceed to the limit, obtain the integral, and use this expression as the *definition* of the physical law in the complicated case.

Now it is plain that no calculus student can be expected to be able to master this procedure immediately when he is confronted with an unfamiliar physical law. However, practice in carrying out the process in familiar situations makes possible an understanding of the physics, the definition, and the integral concept. Invention is a modification of experience. Once the student has a backlog of experience in solving problems involving familiar situations, he is capable of attacking an unfamiliar physical process right from the start.

With this in mind, the student will appreciate the benefits of mastering the exercises in this and the following section. Additional material of the same kind is given in subsequent chapters.

EXERCISES

In problems 1 through 4, a particle is moving along the x-axis from a to b according to the force law, $F(x)$, which is given. Find the work done.

1. $F(x) = x^3 + 2x^2 + 6x - 1, \quad a = 1, b = 2$

2. $F(x) = 8 + 2x - x^2, \quad a = 0, b = 3$

3. $F(x) = \dfrac{x}{(1 + x^2)^2}, \quad a = 1, b = 2$

4. $F(x) = (x^3 + 2x^2 + 1)(3x^2 + 4), \quad a = 0, b = 1$

In problems 5 through 9, assume that each spring obeys Hooke's Law ($F = kx$) as stated in Example 2. Find the work done in each case.

5. Natural length, 8 in.; 20 lb force stretches spring $\frac{1}{2}$ in. Find the work done in stretching the spring from 8 to 11 in.

6. Natural length 6 in.; 500 lb stretches spring $\frac{1}{4}$ in. Find the work done in stretching it 1 in.

7. Natural length 10 in.; 30 lb stretches it to $11\frac{1}{2}$ in. Find the work done in stretching it (a) from 10 to 12 in.; (b) from 12 to 14 in.

8. Natural length 6 in.; 12,000 lb compresses it $\frac{1}{2}$ in. Find the work done in compressing it from 6 in. to 5 in. (Hooke's Law works for compression as well as for extension.)

9. Natural length 6 in.; 1200 lb compresses it $\frac{1}{2}$ in. Find the work done in compressing it from 6 in. to $4\frac{1}{2}$ in. What is the work required to bring the spring to 9 in. from its compressed state of $4\frac{1}{2}$ in.?

10. A cable 100 ft long and weighing 5 lb/ft is hanging from a windlass. Find the work done in winding it up.

11. A boat is anchored so that the anchor is 100 ft directly below the capstan about which the anchor chain is wound. The anchor weighs 3000 lb and the chain weighs 20 lb/ft. How much work is done in bringing up the anchor?

12. A tank full of water is in the form of a right circular cylinder of altitude 5 ft and radius of base 3 ft. How much work is done in pumping the water up to a level 10 ft above the top of the tank?

13. A swimming pool full of water is in the form of a rectangular parallelepiped 5 ft deep, 15 ft wide, and 25 ft long. Find the work required to pump the water up to a level 1 ft above the surface of the pool.

14. The base of one cylindrical tank of radius 6 ft and altitude 10 ft is 3 ft above the top of another tank of the same size and shape. The lower tank is full of oil (50 lb/ft³) and the upper tank is empty. How much work is done in pumping all the oil from the lower tank into the upper through a pipe which enters the upper tank through its base?

15. A trough full of water is 10 ft long, and its cross section is in the shape of an isosceles triangle 2 ft wide across the top and 2 ft high. How much work is done in pumping all the water out of the trough over one of its ends?

16. A trough full of water is 12 ft long and its cross section is in the shape of an isosceles trapezoid 1 ft high, 2 ft wide at the bottom, and 3 ft wide at the top. Find the work done in pumping the water to a point 2 ft above the top of the trough.

17. A trough full of water is 6 ft long and its cross section is in the shape of a semicircle with the diameter at the top 2 ft wide. How much work is required to pump the water out over one of its ends?

18. A steam shovel is excavating sand. Each load weighs 500 lb when excavated. The shovel lifts each load to a height of 15 ft in $\frac{1}{2}$ min, then dumps it. A leak in the shovel lets sand drop out while the shovel is being raised. The rate at which sand leaks out is 160 lb/min; find the amount of work done by the shovel in raising one load.

19. Two unlike charges of amount e_1 and e_2 electrostatic units attract each other with a force $e_1 e_2 / r^2$, where r is the distance between them (assuming appropriate units). A positive charge e_1 of 7 units is held fixed at a certain point P. (See Fig. 8–35.) How much work is done in moving a negative charge e_2 of 1 unit from a point 4 units away from the positive charge to a point 20 units away from that charge along a straight line pointing directly away from the positive charge?

FIGURE 8–35

20. The base of a tank of radius 5 ft and altitude 8 ft is directly above a tank of the same radius but of altitude 6 ft. The lower tank is full of water. How much work is done in pumping the water from the lower tank to the upper tank if the pipe enters the upper tank halfway up its side?

21. A metal bar of length L and cross section A obeys Hooke's Law when stretched. If it is stretched x units the force F required is given by

$$F = \frac{EA}{L}\,x,$$

where E is a constant known as *Young's modulus* or the *modulus of elasticity*. The quantity E depends only on the type of material used, not on the shape or size of the bar. If a steel bar 12 in. long and of uniform cross section 4 in^2 is stretched $\frac{1}{2}$ in., find the work done. (Give answer in terms of E.)

10. FLUID PRESSURE

The definition of pressure, like the definition of work, depends on the notion of force. In the simplest case, suppose a fluid (liquid or gas) is in a container and, at some point in the container, a small flat plate is inserted. The mere presence of the fluid exerts a force on this plate both from the weight of the fluid and from the action of the molecules. The *pressure* is defined as the *force per unit area* of the fluid on the plate.

When a liquid is in an open container so that there is a *free surface* at the top, the pressure at any depth of the liquid is given by a particularly simple law. Suppose that the liquid weighs w lb/ft^3 (i.e., its density is w). *The pressure p at a depth h feet below the surface is*

$$p = w \cdot h.$$

This is a remarkable formula in many ways; it says that the size of the vessel is irrelevant. At a depth of 3 ft in a swimming pool the pressure is the same as it is at a depth of 3 ft in an ocean (assuming that the pool is filled with salt water). The pressure is determined by depth alone, all other dimensions of the vessel being of no consequence.

The following principle is also needed in the study of liquid pressure:

PRINCIPLE 1. *At any point in a liquid the pressure is the same in all directions.*

This means that a plate below the surface has the same pressure on it whether it is located vertically, horizontally, or at an angle. Any skin diver knows that the pressure on his eardrums depends only on how deep he is and not on the angle at which his head happens to be tilted.

The problem we shall concern ourselves with is the determination of the *total force* on a plate situated in a fluid. In the simplest case, if the plate has area A ft^2 and if it is at a depth where the pressure is p lb/ft^2, then the force F is given by

$$F = p \cdot A.$$

If the density of the liquid is w and the plate is h ft below the surface, we may also write

$$F = w \cdot h \cdot A,$$

since $p = w \cdot h$.

If a large plate is located in a fluid either vertically or at an angle, then different portions of it are at different depths. The elementary rule given above for finding the force will not work, since we do not know what depth h to use. To handle problems of this sort we need the following principle:

PRINCIPLE 2. *If a flat plate is divided into several parts, then the total force on the entire plate is the sum of the forces on each of the parts.*

Note the similarity between this principle and those in the previous section on work. We shall now show how Principles 1 and 2 lead to an integral which will define the total force on a plate in a liquid. A specific example will be worked first.

EXAMPLE 1. The face of a dam adjacent to the water is vertical and rectangular in shape with width 50 ft and height 10 ft. Find the total force exerted by the liquid on the face of the dam when the water surface is level with the top of the dam.

Solution. The depth of water varies from 0 to 10 ft and the pressure changes with depth. We divide the dam into horizontal strips $0 = h_0 < h_1 < h_2 < \cdots < h_n = 10$. (See Fig. 8–36.) If the number of subdivisions is large, then the pressure on a strip such as the ith one will be *almost* constant, since all of its points are at approximately the same depth. The width of the strip is $\Delta_i h = h_i - h_{i-1}$. If $\bar{h}_i$ is an average value between h_i and h_{i-1}, then the force on the ith strip is the area $(= 50 \, \Delta_i h)$ times the pressure $(= w\bar{h}_i)$. We have

$$\text{Force on the } i\text{th strip} = 50 w \bar{h}_i \, \Delta_i h.$$

According to Principle 2, we obtain the total force by adding the forces on the individual strips:

$$\text{Total force} = \sum_{i=1}^{n} 50 w \bar{h}_i \, \Delta_i h.$$

This expression is suggestive of the integral

$$\int_0^{10} 50 w h \, dh,$$

which is the *definition of the total force* on the dam. Therefore, by integration,

$$\text{Total force} = 50 w \tfrac{1}{2} h^2 \big]_0^{10} = 2500 w = 156,250 \text{ lb.}$$

FIGURE 8–36

FIGURE 8–37   FIGURE 8–38

The technique for working Example 1 follows the outline given at the end of the previous section:

(1) In the simple case of constant pressure, force = pressure × area. (We know additionally that, for a liquid, pressure = weight × depth.)

(2) A principle is given which says that the total force is the sum of the forces on the various parts.

(3) The sum obtained is of the type used in defining integrals.

(4) We proceed to the limit to obtain an integral defining the total force.

Another example illustrates the procedure in a slightly more complicated case.

EXAMPLE 2. The face of a dam adjacent to the water has the shape of an isosceles trapezoid of altitude 20 ft, upper base 50 ft, and lower base 40 ft. Find the total force exerted by the water on the dam when the water is 15 ft deep.

Solution. Figure 8–37 shows the dam and a typical strip along which the pressure is almost constant. The width of the strip is $\Delta_i h = h_i - h_{i-1}$. The force on this strip is

$$\text{Force on } i\text{th} \quad \text{strip} = w \cdot \bar{h}_i \cdot \text{area},$$

where $\bar{h}_i$ is between h_{i-1} and h_i. The main problem is to find the area of the strip. For practical purposes we suppose it to be a rectangle. Then the area is (length) × ($\Delta_i h$). But what is the length l? Here the shape of the dam plays a role. In order to find l *as a function of the depth h,* we use the method of similar triangles. (Fig. 8–38.) From triangles *ABC* and *DEC* we have

$$\frac{l - 40}{15 - h} = \frac{10}{20} \quad \text{or} \quad l = \frac{95}{2} - \frac{1}{2}h,$$

which is the length of the ith strip. Its area is

$$(\tfrac{95}{2} - \tfrac{1}{2}h)\,\Delta_i h,$$

and the total force on the ith strip is (approximately)

$$w\bar{h}_i(\tfrac{95}{2} - \tfrac{1}{2}\bar{h}_i)\,\Delta_i h.$$

The total force on the dam, according to Principle 2, is (approximately)

$$\tfrac{1}{2}\sum_{i=1}^{n} w\bar{h}_i(95 - \bar{h}_i)\,\Delta_i h.$$

We proceed to the limit and obtain

$$\text{Total force} = \int_0^{15} \tfrac{1}{2}wh(95 - h)\,dh = w[\tfrac{95}{4}h^2 - \tfrac{1}{6}h^3]_0^{15} = 298,828\tfrac{1}{8} \text{ lb.}$$

The essential step in Example 2 is finding the area of the ith strip in terms of the depth h, which is necessary in order that the sum we obtain be of the type used in approximating an integral.

EXERCISES

In problems 1 through 8, the face of a dam adjacent to the water is vertical and has the shape indicated. Find the total force on the dam due to fluid pressure.

  1. A rectangle 200 ft wide, 15 ft high; water 10 ft deep.
  2. A rectangle 150 ft wide, 12 ft high; water 8 ft deep.
  3. An isosceles triangle 30 ft wide at the top, 20 ft high in the center; dam full of water.
  4. An isosceles triangle 30 ft wide at the top, 15 ft high in the center; water 10 ft deep in center.
  5. An isosceles triangle 250 ft across the top, 100 ft high in the center; water 60 ft deep in center.
  6. A right triangle, one leg horizontal (at top) and 10 ft wide, one leg vertical and 20 ft high; dam full of water.
  7. An isosceles trapezoid 90 ft across the top, 60 ft wide at the bottom, 20 ft high; full of water.
  8. An isosceles trapezoid 60 ft across the top, 30 ft wide at the bottom, 10 ft high; water 8 ft deep.
  9. A square of side 5 ft is submerged in water so that its diagonal is perpendicular to the surface. Find the total force on the square (due to the liquid on one side) if one vertex is in the surface.
 10. The vertical ends of a trough are in the shapes of semicircles of diameter 2 ft with diameter horizontal. Find the total force on one end when the trough is full of water.
 11. An oil tank is in the shape of a right circular cylinder of diameter 4 ft with axis horizontal. Find the total force on one end when the tank is half full of oil weighing 50 lb/ft^3.

In problems 12 through 16, it is assumed that in a dam the face of a gate of the shape indicated is vertical. If the gate is adjacent to the water, find the total force on the gate in each case.

 12. A rectangle 4 ft wide, 3 ft high, with upper edge 20 ft below the surface of the water.
 13. An isosceles triangle 4 ft wide at the top, 3 ft high, with upper edge 15 ft below the water surface.
 14. An isosceles triangle 2 ft wide at the bottom, 2 ft high, with top vertex 10 ft below the surface of the water.

15. An isosceles trapezoid 3 ft wide at the top, 4 ft wide at the bottom, and 3 ft high, with upper base 20 ft below the water surface.

16. An isosceles right triangle, length of leg 5 ft, with one leg vertical and the horizontal leg at the bottom. The horizontal leg is 30 ft below the water surface.

In problems 17 through 19 it is assumed that the face of the dam adjacent to the water is a plane figure of the given shape and is inclined at an angle of 30° from the vertical. Find the total force on that face in each case.

17. A rectangle 50 ft wide with slant height 30 ft; dam full of water.

18. An isosceles trapezoid 60 ft wide at the top, 40 ft wide at the bottom, slant height 20 ft; dam full of water.

19. An isosceles trapezoid 200 ft wide at the top, 120 ft wide at the bottom, slant height 50 ft; water $20\sqrt{3}$ ft deep.

20. A swimming pool is 25 ft wide, 40 ft long, 2 ft deep at one end, and 8 ft deep at the other, the bottom being an inclined plane. Find the total force on the bottom.

21. Consider a gas confined to a right circular cylinder closed at one end by a movable piston. Assume that the pressure of the gas is p lb/ft^2 when the volume is v ft^3. The pressure depends on the volume and we write $p = p(v)$. Show that the *work done* by the gas in expanding from a volume v_1 to a volume v_2 may be defined by

$$\int_{v_1}^{v_2} p(v) \, dv \text{ ft-lb.}$$

(*Hint:* Let the area of the cross section be A ft^2, and let x be the variable distance from the piston to the fixed end of the cylinder.)

22. Suppose that v and p are related by the equation $p \cdot v^{1.4} =$ const. Find the work done by such a gas as it expands from a volume of 5 ft^3 to 200 ft^3 if the pressure is 2500 lb/in^2 when $v = 5$ ft^3.

23. Suppose that v and p are related by the equation $p \cdot v^{1.4} =$ const. If $p = 60$ lb/in^2 when $v = 10$ ft^3, (a) find v when $p = 15$ lb/in^2, and (b) find the work done by the gas as it expands until the pressure reaches this value (15 lb/in^2).

CHAPTER 9

Lines and Circles. Trigonometry Review

---

1. DISTANCE FROM A POINT TO A LINE

In this chapter we continue the study of analytic geometry which we started in Chapter 3. The tools of the calculus which we have developed in the interim turn out to be powerful aids in obtaining properties of curves and regions in the plane.

A first-degree equation of the form

$$Ax + By + C = 0$$

represents a straight line. Suppose $P(x_0, y_0)$ is a point not on the line. *The distance from a point to a line* is defined as the length of a perpendicular dropped from this point to the line. The number representing this distance is always positive. The following theorem gives a simple formula.

Theorem 1. *The distance d from the point $P(x_0, y_0)$ to the line L whose equation is $Ax + By + C = 0$ is given by the formula*

$$d = \frac{|Ax_0 + By_0 + C|}{\sqrt{A^2 + B^2}}.$$

Proof. We shall use a proof which is easy to devise but which requires some complicated algebraic manipulation. The steps of the proof are: (1) Find the equation of the line through $P(x_0, y_0)$ which is perpendicular to L (Fig. 9–1). (2) Find the point of intersection of this line with L. Call the point $Q(\bar{x}, \bar{y})$. (3) Find the

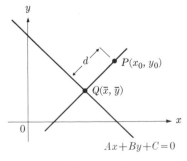

FIGURE 9–1

254

distance PQ. (4) Treat vertical and horizontal lines separately. (The proof will help us review some of the facts and formulas concerning straight lines.)

The slope of the line $Ax + By + C = 0$ is $-A/B$. If the line is neither vertical nor horizontal, the slope of the line through P and perpendicular to L is $+B/A$, the negative reciprocal. The equation of this line, according to the point-slope formula, is $y - y_0 = (B/A)(x - x_0)$ or $Bx - Ay + Ay_0 - Bx_0 = 0$. To find $Q(\bar{x}, \bar{y})$ we solve simultaneously the equations

$$Ax + By + C = 0; \qquad Bx - Ay + Ay_0 - Bx_0 = 0.$$

We multiply the first equation by A and the second by B and add, to get

$$\bar{x} = \frac{B^2 x_0 - ABy_0 - AC}{A^2 + B^2}.$$

Now we multiply the first equation by B and the second by A and subtract, to find

$$\bar{y} = \frac{-ABx_0 + A^2 y_0 - BC}{A^2 + B^2}.$$

The distance d, according to the formula for the distance between two points, is

$$d = \sqrt{(x_0 - \bar{x})^2 + (y_0 - \bar{y})^2}.$$

Substitution of the expressions for $\bar{x}$ and $\bar{y}$ in this formula yields

$$d^2 = \left[x_0 - \frac{B^2 x_0 - ABy_0 - AC}{A^2 + B^2} \right]^2 + \left[y_0 - \frac{-ABx_0 + A^2 y_0 - BC}{A^2 + B^2} \right]^2.$$

We find the least common denominator and simplify, to obtain

$$d^2 = \frac{A^2(Ax_0 + By_0 + C)^2}{(A^2 + B^2)^2} + \frac{B^2(Ax_0 + By_0 + C)^2}{(A^2 + B^2)^2}.$$

This combines even further to yield

$$d^2 = \frac{(Ax_0 + By_0 + C)^2}{A^2 + B^2},$$

and finally, taking the positive square root, we write the result:

$$d = \frac{|Ax_0 + By_0 + C|}{\sqrt{A^2 + B^2}}.$$

If the line L is horizontal, its equation is of the form $y = -C/B$ and the distance from $P(x_0, y_0)$ to L is simply the difference of the y-values (draw a sketch, if necessary). Therefore,

$$d = \left| y_0 - \left(-\frac{C}{B} \right) \right| = \left| \frac{By_0 + C}{B} \right|.$$

Similarly, if the line is vertical,

$$d = \left| \frac{Ax_0 + C}{A} \right|.$$

Note that the distance formula in the statement of the theorem works in *all* cases so long as A and B are not both zero. Furthermore if, by accident, the point $P(x_0, y_0)$ happened to be on the line L the distance d would be zero, since (x_0, y_0) would satisfy the equation $Ax_0 + By_0 + C = 0$.

EXAMPLE 1. Find the distance d from the point $(2, -1)$ to the line $3x + 4y - 5 = 0$.

Solution. We see that $A = 3$, $B = 4$, $C = -5$, $x_0 = 2$, $y_0 = -1$. Substituting in the formula, we get

$$d = \frac{|3 \cdot 2 + 4(-1) - 5|}{\sqrt{3^2 + 4^2}} = \frac{|-3|}{5} = \frac{3}{5}.$$

DEFINITION. *The distance between parallel lines* is the shortest distance from any point on one of the lines to the other line.

EXAMPLE 2. Find the distance between the parallel lines $L_1 : 2x - 3y + 7 = 0$ and $L_2 : 2x - 3y - 6 = 0$.

Solution. First find any point on one of the lines, say L_1. To do this, let x be any value and solve for y in the equation for L_1. If $x = 1$ in L_1, then $y = 3$ and the point $(1, 3)$ is on L_1. The distance from $(1, 3)$ to L_2 is

$$d = \frac{|2(1) - 3(3) - 6|}{\sqrt{2^2 + (-3)^2}} = \frac{|-13|}{\sqrt{13}} = \frac{13}{\sqrt{13}} = \sqrt{13}.$$

The distance between the parallel lines is $\sqrt{13}$. The answer could be checked by taking any point on L_2 and finding its distance to L_1.

EXERCISES

In problems 1 through 8, find the distance from the given points to the given lines. Draw figures.

1. $(2, 1)$, $4x - 3y + 5 = 0$
2. $(2, -3)$, $x + y - 3 = 0$
3. $(-1, 2)$, $12x - 5y + 9 = 0$
4. $(-1, -2)$, $2x - 3y + 5 = 0$
5. $(4, 6)$, $2x - y - 2 = 0$
6. $(3, 2)$, $x + 5 = 0$
7. $(-1, 0)$, $y + 2 = 0$
8. $(2, 1)$, $x - y = 0$

In problems 9 through 12, find the distance between the given parallel lines. Check your results.

9. $3x + 4y - 7 = 0$ and $3x + 4y + 3 = 0$
10. $x + 2y + 4 = 0$ and $2x + 4y - 5 = 0$
11. $5x - 6y = 0$ and $5x - 6y + 1 = 0$
12. $Ax + By + C = 0$ and $Ax + By + C' = 0$

In problems 13 through 16, the vertices of triangles are given. Find the lengths of the altitudes from the first vertex to the side joining the other two. Then find the areas of the triangles.

13. $(3, 2)$, $(-1, 1)$, $(-2, 3)$

14. $(4, -2)$, $(-1, -3)$, $(3, 2)$

15. $(-2, -1)$, $(-1, 4)$, $(3, 2)$

16. $(-3, 4)$, $(1, -2)$, $(3, 4)$

17. Find the two points on the x-axis which are at a distance 2 from $3x - 4y - 6 = 0$.

18. Find the two points on the y-axis which are at a distance 3 from the line $12x + 5y + 9 = 0$.

19. Find the two points on the line $2x + 3y + 4 = 0$ which are at a distance 2 from the line $3x + 4y - 6 = 0$.

20. Find the equations of the two lines parallel to $3x + 4y - 5 = 0$ and at a distance 2 from it.

21. Find the equations of the two lines parallel to $x - 2y + 1 = 0$ and a distance 3 from it.

22. Find the distance from the midpoint of the segment joining $(3, 2)$ and $(-4, 6)$ to the line $2x - 3y + 5 = 0$.

2. FAMILIES OF LINES

The equation

$$y = 2x + k$$

represents a line of slope 2 for each value of k. The totality of lines obtained by letting k have any value — positive, negative, or zero — is called the *family of lines* of slope 2. In this instance, the family consists of a collection of parallel lines. More generally, a family of lines is a collection of lines which have a particular geometric property. The equation

$$y = kx + 3$$

represents for each value of k a line which has y-intercept 3. The totality of such lines obtained by letting k take on all possible values is another example of a family of lines. Note that there is one line which passes through the point $(0, 3)$ which is not in this family: the y-axis itself. Its equation is $x = 0$ and it is not included in the above family. It occasionally happens that families of lines have exceptions, and these must be taken into account. The following examples illustrate other families.

EXAMPLE 1. Write the equation for the family of lines parallel to $3x + 2y + 4 = 0$.

Solution. The slope of every member of the family must be $-\frac{3}{2}$. Therefore $3x + 2y + k = 0$, where k can have any value, represents the family.

EXAMPLE 2. Write the equation for the family of all lines passing through $(3, -2)$.

Solution. The point-slope form for the equation of a line through $(3, -2)$ is

$$y + 2 = m(x - 3),$$

and this represents every line through $(3, -2)$, with one exception. The line $x = 3$ must be added to the above family to get *all* lines through $(3, -2)$.

EXAMPLE 3. Write the equation for the family of all lines having x-intercept -2.

Solution. The two-intercept form for the equation of a line is

$$\frac{x}{a} + \frac{y}{b} = 1.$$

The equation $(x/-2) + (y/b) = 1$, where b can have any value, represents all lines with x-intercept -2 except for two: the x-axis $(y = 0)$ and the line $x = -2$.

The two lines

$$L_1: 3x - 2y + 7 = 0 \quad \text{and} \quad L_2: 2x + y - 6 = 0$$

intersect at a point (call it P) which may be found by solving the equations simultaneously. The first-degree equation

$$(3x - 2y + 7) + k(2x + y - 6) = 0$$

represents a family of lines passing through the intersection of L_1 and L_2. To see this we first note that no matter what k is, the above line must pass through P because $3x - 2y + 7 = 0$ at P and $2x + y - 6 = 0$ at P. As k varies, the equation changes, so the above system represents a family of lines through P. The family consists of *all* lines through P, with one exception. No value of k gives L_2 itself. Recombining the terms, we conclude that the equation

$$(3 + 2k)x + (k - 2)y + 7 - 6k = 0$$

represents the family of all lines through P except for L_2.

EXAMPLE 4. Find the equation of the line passing through $(2, -3)$ and the intersection of the lines

$$L_1: 3x - y + 8 = 0 \quad \text{and} \quad L_2: 2x + 5y + 7 = 0.$$

Solution. We could find the intersection point of L_1 and L_2 and then use the two-point form of the equation of a line to get the answer. Instead we shall use the idea of a family of lines. The equation

$$3x - y + 8 + k(2x + 5y + 7) = 0$$

represents the family through the intersection of L_1 and L_2. The particular member passing through $(2, -3)$ must satisfy

$$3(2) - (-3) + 8 + k(2(2) + 5(-3) + 7) = 0.$$

This equation yields

$$k = \tfrac{17}{4}$$

and, substituting this value of k in the equation of the family, we obtain

$$3x - y + 8 + \tfrac{17}{4}(2x + 5y + 7) = 0, \quad \text{and} \quad 46x + 81y + 151 = 0.$$

EXERCISES

In problems 1 through 12, write the equations of the families of lines satisfying the given conditions:

1. parallel to the line $x - 3y + 7 = 0$
2. having y-intercept -4
3. having x-intercept 2
4. passing through the point $(3, -7)$
5. passing through the point $(2, -1)$
6. perpendicular to the line $3x + 4y - 2 = 0$
7. having equal x- and y-intercepts
8. having x-intercept equal to the negative of the y-intercept
9. having y-intercept equal to twice the x-intercept
10. having the product of the intercepts equal to 9
11. having the sum of the intercepts equal to 10
12. the right triangle formed by the line and the coordinate axes having an area of 12
13. Find the equation of the line passing through $(5, -1)$ and through the intersection of $2x + y - 3 = 0$ and $x + 4y - 7 = 0$.
14. Find the equation of the line passing through $(2, -4)$ and through the intersection of $3x - 4y + 1 = 0$ and $2x - 6y + 3 = 0$.
15. Find the equation of the line passing through the intersection of $2x - y + 3 = 0$ and $x + 3y - 2 = 0$ and having slope 4.
16. Find the equation of the line passing through the intersection of $3x + 4y - 2 = 0$ and $2x + y - 6 = 0$ and having slope -2.
17. Find the equation of the line passing through the intersection of $2x + y - 1 = 0$ and $x - y + 3 = 0$ and having y-intercept -3.
18. Find the equations of the lines which bisect the angle formed by the lines $L_1: x + y - 5 = 0$ and $L_2: 2x - y + 3 = 0$. (*Hint:* Write the condition that the distances from a point (x, y) to L_1 and L_2 be equal.)
19. Find the equations of the lines which pass through the intersection of $L_1: 2x + 3y - 1 = 0$ and $L_2: x - y + 12 = 0$ and which are three units from the origin.

3. THE CIRCLE

Straight lines correspond to equations of the first degree in x and y. A systematic approach to the study of equations in x and y would proceed to equations of the second degree, third degree, and so on. Curves of the second degree are sufficiently simple that we can study them thoroughly in this course. Curves corresponding to equations of the third degree and higher will not be treated systematically, since the complications rapidly become too great. However, the study of equations of any degree — the theory of algebraic curves — is an interesting subject on its own and may be studied in advanced courses.

The set of all points (x, y) which are at a given distance r from a fixed point (h, k) represents a circle. We also use the phrase, *the locus of all such points is a circle.* From the formula for the distance between two points we know that

$$r = \sqrt{(x - h)^2 + (y - k)^2},$$

or, upon squaring,

$$(x - h)^2 + (y - k)^2 = r^2.$$

This is the equation of a circle with center at (h, k) and radius r.

EXAMPLE 1. Find the equation of the circle with center at $(-3, 4)$ and radius 6.

Solution. We have $h = -3, k = 4, r = 6$. Substituting in the equation of the circle, we obtain

$$(x + 3)^2 + (y - 4)^2 = 36.$$

We can multiply out to get

$$x^2 + y^2 + 6x - 8y - 11 = 0$$

as another form for the answer.

We now start the other way around. Suppose that we are given an equation such as

$$x^2 + y^2 - 4x + 7y - 8 = 0;$$

we ask whether or not this represents a circle and, if so, what the center and radius are. The process for determining these facts consists of "completing the square." We write

$$(x^2 - 4x \quad) + (y^2 + 7y \quad) = 8,$$

in which we leave the appropriate spaces, as shown. We add the square of half the coefficient of x and the square of half the coefficient of y to both sides and so obtain

$$(x^2 - 4x + 4) + (y^2 + 7y + \tfrac{49}{4}) = 8 + 4 + \tfrac{49}{4},$$

or

$$(x - 2)^2 + (y + \tfrac{7}{2})^2 = \tfrac{97}{4}.$$

This represents a circle with center at $(2, -\tfrac{7}{2})$ and radius $\tfrac{1}{2}\sqrt{97}$.

The process of completing the square may be performed for a *general* equation of the form

$$x^2 + y^2 + Dx + Ey + F = 0,$$

where D, E, F are any numbers. We get

$$x^2 + Dx + \frac{D^2}{4} + y^2 + Ey + \frac{E^2}{4} = -F + \frac{D^2}{4} + \frac{E^2}{4},$$

or

$$\left(x + \frac{D}{2}\right)^2 + \left(y + \frac{E}{2}\right)^2 = \tfrac{1}{4}(D^2 + E^2 - 4F).$$

We conclude that such an equation represents a circle with center at $(-D/2, -E/2)$ and radius $\tfrac{1}{2}\sqrt{D^2 + E^2 - 4F}$. But there is a problem: If the quantity under the radical is negative, there is no circle and consequently no locus. If it is zero, the circle reduces to a point. *The equation does represent a circle of radius* $\frac{1}{2}\sqrt{D^2 + E^2 - 4F}$ *if* $D^2 + E^2 > 4F$, *and only then.*

A circle is determined if the numbers D, E, and F are given. This means that in general three conditions determine a circle. We all know that there is exactly one circle through three points (not all on a straight line). The following example shows how the equation is found when three points are prescribed.

EXAMPLE 2. Find the equation of the circle passing through the points $(-3, 4)$, $(4, 5)$, and $(1, -4)$. Locate the center and determine the radius.

Solution. If the circle has the equation

$$x^2 + y^2 + Dx + Ey + F = 0,$$

then each point on the circle must satisfy this equation. By substituting, we get

$$(-3, 4): \quad -3D + 4E + F = -25;$$
$$(4, 5): \quad 4D + 5E + F = -41;$$
$$(1, -4): \quad D - 4E + F = -17.$$

We subtract the second equation from the first and the third from the second and eliminate F, to obtain

$$7D + E = -16, \quad 3D + 9E = -24.$$

We solve these simultaneously and get $D = -2$, $E = -2$. Substituting back into any one of the original three equations gives $F = -23$. The equation of the circle is

$$x^2 + y^2 - 2x - 2y - 23 = 0.$$

The center and radius are obtained by completing the square. We write

$$(x^2 - 2x \quad) + (y^2 - 2y \quad) = 23, \quad \text{and} \quad (x - 1)^2 + (y - 1)^2 = 25.$$

The center is at $(1, 1)$; the radius is 5.

The problem of Example 2 could be solved in another way. (1) Find the perpendicular bisector of the line segment joining the first two points. (2) Do the same with the first and third (or second and third) points. (3) The point of intersection of the two perpendicular bisectors is the center of the circle. (4) The formula for the distance from the center of the circle to any of the original three points gives the radius. (5) Knowing the center and radius, we write the equation of the circle. (See Fig. 9–2.)

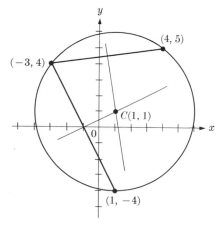

FIGURE 9–2

EXERCISES

In problems 1 through 14, find the equations of the circles determined by the given conditions, where C denotes the center and r the radius.

1. $C = (-3, 4)$, $r = 5$
2. $C = (0, 0)$, $r = 4$
3. $C = (2, 3)$, $r = 2$
4. $C = (2, -1)$, $r = 3$
5. A diameter is the segment from $(4, 2)$ to $(8, 6)$
6. A diameter is the segment from $(-2, 3)$ to $(4, -1)$
7. $C = (3, 4)$, tangent to the x-axis
8. $C = (-2, 3)$, tangent to the y-axis
9. $C = (2, 1)$, passing through $(3, 4)$
10. $C = (-1, -2)$, passing through $(-2, 2)$
11. $C = (2, 3)$, tangent to $3x + 4y + 2 = 0$
12. $C = (3, -2)$, tangent to $5x - 12y = 0$
13. Tangent to both axes, radius 6, in second quadrant
14. Tangent to the x-axis, to the line $y = 2x$ and radius 5 (four solutions)

In problems 15 through 22, determine the loci of the given equations by completing the squares.

15. $x^2 + y^2 + 6x - 8y = 0$
16. $x^2 + y^2 + 2x - 4y - 11 = 0$
17. $x^2 + y^2 - 4x + 2y + 5 = 0$
18. $x^2 + y^2 + 6x - 4y + 15 = 0$
19. $x^2 + y^2 + 3x - 5y - \frac{1}{2} = 0$
20. $x^2 + y^2 + 4x - 3y + 4 = 0$
21. $2x^2 + 2y^2 + 3x + 5y + 2 = 0$
22. $2x^2 + 2y^2 - 5x + 7y + 10 = 0$

23. Show that when $D = E$ the locus of $x^2 + y^2 + Dx + Ey + F = 0$ is always a circle if $F < D^2/2$. Note that if $F < 0$ the locus is always a circle, regardless of the sizes of D and E.

In problems 24 through 27, find the equations of the circles through the given points by the method used in Example 2. Find the centers and radii.

24. $(-5, 2)$, $(-3, 4)$, $(1, 2)$
25. $(-3, 1)$, $(-2, 2)$, $(6, -2)$
26. $(7, -2)$, $(3, -4)$, $(0, -3)$
27. $(1, -1)$, $(0, 1)$, $(-3, -3)$

In problems 28 and 29, find the equations of the circles by the method described after Example 2.

28. $(-2, -4)$, $(2, -6)$, $(4, 2)$
29. $(-2, -1)$, $(0, 2)$, $(4, 1)$
30. Determine whether or not the points $(2, 0)$, $(0, 4)$, $(2, 2)$, and $(1, 1)$ lie on a circle.
31. Find the equation of the circle or circles with center on the y-axis and passing through $(-2, 3)$ and $(4, 1)$.
32. Find the equation of the circle with center on the line $x + y - 1 = 0$ and passing through the points $(0, 5)$ and $(2, 1)$.

4. THE CIRCLE, CONTINUED

A line tangent to a circle is defined in the usual way by the methods of calculus. We also have the elementary definition that a line perpendicular to a radius and passing through the point where the radius meets the circle is tangent to the circle at this point. We consider an example which illustrates the fact that the two definitions agree. The point $(1, 2)$ is on the circle

$$x^2 + y^2 + 2x + 3y - 13 = 0.$$

We pose the problem of finding the equation of the line tangent to the circle at the point $(1, 2)$. (See Fig. 9–3). By implicit differentiation we can find the slope of the tangent line at any point. We have

$$2x + 2y \frac{dy}{dx} + 2 + 3 \frac{dy}{dx} = 0$$

and

$$\frac{dy}{dx} = - \frac{2x + 2}{2y + 3}.$$

At the point $(1, 2)$ we obtain

$$\frac{dy}{dx} = - \frac{2 + 2}{4 + 3} = - \frac{4}{7},$$

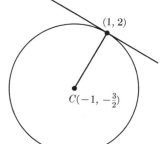

FIGURE 9–3

and the equation of the line, according to the point-slope formula, is

$$y - 2 = -\tfrac{4}{7}(x - 1) \qquad \text{or} \qquad 4x + 7y - 18 = 0.$$

Any line perpendicular to this tangent line has slope $\tfrac{7}{4}$. The particular perpendicular passing through $(1, 2)$ has the equation

$$y - 2 = \tfrac{7}{4}(x - 1),$$

or

$$7x - 4y + 1 = 0. \tag{1}$$

The center C of the circle is at $(-1, -\tfrac{3}{2})$. Since

$$7(-1) - 4(-\tfrac{3}{2}) + 1 = 0,$$

the line (1) passes through the center C. Therefore we see that the tangent line is perpendicular to the radius at the point of contact. Thus the two definitions for a tangent to a circle agree.

Let $P(x_1, y_1)$ be a point outside the circle K which has its center at $C(h, k)$ and has radius r. The equation of K is

$$(x - h)^2 + (y - k)^2 = r^2.$$

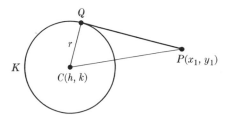

FIGURE 9–4

A tangent from P to the circle has contact at a point Q (Fig. 9–4). Triangle PQC is a right triangle. The length $\overline{PQ} = \sqrt{(\overline{PC})^2 - r^2}$ and, using the distance formula for the length PC, we have

$$\overline{PQ} = \sqrt{(x_1 - h)^2 + (y_1 - k)^2 - r^2}.$$

EXAMPLE 1. A tangent is drawn from $P(8, 4)$ to the circle

$$x^2 + y^2 + 2x + y - 3 = 0.$$

Find the distance from P to the point of tangency.

Solution. $d = \sqrt{8^2 + 4^2 + 2(8) + 4 - 3} = \sqrt{97}.$

Note that it was not necessary to complete the square; mere substitution of $x = 8$ and $y = 4$ has the same effect.

The equation

$$x^2 + (y - k)^2 = 25$$

represents a *family of circles*. All circles of this family have radius 5 and, furthermore, the centers are always on the y-axis. Since a line is determined by two conditions while a circle is fixed by three conditions, families of circles are more extensive than families of lines, from some points of view. For example, all circles of radius 3 comprise a "larger" class than all lines of slope 7. This has meaning in the following sense: consider any point in the plane; only one member of the above family of lines passes through this point; however, an infinite number of circles of radius 3 passes through this same point. The family of lines of slope 7 is called a *one-parameter family*. The equation $y = 7x + k$ has *one* constant k which can take on any real value. The equation

$$(x - h)^2 + (y - k)^2 = 9$$

is a *two-parameter family* of circles. The numbers h and k may independently take on any numerical value.

EXAMPLE 2. Find the equation of the family of circles with centers on the line $y = x$ and radius 7.

Solution. The center $C(h, k)$ must have $h = k$ if the center is on the line $y = x$. The required equation is

$$(x - h)^2 + (y - h)^2 = 49.$$

This is a one-parameter family of circles.

EXAMPLE 3. Find the equation of the family of circles with center at $(3, -2)$.

Solution. The equation is

$$(x - 3)^2 + (y + 2)^2 = r^2.$$

This is a one-parameter family of concentric circles.

––––––––––

The two circles

$$x^2 + y^2 + Dx + Ey + F = 0,$$
$$x^2 + y^2 + D'x + E'y + F' = 0,$$

may or may not intersect. If we subtract one of these equations from the other, we obtain

$$(D - D')x + (E - E')y + (F - F') = 0,$$

which is the equation of a straight line. This straight line has slope $-(D - D')/(E - E')$ (if $E \neq E'$). The circles have centers at $(-D/2, -E/2)$ and $(-D'/2, -E'/2)$, respectively. The line joining the centers has slope

$$\frac{(-E'/2) + (E/2)}{(-D'/2) + (D/2)} = \frac{E - E'}{D - D'},$$

which is the negative reciprocal of $-(D - D')/(E - E')$. *The equation of the line obtained by subtraction of the equations of two circles* is called the *radical axis,* and it *is perpendicular to the line joining the centers of the circles.* Furthermore, if the circles intersect, the points of intersection satisfy *both* equations of circles. These points must therefore be on the radical axis.

––––––––––

EXAMPLE 4. Find the points of intersection of the circles.

$$x^2 + y^2 - 2x - 4y - 4 = 0,$$
$$x^2 + y^2 - 6x - 2y - 8 = 0.$$

Solution. By subtraction we get

$$4x - 2y + 4 = 0,$$

and we solve this equation simultaneously with the equation of either circle. The substitution gives

$$5x^2 - 2x - 8 = 0 \quad \text{or} \quad x = \tfrac{1}{5} \pm \tfrac{1}{5}\sqrt{41}.$$

The points of intersection are $(\tfrac{1}{5} + \tfrac{1}{5}\sqrt{41}, \tfrac{12}{5} + \tfrac{2}{5}\sqrt{41})$ and $(\tfrac{1}{5} - \tfrac{1}{5}\sqrt{41}, \tfrac{12}{5} - \tfrac{2}{5}\sqrt{41})$.

EXERCISES

In problems 1 through 4, find the equations of the lines tangent to the given circles at the points P on the circles.

1. $x^2 + y^2 + 2x - 4y = 0$, $P(1, 3)$
2. $x^2 + y^2 - 3x + 2y - 7 = 0$, $P(-1, 1)$
3. $x^2 + y^2 + 5x - 6y - 21 = 0$, $P(2, -1)$
4. $x^2 + y^2 + 2x - 19 = 0$, $P(-3, 4)$

In problems 5 through 8, find the equations of the lines normal to the given circles at the given points P on the circles. Do each problem in two ways.

5. $x^2 + y^2 + 4y - 1 = 0$, $P(2, -3)$
6. $x^2 + y^2 - 3x - 8y + 18 = 0$, $P(1, 4)$
7. $x^2 + y^2 - 4x - 7y - 6 = 0$, $P(6, 1)$
8. $x^2 + y^2 + 8x + 2y + 16 = 0$, $P(-4, -2)$

In problems 9 through 12, lines are drawn tangent to the given circles through the given points P, not on the circles. Find the equations of these lines.

9. $x^2 + y^2 + 4x + 6y - 21 = 0$, $P(-4, 5)$
10. $x^2 + y^2 - 2x + 5y + 7 = 0$, $P(-1, -2)$
11. $x^2 + y^2 - x - 4y - 7 = 0$, $P(3, 0)$
12. $x^2 + y^2 + 2x + 6y + 2 = 0$, $P(-3, 3)$
13. The slope of the tangent to

$$x^2 + y^2 + 3x + y + 25 = 0 \quad \text{is} \quad \frac{dy}{dx} = -\frac{2x + 3}{2y + 1}, \quad y \neq -\tfrac{1}{2}.$$

What is wrong with this statement? or is it correct?

In problems 14 through 20, write the equations of the families of circles with the given properties.

14. center on the x-axis, radius 3
15. center on the y-axis, radius 4
16. center on the line $x + y - 6 = 0$, radius 1
17. center on the x-axis, tangent to the y-axis
18. center on the line $y = x$, tangent to both coordinate axes
19. center on the line $y = 3x$, tangent to the line $x + 3y + 4 = 0$
20. center on the line $x + 2y - 7 = 0$ and tangent to the line $2x + 3y - 1 = 0$
21. Give a reasonable definition for the statement that two circles intersect at right angles. Do the circles $x^2 + y^2 - 6y = 0$ and $x^2 + y^2 - 6x = 0$ satisfy your definition at their intersection points?

In problems 22 through 25, find the points of intersection of the two circles, if they intersect. If they do not intersect, draw a graph showing the location of the radical axis.

22. $x^2 + y^2 + 6x - 9y = 0$, $x^2 + y^2 - 2x + 3y - 7 = 0$
23. $x^2 + y^2 + x - 3y + 1 = 0$, $x^2 + y^2 - 4x + 2y - 3 = 0$

24. $x^2 + y^2 + 2x + 3y + 1 = 0$, $x^2 + y^2 - 8y - 7 = 0$
25. $2x^2 + 2y^2 + 4x - 2y - 1 = 0$, $3x^2 + 3y^2 + 6x - 9y + 2 = 0$
26. Given the circles $x^2 + y^2 + 2x - 4 = 0$ and $x^2 + y^2 - x - y - 2 = 0$. What is the geometric property of the family of circles

$$(x^2 + y^2 - x - y - 2) + k(x^2 + y^2 + 2x - 4) = 0?$$

   Sketch a few members of this family.

27. Find the locus of all points $P(x, y)$ such that the distance from $(3, 2)$ is always twice the distance from $(4, 1)$. Describe the locus.

28. Find the locus of all points $P(x, y)$ such that the distance from $(1, -4)$ is always $\frac{2}{3}$ the distance from $(2, 1)$. Describe the locus.

29. Given the three circles

$$x^2 + y^2 - x - y = 0,$$
$$x^2 + y^2 + 2x - y - 3 = 0,$$
$$x^2 + y^2 + x - 2y - 4 = 0,$$

   show that the three radical axes obtained from each pair of circles are concurrent (i.e., the three lines meet in one point).

30. Work problem 29 again for the circles

$$x^2 + y^2 + Dx + Ey + F = 0,$$
$$x^2 + y^2 + D'x + E'y + F' = 0,$$
$$x^2 + y^2 + D''x + E''y + F'' = 0.$$

   What conditions are necessary for the result? (*Hint:* Can you think of a pair of circles which do not have a radical axis?)

5. TRIGONOMETRY REVIEW

It is assumed that a student of the calculus has successfully completed a course in trigonometry. However, no matter how well he has learned the formulas of trigonometry, he can forget them unless he has used them repeatedly and frequently. We shall therefore devote this section to a review of the basic notions of trigonometry and a compilation of many of the elementary formulas, for we shall need to use them often from now on. In any case, the formulas serve as handy tools for future use, and the student who has difficulty remembering them should relearn them systematically.

A circle of radius r is drawn and a rectangular coordinate system constructed with origin at the center of this circle. An angle θ is drawn, starting from the positive direction of the x-axis, and is measured counterclockwise. Angles in the first, second, third, and fourth quadrants are shown in Fig. 9–5. The basic definitions of the trigonometric functions are

$$\sin \theta = \frac{y}{r}, \qquad \cos \theta = \frac{x}{r},$$

where (x, y) are the coordinates of the point where the terminating side of the

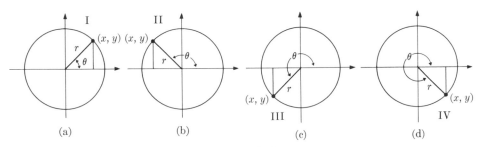

FIGURE 9–5

angle θ intersects the circle. These definitions depend only on the angle θ and not on the size of the circle since, by similar triangles, the ratios are independent of the size of r. The quantity r is always positive, while x and y have the sign that goes with the quadrant: x and y are positive in the first quadrant; x is negative, y is positive in the second quadrant, and so on.

The remaining trigonometric functions are defined by the relations

$$\tan \theta = \frac{\sin \theta}{\cos \theta}, \quad \cot \theta = \frac{\cos \theta}{\sin \theta}, \quad \sec \theta = \frac{1}{\cos \theta}, \quad \csc \theta = \frac{1}{\sin \theta}.$$

We also can define them by the formulas

$$\tan \theta = \frac{y}{x}, \quad \cot \theta = \frac{x}{y}, \quad \sec \theta = \frac{r}{x}, \quad \csc \theta = \frac{r}{y}.$$

For angles larger than $360°$ the trigonometric functions repeat, and for this reason they are called *periodic* functions. This means that for all θ

$$\sin (360° + \theta) = \sin \theta, \quad \cos (360° + \theta) = \cos \theta.$$

Negative angles are measured by starting from the positive x-direction and going *clockwise*. Figure 9–6 shows a negative angle $-\theta$ and its corresponding positive angle θ. By congruent triangles it is easy to see that for *every* θ we have

$$\sin (-\theta) = -\sin \theta \quad \text{and} \quad \cos (-\theta) = \cos \theta,$$

which says that the sine function is an *odd* function of θ, while the cosine function

FIGURE 9–6

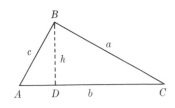

FIGURE 9–7

is an *even* function of θ. It is easy to show that

$$\tan(-\theta) = -\tan\theta, \qquad \cot(-\theta) = -\cot\theta,$$
$$\sec(-\theta) = \sec\theta, \qquad \csc(-\theta) = -\csc\theta.$$

No matter what quadrant the angle θ is in, the Pythagorean theorem tells us that

$$x^2 + y^2 = r^2,$$

or, upon dividing by r^2,

$$\left(\frac{x}{r}\right)^2 + \left(\frac{y}{r}\right)^2 = 1.$$

This formula asserts that for every angle θ,

$$\cos^2\theta + \sin^2\theta = 1.$$

Let ABC be any triangle with sides a, b, c, as shown in Fig. 9–7. We have the *Law of Sines:*

$$\frac{\sin A}{a} = \frac{\sin B}{b} = \frac{\sin C}{c},$$

and the *Law of Cosines:*

$$a^2 = b^2 + c^2 - 2bc\cos A,$$
$$b^2 = a^2 + c^2 - 2ac\cos B,$$
$$c^2 = a^2 + b^2 - 2ab\cos C.$$

The area of $\triangle ABC$ is

$$\text{Area} = \tfrac{1}{2}ab\sin C = \tfrac{1}{2}bc\sin A = \tfrac{1}{2}ac\sin B.$$

The proofs of these statements should be reviewed. An ambitious student may want to rediscover these proofs for himself. As a help in establishing the law of sines, the student should drop the perpendicular from B to side b in Fig. 9–7.

The most common unit for measurement of angles is the degree. The circumference of a circle is divided into 360 equal parts, and the angle from the center to two adjacent subdivision points is *one degree.* Each degree is divided into 60 *minutes* and each minute into 60 *seconds.*

A second type of unit for measuring angles is the *radian.* A circle is drawn and an arc is measured which is equal in length to the radius, as in Fig. 9–8. Note that the arc $\overgroup{AB}$ (*not* the chord) is r units in length. *The angle subtended from the center of the circle is* 1 *radian,* by definition. This angle is the same regardless of the size of the circle and so is a perfectly good unit for measurement. To measure any angle θ in radian units (Fig. 9–9), we measure the arc s intercepted by a circle of radius r. Then division by r gives the radian measure of the angle:

$$\theta = \frac{s}{r} \text{ radians.}$$

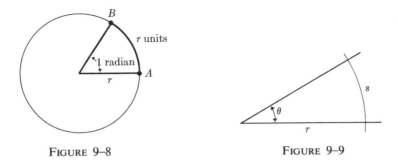

FIGURE 9–8   FIGURE 9–9

We are all familiar with the definition of the number π, which is

$$\pi = \frac{\text{length of circumference of circle}}{\text{length of diameter of circle}} .$$

If C is the length of the circumference and r is the radius, then $2\pi = C/r$. This is the same as saying that the radian measure of the angle we know as 360° is exactly 2π radians. We have the basic relation

$$\pi \text{ radians} = 180 \text{ degrees}.$$

The fundamental formulas upon which many of the trigonometric identities and relations are based are the *addition formulas for the sine and cosine*. These are

$$\sin(\phi + \theta) = \sin\phi\cos\theta + \cos\phi\sin\theta;$$
$$\sin(\phi - \theta) = \sin\phi\cos\theta - \cos\phi\sin\theta;$$
$$\cos(\phi + \theta) = \cos\phi\cos\theta - \sin\phi\sin\theta;$$
$$\cos(\phi - \theta) = \cos\phi\cos\theta + \sin\phi\sin\theta.$$

Proofs of these formulas should be reviewed. Simple proofs, based on the Law of Cosines, may be found in Morrey, *University Calculus*, Section 9–7. See also problems 4 and 5 at the end of this section. Many of the formulas listed below are special cases of the above formulas. Before listing them, we shall indicate some special values of the three principal trigonometric functions in a way that somewhat reduces the strain on memorization. The tangent function tends to infinity as $\theta \to 90°$ and we sometimes say, speaking loosely, that "tan 90° is infinite."

Function \ Angle	0°	30°	45°	60°	90°	120°	135°	150°	180°
sin	$\frac{\sqrt{0}}{2}$	$\frac{\sqrt{1}}{2}$	$\frac{\sqrt{2}}{2}$	$\frac{\sqrt{3}}{2}$	$\frac{\sqrt{4}}{2}$	$\frac{\sqrt{3}}{2}$	$\frac{\sqrt{2}}{2}$	$\frac{\sqrt{1}}{2}$	$\frac{\sqrt{0}}{2}$
cos	$\frac{\sqrt{4}}{2}$	$\frac{\sqrt{3}}{2}$	$\frac{\sqrt{2}}{2}$	$\frac{\sqrt{1}}{2}$	$\frac{\sqrt{0}}{2}$	$-\frac{\sqrt{1}}{2}$	$-\frac{\sqrt{2}}{2}$	$-\frac{\sqrt{3}}{2}$	$-\frac{\sqrt{4}}{2}$
tan	$\sqrt{\frac{0}{4}}$	$\sqrt{\frac{1}{3}}$	$\sqrt{\frac{2}{2}}$	$\sqrt{\frac{3}{1}}$	*	$-\sqrt{\frac{3}{1}}$	$-\sqrt{\frac{2}{2}}$	$-\sqrt{\frac{1}{3}}$	$-\sqrt{\frac{0}{4}}$

From the relation

$$\sin^2\theta + \cos^2\theta = 1,$$

we obtain, when we divide by $\cos^2\theta$, the relation

$$\tan^2\theta + 1 = \sec^2\theta.$$

If we divide by $\sin^2\theta$, the identity

$$1 + \cot^2\theta = \csc^2\theta$$

results.

The *double-angle* formulas are obtained by letting $\theta = \phi$ in the addition formulas. We find that

$$\sin 2\theta = 2\sin\theta\cos\theta;$$
$$\cos 2\theta = \cos^2\theta - \sin^2\theta = 2\cos^2\theta - 1 = 1 - 2\sin^2\theta.$$

Since $\tan(\phi + \theta) = \sin(\phi + \theta)/\cos(\phi + \theta)$, we have

$$\tan(\phi + \theta) = \frac{\tan\phi + \tan\theta}{1 - \tan\phi\tan\theta};$$

$$\tan(\phi - \theta) = \frac{\tan\phi - \tan\theta}{1 + \tan\phi\tan\theta}.$$

The double-angle formula becomes

$$\tan 2\theta = \frac{2\tan\theta}{1 - \tan^2\theta}.$$

The *half-angle* formulas are derived from the double-angle formulas by writing $\theta/2$ for θ. We obtain

$$\sin^2\frac{\theta}{2} = \frac{1 - \cos\theta}{2}, \quad \cos^2\frac{\theta}{2} = \frac{1 + \cos\theta}{2};$$

$$\tan\frac{\theta}{2} = \frac{1 - \cos\theta}{\sin\theta} = \frac{\sin\theta}{1 + \cos\theta}.$$

The following relations may be verified from the addition formulas:

$$\sin\phi + \sin\theta = 2\sin\left(\frac{\phi + \theta}{2}\right)\cos\left(\frac{\phi - \theta}{2}\right);$$

$$\sin\phi - \sin\theta = 2\cos\left(\frac{\phi + \theta}{2}\right)\sin\left(\frac{\phi - \theta}{2}\right);$$

$$\cos\phi + \cos\theta = 2\cos\left(\frac{\phi + \theta}{2}\right)\cos\left(\frac{\phi - \theta}{2}\right);$$

$$\cos\phi - \cos\theta = -2\sin\left(\frac{\phi + \theta}{2}\right)\sin\left(\frac{\phi - \theta}{2}\right).$$

The addition formulas, with one of the angles taken as a special value, yield the following useful relations. Starting with the formula

$$\sin\left(\frac{\pi}{2} - \theta\right) = \sin\frac{\pi}{2}\cos\theta - \cos\frac{\pi}{2}\sin\theta, \quad \left(\frac{\pi}{2} = 90°\right)$$

and noting that $\sin 90° = 1$, $\cos 90° = 0$, we obtain

$$\sin\left(\frac{\pi}{2} - \theta\right) = \cos\theta.$$

In a similar way, we have

$$\cos\left(\frac{\pi}{2} - \theta\right) = \sin\theta;$$

$$\sin\left(\frac{\pi}{2} + \theta\right) = \cos\theta, \qquad \cos\left(\frac{\pi}{2} + \theta\right) = -\sin\theta;$$

$$\cos(\pi - \theta) = -\cos\theta, \qquad \sin(\pi - \theta) = \sin\theta;$$

$$\cos(\pi + \theta) = -\cos\theta, \qquad \sin(\pi + \theta) = -\sin\theta.$$

EXERCISES

1. Prove the Law of Sines.
2. Prove the Law of Cosines.
3. Establish the formula: Area $= \frac{1}{2}ab\sin C$, for the area of a triangle.

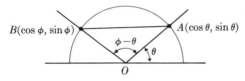

$B(\cos\phi, \sin\phi)$ $\quad$ $A(\cos\theta, \sin\theta)$

$\phi - \theta$ $\quad$ θ

O

FIGURE 9–10

4. Given the diagram in Fig. 9–10 (circle has radius $= 1$). Apply the Law of Cosines to triangle ABO to obtain a formula for $\cos(\phi - \theta)$. Then use the distance formula for the length $\overline{AB}$ to derive

$$\cos(\phi - \theta) = \cos\phi\cos\theta + \sin\phi\sin\theta.$$

5. Derive formulas for $\sin 3\theta$, $\cos 3\theta$ in terms of $\sin\theta$ and $\cos\theta$.
6. Derive formulas for $\sin 4\theta$, $\cos 4\theta$ in terms of $\sin\theta$ and $\cos\theta$.
7. Write out the derivation of the formulas for $\sin\theta/2$ and $\cos\theta/2$ in terms of $\cos\theta$.
8. Derive formulas for $\sin\frac{1}{4}\theta$ and $\cos\frac{1}{4}\theta$ in terms of $\cos\theta$.
9. Without using tables, find the values of the following:

$$\sin 15°, \quad \cos 15°, \quad \sin 22\frac{1}{2}°, \quad \cos 22\frac{1}{2}°, \quad \tan 75°, \quad \sec 75°.$$

10. Without using tables, find the values of the following:

$$\tan 22\frac{1}{2}°, \quad \sin 7\frac{1}{2}°, \quad \cos 7\frac{1}{2}°, \quad \sin 37\frac{1}{2}°, \quad \tan 37\frac{1}{2}°.$$

11. Write formulas in terms of $\sin \theta$ and $\cos \theta$ for

$$\sin \left(\frac{3\pi}{2} - \theta\right), \quad \cos \left(\frac{3\pi}{2} - \theta\right), \quad \sin \left(\frac{3\pi}{2} + \theta\right), \quad \cos \left(\frac{3\pi}{2} + \theta\right),$$

$$\sin (2\pi - \theta), \quad \cos (2\pi - \theta).$$

12. Since $\pi = 3.14^+$ approximately, let

$$x = 0, \quad \frac{\pi}{6}, \quad \frac{\pi}{4}, \quad \frac{\pi}{3}, \quad \frac{\pi}{2}, \quad \frac{2\pi}{3}, \quad \frac{3\pi}{4}, \quad \frac{5\pi}{6}, \quad \pi, \quad \frac{7\pi}{6}, \quad \text{etc.},$$

and plot the curve $y = \sin x$ on a rectangular coordinate system. Extend the graph from -2π to $+4\pi$.

13. Work problem 12 again for $y = \cos x$.

14. Work problem 12 again for $y = \tan x$.

15. Derive (from the addition formulas) the identity

$$\sin \phi + \sin \theta = 2 \sin \left(\frac{\phi + \theta}{2}\right) \cos \left(\frac{\phi - \theta}{2}\right).$$

16. Work problem 15 again for

$$\cos \phi + \cos \theta = 2 \cos \left(\frac{\phi + \theta}{2}\right) \cos \left(\frac{\phi - \theta}{2}\right).$$

17. In terms of $\sin \theta$ and $\cos \theta$, find

$$\sin \left(\frac{\pi}{6} - \theta\right), \quad \cos \left(\frac{\pi}{3} + \theta\right), \quad \cos \left(\frac{5\pi}{6} - \theta\right).$$

18. In terms of $\sin \theta$ and $\cos \theta$, find

$$\sin \left(\frac{\pi}{12} - \theta\right), \quad \cos \left(\frac{\pi}{3} + \frac{\pi}{4} - \theta\right), \quad \sin \left(\frac{\pi}{4} - \frac{\pi}{24} - \theta\right).$$

19. Sketch, in rectangular coordinates, the graph of $y = \cot x$.

20. Sketch, in rectangular coordinates, the graph of $y = \sec x$.

21. Sketch, in rectangular coordinates, the graph of $y = \csc x$.

6. GRAPHS OF TRIGONOMETRIC FUNCTIONS

In the study of trigonometry one occasionally has use for a short table of the values of trigonometric functions in terms of radian measure. However, the most common measure used for angles is the degree, and most tables for the sine, cosine, etc., are in degrees, minutes, and perhaps seconds. In calculus, however, the situation is reversed: the *natural unit* for the study of trigonometric and related functions is the *radian*. Measurement of angles in degrees is awkward and seldom used in calculus, as will become apparent in Chapter 11. In the meantime we shall get some practice in using radians to graph trigonometric functions, and in the process we shall become familiar with many of the properties of these functions.

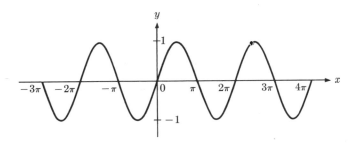

FIGURE 9–11

The graph of the function $y = \sin x$ in a rectangular coordinate system is made by drawing up a table of values and sketching the curve, as shown in Fig. 9–11.

x	0	$\pi/6$	$\pi/4$	$\pi/3$	$\pi/2$	$2\pi/3$	$3\pi/4$	$5\pi/6$	π
y	0	$1/2$	$\sqrt{2}/2$	$\sqrt{3}/2$	1	$\sqrt{3}/2$	$\sqrt{2}/2$	$1/2$	0

x	$7\pi/6$	$5\pi/4$	$4\pi/3$	$3\pi/2$	$5\pi/3$	$7\pi/4$	$11\pi/6$	2π
y	$-1/2$	$-\sqrt{2}/2$	$-\sqrt{3}/2$	-1	$-\sqrt{3}/2$	$-\sqrt{2}/2$	$-1/2$	0

It is necessary to make a table of values only between 0 and 2π. From the relation $\sin(2\pi + x) = \sin x$, we know that the curve then repeats indefinitely to the left and right.

The graph of $y = \cos x$ is found in the same way. A table of values between 0 and 2π and a knowledge of the periodic nature of the function yield the graph shown in Fig. 9–12. Note that the curves are identical except that the cosine function is shifted to the left by an amount $\pi/2$. This fact is not surprising if we recall the relation $\sin[(\pi/2) - x] = \cos x$.

A function f is called *periodic* if there is a number l such that

$$f(x + l) = f(x)$$

for all x, in which case the number l is called a *period* of the function f. For the sine function, 2π is a period, but so are 4π, 6π, 8π, etc., since $\sin(x + 4\pi) =$

FIGURE 9–12

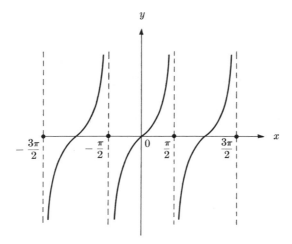

FIGURE 9–13

sin x, sin $(x + 6\pi)$ = sin x, and so on. For periodic functions there is always a
smallest number l for which $f(x + l) = f(x)$. This number is called the *least
period* of f. The least period of sin x is 2π; the same is true for cos x. The function tan x has period 2π, but this is not the least period. A graph of $y = \tan x$
is given in Fig. 9–13 which shows clearly that π is a period of tan x. This is the
least period for the tangent function.

The function $y = \sin kx$ repeats when kx changes by an amount 2π. If k is a
constant, then sin kx repeats when x changes by an amount $2\pi/k$. The least period
of the function sin kx is $2\pi/k$. The same is true for $y = \cos kx$. For example,
$y = \cos 5x$ has as its least period $2\pi/5$.

A periodic function f, which never becomes larger than some number b in value
and never becomes smaller than some number c, is said to have *amplitude* $\frac{1}{2}(b - c)$,
provided that there are points where f actually takes on the values b and c. For
example, the function $y = 3 \sin 2x$ is never larger than 3 or smaller than -3.
The amplitude is 3. Note that $y = 3$ when $x = \pi/4$. The tangent function has
no amplitude.

EXAMPLE 1. Find the amplitude and period of $y = 4 \cos (3x/2)$. Sketch the graph.

Solution. The amplitude is 4; the period is $2\pi/(\frac{3}{2}) = 4\pi/3$. The graph is sketched in
Fig. 9–14.

FIGURE 9–14

FIGURE 9–15

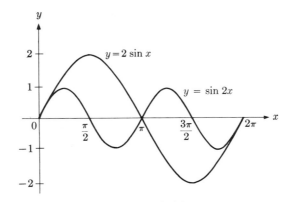

FIGURE 9–16

EXAMPLE 2. Find the amplitude and period of $y = 2.5 \sin [x + (\pi/6)]$ and sketch its graph.

Solution. This function is similar to $2.5 \sin x$, except that it is shifted horizontally. When $x = -\pi/6$, $y = 0$, and we see that the "zero point" is moved to the left an amount $\pi/6$. The period is $2\pi/1 = 2\pi$, and the amplitude is 2.5. With this information it is now easy to sketch the curve, as shown in Fig. 9–15.

Combinations of trigonometric functions may be sketched quickly by a method known as *addition of ordinates*. If the sum of two functions is to be sketched, we start by sketching each function separately. Then, at a particular value of x, the y-values of each of the functions are added to give the result. Incidentally, this method is quite general and may be used for the sum or difference of any functions. An example illustrates the technique.

EXAMPLE 3. Sketch the graph of

$$y = 2 \sin x + \sin 2x.$$

Solution. The function $2 \sin x$ has period 2π and amplitude 2, while $\sin 2x$ has period π and amplitude 1. We sketch the graph of each of these functions on the same coordinate system from 0 to 2π, as shown in Fig. 9–16. At convenient values of x, the y-values of the two graphs are added and the results plotted either on the same graph or on a similar one, as shown in Fig. 9–17.

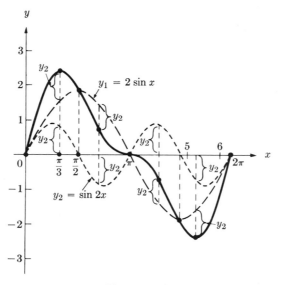

FIGURE 9–17

EXERCISES

In problems 1 through 16, find the amplitudes and the periods of the functions defined by the given expressions and sketch their graphs.

1. $2 \sin \frac{1}{2}x$

2. $3 \cos \frac{3}{2}x$

3. $4 \cos \frac{1}{2}\pi x$

4. $2.5 \sin \frac{1}{3}\pi x$

5. $3 \sin \frac{2}{3}x$

6. $5 \sin \frac{1}{2}\pi x$

7. $2 \cos \left(2x + \dfrac{\pi}{3} \right)$

8. $3 \sin \left(\frac{1}{2}\pi x + \frac{1}{4}\pi \right)$

9. $-2 \sin 2x$

10. $-3 \cos \frac{2}{3}\pi x$

11. $4 \sin \left(2x - \dfrac{\pi}{3} \right)$

12. $3 \cos \left(2x - \dfrac{\pi}{3} \right)$

13. $-3 \sin \left(\frac{1}{2}x + 7 \right)$

14. $\frac{1}{3} \sin \left(2x + \frac{1}{2}\pi \right)$

15. $1 + \sin 2x$

16. $-3 + 2 \cos (x - 1)$

In problems 17 through 24, find the periods and amplitudes (if any), and sketch the graphs.

17. $\tan 2x$

18. $\cot 3x$

19. $\sin x + \cos x$

20. $\sec 2x$

21. $\csc \frac{1}{2}x$

22. $2 \tan (3x - 1)$

23. $2 \cos 2x - 2\sqrt{3} \sin 2x$

24. $-4 \cot (2x - \pi)$

In problems 25 through 32, sketch the graphs of the curves, using the method of addition of ordinates.

25. $y = 2 \sin x + \cos 2x$

26. $y = 3 \cos x - 2 \sin 2x$

27. $y = 3 \sin \frac{1}{2}x - \frac{3}{2} \sin x$

28. $y = 2 \sin \frac{1}{2}\pi x - 3 \cos \pi x$

29. $y = 3 \sin 2x - 2 \cos 3x$

30. $y = 2 \cos 3x - 3 \sin 4x$

31. $y = x + \sin x$

32. $y = 1 - x + \cos x$

33. Sketch the graph of $y = 2 \sin^2 x$. Show that it has period π. How does it compare with the graph of $\cos 2x$?

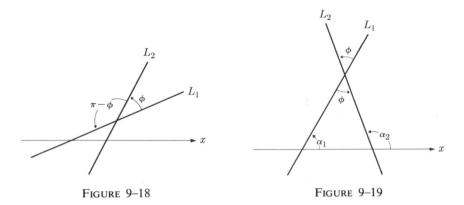

FIGURE 9–18   FIGURE 9–19

7. ANGLE BETWEEN TWO LINES. BISECTORS OF ANGLES

We recall that the *inclination* α of a line L is the angle the line makes with the positive x-direction. If the line is parallel to the x-axis, its inclination is zero. The *slope m* of the line L is $m = \tan \alpha$. Two nonparallel lines L_1 and L_2 make four angles at their intersection: two equal acute angles and two equal obtuse angles (unless the lines are perpendicular). The obtuse angle is the supplement of the acute angle.

The angle swept out when the line L_1 is rotated counterclockwise to L_2 about the point of intersection is called *the angle from L_1 to L_2. The angle from L_2 to L_1* is the one obtained by rotating L_2 into L_1 counterclockwise and is the supplement of the angle from L_1 to L_2. In Fig. 9–18, ϕ is the angle from L_1 to L_2 and $\pi - \phi$ is the angle from L_2 to L_1.

Let L_1 and L_2 be two intersecting lines (neither of which is vertical) with inclinations α_1 and α_2 and slopes $m_1 = \tan \alpha_1$ and $m_2 = \tan \alpha_2$, respectively. Let ϕ be the angle from L_1 to L_2, as shown in Fig. 9–19. Since the exterior angle of a triangle is the sum of the remote interior angles, we have

$$\alpha_2 = \alpha_1 + \phi \quad \text{or} \quad \phi = \alpha_2 - \alpha_1 \quad \text{and} \quad \tan \phi = \tan (\alpha_2 - \alpha_1).$$

Recalling from the trigonometry review the formula for the tangent of the difference of two angles, we obtain

$$\tan \phi = \frac{\tan \alpha_2 - \tan \alpha_1}{1 + \tan \alpha_1 \tan \alpha_2} \quad \text{and} \quad \tan \phi = \frac{m_2 - m_1}{1 + m_1 m_2}, \qquad (1)$$

which is *the formula for the tangent of the angle **from L_1 to L_2**.*

EXAMPLE 1. Find the tangent of the angle from the line given by $2x + 3y - 5 = 0$ to the line given by $4x - 3y - 2 = 0$.

Solution. Here $m_1 = -\frac{2}{3}$ and $m_2 = \frac{4}{3}$. The formula yields

$$\tan \phi = \frac{\frac{4}{3} - (-\frac{2}{3})}{1 + (-\frac{2}{3})(\frac{4}{3})} = 18.$$

Formula (1) fails if one of the lines is vertical. We divide both the numerator and the denominator by m_2 in the formula for $\tan \phi$, getting

$$\tan \phi = \frac{1 - (m_1/m_2)}{(1/m_2) + m_1}.$$

Consider now that L_2 becomes vertical; that is, $m_2 \to \infty$ as L_2 approaches a vertical line. Then $m_1/m_2 \to 0$, $1/m_2 \to 0$. Therefore the formula for the angle from L_1 to L_2 when L_2 is vertical is simply

$$\tan \phi = \frac{1}{m_1}.$$

EXAMPLE 2. Given the curve with equation $y = 2x^2 - 3x - 4$. Find the equations of the lines tangent to the curve at the points where $x = 1$ and $x = 2$. Find the angle between these tangent lines.

Solution. The slope at any point is found by obtaining the derivative:

$$\frac{dy}{dx} = 4x - 3.$$

At $x = 1$ the slope $m_1 = 1$; at $x = 2$ the slope $m_2 = 5$. When $x = 1$, $y = -5$ and when $x = 2$, $y = -2$. The first line has equation

$$y + 5 = 1(x - 1),$$

and the second has equation

$$y + 2 = 5(x - 2).$$

The angle from the first line to the second is

$$\tan \phi = \frac{5 - 1}{1 + 5 \cdot 1} = \frac{2}{3}.$$

Figure 9–20 shows the result.

From plane geometry we recall that the angle bisectors of two given intersecting lines represent the locus of all points which are equidistant from the given lines. The equations of these angle bisectors are found by using the formula for the distance from a point to a line and the methods of solving locus problems. The following example illustrates the technique.

EXAMPLE 3. Find the equations of the bisectors of the angles formed by the lines $3x + 4y - 7 = 0$ and $4x + 3y + 2 = 0$.

Solution. We draw a figure, as shown (Fig. 9–21), and let $P(x, y)$ be a point on the locus (angle bisector, in this case). Let d_1 be the distance from P to the line $3x + 4y - 7 = 0$ and d_2 the distance from P to the line $4x + 3y + 2 = 0$. The conditions of the

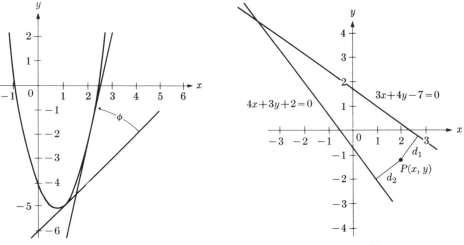

FIGURE 9–20   FIGURE 9–21

locus are $d_1 = d_2$. Then, from the formula for the distance from a point to a line, we have

$$d_1 = \frac{|3x + 4y - 7|}{\sqrt{3^2 + 4^2}} \quad \text{and} \quad d_2 = \frac{|4x + 3y + 2|}{\sqrt{4^2 + 3^2}} .$$

The conditions of the locus state that

$$|3x + 4y - 7| = |4x + 3y + 2|.$$

At this time we make use of our knowledge of absolute values. If $|a| = |b|$, then either $a = b$ or $a = -b$. This tells us that either

$$3x + 4y - 7 = 4x + 3y + 2 \quad \text{or} \quad 3x + 4y - 7 = -(4x + 3y + 2).$$

Simplifying, we obtain

$$x - y + 9 = 0 \quad \text{and} \quad 7x + 7y - 5 = 0$$

as the equations of the two angle bisectors. Note that the angle bisectors have slopes 1 and -1 and are therefore perpendicular, as we know they should be.

To distinguish the bisectors from each other, we have merely to find the tangent of the angle from one of the given lines to the other, and then the tangent of the angle from one of the given lines to the angle bisectors. A comparison of the sizes indicates where the lines fall.

EXERCISES

In problems 1 through 9, find $\tan \phi$, where ϕ is the angle from L_1 to L_2.

1. L_1: $2x - y + 3 = 0$, L_2: $x + y - 2 = 0$
2. L_1: $2x + y - 5 = 0$, L_2: $x - 2y + 1 = 0$
3. L_1: $x - 3y + 4 = 0$, L_2: $2x + y - 3 = 0$

4. L_1: $x - y - 1 = 0$, L_2: $x - 2y = 3$

5. L_1: $2x + 3y = 5$, L_2: $3x + 2y = 1$

6. L_1: $5x + y = 0$, L_2: $3x + 2y = 5$

7. L_1: $3x - 2y = 2$, L_2: $y = 2$

8. L_1: $x + y = 2$, L_2: $x = 3$

9. L_1: $4x - 7y = 3$, L_2: $x = -2$

In problems 10 through 13, find the tangents of the angles of the triangles ABC with the vertices given.

10. $A(3, 0)$, $B(1, 2)$, $C(5, 6)$ 11. $A(-1, 2)$, $B(4, 1)$, $C(0, 5)$

12. $A(-1, -3)$, $B(2, -1)$, $C(-3, 4)$ 13. $A(-1, 4)$, $B(5, 1)$, $C(5, 6)$

14. Given a triangle with vertices at $A(0, 0)$, $B(5, 0)$, $C(3, 4)$; show that the three angle bisectors meet in a point.

15. Show that the bisectors of the angles of any triangle meet in a point.

In problems 16 through 20, find the equations of the lines through the given point P_0 making the given angle θ with the given line L.

16. $P_0 = (2, -3)$, $\theta = \pi/4$, L: $3x - 2y = 5$

17. $P_0 = (-1, 2)$, $\tan \theta = \frac{1}{2}$, L: $2x + y - 3 = 0$

18. $P_0 = (4, 1)$, $\tan \theta = 3$, L: $3x + 4y - 5 = 0$

19. $P_0 = (-1, -2)$, $\theta = \pi/6$, L: $x + y = 1$

20. $P_0 = (3, 1)$, $\theta = \pi/2$, L: $2x - y = 3$

21. Tangent lines are drawn to the curve of $y = x^2 - 2x + 4$ at the points $(1, 3)$ and $(-2, 12)$. Find the tangent of the angle at which the first tangent intersects the second. Is it necessary to find the equations of the lines?

22. Tangent lines are drawn to the curve given by $y = x^3 - 2x^2 + 3x - 4$ at $(2, 2)$ and $(-1, -10)$. Find the tangent of the angles at which these lines intersect.

23. Two tangent lines are drawn to the circle

$$x^2 + y^2 - 2x + 5y + 7 = 0$$

from the point $(-1, -2)$. Find the tangent of the angle at which these lines intersect.

In problems 24 through 28, find the equations of the two bisectors of the angles formed by the given lines. Draw figures.

24. $x - 2y = 0$, $11x + 2y = 0$ 25. $2x + 3y = 0$, $18x + y = 0$

26. $2x + y + 5 = 0$, $x + 2y - 3 = 0$ 27. $y = 0$, $4x - 3y = 0$

28. $x = 4$, $2x + 3y - 1 = 0$

In problems 29 through 31, find the equation of the bisector of $\angle AVB$. Draw a figure.

29. $A(6, -2)$, $V(2, 1)$, $B(5, 5)$ 30. $A(3, -3)$, $V(1, -1)$, $B(8, 0)$

31. $A(2, 4)$, $V(-1, 3)$, $B(7, 3)$

8. ASYMPTOTES

We discussed asymptotes earlier (Chapter 2, Section 5) in an informal way. Now we shall give some precise definitions of various kinds of asymptotes.

DEFINITIONS. A line $x = a$ is a *vertical asymptote* of the curve with equation $y = g(x)$ if $g(x) \to \infty$ as $x \to a$. A line $y = b$ is a *horizontal asymptote* of $y = g(x)$ if $g(x) - b \to 0$ as $x \to \infty$. The line $y = mx + b$ *is an asymptote* of $y = g(x)$ if $[g(x) - (mx + b)] \to 0$ as $x \to \infty$.

We shall give some examples of curves with asymptotes and shall recall from Chapter 2 the methods for obtaining them.

————————

EXAMPLE 1. Find the asymptotes of $y = 3 + 1/(x - 2)$. Sketch the graph.

Solution.   Since $1/(x - 2) \to \infty$ as $x \to 2$, the curve has a vertical asymptote at $x = 2$. To obtain the horizontal asymptotes, if any, we solve for x in terms of y, obtaining

$$x = 2 + \frac{1}{y - 3}.$$

An inspection of this equation with y as independent variable and x as dependent variable shows that $x \to \infty$ as $y \to 3$. Therefore the line $y = 3$ is a horizontal asymptote of the curve. The graph is shown in Fig. 9–22.

EXAMPLE 2. Find the asymptotes of the curve given by

$$y^2 = \frac{x}{x^3 + 1},$$

and sketch the graph.

Solution.   First we note the symmetry with respect to the x-axis. If y is replaced by $-y$, the equation is unchanged. Second, since $y = \pm\sqrt{x/(x^3 + 1)}$, there are no points

FIGURE 9–22

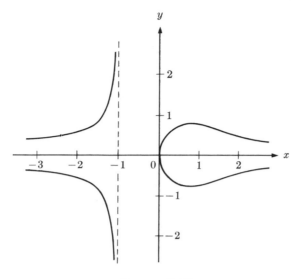

FIGURE 9–23

on the curve wherever $x/(x^3 + 1)$ is negative. This occurs only if $-1 < x < 0$, since in this range the numerator is negative and the denominator is positive. If $x < -1$, both the numerator and the denominator are negative, while if $x > 0$ the expression is positive.

A vertical asymptote occurs at $x = -1$, since the denominator is zero at this value. It is not easily possible to obtain the horizontal asymptotes by solving for x in terms of y, but by now our knowledge of limits enables us to find the value of

$$\lim_{x\to\infty} \sqrt{x/(x^3 + 1)}.$$

We divide both the numerator and the denominator by x and get

$$\lim_{x\to\infty} \sqrt{\frac{1}{x^2 + (1/x)}}.$$

The denominator tends to infinity as $x \to \infty$ and so the limit is zero. The line $y = 0$ is a horizontal asymptote.

We now plot a few points.

x	-3	-2	$-\frac{3}{2}$	-1.1	0	$\frac{1}{2}$	1	2
y	$\pm\sqrt{\frac{3}{26}}$	$\pm\sqrt{\frac{2}{7}}$	$\pm\sqrt{\frac{12}{19}}$	$\pm\sqrt{\frac{1100}{331}}$	0	$\pm\frac{2}{3}$	$\pm\sqrt{\frac{1}{2}}$	$\pm\sqrt{\frac{2}{9}}$

The graph is sketched in Fig. 9–23.

Certain trigonometric functions have asymptotes. The next example illustrates their behavior.

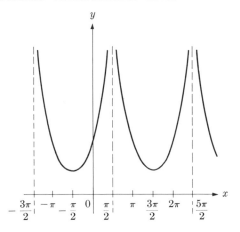

FIGURE 9–24

EXAMPLE 3. Find the asymptotes and sketch the graph of

$$y = \frac{1 + \cos^2 x}{1 - \sin x}.$$

Solution. A vertical asymptote occurs whenever the denominator is zero — that is, whenever $\sin x = 1$. This equation holds when $x = \pi/2,\ \pi/2 + 2\pi,\ \pi/2 + 4\pi, \ldots$, and also when $x = \pi/2 - 2\pi,\ \pi/2 - 4\pi, \ldots$. We write the solutions of $\sin x = 1$ compactly in the form $x = (\pi/2) + 2n\pi$, where n is any integer, positive, negative, or zero. After obtaining a few points on the graph from a table of values for x between 0 and 2π, we sketch the curve, as shown in Fig. 9–24.

———————

Discovering asymptotes which are neither horizontal nor vertical is not a routine matter, and each case must be studied individually. However, if a backlog of experience is built up, the chances are improved of finding the asymptotes in the next problem to come along. The following example shows one way of finding such asymptotes.

———————

EXAMPLE 4. Find the asymptotes, if any, and sketch the graph of

$$y = \sqrt{4x^2 - 1}, \qquad x \geq \tfrac{1}{2}.$$

Solution. There are no vertical or horizontal asymptotes. A line $y = mx + b$ is an asymptote if

$$[\sqrt{4x^2 - 1} - (mx + b)] \to 0 \quad \text{as} \quad x \to \infty \text{ (and } x > 0).$$

We select $m = 2$ and $b = 0$ (for reasons which will become clear in a moment) and write

$$\sqrt{4x^2 - 1} - 2x.$$

Now we *rationalize* the numerator:

$$\frac{\sqrt{4x^2 - 1} - 2x}{1} \cdot \frac{\sqrt{4x^2 - 1} + 2x}{\sqrt{4x^2 - 1} + 2x}.$$

This yields

$$\frac{(4x^2 - 1) - (2x)^2}{\sqrt{4x^2 - 1} + 2x} = \frac{-1}{2x + \sqrt{4x^2 - 1}}.$$

The evaluation of

$$\lim_{x \to \infty} \frac{-1}{2x + \sqrt{4x^2 - 1}}$$

is easy. It has the value zero, and so the line $y = 2x$ is an asymptote. The reason for selecting $m = 2$, $b = 0$ is now clear. It was done so that the quantities involving x in the numerator would cancel when the rationalizing process took place.

For example, the function $y = \sqrt{8x^2 - 1} + 3$ would have the asymptote $y = mx + b$ with $m = \sqrt{8}$ and $b = 3$.

EXERCISES

Find the asymptotes, if any, and sketch the graphs.

1. $y = \dfrac{2x}{3x - 2}$

2. $y = \dfrac{x - 1}{x + 2} + 3$

3. $y = (x - 3)^2$

4. $x^2 y^2 (x - 1) = 1$

5. $y = \dfrac{2x}{x^3 + 1}$

6. $y^2 = \dfrac{1 - x}{1 + x}$

7. $y^2 = x(x - 1)^2$

8. $y^2 = x^3 - 4x$

9. $x^2 y - y^3 = 1$

10. $x^2 y^3 - y = 1$

11. $(1 + y)x^2 = y^2(1 - y)$

12. $y = \tan 2x$

13. $y = \csc\left(x + \dfrac{\pi}{6}\right)$

14. $y = \dfrac{1 + \sin^2 x}{\cos x}$

15. $y = \sec x + \cos x$

16. $y = \dfrac{1 + \sin^2 x}{1 + \sin x}$

17. $y = \dfrac{1}{1 + \cos^2 x}$

18. $y = \dfrac{1 + |\cos x|}{1 - \cos x}$

19. $x^2 - 4y^2 = 1$

20. $9x^2 - y^2 = 4$

21. $y = \sqrt{x^2 - 4} - 2$

22. $y = -\sqrt{4x^2 + 1}$

23. $y = \sqrt[3]{x^3 - 1}$

24. $y = \sqrt[3]{8x^3 + 2}$

CHAPTER 10

The Conics

1. THE PARABOLA

In the sections of Chapter 9 dealing with the circle, we began a systematic study of equations of the second degree in x and y. We shall now continue our analysis of second-degree curves.

DEFINITIONS. A *parabola* is the locus of all points whose distances from a fixed point equal their distances from a fixed line. The fixed point is called the *focus* and the fixed line the *directrix*.

The definition of the parabola is purely geometric in the sense that it says nothing about coordinates — that is, the values of x and y. Recall that the definition of the circle as the locus of points at a given distance from a fixed point is also a geometric one. It will turn out, of course, that parabolas are always given by second-degree equations, as is true in the case of the circle.

Figure 10–1 shows a typical situation. The line L is the directrix, the point F is the focus, and P, Q, R, S are points which satisfy the conditions of the locus. That is, $AP = PF$, $BQ = QF$, $CR = RF$, and $DS = SF$. The perpendicular to L through the focus intersects the parabola at a point V. This point is called the *vertex* of the parabola.

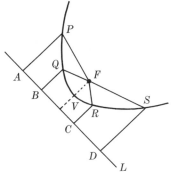

FIGURE 10–1

To find an equation for a parabola, we set up a coordinate system and locate the directrix and the focus at convenient places. Suppose that the distance from the focus F to the directrix L is p units. We place the focus at $(p/2, 0)$ and let the line L be $x = -p/2$, as shown in Fig. 10–2. If $P(x, y)$ is a typical point on the locus, the conditions are such that the distance $PF = \sqrt{[x - (p/2)]^2 + (y - 0)^2}$

286

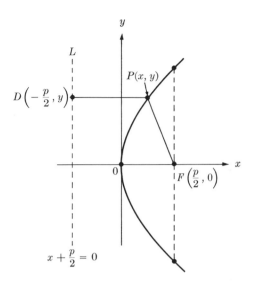

FIGURE 10–2

is equal to the distance from P to the line L. From an examination of the figure (or from the formula for the distance from a point to a line) we easily deduce that the distance from P to the line L is $|x - (-p/2)|$. Therefore we have

$$\sqrt{\left(x - \frac{p}{2}\right)^2 + y^2} = \left|x + \frac{p}{2}\right|,$$

and, since both sides are positive, we may square to obtain

$$\left(x - \frac{p}{2}\right)^2 + y^2 = \left(x + \frac{p}{2}\right)^2,$$

and

$$x^2 - px + \frac{p^2}{4} + y^2 = x^2 + px + \frac{p^2}{4}.$$

This equation yields

$$y^2 = 2px, \qquad p > 0.$$

Each point on the locus satisfies this equation. Conversely, by reversing the steps, it can be shown that every point which satisfies this equation fulfills the conditions of the locus. We call this *the equation of the parabola with focus at* $(p/2, 0)$ *and with the line* $x = -p/2$ *as directrix.* The vertex of the parabola is at the origin. It is apparent from the equation that the x-axis is an axis of symmetry, for if y is replaced by $-y$, the equation is unchanged. The line of symmetry of a parabola is called the *axis of the parabola*.

If the focus and directrix are placed in other positions, the equation will of course be different. There are four *standard positions* for the focus-directrix combination, of which the first has just been described. The second standard position has its focus at $(-p/2, 0)$ and the line $x = p/2$ as its directrix. Using the same method as

FIGURE 10–3

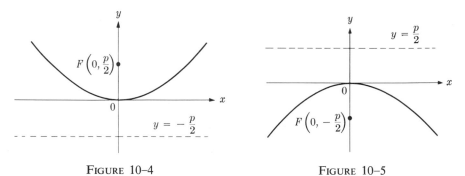

FIGURE 10–4   FIGURE 10–5

before, we solve the locus problem which defines the parabola. We obtain the equation

$$y^2 = -2px, \qquad p > 0,$$

and a parabola in the position shown in Fig. 10–3. The third position has its focus at $(0, p/2)$ and the line $y = -p/2$ as the directrix. The resulting equation is

$$x^2 = 2py, \qquad p > 0,$$

and the parabola is in the position shown in Fig. 10–4. In position (4) the focus is at $(0, -p/2)$ and the directrix is the line $y = p/2$. The equation then becomes

$$x^2 = -2py, \qquad p > 0,$$

and the parabola is in the position shown in Fig. 10–5. In all four positions the vertex is at the origin.

EXAMPLE 1. Given the parabola $y^2 = -12x$, find the focus, directrix, and axis. Sketch the curve.

Solution. Since $2p = 12, p = 6$ and, since the equation is in the second of the standard forms, the focus is at $(-3, 0)$. The directrix is the line $x = 3$, and the x-axis is the axis of the parabola. The curve is sketched in Fig. 10–6.

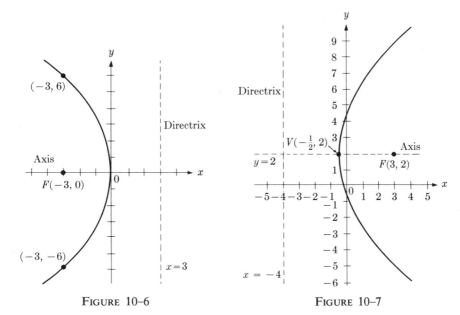

FIGURE 10–6   FIGURE 10–7

When the parabola is not in one of the standard positions, the equation is more complicated. If the directrix is horizontal or vertical, the equation is only slightly different; however, if the directrix is parallel to neither axis, the equation is altered considerably. The following example shows how the equation of the parabola may be obtained directly from the definition.

EXAMPLE 2. Find the equation of the parabola with focus at $F(3, 2)$ and with the line $x = -4$ as directrix. Locate the vertex and the axis of symmetry.

Solution. From the definition of parabola, if $P(x, y)$ is a point on the curve, then $PF = \sqrt{(x - 3)^2 + (y - 2)^2}$ must be equal to the distance from P to the directrix, which is $|x + 4|$. We have

$$\sqrt{(x - 3)^2 + (y - 2)^2} = |x + 4|.$$

Multiplying out, we find that

$$x^2 - 6x + 9 + y^2 - 4y + 4 = x^2 + 8x + 16.$$

This yields

$$(y - 2)^2 = 14x + 7 \quad \text{or} \quad (y - 2)^2 = 14(x + \tfrac{1}{2}).$$

A sketch of the equation (Fig. 10–7) shows that the axis is the line $y = 2$ and the vertex is at the point $(-\tfrac{1}{2}, 2)$.

The four forms for the parabola when the axis is vertical or horizontal and the vertex is at the point (a, b) instead of the origin are:

(1) $(y - b)^2 = 2p(x - a), \qquad p > 0,$

with focus at $(a + p/2, b)$; directrix, $x = a - p/2$;

(2) $(y - b)^2 = -2p(x - a), \qquad p > 0,$

with focus at $(a - p/2, b)$; directrix, $x = a + p/2$;

(3) $(x - a)^2 = 2p(y - b), \qquad p > 0,$

with focus at $(a, b + p/2)$; directrix, $y = b - p/2$;

(4) $(x - a)^2 = -2p(y - b), \quad p > 0,$

with focus at $(a, b - p/2)$; directrix, $y = b + p/2$.

EXAMPLE 3. Given the parabola $x^2 = -4y - 3x + 2$, find the vertex, focus, directrix, and axis. Sketch the curve.

Solution. We complete the square in x, writing

$$x^2 + 3x \qquad = -4y + 2,$$

and then obtain

$$(x + \tfrac{3}{2})^2 = -4y + 2 + \tfrac{9}{4} = -4y + \tfrac{17}{4}.$$

This yields

$$(x + \tfrac{3}{2})^2 = -4(y - \tfrac{17}{16}),$$

which is in the fourth form above. We read off that the vertex is at $(-\tfrac{3}{2}, \tfrac{17}{16})$. Since $2p = 4$ we know that $p = 2$ and the focus is at $(-\tfrac{3}{2}, \tfrac{1}{16})$; the directrix is the line $y = \tfrac{33}{16}$, and the axis is the line $x = -\tfrac{3}{2}$. The curve is sketched in Fig. 10–8.

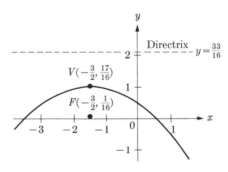

FIGURE 10–8

A problem which combines a number of ideas we have already studied is solved in the next illustration.

EXAMPLE 4. In the family of lines $3x + 2y - k = 0$ find the member which is tangent to the parabola $y = 3x^2 - 2x + 1$.

Solution. If a line is tangent to a parabola, the slope of the line and of the parabola must be the same at the point of contact. The above family consists of all lines of slope

$-\frac{3}{2}$. The slope of the parabola at any point is

$$\frac{dy}{dx} = 6x - 2.$$

Then $6x - 2 = -\frac{3}{2}$ or $x = \frac{1}{12}$ occurs when the slope of the parabola and the slope of the line are the same. Substituting $x = \frac{1}{12}$ in the equation for the parabola, we get $y = 3(\frac{1}{144}) - \frac{2}{12} + 1 = \frac{123}{144}$. The point on the parabola where the slope is $-\frac{3}{2}$ is $(\frac{1}{12}, \frac{123}{144})$. This point must also be on the line. Therefore

$$3(\tfrac{1}{12}) + 2(\tfrac{123}{144}) - k = 0,$$

or $k = \frac{47}{24}$, and the desired line has the equation

$$3x + 2y - \tfrac{47}{24} = 0.$$

EXERCISES

In problems 1 through 6, find the coordinates of the foci and the equations of the directrices. Sketch the curves.

1. $y^2 = 8x$ 2. $x^2 = 6y$ 3. $y^2 = -12x$
4. $x^2 = -16y$ 5. $2y^2 = -7x$ 6. $4x^2 = 9y$

In problems 7 through 14, find the equation of the parabola with vertex at the origin which satisfies the given additional condition.

7. Focus at $(-3, 0)$ 8. Focus at $(0, 2)$ 9. Directrix: $y = 2$
10. Directrix: $x = \frac{7}{3}$ 11. Focus at $(0, -\frac{3}{2})$ 12. Directrix: $y = -\frac{4}{3}$
13. Passing through $(2, 3)$ and axis along the x-axis.
14. Passing through $(2, 3)$ and axis along the y-axis.

In problems 15 through 22, find the focus, vertex, directrix, and axis of the parabola. Sketch the curve.

15. $y = x^2 - 2x + 3$ 16. $x = y^2 + 2y - 4$ 17. $y = -2x^2 + 4x + 5$
18. $y = -4x^2 + 3x$ 19. $x = -y^2 + 2y - 7$ 20. $x^2 + 2y - 3x + 5 = 0$
21. $y^2 + 2x - 4y + 7 = 0$ 22. $3y^2 - x + y = 0$

In problems 23 through 28, find the equations of the parabolas from the definition.

23. Directrix $x = 0$, focus at $(6, 0)$ 24. Directrix $y = 0$, focus at $(0, 5)$
25. Vertex $(0, 4)$, focus $(0, 2)$ 26. Vertex $(-2, 0)$, directrix $x = 1$
27. Focus $(-1, -2)$, directrix $x - 2y + 3 = 0$
28. Focus $(2, 3)$, directrix $x + y + 1 = 0$
29. Find the member of the family $4x - y - k = 0$ which is tangent to the parabola $y = 2x^2 - x + 1$.
30. Find a member of the family $kx - y - 5 = 0$ which is tangent to the parabola $y = 3x^2 + 2x + 4$.
31. Find the member of the family of parabolas $y = kx^2 + 4x - 3$ which is tangent to the line $2x - y + 1 = 0$.

32. An arch has the shape of a parabola with vertex at the top and axis vertical. If it is 45 ft wide at the base and 18 ft high in the center, how wide is it 10 ft above the base?

33. The line through the focus of a parabola and parallel to the directrix is called the *line of the latus rectum*. The portion of this line cut off by the parabola is called the *latus rectum*. Show that for the parabola $y^2 = 2px$ the length of the latus rectum is $2p$. Is this true for any parabola where the distance from the focus to the directrix is p units?

34. Find the locus of a point whose distance from $(4, 0)$ is 1 unit less than its distance from the line $x = -6$. Describe the curve.

2. THE PARABOLA, CONTINUED

Suppose that (x_1, y_1) is a point on a parabola. We shall now show how to find the equation of the line tangent to the parabola at (x_1, y_1). If, for example, the parabola has the equation

$$y^2 = 2px,$$

then the slope at any point is given (by implicit differentiation) as

$$2y \frac{dy}{dx} = 2p \quad \text{and} \quad \frac{dy}{dx} = \frac{p}{y}.$$

The equation of any line through (x_1, y_1) is

$$y - y_1 = m(x - x_1).$$

If the slope is p/y_1 the equation becomes

$$y - y_1 = \frac{p}{y_1}(x - x_1).$$

This formula can be simplified: Since (x_1, y_1) is on the parabola, we know that $y_1^2 = 2px_1$. Therefore the above equation may be written

$$y_1 y - y_1^2 = px - px_1,$$

or

$$y_1 y - 2px_1 = px - px_1 \quad \text{and} \quad y_1 y = p(x + x_1).$$

EXAMPLE 1. Find the equation of the line tangent to $y^2 = 20x$ at the point $(3, 2\sqrt{15})$.

Solution. In this case $x_1 = 3$, $y_1 = 2\sqrt{15}$, $p = 10$, and the equation is

$$2\sqrt{15}\, y = 10(x + 3).$$

EXAMPLE 2. Find the equation of the line tangent to the parabola $y^2 + 3y - 2x + 4 = 0$, at the point on the parabola where $y = 2$.

Solution. When $y = 2$, by substitution in the equation we obtain $x = 7$. The slope at any point is given by the relation

$$2y \frac{dy}{dx} + 3 \frac{dy}{dx} - 2 = 0,$$

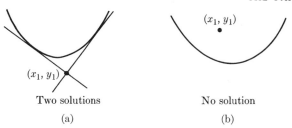

Two solutions   No solution

(a)   (b)

FIGURE 10–9

and at (7, 2) we find

$$\frac{dy}{dx} = \frac{2}{2y + 3} = \frac{2}{7}.$$

The equation of the tangent line is $y - 2 = \frac{2}{7}(x - 7)$.

A somewhat more difficult problem is that of finding the line tangent to a parabola when the given point (x_1, y_1) is *not* on the parabola. There will be either two solutions or no solution to this problem, as Fig. 10–9 shows. Let the parabola have equation $x^2 = 2py$, and suppose that $y - y_1 = m(x - x_1)$ is the equation of the desired line. The slope of the parabola at any point is

$$\frac{dy}{dx} = \frac{x}{p}.$$

Let (x_0, y_0) be a point of tangency. Since this point is on both the parabola and the line, we have $x_0^2 = 2py_0$ and $y_0 - y_1 = (x_0/p)(x_0 - x_1)$. We have two equations in the unknowns x_0 and y_0. Once these are solved simultaneously the problem is done, since the value x_0/p may be substituted in the equation of the line. The following example illustrates the method in a particular case.

EXAMPLE 3.   Find the equations of the lines which are tangent to the parabola $y^2 - y - 2x + 4 = 0$ and which pass through the point $(-5, 2)$.

Solution. Any line through $(-5, 2)$ has equation

$$y - 2 = m(x + 5)$$

and the slope of the curve at any point on the parabola is given by

$$2y \frac{dy}{dx} - \frac{dy}{dx} - 2 = 0 \quad \text{or} \quad \frac{dy}{dx} = \frac{2}{2y - 1}.$$

If (x_0, y_0) is the point of tangency, then $m = 2/(2y_0 - 1)$. We have the equations

$$y_0^2 - y_0 - 2x_0 + 4 = 0 \quad \text{and} \quad y_0 - 2 = \frac{2}{2y_0 - 1}(x_0 + 5).$$

These are solved simultaneously by eliminating x_0, and the two solutions are $x_0 = 17$, $y_0 = 6$ and $x_0 = 5$, $y_0 = -2$. The corresponding slopes are $m_0 = \frac{2}{11}$, $-\frac{2}{5}$. The

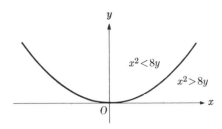

FIGURE 10–10

desired lines have equations

$$y - 2 = \tfrac{2}{11}(x + 5) \quad \text{and} \quad y - 2 = -\tfrac{2}{5}(x + 5).$$

If there were no solution, the attempt to solve the quadratic equation for y_0 would give complex numbers for the roots. That there is no solution may also be determined in another way. As we know, a parabola such as $x^2 = 8y$ divides the plane into two regions; in one of them $x^2 > 8y$ and in the other $x^2 < 8y$. Any point (x_1, y_1) such that $x_1^2 > 8y_1$ is a point such that two tangents to the parabola may be constructed (Fig. 10–10). If $x_1^2 < 8y_1$, no tangents can be drawn.

EXAMPLE 4. Given the parabola $-2x^2 + 3y - 2x + 1 = 0$ and the points $P(1, -2)$, $Q(2, 9)$, decide whether or not tangents to the parabola may be drawn from P and Q.

Solution. First write the equation with the quadratic coefficient positive:

$$2x^2 - 3y + 2x - 1 = 0.$$

Now substitute the coordinates of $P(1, -2)$ in the left side. This yields

$$2 - 3(-2) + 2 - 1 = 9.$$

Since the result is positive, two tangents may be drawn. For the point $Q(2, 9)$ the result is

$$2 \cdot 2^2 - 3(9) + 2(2) - 1 = -16,$$

and, since this result is negative, no tangents can be constructed.

The parabola has many interesting geometrical properties that make it suitable for practical applications. Probably the most familiar application is the use of parabolic shapes in headlights of cars, flashlights, and so forth. If a parabola is revolved about its axis, the surface generated is called a *paraboloid*. Such surfaces are used in headlights, optical and radio telescopes, radar, etc., because of the following geometric property. If a source of light (or sound or other type of wave) is placed at the focus of a parabola, and if the parabola is a reflecting surface, then the wave will bounce back in a line parallel to the axis of the parabola (Fig. 10–11). This creates a parallel beam without dispersion. (In actual practice there will be some dispersion, since the source of light must occupy more than one

FIGURE 10–11

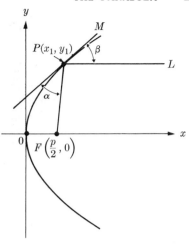

FIGURE 10–12

point.) Clearly the converse is also true. If a series of incoming waves is parallel
to the axis of the reflecting paraboloid, the resulting signal will be concentrated
at the focus (where the receiving equipment is therefore located).

We shall establish the reflecting property for the parabola $y^2 = 2px$. Let
$P(x_1, y_1)$ be a point (not the origin) on the parabola, and draw the line segment
from P to the focus (Fig. 10–12). Now construct a line L through P parallel to
the x-axis and the line M tangent to the parabola at P. The law for the reflecting
property of the parabola states that the angle formed by M and PF (α in the
figure) must be equal to the angle formed by L and M (β in the figure). The slope
of the line M is $\tan \beta$, which is also the slope of the parabola at (x_1, y_1). The
result is

$$2y \frac{dy}{dx} = 2p \qquad \text{and} \qquad \tan \beta = \frac{p}{y_1}.$$

We now find $\tan \alpha$ from the formula for the angle between two lines. The slope of
PF is

$$\frac{y_1 - 0}{x_1 - \frac{p}{2}}.$$

Therefore

$$\tan \alpha = \frac{\dfrac{y_1}{x_1 - \dfrac{p}{2}} - \dfrac{p}{y_1}}{1 + \dfrac{y_1}{x_1 - \dfrac{p}{2}} \dfrac{p}{y_1}},$$

and

$$\tan \alpha = \frac{y_1^2 - px_1 + \frac{1}{2}p^2}{x_1 y_1 - \frac{1}{2}py_1 + py_1}.$$

Since $y_1^2 = 2px_1$, this simplifies to

$$\tan \alpha = \frac{p}{y_1},$$

and the result is established.

The main cables of suspension bridges are usually parabolic in shape, since it can be shown that if the total weight of a bridge is distributed uniformly along its length, a cable in the shape of a parabola bears the load evenly. It is a remarkable fact that no other shape will perform this task.

EXERCISES

In problems 1 through 8, find the equation of the line tangent to the parabola at the given point P on the parabola.

1. $y^2 = 9x$, $P(1, 3)$
2. $y^2 = -3x$, $P(-3, -3)$
3. $x^2 = 12y + 7$, $P(1, -\frac{1}{2})$
4. $x^2 - 2y + 3x - 4 = 0$, $P(-2, -3)$
5. $y^2 - 3x + 2y + 4 = 0$, $P(\frac{4}{3}, 0)$
6. $(y - 2)^2 = -4(x + 3)$, $P(-4, 4)$
7. $x^2 - 2x + y = 0$, $P(-3, -15)$
8. $-x^2 - 2y + 2x + 4 = 0$, $P(4, -2)$
9. Find the equation of the line tangent to the parabola $y^2 - 3y + 4x - 8 = 0$ at the point on the parabola where $x = 1$.

In problems 10 through 20, first decide whether lines tangent to the given parabola which pass through the given point P can be constructed. When they can, determine the equations of the lines.

10. $y^2 = 8x$, $P(-3, 1)$
11. $y^2 = -4x$, $P(1, 5)$
12. $y^2 = 8x$, $P(3, 1)$
13. $y^2 = -4x$, $P(1, -5)$
14. $x^2 = -4y$, $P(4, 1)$
15. $x^2 = 12y$, $P(-1, -3)$
16. $x^2 - 4x + 2y - 1 = 0$, $P(-1, 3)$
17. $2y^2 - 3y + x - 4 = 0$, $P(1, -1)$
18. $x^2 - 4x + 2y - 1 = 0$, $P(1, -8)$
19. $x + 2y - 2x^2 + 1 = 0$, $P(1, 3)$
20. $x + 2y - 2x^2 + 1 = 0$, $P(1, -3)$
21. For the parabola $x^2 = 2py$, establish the "optical property." That is, if (x_1, y_1) is a point on the parabola and M is the line tangent at (x_1, y_1), show that the angle formed between M and a line from (x_1, y_1) through the focus is equal to the angle M forms with a line through (x_1, y_1) parallel to the axis.
22. Let $P(x_1, y_1)$ be a point (not the vertex) on the parabola $y^2 = 2px$. Find the equation of the line normal to the parabola at this point. Show that this normal line intersects the x-axis at the point $Q(x_1 + p, 0)$.
23. A line through the focus of the parabola $x^2 = -12y$ intersects the parabola at the point $(5, -\frac{25}{12})$. Find the other point of intersection of this line with the parabola.
24. The two towers of a suspension bridge are 300 ft apart and extend 80 ft above the road surface. If the cable is tangent to the road at the center of the bridge, find the height of the cable above the road at 50 ft and also at 100 ft from the center of the bridge. (Assume that the road is horizontal.)
25. At a point P on a parabola a tangent line is drawn. This line intersects the axis of the parabola at a point A. If F denotes the focus, show that $\triangle APF$ is isosceles.

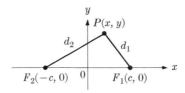

FIGURE 10–13

3. THE ELLIPSE

Continuing our discussion of curves of the second degree, we now take up the ellipse.

DEFINITIONS. An *ellipse* is the locus of all points the sum of whose distances from two fixed points is constant. The two fixed points are called the *foci*.

For the definition to make sense, the constant (the sum of the distances from the foci) must be larger than the distance between the foci. Note that the definition is purely geometric and says nothing about coordinates or equations. It will turn out, of course, that the equation of an ellipse is of the second degree.

Suppose that the distance between the foci is $2c$ $(c > 0)$. We place the foci — label them F_1 and F_2 — at convenient points, say F_1 at $(c, 0)$ and F_2 at $(-c, 0)$. Let $P(x, y)$ be a point on the ellipse, d_1 the distance from P to F_1, and d_2 the distance from P to F_2 (Fig. 10–13). The conditions of the locus state that $d_1 + d_2$ is always constant. As we said, this constant (which we shall denote by $2a$) must be larger than $2c$. Thus we have

$$d_1 + d_2 = 2a,$$

or, from the distance formula,

$$\sqrt{(x - c)^2 + (y - 0)^2} + \sqrt{(x + c)^2 + (y - 0)^2} = 2a.$$

We simplify by transferring one radical to the right and squaring both sides:

$$(x - c)^2 + y^2 = 4a^2 - 4a\sqrt{(x + c)^2 + y^2} + (x + c)^2 + y^2.$$

By multiplying out and combining, we obtain

$$\sqrt{(x + c)^2 + y^2} = a + \frac{c}{a} x.$$

We square again to find

$$(x + c)^2 + y^2 = a^2 + 2cx + \frac{c^2}{a^2} x^2,$$

and this becomes

$$\frac{x^2}{a^2} + \frac{y^2}{a^2 - c^2} = 1.$$

Since $a > c$, we can introduce a new quantity,

$$b = \sqrt{a^2 - c^2},$$

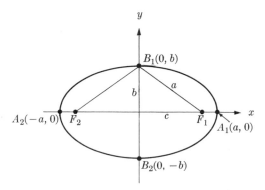

FIGURE 10–14

and we can write

$$\frac{x^2}{a^2} + \frac{y^2}{b^2} = 1.$$

This is *the equation of an ellipse.*

We have shown that every point on the locus satisfies this equation. Conversely (by reversing the steps*), it can be shown that each point which satisfies this equation is on the ellipse. A sketch of such an equation is shown in Fig. 10–14. From the equation, we see immediately that the curve is symmetric with respect to both the x- and y-axes.

> DEFINITIONS. The line passing through the two foci F_1 and F_2 is called the *major axis*. The perpendicular bisector of the line segment $F_1 F_2$ is called the *minor axis*. The intersection of the major and minor axes is called the *center*.

The equation of the ellipse as we have obtained it indicates that the ellipse intersects the x-axis at $(a, 0)$, $(-a, 0)$. These points are called the *vertices* of the ellipse. The distance between them, $2a$, is called the *length of the major axis*. (Sometimes this segment is called simply the major axis.) The ellipse intersects the y-axis at $(0, b)$ and $(0, -b)$. The distance between them, $2b$, is called the *length of the minor axis*. (Sometimes this segment is called the minor axis.)

The *eccentricity e* of an ellipse is defined as

$$e = \frac{c}{a}.$$

---

*In the process of reversing the steps it must be verified that

$$a + \frac{c}{a} x \geq 0 \qquad \text{and} \qquad 2a - \sqrt{(x + c)^2 + y^2} \geq 0.$$

However,

$$2a - \sqrt{(x + c)^2 + y^2} = 2a - \left(a + \frac{c}{a} x\right) = a - \frac{c}{a} x.$$

Since $-a \leq x \leq a$ for every point satisfying the equation, and since $c < a$, the verification is immediate.

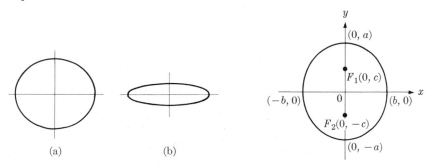

FIGURE 10–15   FIGURE 10–16

Note that since $c < a$, the eccentricity is always between 0 and 1. Further, it is dimensionless, being the ratio of two lengths. The eccentricity measures the flatness of an ellipse. If a is kept fixed and c is very "small," then e is close to zero. But this means that the foci are close together, and the ellipse is almost a circle, as in Fig. 10–15(a). On the other hand, if c is close to a, then e is near 1 and the ellipse is quite flat, as shown in Fig. 10–15(b). The limiting position of an ellipse as $e \to 0$ is a circle of radius a. The limiting position as $e \to 1$ is a line segment of length $2a$.

In developing the equation of an ellipse we placed the foci at $(c, 0)$ and $(-c, 0)$. If instead we put them on the y-axis at $(0, c)$ and $(0, -c)$ and carry through the same argument, then the equation of the ellipse we obtain is

$$\frac{x^2}{b^2} + \frac{y^2}{a^2} = 1.$$

The y-axis is now the major axis, the x-axis is the minor axis, and the vertices are at $(0, a)$ and $(0, -a)$. The quantity $b = \sqrt{a^2 - c^2}$ and the eccentricity $e = c/a$ are defined as before. Figure 10–16 shows an ellipse with foci on the y-axis.

———————————

EXAMPLE 1. Given the ellipse with equation $9x^2 + 25y^2 = 225$, find the major and minor axes, the eccentricity, the coordinates of the foci and the vertices. Sketch the ellipse.

Solution. We put the equation in "standard form" by dividing by 225. We obtain

$$\frac{x^2}{25} + \frac{y^2}{9} = 1,$$

which tells us that $a = 5, b = 3$. Since

$$a^2 = b^2 + c^2,$$

we find that $c = 4$. The eccentricity $e = c/a = \frac{4}{5}$. The major axis is along the x-axis, the minor axis is along the y-axis, the vertices are at $(\pm 5, 0)$, and the foci are at $(\pm 4, 0)$. The ellipse is sketched in Fig. 10–17.

EXAMPLE 2. Given the ellipse with equation $16x^2 + 9y^2 = 144$, find the major and minor axes, the eccentricity, the coordinates of the foci, and the vertices. Sketch the ellipse.

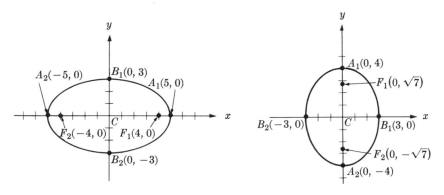

FIGURE 10–17   FIGURE 10–18

Solution. We divide by 144 to get

$$\frac{x^2}{9} + \frac{y^2}{16} = 1.$$

We note that *the number under the y-term is larger.* Therefore $a = 4, b = 3, c^2 = a^2 - b^2$, and $c = \sqrt{7}$. The eccentricity $e = \sqrt{7}/4$, the major axis is along the y-axis, the minor axis is along the x-axis, the foci are at $(0, \pm\sqrt{7})$, and the vertices at $(0, \pm 4)$. The ellipse is sketched in Fig. 10–18.

The foregoing examples illustrate the fact that when we have an equation of the form

$$\frac{x^2}{(\ \ )^2} + \frac{y^2}{(\ \ )^2} = 1,$$

the equation represents an ellipse (or a circle if the denominators are equal in size), and the *larger denominator* determines whether the foci, vertices, and major axes are along the x-axis or the y-axis.

EXAMPLE 3.   Find the equation of the ellipse with axes along the x-axis and y-axis which passes through the points $P(6, 2)$ and $Q(-4, 3)$.

Solution. Let the equation be

$$\frac{x^2}{A^2} + \frac{y^2}{B^2} = 1;$$

we don't know whether A is larger than B or B is larger than A. Since the points P and Q are on the ellipse, we have

$$36\left(\frac{1}{A^2}\right) + 4\left(\frac{1}{B^2}\right) = 1,$$

$$16\left(\frac{1}{A^2}\right) + 9\left(\frac{1}{B^2}\right) = 1,$$

which gives us two equations in the unknowns $1/A^2$, $1/B^2$. Solving simultaneously, we obtain

$$\frac{1}{A^2} = \frac{1}{52}, \quad \frac{1}{B^2} = \frac{1}{13},$$

and the resulting ellipse is

$$\frac{x^2}{52} + \frac{y^2}{13} = 1.$$

The major axis is along the x-axis.

EXERCISES

In problems 1 through 10, find the lengths of the major and minor axes, the coordinates of the foci and vertices, and the eccentricity. Sketch the curve.

1. $16x^2 + 25y^2 = 400$
2. $25x^2 + 169y^2 = 4225$
3. $9x^2 + 16y^2 = 144$
4. $25x^2 + 16y^2 = 400$
5. $3x^2 + 2y^2 = 6$
6. $3x^2 + 4y^2 = 12$
7. $5x^2 + 2y^2 = 10$
8. $5x^2 + 3y^2 = 15$
9. $2x^2 + 3y^2 = 11$
10. $5x^2 + 4y^2 = 17$

In problems 11 through 21, find the equation of the ellipse satisfying the given conditions.

11. Vertices at $(\pm 5, 0)$, foci at $(\pm 4, 0)$
12. Vertices at $(0, \pm 5)$, foci at $(0, \pm 3)$
13. Vertices at $(0, \pm 10)$, eccentricity $\frac{4}{5}$
14. Vertices at $(\pm 6, 0)$, eccentricity $\frac{2}{3}$
15. Foci at $(0, \pm 4)$, eccentricity $\frac{4}{5}$
16. Vertices at $(0, \pm 5)$, passing through $(3, 3)$
17. Axes along the coordinate axes, passing through $(4, 3)$ and $(-1, 4)$
18. Axes along the coordinate axes, passing through $(-5, 2)$ and $(3, 7)$
19. Foci at $(\pm 3, 0)$, passing through $(4, 1)$
20. Eccentricity $\frac{3}{4}$, foci along x-axis, center at origin, and passing through $(6, 4)$
21. Eccentricity $\frac{3}{4}$, foci on the y-axis, center at origin, and passing through $(6, 4)$
22. Find the locus of a point which moves so that the sum of its distances from $(6, 0)$ and $(-6, 0)$ is always 20.
23. Find the locus of a point which moves so that the sum of its distances from $(3, 0)$ and $(9, 0)$ is always 12.

4. THE ELLIPSE, CONTINUED

A mechanical construction of an ellipse can be made directly from the facts given in the definition, as shown in Fig. 10–19. Select a piece of string of length $2a$. Fasten its ends with thumbtacks at the foci, insert a pencil so as to draw the string taut, and trace out an arc. The curve will be an ellipse.

The ellipse has many interesting geometrical properties. The paths of the planets about the sun are approximately elliptical; whispering galleries are ellip-

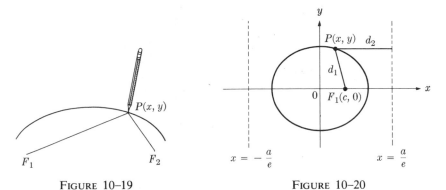

FIGURE 10–19   FIGURE 10–20

soidal (an ellipse revolved about the major axis) in shape. If a signal (in the form of a light, sound, or other type of wave) has its source at one focus of an ellipse, *all* reflected waves will pass through the other focus.

We have seen that a parabola has a focus and a directrix. The ellipse has two foci and also two directrices. If the ellipse has foci at $(\pm c, 0)$ and vertices at $(\pm a, 0)$, *the directrices are the lines*

$$x = \frac{a^2}{c} = \frac{a}{e} \quad \text{and} \quad x = -\frac{a^2}{c} = -\frac{a}{e}.$$

To draw an analogy with the parabola, we can show that such an ellipse is the locus of all points whose distances from a fixed point (F_1) are equal to $e \ (0 < e < 1)$ times their distances from a fixed line $(x = a/e)$. As Fig. 10–20 shows, the conditions of the locus are

$$d_1 = ed_2, \quad \text{or} \quad \sqrt{(x - c)^2 + y^2} = e \left| x - \frac{a}{e} \right|.$$

If we square both sides and simplify, we obtain $(x^2/a^2) + (y^2/b^2) = 1$, which we know to be the equation of an ellipse. The same situation holds true if the focus $F_2(-c, 0)$ and the directrix $x = -a/e$ are used.

EXAMPLE 1. Find the equation of the ellipse with foci at $(\pm 5, 0)$ and with the line $x = 36/5$ as one directrix.

Solution. We have $c = 5$, $a/e = 36/5$. Since $e = c/a$, we obtain $a^2/c = 36/5$, or $a = 6$. Then $b = \sqrt{36 - 25} = \sqrt{11}$, and the equation is

$$\frac{x^2}{36} + \frac{y^2}{11} = 1.$$

Given that $P(x_1, y_1)$ is a point on the ellipse

$$\frac{x^2}{a^2} + \frac{y^2}{b^2} = 1,$$

it is a simple matter to find the equation of the line tangent to the ellipse at this point. The slope of the ellipse is obtained by implicit differentiation:

$$\frac{2x}{a^2} + \frac{2y}{b^2}\frac{dy}{dx} = 0, \qquad \text{and} \qquad \frac{dy}{dx} = -\frac{b^2}{a^2}\frac{x}{y}.$$

The equation of the line tangent at $P(x_1, y_1)$ is

$$y - y_1 = -\frac{b^2}{a^2}\frac{x_1}{y_1}(x - x_1),$$

or

$$a^2 y_1 y - a^2 y_1^2 = -b^2 x_1 x + b^2 x_1^2.$$

But $b^2 x_1^2 + a^2 y_1^2 = a^2 b^2$, since (x_1, y_1) is on the ellipse. Therefore

$$\frac{x_1 x}{a^2} + \frac{y_1 y}{b^2} = 1$$

is the equation of the tangent line.

EXAMPLE 2. Find the equation of the line tangent to the ellipse

$$\frac{x^2}{9} + \frac{y^2}{16} = 1$$

at the point $(2, -\frac{4}{3}\sqrt{5})$.

Solution. The point $(2, -\frac{4}{3}\sqrt{5})$ is on the ellipse and, even though the major axis is along the y-axis, it is easily seen that the analogous formula for the tangent line holds. We obtain

$$\frac{2x}{9} + \frac{-\frac{4}{3}\sqrt{5}\,y}{16} = 1, \qquad \text{or} \qquad 8x - 3\sqrt{5}\,y - 36 = 0.$$

The reflected-wave property of ellipses is exhibited by the following procedure. Let $P(x_1, y_1)$ be a point on the ellipse (not a vertex), as shown in Fig. 10–21. Construct a tangent line M at this point. Then the angle made by M and the line PF_1 (α in the figure) is equal to the angle made by M and the line PF_2 (β in the figure). This result may be established by setting up the formulas for $\tan \alpha$ and $\tan \beta$ as the angles between two lines and showing them to be equal.

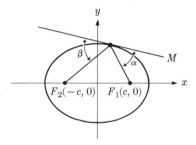

FIGURE 10–21

An ellipse divides the plane into two regions, one inside and one outside the curve itself. Every point inside the ellipse $(x^2/a^2) + (y^2/b^2) = 1$ satisfies the inequality

$$\frac{x^2}{a^2} + \frac{y^2}{b^2} < 1.$$

From any point outside the ellipse two tangents may be drawn, and clearly no tangents to the ellipse can be constructed which pass through a point inside the ellipse itself.

EXAMPLE 3. Given the ellipse $(x^2/25) + (y^2/9) = 1$, and the points $P(1, 2)$, $Q(0, 6)$, and $R(3, 2)$. For each point, decide whether tangents to the ellipse passing through the point can be constructed. If they can, find the equations of the tangent lines.

Solution. For the point P we have

$$\frac{1^2}{25} + \frac{2^2}{9} < 1,$$

and no tangents exist. Similarly, for the point R we have $(9/25) + (4/9) < 1$. The point Q is outside the ellipse, since $(0^2/25) + (6^2/9) > 1$, and we proceed to find the tangent lines through Q. Any line through Q has the equation

$$y - 6 = m(x - 0).$$

The slope of the ellipse at any point is, by implicit differentiation,

$$\frac{2x}{25} + \frac{2y}{9}\frac{dy}{dx} = 0, \quad \text{or} \quad \frac{dy}{dx} = -\frac{9}{25}\frac{x}{y}.$$

Suppose that $P_1(x_1, y_1)$ is a point where the desired line is tangent to the ellipse. We have $m = -9x_1/25y_1$ and

$$\frac{x_1^2}{25} + \frac{y_1^2}{9} = 1, \quad y_1 - 6 = -\frac{9}{25}\frac{x_1}{y_1}x_1.$$

We solve these equations simultaneously and obtain

$$(\tfrac{5}{2}\sqrt{3}, \tfrac{3}{2}) \quad \text{and} \quad (-\tfrac{5}{2}\sqrt{3}, \tfrac{3}{2})$$

as the points of tangency. The equations of the lines are

$$y - 6 = -\frac{9}{25}\cdot\frac{\tfrac{5}{2}\sqrt{3}}{\tfrac{3}{2}}x, \quad y - 6 = -\frac{9}{25}\cdot\frac{-\tfrac{5}{2}\sqrt{3}}{\tfrac{3}{2}}x,$$

and, when we simplify, we find

$$3\sqrt{3}\,x + 5y - 30 = 0, \quad 3\sqrt{3}\,x - 5y + 30 = 0.$$

EXERCISES

In problems 1 through 6, find the equation of the ellipse satisfying the given conditions.

1. Foci at $(\pm 4, 0)$, directrices $x = \pm 6$
2. Eccentricity $\frac{1}{2}$, directrices $x = \pm 8$
3. Foci at $(0, \pm 4)$, directrices $y = \pm 7$
4. Vertices at $(\pm 6, 0)$, directrices $x = \pm 9$
5. Vertices at $(0, \pm 7)$, directrices $y = \pm 12$
6. Eccentricity $\frac{2}{3}$, directrices $y = \pm 9$
7. Find the locus of a point whose distance from $(3, 0)$ is always $\frac{1}{3}$ of its distance from the line $x = 27$.
8. Find the locus of a point whose distance from $(0, 4)$ is always $\frac{2}{3}$ of its distance from the line $y = 9$.
9. Find the locus of a point whose distance from $(4, 0)$ is always $\frac{1}{2}$ of its distance from the line $x = 6$. Locate the major and minor axes.
10. Find the locus of a point whose distance from $(0, 5)$ is always $\frac{3}{4}$ of its distance from the line $y = 8$. Locate the major and minor axes.
11. Find the equation of the line tangent to the ellipse

$$\frac{x^2}{9} + \frac{y^2}{4} = 1$$

at the point $P(1, -\frac{4}{3}\sqrt{2})$.

12. Find the equation of the line tangent to the ellipse $4x^2 + 12y^2 = 1$ at the point $P(\frac{1}{4}, \frac{1}{4})$.
13. Find the equation of the line normal to the ellipse $4x^2 + 9y^2 = 36$ at the point $P(2, \frac{2}{3}\sqrt{5})$.
14. Find the equation of the line normal to the ellipse $16x^2 + 25y^2 = 400$ at the point $P(-3, \frac{16}{5})$.
15. Prove the reflected-wave property of an ellipse, as described in this section.
16. Prove that the segment of a tangent to an ellipse between the point of contact and a directrix subtends a right angle at the corresponding focus.
17. A line through a focus parallel to a directrix is called a *latus rectum*. The segment of this line is called the *length of the latus rectum*. Show that the length of the latus rectum of $(x^2/a^2) + (y^2/b^2) = 1$ is $2b^2/a$.
18. Prove that the line joining a point P_0 of an ellipse to the center and the line through a focus and perpendicular to the tangent at P_0 intersect on the corresponding directrix.
19. The tangent to an ellipse at a point P_0 meets the tangent at a vertex in a point Q. Prove that the line joining the other vertex to P_0 is parallel to the line joining the center to Q.
20. Given the ellipse $(x^2/4) + (y^2/2) = 1$. Decide whether or not the points $P(1, \frac{1}{2})$, $Q(1, 4)$, and $R(0, 1)$ are outside the ellipse. Construct the tangent lines passing through the points wherever possible.
21. Given the ellipse $(x^2/1) + (y^2/9) = 1$. Rework problem 20 for the points $P(\frac{1}{2}, 1)$, $Q(2, 3)$, and $R(5, 0)$.

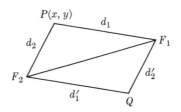

FIGURE 10–22

5. THE HYPERBOLA

A study of the hyperbola will complete our discussion of second-degree curves in the plane.

DEFINITIONS.   A *hyperbola* is the locus of all points the difference of whose distances from two fixed points is a positive constant.   The two fixed points are called the *foci*.

A typical situation is shown in Fig. 10–22, where the two fixed points (foci) are labeled F_1 and F_2.   For a point P to be on the locus, the distance PF_1 minus the distance PF_2 must be equal to a positive constant.   Also, a point, say Q, will be on the locus if the distance QF_2 minus QF_1 is this same constant.   We remark that the definition of a hyperbola, like that of a parabola and an ellipse, is purely geometric and makes no mention of coordinate systems.   It is true, of course, that hyperbolas are second-degree curves.

Suppose that the distance between the foci is $2c$ $(c > 0)$.   We place the foci at convenient points, F_1 at $(c, 0)$ and F_2 at $(-c, 0)$.   Let $P(x, y)$ be a point on the hyperbola; then the conditions of the locus assert that $d_1 - d_2$ or $d_2 - d_1$ is always a positive constant (Fig. 10–23), which we label $2a$ $(a > 0)$.   We write the conditions of the locus as

$$d_1 - d_2 = 2a \qquad \text{or} \qquad d_2 - d_1 = 2a,$$

which may be combined as

$$d_1 - d_2 = \pm 2a.$$

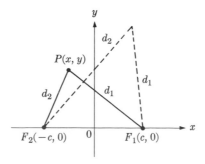

FIGURE 10–23

Using the distance formula, we obtain

$$\sqrt{(x - c)^2 + y^2} - \sqrt{(x + c)^2 + y^2} = \pm 2a.$$

We transfer one radical to the right side and square both sides to get

$$(x - c)^2 + y^2 = (x + c)^2 + y^2 \pm 4a\sqrt{(x + c)^2 + y^2} + 4a^2.$$

Some terms may be canceled to yield

$$\pm 4a\sqrt{(x + c)^2 + y^2} = 4a^2 + 4cx.$$

We divide by $4a$ and once again square both sides, to find

$$x^2 + 2cx + c^2 + y^2 = a^2 + 2cx + \frac{c^2}{a^2} x^2,$$

or

$$\left(\frac{c^2}{a^2} - 1\right) x^2 - y^2 = c^2 - a^2.$$

We now divide through by $c^2 - a^2$, with the result that we have

$$\frac{x^2}{a^2} - \frac{y^2}{c^2 - a^2} = 1.$$

We shall show that the quantity c must be larger than a. We recall that the sum of the lengths of any two sides of a triangle must be greater than the length of the third side. When we refer to Fig. 10–23, we observe that $2c + d_2 > d_1$ and $2c + d_1 > d_2$. Therefore $2c > d_1 - d_2$ and $2c > d_2 - d_1$; combined, these inequalities give $2c > |d_1 - d_2|$. But $|d_1 - d_2| = 2a$, and so $c > a$.

We define the positive number b by the relation

$$b = \sqrt{c^2 - a^2},$$

and we write *the equation of the hyperbola:*

$$\frac{x^2}{a^2} - \frac{y^2}{b^2} = 1.$$

Conversely, by showing that all the steps are reversible, we could have demonstrated that every point which satisfies the above equation is on the locus. (We shall not enter into the discussion required for the proof of this fact.)

The equation of the hyperbola in the above form shows at once that it is symmetric with respect to both the x-axis and the y-axis.

DEFINITIONS. The line passing through the foci F_1 and F_2 is called the *transverse axis*. The perpendicular bisector of the segment F_1F_2 is called the *conjugate axis*. The intersection of these axes is called the *center*.

[See Fig. 10–24, where the foci are at $(c, 0)$ and $(-c, 0)$, the transverse axis is the x-axis, the conjugate axis is the y-axis, and the center is at the origin.]

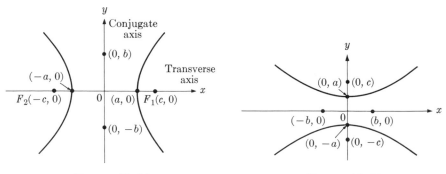

FIGURE 10–24   FIGURE 10–25

The points of intersection of a hyperbola with the transverse axis are called its *vertices*. In Fig. 10–24, corresponding to the equation

$$\frac{x^2}{a^2} - \frac{y^2}{b^2} = 1,$$

these vertices occur at $(a, 0)$ and $(-a, 0)$. The length $2a$ is called the *length of the transverse axis*. Even though the points $(0, b)$ and $(0, -b)$ are not on the locus, the length $2b$ is a useful quantity. It is called the *length of the conjugate axis*.

The *eccentricity* of a hyperbola is defined as

$$e = \frac{c}{a}.$$

Note that since $c > a$, *the eccentricity of a hyperbola is always larger than* 1.

If the foci of the hyperbola are placed along the y-axis at the points $(0, c)$ and $(0, -c)$, the equation takes the form

$$\frac{y^2}{a^2} - \frac{x^2}{b^2} = 1,$$

where, as before,

$$b = \sqrt{c^2 - a^2}.$$

The curve has the general appearance of the curve shown in Fig. 10–25.

In contrast with the equation of an ellipse, the equation for a hyperbola indicates that the relative sizes of a and b play no role in determining where the foci and axes are. An equation of the form

$$\frac{x^2}{(\ )^2} - \frac{y^2}{(\ )^2} = 1$$

always has its transverse axis (and foci) on the x-axis, while an equation of the form

$$\frac{y^2}{(\ )^2} - \frac{x^2}{(\ )^2} = 1$$

always has its transverse axis (and foci) on the y-axis. In the first case, the quantity

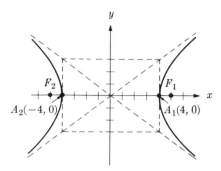

FIGURE 10–26

under the x^2 term is labeled a^2 and that under the y^2 term is labeled b^2. In the second case the quantity under the y^2 term is labeled a^2 and that under the x^2 term is labeled b^2. In *both cases* we have

$$c^2 = a^2 + b^2.$$

EXAMPLE 1. Given the hyperbola with equation $9x^2 - 16y^2 = 144$. Find the axes, the coordinates of the vertices and the foci, and the eccentricity. Sketch the curve.

Solution. Dividing by 144, we find that

$$\frac{x^2}{16} - \frac{y^2}{9} = 1,$$

and, therefore,

$$a = 4, b = 3, c^2 = a^2 + b^2 = 25, c = 5.$$

The transverse axis is along the x-axis; the conjugate axis is along the y-axis. The vertices are at $(\pm 4, 0)$. The foci are at $(\pm 5, 0)$. The eccentricity $= c/a = 5/4$. The curve is sketched in Fig. 10–26, where we have constructed a rectangle by drawing parallels to the axes through the points $(a, 0)$, $(-a, 0)$, $(0, b)$, and $(0, -b)$. This is called the *central rectangle*. Note that the diagonal from the origin to one corner of this rectangle has length c.

EXAMPLE 2. Find the equation of the hyperbola with vertices at $(0, \pm 6)$ and eccentricity $\frac{5}{3}$. Locate the foci.

Solution. Since the vertices are along the y-axis, the equation is of the form

$$\frac{y^2}{a^2} - \frac{x^2}{b^2} = 1,$$

with $a = 6$, $e = c/a = \frac{5}{3}$, and $c = (5 \cdot 6)/3 = 10$. Therefore $b = \sqrt{100 - 36} = 8$, and the equation is

$$\frac{y^2}{36} - \frac{x^2}{64} = 1.$$

The foci are at the points $(0, \pm 10)$.

EXERCISES

In problems 1 through 10, find the lengths of the transverse and conjugate axes, the coordinates of the foci and the vertices, and the eccentricity. Sketch the curve.

1. $16x^2 - 9y^2 = 144$ 2. $16x^2 - 9y^2 + 576 = 0$
3. $25x^2 - 144y^2 + 3600 = 0$ 4. $25x^2 - 144y^2 - 900 = 0$
5. $2x^2 - 3y^2 - 6 = 0$ 6. $2x^2 - 3y^2 + 6 = 0$
7. $5x^2 - 2y^2 = 10$ 8. $5x^2 - 4y^2 + 13 = 0$
9. $3x^2 - 2y^2 = 1$ 10. $2x^2 - 3y^2 = -1$

In problems 11 through 20, find for each case the equation of the hyperbola (or hyperbolas) satisfying the given conditions.

11. Vertices at $(\pm 5, 0)$, foci at $(\pm 7, 0)$ 12. Vertices at $(\pm 4, 0)$, foci at $(\pm 6, 0)$
13. Vertices at $(0, \pm 7)$, eccentricity $\frac{4}{3}$ 14. Foci at $(\pm 6, 0)$, eccentricity $\frac{3}{2}$
15. Eccentricity $\sqrt{5}$, foci on x-axis, center at origin, passing through the point $(3, 2)$
16. Vertices at $(0, \pm 4)$, passing through $(-2, 5)$
17. Foci at $(0, \pm \sqrt{10})$, passing through $(2, 3)$
18. Axes along the coordinate axes, passing through $(4, 2)$ and $(-6, 7)$
19. Axes along the coordinate axes, passing through $(-3, 4)$ and $(5, 6)$
20. Foci at $(\pm 8, 0)$, length of conjugate axis 6
21. Find the locus of a point such that the difference of its distances from $(4, 0)$ and $(-4, 0)$ is always equal to 2.
22. Find the locus of a point such that the difference of its distances from $(0, 7)$ and $(0, -7)$ is always equal to 3.
23. Find the locus of a point such that the difference of its distances from $(10, 0)$ and $(2, 0)$ is always 1.
24. Find the locus of a point such that the difference of its distances from $(2, 0)$ and $(2, 12)$ is always equal to 3.

6. THE HYPERBOLA, CONTINUED

The hyperbola, like the ellipse, has two directrices. For the hyperbola

$$\frac{x^2}{a^2} - \frac{y^2}{b^2} = 1,$$

the directrices are the lines

$$x = \pm \frac{a}{e},$$

and for the hyperbola

$$\frac{y^2}{a^2} - \frac{x^2}{b^2} = 1,$$

the directrices are the lines

$$y = \pm \frac{a}{e}.$$

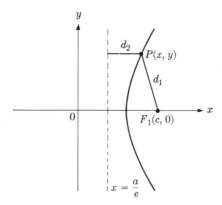

FIGURE 10–27

A hyperbola has the property that it is the locus of all points $P(x, y)$ whose distances from a fixed point (F_1) are equal to e ($e > 1$) times their distances from a fixed line (say $x = a/e$). As Fig. 10–27 shows, the conditions of the locus are

$$d_1 = ed_2 \quad \text{or} \quad \sqrt{(x - c)^2 + y^2} = e\left|x - \frac{a}{e}\right|.$$

If we square both sides and simplify, we obtain $(x^2/a^2) - (y^2/b^2) = 1$. The same is true if we start with $F_2(-c, 0)$ and the line $x = -a/e$.

EXAMPLE 1. Find the equation of the hyperbola if the foci are at the points $(\pm 6, 0)$ and one directrix is the line $x = 3$.

Solution. We have $c = 6$ and $a/e = 3$. Since $e = c/a$, we may also write $a^2/c = 3$ and $a^2 = 18$, $a = \sqrt{18}$. In addition, $c^2 = a^2 + b^2$, from which we obtain $b^2 = 18$. The equation is

$$\frac{x^2}{18} - \frac{y^2}{18} = 1.$$

If $P(x_1, y_1)$ is a point on the hyperbola

$$\frac{x^2}{a^2} - \frac{y^2}{b^2} = 1,$$

we can get the formula for the line tangent to the hyperbola at P in a way that precisely parallels the work we did to obtain the formula for the line tangent to the ellipse. The slope of the hyperbola at any point, by implicit differentiation, is

$$\frac{2x}{a^2} - \frac{2y}{b^2}\frac{dy}{dx} = 0, \quad \text{or} \quad \frac{dy}{dx} = \frac{b^2}{a^2}\frac{x}{y}.$$

The equation of the line tangent at $P(x_1, y_1)$ is

$$y - y_1 = +\frac{b^2}{a^2}\frac{x_1}{y_1}(x - x_1), \quad \text{or} \quad a^2 y_1 y - a^2 y_1^2 = b^2 x_1 x - b^2 x_1^2.$$

But since P is on the hyperbola we know that $b^2x_1^2 - a^2y_1^2 = a^2b^2$, and so

$$\frac{x_1x}{a^2} - \frac{y_1y}{b^2} = 1$$

is the equation of the tangent line.

EXAMPLE 2. Find the equations of the tangent line and the normal line to the hyperbola

$$\frac{x^2}{9} - \frac{y^2}{16} = 1,$$

at the point $(5, -\frac{16}{3})$.

Solution. The point $(5, -\frac{16}{3})$ is on the hyperbola, and so the equation of the tangent line is

$$\frac{5x}{9} + \frac{\frac{16}{3}y}{16} = 1, \quad \text{or} \quad 5x + 3y - 9 = 0.$$

The normal line will have slope $\frac{3}{5}$, and the equation is

$$y + \tfrac{16}{3} = \tfrac{3}{5}(x - 5).$$

Among all the second-degree equations the hyperbola is the only one which has asymptotes. We shall now show that the hyperbola

$$\frac{x^2}{a^2} - \frac{y^2}{b^2} = 1$$

has, as its asymptotes, the lines $y = (b/a)x$ and $y = -(b/a)x$. First we recall (from Chapter 9, Section 8) that the line $y = mx + k$ is an asymptote of the function $y = g(x)$, if $[g(x) - (mx + k)] \to 0$ as $x \to \infty$. The equation of a hyperbola gives y not as one but as *two* functions of x. Therefore, when we solve for y, we have

$$y = \pm \frac{b}{a} \sqrt{x^2 - a^2}$$

as the functions. Let us take one of them, say $+(b/a)\sqrt{x^2 - a^2}$, as $g(x)$, and show that the line $(b/a)x$ ($m = b/a$, $k = 0$) is an asymptote. Figure 10–28 shows

FIGURE 10–28

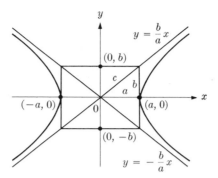

$$y = \frac{b}{a} x$$

$(0, b)$

c

b

a

$(-a, 0)$

0

$(a, 0)$

x

$(0, -b)$

$$y = -\frac{b}{a} x$$

FIGURE 10–29

the situation. We must prove that

$$\frac{b}{a} \sqrt{x^2 - a^2} - \frac{b}{a} x \to 0 \quad \text{as} \quad x \to \infty.$$

The trick we use is the familiar one of rationalizing the numerator (after factoring out b/a). We obtain

$$\frac{b}{a} \left(\frac{\sqrt{x^2 - a^2} - x}{1} \right) \frac{\sqrt{x^2 - a^2} + x}{\sqrt{x^2 - a^2} + x} = \frac{b}{a} \frac{x^2 - a^2 - x^2}{\sqrt{x^2 - a^2} + x} = \frac{-ab}{\sqrt{x^2 - a^2} + x}.$$

The denominator tends to infinity and the numerator remains fixed as $x \to +\infty$. We conclude that the ratio approaches zero, and therefore $y = (b/a)x$ is an asymptote. Similarly, $y = -(b/a)x$ is an asymptote and, furthermore, both lines are asymptotes of the function $-(b/a)\sqrt{x^2 - a^2}$. Figure 10–29 shows the hyperbola $(x^2/a^2) - (y^2/b^2) = 1$ and its asymptotes.

Now we can see one of the uses of the central rectangle. *The asymptotes are the lines which contain the diagonals of the central rectangle.* In an analogous way the hyperbola

$$\frac{y^2}{a^2} - \frac{x^2}{b^2} = 1$$

has the asymptotes

$$y = \frac{a}{b} x \quad \text{and} \quad y = -\frac{a}{b} x.$$

These lines contain the diagonals of the appropriately constructed central rectangle.

EXAMPLE 3. Given the hyperbola $25x^2 - 9y^2 = 225$, find the foci, vertices, eccentricity, directrices, and asymptotes. Sketch the curve.

Solution. When we divide by 225, we obtain $(x^2/9) - (y^2/25) = 1$, and therefore $a = 3$, $b = 5$, $c^2 = 9 + 25$, and $c = \sqrt{34}$. The foci are at $(\pm\sqrt{34}, 0)$, vertices at $(\pm 3, 0)$; the eccentricity is $e = c/a = \sqrt{34}/3$, and the directrices are the lines $x = \pm a/e = \pm 9/\sqrt{34}$. To find the asymptotes we merely write $y = \pm(b/a)x = \pm\frac{5}{3}x$.

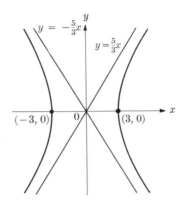

FIGURE 10–30

Since the asymptotes are a great help in sketching the curve, we draw them first (Fig. 10–30); knowing the vertices and one or two additional points helps us obtain a fairly accurate graph.

_____

An easy way to remember the equations of the asymptotes is to recognize that if the hyperbola is

$$\frac{x^2}{a^2} - \frac{y^2}{b^2} = 1, \quad \text{the asymptotes are} \quad \frac{x^2}{a^2} - \frac{y^2}{b^2} = 0,$$

and if the hyperbola is

$$\frac{y^2}{a^2} - \frac{x^2}{b^2} = 1, \quad \text{the asymptotes are} \quad \frac{y^2}{a^2} - \frac{x^2}{b^2} = 0.$$

A hyperbola divides the plane into *three* regions. For example, the hyperbola

$$\frac{x^2}{4} - \frac{y^2}{16} = 1$$

divides the plane into the regions

$$\frac{x^2}{4} - \frac{y^2}{16} < 1,$$

$$\frac{x^2}{4} - \frac{y^2}{16} > 1 \quad and \quad x > 2,$$

$$\frac{x^2}{4} - \frac{y^2}{16} > 1 \quad and \quad x < -2.$$

For any given point P in the first of these regions, tangents to the hyperbola which pass through this point may be constructed, while no tangents can be constructed which pass through a point (such as Q) of the other two regions (Fig. 10–31).

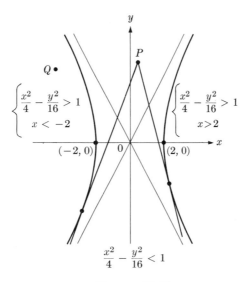

$$\begin{cases} \dfrac{x^2}{4} - \dfrac{y^2}{16} > 1 \\ x < -2 \end{cases}$$

$$\begin{cases} \dfrac{x^2}{4} - \dfrac{y^2}{16} > 1 \\ x > 2 \end{cases}$$

$$\dfrac{x^2}{4} - \dfrac{y^2}{16} < 1$$

FIGURE 10–31

EXAMPLE 4.   Given the hyperbola $(x^2/4) - (y^2/3) = 1$.   Decide whether or not tangents to the hyperbola can be constructed which pass through any of the points $P(3, 1)$, $Q(-4, 2)$, $R(1, 3)$. If they can, find the equations of the tangent lines.

Solution. For the point P we have $(3^2/4) - (1^2/3) > 1$, and no tangents can be constructed.   Similarly, no tangents can be constructed which pass through Q, since $((-4)^2/4) - (2^2/3) > 1$. The point R satisfies the inequality $(1^2/4) - (3^2/3) < 1$, and we proceed to find the tangent lines. Any line through R has the equation

$$y - 3 = m(x - 1),$$

and the slope of the hyperbola at any point is

$$\frac{dy}{dx} = \frac{3}{4}\frac{x}{y}.$$

If (x_1, y_1) is a point of tangency, then $m = \frac{3}{4}(x_1/y_1)$, and the two equations

$$\frac{x_1^2}{4} = \frac{y_1^2}{3} + 1, \qquad y_1 - 3 = \frac{3}{4}\frac{x_1}{y_1}(x_1 - 1)$$

hold. We solve these simultaneously and find

$$\left(\frac{-4 + 12\sqrt{5}}{11}, \ \frac{-12 + 3\sqrt{5}}{11} \right), \qquad \left(\frac{-4 - 12\sqrt{5}}{11}, \ \frac{-12 - 3\sqrt{5}}{11} \right).$$

The equations of the lines are

$$(1 - 3\sqrt{5})x + (-4 + \sqrt{5})y + 11 = 0, \qquad (1 + 3\sqrt{5})x - (4 + \sqrt{5})y + 11 = 0.$$

EXERCISES

In problems 1 through 8, find the vertices, foci, eccentricity, equations of the asymptotes, and directrices. Construct the central rectangle and sketch the hyperbola.

1. $4x^2 - 9y^2 = 36$ 2. $9x^2 - 4y^2 = 36$ 3. $x^2 - 4y^2 = 4$
4. $9x^2 - y^2 = -9$ 5. $x^2 - y^2 = 1$ 6. $x^2 - y^2 = -1$
7. $25x^2 - 8y^2 = -200$ 8. $2x^2 - 3y^2 = 8$

In problems 9 through 17, find in each case the equation of the hyperbola (or hyperbolas) satisfying the given conditions.

9. Asymptotes $y = \pm 2x$, vertices $(\pm 6, 0)$
10. Asymptotes $y = \pm 2x$, vertices $(0, \pm 4)$
11. Eccentricity $\frac{4}{3}$, directrices $x = \pm 2$
12. Foci at $(\pm 6, 0)$, directrices $x = \pm 4$
13. Asymptotes $3y = \pm 4x$, foci at $(\pm 6, 0)$
14. Directrices $y = \pm 4$, asymptotes $y = \pm \frac{3}{2}x$
15. Asymptotes $2y = \pm 3x$, passing through $(5, 3)$
16. Directrices $x = \pm 1$, passing through $(-4, 6)$, center at origin
17. Directrices $y = \pm 1$, passing through $(1, \sqrt{3})$, center at origin
18. Find the equations of the tangent and normal lines to the hyperbola

$$(x^2/16) - (y^2/4) = 1 \qquad \text{at the point} \qquad (-5, \tfrac{3}{2}).$$

19. Find the point of intersection of the lines tangent to the hyperbola

$$(y^2/36) - (x^2/9) = 1 \qquad \text{at the points} \qquad (1, -2\sqrt{10}), (-4, 10).$$

20. Prove that the lines $y = \pm(a/b)x$ are asymptotes of the hyperbola

$$(y^2/a^2) - (x^2/b^2) = 1.$$

21. A line through a focus of a hyperbola and parallel to the directrix is called a *latus rectum*. The length of the segment cut off by the hyperbola is called the *length of the latus rectum*. Show that for the hyperbola $(x^2/a^2) - (y^2/b^2) = 1$ the length of the latus rectum is $2b^2/a$.
22. Find the locus of a point such that its distance from $(5, 0)$ is always $\frac{5}{3}$ times its distance from the line $x = \frac{9}{5}$.
23. Find the locus of a point such that its distance from the point $(0, \sqrt{41})$ is always $\sqrt{41}/5$ times its distance from the line $y = 25/\sqrt{41}$.
24. Find the locus of a point such that its distance from the point $(8, 0)$ is always 3 times its distance from the line $x = 1$.
25. Show that an asymptote, a directrix, and the line through the corresponding focus perpendicular to the asymptote pass through a point.
26. Given the hyperbola $(x^2/4) - y^2 = 1$. Find the equations of the lines tangent to this hyperbola passing through the point $(1, 2)$.
27. Given the hyperbola $(y^2/4) - (x^2/6) = 1$. Decide whether or not tangents to this hyperbola can be drawn which pass through any of the points $P(0, 8)$, $Q(1, 5)$, $R(4, 0)$, and $S(-8, -9)$. Find the equations of the lines, wherever possible.

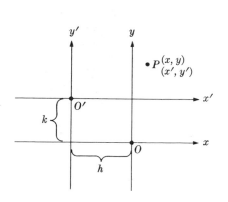

FIGURE 10–32   FIGURE 10–33

7. TRANSLATION OF AXES

Coordinate systems were not employed in our definitions and descriptions of the principal properties of second-degree curves. However, when we want to find equations for such curves and when we wish to use the methods of analytic geometry, coordinate systems become essential.

When we use the method of coordinate geometry we place the axes at a position "convenient" with respect to the curve under consideration. In the examples of ellipses and hyperbolas which we studied, the foci were located on one of the axes and were situated symmetrically with respect to the origin. But now suppose that we have a problem in which the curve (hyperbola, parabola, ellipse, etc.) is *not* situated so conveniently with respect to the axes. We would then like to change the coordinate system in order to have the curve at a convenient and familiar location. The process of making this change is called a *transformation of coordinates*.

The first type of transformation we shall consider is one of the simplest, and is called the *translation of axes*. Figure 10–32 shows the usual rectangular xy-coordinate system. We now introduce an additional coordinate system, with axis x' parallel to x and k units away, and axis y' parallel to y and h units away. This means that the origin O' of the new coordinate system has coordinates (h, k) in the original system. The positive x'- and y'-directions are taken to be the same as the positive x- and y-directions. When P is any point in the plane, what are its coordinates in each of the systems? When P has coordinates (x, y) in the original system and (x', y') in the new system, they are related in the manner shown in Fig. 10–33:

$$x' = x - h, \qquad y' = y - k,$$

or, equivalently,

$$x = x' + h, \qquad y = y' + k.$$

Two coordinate systems xy and $x'y'$ which satisfy these equations are said to be related by a *translation of axes*.

The most general equation of the second degree has the form

$$Ax^2 + Bxy + Cy^2 + Dx + Ey + F = 0,$$

where A, B, C, D, E, and F represent numbers. We also assume that A, B, and C are not all zero, since then the equation would be in the first degree. We recognize that the equations we have been discussing are all special cases of the above equation.   For example, the circle $x^2 + y^2 - 16 = 0$ has $A = 1$, $B = 0$, $C = 1$, $D = E = 0$, $F = -16$.   The ellipse $(x^2/9) + (y^2/4) = 1$ has $A = \frac{1}{9}$, $B = 0$, $C = \frac{1}{4}$, $D = E = 0$, $F = -1$.   Similarly, we see that parabolas and hyperbolas are of the above form.

An interesting case is $A = 1$, $B = 0$, $C = -1$, $D = E = F = 0$.   We get $x^2 - y^2 = 0$ or $y = \pm x$, and the locus is two intersecting lines.   Second-degree curves whose loci reduce to lines or points are frequently called *degenerate*.

We now illustrate how to use translation of axes to reduce an equation of the form

$$Ax^2 + Cy^2 + Dx + Ey + F = 0$$

to an equation of the same form but with new letters (x', y'), and with D and E both equal to zero (with certain exceptions).   Although presented in a new way, the equation will be easily recognized as one of the second-degree curves we have studied.   *The principal tool in this process is "completing the square."*

———————

EXAMPLE 1.   Given the equation

$$9x^2 + 25y^2 + 18x - 100y - 116 = 0,$$

by using a translation of axes determine whether the locus of the equation is a parabola, ellipse, or hyperbola.   Determine foci (or focus), vertices (or vertex), directrices (or directrix), eccentricity, and asymptotes, if any.   Sketch the curve.

Solution.   To complete the square in x and y, we write the equation in the form

$$9(x^2 + 2x \qquad) + 25(y^2 - 4y \qquad) = 116.$$

We add 1 in the parentheses for x, which means adding 9 to the left side, and we add 4 in the parentheses for y, which means adding 100 to the left side.   We obtain

$$9(x^2 + 2x + 1) + 25(y^2 - 4y + 4) = 116 + 9 + 100,$$

or

$$9(x + 1)^2 + 25(y - 2)^2 = 225.$$

Now we have the clue for translation of axes.   We define

$$x' = x + 1 \qquad \text{and} \qquad y' = y - 2.$$

That is, the translation is made with $h = -1$, $k = 2$.   The equation becomes

$$9x'^2 + 25y'^2 = 225.$$

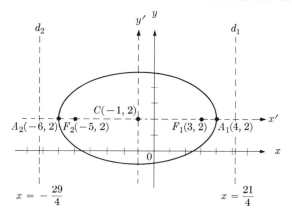

FIGURE 10–34

Dividing by 225, we find

$$\frac{x'^2}{25} + \frac{y'^2}{9} = 1,$$

which we recognize as an ellipse with $a = 5, b = 3, c^2 = a^2 - b^2 = 16, c = 4, e = \frac{4}{5}$. In the $x'y'$-system, we have: center $(0, 0)$; vertices $(\pm 5, 0)$; foci $(\pm 4, 0)$; directrices, $x' = \pm\frac{25}{4}$.

In the xy-system, we use the relations $x = x' - 1, y = y' + 2$ to obtain: center $(-1, 2)$; vertices $(4, 2), (-6, 2)$; foci $(3, 2), (-5, 2)$; directrices, $x = \frac{21}{4}, x = -\frac{29}{4}$. The curve is sketched in Fig. 10–34.

EXAMPLE 2. Discuss, as in Example 1, the locus of the equation

$$x^2 + 4x + 4y - 4 = 0.$$

Solution. Here we have $A = 1, C = 0, D = 4, E = 4, F = -4$. There is only one second-degree term, and we complete the square to obtain

$$(x^2 + 4x + 4) = -4y + 4 + 4,$$
$$(x + 2)^2 = -4(y - 2).$$

We read off the appropriate translation of axes. It is

$$x' = x + 2, \qquad y' = y - 2,$$

and we have

$$x'^2 = -4y',$$

which we recognize as a parabola. In the $x'y'$-system, the vertex is at $(0, 0)$, focus at $(0, -1)$ (since $p = 2$); directrix, $y' = 1$. In the xy-system (since $h = -2, k = 2$), we have the vertex at $(-2, 2)$, focus at $(-2, 1)$, and directrix $y = 3$. The curve is sketched in Fig. 10–35.

EXAMPLE 3. Find the equation of the ellipse with eccentricity $\frac{1}{2}$ and foci at $(4, 2)$ and $(2, 2)$.

Solution. The center of the ellipse is halfway between the foci and therefore is at the point $(3, 2)$. The major axis of the ellipse is along the line $y = 2$. To move the origin

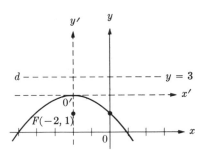

FIGURE 10–35

to the center of the ellipse by a translation of coordinates, we let

$$x' = x - 3, \qquad y' = y - 2.$$

In this system the foci are at $(\pm 1, 0)$; $e = c/a = \tfrac{1}{2}$ and, since $c = 1$, we have $a = 2$. Also, $c^2 = a^2 - b^2$ gives us $b^2 = 3$. In the $x'y'$-system, the equation is

$$\frac{x'^2}{4} + \frac{y'^2}{3} = 1.$$

In the xy-system, the equation is

$$\frac{(x - 3)^2}{4} + \frac{(y - 2)^2}{3} = 1,$$

or

$$3(x - 3)^2 + 4(y - 2)^2 = 12,$$

and

$$3x^2 + 4y^2 - 18x - 16y + 31 = 0.$$

We are now in a position to discuss all the curves that an equation

$$Ax^2 + Cy^2 + Dx + Ey + F = 0$$

can possibly represent, presented here in the form of a theorem:

Theorem 1. (a) *If A and C are both positive or both negative, then the locus is an ellipse, a circle (if A = C), a point, or nothing.* (b) *If A and C are of opposite signs, the locus is a hyperbola or two intersecting lines.* (c) *If either A or C is zero, the locus is a parabola, two parallel lines, one line, or nothing.*

We shall not prove this theorem, but some of its possible uses will be illustrated by examples.

The equation $3x^2 + y^2 + 5 = 0$ has no locus, since the sum of positive quantities can never add up to zero. This exhibits the last case under (a) of Theorem 1. Under (c), the equation $x^2 - 2x = 0$ ($A = 1, C = 0, D = -2$, $E = 0, F = 0$) is an example of two parallel lines, while $x^2 - 2x + 1 = 0$ ($A = 1, C = 0, D = -2, E = 0, F = 1$) is an example of one line.

A proof of this theorem is within the scope of any curious student.

EXERCISES

1. A rectangular system of coordinates is translated to a new $x'y'$-system, whose origin is at $(-3, 4)$. The points P, Q, R, and S have coordinates $(4, 3)$, $(-2, 7)$, $(-6, \frac{3}{2})$, and $(-5, -2)$, respectively, in the original system. Find the coordinates of these points in the new system.

2. A translation of coordinates moves the origin to the point of intersection of the lines $2x + 3y - 4 = 0$ and $x + 4y - 1 = 0$. Find the translation of coordinates and the equations of these lines in the new system.

3. A translation of coordinates moves the origin to the point of intersection of the lines $3x - 7y + 1 = 0$ and $2x - 5y - 6 = 0$. Find the equations of these lines in the new coordinate system.

In problems 4 through 17, translate the coordinates so as to eliminate the first-degree terms (or one first-degree term in the case of parabolas), describe the principal properties (as in Example 1) and sketch the curves.

4. $y^2 + 8x - 6y + 1 = 0$

5. $25x^2 + 16y^2 + 50x - 64y - 311 = 0$

6. $9x^2 + 16y^2 - 36x - 32y - 92 = 0$

7. $9x^2 - 4y^2 + 18x + 16y + 29 = 0$

8. $x^2 - 4x + 6y + 16 = 0$

9. $4x^2 + 9y^2 + 8x - 36y + 4 = 0$

10. $y^2 - 4x + 10y + 5 = 0$

11. $9x^2 + 4y^2 - 18x + 8y + 4 = 0$

12. $4x^2 - 9y^2 + 8x + 18y + 4 = 0$

13. $3x^2 + 4y^2 - 12x + 8y + 4 = 0$

14. $x^2 + 6x - 8y + 1 = 0$

15. $3x^2 - 2y^2 + 6x - 8y - 17 = 0$

16. $2x^2 + 3y^2 - 8x - 6y + 11 = 0$

17. $4x^2 - 3y^2 + 8x + 12y - 8 = 0$

In problems 18 through 23, find the equation of the locus indicated; sketch the curve.

18. Parabola: vertex at $(2, 1)$; directrix $y = 3$

19. Ellipse: vertices at $(2, -3)$ and $(2, 5)$; foci at $(2, -2)$ and $(2, 4)$

20. Ellipse: foci at $(-2, 3)$ and $(4, 3)$; directrices $x = -5$ and $x = 7$

21. Hyperbola: vertices at $(-3, 1)$ and $(5, 1)$; passing through $(-5, 3)$

22. Hyperbola: asymptotes $2x - 3y + 7 = 0$ and $2x + 3y + 1 = 0$; passing through $(1, 5)$

23. Parabola: axis $y = -1$; directrix $x = 2$; focus, $(5, -1)$

In problems 24 through 28, find the equation of the given locus. Identify the curve.

24. The locus of all points whose distances from $(4, 3)$ equal their distances from the line $x = 6$

25. The locus of all points whose distances from $(2, 1)$ are equal to one-half their distances from the line $y = -2$

26. The locus of all points whose distances from $(-1, 2)$ are equal to twice their distances from the line $x = -4$

27. The locus of all points whose distances from $(2, -3)$ are equal to twice their distances from $(-4, 3)$

28. The locus of all points whose distances from $(1, 2)$ are equal to their distances from the line $3x - 4y - 5 = 0$

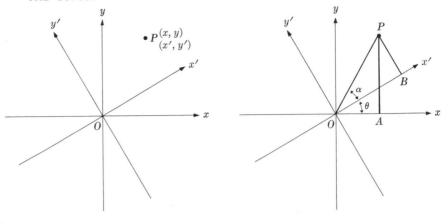

FIGURE 10–36   FIGURE 10–37

8. ROTATION OF AXES. THE GENERAL EQUATION OF THE SECOND DEGREE

Suppose that we make a transformation of coordinates from an xy-system to an $x'y'$-system in the following way. The origin is kept fixed, and the x' and y' axes are obtained by rotating the x- and y-axes counterclockwise an amount θ, as shown in Fig. 10–36. Every point P will have coordinates (x, y) with respect to the original system and coordinates (x', y') with respect to the new system. We now find the relationship between (x, y) and $x', y')$. Draw the lines OP, AP, and BP, as shown in Fig. 10–37, and note that $x = \overline{OA}$, $y = \overline{AP}$, $x' = \overline{OB}$, $y' = \overline{BP}$. We have

$$x = \overline{OA} = \overline{OP} \cos (\theta + \alpha), \qquad y = \overline{AP} = \overline{OP} \sin (\theta + \alpha).$$

Recalling from trigonometry the formula for the sine and cosine of the sum of two angles, we obtain

$$x = \overline{OP} \cos \theta \cos \alpha - \overline{OP} \sin \theta \sin \alpha,$$
$$y = \overline{OP} \sin \theta \cos \alpha + \overline{OP} \cos \theta \sin \alpha.$$

But $\overline{OP} \cos \alpha = \overline{OB} = x'$ and $\overline{OP} \sin \alpha = \overline{BP} = y'$. Therefore

$$x = x' \cos \theta - y' \sin \theta,$$
$$y = x' \sin \theta + y' \cos \theta.$$

When two coordinate systems, xy and $x'y'$, satisfy these equations, we say that they are related by a *rotation of axes;* more specifically, we can say that the x'- and y'-axes are obtained by rotating the x- and y-axes through the angle θ.

To express x' and y' in terms of x and y, we merely solve the above equations for x' and y'. Multiplying the first equation by $\cos \theta$, the second by $\sin \theta$, and adding, we find

$$x \cos \theta + y \sin \theta = x' (\cos^2 \theta + \sin^2 \theta), \qquad \text{or} \qquad x' = x \cos \theta + y \sin \theta.$$

Similarly, we get

$$y' = -x \sin \theta + y \cos \theta.$$

EXAMPLE 1. A rectangular coordinate system is rotated 60°. Find the coordinates of the point $P(3, -1)$ in the new system. What is the equation of the line $2x - 3y + 1 = 0$ in the rotated system?

Solution. We have $\sin 60° = \frac{1}{2}\sqrt{3}$, $\cos 60° = \frac{1}{2}$. The equations relating the xy-system and the $x'y'$-system are

$$x' = \tfrac{1}{2}x + \tfrac{1}{2}\sqrt{3}\,y, \qquad y' = -\tfrac{1}{2}\sqrt{3}\,x + \tfrac{1}{2}y.$$

The coordinates of P are $x' = \frac{3}{2} - \frac{1}{2}\sqrt{3}$, $y' = -\frac{3}{2}\sqrt{3} - \frac{1}{2}$. The relationships giving the xy-system in terms of the $x'y'$-system are

$$x = \tfrac{1}{2}x' - \tfrac{1}{2}\sqrt{3}\,y', \qquad y = \tfrac{1}{2}\sqrt{3}\,x' + \tfrac{1}{2}y';$$

and so the equation of the line in the new system is

$$2(\tfrac{1}{2}x' - \tfrac{1}{2}\sqrt{3}\,y') - 3(\tfrac{1}{2}\sqrt{3}\,x' + \tfrac{1}{2}y') + 1 = 0,$$

or

$$(1 - \tfrac{3}{2}\sqrt{3})x' - (\tfrac{3}{2} + \sqrt{3})y' + 1 = 0.$$

We recall that the most general equation of the second degree has the form

$$Ax^2 + Bxy + Cy^2 + Dx + Ey + F = 0 \quad (A, B, C \text{ not all zero}).$$

In Section 7 we showed (when $B = 0$) how the axes could be translated so that in the new system $D = E = 0$ (except in the case of parabolas, when we could make only one of them zero).

Now we shall show that *it is always possible to rotate the coordinates in such a way that in the new system there is no $x'y'$-term.* To do this we take the equations

$$x = x' \cos \theta - y' \sin \theta, \qquad y = x' \sin \theta + y' \cos \theta,$$

and we substitute in the general equation of the second degree. Then we have

$$\begin{aligned}
Ax^2 &= A(x' \cos \theta - y' \sin \theta)^2, \\
Bxy &= B(x' \cos \theta - y' \sin \theta)(x' \sin \theta + y' \cos \theta), \\
Cy^2 &= C(x' \sin \theta + y' \cos \theta)^2, \\
Dx &= D(x' \cos \theta - y' \sin \theta), \\
Ey &= E(x' \sin \theta + y' \cos \theta), \\
F &= F.
\end{aligned}$$

We add these equations and obtain (after multiplying out the right side)

$$\begin{aligned}
Ax^2 &+ Bxy + Cy^2 + Dx + Ey + F \\
&= A'x'^2 + B'x'y' + C'y'^2 + D'x' + E'y' + F' = 0,
\end{aligned}$$

where A', B', C', D', E', and F' are the abbreviations of

$$A' = A\cos^2\theta + B\sin\theta\cos\theta + C\sin^2\theta,$$
$$B' = 2(C - A)\sin\theta\cos\theta + B(\cos^2\theta - \sin^2\theta),$$
$$C' = A\sin^2\theta - B\sin\theta\cos\theta + C\cos^2\theta,$$
$$D' = D\cos\theta + E\sin\theta,$$
$$E' = -D\sin\theta + E\cos\theta,$$
$$F' = F.$$

Our purpose is to select θ so that the $x'y'$-term is missing, in order that B' will be zero. Let us set it equal to zero and see what happens:

$$2(C - A)\sin\theta\cos\theta + B(\cos^2\theta - \sin^2\theta) = 0.$$

We recall from trigonometry the double-angle formulas $\sin 2\theta = 2\sin\theta\cos\theta$, and $\cos 2\theta = \cos^2\theta - \sin^2\theta$, and we write

$$(C - A)\sin 2\theta + B\cos 2\theta = 0,$$

or

$$\cot 2\theta = \frac{A - C}{B}.$$

In other words, if we select θ so that $\cot 2\theta = (A - C)/B$ we will obtain $B' = 0$. There is always an angle between 0 and π which solves this equation.

The next example will illustrate the process.

EXAMPLE 2. Given the equation $8x^2 - 4xy + 5y^2 = 36$. Choose new axes by rotation so as to eliminate the $x'y'$-term; sketch the curve and locate the principal quantities.

Solution. We have $A = 8$, $B = -4$, $C = 5$, $D = E = 0$, $F = -36$. We select $\cot 2\theta = (A - C)/B = (8 - 5)/(-4) = -\frac{3}{4}$. This means that 2θ is in the second quadrant and $\cos 2\theta = -\frac{3}{5}$.

We remember from trigonometry the half-angle formulas

$$\sin\theta = \sqrt{(1 - \cos 2\theta)/2}, \qquad \cos\theta = \sqrt{(1 + \cos 2\theta)/2},$$

and we use these to get

$$\sin\theta = \sqrt{\tfrac{4}{5}}, \qquad \cos\theta = \sqrt{\tfrac{1}{5}},$$

which gives the rotation

$$x = \frac{1}{\sqrt{5}}x' - \frac{2}{\sqrt{5}}y' = \frac{x' - 2y'}{\sqrt{5}},$$

$$y = \frac{2}{\sqrt{5}}x' + \frac{1}{\sqrt{5}}y' = \frac{2x' + y'}{\sqrt{5}}.$$

Substituting in the given equation, we obtain

$$\tfrac{8}{5}(x' - 2y')^2 - \tfrac{4}{5}(x' - 2y')(2x' + y') + \tfrac{5}{5}(2x' + y')^2 = 36;$$

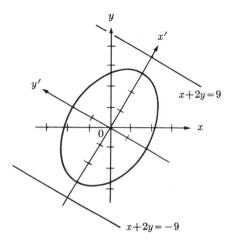

FIGURE 10–38

when we multiply out, we find that

$$4x'^2 + 9y'^2 = 36 \quad \text{or} \quad \frac{x'^2}{9} + \frac{y'^2}{4} = 1.$$

The locus is an ellipse, which is sketched in Fig. 10–38. The $x'y'$-coordinates of the vertices are at $(\pm 3, 0)$, and the foci are at $(\pm\sqrt{5}, 0)$. The eccentricity is $\sqrt{5}/3$; the directrices are the lines $x' = \pm 9/\sqrt{5}$. In the original system, the vertices are at $(3/\sqrt{5}, 6/\sqrt{5})$, $(-3/\sqrt{5}, -6/\sqrt{5})$. The foci are at $(1, 2)$, $(-1, -2)$. The directrices are the lines $x + 2y = \pm 9$.

In Example 2 the coefficients D and E are zero. When a problem arises with B, D, and E all different from zero, we may eliminate them by performing in succession a rotation (eliminating B) and a translation (eliminating the D and E terms). Here we have an example of the way processes develop in mathematics: a complicated structure is erected by combining simple building blocks. The technique of performing several transformations in succession occurs frequently in mathematical problems.

EXAMPLE 3. Given the equation

$$2x^2 - 4xy - y^2 + 20x - 2y + 17 = 0.$$

Reduce the equation to standard form by eliminating B, D, and E. Identify the curve and locate the vertices and foci.

Solution. We choose θ so that

$$\cot 2\theta = \frac{A - C}{B} = \frac{2 + 1}{-4} = -\frac{3}{4}.$$

This puts 2θ in the second quadrant and $\cos 2\theta = -\frac{3}{5}$ and, as in Example 2, $\cos \theta = \sqrt{\frac{1}{5}}$,

$\sin \theta = \sqrt{\frac{4}{5}}$. The rotation is

$$x = \frac{1}{\sqrt{5}}(x' - 2y'), \qquad y = \frac{1}{\sqrt{5}}(2x' + y').$$

Substituting into the given equation, we obtain

$$\frac{2}{5}(x' - 2y')^2 - \frac{4}{5}(x' - 2y')(2x' + y') - \frac{1}{5}(2x' + y')^2$$
$$+ \frac{20}{\sqrt{5}}(x' - 2y') - \frac{2}{\sqrt{5}}(2x' + y') + 17 = 0.$$

Simplification yields

$$2x'^2 - 3y'^2 - \frac{16}{\sqrt{5}}x' + \frac{42}{\sqrt{5}}y' - 17 = 0,$$

which we recognize as a hyperbola. To eliminate the coefficients of x' and y', we proceed as in the preceding section and translate the coordinates. Completing the square is the standard method, and we write

$$2\left(x'^2 - \frac{8}{\sqrt{5}}x' \qquad\right) - 3\left(y'^2 - \frac{14}{\sqrt{5}}y' \qquad\right) = 17.$$

Then we have

$$2\left(x'^2 - \frac{8}{\sqrt{5}}x' + \frac{16}{5}\right) - 3\left(y'^2 - \frac{14}{\sqrt{5}}y' + \frac{49}{5}\right) = 17 + \frac{32}{5} - \frac{147}{5},$$

and

$$2\left(x' - \frac{4}{\sqrt{5}}\right)^2 - 3\left(y' - \frac{7}{\sqrt{5}}\right)^2 = -6.$$

The translation of axes is read off from this equation. It is

$$x'' = x' - \frac{4}{\sqrt{5}}, \qquad y'' = y' - \frac{7}{\sqrt{5}};$$

the equation becomes

$$\frac{y''^2}{2} - \frac{x''^2}{3} = 1.$$

Figure 10–39 shows the transformations. In the $x''y''$-system, the vertices are at $(0, \pm\sqrt{2})$ and the foci are at $(0, \pm\sqrt{5})$. This puts the vertices at $(4/\sqrt{5}, \pm\sqrt{2} + 7/\sqrt{5})$ and the foci at $(4/\sqrt{5}, \pm\sqrt{5} + 7/\sqrt{5})$ in the $x'y'$-system. Substituting in the equations

$$x = \frac{1}{\sqrt{5}}(x' - 2y') \qquad \text{and} \qquad y = \frac{1}{\sqrt{5}}(2x' + y'),$$

we get the vertices at

$$\left(-\frac{10 + 2\sqrt{10}}{5}, \frac{15 + \sqrt{10}}{5}\right), \qquad \left(\frac{-10 + 2\sqrt{10}}{5}, \frac{15 - \sqrt{10}}{5}\right),$$

and the foci at

$$(-4, 4), \qquad (0, 2),$$

in the xy-system.

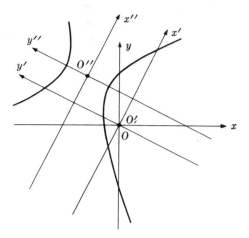

FIGURE 10–39

The next example illustrates a somewhat different situation.

EXAMPLE 4. Given the equation

$$4x^2 - 12xy + 9y^2 - 52x + 26y + 81 = 0,$$

reduce it to standard form by eliminating B, D, and E. Identify the curve and locate the principal quantities.

Solution. We first rotate and choose θ so that

$$\cot 2\theta = \frac{A - C}{B} = \frac{4 - 9}{-12} = \frac{5}{12}.$$

Then 2θ is in the first quadrant and $\cos 2\theta = \frac{5}{13}$. From the half-angle formulas (as in Example 2),

$$\cos \theta = \sqrt{\tfrac{9}{13}}, \qquad \sin \theta = \sqrt{\tfrac{4}{13}}.$$

The desired rotation of coordinates is

$$x = \frac{1}{\sqrt{13}} (3x' - 2y'), \qquad y = \frac{1}{\sqrt{13}} (2x' + 3y').$$

Substituting in the given equation, we obtain

$$\tfrac{4}{13}(9x'^2 - 12x'y' + 4y'^2) - \tfrac{12}{13}(6x'^2 + 5x'y' - 6y'^2)$$
$$+ \tfrac{9}{13}(4x'^2 + 12x'y' + 9y'^2) - 4\sqrt{13}(3x' - 2y')$$
$$+ 2\sqrt{13}(2x' + 3y') + 81 = 0,$$

and, after simplification,

$$13y'^2 - 8\sqrt{13}\, x' + 14\sqrt{13}\, y' + 81 = 0.$$

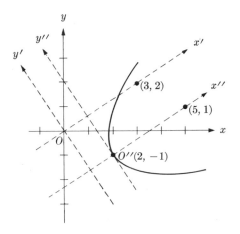

FIGURE 10–40

Note that in the process of eliminating the $x'y'$-term we also eliminated the x'^2-term. We now realize that the curve must be a parabola. To translate the coordinates properly, we complete the square in y. This yields

$$13(y'^2 + \tfrac{14}{13}\sqrt{13}\, y' \qquad) = 8\sqrt{13}\, x' - 81,$$

and

$$13\left(y' + \frac{7}{\sqrt{13}}\right)^2 = 8\sqrt{13}\left(x' - \frac{4}{\sqrt{13}}\right).$$

The translation of axes,

$$x'' = x' - \frac{4}{\sqrt{13}}, \qquad y'' = y' + \frac{7}{\sqrt{13}},$$

leads to the equation

$$y''^2 = \frac{8}{\sqrt{13}}\, x''.$$

In the $x''y''$-system, $p = 4/\sqrt{13}$, the vertex is at the origin, the focus is at $(2/\sqrt{13}, 0)$, the directrix is the line $x'' = -2/\sqrt{13}$, and the x''-axis is the axis of the parabola. In the $x'y'$-system, the focus is at $(6/\sqrt{13}, -7/\sqrt{13})$, and the directrix is the line $x' = 2/\sqrt{13}$. As for the original xy-system, we find that the focus is at $(\tfrac{32}{13}, -\tfrac{9}{13})$. The directrix is the line $3x + 2y = 2$. The parabola and all sets of axes are sketched in Fig. 10–40.

In the rotation of the coordinates, the general equation of the second degree,

$$Ax^2 + Bxy + Cy^2 + Dx + Ey + F = 0,$$

goes into the equation

$$A'x^2 + B'xy + C'y^2 + D'x + E'y + F = 0,$$

with

$$A' = A \cos^2 \theta + B \sin \theta \cos \theta + C \sin^2 \theta,$$
$$B' = 2(C - A) \sin \theta \cos \theta + B (\cos^2 \theta - \sin^2 \theta),$$
$$C' = A \sin^2 \theta - B \sin \theta \cos \theta + C \cos^2 \theta.$$

The quantity $A' + C'$, when calculated, is

$$A' + C' = A (\cos^2 \theta + \sin^2 \theta) + C (\sin^2 \theta + \cos^2 \theta) = A + C.$$

In other words, even though A changes to A' and C changes to C' when a rotation through *any* angle is made, the quantity $A + C$ does not change at all. We say that $A + C$ is *invariant* under a rotation of coordinates.

If we compute the expression $B'^2 - 4A'C'$ (a tedious computation) and use some trigonometry, we find that

$$B'^2 - 4A'C' = B^2 - 4AC.$$

In other words, $B^2 - 4AC$ is also an *invariant* under rotation of axes.

It can readily be checked that $A + C$ and $B^2 - 4AC$ are invariant under translation of axes, and therefore we can formulate the following theorem for *general equations of the second degree.*

Theorem 2. (a) *If* $B^2 - 4AC < 0$, *the curve is an ellipse, a circle, a point, or there is no curve.* (b) *If* $B^2 - 4AC > 0$, *the curve is a hyperbola or two intersecting straight lines.* (c) *If* $B^2 - 4AC = 0$, *the curve is a parabola, two parallel lines, one line, or there is no curve.*

The circle, ellipse, parabola, and hyperbola are often called *conic sections*, for all of them can be obtained as sections cut from a right circular cone by planes. The cone is thought of as extending indefinitely on both sides of its vertex; the part of the cone on one side of the vertex is called a *nappe*.

Ellipse Parabola Hyperbola

FIGURE 10–41

If the plane intersects only one nappe, as in Fig. 10–41(a), the curve of the intersection is an ellipse. (A circle is a special case of the ellipse, and occurs when the plane is perpendicular to the axis of the cone.) If the plane is parallel to one of the generators of the cone, the intersection is a parabola, as shown in Fig. 10–41(b). If the plane intersects both nappes, the curve is a hyperbola, one branch coming from each nappe, as in Fig. 10–41(c).

Certain degenerate cases also occur; the locus is two intersecting lines when the plane intersects both nappes and also passes through the vertex. If the plane contains one of the generators, the locus of the intersection is a single straight line. Finally, the locus is a single point if the plane contains the vertex and does not intersect either nappe of the cone. The degenerate locus of two parallel lines cannot be obtained as a plane section of a cone.

EXERCISES

In problems 1 through 12, in each case change from an xy-system to an $x'y'$-system such that the $x'y'$-term is missing. For the ellipses and hyperbolas, find the coordinates of the vertices. For each parabola find the xy-coordinates of the focus and the xy-equation of the directrix. If the locus consists of lines, find their xy-equations.

1. $x^2 + 4xy + 4y^2 = 9$
2. $7x^2 - 4xy + 4y^2 = 240$
3. $2x^2 + 3xy - 2y^2 = 25$
4. $7x^2 - 6xy - y^2 = 0$
5. $x^2 + 2xy + y^2 - 8x + 8y = 0$
6. $x^2 + 4xy + y^2 + 32 = 0$
7. $8x^2 + 12xy + 13y^2 = 884$
8. $x^2 - 4xy + 4y^2 - 40x - 20y = 0$
9. $x^2 - 2xy = 10$
10. $xy = 4$
11. $2xy - 3y^2 = 5$
12. $xy = -3$

In problems 13 through 22, in each case rotate the axes to an $x'y'$-system such that the $x'y'$-term is missing. Then translate the axes so that the first-degree terms are absent. Sketch the loci and identify the principal quantities.

13. $3x^2 + 10xy + 3y^2 - 2x - 14y - 5 = 0$
14. $4x^2 - 8xy - 2y^2 + 20x - 4y + 15 = 0$
15. $4x^2 + 4xy + y^2 - 24x + 38y - 139 = 0$
16. $16x^2 - 24xy + 9y^2 + 56x - 42y + 49 = 0$
17. $12x^2 + 24xy + 19y^2 - 12x - 40y + 31 = 0$
18. $4x^2 - 4\sqrt{5}\, xy + 5y^2 + 8x - 4\sqrt{5}\, y - 21 = 0$
19. $31x^2 + 10\sqrt{3}\, xy + 21y^2 - (124 - 40\sqrt{3})x + (168 - 20\sqrt{3})y + 316 - 80\sqrt{3} = 0$
20. $x^2 + 2xy + y^2 - 4x - 4y + 4 = 0$
21. $x^2 - \sqrt{3}\, xy + 3x - 2y - 5 = 0$
22. $3xy - 4y^2 + x - 2y + 1 = 0$
23. Prove that a second-degree equation with an xy-term in it can never represent a circle.
24. Prove that $B^2 - 4AC$ is invariant under rotation and translation of axes.
25. Given the transformation of coordinates

$$x' = ax + by, \qquad y' = cx + dy,$$

with a, b, c, and d numbers such that $ad - bc$ is positive. If the general equation of the second degree undergoes such a transformation, what can be said about $B^2 - 4AC$?

CHAPTER 11

The Trigonometric
and Exponential Functions

1. SOME SPECIAL LIMITS

In Chapter 4 we learned several techniques for evaluating the limits of various algebraic expressions. We shall now employ a new device for finding the limit in a special case. We consider the function

$$f(\theta) = \frac{\sin \theta}{\theta}$$

and suppose that θ is measured in *radians*. This function is defined for all values of θ except $\theta = 0$. Since $\sin 0 = 0$, straight substitution gives $f(0) = 0/0$, a meaningless expression. Nevertheless, we can find the value of

$$\lim_{\theta \to 0} \frac{\sin \theta}{\theta}.$$

We shall start by supposing that θ is positive and less than $\pi/2$. Figure 11-1 shows a typical value of θ. We draw an arc $\widehat{IP}$ of a circle of radius 1 and construct the perpendiculars $\overline{PQ}$ and $\overline{TI}$, as shown. From this figure, it is obvious that

$$\text{area } \triangle IOP < \text{area sector } IOP < \text{area } \triangle IOT.$$

Since $\overline{OI} = \overline{OP} = 1$, we have

$$\text{area } \triangle IOP = \tfrac{1}{2}\overline{PQ} \cdot \overline{OI} = \tfrac{1}{2}\overline{PQ};$$
$$\text{area sector } IOP = \tfrac{1}{2}\theta r^2 = \tfrac{1}{2}\theta \quad (\theta \text{ in radians});$$
$$\text{area } \triangle IOT = \tfrac{1}{2}\overline{IT} \cdot \overline{OI} = \tfrac{1}{2}\overline{IT}.$$

On the other hand, we know that

$$\sin \theta = \frac{\overline{PQ}}{\overline{OP}} = \overline{PQ}; \qquad \tan \theta = \frac{\overline{IT}}{\overline{OI}} = \overline{IT}.$$

Therefore the above area inequalities are the same as the inequalities

$$\tfrac{1}{2}\sin \theta < \tfrac{1}{2}\theta < \tfrac{1}{2}\tan \theta.$$

We multiply by 2 and divide by $\sin \theta$. (This keeps the same direction for the

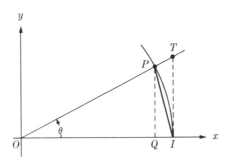

FIGURE 11–1

inequalities, since everything is positive.) We obtain

$$1 < \frac{\theta}{\sin \theta} < \frac{1}{\cos \theta}.$$

Now we take reciprocals; this has the effect of reversing the direction. (Recall that if a and b are any positive numbers and $a > b$, then $1/a < 1/b$.) We conclude that

$$1 > \frac{\sin \theta}{\theta} > \cos \theta.$$

As θ tends to zero, we know that $\cos \theta \to 1$. Since $\sin \theta/\theta$ is always between 1 and a number tending to 1, it also must approach 1 as θ approaches zero. In the proof we considered θ positive, but now we note that $f(\theta) = \sin \theta/\theta$ is an *even* function of θ. For, if we replace θ by $-\theta$, we have

$$f(-\theta) = \frac{\sin (-\theta)}{-\theta} = \frac{-\sin \theta}{-\theta} = \frac{\sin \theta}{\theta} = f(\theta).$$

Therefore, as $\theta \to 0$ through negative values, the result must be identical with the one obtained when $\theta \to 0$ through positive values. The above development gives the following result.

Theorem 1. *If θ is measured in radians, then*

$$\lim_{\theta \to 0} \frac{\sin \theta}{\theta} = 1.$$

Corollary.

$$\lim_{\theta \to 0} \frac{1 - \cos \theta}{\theta} = 0.$$

Proof. This result may be obtained from Theorem 1 by using the identity

$$\frac{1 - \cos \theta}{\theta} = \frac{(1 - \cos \theta)(1 + \cos \theta)}{\theta(1 + \cos \theta)} = \frac{\sin^2 \theta}{\theta(1 + \cos \theta)} = \frac{\sin \theta}{\theta} \cdot \frac{\sin \theta}{1 + \cos \theta}.$$

We know that

$$\lim_{\theta \to 0} \frac{\sin \theta}{\theta} = 1 \quad \text{and} \quad \lim_{\theta \to 0} \frac{\sin \theta}{1 + \cos \theta} = 0,$$

since the second limit may be obtained by straight substitution. From the fact that the limit of a product is the product of the limits, we obtain the result given by the corollary.

EXAMPLE 1. Find the value of

$$\lim_{\theta \to 0} \frac{\sin 2\theta}{\theta},$$

θ measured in radians.

Solution. We write

$$\frac{\sin 2\theta}{\theta} = \frac{2 \sin (2\theta)}{(2\theta)}.$$

Therefore

$$\lim_{\theta \to 0} \frac{\sin 2\theta}{\theta} = 2 \lim_{(2\theta) \to 0} \frac{\sin (2\theta)}{(2\theta)} = 2 \cdot 1.$$

We made use of the fact that when $\theta \to 0$, so does 2θ.

EXAMPLE 2. Find the value of

$$\lim_{\alpha \to 0} \frac{\sin \alpha}{\alpha},$$

α measured in degrees.

Solution. The functions $\sin \alpha$ and $\sin \pi\alpha/180$ have the same values, one being measured in degrees and the other in radians. We have

$$\lim_{\alpha \to 0} \frac{\sin \alpha}{\alpha} = \lim_{\alpha \to 0} \frac{\pi}{180} \frac{\sin \dfrac{\pi\alpha}{180}}{\dfrac{\pi\alpha}{180}} = \frac{\pi}{180} \lim_{\frac{\pi\alpha}{180} \to 0} \frac{\sin \dfrac{\pi\alpha}{180}}{\dfrac{\pi\alpha}{180}} = \frac{\pi}{180}.$$

Example 2 exhibits one of the reasons why radian measure is used throughout calculus. The limit of $\sin \theta/\theta$ is 1 if θ is measured in radians and $\pi/180$ if θ is measured in degrees. In the following section we shall see why the first is highly preferable to the second.

2. THE DIFFERENTIATION OF TRIGONOMETRIC FUNCTIONS

With the help of the limits obtained in the preceding section, we can find the derivatives of all the trigonometric functions.

Theorem 2. *If $f(x) = \sin x$, then $f'(x) = \cos x$.*

Proof. We can apply the five-step rule.

Step 1: $f(x) = \sin x$.

Step 2: $f(x + h) = \sin (x + h)$.

Step 3: $f(x + h) - f(x) = \sin (x + h) - \sin x$.

Step 4: $\dfrac{f(x + h) - f(x)}{h} = \dfrac{\sin (x + h) - \sin x}{h}.$

As usual, it is at this point that we must employ ingenuity. We first use the fact that $\sin (x + h) = \sin x \cos h + \cos x \sin h$ and write

$$\frac{f(x + h) - f(x)}{h} = \frac{\sin x \cos h + \cos x \sin h - \sin x}{h}$$

$$= \cos x \frac{\sin h}{h} + \sin x \frac{\cos h - 1}{h}.$$

Then, taking the limit as $h \to 0$, we use the theorem and corollary of the preceding section to perform *Step* 5 and conclude that

$$f'(x) = \lim_{h \to 0} \frac{f(x + h) - f(x)}{h} = \cos x.$$

The simplicity of the result — that the derivative of $\sin x$ is $\cos x$ — is due to the use of radians. If, for example, degrees were used, then $\lim_{h \to 0} (\sin h/h)$ would be $\pi/180$, and all the derivative formulas for trigonometric functions would have an extra, inconvenient factor in them. Later, we shall see that a similar situation occurs in the study of logarithms.

Suppose that u is a function of x; that is, $u = u(x)$. Then, by using the chain rule, we easily find the formula for the derivative of $\sin u$. If we write

$$y = \sin u,$$

then

$$\frac{dy}{dx} = \cos u \frac{du}{dx}.$$

In differentials this becomes

$$d \sin u = \cos u \, du.$$

EXAMPLE 1. Find the derivative of $y = \sin (3x^2 - 6x + 1)$.

Solution. Taking $u = 3x^2 - 6x + 1$, we obtain

$$\frac{dy}{dx} = \cos (3x^2 - 6x + 1) \cdot (6x - 6) = 6(x - 1) \cos (3x^2 - 6x + 1).$$

Theorem 3. *If* $f(x) = \cos x$, *then* $f'(x) = -\sin x$.

Proof. This result can be obtained by the five-step rule. A simpler method results from writing

$$f(x) = \cos x = \sin \left(\frac{\pi}{2} - x\right).$$

Then

$$f'(x) = \frac{d}{dx} \sin \left(\frac{\pi}{2} - x\right) = \cos \left(\frac{\pi}{2} - x\right)(-1), \quad \text{since} \quad \frac{d}{dx} \left(\frac{\pi}{2} - x\right) = -1.$$

Therefore

$$f'(x) = -\cos \left(\frac{\pi}{2} - x\right) = -\sin x.$$

The chain rule again shows that if

$$y = \cos u, \qquad \text{then} \qquad \frac{dy}{dx} = -\sin u \, \frac{du}{dx}$$

and, in differentials,

$$d \cos u = -\sin u \, du.$$

With the help of the derivatives of the sine and cosine functions, we may find the derivatives of the remaining trigonometric functions. The following example shows the method.

EXAMPLE 2. Find the derivative of $y = \tan x$.

Solution. We write

$$y = \frac{\sin x}{\cos x}$$

and use the formula for the derivative of a quotient. We have

$$\frac{dy}{dx} = \frac{\cos x \, (\cos x) - \sin x \, (-\sin x)}{\cos^2 x}.$$

This yields

$$\frac{dy}{dx} = \frac{1}{\cos^2 x} = \sec^2 x.$$

The formulas for differentiating trigonometric functions are summarized in the following table (expressed in terms of differentials):

$$d \sin u = \cos u \, du \qquad\qquad d \cot u = -\csc^2 u \, du$$
$$d \cos u = -\sin u \, du \qquad\qquad d \sec u = \sec u \tan u \, du$$
$$d \tan u = \sec^2 u \, du \qquad\qquad d \csc u = -\csc u \cot u \, du$$

The general rules for differentiating polynomials and rational functions, together with the formulas for products and quotients, open up vast possibilities for differentiating complicated expressions. The succeeding examples show some of the ramifications.

EXAMPLE 3. Given that $f(x) = \sin^3 x$, find $f'(x)$.

Solution. $f(x) = (\sin x)^3$, and so

$$f'(x) = 3 \, (\sin x)^2 \cdot \frac{d \, (\sin x)}{dx} = 3 \sin^2 x \cos x.$$

EXAMPLE 4. Given that $y = \tan^4 (2x + 1)$, find dy/dx.

Solution. $y = [\tan (2x + 1)]^4$;

$$\frac{dy}{dx} = 4 \, [\tan (2x + 1)]^3 \cdot \frac{d}{dx} \tan (2x + 1).$$

But

$$\frac{d}{dx} \tan (2x + 1) = \sec^2 (2x + 1) \cdot \frac{d}{dx} (2x + 1) = \sec^2 (2x + 1) \cdot (2).$$

Therefore

$$\frac{dy}{dx} = 4 \tan^3 (2x + 1) \cdot 2 \sec^2 (2x + 1) = 8 \tan^3 (2x + 1) \sec^2 (2x + 1).$$

EXAMPLE 5. Given that $f(x) = x^3 \sec^2 3x$, find $f'(x)$.

Solution. $f(x) = x^3 [\sec (3x)]^2$. We see that this is in the form of a product, and write

$$f'(x) = x^3 \cdot 2 [\sec (3x)] \frac{d}{dx} (\sec 3x) + [\sec (3x)]^2 \cdot 3x^2$$

$$= 2x^3 \sec 3x \cdot \left[\sec 3x \tan 3x \cdot \frac{d(3x)}{dx} \right] + 3x^2 \sec^2 3x$$

$$= 3x^2 (\sec^2 3x)(2x \tan 3x + 1).$$

EXAMPLE 6. Given that $v = \sin^3 (s/2) \cos^2 (s/2)$, find dv/ds.

Solution. This is in the form of a product of $\sin^3 (s/2)$ and $\cos^2 (s/2)$. We use differentials and write

$$dv = \left(\sin^3 \frac{s}{2} \right) \cdot 2 \cos \frac{s}{2} d \left(\cos \frac{s}{2} \right) + \left(\cos^2 \frac{s}{2} \right) \cdot 3 \sin^2 \frac{s}{2} d \left(\sin \frac{s}{2} \right) \cdot$$

But

$$d \left(\cos \frac{s}{2} \right) = -\sin \frac{s}{2} \cdot \frac{1}{2} ds,$$

$$d \left(\sin \frac{s}{2} \right) = \cos \frac{s}{2} \cdot \frac{1}{2} ds,$$

and therefore

$$\frac{dv}{ds} = -\sin^4 \frac{s}{2} \cos \frac{s}{2} + \frac{3}{2} \sin^2 \frac{s}{2} \cos^3 \frac{s}{2} \cdot$$

EXERCISES

In problems 1 through 12, evaluate the limits.

1. $\displaystyle\lim_{h \to 0} \frac{\sin 3h}{h}$

2. $\displaystyle\lim_{\theta \to 0} \frac{\sin 2\sqrt{\theta}}{\sqrt{\theta}}$

3. $\displaystyle\lim_{h \to 0} \frac{\sin 4h}{\sin 7h}$ (*Hint:* Multiply and divide by h.)

4. $\displaystyle\lim_{h \to 0} \frac{\tan h}{h}$

5. $\displaystyle\lim_{x \to 0} \frac{1 - \cos x}{2x^2}$

6. $\displaystyle\lim_{\theta \to 0} \frac{\theta}{\cos \theta}$

7. $\displaystyle\lim_{\phi \to 0} \frac{1}{\phi \cot \phi}$

8. $\displaystyle\lim_{\theta \to \pi/2} \frac{\cos \theta}{(\pi/2) - \theta}$

9. $\displaystyle\lim_{x \to 0} \frac{x}{\csc^2 x}$

10. $\displaystyle\lim_{x \to 0} \frac{\cot^2 x}{4x^2}$

11. $\displaystyle\lim_{x \to 0} \frac{x^3}{\tan^3 2x}$

12. $\displaystyle\lim_{x \to 0} \frac{4x^3}{1 - \cos^2 \frac{1}{2}x}$

In problems 13 through 38, differentiate the trigonometric functions.

13. $f(x) = \tan 3x$

14. $g(y) = 2 \sin y \cos y$

15. $f(s) = \sec (s^2)$

16. $\phi(t) = \sin^2 3t$

17. $f(y) = \csc^3 \frac{1}{3}y$

18. $g(x) = \sin 2x - \frac{1}{3}(\sin^3 2x)$

19. $f(x) = 2x + \cot 2x$

20. $h(u) = u \sin u + \cos u$

21. $x(s) = \sqrt{\tan 2s}$

22. $h(t) = \sec^2 2t - \tan^2 2t$

23. $f(x) = x^2 \tan^2 (x/2)$

24. $g(x) = (\tan^3 4x)/3 + \tan 4x$

25. $f(x) = \frac{1}{3}(\sec^3 2x) - \sec 2x$

26. $f(x) = \sqrt{1 + \cos x}$

27. $f(x) = (\sin 2x)/x^2$

28. $f(x) = (\sin 2x)/x^5$

29. $f(x) = (\cos^2 3x)/(1 + x^2)$

30. $f(x) = \sin^3 2x \tan^2 3x$

31. $f(x) = \cos^2 3x \csc^3 2x$

32. $f(x) = (\sin 2x)/(1 + \cos 2x)$

33. $f(x) = (\cot^2 ax)/(1 + x^2)$

34. $f(x) = (1 + \tan 3x)^{2/3}$

35. $f(x) = (1 + \sin^2 2x)^{1/2}$

36. $f(x) = \sin nx \sin^n x$

37. $f(x) = \sin (\cos x)$

38. $f(x) = \dfrac{\cot (x/2)}{\sqrt{1 - \cot^2 (x/2)}}$

39. $f(x) = \dfrac{(1 + \cos^2 3x)^{1/3}}{(1 + x^2)^{1/2}}$

40. If $f(x) = \cos x$ prove, by using the five-step rule, that $f'(x) = -\sin x$.

41. Prove that if $f(x) = \cot x$, then $f'(x) = -\csc^2 x$.

42. Prove that if $f(x) = \sec x$, then $f'(x) = \sec x \tan x$.

43. Prove that if $f(x) = \csc x$, then $f'(x) = -\csc x \cot x$.

3. INTEGRATION OF TRIGONOMETRIC FUNCTIONS

Every differentiation formula automatically gives us a corresponding integration formula. From our knowledge of the derivatives of the trigonometric functions, we obtain at once the following indefinite integral formulas:

$$\int \cos u \, du = \sin u + c,$$

$$\int \sin u \, du = -\cos u + c,$$

$$\int \sec^2 u \, du = \tan u + c,$$

$$\int \csc^2 u \, du = -\cot u + c,$$

$$\int \sec u \tan u \, du = \sec u + c,$$

$$\int \csc u \cot u \, du = -\csc u + c.$$

In the above formulas u may be any function of x, and du is the differential of u. These formulas may be combined with the methods of integration of Chapter 8, Section 7, to help us integrate a wide variety of functions. We shall illustrate the technique with some examples.

EXAMPLE 1. Find the value of $\int \sin 4x \, dx$.

Solution. We let $u = 4x$ and $du = 4 \, dx$. Then the above integral becomes

$$\int \sin u \cdot \tfrac{1}{4} \, du = \tfrac{1}{4} \int \sin u \, du = -\tfrac{1}{4} \cos u + c = -\tfrac{1}{4} \cos 4x + c.$$

EXAMPLE 2. Find the value of

$$\int \tan^2 (2x - 3) \, dx.$$

Solution. This does not seem to fit any of the formulas for integration until we recall the trigonometric identity $1 + \tan^2 \theta = \sec^2 \theta$. Then the above integral becomes

$$\int [\sec^2 (2x - 3) - 1] \, dx = \int \sec^2 (2x - 3) \, dx - \int dx.$$

We now let $u = 2x - 3$, $du = 2 \, dx$, and the first integral becomes

$$\int \sec^2 u \cdot \tfrac{1}{2} \, du = \tfrac{1}{2} \int \sec^2 u \, du = \tfrac{1}{2} \tan u + c = \tfrac{1}{2} \tan (2x - 3) + c.$$

The second integral gives us merely $x + c$ and so, combining the constants of integration, we have

$$\int \tan^2 (2x - 3) \, dx = \tfrac{1}{2} \tan (2x - 3) - x + c.$$

EXAMPLE 3. Find the value of $\int \sin^3 x \, dx$.

Solution. We again make use of trigonometric identities and write

$$\sin^3 x = \sin x \sin^2 x = \sin x (1 - \cos^2 x) = \sin x - \sin x \cos^2 x.$$

Therefore

$$\int \sin^3 x \, dx = \int \sin x \, dx - \int \sin x \cos^2 x \, dx.$$

The first integral is easy and gives us $-\cos x + c$. The second integral is a little harder but still manageable, if we let $u = \cos x$. Then $du = -\sin x \, dx$, and we obtain

$$\int \sin x \cos^2 x \, dx = -\int u^2 \, du = -\tfrac{1}{3} u^3 + c = -\tfrac{1}{3} \cos^3 x + c.$$

The final result is

$$\int \sin^3 x \, dx = -\cos x + \tfrac{1}{3} \cos^3 x + c.$$

EXERCISES

In the following problems, perform the integrations.

1. $\displaystyle\int \sin 7x \, dx$ 2. $\displaystyle\int \cos 8t \, dt$ 3. $\displaystyle\int \sec^2 \left(\frac{x - 5}{2} \right) dx$

4. $\displaystyle\int \sec (3 - x) \tan (3 - x) \, dx$ 5. $\displaystyle\int \frac{\cos 2x}{\sin^2 2x} \, dx$

6. $\displaystyle\int \frac{\sin 3x}{\cos^2 3x}\, dx$ 7. $\displaystyle\int \cot^2 (2x - 6)\, dx$ 8. $\displaystyle\int \cos^3 2x\, dx$

9. $\displaystyle\int \sin^5 x\, dx$ 10. $\displaystyle\int \cos^5 x\, dx$ 11. $\displaystyle\int x \sin (x^2)\, dx$

12. $\displaystyle\int x^2 \sec^2 (4x^3)\, dx$ 13. $\displaystyle\int \frac{\sin x\, dx}{\cos^5 x}$ 14. $\displaystyle\int \cos^6 2x \sin 2x\, dx$

15. $\displaystyle\int \tan^5 x \sec^2 x\, dx$ 16. $\displaystyle\int \csc^7 2x \cot 2x\, dx$ 17. $\displaystyle\int \frac{\csc^2 (3 - 2x)}{\cot^4 (3 - 2x)}\, dx$

18. $\displaystyle\int \cos^2 \tfrac{1}{2} x\, dx$ (*Hint:* Use half-angle formula.)   19. $\displaystyle\int \sin^2 3x\, dx$

20. $\displaystyle\int \sin^4 x\, dx$

4. RELATIONS AND INVERSE FUNCTIONS

The equation

$$y^2 - x^2 = 1$$

defines a *relation* between x and y. The variable y is not a *function* of x, since (as is evident in Fig. 11–2) for each value of x there are two values of y. Nor is x a function of y, because for each value of y larger than 1 or less than -1 there correspond two values of x. As we know, the functional relation requires that exactly *one* value of the dependent variable correspond to a single value of the independent variable.

The equation

$$y = (x - 2)^2$$

also defines a relation between x and y. In this case, however, y is a function of x. To each value of x there corresponds exactly one value of y. But x is not a function of y, because to each positive value of y there correspond two values of x (Fig. 11–3).

FIGURE 11–2   FIGURE 11–3

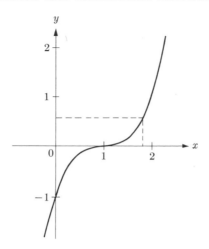

FIGURE 11–4

A relation such as

$$y = (x - 1)^3$$

expresses y as a function of x; also, if we solve for x and write

$$x = 1 + \sqrt[3]{y},$$

we see that to each value of y there corresponds exactly one value of x. Therefore x is a function of y. Thinking of y as a function of x, we write

$$y = f(x) = (x - 1)^3.$$

On the other hand, thinking of x as a function of y, we could write

$$x = g(y) = 1 + \sqrt[3]{y}.$$

The relation is shown in Fig. 11–4. The functions f and g are called *inverse functions*, and we also say that *g is the function inverse to f* and *f is the function inverse to g*. To express this symbolically, we introduce a new notation by writing

$$x = f^{-1}(y)$$

for the function inverse to f. The quantity -1 is to be thought of not as an exponent but as a special symbol standing for "inverse." There is a certain danger of confusing this new symbol with the exponent -1, but the meaning will always be clear from the context.

The example of a function and its inverse shown in Fig. 11–4 is typical of a much more general situation. Intuitively we see that if a function f is steadily increasing as we move from left to right along the x-axis, then to each point on the y-axis in the range of the function there can correspond but one value of x. This means that the function has an inverse (at least in the interval when f is increasing). A similar statement holds if the function is decreasing. [See Figs. 11–5(a) and 11–5(b)].

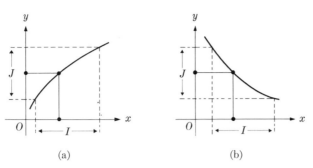

(a) (b)

FIGURE 11–5

A proof of the following theorem is given in Morrey, *University Calculus,* Section 11–4.

Theorem 4. (Inverse function theorem.) *Assume that a function f has an interval I as its domain, is continuous and increasing (or decreasing) on I, and has the range J. (See Fig. 11–5.) Then J is an interval and the function f has a continuous inverse function g with domain J and range I.*
We have

$$g[f(x)] = x \qquad \text{for } x \text{ on } I,$$

and

$$f[g(y)] = y \qquad \text{for } y \text{ on } J.$$

EXAMPLE 1. Given the function

$$y = f(x) = \frac{x}{1 + x^2} \qquad \text{for } 1 < x < \infty.$$

Determine the range of this function and decide whether or not it has an inverse.

Solution. We first compute the derivative of f:

$$y' = \frac{1 - x^2}{(1 + x^2)^2}.$$

Since the derivative is negative for $1 < x < \infty$, the function is decreasing. We have $f(1) = \frac{1}{2}$ and $\lim_{x \to \infty} f(x) = 0$. Therefore the range of the function is $0 < y < \frac{1}{2}$. By the Inverse Function Theorem we know that

$$x = f^{-1}(y)$$

is the inverse function with domain the interval $(0, \frac{1}{2})$ and range $(1, \infty)$. In fact, solving for x in terms of y, we write

$$yx^2 - x + y = 0,$$

and find that

$$x = \frac{1 + \sqrt{1 - 4y^2}}{2y}.$$

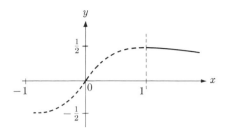

FIGURE 11–6

The plus sign is selected in order to obtain the proper branch. (See Fig. 11–6.)

EXAMPLE 2. Given the function

$$y = f(x) = \frac{x^5 + 2x}{1 + x^5}$$

defined for $-\infty < x < -1$. Decide whether or not this function has an inverse. Does the function have an inverse if the domain is $0 \le x < \infty$?

Solution. We calculate the derivative, obtaining

$$\frac{dy}{dx} = \frac{2 + 5x^4 - 8x^5}{(1 + x^5)^2}.$$

This derivative is positive for all values of x in the interval $-\infty < x < -1$, and therefore the function does have an inverse. The derivative is positive for $x = 0$ and negative for large values of x, since the term $-8x^5$ dominates. Therefore the Inverse Function Theorem fails if x is in $(0, \infty)$. To show that the function does not have an inverse, we set y equal to some value, say y_0, in the range and show that there are two or more values of x corresponding to this particular value of y. We must therefore solve for x the fifth-degree equation

$$y_0(1 + x^5) = x^5 + 2x,$$

which can be done numerically. If $y_0 = \frac{3}{2}$, we obtain $x = 1$ and $x = 0.897$, approximately.

EXERCISES

For each of the following functions f, determine whether or not there is an inverse g. If there is, determine the domain of g.

1. $f(x) = 3x + 2$, $\quad -\infty < x < \infty$
2. $f(x) = x^2 + 2x - 3$, $\quad 0 \le x < \infty$
3. $f(x) = x^3 + 4x - 5$, $\quad -\infty < x < \infty$
4. $f(x) = \dfrac{x}{x + 1}$, $\quad -1 < x < \infty$
5. $f(x) = 3 - 2x - x^2$, $\quad -\infty < x < 0$
6. $f(x) = 3 - 2x - x^2$, $\quad -5 < x < 1$
7. $f(x) = 3 - 2x - x^2$, $\quad 0 < x < \infty$

8. $f(x) = \dfrac{x^2}{(x+1)^2}$, $-2 < x < 2$

9 $f(x) = \dfrac{1}{x^2}$, $0 < x \le 1$

10. $f(x) = \dfrac{2+x}{2-x}$, $0 \le x < 2$

For each of the following functions f, find a domain, if any, for which the Inverse Function Theorem applies. Find the inverse function g and give its domain if possible.

11. $f(x) = x^2 + 4x - 1$ 12. $f(x) = 6x - x^2$

13. $f(x) = 2x^2 + 3x + 4$ 14. $f(x) = 5x + 6 - 2x^2$

15. $f(x) = \dfrac{x}{x+1}$ 16. $f(x) = \dfrac{2x}{1+x^2}$

17. $f(x) = \dfrac{2x-1}{x+2}$ 18. $f(x) = x + \dfrac{1}{x}$

19. $f(x) = x^3 + 3x^2 - 9x + 7$ 20. $f(x) = 2x^3 + 3x^2 - 3x$

21. $f(x) = x^3 + 3x^2 + 6x - 3$ 22. $f(x) = x^4 + \tfrac{4}{3}x^3 - 4x^2 + \tfrac{2}{3}$

5. THE INVERSE TRIGONOMETRIC FUNCTIONS

The relation

$$y = \sin x$$

expresses y as a function of x but does not give x as a function of y. We observe that if we give y the value $\tfrac{1}{2}$, there correspond the values

$$x = \begin{cases} \dfrac{\pi}{6}, \dfrac{5\pi}{6}, \dfrac{13\pi}{6}, \dfrac{17\pi}{6}, \dots, \\[2ex] -\dfrac{7\pi}{6}, -\dfrac{11\pi}{6}, -\dfrac{19\pi}{6}, -\dfrac{23\pi}{6}, \dots \end{cases}$$

This property is exhibited in Fig. 11–7, which shows that the line $y = \tfrac{1}{2}$ intersects the curve of $y = \sin x$ infinitely often. If we restrict our considerations to the interval along the x-axis from $-\pi/2$ to $+\pi/2$, we note that the function $y = \sin x$ is steadily increasing. With this fact in mind, we apply the Inverse Function Theorem of Section 4 to $y = \sin x$, for x restricted to the interval $[-\pi/2, \pi/2]$, and

FIGURE 11–7

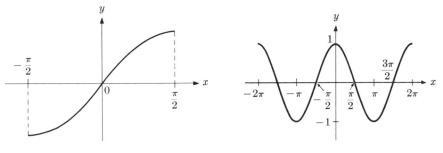

FIGURE 11–8   FIGURE 11–9

conclude that there is an inverse function. Figure 11–8 shows the relation between $f(x) = \sin x$ and $f^{-1}(y)$, the inverse function.

There are several notations for this inverse function, of which

$$\sin^{-1} y \quad \text{and} \quad \arcsin y$$

are the most common. We read them "inverse sine of y," "arc sine of y," or sometimes "the angle whose sine is y."

The restriction of the values of the angle to the interval $[-\pi/2, \pi/2]$ (or an equivalent interval) is essential if we are to get an inverse function. The values of x in the interval $-\pi/2 \le x \le \pi/2$ are frequently called the *principal values of the sine function.*

The graph of the function

$$y = \cos x$$

is shown in Fig. 11–9. This function is decreasing for x in the interval $[0, \pi]$. With x restricted to this domain, the cosine function has an inverse. We use the expressions

$$\cos^{-1} y \quad \text{and} \quad \arccos y$$

to denote this inverse function. The angles in the interval $0 \le x \le \pi$ are called the *principal values of the cosine function.*

In defining inverse trigonometric functions we always specify x as the independent variable and y as the dependent variable. For example, in the graph of

$$y = \arcsin x$$

(Fig. 11–10) the domain of the function is seen to be the interval $-1 \le x \le 1$ and the range, the interval $-\pi/2 \le y \le \pi/2$.

DEFINITIONS. We define:
(i)   arcsin x as the number y for which $-\pi/2 \le y \le \pi/2$ and $\sin y = x$, $|x| \le 1$ (Fig. 11–10).
(ii)   arccos x as the number y for which $0 \le y \le \pi$ and $\cos y = x$, $|x| \le 1$ (Fig. 11–11).
(iii) arctan x as the number y for which $-\pi/2 < y < \pi/2$ and $\tan y = x$ (Fig. 11–12).

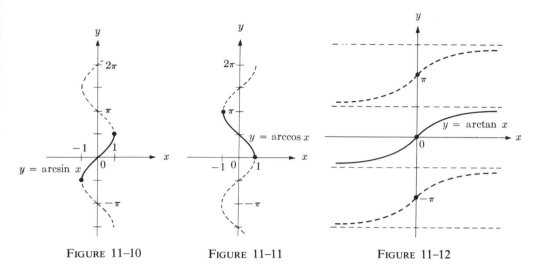

FIGURE 11–10   FIGURE 11–11   FIGURE 11–12

(iv) arccot x as the number y for which $0 < y < \pi$ and $\cot y = x$ (Fig. 11–13).

(v) for $x \geq 1$, arcsec x as the number y such that $0 \leq y < \pi/2$ and $\sec y = x$; for $x \leq -1$ arcsec x as the number y such that $-\pi \leq y < -\pi/2$ and $\sec y = x$ (Fig. 11–14).

(vi) for $x \geq 1$, arccsc x as the number y such that $0 < y \leq \pi/2$ and $\csc y = x$; for $x \leq -1$, arccsc x as the number y such that $-\pi < y \leq -\pi/2$ and $\csc y = x$ (Fig. 11–15).

To sum up, we have:

(a) the values of arcsin x and arctan x are between $-\pi/2$ and $\pi/2$;

(b) the values of arccos x and arccot x are between 0 and π;

(c) the values of arcsec x and arccsc x are between 0 and $\pi/2$ if $x \geq 1$ and between $-\pi$ and $-\pi/2$ if $x \leq -1$.

FIGURE 11–13   FIGURE 11–14

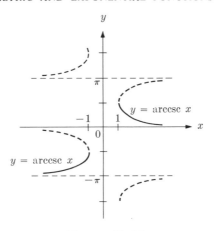

FIGURE 11–15

EXAMPLE 1. Evaluate (a) arcsin $\frac{1}{2}$, (b) arccot (-1), (c) arctan $(-\sqrt{3})$, (d) arcsec (-2).

Solution. (a) We set $y = $ arcsin $\frac{1}{2}$, and this gives us sin $y = \frac{1}{2}$ or $y = \pi/6$. In the same way we have (b) arccot $(-1) = 3\pi/4$ and (c) arctan $(-\sqrt{3}) = -\pi/3$. As for (d), by setting $y = $ arcsec (-2), we obtain sec $y = -2$, and y must be in the third quadrant. Therefore $y = -2\pi/3$ (cos $y = -\frac{1}{2}, y = -120°$).

The following theorems tell us how to find the derivatives of the inverse trigonometric functions.

Theorem 5. *Let $y = $ arcsin x. Then*

$$\frac{dy}{dx} = \frac{1}{\sqrt{1 - x^2}} \qquad \text{if } -1 < x < 1.$$

Proof. From the definition of inverse trigonometric functions, we have

$$\sin y = x, \qquad -\frac{\pi}{2} < y < \frac{\pi}{2}.$$

By the Chain Rule for Derivatives, we get

$$\cos y \cdot \frac{dy}{dx} = 1,$$

and we note that cos $y > 0$ so long as y is in the interval $(-\pi/2, \pi/2)$. Therefore, from the relation

$$\sin^2 y + \cos^2 y = 1,$$

we conclude that

$$\cos y = +\sqrt{1 - \sin^2 y}, \qquad -\frac{\pi}{2} < y < \frac{\pi}{2},$$

or

$$\cos y = \sqrt{1 - x^2}.$$

Therefore

$$\frac{dy}{dx} = \frac{1}{\cos y} = \frac{1}{\sqrt{1 - x^2}}.$$

Theorem 6. *If* $y = \arccos x$, *then*

$$\frac{dy}{dx} = -\frac{1}{\sqrt{1 - x^2}}, \qquad -1 < x < 1.$$

Proof. We have

$$\cos y = x, \qquad 0 < y < \pi,$$

and by the Chain Rule for Derivatives,

$$-\sin y \, \frac{dy}{dx} = 1.$$

We see that $\sin y > 0$ for $0 < y < \pi$, and so

$$\sin y = +\sqrt{1 - \cos^2 y} = \sqrt{1 - x^2}, \qquad -1 < x < 1,$$

from which we conclude that

$$\frac{dy}{dx} = -\frac{1}{\sqrt{1 - x^2}}, \qquad -1 < x < 1.$$

The next two formulas for derivatives are established in a similar way.

Theorem 7. *If* $y = \arctan x$, *then*

$$\frac{dy}{dx} = \frac{1}{1 + x^2}.$$

Theorem 8. *If* $y = \text{arccot } x$, *then*

$$\frac{dy}{dx} = -\frac{1}{1 + x^2}.$$

We prove the following theorem.

Theorem 9. *If* $y = \text{arcsec } x$, *then*

$$\frac{dy}{dx} = \frac{1}{x\sqrt{x^2 - 1}}, \qquad \text{if } |x| > 1.$$

Proof. From the definition of the inverse secant function, we may write

$$\sec y = x, \qquad 0 < y < \frac{\pi}{2}, \qquad -\pi < y < -\frac{\pi}{2}.$$

We note that $\tan y > 0$ in the first and third quadrants, and therefore from $\tan^2 y + 1 = \sec^2 y$ we obtain

$$\tan y = +\sqrt{\sec^2 y - 1} = \sqrt{x^2 - 1}, \qquad |x| > 1.$$

By the Chain Rule for Derivatives we see that

$$\sec^2 y \, \frac{dy}{dx} = \frac{1}{2} (x^2 - 1)^{-1/2}(2x) = \frac{x}{\sqrt{x^2 - 1}}.$$

Now we substitute in the expression for dy/dx, to obtain

$$\frac{dy}{dx} = \frac{1}{x\sqrt{x^2 - 1}}.$$

Theorem 10. *If* $y = \operatorname{arccsc} x$, *then*

$$\frac{dy}{dx} = \frac{-1}{x\sqrt{x^2 - 1}}, \qquad |x| > 1.$$

The proof of this result follows the same lines as the proof of Theorem 9.

If u is any function of x, we may use the chain rule to find derivatives of the inverse trigonometric functions of u. We shall state the basic formulas in terms of differentials:

$$d \arcsin u = \frac{du}{\sqrt{1 - u^2}}, \qquad d \arccos u = \frac{-du}{\sqrt{1 - u^2}},$$

$$d \arctan u = \frac{du}{1 + u^2}, \qquad d \operatorname{arccot} u = \frac{-du}{1 + u^2},$$

$$d \operatorname{arcsec} u = \frac{du}{u\sqrt{u^2 - 1}}, \qquad d \operatorname{arccsc} u = \frac{-du}{u\sqrt{u^2 - 1}}.$$

EXAMPLE 2. Given that $y = \arcsin (\tfrac{5}{3}x)$, find dy/dx.

Solution. We let $u = \tfrac{5}{3}x$ and $du = \tfrac{5}{3}dx$. Therefore

$$\frac{dy}{dx} = \frac{\tfrac{5}{3}}{\sqrt{1 - (\tfrac{5}{3}x)^2}} = \frac{5}{\sqrt{9 - 25x^2}}.$$

EXAMPLE 3. Given that $f(x) = x \tan^{-1} (x^2)$, find $f'(x)$.

Solution. This is in the form of the product of x and $\arctan (x^2)$. From the product formula we have

$$f'(x) = x \cdot \frac{d}{dx} (\arctan (x^2)) + \arctan (x^2) \cdot 1.$$

Since

$$\frac{d}{dx} (\arctan (x^2)) = \frac{2x}{1 + (x^2)^2} = \frac{2x}{1 + x^4},$$

we conclude that

$$f'(x) = \frac{2x^2}{1 + x^4} + \tan^{-1} (x^2).$$

EXERCISES

In problems 1 through 4, find the value of each of the expressions.

1. (a) $\arcsin (\sqrt{3}/2)$,   (b) $\arccos (-1/\sqrt{2})$,   (c) $\arctan (-1)$
2. (a) $\cos^{-1} (-\frac{1}{2})$,   (b) $\sec^{-1} (-2/\sqrt{3})$,   (c) $\csc^{-1} (-2)$
3. (a) $\operatorname{arccot} \sqrt{3}$,   (b) $\operatorname{arcsec} 2$,   (c) $\arctan (-1/\sqrt{3})$
4. (a) $\arcsin (-\frac{1}{2})$,   (b) $\operatorname{arccot} (-\sqrt{3})$,   (c) $\operatorname{arccsc} (-2/\sqrt{3})$

In problems 5 through 21, perform the differentiations.

5. $f(x) = \arctan 2x$ 6. $g(s) = \operatorname{arccot} s^2$
7. $\phi(y) = \arccos \sqrt{y}$ 8. $f(t) = \operatorname{arcsec} (1/t)$
9. $y = x \cos^{-1} x$ 10. $f(u) = u^2 \arcsin 2u$
11. $f(x) = (\operatorname{arccot} 3x)/(1 + x^2)$ 12. $f(x) = \arctan (x/\sqrt{1 - x^2})$
13. $f(x) = \arcsin (x/\sqrt{1 + x^2})$ 14. $f(x) = \operatorname{arccot} [(1 - x)/(1 + x)]$
15. $f(x) = \arctan [(x - 3)/(1 + 3x)]$ 16. $f(x) = (\arccos 2x)/\sqrt{1 + 4x^2}$
17. $f(x) = x \arcsin 2x + \frac{1}{2}\sqrt{1 - 4x^2}$ 18. $f(x) = \arctan (3 \tan x)$
19. $f(x) = \sqrt{x^2 - 4} - 2 \arctan [\frac{1}{2}\sqrt{x^2 - 4}]$
20. $f(x) = \sec^{-1} (\sqrt{1 + x^2}/x)$
21. $f(x) = \arctan [(3 \sin x)/(4 + 5 \cos x)]$
22. Given that $f(x) = \arcsin x + \arccos x$, find $f'(x)$. What can you conclude about $f(x)$?
23. Given that $f(x) = \operatorname{arcsec} x + \operatorname{arccsc} x$, find $f'(x)$. What can you conclude about $f(x)$?
24. (a) Prove Theorem 7; (b) prove Theorem 8; (c) prove Theorem 10.

6. INTEGRATIONS YIELDING INVERSE TRIGONOMETRIC FUNCTIONS

Each new derivative formula carries with it a new integration formula. Therefore the Theorems of Section 5 may be rephrased to give the following integration formulas:

$$\int \frac{du}{\sqrt{1 - u^2}} = \arcsin u + c,$$

$$\int \frac{du}{1 + u^2} = \arctan u + c,$$

$$\int \frac{du}{u\sqrt{u^2 - 1}} = \operatorname{arcsec} u + c,$$

EXAMPLE 1. Find the value of

$$\int \frac{dx}{\sqrt{1 - 4x^2}}.$$

Solution. Let $u = 2x$ and $du = 2\,dx$. Then

$$\int \frac{dx}{\sqrt{1 - 4x^2}} = \int \frac{\frac{1}{2}\,du}{\sqrt{1 - u^2}} = \frac{1}{2} \arcsin u + c = \frac{1}{2} \arcsin 2x + c.$$

EXAMPLE 2. Find the value of

$$\int \frac{dx}{9 + x^2}.$$

Solution. We write

$$\int \frac{dx}{9 + x^2} = \int \frac{dx}{9[1 + (x/3)^2]} = \frac{1}{9} \int \frac{dx}{1 + (x/3)^2}.$$

Making the substitution $u = x/3$, $du = \frac{1}{3}\,dx$, we obtain

$$\frac{1}{9} \int \frac{3\,du}{1 + u^2} = \frac{1}{3} \tan^{-1} u + c = \frac{1}{3} \tan^{-1} \frac{x}{3} + c.$$

The reader may wonder why three of the formulas for integration were omitted. For example, we did not include the formula

$$\int \frac{du}{\sqrt{1 - u^2}} = -\arccos u + c.$$

This is not a new formula because it can be verified that for all values of u between -1 and $+1$ we have

$$\arccos u = \frac{\pi}{2} - \arcsin u.$$

(See problem 22 of Section 5.) Therefore the above integration formula is the same as the one leading to arcsin u. The other two formulas present similar situations.

EXERCISES

In problems 1 through 10, perform the integrations.

1. $\displaystyle\int \frac{dx}{\sqrt{1 - 9x^2}}$ 2. $\displaystyle\int \frac{dx}{1 + 16x^2}$ 3. $\displaystyle\int \frac{dx}{x\sqrt{4x^2 - 1}}$

4. $\displaystyle\int \frac{dx}{\sqrt{4 - 9x^2}}$ 5. $\displaystyle\int \frac{dx}{1 + 7x^2}$ 6. $\displaystyle\int \frac{dx}{16 + 9x^2}$

7. $\displaystyle\int \frac{dx}{x\sqrt{x^2 - 4}}$ 8. $\displaystyle\int \frac{dx}{\sqrt{12 - 5x^2}}$ 9. $\displaystyle\int \frac{dx}{x\sqrt{2x^2 - 10}}$

10. $\displaystyle\int \frac{dx}{7 + (\frac{1}{3}x)^2}$

In problems 11 through 14, evaluate the integrals.

11. $\displaystyle\int_{-1/2}^{(1/2)\,\sqrt{3}} \frac{dx}{\sqrt{1-x^2}}$ 12. $\displaystyle\int_{-1}^{\sqrt{3}} \frac{dx}{1+x^2}$ 13. $\displaystyle\int_{(2/3)\,\sqrt{3}}^{2} \frac{dx}{x\sqrt{x^2-1}}$

14. $\displaystyle\int_{-2}^{-\sqrt{2}} \frac{dx}{x\sqrt{x^2-1}}$

15. Show that $\arctan x + \text{arccot } x = \text{const.}$ What is the value of the constant?

7. THE LOGARITHM FUNCTION

The student has undoubtedly learned the basic ideas of logarithms in elementary courses in algebra and trigonometry. The underlying principle occurs in the law of exponents, which states that

$$b^\alpha \cdot b^\beta = b^{\alpha+\beta},$$

where α, β, and b are any numbers. If the exponents α and β are integers, the meaning of the above equation is clear from the very definition of an exponent as a symbol for repeated multiplication. Similarly, if the exponents are rational and b is positive, the notion of the nth root of a number allows us to derive the above law of exponents. However, it is not so clear how we would go about defining the number

$$3^{\sqrt{2}}.$$

The definition of numbers with irrational exponents requires an additional effort. The customary introduction of logarithms proceeds on the assumption that all such numbers are known. In particular, if b and N are any numbers, with $b > 0$, $b \neq 1$, it is assumed that the equation

$$b^y = N$$

may always be solved uniquely for y. The value of y which solves this equation is written as

$$\log_b N.$$

The usual laws of logarithms, such as

$$\log_b M + \log_b N = \log_b (MN), \qquad \log_b M - \log_b N = \log_b \left(\frac{M}{N}\right),$$

follow immediately from the law of exponents.

Rather than following the traditional method of elementary mathematics to define logarithms, we shall use the help of the calculus. First we recall the formula

$$\int t^n \, dt = \frac{t^{n+1}}{n+1} + c, \qquad n \neq -1.$$

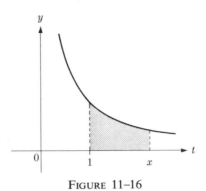

FIGURE 11–16

This integration formula fails for $n = -1$. Nevertheless, if we plot the graph (Fig. 11–16) of $y = 1/t$ for positive values of t, the expression

$$\int_1^x \frac{1}{t}\, dt, \qquad x > 0,$$

has meaning, as it is simply the area under the curve between the points 1 and x. Its value will depend on x and, in fact, it is a function of x so long as x is positive. We define a new function in the following way.

DEFINITION. For values of $x > 0$, we define

$$\ln x = \int_1^x \frac{1}{t}\, dt.$$

Remark. For the present, read ln x as "ell-en x" or "ell-en of x."

The integral of the function $1/t$ has a useful property which we shall state in the form of a lemma.

Lemma. If a and b are any positive numbers, then

$$\int_a^{a \cdot b} \frac{dt}{t} = \int_1^b \frac{du}{u}.$$

Proof. We let $u = (1/a)t$ in the integral on the left; then $du = (1/a)\, dt$. After making this change, we have for the limits of integration: $t = a$ corresponds to $u = 1$, and $t = ab$ corresponds to $u = b$. Therefore

$$\int_a^{a \cdot b} \frac{dt}{t} = \int_1^b \frac{a\, du}{au} = \int_1^b \frac{du}{u}.$$

Geometrically, the lemma states that the shaded areas shown in Figs. 11–17 and 11–18 are equal. With the aid of this lemma the following basic theorem is easy to establish.

Theorem 11. *If a and b are any positive numbers, then*
(i) $\ln (a \cdot b) = \ln a + \ln b$,   (iii) $\ln 1 = 0$,
(ii) $\ln (a/b) = \ln a - \ln b$,   (iv) $\ln a^r = r \ln a$, *if r is any rational number.*

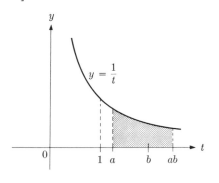

FIGURE 11–17　　　　　　　　FIGURE 11–18

Proof. To prove (i), we have from the definition of the ln function that

$$\ln (a \cdot b) = \int_1^{a \cdot b} \frac{dt}{t}.$$

This integral may be written in the form

$$\int_1^{a \cdot b} \frac{dt}{t} = \int_1^a \frac{dt}{t} + \int_a^{a \cdot b} \frac{dt}{t},$$

and the equality holds whether or not a falls between 1 and $a \cdot b$. At this point we use the lemma to replace the second integral on the right and get

$$\ln (a \cdot b) = \int_1^a \frac{dt}{t} + \int_1^b \frac{dt}{t} = \ln a + \ln b.$$

To prove (ii), we write $a = b \cdot (a/b)$ and apply (i) to the product of b and a/b. We then have

$$\ln a = \ln \left(b \cdot \frac{a}{b} \right) = \ln b + \ln \left(\frac{a}{b} \right),$$

and when we transfer $\ln b$ to the left side, we see that

$$\ln \frac{a}{b} = \ln \left(b \cdot \frac{a}{b} \right) - \ln b = \ln a - \ln b.$$

As for (iii), we apply (ii) with $b = a$. This says that

$$\ln 1 = \ln \frac{a}{a} = \ln a - \ln a = 0.$$

To establish (iv) we proceed in stages. If the exponent is a positive integer, we use (i) and induction. If $b = a$, we observe that (i) states that

$$\ln a^2 = \ln (a \cdot a) = \ln a + \ln a = 2 \ln a.$$

Using a step-by-step method, we obtain

$$\ln a^n = n \ln a, \quad \text{if } n \text{ is a positive integer.}$$

If n is a negative integer, we write $a^{-n} = 1/a^n$ and use (ii) to get

$$\ln (a^{-n}) = \ln \left(\frac{1}{a^n}\right) = \ln 1 - \ln a^n.$$

Since $\ln 1 = 0$ and $\ln a^n = n \ln a$, we find that

$$\ln (a^{-n}) = -n \ln a.$$

If r is any rational number, then $r = p/q$, where p and q are integers (we take q as positive). We define $u = a^{1/q}$; then $u^q = a$ and $\ln a = q \ln u$, since q is an integer. Also we have $u^p = a^{p/q} = a^r$. Therefore

$$\ln (a^r) = \ln (u^p) = p \ln u = \frac{p}{q} q \ln u = \frac{p}{q} \ln a;$$

and so

$$\ln (a^r) = r \ln a.$$

The *domain* of the function $\ln x$ consists of all positive numbers. The next theorem establishes some of the basic properties of this function and also tells us that the *range* of $\ln x$ consists of all real numbers.

Theorem 12. *If $f(x) = \ln x$, then*
(i) $f'(x) = 1/x, \; x > 0,$
(ii) *f is increasing*,
(iii) $\frac{1}{2} \leq \ln 2 \leq 1,$
(iv) $\ln x \to +\infty$ *as* $x \to +\infty,$
(v) $\ln x \to -\infty$ *as* $x \to 0,$
(vi) *the range of f consists of all real numbers.*

Proof. Item (i) is simply the statement that differentiation and integration are inverse processes (Fundamental Theorem of Calculus). The derivative is positive, and part (ii) states that a function with a positive derivative is increasing, a fact which we have already learned. To establish (iii), we make use of our knowledge of integrals as areas. The value of

$$\ln 2 = \int_1^2 \frac{1}{t} \, dt$$

is shown as the shaded area in Fig. 11–19. From the theorem on integrals which gives upper and lower bounds, we have

$$\text{area } ADFE \leq \ln 2 \leq \text{area } BCFE,$$

or

$$\tfrac{1}{2} \leq \ln 2 \leq 1.$$

To prove (iv), we must show that $\ln x$ increases without bound as x does. Let n be any positive integer. If $x > 2^n$, then

$$\ln x > \ln (2^n),$$

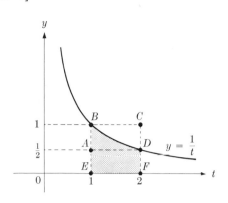

FIGURE 11–19   FIGURE 11–20

since we know from (ii) that ln x is an increasing function. But

$$\ln x > \ln 2^n = n \ln 2 \geq \tfrac{1}{2}n \qquad \text{(by (iii))}.$$

Since $\tfrac{1}{2}n \to \infty$ as $n \to \infty$, we have

$$\ln x \to \infty \quad \text{as} \quad x \to \infty.$$

To obtain (v), we use a device similar to that used for (iv). If n is a positive integer, $(1/2^n) \to 0$ as $n \to \infty$. If $0 < x < 1/2^n$, we know that

$$\ln x < \ln \left(\frac{1}{2^n} \right) = -n \ln 2.$$

Since $\ln 2 > \tfrac{1}{2}$, we can say that

$$\ln x < -\frac{n}{2}.$$

As $n \to \infty$, $x \to 0$ and $\ln x \to -\infty$. Note that x must tend to zero through positive values, since $\ln x$ is not defined for $x \leq 0$.

Items (iv) and (v) show that the range of $\ln x$ extends from $-\infty$ to $+\infty$. The Intermediate Value Theorem then allows us to conclude that no numbers in the range are omitted, thus proving (vi).

A graph of the function $\ln x$ is given in Fig. 11–20.

EXAMPLE 1. Given that $\ln 2 = 0.69315$ and $\ln 3 = 1.09861$, find $\ln 24$, $\ln 0.1875$.

Solution. We write $24 = 2^3 \cdot 3$ and use the properties of Theorem 11 to obtain

$$\ln 24 = 3 \ln 2 + \ln 3 = 3(0.69315) + 1.09861 = 3.17806.$$

We observe that $0.1875 = \tfrac{3}{16}$, and so

$$\ln 0.1875 = \ln 3 - 4 \ln 2 = -1.67399.$$

EXAMPLE 2. Use the theorem giving upper and lower bounds for integrals to obtain an upper and lower bound for $\ln 5$.

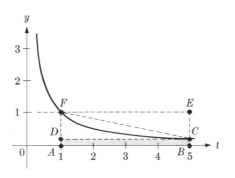

FIGURE 11–21   FIGURE 11–22

Solution. From Fig. 11–21, we see that a lower bound is given by the shaded area *ABCD;* it is $\frac{4}{5}$. An upper bound is given by the area *ABEF;* it is 4. In other words,

$$\tfrac{4}{5} \leq \ln 5 \leq 4.$$

A refined upper bound is given by the area of the trapezoid *ABCF;* it is

$$\tfrac{1}{2}(4)(\tfrac{1}{5} + 1) = \tfrac{12}{5}.$$

A more precise lower bound may be obtained by dividing the interval from 1 to 5 into sections and computing the areas separately, as shown in Fig. 11–22:

$$\text{Area} = 1 \cdot (\tfrac{1}{2}) + 1 \cdot (\tfrac{1}{3}) + 1(\tfrac{1}{4}) + 1(\tfrac{1}{5}) = \tfrac{77}{60}.$$

The estimates for ln 5 are

$$\tfrac{77}{60} \leq \ln 5 \leq \tfrac{12}{5}.$$

EXAMPLE 3. Given that $F(x) = \ln (x^2 + 5)$, find $F'(x)$.

Solution. The chain rule tells us that

$$\frac{d}{dx} \ln u = \frac{1}{u} \cdot \frac{du}{dx}.$$

Therefore, letting $u = x^2 + 5$, we obtain

$$F'(x) = \frac{1}{x^2 + 5} \cdot 2x = \frac{2x}{x^2 + 5}.$$

EXAMPLE 4. Given that $G(x) = \ln \sqrt{(1 + x)/(1 - x)}$ $(-1 < x < 1)$, find $G'(x)$.

Solution. The use of the properties of logarithms simplifies the work of differentiation. We first write

$$G(x) = \frac{1}{2} \ln \frac{1 + x}{1 - x} = \frac{1}{2} \ln (1 + x) - \frac{1}{2} \ln (1 - x).$$

Then

$$G'(x) = \frac{1}{2} \frac{1}{1 + x} - \frac{1}{2} \frac{1}{1 - x} \cdot (-1) = \frac{1}{2} \left(\frac{1}{1 + x} + \frac{1}{1 - x} \right) = \frac{1}{1 - x^2}.$$

EXERCISES

In problems 1 through 5, compute the required quantities, using the fact that $\ln 2 = 0.69315$, $\ln 3 = 1.09861$, and $\ln 10 = 2.30259$.

1. $\ln 4$, $\ln 5$, $\ln 6$, $\ln 8$, $\ln 9$
2. $\ln 12$, $\ln 15$, $\ln 16$, $\ln 18$, $\ln 20$
3. $\ln 24$, $\ln 25$, $\ln 27$, $\ln 30$, $\ln 32$
4. $\ln 1.5$, $\ln 2.7$, $\ln 0.25$, $\ln 1.25$
5. $\ln \sqrt{30}$, $\ln \sqrt[3]{270}$, $\ln \sqrt{2/3}$, $\ln \sqrt[4]{7.2}$

In problems 6 through 15, use the definition of the function $\ln x$ and the properties of the area of elementary figures to obtain upper and lower bounds for the given quantities (method of Example 2).

6. $\ln 4.5$ 7. $\ln 7$ 8. $\ln 14$ 9. $\ln 3.2$
10. $\ln 1.05$ 11. $\ln \frac{1}{2}$ 12. $\ln 0.15$ 13. $\ln 0.001$
14. $\ln 0.95$ 15. $\ln 0.995$

In problems 16 through 31, perform the differentiations.

16. $f(x) = \ln (2x + 3)$
17. $f(x) = \ln x^4$
18. $f(x) = \ln (x^2 + 2x + 3)$
19. $f(x) = \ln (x^3 - 3x + 1)$
20. $g(x) = 2 \ln \sin x$
21. $h(x) = \ln \sec 2x$
22. $F(x) = \ln (\sec x + \tan x)$
23. $F(x) = (\ln x)^4$
24. $G(x) = \ln (\ln x)$, $(x > 1)$
25. $G(x) = x \ln x$
26. $H(x) = \ln \sqrt{1 - x^2}$
27. $f(x) = \ln (x + \sqrt{x^2 + a^2})$
28. $H(x) = \ln (x^2 \sqrt{x^2 + 1})$
29. $H(x) = \ln [(x^2 + 1)/(x^2 - 1)]$
30. $T(x) = \ln \sqrt{(1 + \cos x)/(1 - \cos x)}$
31. $f(x) = (\ln x)^2/(1 + x^2)$

Using the definition of the function $\ln x$ and the values of $\ln 2$, $\ln 3$, and $\ln 10$ which are given at the beginning of the exercises, evaluate the following integrals.

32. $\displaystyle\int_1^5 \frac{1}{x}\, dx$ 33. $\displaystyle\int_4^{10} \frac{dx}{x}$ 34. $\displaystyle\int_3^{15} \frac{du}{u}$

35. $\displaystyle\int_5^8 \frac{du}{u}$ 36. $\displaystyle\int_1^{1/4} \frac{du}{u}$ 37. $\displaystyle\int_{1/3}^1 \frac{du}{u}$

38. $\displaystyle\int_{1/2}^{12} \frac{du}{u}$ 39. $\displaystyle\int_{1/8}^{1/5} \frac{du}{u}$ 40. $\displaystyle\int_{0.01}^{10} \frac{du}{u}$

8. THE EXPONENTIAL FUNCTION

Theorem 12 of Section 7 states that the domain of $\ln x$ consists of all positive numbers, while the range consists of all real numbers. Since the derivative of $\ln x$ is always positive, it makes sense to speak of the *inverse function* of $\ln x$. This function is defined in the following way:

DEFINITION. *The exponential function*, denoted by exp, is defined to be the inverse of the function $\ln$.

Remark. From the paragraph above it is clear that the domain of exp x consists of all real numbers, and the range consists of all positive numbers.

The basic properties of exp x are given in the next theorem.

Theorem 13. *If $f(x) = \exp x$, then*
(i)   *f is increasing for all values of x,*
(ii) $\exp (x_1 + x_2) = (\exp x_1)(\exp x_2)$,
(iii) $\exp (x_1 - x_2) = (\exp x_1)/(\exp x_2)$,
(iv) $\exp rx = (\exp x)^r$ *if r is rational,*
(v) $f(x) \to +\infty$ *as* $x \to +\infty$,
(vi) $f(x) \to 0$ *as* $x \to -\infty$.

Proof. To establish (i), let $y_1 = \exp x_1$ and $y_2 = \exp x_2$, with $x_2 > x_1$. We wish to show that $y_2 > y_1$. From the definition of inverse functions we know that

$$x_1 = \ln y_1 \qquad \text{and} \qquad x_2 = \ln y_2.$$

Since ln is an increasing function, the only way that the inequality $x_2 > x_1$ can hold is if $y_2 > y_1$.

Item (ii) is proved by the same technique — going back to the ln function. Let

$$y_1 = \exp x_1 \qquad \text{and} \qquad y_2 = \exp x_2.$$

Then $x_1 = \ln y_1$, $x_2 = \ln y_2$, and $x_1 + x_2 = \ln y_1 + \ln y_2 = \ln y_1 y_2$. This last statement asserts that

$$y_1 y_2 = \exp (x_1 + x_2), \qquad \text{or} \qquad (\exp x_1)(\exp x_2) = \exp (x_1 + x_2).$$

The argument for (iii) is analogous to that for (ii).

We prove part (iv) by induction. We know that

$$\exp (2x) = \exp (x + x) = (\exp x)(\exp x) = (\exp x)^2,$$

and therefore, by induction, that

$$\exp (nx) = (\exp x)^n, \qquad \text{for } n \text{ a positive integer.}$$

The remaining argument parallels the proof of (iv) in Theorem 11, Section 7. Parts (v) and (vi) are derived by appealing to the analogous result for the function ln. To state that ln and exp are inverse functions is equivalent to writing the compact formulas

$$\ln (\exp x) = x \text{ for all } x \qquad \text{and} \qquad \exp (\ln x) = x, \qquad \text{if } x > 0.$$

Figure 11–23 shows the functions ln and exp. They are the reflections of each other in the line $y = x$, since an interchange of the roles of x and y sends one function into the other.

If a is any positive number and r is any rational number, the formula

$$\exp (\ln x) = x \qquad \text{becomes, for } x = a^r, \qquad \exp (\ln a^r) = a^r.$$

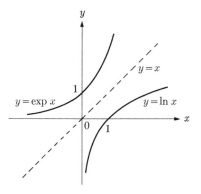

FIGURE 11–23

But $\ln a^r = r \ln a$, and so we have

$$\exp{(r \ln a)} = a^r, \qquad \text{if } a > 0 \text{ and } r \text{ is rational.}$$

The right side of this expression has meaning if r is rational. The left side has meaning if r is any real number. This gives us a clue for defining a^r when r is any real number.

DEFINITION. If $a > 0$, we define

$$a^x = \exp{(x \ln a)}, \qquad \text{for any } x.$$

Remark. The procedure used in defining a^x for any real number x is typical of a technique that is used in many branches of mathematics. The process is one that starts with an equation which holds under certain restrictions. If one side of the equation has meaning without these restrictions while the other side is *undefined* if the restrictions are relaxed, the equation itself may be used to define the hitherto meaningless side.*

Now that numbers of the form a^x have meaning for any real number x, we are in a position to define logarithm in the familiar way.

DEFINITION. If $b > 0$ and $N > 0$, we define $\log_b N$ as that number y such that $b^y = N$. In words:

The logarithm of a positive number N to the positive base b is that power to which b must be raised to obtain N.

The familiar properties of exponents and logarithms to any base may now be established from the definition of a^x and from the properties of the ln and exp

---

*An example of this is given by the equation $x^2 = b$, where b is a number. The equation determines the square root of a number b if it is nonnegative; but the right side has meaning if b is *any real number*. This equation may be used as the *definition* of imaginary numbers.

functions as given in Theorems 11, 12, and 13. Some of these properties are:
(i) $a^x \cdot a^y = a^{x+y}$, $a^x/a^y = a^{x-y}$; $(a^x)^y = a^{xy}$, $(ab)^x = a^x \cdot b^x$;
(ii) $\log_b (x \cdot y) = \log_b x + \log_b y$, $b \neq 1$;
(iii) $\log_b (x/y) = \log_b x - \log_b y$, $b \neq 1$;
(iv) $\log_b (x^y) = y \log_b x$, if $x > 0$, $b \neq 1$.

DEFINITION. We define a number which we designate e by the formula

$$e = \exp 1.$$

The importance of this number is exhibited in the following theorems.

Theorem 14. *If $x > 0$, then*

$$\ln x = \log_e x.$$

Proof. Since, by definition, $e = \exp 1$, we have $\ln e = \ln \exp 1$. However, because ln and exp are inverse functions, we know that $\ln \exp 1 = 1$. Therefore,

$$\ln e = 1.$$

If we set $y = \log_e x$, then $x = e^y$ and, further, $\ln x = \ln e^y = y \ln e = y$.

Theorem 14 states that the function we have been calling "ell-en of x" is simply a logarithm function to the base e.

DEFINITIONS. Logarithms to the base e are called *natural logarithms* (also *Napierian logarithms*). Logarithms to the base 10 are called *common logarithms*.

Theorem 15. *We have*
(i) $\exp x = e^x$ *for all x,*
(ii) e *lies between* 2 *and* 4.

Proof. For the first part, we know by definition of a number to an exponent, as given on p. 359, that

$$e^x = \exp (x \ln e).$$

But we saw in the proof of Theorem 14 that $\ln e = 1$. This yields $e^x = \exp x$. To establish (ii), we first recall that in Theorem 12, part (iii), we found that

$$\tfrac{1}{2} \leq \ln 2 \leq 1.$$

The inequality

$$\ln 2 = \log_e 2 \leq 1$$

is interpreted from the definition of logarithm as $2 \leq e^1 = e$. From the relation $\ln 4 = \ln 2 + \ln 2 \geq \tfrac{1}{2} + \tfrac{1}{2} = 1$, we see that $\log_e 4 \geq 1$, and therefore

$$4 \geq e^1 = e.$$

The actual numerical value of e is 2.71828^+, correct to the number of decimal places given. Methods for computing e to any desired number of places will be given later. The notations $\ln x$ and $\log_e x$ are sometimes replaced by $\log x$, it being understood that the base is e.

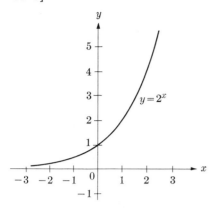

FIGURE 11–24   FIGURE 11–25

EXAMPLE 1. Find the value of $\log_2 \frac{1}{8}$.

Solution. Letting $x = \log_2 \frac{1}{8}$, we see from the definition of logarithm that

$$2^x = \tfrac{1}{8}.$$

Writing $\frac{1}{8}$ as 2^{-3}, we obtain $x = -3$.

EXAMPLE 2. Sketch the graph of $y = 2^x$.

Solution. We construct a table of values, as shown. We observe that $y \to +\infty$ as $x \to +\infty$, and $y \to 0$ as $x \to -\infty$. The curve is sketched in Fig. 11–24.

x	0	1	2	3	4	-1	-2	-3	-4
y	1	2	4	8	16	$\frac{1}{2}$	$\frac{1}{4}$	$\frac{1}{8}$	$\frac{1}{16}$

EXAMPLE 3. Sketch the graph of $y = \log_3 x$.

Solution. One way to get a table of values is to note that the equation $y = \log_3 x$ is equivalent to $3^y = x$. Letting y take on a succession of values, we formulate the table and then sketch the curve, as shown in Fig. 11–25.

y	0	1	2	3	4	-1	-2	-3	-4
$x = 3^y$	1	3	9	27	81	$\frac{1}{3}$	$\frac{1}{9}$	$\frac{1}{27}$	$\frac{1}{81}$

EXAMPLE 4. Prove that if $x > 0, b > 0$, and $b \neq 1$, then

$$\log_b x = \frac{\ln x}{\ln b}.$$

Solution. We set $y = \log_b x$ and write the equivalent expression $b^y = x$. This yields

$$\ln (b^y) = \ln x$$

and, consequently,

$$y \ln b = \ln x \qquad \text{or} \qquad y = \frac{\ln x}{\ln b}.$$

EXERCISES

In problems 1 through 14, sketch the curves.

1. $y = 4^x$ 2. $y = 3^x$ 3. $y = (\frac{1}{2})^x$ 4. $y = (\frac{1}{3})^{2x}$

5. $y = 2^{-x}$ 6. $y = 3^{-2x}$ 7. $y = 2^{x+1}$ 8. $y = 2^{3-x}$

9. $y = \log_2 x$ 10. $y = \log_4 x$ 11. $y = \log_{1/2} x$ 12. $y = \log_{1/5} x$

13. $y = \log_3 2x$ 14. $y = \log_2 (x + 1)$

In problems 15 through 18, find the values of the given expressions.

15. (a) $\log_3 81$;   (b) $\log_4 16$;   (c) $\log_2 \frac{1}{32}$

16. (a) $\log_3 \frac{1}{27}$;   (b) $\log_5 125$;   (c) $\log_4 \frac{1}{64}$

17. (a) $\log_2 1$;   (b) $\log_7 \frac{1}{49}$;   (c) $\log_a a$

18. (a) $\log_{1/2} (8)$;   (b) $\log_{1/6} 216$;   (c) $\log_{1/4} \frac{1}{16}$

19. From the definition of the function a^x, prove that $a^x \cdot a^y = a^{x+y}$ for any real numbers x and y and $a > 0$.

20. (a) Prove that $(2^{\sqrt{3}})^{\sqrt{3}} = 8$.   (b) If x and y are any real numbers, prove that $(a^x)^y = a^{xy}$.

21. From the definition of the ln function, show that ln $2.4 \le 1$ and, consequently, that $2.4 \le e$.

22. From the definition of the ln function, show that ln $3.5 \ge 1$ and, consequently, that $3.5 \ge e$.

Using the results of Example 4, express the following quantities in terms of natural logarithms.

23. $\log_3 8$, $\log_7 12$, $\log_2 15$ 24. $\log_{1/3} 28$, $\log_{1/3} x^2$, $\log_8 12$

Without using tables, find the value of the following, given that ln $2 = 0.693$, ln $3 = 1.099$, ln $10 = 2.303$.

25. $\log_3 16$ 26. $\log_2 30$ 27. $\log_{1/5} 6$

28. $\log_{10} 24$ 29. $\log_6 18$ 30. $\log_{15} 9$

9. DIFFERENTIATION OF EXPONENTIAL FUNCTIONS; LOGARITHMIC DIFFERENTIATION.

In Section 7 we saw that the derivative of ln x is $1/x$. In Section 8 we showed that ln x is $\log_e x$ and, therefore, we have the formula

$$\frac{d}{dx} (\log_e x) = \frac{1}{x}, \quad x > 0.$$

The following theorem is convenient when x may have negative values.

Theorem 16. *If* $f(x) = \log_e |x|$, *then* $f'(x) = 1/x$, $x \ne 0$.

Proof. If x is positive, $\log_e |x| = \log_e x$, and the result is immediate. If x is negative, then $-x$ is positive and

$$\frac{d}{dx} \log_e (-x) = \frac{1}{-x} \frac{d(-x)}{dx} = \frac{1}{x}.$$

Therefore, whatever x is, we have

$$\frac{d}{dx} \log_e |x| = \frac{1}{x}.$$

The derivative of the exponential function is obtained by using the fact that it is the inverse of the natural logarithm.

Theorem 17. *If* $f(x) = e^x$, *then* $f'(x) = e^x$.

Proof. By letting $y = e^x = \exp x$, we may write $\ln y = x$. Then, by the chain rule, we have

$$\frac{1}{y} \frac{dy}{dx} = 1, \quad \text{or} \quad f'(x) = \frac{dy}{dx} = y = e^x.$$

The problem of finding the derivative of a^x is readily reduced to that of obtaining the derivative of the exponential function.

Theorem 18. *If* $f(x) = a^x$, *then* $f'(x) = a^x \log_e a$.

Proof. We set $y = a^x$. Then $\log_e y = x \log_e a$ and, by differentiating, we find

$$\frac{1}{y} \frac{dy}{dx} = \log_e a$$

and

$$f'(x) = \frac{dy}{dx} = y \log_e a = a^x \log_e a.$$

We summarize the formulas in the following table:

$\ln u = \log_e u,$	$\exp u = e^u,$	$a^u = e^{u \ln a},$
$d \ln u = \dfrac{du}{u},$	$d \log_a u = \dfrac{du}{u \ln a},$	
$de^u = e^u \, du,$	$da^u = a^u (\ln a) \, du.$	

EXAMPLE 1. Given that $f(x) = \ln |\sin x|$, find $f'(x)$.

Solution.

$$d \ln |\sin x| = \frac{1}{\sin x} d (\sin x) = \frac{\cos x \, dx}{\sin x}.$$

Therefore

$$f'(x) = \cot x.$$

EXAMPLE 2. Given that $f(x) = x^2 e^{-x^2}$, find $f'(x)$.

Solution.

$$d(x^2 e^{-x^2}) = x^2\, d(e^{-x^2}) + e^{-x^2}\, d(x^2)$$
$$= x^2 e^{-x^2}\, d(-x^2) + 2x e^{-x^2}\, dx$$
$$= e^{-x^2}(-2x^3 + 2x)\, dx.$$

Therefore

$$f'(x) = 2x e^{-x^2}(1 - x^2).$$

EXAMPLE 3. Given that $f(x) = a^{4x}/\ln|5x - 1|$, find $f'(x)$ $(x \neq \frac{1}{5}, a > 0)$.

Solution. The formula for the differential of a quotient gives us

$$df = \frac{\ln|5x - 1|\, d(a^{4x}) - a^{4x}\, d\ln|5x - 1|}{[\ln|5x - 1|]^2}.$$

Since $d(a^{4x}) = a^{4x} \ln a\, d(4x) = 4a^{4x} \ln a\, dx$, and

$$d\ln|5x - 1| = \frac{1}{5x - 1}\, d(5x - 1) = \frac{5\, dx}{5x - 1},$$

we obtain

$$f'(x) = \frac{4a^{4x} \ln a \ln|5x - 1| - [5a^{4x}/(5x - 1)]}{[\ln|5x - 1|]^2}$$

$$= a^{4x}\frac{4(5x - 1)\ln a \ln|5x - 1| - 5}{(5x - 1)\ln^2|5x - 1|}.$$

———————————

The function x^n is now defined for n any *real* number (see definition on p. 359). The next theorem shows how we can extend to the case for any real number the differentiation formulas obtained previously for the case n a rational number.

Theorem 19.   *If n is any real number and f is defined by $f(x) = x^n$, then $f'(x) = nx^{n-1}$, $x > 0$.*

Proof. We let $y = x^n$. From the definition on p. 359, we have

$$y = x^n = \exp(n \log x) = e^{n \log x}.$$

From the derivative formulas, we get

$$\frac{dy}{dx} = e^{n \log x} \frac{d}{dx}(n \log x) = e^{n \log x} n\left(\frac{1}{x}\right).$$

Therefore

$$\frac{dy}{dx} = x^n \cdot n \frac{1}{x} = nx^{n-1}.$$

We have learned how to differentiate functions of the form a^u where a is constant and u is variable, and Theorem 19 yields the formula for u^a where u is variable and a is any constant. Sometimes we get functions of the form $u(x)^{v(x)}$, where u and v are both functions of x. If u and v can each be differentiated by known methods it is possible to develop a formula for the derivative of u^v. The following examples illustrate the procedure, called *logarithmic differentiation*.

EXAMPLE 4. Given that $f(x) = x^x$, find $f'(x)$.

Solution. Write $y = x^x$, and take logarithms of both sides of this equation. Then
$\log y = x \log x$.
Differentiate:

$$\frac{1}{y}\frac{dy}{dx} = x \cdot \frac{1}{x} + \log x \cdot 1 = 1 + \log x.$$

Therefore

$$f'(x) = \frac{dy}{dx} = y(1 + \log x) = x^x(1 + \log x).$$

EXAMPLE 5. Given that

$$f(x) = \left| \frac{x^2\sqrt[3]{3x+2}}{(2x-3)^3} \right|, \qquad x \neq \tfrac{3}{2}, 0, -\tfrac{2}{3},$$

find $f'(x)$.

Solution. Taking logs, we have

$$\log f(x) = 2 \log |x| + \tfrac{1}{3} \log |3x+2| - 3 \log |2x - 3|.$$

Therefore

$$\frac{1}{f} f' = \frac{2}{x} + \frac{1}{3x+2} - \frac{6}{2x-3},$$

and

$$f'(x) = \left| \frac{x^2\sqrt[3]{3x+2}}{(2x-3)^3} \right| \left(\frac{2}{x} + \frac{1}{3x+2} - \frac{6}{2x-3} \right).$$

EXERCISES

In the following problems, perform the differentiations.

1. $f(x) = e^{2x}$

2. $f(x) = e^{x^2 - 3x + 7}$

3. $f(x) = x^4 e^{-3x}$

4. $f(x) = x^{-2} e^{-x^2}$

5. $G(x) = e^{2x} \ln x$

6. $f(x) = x^3 e^{3x} \ln (x^2)$

7. $g(x) = e^{\tan x}$

8. $F(x) = \exp (\sin x)$

9. $f(x) = 3^{5x}$

10. $f(x) = 4^{-2x}$

11. $f(x) = (x^3 + 3)2^{-7x}$

12. $F(x) = 2^{5x} \cdot 3^{4x^2}$

13. $F(x) = x^{\sin x}$

14. $F(x) = x^{\ln x}$

15. $G(x) = x^{\sqrt{x}}$

16. $G(x) = (\sin x)^x$

17. $H(x) = (\ln x)^x$

18. $H(x) = (3/x)^x$

19. $f(x) = \dfrac{x^2\sqrt{2x+3}}{(x^2+1)^4}$

20. $f(x) = |x\sqrt{2x-1}\sqrt[3]{3x+3}|$

21. $g(x) = \sqrt{[(x + 2)(x + 3)]/(x + 1)}$ 22. $g(x) = \left| \dfrac{(x + 2)^2(2x - 3)^{1/2}}{\sqrt[3]{3x - 2}} \right|$

23. $g(x) = \left| \dfrac{x^2 \arctan x}{1 + x^2} \right|$ 24. $f(x) = \dfrac{\exp(x^2)}{\sqrt{x^2 + 1}\,\sqrt[4]{2x^2 + 3}}$

10. THE NUMBER e

The function $f(x) = \log_e x$ has as its derivative the function $1/x$. We shall use this fact to gain additional insight into the number e. Suppose that we wish to find the derivative of $\log_e x$ from the very definition of derivative. We proceed in the following way (Five-Step Rule).

Step 1: $f(x) = \log_e x$.
Step 2: $f(x + h) = \log_e (x + h)$.
Step 3: $\Delta f = f(x + h) - f(x) = \log_e (x + h) - \log_e x$.
Step 4: $(1/h)\,\Delta f = (1/h)[\log_e (x + h) - \log_e x]$.

We use the properties of logarithms to write this last expression in the form

$$\frac{1}{h}\,\Delta f = \frac{1}{h}\log_e \frac{x + h}{x} = \frac{1}{h}\log_e \left(1 + \frac{h}{x}\right).$$

Before letting $h \to 0$ we multiply and divide by x, getting

$$\frac{1}{h}\,\Delta f = \frac{1}{x}\cdot\frac{x}{h}\log_e \left(1 + \frac{h}{x}\right) = \frac{1}{x}\cdot\log_e \left(1 + \frac{h}{x}\right)^{x/h}.$$

Now we are ready to let h tend to zero. We have (*Step* 5)

$$\lim_{h\to 0}\frac{1}{h}\,\Delta f = f'(x) = \frac{1}{x}\lim_{h\to 0}\log_e \left(1 + \frac{h}{x}\right)^{x/h}.$$

Since the answer must be $1/x$, we conclude that

$$\lim_{h\to 0}\log_e \left(1 + \frac{h}{x}\right)^{x/h} = 1.$$

This answer is possible only if

$$\lim_{h\to 0}\left(1 + \frac{h}{x}\right)^{x/h} = e.$$

Letting $t = h/x$, we find that e is obtainable in the limiting form:

$$e = \lim_{t\to 0}(1 + t)^{1/t}.$$

By simple substitution, we can get an idea of how the function $G(t) = (1 + t)^{1/t}$ behaves as $t \to 0$. We have $G(1) = 2$, $G(\frac{1}{2}) = \frac{9}{4}$, $G(\frac{1}{3}) = \frac{64}{27}$, $G(\frac{1}{4}) = \frac{625}{256} = 2.4^+$, $G(\frac{1}{10}) = 2.59^+$.

EXERCISES

1. Compute values of the function $G(t) = (1 + t)^{1/t}$ for $t = \frac{1}{5}, \frac{1}{6}, \frac{1}{7}, \frac{1}{8}.$ Use logarithms to find $G(\frac{1}{20})$, $G(\frac{1}{50})$.

2. Compute $G(2)$, $G(3)$, $G(4)$, $G(5)$. Sketch the graph.

3. Show that the function $H(t) = [1 + (1/t)]^t$ is an increasing function of t.

11. APPLICATIONS

In Chapter 7 various applications of differentiation were discussed. Now we are able to differentiate many more types of functions than we were at that time—including logarithmic, exponential, trigonometric, and inverse trigonometric functions. Although the general methods are the same as those described in Chapter 7, the degree of permissible complication has expanded greatly.   The following examples illustrate the techniques which may be used.

EXAMPLE 1. Find the equation of the line tangent to the curve $y = xe^{2x}$ at the point where $x = 2$.

Solution. We have

$$\frac{dy}{dx} = 2xe^{2x} + e^{2x}$$

and, at $x = 2$,

$$\frac{dy}{dx} = 4e^4 + e^4 = 5e^4.$$

Further, at $x = 2$, $y = 2e^4$. The tangent line has the equation

$$y - 2e^4 = 5e^4(x - 2), \quad \text{or} \quad 5e^4x - y = 8e^4.$$

EXAMPLE 2. A gutter is to be made out of a long sheet of metal 12 in. wide by turning up strips of width 4 in. along each side so that they make equal angles θ with the vertical, as in Fig. 11–26. For what value of θ will the carrying capacity be greatest?

Solution. The carrying capacity is proportional to the area A of a cross section. If we find the maximum value for A, the capacity will also be a maximum. From Fig. 11–26 we see that the area of each of the triangles is $8 \sin \theta \cos \theta$.

FIGURE 11–26

Therefore

$$A = 16 \cos \theta + 16 \sin \theta \cos \theta, \qquad 0 \le \theta < \frac{\pi}{2}.$$

$$\frac{dA}{d\theta} = -16 \sin \theta - 16 \sin^2 \theta + 16 \cos^2 \theta$$

$$= 16(1 - \sin \theta - 2 \sin^2 \theta).$$

Setting the derivative equal to zero, we get

$$0 = 1 - \sin \theta - 2 \sin^2 \theta$$

$$= (1 + \sin \theta)(1 - 2 \sin \theta).$$

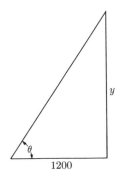

1200

FIGURE 11–27

The equation $\sin \theta + 1 = 0$ gives no root for $0 \le \theta < (\pi/2)$, while $1 - 2 \sin \theta = 0$ yields

$$\theta = \frac{\pi}{6}.$$

The corresponding value of $\cos \theta$ is $\frac{1}{2}\sqrt{3}$, and we find that

$$A\left(\frac{\pi}{6}\right) = 12\sqrt{3}.$$

Since $A(0) = 16$ and $A(\theta) \to 0$ as $\theta \to (\pi/2)$, the maximum carrying capacity occurs at $\pi/6$, with $A \approx 20.8$.

EXAMPLE 3. A balloon leaving the ground 1200 ft from an observer rises at the rate of 200 ft/min. How fast is the angle of elevation of the observer's line of sight increasing when the balloon is at an altitude of 1600 ft?

Solution. As shown in Fig. 11–27, the angle of elevation is θ and the rate of change of this angle is $d\theta/dt$, where t denotes the time in minutes. We have the formula

$$\theta = \arctan\left(\frac{y}{1200}\right),$$

where y is the height of the balloon at time t. Differentiating with respect to t, we obtain

$$\frac{d\theta}{dt} = \frac{1}{1 + (y/1200)^2} \frac{d}{dt}\left(\frac{y}{1200}\right) = \frac{1200}{(1200)^2 + y^2} \frac{dy}{dt}.$$

Inserting $y = 1600$ and $dy/dt = 200$, we find $d\theta/dt = 0.06$ rad/min.

EXERCISES

In problems 1 through 8, find in each case the equations of the lines tangent and normal to the given curve at the point on the curve corresponding to the given value of x.

1. $y = \arctan x, \ x = 1$
2. $y = 2^x, \ x = -1$
3. $y = \text{arcsec } x, \ x = -2$
4. $y = \arcsin x, \ x = -\frac{1}{2}$
5. $y = \ln x, \ x = e$
6. $y = x^2 e^{-x}, \ x = 1$
7. $y = x \ln x, \ x = e$
8. $y = x^{-2} e^{2x}, \ x = -1$

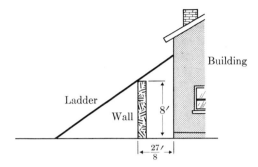

FIGURE 11–28

In problems 9 through 15, find in each case the point or points of intersection of the curves given; then find the tangent of the acute angle between the curves at these intersection points.

9. $y = \arcsin x$, $y = \arccos x$
10. $y = \arctan x$, $y = \arcsin (x/2)$
11. $y = e^{2x}$, $y = 2e^x$
12. $y = \ln x$, $y = \ln x^2$
13. $y = \text{arccot } x$, $y = \frac{1}{2} \arcsin (x)$
14. $y = xe^x$, $y = x^2 e^x$
15. $y = xe^{-x}$, $y = x^2 e^{-x}$

In problems 16 through 27, find in each case the relative maxima and minima, the points of inflection, the intervals in which f is increasing, those in which f is decreasing, those in which the graph is concave upward, and those in which it is concave downward. Sketch the graph.

16. $f(x) = e^{-x}$
17. $f(x) = xe^{-x}$
18. $f(x) = x^2 e^{-x}$
19. $f(x) = e^{-x^2}$
20. $f(x) = 2xe^{-(1/2)x^2}$
21. $f(x) = x^2 e^{-x^2}$
22. $f(x) = \ln (1 + x)$
23. $f(x) = x \ln x$
24. $f(x) = 2x^2 \ln x$
25. $f(x) = 2x (\ln x)^2$
26. $f(x) = e^{-x} \sin x$
27. $f(x) = e^{-x} \cos x$

28. Find the minimum value of x^x for $x > 0$.

29. A revolving light 3 mi from a straight shoreline makes 2 revolutions/min. Find the speed of the spot of light along the shore when it is 2 mi away from the point on the shore nearest the light.

30. A wall 8 ft high is $\frac{27}{8}$ ft from a building. Find the length of the shortest ladder which will clear the wall and rest with one end on the ground and the other end on the building. Also find the angle which this ladder makes with the horizontal (see Fig. 11–28).

31. An airplane at an altitude of 4400 ft is flying horizontally directly away from an observer. At the instant when the angle of elevation is 45°, the angle is decreasing at the rate of 0.05 radians/sec. How fast is the airplane flying at that instant?

32. A cone whose generators make an angle θ with its axis is inscribed in a sphere of radius R. For what value of θ will the lateral area of the cone be greatest?

33. A man is walking along a sidewalk at the rate of 5 ft/sec. A searchlight on the ground 30 ft from the walk is kept trained on him. At what rate is the searchlight revolving when the man is 20 ft away from the point on the sidewalk nearest the light?

FIGURE 11–29   FIGURE 11–30

34. A tablet 7 ft high is placed on a wall with its base 9 ft above the level of an observer's eye. How far from the wall should an observer stand in order that the angle subtended at his eye by the tablet be a maximum?

35. A steel girder 27 ft long is moved horizontally along a corridor 8 ft wide and around a corner into a hall at right angles to the corridor. How wide must the hall be to permit this? Neglect the width of the girder (see Fig. 11–29).

36. A man on a wharf is pulling in a small boat. His hands are 20 ft above the level of the point on the boat where the rope is tied. If he is pulling in the rope at 2 ft/sec, how fast is the angle that the rope makes with the horizontal increasing when there are 52 ft of rope out?

37. Find the angle of the sector which should be removed from a circular piece of canvas of radius 12 ft so that the conical tent made from the remaining piece will have the greatest volume. Repeat the problem for a circular piece of canvas of radius R ft.

38. The end B of a piston rod moves back and forth on a line through O; B is attached to a rod AB of length 10 in. which, in turn, is attached to a crank OA of length 4 in., which revolves about O. Find an expression for the velocity of B if OA makes 10 rev/sec (see Fig. 11–30).

39. A hemispherical dome is 50 ft in diameter. Just at sunset a ball is dropped from a point on the line joining the top of the dome with the sun. Assuming that the ball drops according to the law $s = 16t^2$ (s in ft, t in sec), obtain an expression for the speed of its shadow along the dome in terms of t. Find its speed when $t = 1$ and the limit of its speed as $t \to 0$.

40. A weight is drawn along a level table by means of a rope, attached to a point P, which passes over a windlass whose axle is fixed horizontally at the level of the table and perpendicular to the line of motion of P. If the windlass, which has a radius of 1 ft, turns at the rate of $\frac{1}{2}$ rev/sec, find an expression for the rate of change of the angle which the rope makes with the table. Assume that P is at the level of the table.

12. THE HYPERBOLIC FUNCTIONS

Exponential functions appear in many investigations in engineering, physics, chemistry, biology, etc. Certain combinations of them occur so often that they have been tabulated and given special names. We define the two basic hyperbolic functions in terms of exponentials by the formulas

$$\sinh x = \tfrac{1}{2}(e^x - e^{-x}), \qquad \cosh x = \tfrac{1}{2}(e^x + e^{-x}).$$

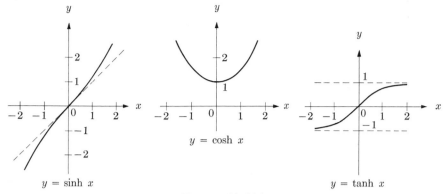

$y = \sinh x$ $y = \cosh x$ $y = \tanh x$

FIGURE 11–31A

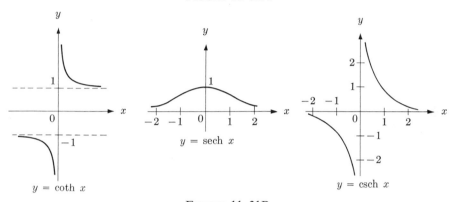

$y = \coth x$ $y = \operatorname{sech} x$ $y = \operatorname{csch} x$

FIGURE 11–31B

We read these "hyperbolic sine of x" and "hyperbolic cosine of x." We shall see that these functions satisfy many relations which are reminiscent of the sine and cosine functions.

In analogy with trigonometric functions, there are four more hyperbolic functions defined in terms of $\sinh x$ and $\cosh x$, as follows:

$$\tanh x = \frac{\sinh x}{\cosh x}, \qquad \coth x = \frac{\cosh x}{\sinh x},$$

$$\operatorname{sech} x = \frac{1}{\cosh x}, \qquad \operatorname{csch} x = \frac{1}{\sinh x}.$$

These are called "hyperbolic tangent of x," etc.

Sketches of the hyperbolic functions are shown in Fig. 11–31. It is evident that, unlike the trigonometric functions, none of the hyperbolic functions is periodic. $\sinh x$, $\tanh x$, $\coth x$, and $\operatorname{csch} x$ are odd functions, while $\cosh x$ and $\operatorname{sech} x$ are even. To see this, we appeal directly to the definition, noting for example that

$$\sinh(-x) = \tfrac{1}{2}(e^{-x} - e^{-(-x)}) = -\tfrac{1}{2}(e^{x} - e^{-x}) = -\sinh x,$$

and

$$\cosh(-x) = \tfrac{1}{2}(e^{-x} + e^{-(-x)}) = \tfrac{1}{2}(e^{x} + e^{-x}) = \cosh x.$$

The relation

$$\cosh^2 x - \sinh^2 x = 1$$

is established by observing that

$$[\tfrac{1}{2}(e^x + e^{-x})]^2 - [\tfrac{1}{2}(e^x - e^{-x})]^2 = \tfrac{1}{4}(e^{2x} + 2 + e^{-2x}) - \tfrac{1}{4}(e^{2x} - 2 + e^{-2x}) = 1.$$

The formulas

$$\tanh^2 x + \operatorname{sech}^2 x = 1,$$
$$\coth^2 x - \operatorname{csch}^2 x = 1,$$

are then easily verified from the definitions of the functions and from the relation $\cosh^2 x - \sinh^2 x = 1$.

The addition formulas for the hyperbolic functions are:

$$\sinh (x \pm y) = \sinh x \cosh y \pm \cosh x \sinh y,$$
$$\cosh (x \pm y) = \cosh x \cosh y \pm \sinh x \sinh y,$$
$$\tanh (x \pm y) = \frac{\tanh x \pm \tanh y}{1 \pm \tanh x \tanh y}.$$

These formulas are easier to establish than are the corresponding trigonometric addition formulas. For example, to prove the first one we merely substitute the appropriate exponentials in the left and right sides and see if they are equal. We have

$$\sinh (x + y) = \tfrac{1}{2}(e^{x+y} - e^{-x-y})$$

and
$$\sinh x \cosh y + \cosh x \sinh y$$

$$= \tfrac{1}{2}(e^x - e^{-x})\tfrac{1}{2}(e^y + e^{-y}) + \tfrac{1}{2}(e^x + e^{-x})\tfrac{1}{2}(e^y - e^{-y})$$
$$= \tfrac{1}{4}(e^{x+y} + e^{x-y} - e^{-x+y} - e^{-x-y} + e^{x+y} - e^{x-y} + e^{-x+y} - e^{-x-y})$$
$$= \tfrac{1}{2}(e^{x+y} - e^{-x-y}) = \sinh (x + y).$$

The remaining formulas are obtained in a similar way.

Theorem 20. *The following differentiation formulas hold:*

(i) $d \sinh u = \cosh u \, du$ (ii) $d \cosh u = \sinh u \, du$
(iii) $d \tanh u = \operatorname{sech}^2 u \, du$ (iv) $d \coth u = -\operatorname{csch}^2 u \, du$
(v) $d \operatorname{sech} u = -\operatorname{sech} u \tanh u \, du$ (vi) $d \operatorname{csch} u = -\operatorname{csch} u \coth u \, du.$

Proof. To prove (i) we write

$$\sinh u = \tfrac{1}{2}(e^u - e^{-u}),$$

$$d \sinh u = \tfrac{1}{2} d(e^u - e^{-u}) = \tfrac{1}{2}(e^u + e^{-u}) \, du = \cosh u \, du.$$

The remaining formulas, (ii) through (vi), follow in the same way, by appeal to the definition and by differentiation of the exponential function.

EXAMPLE 1. Given that $\sinh x = -\frac{3}{4}$, find the values of the other hyperbolic functions.

Solution. $\cosh^2 x = 1 + \sinh^2 x = \frac{25}{16}$. Since $\cosh x$ is always positive, we have $\cosh x = \frac{5}{4}$. Therefore

$$\tanh x = \frac{\sinh x}{\cosh x} = -\frac{3}{5}, \qquad \coth x = -\frac{5}{3},$$

$$\operatorname{sech} x = \frac{1}{\cosh x} = \frac{4}{5}, \qquad \operatorname{csch} x = \frac{1}{\sinh x} = -\frac{4}{3}.$$

EXAMPLE 2. Given $f(x) = \sinh^3 (2x^2 + 3)$, find $f'(x)$.

Solution. We have, by the chain rule,

$$df = 3 \sinh^2 (2x^2 + 3)\, d\,[\sinh (2x^2 + 3)],$$

and from the formula for the derivative of the sinh function,

$$df = 3 \sinh^2 (2x^2 + 3) \cosh (2x^2 + 3)\, d(2x^2 + 3),$$
$$f'(x) = 12x \sinh^2 (2x^3 + 3) \cosh (2x^2 + 3).$$

EXERCISES

In problems 1 through 17, establish the formulas.

1. $\sinh (x - y) = \sinh x \cosh y - \cosh x \sinh y$
2. $\cosh (x + y) = \cosh x \cosh y + \sinh x \sinh y$
3. $\cosh (x - y) = \cosh x \cosh y - \sinh x \sinh y$
4. $\tanh (x + y) = \dfrac{\tanh x + \tanh y}{1 + \tanh x \tanh y}$ 5. $\tanh (x - y) = \dfrac{\tanh x - \tanh y}{1 - \tanh x \tanh y}$
6. $\sinh 2x = 2 \sinh x \cosh x$
7. $\cosh 2x = \cosh^2 x + \sinh^2 x = 2 \cosh^2 x - 1 = 2 \sinh^2 x + 1$
8. $\tanh 2x = \dfrac{2 \tanh x}{1 + \tanh^2 x}$
9. $\sinh A + \sinh B = 2 \sinh \dfrac{A + B}{2} \cosh \dfrac{A - B}{2}$
10. $\cosh A + \cosh B = 2 \cosh \dfrac{A + B}{2} \cosh \dfrac{A - B}{2}$
11. $\cosh (x/2) = \sqrt{(1 + \cosh x)/2}$ 12. $\sinh (x/2) = \pm\sqrt{(\cosh x - 1)/2}$
13. $d \cosh u = \sinh u\, du$ 14. $d \tanh u = \operatorname{sech}^2 u\, du$
15. $d \coth u = -\operatorname{csch}^2 u\, du$ 16. $d \operatorname{sech} u = -\operatorname{sech} u \tanh u\, du$
17. $d \operatorname{csch} u = -\operatorname{csch} u \coth u\, du$

In problems 18 through 23, find the values of the remaining hyperbolic functions.

18. $\sinh x = -\frac{12}{5}$ 19. $\tanh x = -\frac{4}{5}$ 20. $\coth x = 2$
21. $\operatorname{csch} x = -2$ 22. $\cosh x = 4,\ x > 0$ 23. $\cosh x = 2,\ x < 0$

In problems 24 through 29, examine the curves for maximum points, minimum points, and points of inflection. State where the curves are concave upward and where they are concave downward. Sketch the graphs.

24. $y = \sinh 2x$ 25. $y = \cosh (x/2)$ 26. $y = \tanh 3x$

27. $y = \coth \frac{1}{3}x$ 28. $y = \operatorname{sech} (x + 1)$ 29. $y = \operatorname{csch} (1 - x)$

13. THE INVERSE HYPERBOLIC FUNCTIONS

The function $f(x) = \sinh x$ is an increasing function for all values of x. This is so because the derivative of $\sinh x$ is $\cosh x$, a positive quantity for all values of x, and we know that a function with a positive derivative is an increasing function.

A function which is steadily increasing has an inverse. We define

$$y = \operatorname{argsinh} x$$

to be the inverse of the sinh function. Its domain consists of all real numbers. The graph is sketched in Fig. 11–32.

Similarly, the functions $\tanh x$, $\coth x$, and $\operatorname{csch} x$ are all increasing or decreasing functions for all values of x and so have inverse functions, which we denote by

$$\operatorname{argtanh} x, \quad \operatorname{argcoth} x, \quad \operatorname{argcsch} x.$$

The domain of $\operatorname{argtanh} x$ is the set of numbers $-1 < x < 1$, while the range consists of all real numbers. Its graph is sketched in Fig. 11–33.

The function $\cosh x$ is an increasing function, and $\operatorname{sech} x$ is a decreasing function, for nonnegative values of x. We define

$$\operatorname{argcosh} x, \quad \operatorname{argsech} x$$

to be the inverse of the cosh and sech functions respectively, restricted to non-negative values. The domain of $f(x) = \operatorname{argcosh} x$ consists of all numbers $x \geq 1$, and the range is the set of nonnegative real numbers.

The hyperbolic functions are defined in terms of exponentials. The exponential and logarithmic functions are the inverse of each other. It is therefore natural to ask what relation, if any, exists between the logarithmic function and the inverse hyperbolic functions. The direct connection between the natural logarithm and the inverse hyperbolic functions is exhibited in the next theorem.

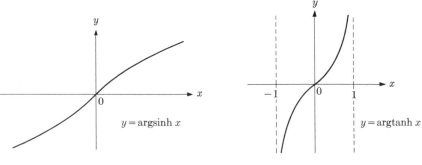

FIGURE 11–32   FIGURE 11–33

Theorem 21.

(i) $\operatorname{argsinh} x = \ln(x + \sqrt{x^2 + 1})$ *for all* x,

(ii) $\operatorname{argtanh} x = \frac{1}{2} \ln[(1 + x)/(1 - x)]$, $-1 < x < 1$,

(iii) $\operatorname{argcoth} x = \frac{1}{2} \ln[(x + 1)/(x - 1)]$, $|x| > 1$,

(iv) $\operatorname{argcosh} x = \ln(x + \sqrt{x^2 - 1})$, $x \geq 1$.

Proof. To prove (i), we write $y = \operatorname{argsinh} x$ and, equivalently, $x = \sinh y$. We wish to find an expression for y in terms of the logarithm. The definition of $\sinh y$ gives us

$$x = \tfrac{1}{2}(e^y - e^{-y})$$

and

$$e^y - \frac{1}{e^y} - 2x = 0.$$

We solve this for e^y by first writing

$$(e^y)^2 - 2x(e^y) - 1 = 0$$

and then applying the quadratic formula to obtain

$$e^y = x \pm \sqrt{x^2 + 1}.$$

The plus sign must be chosen, since $e^y > 0$ always. Taking natural logs of both sides, we find that

$$y = \ln(x + \sqrt{x^2 + 1}),$$

which proves (i).

The proofs of (ii), (iii), and (iv) follow the same pattern: first, we express the hyperbolic function in terms of exponentials; second, we solve for the exponential by the quadratic formula; third, we make the correct choice of the plus or minus sign in the quadratic formula; and fourth, we take logarithms of both sides. We shall exhibit the steps again in the proof of (iv). Let $y = \operatorname{argcosh} x$, $x \geq 1$, and write $\cosh y = x$, $y \geq 0$. Then we have

$$e^y + e^{-y} = 2x, \qquad y \geq 0,$$

and

$$(e^y)^2 - 2x(e^y) + 1 = 0, \qquad y \geq 0.$$

Solving by the quadratic formula, we obtain

$$e^y = x \pm \sqrt{x^2 - 1}, \qquad y \geq 0.$$

For $y \geq 0$ we must have $e^y \geq 1$. Since

$$(x + \sqrt{x^2 - 1})(x - \sqrt{x^2 - 1}) = 1,$$

it follows that for $x > 1$, $x + \sqrt{x^2 - 1} > 1$, and $x - \sqrt{x^2 - 1} < 1$. We therefore choose the plus sign. Taking logarithms, we get

$$y = \ln(x + \sqrt{x^2 - 1}), \qquad x \geq 1.$$

EXAMPLE 1. Express argcosh 2, argtanh $(-\frac{1}{2})$ in terms of the ln function.

Solution. From Theorem 21, we obtain

$$\text{argcosh } 2 = \ln (2 + \sqrt{3}),$$

$$\text{argtanh } (-\tfrac{1}{2}) = \tfrac{1}{2} \ln \frac{1/2}{3/2} = -\tfrac{1}{2} \ln 3 = \ln \frac{1}{\sqrt{3}} \cdot$$

By expressing the inverse hyperbolic functions in terms of logarithms, we have simplified the problem of computing the derivatives of these functions.

Theorem 22. *The inverse hyperbolic functions have the following differentiation formulas:*

(i) $d \text{ argsinh } u = \dfrac{du}{\sqrt{u^2 + 1}}$,

(ii) $d \text{ argcosh } u = \dfrac{du}{\sqrt{u^2 - 1}}$, $u > 1$,

(iii) $d \text{ argtanh } u = \dfrac{du}{1 - u^2}$, $-1 < u < 1$,

(iv) $d \text{ argcoth } u = \dfrac{du}{1 - u^2}$, $|u| > 1$,

(v) $d \text{ argsech } u = -\dfrac{du}{u\sqrt{1 - u^2}}$, $0 < u < 1$,

(vi) $d \text{ argcsch } u = -\dfrac{du}{|u|\sqrt{u^2 + 1}}$, $u \neq 0$.

Proof. To prove (i), we write

$$y = \text{argsinh } u = \ln (u + \sqrt{u^2 + 1}).$$

Therefore

$$dy = \frac{1}{u + \sqrt{u^2 + 1}} d(u + \sqrt{u^2 + 1})$$

$$= \frac{1}{u + \sqrt{u^2 + 1}} \left(1 + \frac{u}{\sqrt{u^2 + 1}}\right) du = \frac{du}{\sqrt{u^2 + 1}} \cdot$$

The remaining formulas, (ii) through (vi), are proved in a similar manner.

EXAMPLE 2. Given $f(x) = \text{argcosh } (x^2 + 2x + 2)$, find $f'(x)$.

Solution. Letting $u = x^2 + 2x + 2$, we have

$$df = \frac{du}{\sqrt{u^2 - 1}} = \frac{2(x + 1) \, dx}{\sqrt{(x^2 + 2x + 2)^2 - 1}},$$

and, since $x^2 + 2x + 2 = (x + 1)^2 + 1$,

$$f'(x) = \frac{2(x + 1)}{\sqrt{(x + 1)^4 + 2(x + 1)^2}} = \frac{2}{\sqrt{(x + 1)^2 + 2}}, \qquad (x + 1 > 0).$$

EXAMPLE 3. Evaluate

$$\int_{-1}^{2} \frac{dx}{\sqrt{1 + x^2}}$$

and express the result in terms of the ln function.

Solution. Since every differentiation formula carries with it an integration formula, Theorem 22(i) gives us

$$\int_{-1}^{2} \frac{dx}{\sqrt{1 + x^2}} = \operatorname{argsinh} x]_{-1}^{2} = \operatorname{argsinh} 2 - \operatorname{argsinh} (-1)$$

$$= \ln (2 + \sqrt{5}) - \ln (-1 + \sqrt{2}) = \ln \frac{2 + \sqrt{5}}{\sqrt{2} - 1}.$$

EXERCISES

In problems 1 through 6, express the given quantities in terms of the natural logarithm.

1. $\operatorname{argsinh} (\frac{1}{2})$ 2. $\operatorname{argtanh} (\frac{3}{5})$ 3. $\operatorname{argcosh} 2$
4. $\operatorname{argcoth} (-2)$ 5. $\operatorname{argsech} (\frac{3}{5})$ 6. $\operatorname{argcosh} (2.6)$

In problems 7 through 12, examine the curves for maximum points, minimum points, and points of inflection. State where the curves are concave upward and where they are concave downward. Sketch the graphs.

7. $y = \operatorname{argsinh} 2x$ 8. $y = \operatorname{argcosh} (x + 1)$ 9. $y = \operatorname{argtanh} \frac{1}{2}x$
10. $y = \operatorname{argcoth} (x - 1)$ 11. $y = \operatorname{argsech} 4x$ 12. $y = \operatorname{argcsch} (2x - 1)$

In problems 13 through 20, perform the differentiations.

13. $f(x) = \operatorname{argsinh} 2x$ 14. $f(x) = x^2 \operatorname{argcosh} 3x$
15. $g(x) = x^{-1} \operatorname{argtanh} x^2$ 16. $f(x) = e^{-2x} \operatorname{argsinh} (3x - 2)$
17. $G(x) = \operatorname{argsinh} (\tan x)$ 18. $F(x) = (\operatorname{argsinh} \sqrt{x})/\sqrt{x}$
19. $f(x) = \operatorname{argsinh}^2 (2x)$ 20. $H(x) = xe^{-x} \operatorname{argcosh} (1 - x)$

In problems 21 through 26, evaluate the integrals, giving the answers in terms of the ln function.

21. $\displaystyle\int_{2}^{5} \frac{dx}{\sqrt{x^2 - 1}}$ 22. $\displaystyle\int_{-1/2}^{3/5} \frac{dx}{1 - x^2}$ 23. $\displaystyle\int_{-2}^{-1} \frac{dx}{\sqrt{x^2 + 1}}$

24. $\displaystyle\int_{-3}^{-2} \frac{dx}{1 - x^2}$ 25. $\displaystyle\int_{3}^{5} \frac{dx}{\sqrt{x^2 - 4}}$ 26. $\displaystyle\int_{1}^{3} \frac{dx}{16 - x^2}$

27. Prove that argtanh $x = \frac{1}{2} \ln (1 + x)/(1 - x)$, $-1 < x < 1$.
28. Prove that argcoth $x = \frac{1}{2} \ln (x + 1)/(x - 1)$, $|x| > 1$.
29. Sketch the graph of $y = $ argcoth x; of $y = $ argcsch x.

30. Prove that d argcosh $u = \dfrac{du}{\sqrt{u^2 - 1}}$, $u > 1$.

31. Prove that d argtanh $u = \dfrac{du}{1 - u^2}$, $-1 < u < 1$.

32. Prove that d argcoth $u = \dfrac{du}{1 - u^2}$, $|u| > 1$.

33. Prove that d argsech $u = -\dfrac{du}{u\sqrt{1 - u^2}}$, $0 < u < 1$.

34. Prove that d argcsch $u = -\dfrac{du}{|u|\sqrt{u^2 + 1}}$, $u \neq 0$.

35. Let $x = \cosh t$, $y = \sinh t$. Draw a table of values for x and y as t assumes values in the interval $-10 \leq t \leq 10$. Sketch the graph in the xy-plane. Can you identify the curve?

CHAPTER 12

Parametric Equations. Arc Length

1. PARAMETRIC EQUATIONS

The equations

$$x = t^2 + 2t, \qquad y = t - 2,$$

express x and y as functions of t. However, x and y are related, since whenever we assign a value to t *both* x and y are determined. This relation may be exhibited graphically in the following way. First we set up a table of values for t, x, and y by letting t take on various values and then computing x and y from the given equations. The points (x, y) are then plotted in the usual way on a rectangular coordinate system (Fig. 12–1). The t-scale (Fig. 12–2) is completely separate

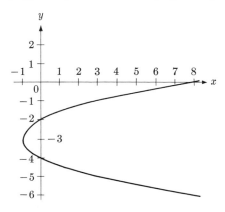

FIGURE 12–1

and does not appear in the graph. The variable t is called a *parameter*, and the equations for x and y in terms of t are called the *parametric equations* of the locus shown in Fig. 12–1.

t	0	1	2	3	4	-1	-2	-3	-4
x	0	3	8	15	24	-1	0	3	8
y	-2	-1	0	1	2	-3	-4	-5	-6

379

t scale

FIGURE 12–2

In general, if *x* and *y* are functions of a variable *t*, so that

$$x = f(t), \qquad y = g(t),$$

we say that they form a set of *parametric equations*. The values of the parameter *t* will lie in some domain of real numbers. The locus of this pair of equations will be the set of points in the *xy*-plane which result when *t* takes on all values in its domain.

Sometimes it is possible to *eliminate the parameter* by solving one of the equations for *t* and then substituting into the other. In the example we considered, we have

$$t = y + 2$$

and, substituting this value for *t* in the equation for *x* in terms of *t*, we obtain

$$x = (y + 2)^2 + 2(y + 2) = y^2 + 6y + 8.$$

We recognize the equation $x = y^2 + 6y + 8$ as that of a parabola, as indeed Fig. 12–1 shows.

The equations

$$x = t^7 + 3t^2 - 1, \qquad y = e^t + 2t^2 - 3\sqrt{t},$$

are a pair of parametric equations. Because of the square-root sign, it is clear that the domain for *t* is restricted to nonnegative real numbers. It is not possible to eliminate the parameter in any simple way, since solving either equation for *t* gives the appearance of being a herculean task.

EXAMPLE 1. Plot the locus of the equations

$$x = t^2 + 2t - 1, \qquad y = t^2 + t - 2.$$

Eliminate the parameter, if possible.

Solution. We construct the following table:

t	−4	−3	−2	−1	0	1	2	3
x	7	2	−1	−2	−1	2	7	14
y	10	4	0	−2	−2	0	4	10

By plotting these points, we obtain the curve shown in Fig. 12–3. To eliminate the parameter, we first subtract the equations, obtaining

$$x - y = t + 1 \qquad \text{and} \qquad t = x - y - 1.$$

FIGURE 12–3

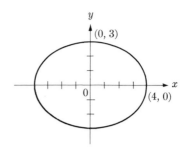

FIGURE 12–4

Substituting for t in the second of the equations, we find that

$$y = (x - y - 1)^2 + (x - y - 1) - 2,$$

and, simplifying,

$$x^2 - 2xy + y^2 - x - 2 = 0.$$

EXAMPLE 2. Plot the locus of the equations

$$x = 4 \cos \theta, \qquad y = 3 \sin \theta,$$

and eliminate the parameter, if possible.

Solution. In this problem the parameter is θ. While the domain for θ consists of all real numbers, only those values between 0 and 2π are needed, since both functions have period 2π. Rather than set up a table of values for θ, x, and y, we find it simpler first to write

$$\cos \theta = \frac{x}{4}, \qquad \sin \theta = \frac{y}{3}.$$

Then, by squaring and adding, we get

$$1 = \cos^2 \theta + \sin^2 \theta = \frac{x^2}{16} + \frac{y^2}{9},$$

which we recognize to be an ellipse, as shown in Fig. 12–4.

EXAMPLE 3. A projectile moves approximately according to the law

$$x = (v_0 \cos \alpha)t, \qquad y = (v_0 \sin \alpha)t - 16t^2,$$

where v_0 and α are constants and t is the time, in seconds, after the projectile is fired. The equations give the rectangular coordinates x, y (in feet) of the center of the projectile in the vertical plane of motion with the muzzle of the gun at the origin of the coordinate system, the x-axis horizontal, and the y-axis vertical; v_0 is the muzzle velocity, i.e., the velocity of the projectile at the instant it leaves the gun; α is the angle of inclination of the projectile as it leaves the gun [Fig. 12–5(a)]. If $v_0 = 100$ ft/sec, $\cos \alpha = \frac{3}{5}$, and $\sin \alpha = \frac{4}{5}$, what are the coordinates of the center of the projectile at times $t = 1, 2, 3, 4$, and 5? Find the time T when the projectile hits the ground, and find the distance R from the muzzle of the gun to the place where the projectile strikes the ground.

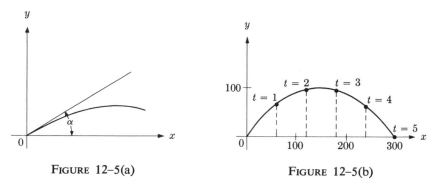

FIGURE 12-5(a)   FIGURE 12-5(b)

Solution. We have $v_0 \cos \alpha = 60$, $v_0 \sin \alpha = 80$, and so

$$x = 60t, \qquad y = 80t - 16t^2.$$

The projectile hits the ground when $y = 0$. Therefore $0 = 80t - 16t^2$ and $t = 0, 5$. Consequently, $T = 5$. To find R, we insert $t = 5$ in $x = 60t$, obtaining $R = 300$ ft. We construct the table:

t	0	1	2	3	4	5
x	0	60	120	180	240	300
y	0	64	96	96	64	0

Plotting the points yields the curve shown in Fig. 12-5(b). The domain of the relation is the interval $0 \le t \le 5$.

A circular hoop starts rolling along a stretch of level ground. A point on the rim of the hoop has a mark on it. We wish to find the path traced out by the marked point. Figure 12-6 shows the hoop in a number of different positions as it rolls along. The curve traced out by the marked point, which we denote by P, may be expressed in terms of parametric equations. Let a be the radius of the hoop, and suppose that when the hoop begins rolling the point P is on the ground at the point labeled O in Fig. 12-7. Figure 12-7 shows the position of the point P after the hoop has turned through an angle θ. Since the hoop is assumed to roll without slipping, we have, from the diagram,

$$\overline{OM} = \text{arc } \widehat{MP} = a\theta, \quad \theta \text{ in radians.}$$

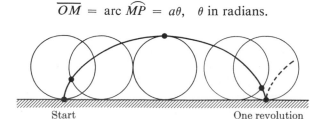

Start   One revolution

FIGURE 12-6

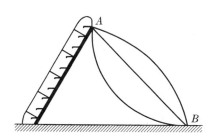

FIGURE 12–7   FIGURE 12–8

From $\triangle CPQ$ we read off

$$\overline{PQ} = a \sin \theta, \qquad 0 \le \theta \le \frac{\pi}{2},$$

$$\overline{QC} = a \cos \theta, \qquad 0 \le \theta \le \frac{\pi}{2}.$$

Denoting the coordinates of P by (x, y) we see that

$$x = \overline{ON} = \overline{OM} - \overline{NM} = \text{arc } \widehat{MP} - \overline{PQ} = a\theta - a \sin \theta,$$
$$y = \overline{NP} = \overline{MC} - \overline{QC} = a - a \cos \theta.$$

Even though these equations were derived for θ between 0 and $\pi/2$, it can be shown that for all values of θ the parametric equations

$$x = a(\theta - \sin \theta), \qquad y = a(1 - \cos \theta)$$

represent the path of the marked point on the rim. This curve is called a *cycloid*.

The cycloid is a particularly good example of a curve which is obtained without too much difficulty by use of parametric equations, while any attempt to find the relation between x and y without resorting to a parameter would lead to an almost unsurmountable problem.

The cycloid is of interest because it crops up in some problems in mathematical physics. Suppose a manufacturer of slides for playgrounds wishes to make a slide so that children can descend from a point A above ground to a point B on the ground as rapidly as possible (Fig. 12–8). He is not sure what shape the slide should be, but he assumes that it is so slippery and the children's clothes so smooth that friction may be neglected and that only gravity has an effect. Figure 12–8 shows several possible shapes. At first glance, it may seem that the straight line is the best, but this becomes doubtful when we realize that if we make the path steep at the beginning the child will gather speed and coast rapidly to B. The solution to the manufacturer's problem is the cycloid. A curve going from A to B which is a piece of a cycloid is the "curve of fastest descent." Proving such an assertion involves solving a problem in the calculus of variations. Questions of this type are considered in more advanced courses in mathematics.

EXERCISES

In problems 1 through 16, plot the curves as in Example 1; in each case eliminate the parameter and get a relation between x and y.

1. $x = 2t$, $y = -5t$

2. $x = t - 1$, $y = t^2$

3. $x = t$, $y = 1/t$

4. $x = 2 + (s^2/2)$, $y = -1 + \frac{1}{8}s^3$

5. $x = -1 + 2 \cos \theta$,
   $y = 2 + 2 \sin \theta$

6. $x = 3 \cos \theta$,
   $y = 2 \sin \theta$

7. $x = 2 \cos^3 \theta$, $y = 2 \sin^3 \theta$

8. $x = 3 \sec t$, $y = 2 \tan t$

9. $x = 2 + 3 \cosh u$,
   $y = -1 + 2 \sinh u$

10. $x = 1 + 2 \operatorname{sech} u$,
    $y = 2 + 3 \tanh u$

11. $x = t^2 + 2t + 3$,
    $y = t^2 + t - 1$

12. $x = t^2 + t + 1$,
    $y = \frac{1}{2}t^2 + t - 1$

13. $x = \dfrac{20t}{4 + t^2}$,

    $y = \dfrac{5(4 - t^2)}{4 + t^2}$

14. $x = \dfrac{3(2 - t)^2(2 + t)}{6t^2 + 8}$,

    $y = \dfrac{3(2 - t)(2 + t)^2}{6t^2 + 8}$

15. $x = e^t$, $y = e^{-t}$

16. $x = \ln s$, $y = e^{2s}$

17. Assuming that the equations of Example 3 hold, and given that $v_0 = 500$ ft/sec, $\cos \alpha = \frac{4}{5}$, $\sin \alpha = \frac{3}{5}$, find x and y for $t = 2, 4, 6, 8$, and 10. Also find T and R and plot the trajectory.

18. Assuming that the equations of Example 3 hold, find T and R in terms of v_0 and α. Find y in terms of x (i.e., eliminate the parameter).

19. A wheel of radius a rolls without slipping along a level stretch of ground. A point on one of the spokes of the wheel is marked. Find the path traced by this point if it is at a distance b from the center.

20. Find the locus of a point P on a circle of radius a which rolls without slipping on the inside of a circle of radius $4a$. Choose the center of the large circle as origin, choose the positive x-axis through a point where P touches the large circle, and choose the parameter θ as the angle xOC, where C is the center of the small circle (Fig. 12–9). (*Hint:* Note that arc $\overset{\frown}{BHP}$ = arc $\overset{\frown}{MB}$.)

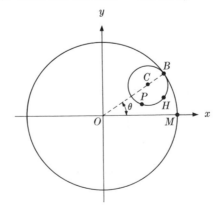

FIGURE 12–9

2. DERIVATIVES AND PARAMETRIC EQUATIONS

In previous chapters we learned how to use the first and second derivatives as aids in drawing graphs of functions. Such aids can also be used with parametric equations, even when the parameter cannot be eliminated. Suppose we have the equations

$$x = f(t), \qquad y = g(t),$$

which represent a relation between x and y. It is only in rather special circumstances that such a relation yields y as a function of x. For example, if $f'(t)$ is positive for t in an interval $[a, b]$, then we know that the values of x move steadily to the right as t goes from a to b. Therefore y will be a function of x for x in the interval $[f(a), f(b)]$. However, in general, x and y will be related by an equation in which neither variable is a function of the other. As in the case of implicit functions, it nevertheless is still possible to find the derivative dy/dx and identify it with the slope of the tangent to the curve at a point. The derivative may be found by the chain rule. We have

$$\frac{dy}{dx} = \frac{dy}{dt} \cdot \frac{dt}{dx} = \frac{dy/dt}{dx/dt}.$$

This derivative will be given in terms of t. If t cannot be expressed in terms of x or y — as is frequently the case — the process of getting the second derivative requires some explanation. The idea is to use the chain rule again. We write

$$\frac{d^2y}{dx^2} = \frac{d}{dx}\left(\frac{dy}{dx}\right) = \frac{d}{dt}\left(\frac{dy}{dx}\right)\frac{dt}{dx} = \frac{d}{dt}\left(\frac{dy}{dx}\right) \div \frac{dx}{dt}.$$

Since dy/dx is given in terms of t, finding $(d/dt)(dy/dx)$ is a routine matter. Furthermore, we calculated dx/dt previously, when we obtained dy/dx.

EXAMPLE 1. Find dy/dx, d^2y/dx^2, and d^3y/dx^3, given that $x = t^2 + 3t - 2$, $y = 2 - t - t^2$.

Solution. We have

$$\frac{dx}{dt} = 2t + 3, \qquad \frac{dy}{dt} = -1 - 2t.$$

Therefore,

$$\frac{dy}{dx} = \frac{dy/dt}{dx/dt} = \frac{-(2t + 1)}{2t + 3}.$$

The second derivative is given by

$$\frac{d^2y}{dx^2} = \frac{\dfrac{d}{dt}\left(\dfrac{dy}{dx}\right)}{dx/dt},$$

and since

$$\frac{d}{dt}\left(\frac{dy}{dx}\right) = \frac{d}{dt}\left(-\frac{2t+1}{2t+3}\right) = -\frac{(2t+3)(2) - (2t+1)(2)}{(2t+3)^2} = \frac{-4}{(2t+3)^2},$$

we get

$$\frac{d^2y}{dx^2} = -\frac{4/(2t+3)^2}{2t+3} = \frac{-4}{(2t+3)^3}.$$

We have not derived a formula for the third derivative, but the process is analogous. We write

$$\frac{d^3y}{dx^3} = \frac{d}{dx}\left(\frac{d^2y}{dx^2}\right) = \frac{d}{dt}\left(\frac{d^2y}{dx^2}\right)\cdot\frac{dt}{dx} = \frac{\frac{d}{dt}\left(\frac{d^2y}{dx^2}\right)}{dx/dt}.$$

For the numerator, we obtain

$$\frac{d}{dt}\left(\frac{d^2y}{dx^2}\right) = \frac{d}{dt}\left(\frac{-4}{(2t+3)^3}\right) = \frac{24}{(2t+3)^4},$$

and so

$$\frac{d^3y}{dx^3} = \frac{24/(2t+3)^4}{2t+3} = \frac{24}{(2t+3)^5}.$$

EXAMPLE 2.   Given that $x = x(t) = t^2 - t$, $y = y(t) = t^3 - 3t$. Find dy/dx and d^2y/dx^2. Plot the graph.

Solution. We compute

$$\frac{dx}{dt} = 2t - 1, \qquad \frac{dy}{dt} = 3(t^2 - 1);$$

$$\frac{dy}{dx} = \frac{3(t^2 - 1)}{2t - 1}, \qquad \frac{d^2y}{dx^2} = \frac{\frac{d}{dt}\left(\frac{dy}{dx}\right)}{dx/dt} = 6\,\frac{t^2 - t + 1}{(2t - 1)^3}.$$

We construct the table of values:

t	-3	-2	$-\sqrt{3}$	-1	0	$\frac{1}{2}$	1	$\sqrt{3}$	2	3
x	12	6	$3 + \sqrt{3}$	2	0	$-\frac{1}{4}$	0	$3 - \sqrt{3}$	2	6
x'	$-$	$-$	$-$	$-$	$-$	0	$+$	$+$	$+$	$+$
y	-18	-2	0	2	0	$-\frac{11}{8}$	-2	0	2	18
y'	$+$	$+$	$+$	0	$-$	$-$	0	$+$	$+$	$+$

We draw the graph, as in Fig. 12–10.

EXAMPLE 3. Find the equation of the line tangent to the curve

$$x = t^2 - 2, \qquad y = t^3 - 2t + 1,$$

at the point where $t = 2$.

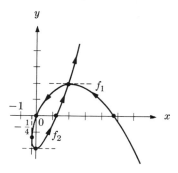

FIGURE 12–10

Solution. When $t = 2$, we have $x = 2$, $y = 5$. Further, $dx/dt = 2t$, $dy/dt =. 3t^2 - 2$, and $dy/dx = (3t^2 - 2)/2t$. The slope of the tangent line is

$$\frac{3(2)^2 - 2}{2(2)} = \frac{5}{2}.$$

The equation of the desired line is

$$y - 5 = \tfrac{5}{2}(x - 2), \qquad \text{or} \qquad 5x - 2y = 0.$$

EXERCISES

In problems 1 through 10, find dy/dx and d^2y/dx^2 in terms of the parameters.

1. $x = 3t - 2$, $y = 4 - 5t$
2. $x = t^2 + 4$, $y = 2t^2 - 3t + 1$
3. $x = t^2 + 1$, $y = t^3 + 2t$
4. $x = 5 \cos t$, $y = 4 \sin t$
5. $x = e^{2t}$, $y = 2 + t^2$
6. $x = t^2 - 1$, $y = 2e^t$
7. $x = 4 \cos t$, $y = 2 \sin^2 t$
8. $x = 2 \sin 2\theta$, $y = 2 \sin \theta$
9. $x = a \cos^3 \theta$, $y = a \sin^3 \theta$
10. $x = a\theta - a \sin \theta$, $y = a - a \cos \theta$ (cycloid)
11. Find dy/dx, d^2y/dx^2, d^3y/dx^3, d^4y/dx^4, given that $x = t^3 + t$, $y = \tfrac{3}{2}t^4 + t^2$
12. Rework problem 11, given that $x = e^{2t}$, $y = e^t + e^{-t}$

In problems 13 through 20, find in each case the equations of the lines tangent and normal to the specified curve at the point corresponding to the given value of the parameter.

13. $x = t^2 + 1$, $y = t^3 + 2t$, $t = -2$
14. $x = e^{2t}$, $y = 2 + t^2$, $t = 1$
15. $x = 4 \cos t$, $y = 2 \sin^2 t$, $t = \pi/3$
16. $x = 5 \cos t$, $y = 4 \sin t$, $t = \pi/3$
17. $x = t^2 - 1$, $y = 2e^t$, $t = -1$
18. $x = 2 \sin 2\theta$, $y = 2 \sin \theta$, $\theta = \pi/4$
19. $x = 2 \cos^3 \theta$, $y = 2 \sin^3 \theta$, $\theta = \pi/4$
20. $x = 3\theta - 3 \sin \theta$, $y = 3 - 3 \cos \theta$, $\theta = \pi/2$

In problems 21 through 26, find in each case the intervals of values of the parameter when x and y are increasing and decreasing. Plot the curve. Solve for y in terms of x.

21. $x = 2 \tan \phi$, $y = \sec \phi$, $-\pi/2 < \phi < 3\pi/2$
22. $x = 2 \tan \theta$, $y = 4 \cos^2 \theta$, $-\pi/2 < \theta < \pi/2$

23. $x = t^2 + 2t$, $y = t^2 + t$, $-\infty < t < \infty$

24. $x = \cos\theta$, $y = \sin 2\theta$, $0 \le \theta \le 2\pi$

25. $x = e^{2t} + 1$, $y = 1 - e^{-t}$, $-\infty < t < \infty$

26. $x = t^2(t - 2)$, $y = t(t - 2)^2$, $-\infty < t < \infty$. (Do not attempt to solve for y in terms of x.)

3. ARC LENGTH

We frequently draw the graph of a function $y = f(x)$ and refer to it as the locus or curve representing the function. When picturing such a graph, we automatically associate a length with any part of it (e.g., the portion going from P_1 to P_2 in Fig. 12–11). We now raise three questions: (1) What are the kinds of curves (or loci) with which we shall associate a length? (2) How do we define length? (3) Once we have defined length how do we measure it?

These questions are easily answered for straight lines. Every straight line segment has a length given by the distance formula

$$d = \sqrt{(x_1 - x_2)^2 + (y_1 - y_2)^2},$$

where (x_1, y_1) and (x_2, y_2) are the coordinates of the endpoints of the segment. We are familiar with the formula for the length of a circular arc, but for many students the derivation of this formula is but a vague memory from high-school geometry or trigonometry. A first step in a precise discussion of the length of curves, of which a circular arc is a special case, is the definition of what we call an *arc*.

DEFINITION. If a locus is given in the form of a function so that $y = f(x)$, $a \le x \le b$, and if f is continuous in this interval, then the locus of f is called an *arc*. When the locus is given by the parametric equations

$$x = F(t), \qquad y = G(t), \qquad c \le t \le d,$$

it is called an *arc* if F and G are continuous on the interval $[c, d]$ and if for two

FIGURE 12–11   FIGURE 12–12

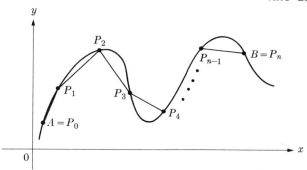

FIGURE 12–13

different values of the parameter, t_1 and t_2, it can never happen that both $F(t_1) = F(t_2)$ and $G(t_1) = G(t_2)$.

Remark. This last condition, which guarantees that the locus does not intersect itself, may be written more compactly as

$$[F(t_1) - F(t_2)]^2 + [G(t_1) - G(t_2)]^2 > 0 \quad \text{if} \quad t_1 \neq t_2.$$

The first of the three questions we raised may now be answered by stating that we shall discuss the lengths of only those curves which are arcs. Turning to the second question — that of defining length — we shall proceed by making use of the one type of arc whose length we know how to measure: the line segment.

We let C be an arc in the plane, as shown in Fig. 12–12. Suppose that we wish to define the length of such an arc between the points A and B. The definition of length requires a limiting process. As a first step we mark off a number of points on the arc between A and B and label them $P_1, P_2, \ldots, P_{n-1}$. Setting $P_0 = A$ and $P_n = B$, we draw a straight line segment from each point P_i to the next point P_{i+1}, as in Fig. 12–13. From the distance formula for the length of a line segment, we compute the lengths

$$\overline{P_0P_1}, \qquad \overline{P_1P_2}, \qquad \overline{P_2P_3}, \qquad \ldots, \qquad \overline{P_{n-1}P_n},$$

and add them. We can write the sum concisely in the form

$$\sum_{i=1}^{n} \overline{P_{i-1}P_i}.$$

If the points P_i are "close together," we feel intuitively that the total length of the line segments will be "close to" the as yet undefined length of the curve. Therefore, if a sequence of subdivisions is made with an increasing number of points in succeeding subdivisions, we would expect that in the limit the length of the arc would be attained. This is indeed the case. In any subdivision of C we denote the length of the longest line segment connecting successive points by $\|\Delta\|$ and call this the *norm of the subdivision.* We recall that the norm of a subdivision of a section of the x-axis was encountered in the definition of integral.

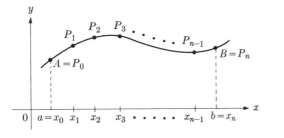

FIGURE 12–14   FIGURE 12–15

DEFINITION. *An arc C from A to B has length if there is a number L with the following property:* For each $\epsilon > 0$ there is a $\delta > 0$ such that

$$\left| \sum_{i=1}^{n} \overline{P_{i-1}P_i} - L \right| < \epsilon$$

for every subdivision $A = P_0, P_1, P_2, \ldots, P_{n-1}, P_n = B$ with $\|\Delta\| < \delta$. The number L is called the *length* of the arc C.

Any arc which has a length is called *rectifiable*. According to the definition, the length L is the limit of the lengths of inscribed polygons, as the maximum distance between successive points of these inscribed polygons tends to zero.

We now turn to the third question — that of actually finding ways of computing the length of an arc. Suppose that the arc C is given in the form $y = f(x)$, with f possessing a continuous derivative and with the endpoints of the arc at $A(a, f(a))$, $B(b, f(b))$, as shown in Fig. 12–14. We introduce subdivision points $P_1, P_2, \ldots,$ P_{n-1}, with coordinates $P_i(x_i, y_i)$. The length of the inscribed polygon is given by the formula

$$\sum_{i=1}^{n} \overline{P_{i-1}P_i} = \sum_{i=1}^{n} \sqrt{(x_i - x_{i-1})^2 + (y_i - y_{i-1})^2},$$

where we have denoted $a = x_0, f(a) = y_0, b = x_n$, and $f(b) = y_n$. At this point we recall the Theorem of the Mean (Chapter 7, Section 2), which states that if a function f has a continuous derivative on an interval $[c, d]$, then there is a value ξ between c and d such that

$$\frac{f(d) - f(c)}{d - c} = f'(\xi), \qquad c < \xi < d.$$

This theorem can be used in the present situation. A typical line segment is shown in Fig. 12–15, and we remember that $y_{i-1} = f(x_{i-1})$, $y_i = f(x_i)$, and therefore there is a value ξ_i between x_{i-1} and x_i such that

$$\frac{f(x_i) - f(x_{i-1})}{x_i - x_{i-1}} = f'(\xi_i), \qquad x_{i-1} < \xi_i < x_i,$$

or

$$(y_i - y_{i-1}) = f'(\xi_i)(x_i - x_{i-1}).$$

We find such an equation for every i from 1 to n, and we substitute in the formula for the length of the inscribed polygons, getting

$$\sum_{i=1}^{n} \overline{P_{i-1}P_i} = \sum_{i=1}^{n} \sqrt{1 + [f'(\xi_i)]^2}\,(x_i - x_{i-1}).$$

We now set $\Delta_i x = x_i - x_{i-1}$ and, recalling the definition of an integral, we see that the limit of

$$\sum_{i=1}^{n} \sqrt{1 + [f'(\xi_i)]^2}\,\Delta_i x$$

is nothing but

$$\int_a^b \sqrt{1 + [f'(x)]^2}\,dx.$$

This is the desired formula for the length of an arc.

EXAMPLE 1. Find the length of the arc $y = x^{3/2}$ from the point $A(1, 1)$ to $B(2, 2\sqrt{2})$.

Solution. We have $dy/dx = \frac{3}{2}x^{1/2}$ and $(dy/dx)^2 = \frac{9}{4}x$.

The length of arc, s, is given by

$$s = \int_1^2 \sqrt{1 + \frac{9}{4}x}\,dx.$$

To integrate this we set $u = 1 + \frac{9}{4}x$, $du = \frac{9}{4}dx$, and obtain

$$s = \int_{13/4}^{11/2} u^{1/2} \cdot \frac{4}{9}\,du,$$

new limits having been inserted because $u = \frac{13}{4}$ when $x = 1$ and $u = \frac{11}{2}$ when $x = 2$. Therefore

$$s = \left[\frac{4}{9} \cdot \frac{2}{3} u^{3/2}\right]_{13/4}^{11/2} = \frac{2}{27}(11\sqrt{22} - \frac{13}{2}\sqrt{13}).$$

Suppose that an arc C is given in the parametric form

$$x = x(t), \qquad y = y(t), \qquad a \le t \le b.$$

We proceed as before, by introducing a number of subdivision points between the endpoints, $A(x(a), y(a))$ and $B(x(b), y(b))$. The sum of the lengths of the inscribed polygon is given by the formula

$$\sum_{i=1}^{n} \overline{P_{i-1}P_i} = \sum_{i=1}^{n} \sqrt{[x(t_i) - x(t_{i-1})]^2 + [y(t_i) - y(t_{i-1})]^2}.$$

Assuming that $x(t)$ and $y(t)$ have continuous first derivatives on the interval $[a, b]$, we may apply the Theorem of the Mean to both functions, getting

$$x(t_i) - x(t_{i-1}) = x'(\xi_i)(t_i - t_{i-1}), \qquad t_{i-1} < \xi_i < t_i,$$
$$y(t_i) - y(t_{i-1}) = y'(\eta_i)(t_i - t_{i-1}), \qquad t_{i-1} < \eta_i < t_i.$$

We find

$$\sum_{i=1}^{n} \overline{P_{i-1}P_i} = \sum_{i=1}^{n} \sqrt{[x'(\xi_i)]^2 + [y'(\eta_i)]^2}\,(t_i - t_{i-1}).$$

Proceeding to the limit as the norm of the subdivision tends to zero and taking into account the definition of integral,* we obtain the formula for arc length:

$$s = \int_a^b \sqrt{[x'(t)]^2 + [y'(t)]^2}\; dt.$$

From the Fundamental Theorem of the Calculus, which states that differentiation and integration are inverse processes, it follows that

$$s'(t) = \frac{ds}{dt} = \sqrt{(dx/dt)^2 + (dy/dt)^2} \qquad \text{or} \qquad ds^2 = dx^2 + dy^2.$$

If the arc is in the form $y = f(x)$ or $x = g(y)$ we obtain, respectively,

$$\frac{ds}{dx} = \sqrt{1 + (dy/dx)^2} \qquad \text{and} \qquad \frac{ds}{dy} = \sqrt{1 + (dx/dy)^2}.$$

EXAMPLE 2. Given that $x = t^3 + 1$, $y = 2t^{9/2} - 4$. Find the length of the arc from the point where $t = 1$ to the point where $t = 3$.

Solution. We have $x'(t) = 3t^2$, $y'(t) = 9t^{7/2}$. Therefore,

$$s = \int_1^3 \sqrt{9t^4 + 81t^7}\; dt = 9 \int_1^3 \sqrt{\tfrac{1}{9} + t^3}\; t^2\, dt.$$

Letting $u = \tfrac{1}{9} + t^3$, $du = 3t^2\, dt$ and integrating, we get

$$s = [2(\tfrac{1}{9} + t^3)^{3/2}]_1^3 = \tfrac{2}{27}(244\sqrt{244} - 10\sqrt{10}).$$

EXAMPLE 3. Find the length of one arch of a cycloid, given that

$$x = a(\theta - \sin\theta), \qquad y = a(1 - \cos\theta), \qquad 0 \le \theta \le 2\pi.$$

Solution. We have $dx/d\theta = a(1 - \cos\theta)$, $dy/d\theta = a\sin\theta$, and therefore

$$s = \int_0^{2\pi} \sqrt{a^2(1 - \cos\theta)^2 + a^2\sin^2\theta}\; d\theta = a \int_0^{2\pi} \sqrt{2 - 2\cos\theta}\; d\theta.$$

---

*The argument given is intuitive and not quite precise. To apply the definition of integral directly, it would be necessary that ξ_i and η_i be the same. A proof of the fact that the result is valid with $\xi_i \ne \eta_i$ is established in Morrey, *University Calculus*, Theorem 8–23.

Making use of the formula $\sin (\theta/2) = \sqrt{(1 - \cos \theta)/2}$, we obtain

$$s = 2a \int_0^{2\pi} \sin \frac{\theta}{2} \, d\theta = \left[-4a \cos \frac{\theta}{2} \right]_0^{2\pi} = 8a.$$

EXERCISES

In problems 1 through 9, find the length of the arc in each case.

1. $y = x^{3/2}$, $0 \leq x \leq 3$

2. $y = x^2/4 - \frac{1}{2} \ln x$, $1 \leq x \leq 3$

3. $y = \frac{1}{6}x^3 + 1/(2x)$, $1 \leq x \leq 3$

4. $y = 3 \cosh \frac{1}{3}x$, $0 \leq x \leq 2$

5. $y = \sqrt{36 - x^2}$, $0 \leq x \leq 3$

6. $x = 6 \cos t$, $y = 6 \sin t$, $\pi/3 \leq t \leq \pi/2$

7. $y = (9 - x^{2/3})^{3/2}$, $1 \leq x \leq 2$

8. $y = x^{2/3}$, $-8 \leq x \leq -2$

9. $x = e^{-t} \cos t$, $y = e^{-t} \sin t$, $0 \leq t \leq \pi/2$

In problems 10 through 18, in each case set up the integral for arc length but do not attempt to evaluate the integral.

10. $y = \sqrt{x}$, $1 \leq x \leq 4$

11. $y = x^3$, $1 \leq x \leq 2$

12. $x = y^4 - 2y^2 + 3$, $1 \leq y \leq 2$

13. $y = \frac{1}{3}(x - 3)\sqrt{x}$, $1 \leq x \leq 2$

14. $x = \frac{1}{6}t^3$, $y = 1/2t$, $1 \leq t \leq 3$

15. $x = t^3 + 2t - 1$, $y = t^2 - t + 5$, $1 \leq t \leq 5$

16. $x = 5 \cos t$, $y = 4 \sin t$, $0 \leq t \leq \pi/2$

17. $y = \frac{4}{5}\sqrt{25 - x^2}$, $0 \leq x \leq 5$

18. $x = t \cos t$, $y = t \sin t$, $0 \leq t \leq \pi$

In problems 19 through 22, in each case subdivide the given interval into the number of equal subintervals indicated by the integer n. Compute the quantity

$$\sum_{i=1}^{n} \sqrt{1 + [f'(\xi_i)]^2}(x_i - x_{i-1}),$$

by taking the value ξ_i at the midpoint of the ith subinterval, and in this way approximate the length of the arc.

19. $y = x^3$, $0 \leq x \leq 2$, $n = 4$

20. $y = x^3$, $0 \leq x \leq 2$, $n = 8$

21. $y = \frac{4}{5}\sqrt{25 - x^2}$, $0 \leq x \leq 3$, $n = 6$

22. $y = \dfrac{1}{x^2 + 1}$, $0 \leq x \leq 2$, $n = 8$

In problems 23 through 25, follow the directions for problems 19 through 22, except that the quantity

$$\sum_{i=1}^{n} \sqrt{[x'(\xi_i)]^2 + [y'(\xi_i)]^2}(t_i - t_{i-1})$$

is to be computed, with ξ_i the midpoint of $[t_{i-1}, t_i]$.

23. $x = t^3 + 1, \quad y = t + 2, \quad 0 \le t \le 1, \quad n = 5$

24. $x = 5 \cos t, \quad y = 4 \sin t, \quad 0 \le t \le \pi/2, \quad n = 6$

25. $x = \dfrac{t+1}{t}, \quad y = \dfrac{t^2 - 2}{1 + t^2}, \quad 0 \le t \le 2, \quad n = 4$

4. CURVATURE

Our aim in this section is to obtain a measure of the rapidity with which curves change direction. Suppose that a curve is given by the equation $y = f(x)$ and f has a continuous second derivative. At a particular point $P_0(x_0, y_0)$ the tangent to the curve makes an angle with the positive x-direction which we call ϕ (Fig. 12-16). From the definition of derivative we know that $\tan \phi = f'(x_0)$ or that at a point $P(x, y)$,

$$\phi(x) = \arctan f'(x).$$

The way ϕ changes as we move along the curve is a measure of the sharpness of the curve. Note that for a straight line ϕ doesn't change at all, and it changes very little even after traversing a long section of the arc of a gradual curve.

DEFINITION. The *curvature* κ of an arc given in the form $y = f(x)$ is the rate of change of the angle ϕ with respect to the arc length s. That is,

$$\kappa = \frac{d\phi}{ds}.$$

The following theorem tells us how to compute the curvature when we are given the function f.

Theorem 1. *For an arc of the form $y = f(x)$, we have*

$$\kappa(x) = \frac{f''(x)}{\{1 + [f'(x)]^2\}^{3/2}}.$$

FIGURE 12-16

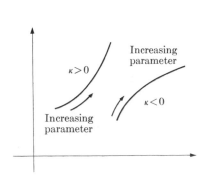

FIGURE 12-17

Proof. From the Chain Rule, we know that

$$\kappa = \frac{d\phi}{ds} = \frac{d\phi}{dx} \cdot \frac{dx}{ds}.$$

We first find $d\phi/dx$:

$$\frac{d\phi}{dx} = \frac{d}{dx} (\arctan f'(x)) = \frac{1}{1 + [f'(x)]^2} \cdot f''(x).$$

To obtain dx/ds, we recall that since differentiation and integration are inverse processes, the formula

$$s = \int \sqrt{1 + [f'(x)]^2} \, dx$$

may be differentiated to give

$$ds = \sqrt{1 + [f'(x)]^2} \, dx,$$

or

$$\frac{dx}{ds} = \frac{1}{\sqrt{1 + [f'(x)]^2}}.$$

Therefore we get

$$\kappa = \frac{f''(x)}{1 + [f'(x)]^2} \cdot \frac{1}{\sqrt{1 + [f'(x)]^2}} = \frac{f''(x)}{\{1 + [f'(x)]^2\}^{3/2}}.$$

If a curve is given in the form $x = g(y)$, or in the parametric form $x = x(t)$, $y = y(t)$, the angle ϕ which the tangent line forms with the positive x-direction may still be defined. It can be shown that for an arc of the form $x = g(y)$ the curvature is given by the formula

$$\kappa(y) = -\frac{g''(y)}{\{1 + [g'(y)]^2\}^{3/2}},$$

while for arcs in parametric form $x = x(t)$, $y = y(t)$, κ is given by the formula

$$\kappa(t) = \frac{x'(t)y''(t) - x''(t)y'(t)}{(x'^2 + y'^2)^{3/2}}.$$

The curvature may be positive, negative, or zero. We see that for arcs such as $y = f(x)$, the curvature has the same sign as $f''(x)$. If ϕ is increasing so that the curve is "turning to the left" as the parameter increases, then κ is positive; κ is negative if ϕ is decreasing. This is equivalent to saying that the concave side of the curve is on the left if $\kappa > 0$ and is on the right if $\kappa < 0$ (Fig. 12–17).

EXAMPLE 1. Find the curvature of the circle $x = a \cos t$, $y = a \sin t$.

Solution. Differentiation yields

$$x' = -a \sin t, \quad x'' = -a \cos t, \quad y' = a \cos t, \quad y'' = -a \sin t.$$

Therefore

$$\kappa = \frac{a^2 \sin^2 t + a^2 \cos^2 t}{(a^2 \sin^2 t + a^2 \cos^2 t)^{3/2}} = \frac{a^2}{a^3} = \frac{1}{a}.$$

We conclude that a circle of radius a has constant curvature equal to $1/a$.

DEFINITIONS. *The radius of curvature R of an arc at a point* is defined as the reciprocal of the absolute value of the curvature at that point; that is,

$$R = \frac{1}{|\kappa|}.$$

The *circle of curvature of an arc at a point P* is that circle passing through P which has radius equal to R, the radius of curvature, and whose center C lies on the concave side of the curve along the normal through P (see Fig. 12–18).

 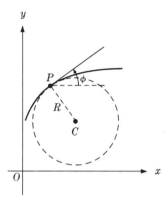

FIGURE 12–18

EXAMPLE 2.   Find the curvature κ and the radius of curvature R for the parabola $y = x^2$. Find the center of the circle of curvature at the point $(1, 1)$.

Solution. We have $dy/dx = 2x$, $d^2y/dx^2 = 2$, and therefore

$$\kappa = \frac{2}{(1 + 4x^2)^{3/2}}; \qquad R = \tfrac{1}{2}(1 + 4x^2)^{3/2}.$$

At $(1, 1)$ the slope is 2 and the equation of the normal line is $y - 1 = -\tfrac{1}{2}(x - 1)$, or $x + 2y - 3 = 0$. The radius of curvature R is $\tfrac{5}{2}\sqrt{5}$. To find the center C of the circle of curvature we first write the equation of the circle through $(1, 1)$, of radius $\tfrac{5}{2}\sqrt{5}$. It is

$$(x - 1)^2 + (y - 1)^2 = \tfrac{125}{4}.$$

Solving this simultaneously with $x + 2y - 3 = 0$, the equation of the normal line, we obtain, for the coordinates x_c, y_c of C, the values

$$x_c = -4, \qquad y_c = \tfrac{7}{2}.$$

EXAMPLE 3. Find the curvature and radius of curvature of the cycloid

$$x = a(\theta - \sin \theta), \quad y = a(1 - \cos \theta), \quad 0 < \theta < 2\pi.$$

Solution. We have

$$x'(\theta) = a(1 - \cos \theta), \qquad x''(\theta) = a \sin \theta,$$
$$y'(\theta) = a \sin \theta, \qquad\qquad y''(\theta) = a \cos \theta.$$

Therefore

$$\kappa(\theta) = \frac{a(1 - \cos \theta)a \cos \theta - a \sin \theta\, a \sin \theta}{[a^2(1 - \cos \theta)^2 + a^2 \sin \theta]^{3/2}}$$

$$= \frac{1}{a} \frac{\cos \theta - 1}{[2(1 - \cos \theta)]^{3/2}} = -\frac{1}{a2\sqrt{2}\sqrt{1 - \cos \theta}}$$

$$= -\frac{1}{4a \sin (\theta/2)}.$$

$$R(\theta) = 4a \sin \frac{\theta}{2}, \qquad 0 < \theta < 2\pi.$$

EXERCISES

In problems 1 through 12, find in each case the curvature $\kappa(x)$ and the radius of curvature $R(x)$.

1. $y = 2\sqrt{x}$

2. $y = x + 1/x, \quad x > 0$

3. $y = x^2 + 3$

4. $y = e^x$

5. $y = \sin x$

6. $y = \cos 2x$

7. $y = a \cosh (x/a)$

8. $y = \tan x$

9. $y = \arcsin x$

10. $y = (a^{2/3} - x^{2/3})^{3/2}$

11. $y = \dfrac{b}{a}\sqrt{a^2 - x^2}, \quad |x| < a$

12. $y = \dfrac{b}{a}\sqrt{x^2 - a^2}, \quad |x| > a$

In problems 13 through 16, find in each case $\kappa(y)$ and $R(y)$.

13. $x = \cot y$

14. $x = \ln y$

15. $x = -\sqrt{a^2 - y^2}$

16. $x = \frac{1}{3}y^3$

In problems 17 through 22, find in each case κ and R in terms of the parameter.

17. $x = \frac{1}{2}t^2, \quad y = \frac{1}{3}t^3$

18. $x = e^t, \quad y = t^2$

19. $x = e^t \sin t, \quad y = e^t \cos t$

20. $x = e^{-2t} \cos t, \quad y = e^{-2t} \sin t$

21. $x = a \cos^3 \theta, \quad y = a \sin^3 \theta$

22. $x = a \cos \theta, \quad y = b \sin \theta$

In problems 23 through 26, find $\kappa(x)$ in each case, and locate the values of x for which κ has relative maxima and minima.

23. $y = \frac{1}{2}x^2$

24. $y = \ln x$

25. $y = 1/x$

26. $y = \ln (\sin x)$

27. Prove that the coordinates of the center of the circle of curvature C are given by

$$x_c = x - \frac{\sin \phi}{\kappa}, \qquad y_c = y + \frac{\cos \phi}{\kappa}.$$

In problems 28 through 31, in each case find κ and R, and locate the center of the circle of curvature at the point indicated.

28. $y = x^2$, $(-1, 1)$ 29. $y = \cos x$, $(\pi/3, \frac{1}{2})$
30. $y = x^3 - 2x^2 + 3x - 5$, $(1, -3)$ 31. $y = e^x$, $(0, 1)$

In problems 32 through 34, find in terms of t the coordinates of the centers of the circles of curvature.

32. $x = a \cos t$, $y = b \sin t$ 33. $x = a \sec t$, $y = b \tan t$
34. $x = a \cosh t$, $y = b \sinh t$

CHAPTER 13

Polar Coordinates

1. POLAR COORDINATES

A coordinate system in the plane allows us to associate a pair of numbers with each point in the plane. Until now we have considered rectangular coordinate systems exclusively. In Chapter 2 we saw that there are many possible ways of identifying number pairs with points in the plane; we shall now describe the system known as *polar coordinates*.

We begin by selecting a point in the plane which we call the *pole* or *origin* and label it *O*. From this point we draw a half-line starting at the pole and extending indefinitely in one direction. This line is usually drawn horizontally and to the right of the pole, as shown in Fig. 13–1. It is called the *initial line* or *polar axis*.

O   Initial line

FIGURE 13–1

FIGURE 13–2

Let *P* be any point in the plane. Its position will be determined by its distance from the pole and by the angle that the line *OP* makes with the initial line. We measure angles θ from the initial line as in trigonometry — positive in a counter-clockwise direction and negative in a clockwise direction. The distance *r* from the origin to the point *P* will be taken as positive. The coordinates of *P* (Fig. 13–2) in the polar coordinate system are (r, θ). There is a sharp distinction between rectangular and polar coordinates, in that a point *P* may be represented in just one way by a pair of rectangular coordinates, but it may be represented in many ways by polar coordinates. For example, the point *Q* with polar coordinates $(2, \pi/6)$ also has polar coordinates

$$\left(2, 2\pi + \frac{\pi}{6}\right), \quad \left(2, 4\pi + \frac{\pi}{6}\right), \quad \left(2, 6\pi + \frac{\pi}{6}\right),$$
$$\left(2, -2\pi + \frac{\pi}{6}\right), \quad \left(2, -4\pi + \frac{\pi}{6}\right), \quad \text{etc.}$$

In other words, there are infinitely many representations of the same point. Furthermore, it is convenient to allow *r*, the distance from the origin, to take on negative values. We establish the convention that a pair of coordinates such as

FIGURE 13–3

$(-3, \theta)$ is simply another representation of the point with coordinates $(3, \theta + \pi)$. Figure 13–3 shows the relationship of the points (r, θ) and $(-r, \theta)$.

EXAMPLE 1. Plot the points whose polar coordinates are

$$P\left(3, \frac{\pi}{3}\right), \quad Q\left(-2, \frac{2\pi}{3}\right), \quad R\left(-2, \frac{\pi}{4}\right), \quad S\left(2, \frac{3\pi}{4}\right), \quad T\left(3, -\frac{\pi}{6}\right).$$

Solution. The points are plotted in Fig. 13–4.

It is important to know the connection between rectangular and polar coordinate systems. To find this relationship, let us consider a plane with one system superimposed on the other in such a way that the origin of the rectangular system is at the pole and the positive *x*-axis coincides with the initial line (Fig. 13–5). The relationship between the rectangular coordinates (x, y) and the polar coordinates (r, θ) of a point P is given by the equations

$$x = r \cos \theta, \qquad y = r \sin \theta.$$

When we are given r and θ, these equations tell us how to find x and y. We also have the formulas

$$r = \pm\sqrt{x^2 + y^2}, \qquad \tan \theta = \frac{y}{x},$$

which give us r and θ when the rectangular coordinates are known.

FIGURE 13–4

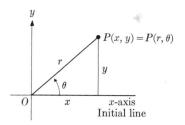

FIGURE 13–5

EXAMPLE 2. The rectangular coordinates of a point are $(\sqrt{3}, -1)$. Find a set of polar coordinates for this point.

Solution. We have $r = \sqrt{3+1} = 2$ and $\tan \theta = -1/\sqrt{3}$. Since the point is in the fourth quadrant, we select for θ the value $-\pi/6$ (or $11\pi/6$). The answer is $(2, -\pi/6)$.

EXERCISES

In problems 1 through 4, the polar coordinates of points are given. Find the rectangular coordinates of the same points and plot them on graphs.

1. $(4, \pi/6)$, $(3, 3\pi/4)$, $(2, \pi)$, $(1, 0)$, $(-2, \pi)$
2. $(2, \pi/4)$, $(1, \pi/3)$, $(3, \pi/2)$, $(4, 3\pi/2)$, $(-1, 7\pi/6)$
3. $(-1, 0)$, $(2, -\pi/6)$, $(4, -\pi/3)$, $(-3, 3\pi/4)$, $(0, \pi/2)$
4. $(2, -\pi/2)$, $(-1, -3\pi/2)$, $(2, 4\pi/3)$, $(-1, -\pi/4)$, $(0, -\pi)$

In problems 5 through 8, the rectangular coordinates of points are given. Find a pair of polar coordinates for each of the points and plot on graphs.

5. $(3, 3)$, $(0, 4)$, $(-1, \sqrt{3})$, $(0, -1)$, $(2, 0)$
6. $(-2, -2)$, $(-4, 0)$, $(\sqrt{3}, 1)$, $(-\sqrt{3}, -1)$, $(0, -2)$
7. $(-2, 2)$, $(3, -3)$, $(-\sqrt{3}, 1)$, $(2\sqrt{3}, 2)$ $(2, 2\sqrt{3})$
8. $(4, 0)$, $(0, 0)$, $(6, 6)$, $(\sqrt{6}, \sqrt{2})$, $(\frac{3}{2}, -\frac{3}{2})$
9. Describe the locus of all points which, in polar coordinates, satisfy the condition $r = 5$; do the same for the condition $\theta = \pi/3$ and for the condition $\theta = -5\pi/6$. What can be said about the angle of intersection of the curve $r = $ const, with $\theta = $ const?
10. Find the distance between the points with polar coordinates $(3, \pi/4)$, $(2, \pi/3)$.
11. Find the distance between the points with polar coordinates $(1, \pi/2)$, $(4, 5\pi/6)$.
12. Find a formula for the distance between the points (r_1, θ_1) and (r_2, θ_2).

2. GRAPHS IN POLAR COORDINATES

Suppose that r and θ are connected by some equation such as $r = 3 \cos 2\theta$ or $r^2 = 4 \sin 3\theta$. *We define the locus of an equation in polar coordinates (r, θ) as the set of all points P each of which has at least one pair of polar coordinates (r, θ) which satisfies the given equation.* To plot the locus of such an equation we must find all ordered pairs (r, θ) which satisfy the given equation and then plot the

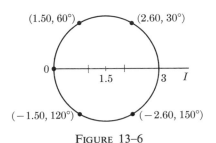

FIGURE 13–6

points obtained. We can obtain a good approximation of the locus in polar co-ordinates, as we can in the case of rectangular coordinates, by making a sufficiently complete table of values, plotting the points, and connecting them by a smooth curve.

EXAMPLE 1. Draw the graph of the equation $r = 3 \cos \theta$.

Solution. We construct the table:

θ	0	$\pi/6$	$\pi/3$	$\pi/2$	$2\pi/3$	$5\pi/6$
$\theta°$	0	30	60	90	120	150
r	3	$\frac{3}{2}\sqrt{3}$	$\frac{3}{2}$	0	$-\frac{3}{2}$	$-\frac{3}{2}\sqrt{3}$
r approx.	3.00	2.60	1.50	0	−1.50	−2.60

θ	π	$7\pi/6$	$4\pi/3$	$3\pi/2$	$5\pi/3$	$11\pi/6$
$\theta°$	180	210	240	270	300	330
r	−3	$-\frac{3}{2}\sqrt{3}$	$-\frac{3}{2}$	0	$\frac{3}{2}$	$\frac{3}{2}\sqrt{3}$
r approx.	−3.00	−2.60	−1.50	0	1.50	2.60

The graph is shown in Fig. 13–6. It is a circle with center at $(\frac{3}{2}, 0)$ and radius $\frac{3}{2}$. It is worth noting that even though there are 12 entries in the table, only 6 points are plotted. The curve is symmetric with respect to the initial line, and we could have saved effort if this fact had been taken into account. Since $\cos(-\theta) = \cos \theta$ for all values of θ, we could have obtained the points on the graph for values of θ between 0 and $-\pi$ without extra computation.

We shall set forth the rules of symmetry, as we did in Chapter 2. These rules, which are useful as aids in graphing, are described in terms of symmetries with respect to x- and y-axes in rectangular coordinates. That is, we suppose that the positive x-axis coincides with the initial line of the polar coordinate system.

RULE I. *If the substitution of $(r, -\theta)$ for (r, θ) yields the same equation, the locus is symmetric with respect to the x-axis.*

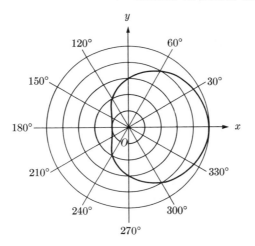

FIGURE 13-7

RULE II. *If the substitution of* $(r, \pi - \theta)$ *for* (r, θ) *yields the same equation, the locus is symmetric with respect to the y-axis.*

RULE III. *If the substitution of* $(-r, \theta)$ *for* (r, θ) *yields the same equation, the locus is symmetric with respect to the pole.*

It is easy to see that if any two of the three symmetries hold, the remaining one holds automatically.

EXAMPLE 2. Discuss for symmetry and plot the locus of the equation

$$r = 3 + 2 \cos \theta.$$

Solution. The locus is symmetric with respect to the x-axis, since $\cos(-\theta) = \cos \theta$ and Rule I applies. We construct the table:

θ	0	$\pm\pi/6$	$\pm\pi/3$	$\pm\pi/2$	$\pm 2\pi/3$	$\pm 5\pi/6$	$\pm\pi$
$\theta°$	0	$\pm30°$	$\pm60°$	$\pm90°$	$\pm120°$	$\pm150°$	$\pm180°$
r	5	$3 + \sqrt{3}$	4	3	2	$3 - \sqrt{3}$	1
r approx.	5.00	4.73	4.00	3.00	2.00	1.27	1.00

We use values of θ from $-\pi$ to $+\pi$ only, since $\cos(\theta + 2\pi) = \cos \theta$ and no new points could possibly be obtained with higher values of θ. The graph, called a limaçon, is shown in Fig. 13-7.

EXAMPLE 3. Given that $r^2 = \sin \theta$, discuss for symmetry and plot the locus of the equation.

Solution. When we replace r by $-r$ we get the same equation and, therefore, by Rule III, the locus is symmetric with respect to the pole. If we replace θ by $\pi - \theta$ we see that $\sin(\pi - \theta) = \sin \theta$ and, by Rule II, the locus is symmetric with respect to the y-axis.

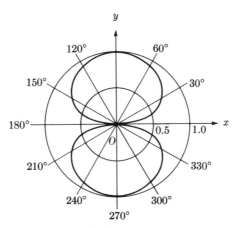

FIGURE 13–8

Since Rules II and III hold, the symmetry of Rule I also holds, and the curve is symmetric with respect to the x-axis. If $\sin \theta$ is negative we have no locus, and so we must restrict θ to the interval $0 \leq \theta \leq \pi$. We make the table:

θ	0	$\pi/6$	$\pi/3$	$\pi/2$	$2\pi/3$	$5\pi/6$	π
$\theta°$	0	30°	60°	90°	120°	150°	180°
r	0	$\pm\sqrt{2}/2$	$\pm\sqrt{\sqrt{3}/2}$	± 1	$\pm\sqrt{\sqrt{3}/2}$	$\pm\sqrt{2}/2$	0
r approx.	0	± 0.71	± 0.93	± 1	± 0.93	± 0.71	0

The graph, shown in Fig. 13–8, has the appearance of a figure eight.

EXAMPLE 4.   Test for symmetry and plot the graph of the equation

$$r = 2 \cos 2\theta.$$

Solution. If we replace θ by $-\theta$ the equation is unchanged and, therefore, by Rule I, we have symmetry with respect to the x-axis. When we replace θ by $\pi - \theta$ we get

$$\cos 2(\pi - \theta) = \cos 2\pi \cos 2\theta + \sin 2\pi \sin 2\theta = \cos 2\theta$$

and, by Rule II, the locus is symmetric with respect to the y-axis. Consequently, the locus is symmetric with respect to the pole. We construct the table:

θ	0	$\pi/12$	$\pi/6$	$\pi/4$	$\pi/3$	$5\pi/12$	$\pi/2$
2θ	0	$\pi/6$	$\pi/3$	$\pi/2$	$2\pi/3$	$5\pi/6$	π
$2\theta°$	0	30	60	90	120	150	180
r	2	$\sqrt{3}$	1	0	-1	$-\sqrt{3}$	-2
r approx.	2.00	1.73	1.00	0	-1.00	-1.73	-2.00

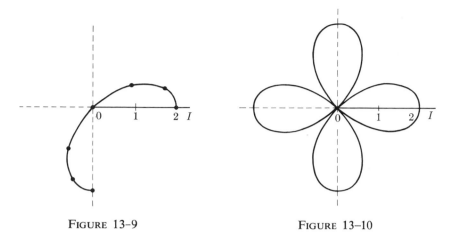

FIGURE 13–9   FIGURE 13–10

We plot the points as shown in Fig. 13–9. Now, making use of the symmetries, we can easily complete the graph (Fig. 13–10). This curve is called a four-leaved rose. Equations of the form

$$r = a \sin n\theta, \qquad r = a \cos n\theta,$$

where n is a positive integer, have loci which are called *rose* or *petal* curves. The number of petals is equal to n if n is an odd integer and is equal to $2n$ if n is an even integer. If $n = 1$, there is one petal and it is circular.

EXERCISES

In the following problems, discuss for symmetry and plot the loci of the equations.

1. $r = 2 \cos \theta$
2. $r = 2 \sin \theta$
3. $r = -2 \sin \theta$
4. $r = 2 \cos (\theta + \pi/4)$
5. $r = 3 \sin (\theta - \pi/3)$
6. $r = 2(1 - \cos \theta)$
7. $r = 2(1 + \cos \theta)$
8. $r = 2(1 + \sin \theta)$
9. $r = 4 - 2 \sin \theta$
10. $r \cos \theta = 2$
11. $r = 2 + 4 \cos \theta$
12. $r = 2 - 4 \sin \theta$
13. $r \sin \theta = 1$
14. $r^2 = 2 \cos \theta$
15. $r^2 = \cos 2\theta$
16. $r^2 = 4 \sin 2\theta$
17. $r = 5 \cos 2\theta$
18. $r = 5 \sin 2\theta$
19. $r = 5 \cos 3\theta$
20. $r = 5 \sin 3\theta$
21. $r = 4 \sin^2 \frac{1}{2}\theta$
22. $r = 2 \cos \frac{1}{2}\theta$
23. $r = \tan \theta$
24. $r = 5 \cos 4\theta$
25. $r = 5 \sin 4\theta$
26. $r = \cot \theta$
27. $r = 2 \csc \theta$
28. $r(2 - \cos \theta) = 4$
29. $r(1 - \cos \theta) = 2$
30. $r(1 + 2 \cos \theta) = 4$
31. $r(1 + 2 \sin \theta) = 2$
32. $r(1 + \cos \theta) = -1$

3. EQUATIONS IN RECTANGULAR AND POLAR COORDINATES

The curves discussed in Section 2 find their natural setting in polar coordinates. However, the equations of some curves may be simpler in appearance or their properties more transparent in one coordinate system than in another. For this reason it is useful to be able to transform an equation given in one coordinate system into the corresponding equation in another system.

Suppose that we are given the equation of a curve in the form $y = f(x)$ in a rectangular system. If we simply make the substitution

$$x = r \cos \theta, \qquad y = r \sin \theta,$$

we have the same equation in a polar coordinate system. We can also go the other way, so that if we are given $r = g(\theta)$ in polar coordinates, the substitution

$$r^2 = x^2 + y^2, \qquad \theta = \arctan \frac{y}{x}, \qquad \left(\text{i.e., } \tan \theta = \frac{y}{x} \right)$$

transforms the relation into one in rectangular coordinates. In this connection, it is frequently useful to make the substitutions

$$\sin \theta = \frac{y}{\sqrt{x^2 + y^2}}, \qquad \cos \theta = \frac{x}{\sqrt{x^2 + y^2}}, \qquad \tan \theta = \frac{y}{x},$$

rather than use the formula for θ itself.

EXAMPLE 1. Find the equation in polar coordinates which corresponds to the locus of the equation

$$x^2 + y^2 - 3x = 0$$

in rectangular coordinates.

Solution. Substituting $x = r \cos \theta$, $y = r \sin \theta$, we obtain

$$r^2 - 3r \cos \theta = 0 \qquad \text{or} \qquad r(r - 3 \cos \theta) = 0.$$

Therefore the locus is $r = 0$ or $r - 3 \cos \theta = 0$. Because the pole is part of the locus of $r - 3 \cos \theta = 0$ (since $r = 0$ when $\theta = \pi/2$), the result is

$$r = 3 \cos \theta.$$

We recognize this locus as the circle of Example 1, Section 2. [In rectangular coordinates, the equation is $(x - \frac{3}{2})^2 + y^2 = \frac{9}{4}$.]

EXAMPLE 2. Given the polar coordinate equation

$$r = \frac{1}{1 - \cos \theta},$$

find the corresponding equation in rectangular coordinates.

Solution. We write

$$r - r \cos \theta = 1 \qquad \text{or} \qquad r = 1 + r \cos \theta.$$

Substituting for r and $\cos \theta$, we get

$$\pm \sqrt{x^2 + y^2} = 1 + x.$$

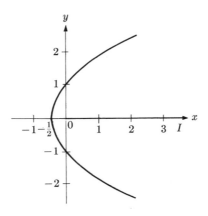

FIGURE 13–11

Squaring both sides (a dangerous operation, since this may introduce extraneous solutions), we obtain

$$x^2 + y^2 = 1 + 2x + x^2 \quad \text{or} \quad y^2 = 2x + 1.$$

When we squared both sides we introduced the extraneous locus $r = -(1 + r \cos \theta)$. But the locus of $r = -(1 + r \cos \theta)$ is the same as the locus of $r = 1 + r \cos \theta$ (see Fig. 13–11). Therefore the correct result is $y^2 = 2x + 1$.

EXERCISES

In problems 1 through 12, in each case find a polar coordinate equation of the locus whose corresponding equation is given in rectangular coordinates.

1. $x = 3$
2. $y = -2$
3. $x + y = 0$
4. $2x - 3y = 0$
5. $3x + y\sqrt{3} = 6$
6. $2x + 2y = 5$
7. $xy = 4$
8. $y^2 = 2x$
9. $x^2 + y^2 + 2x - 4y = 0$
10. $x^2 + y^2 - 4x = 0$
11. $x^2 + y^2 + 2x + 6y = 0$
12. $x^2 + y^2 - 4x + 4y + 4 = 0$

In problems 13 through 32, in each case find a polynomial equation in rectangular coordinates whose locus corresponds to the equation given in polar coordinates. Discuss possible extraneous solutions.

13. $r = 7$
14. $\theta = \pi/3$
15. $r = 3 \cos \theta$
16. $r = 4 \sin \theta$
17. $r \cos \theta = 5$
18. $r \sin \theta = -2$
19. $r \cos (\theta - \pi/4) = 2$
20. $r \cos (\theta + \pi/6) = 1$
21. $r^2 \cos 2\theta = 4$
22. $r^2 \sin 2\theta = 2$
23. $r^2 = \sin 2\theta$
24. $r^2 = \cos 2\theta$
25. $r = 2 \sec \theta \tan \theta$
26. $r(2 - \cos \theta) = 2$
27. $r(1 - 2 \cos \theta) = 2$
28. $r = a \cos 3\theta$
29. $r = a \sin 3\theta$
30. $r = 1 - \cos \theta$
31. $r = 1 - 2 \sin \theta$
32. $r = a \cos 2\theta$

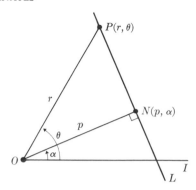

FIGURE 13–12

4. STRAIGHT LINES, CIRCLES, AND CONICS

The straight line was discussed in detail in Chapters 3 and 9. We found that every straight line has an equation (in rectangular coordinates) of the form

$$Ax + By + C = 0.$$

To obtain the equation in polar coordinates we can simply substitute $x = r \cos \theta$, $y = r \sin \theta$. However, it is also possible to find the desired equation directly. In Fig. 13–12, we consider a line L (not passing through the pole), and we draw a perpendicular from the pole to L. Call the point of intersection N and suppose that the coordinates of N are (p, α). The quantities p and α are sufficient to determine the line L completely. To see this, we let $P(r, \theta)$ be any point on L, and we note, according to Fig. 13–12, that $\angle PON = \theta - \alpha$. Therefore we have

$$r \cos (\theta - \alpha) = p.$$

When α and p are given, this is the equation of a straight line. The student may verify that the same equation results regardless of the positions of L and p. The above equation can also be written as

$$r \cos \theta \cos \alpha + r \sin \theta \sin \alpha = p,$$

and changing to rectangular coordinates yields

$$x \cos \alpha + y \sin \alpha = p,$$

which is known as the *normal form of the equation of a straight line*. Whenever the coefficients of x and y are the cosine and sine of an angle, respectively, the constant term gives the distance from the origin. Any equation may be put in normal form. For example,

$$3x + 4y = 7$$

may be written (upon division by $\sqrt{3^2 + 4^2} = 5$) as

$$\tfrac{3}{5}x + \tfrac{4}{5}y = \tfrac{7}{5}.$$

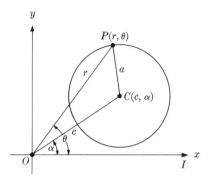

FIGURE 13–13

This equation is now in normal form, and the distance from the origin to the line is $\frac{7}{5}$ units. (Note that this procedure is the same as the one using the formula for the distance from a point to a line, as given in Chapter 9, Section 1).

A line through the pole has $p = 0$, and its polar coordinate equation is

$$\cos(\theta - \alpha) = 0.$$

This is equivalent to the statement

$$\theta = \text{const},$$

a condition which we already know represents straight lines passing through the pole.

We shall employ a direct method for obtaining the equation of a circle in polar coordinates. Let the circle have radius a and center at the point C with coordinates (c, α), as shown in Fig. 13–13. If $P(r, \theta)$ is any point on the circle, then in $\triangle POC$, side $\overline{OP} = r$, side $\overline{OC} = c$, side $\overline{PC} = a$, and $\angle POC = \theta - \alpha$. We use the law of cosines in triangle POC, obtaining

$$r^2 - 2cr\cos(\theta - \alpha) + c^2 = a^2.$$

If c, α, and a are given, the equation of the circle is completely determined. It is instructive to draw a figure similar to 13–13 but with $a > c$ and to repeat the proof with $P(r, \theta)$ in various positions.

EXAMPLE 1. A circle has center at $(5, \pi/3)$ and radius 2. Find its equation in polar coordinates.

Solution. We have $c = 5$, $\alpha = \pi/3$, $a = 2$. Therefore

$$r^2 - 10r\cos\left(\theta - \frac{\pi}{3}\right) + 25 = 4,$$

or

$$r^2 - 10r\cos\left(\theta - \frac{\pi}{3}\right) + 21 = 0.$$

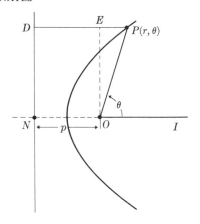

FIGURE 13–14

If a circle passes through the origin, so that $c = \pm a$, the equation reduces to

$$r = 2c \cos (\theta - \alpha).$$

(With $c = \frac{3}{2}$ and $\alpha = 0$, we get the equation of Example 1, Section 2.)

———————

We now recall the focus-directrix definition of parabolas, ellipses, and hyperbolas, as given in Chapter 10. It states that *the locus of a point which moves so that the ratio of its distance from a fixed point (the focus) to its distance from a fixed line (the directrix) remains constant is*

> *a parabola*   if the ratio is 1,
> *an ellipse*   if the ratio is between 0 and 1,
> *a hyperbola* if the ratio is larger than 1.

Polar coordinates are particularly suited to conics, since all three types have equations of the same form in this system. To derive the equation, we place the focus at the pole and let the directrix L be a line perpendicular to the initial line and p units to the left of the pole (Fig. 13–14). If $P(r, \theta)$ is a point on the locus, then the conditions say that $\overline{OP}/\overline{PD} =$ a constant which we call the eccentricity, e, and we write (since $\overline{OP} = r$),

$$r = e\overline{PD}.$$

We can see from Fig. 13–14 that $\overline{PD} = \overline{PE} + \overline{ED} = r \cos \theta + p$. Therefore we have

$$r = er \cos \theta + ep,$$

or

$$r = \frac{ep}{1 - e \cos \theta}. \tag{1}$$

Equation (1) represents an ellipse if $0 < e < 1$, a parabola if $e = 1$, and a hyperbola if $e > 1$.

EXAMPLE 2. Find the equation of the conic with focus at the origin, eccentricity $\frac{1}{2}$ and directrix the line $r \cos \theta = -3$.

Solution. We have $p = 3$, and so

$$r = \frac{\frac{1}{2}(3)}{1 - \frac{1}{2} \cos \theta} = \frac{3}{2 - \cos \theta}.$$

The curve is an ellipse.

EXAMPLE 3. Given the conic $r = 7/(4 - 5 \cos \theta)$, find the eccentricity and locate the directrix. Identify the conic.

Solution. We write the equation in the form

$$r = \frac{\frac{7}{4}}{1 - \frac{5}{4} \cos \theta}.$$

Then we read off the eccentricity $e = \frac{5}{4}$ and $ep = \frac{7}{4}$. This gives $p = \frac{7}{5}$, and the directrix is the line $r \cos \theta = -\frac{7}{5}$. The curve is a hyperbola.

It can be shown that the equation

$$r = \frac{ep}{1 - e \cos (\theta - \alpha)}$$

is a conic of eccentricity e with focus at the pole and directrix the line

$$r \cos (\theta - \alpha) = -p.$$

EXERCISES

In problems 1 through 8, in each case the line L passes through the point N and is perpendicular to the line going through N and the pole O. Find the equation of L in polar coordinates when the coordinates of N are as given.

1. $N(3, \pi/4)$ 　　　　　　　2. $N(-2, \pi/2)$ 　　　　　　　3. $N(4, 5\pi/6)$
4. $N(5, 7\pi)$ 　　　　　　　　5. $N(3, 0)$ 　　　　　　　　　6. $N(-2, -3\pi/2)$
7. $N(\pi, \pi)$ 　　　　　　　　8. $N(-7, -\pi)$

In problems 9 through 15, in each case find in polar coordinates the equation of the circle satisfying the given conditions.

9. Center $(3, \pi/6)$, radius 2 　　　　　　　10. Center $(-2, 5\pi/6)$, radius 3
11. Center $(4, 0)$, radius 4 　　　　　　　　12. Center $(5, \pi/2)$, radius 5
13. Center $(4, \pi/3)$, passing through $(7, \pi/4)$
14. Center $(5, \pi/4)$ passing through $(6, 0)$
15. Center on the line $\theta = \pi/3$ and passing through $(5, \pi/2)$ and $(0, 0)$

In problems 16 through 21 find, in polar coordinates, the equation of the conic with focus at the pole and having the given eccentricity and directrix.

16. $e = 1$, directrix $r \cos \theta = -4$ 17. $e = 2$, directrix $r \cos \theta = -5$

18. $e = \frac{1}{2}$, directrix $r \cos \theta = 2$ 19. $e = \frac{1}{2}$, directrix $r \cos (\theta - \pi/2) = 1$

20. $e = 1$, directrix $r \cos (\theta - \pi/4) = 2\sqrt{2}$

21. $e = 2$, directrix $r \cos (\theta + \pi/3) = 3$

22. Given the line with equation $r \cos (\theta - \pi/3) = 2$, find the distance from the point $(2, \pi/2)$ to this line.

23. Given the line with equation $r \cos (\theta - \alpha) = p$, find a formula for the distance d from a point (r_1, θ_1) to this line.

In problems 24 through 31, conics are given. Find the eccentricity and directrix of each and sketch the curve.

24. $r = \dfrac{6}{1 - \cos \theta}$ 25. $r = \dfrac{9}{2 - \cos \theta}$

26. $r = \dfrac{4}{2 - 3 \cos (\theta - \pi/4)}$

27. $r = \dfrac{2}{1 - \sin \theta}$ $\left[\textit{Hint: } \sin \theta = \cos \left(\theta - \dfrac{\pi}{2} \right). \right]$

28. $r = \dfrac{4}{2 - 4 \sin \theta}$ 29. $r = \dfrac{5}{1 - 2 \cos (\theta - \pi/3)}$

30. $r = \dfrac{2}{2 + \cos \theta}$ 31. $r = \dfrac{4}{6 + \sin \theta}$

5. DERIVATIVES IN POLAR COORDINATES

Consider a curve given in polar coordinates by an equation of the form $r = f(\theta)$. We wish to investigate the meaning of the derivative. Before doing so, however, we shall examine the graph of one of the simplest equations in polar coordinates. The equation

$$r = \theta$$

has a graph known as the *spiral of Archimedes*. We make the table:

θ	0	$\pi/6$	$\pi/3$	$\pi/2$	π	$3\pi/2$	2π	$5\pi/2$	3π
$\theta°$	0°	30°	60°	90°	180°	270°	360°	450°	540°
r	0	$\pi/6$	$\pi/3$	$\pi/2$	π	$3\pi/2$	2π	$5\pi/2$	3π
r approx.	0	0.52	1.05	1.57	3.14	4.71	6.28	7.85	10.42

The curve spirals around the origin indefinitely, as shown in Fig. 13–15. The dotted portion corresponds to negative values of θ.

We know that for a function given in rectangular coordinates, the derivative gives the slope of the tangent line. If we plunge ahead blindly and take derivatives in polar coordinates with the intention of obtaining the slope, trouble arises at once. In the example of the spiral of Archimedes we have $dr/d\theta = 1$, and the

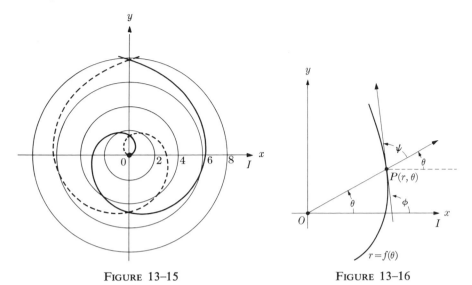

FIGURE 13–15   FIGURE 13–16

derivative is clearly not the slope. We need more information before we can learn about slopes in polar coordinates.

If r is a function of θ, $r = f(\theta)$, then the equations in rectangular coordinates,

$$x = r \cos \theta, \qquad y = r \sin \theta,$$

may be considered as the parametric equations of a curve with θ as parameter when we substitute for r its function of θ. We then have

$$x = f(\theta) \cos \theta, \qquad y = f(\theta) \sin \theta.$$

Differentiating, we find that

$$\frac{dx}{d\theta} = f'(\theta) \cos \theta - f(\theta) \sin \theta, \qquad \frac{dy}{d\theta} = f'(\theta) \sin \theta + f(\theta) \cos \theta.$$

The slope is

$$\frac{dy}{dx} = \frac{dy/d\theta}{dx/d\theta}.$$

Suppose that the curve $r = f(\theta)$ has the appearance of the one in Fig. 13–16. At a point P the tangent line is drawn, and we recognize the slope of this line to be $\tan \phi$. The slope is not particularly convenient in polar coordinates, but the angle ψ between the tangent line and the line from P passing through the pole turns out to be convenient. As seen in Fig. 13–16, ψ and ϕ bear the simple relationship

$$\psi = \phi - \theta,$$

and so

$$\tan \psi = \tan (\phi - \theta)$$

$$= \frac{\tan \phi - \tan \theta}{1 + \tan \phi \tan \theta}.$$

We know that

$$\tan \phi = \frac{dy}{dx} = \frac{dy/d\theta}{dx/d\theta} = \frac{f'(\theta)\sin\theta + f(\theta)\cos\theta}{f'(\theta)\cos\theta - f(\theta)\sin\theta}.$$

It is a good exercise in algebraic manipulation to substitute the above expression for $\tan \phi$ into the formula for $\tan \psi$ and obtain the simple relation

$$\tan \psi = \frac{f(\theta)}{f'(\theta)}.$$

We can also write

$$\cot \psi = \frac{f'(\theta)}{f(\theta)} = \frac{1}{r}\frac{dr}{d\theta}, \qquad r \neq 0.$$

The significance of the derivative in polar coordinates is now becoming clearer. The derivative at a point P is related to the angle that the tangent line forms with the line through the point P and the pole, according to the above formula for $\cot \psi$.

————————

EXAMPLE 1. Given the circle $r = 4\cos\theta$, find the angle between the tangent line and the line from the pole through the point of tangency. Evaluate this at $(2, \pi/3)$.

Solution. We have

$$\cot \psi = \frac{1}{r}\frac{dr}{d\theta} = \frac{1}{4\cos\theta}(-4\sin\theta) = -\tan\theta,$$

and so

$$\psi = \theta + \frac{\pi}{2}.$$

For $\theta = \pi/3$, we obtain $\psi = 5\pi/6$.

EXAMPLE 2. Given the curve $r = 3e^{2\theta}$. Find $\cot \psi$ at any point, and sketch the curve.

Solution. We have

$$\cot \psi = \frac{1}{r}\frac{dr}{d\theta} = \frac{1}{3e^{2\theta}} \cdot 3 \cdot 2e^{2\theta} = 2.$$

In other words, the angle which the tangent makes with the line from the pole through the point of tangency is always the same. The curve, called a *logarithmic spiral*, is shown in Fig. 13–17.

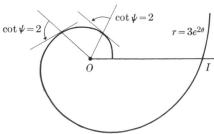

FIGURE 13–17

To obtain a formula for *arc length* in polar coordinates, we start with the formula

$$ds^2 = dx^2 + dy^2,$$

which we obtained in Chapter 12. If $r = f(\theta)$ has a continuous first derivative, we then write, as before,

$$\frac{dx}{d\theta} = f'(\theta) \cos \theta - f(\theta) \sin \theta,$$

$$\frac{dy}{d\theta} = f'(\theta) \sin \theta + f(\theta) \cos \theta.$$

Substitution of these expressions in the formula

$$\frac{ds}{d\theta} = \sqrt{(dx/d\theta)^2 + (dy/d\theta)^2}$$

yields (after some algebraic manipulation)

$$\frac{ds}{d\theta} = \sqrt{[f'(\theta)]^2 + [f(\theta)]^2}$$

and, upon integration,

$$s = \int_{\theta_0}^{\theta_1} \sqrt{(dr/d\theta)^2 + r^2}\, d\theta.$$

EXAMPLE 3. Find the arc length of the curve $r = 3e^{2\theta}$ from $\theta = 0$ to $\theta = \pi/6$.

Solution. We have $dr/d\theta = 6e^{2\theta}$, and so

$$s = \int_0^{\pi/6} \sqrt{36e^{4\theta} + 9e^{4\theta}}\, d\theta = 3\sqrt{5} \int_0^{\pi/6} e^{2\theta}\, d\theta = [\tfrac{3}{2}\sqrt{5}\, e^{2\theta}]_0^{\pi/6}.$$

Therefore

$$s = \tfrac{3}{2}\sqrt{5}\,[e^{\pi/3} - 1] = 6.2 \text{ approx.}$$

EXERCISES

In problems 1 through 14, find $ds/d\theta$ and $\cot \psi$ for each equation.

1. $r = 2a \cos \theta$
2. $r = 4 \cos \theta + 3 \sin \theta$
3. $r = 2(1 + \cos \theta)$
4. $r = 2(1 - \sin \theta)$
5. $r = 4\theta$
6. $r = 2\theta^2$
7. $r = 3 + 2 \cos \theta$
8. $r = 1 - 2 \cos \theta$
9. $r = e^{5\theta}$
10. $r = e^{-4\theta}$
11. $r(2 - \sin \theta) = 2$
12. $r(1 + \cos \theta) = 3$
13. $r(1 + 2 \cos \theta) = 2$
14. $r(5 - 6 \sin \theta) = -1$

In problems 15 through 18, find the length of arc as indicated.

15. $r = 3\theta^2$ from $\theta = 1$ to $\theta = 2$
16. $r = 2e^{3\theta}$ from $\theta = 0$ to $\theta = 3$

17. $r = 3 \cos \theta$ from $\theta = 0$ to $\theta = \pi/4$ 18. $r = 3(1 + \cos \theta)$ from $\theta = 0$ to $\theta = \pi/2$

19. Suppose that $r = f(\theta)$ and $x = f(\theta) \cos \theta$, $y = f(\theta) \sin \theta$. Find an expression for d^2y/dx^2 in terms of θ.

$$\left[Hint: \quad \frac{d^2 y}{dx^2} = \frac{\dfrac{d}{d\theta}\left(\dfrac{dy}{dx}\right)}{dx/d\theta}. \right]$$

20. Using the result of problem 19, show that the curvature κ is given by the formula

$$\kappa = \frac{r^2 + 2(dr/d\theta)^2 - r(d^2r/d\theta^2)}{[r^2 + (dr/d\theta)^2]^{3/2}}.$$

21. Using the formula in problem 20, find κ, given that $r = 2a \sin \theta$.

22. Using the formula of problem 20, find κ, given that $r = 1 - \cos \theta$.

23. Draw the curve of $r = 1 - \cos \theta$ and construct the tangent at the point where $\theta = \pi/3$. Find the equation of the tangent line at this point in rectangular co-ordinates.

24. Draw the curve of $r = 2 + \sqrt{2} \cos \theta$ and construct the tangent at the point where $\theta = 3\pi/4$. Find the equation of this tangent in rectangular coordinates.

6. AREA IN POLAR COORDINATES

Two basic concepts are needed for the development of area in rectangular co-ordinate systems. They are (1) the idea of the limit of a sum, and (2) the formula for the area of a rectangle: length times width.

To find areas enclosed by curves given in polar coordinates, again two concepts are necessary. They are, first, the idea of the limit of a sum (as in rectangular co-ordinates) and second, the formula for the area of a sector of a circle. We recall that the area of a sector of a circle of radius a with angle opening θ (measured in radians) is

$$\tfrac{1}{2}\theta a^2.$$

Suppose that $r = f(\theta)$ is a continuous, positive function defined for values of θ between $\theta = \alpha$ and $\theta = \beta$, with $0 \le \alpha < \beta \le 2\pi$. We construct the lines $\theta = \alpha$ and $\theta = \beta$, and we pose the problem of determining the area of the region bounded by these straight lines and the curve with equation $r = f(\theta)$ (Fig. 13–18). We subdivide the θ-scale into n parts between α and β by introducing the values $\alpha = \theta_0 < \theta_1 < \theta_2 < \cdots < \theta_{n-1} < \theta_n = \beta$. In this way we obtain n sub-intervals; in each subinterval we select a value of θ which we call ξ_i. We then compute the area of the circular sector of radius $f(\xi_i)$ and angle opening $\Delta_i\theta = \theta_i - \theta_{i-1}$, as shown in Fig. 13–19. According to the formula for the area of a sector of a circle, the area is

$$\tfrac{1}{2}[f(\xi_i)]^2 \, \Delta_i\theta.$$

We add these areas for i between 1 and n, getting

$$\tfrac{1}{2}[f(\xi_1)]^2 \, \Delta_1\theta + \tfrac{1}{2}[f(\xi_2)]^2 \, \Delta_2\theta + \tfrac{1}{2}[f(\xi_3)]^2 \, \Delta_3\theta + \cdots + \tfrac{1}{2}[f(\xi_n)]^2 \, \Delta_n\theta,$$

FIGURE 13–18

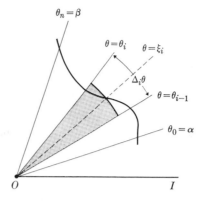

FIGURE 13–19

or, concisely,

$$\tfrac{1}{2} \sum_{i=1}^{n} [f(\xi_i)]^2 \, \Delta_i\theta.$$

It can be shown that as the number of subdivision points increases without bound and as the norm of the subdivision (length of the largest $\Delta_i\theta$) tends to zero, the area A, bounded by the lines $\theta = \alpha$, $\theta = \beta$, and by the curve $r = f(\theta)$, is given by

$$A = \tfrac{1}{2} \int_{\alpha}^{\beta} [f(\theta)]^2 \, d\theta.$$

We have just obtained the desired formula for area in polar coordinates.

———————

EXAMPLE 1. Find the area bounded by the curve

$$r = 2 + \cos \theta$$

and the lines $\theta = 0$, $\theta = \pi/2$ (see Fig. 13–20).

FIGURE 13–20

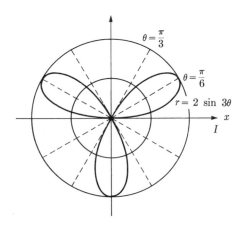

FIGURE 13–21

Solution. We have

$$A = \tfrac{1}{2} \int_0^{\pi/2} [2 + \cos \theta]^2 \, d\theta$$

$$= \tfrac{1}{2} \int_0^{\pi/2} [4 + 4 \cos \theta + \cos^2 \theta] \, d\theta$$

$$= [2\theta + 2 \sin \theta]_0^{\pi/2} + \tfrac{1}{2} \int_0^{\pi/2} \cos^2 \theta \, d\theta$$

$$= \pi + 2 + \tfrac{1}{2} \int_0^{\pi/2} \cos^2 \theta \, d\theta.$$

To perform the remaining integration we use the formula $\cos^2 \theta = (1 + \cos 2\theta)/2$, and obtain

$$\tfrac{1}{2} \int_0^{\pi/2} \cos^2 \theta \, d\theta = \tfrac{1}{4} \int_0^{\pi/2} (1 + \cos 2\theta) \, d\theta = \left[\tfrac{1}{4}(\theta + \tfrac{1}{2} \sin 2\theta) \right]_0^{\pi/2}.$$

Therefore

$$A = \pi + 2 + \frac{\pi}{8} = \frac{9\pi}{8} + 2.$$

EXAMPLE 2. Find the entire area enclosed by the curve $r = 2 \sin 3\theta$.

Solution. We first draw the curve, as shown in Fig. 13–21. In fact, in all area problems in polar coordinates, a sketch should be made. The curve is a rose curve with three congruent petals. *The main difficulty in this problem is determining the limits of integration.* To find the area of the loop in the first quadrant, we observe that $r = 0$ when $\theta = 0$, and that the value of r increases steadily to a maximum when $\theta = \pi/6$ and $r = 2$; then r decreases steadily until $\theta = \pi/3$ when $r = 0$. In other words, the petal is described completely as θ goes from 0 to $\pi/3$. The total area A is three times the area of this loop. Therefore we have

$$\tfrac{1}{3} A = \tfrac{1}{2} \int_0^{\pi/3} (2 \sin 3\theta)^2 \, d\theta, \qquad A = 6 \int_0^{\pi/3} \frac{1 - \cos 6\theta}{2} \, d\theta,$$

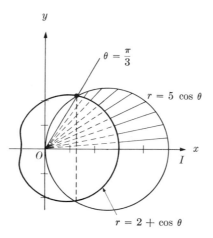

FIGURE 13–22

where we have used the half-angle formula, $\sin^2 \phi = (1 - \cos 2\phi)/2$. Integration yields

$$A = 6 \left[\frac{\theta}{2} - \frac{1}{12} \sin 6\theta \right]_0^{\pi/3} = \pi.$$

EXAMPLE 3.   Find the area inside the circle $r = 5 \cos \theta$ and outside the curve $r = 2 + \cos \theta$.

Solution. We make a sketch, as shown in Fig. 13–22. The two curves intersect when

$$5 \cos \theta = 2 + \cos \theta, \qquad \cos \theta = \tfrac{1}{2},$$

or

$$\theta = \frac{\pi}{3}, \quad -\frac{\pi}{3}.$$

The limits of integration are $-\pi/3$ and $+\pi/3$. The area A inside $5 \cos \theta$ and outside $2 + \cos \theta$ is given by

$$A = \tfrac{1}{2} \int_{-\pi/3}^{+\pi/3} (5 \cos \theta)^2 \, d\theta - \tfrac{1}{2} \int_{-\pi/3}^{+\pi/3} (2 + \cos \theta)^2 \, d\theta.$$

We can shorten the work in two ways: (1) we observe that both curves are symmetric with respect to the x-axis, and (2) the integrals may be combined, since the limits of integration are the same. In this way we obtain

$$A = \int_0^{\pi/3} [25 \cos^2 \theta - (4 + 4 \cos \theta + \cos^2 \theta)] \, d\theta$$

$$= \int_0^{\pi/3} (8 + 12 \cos 2\theta - 4 \cos \theta) \, d\theta$$

$$= [8\theta + 6 \sin 2\theta - 4 \sin \theta]_0^{\pi/3} = \frac{8\pi}{3} + \sqrt{3}.$$

EXERCISES

In problems 1 through 5, find in each case the area enclosed by the curve and the two lines.

1. $r = \theta$, $\theta = 0$, $\theta = 2\pi$ 2. $r = 2\tan\theta$, $\theta = 0$, $\theta = \pi/3$

3. $r = e^{\theta/2}$, $\theta = 0$, $\theta = \pi/2$ 4. $r = 2\cos 2\theta$, $\theta = -\pi/6$, $\theta = \pi/6$

5. $r = \theta^3$, $\theta = 0$, $\theta = \pi/2$

In problems 6 through 14, sketch each curve and find the entire area bounded by it.

6. $r = 3 + 2\cos\theta$ 7. $r = 2\cos 3\theta$ 8. $r^2 = \sin\theta$

9. $r^2 = 2\sin 2\theta$ 10. $r = 2\sin 2\theta$ 11. $r = 2(1 + \cos\theta)$

12. $r = \cos n\theta$, n a positive integer

13. $r = \sin n\theta$, n a positive integer

14. $r = 4 + 2\sin\theta$

In problems 15 through 21, find the indicated area.

15. Inside the circle $r = 4\cos\theta$ and outside $r = 2$

16. Inside $r = 2 + 2\cos\theta$ and outside $r = 1$

17. Inside $r^2 = 8\cos 2\theta$ and outside $r = 2$

18. Inside $r = \sqrt{2\cos\theta}$ and outside $r = 2(1 - \cos\theta)$

19. Inside the curves $r = 3\cos\theta$ and $r = 2 - \cos\theta$

20. Inside the curves $r = 2\sin\theta$ and $r^2 = 2\cos 2\theta$

21. Inside the small loop of the curve $r = 1 + 2\cos\theta$

22. Find the area bounded by $r = a\cos\theta$ and the lines $\theta = \alpha$, $\theta = \pi/2$. By elementary methods, verify that the result is the formula for the area of a segment of a circle.

CHAPTER 14

Vectors in a Plane

1. DIRECTED LINE SEGMENTS AND VECTORS

Let A and B be two points in the plane. We call the line segment going *from A to B a directed line segment*, and we designate it $\overrightarrow{AB}$. The point A is the *base* of the directed line segment and B is its *head*. The segment going *from B to A* is oppositely directed and designated $\overrightarrow{BA}$. To distinguish base and head, we usually draw an arrow at the head, as shown in Fig. 14–1. The *magnitude* of a directed line segment is its length. The *direction* of a directed line segment is indicated by the arrow at the head. Two directed line segments $\overrightarrow{AB}$ and $\overrightarrow{CD}$ are said to *have the same magnitude and direction* if (1) they have the same length and (2) they lie along parallel lines (or the same line) with the arrows pointing in the same direction. Figure 14–2 shows several directed line segments with the same magnitude and direction.

Directed line
segment $\overrightarrow{AB}$

FIGURE 14–1

FIGURE 14–2

Whenever two directed line segments $\overrightarrow{AB}$ and $\overrightarrow{CD}$ have the same magnitude and direction, we say that they are *equivalent* and write

$$\overrightarrow{AB} \approx \overrightarrow{CD}.$$

If we are given a directed line segment $\overrightarrow{AB}$, we see at once that there is an unlimited number of equivalent ones. In fact, if C is any point in the plane, we may draw a line through C parallel to $\overrightarrow{AB}$, mark off a length beginning at C and equal to that of $\overrightarrow{AB}$, and so obtain an equivalent directed line segment with base at C. *Through any point P in the plane there is a directed line segment equivalent to $\overrightarrow{AB}$ and having P as base.*

The definition of a vector involves an abstract concept — that of a collection of directed line segments.

DEFINITION. A *vector* is the collection of all directed line segments having a given magnitude and a given direction. When we write the boldface letter **v** to stand for a vector, we mean the entire collection of directed line segments. A

421

particular directed line segment in the collection is called a *representative* of the vector **v**. Any member of the collection may be used as a representative.

Figure 14–2 shows five representatives of the same vector. Since any two representative directed line segments of the same vector are equivalent, the collection used to define a vector is called an *equivalence class*.

[The vector as we have defined it is sometimes called a *free vector*. There are other ways of introducing vectors; one is to call a directed line segment a vector. We then would make the convention that directed line segments with the same magnitude and direction (i.e., equivalent) are equal vectors. This leads to certain logical difficulties which we wish to avoid.]

Vectors occur with great frequency in various branches of physics and engineering. Problems in mechanics, especially those involving forces, are concerned with "lines of action," i.e., the direction in which forces act. In such problems it is convenient to define a vector as the equivalence class of all directed line segments which lie along a given straight line and have a given magnitude.

DEFINITIONS. The *length* of a vector is the common length of all its representative segments. A *unit vector* is a vector of length one. Two vectors are said to be *orthogonal* (or *perpendicular*) if any representative of one vector is perpendicular to any representative of the other (i.e., the representatives lie along perpendicular lines).

For convenience, we consider directed line segments of zero length; these are simply points. The *zero vector*, denoted by **0**, is the class of directed line segments of zero length. We make the convention that the zero vector is orthogonal to all vectors.

2. OPERATIONS WITH VECTORS

Vectors may be added to yield other vectors. Suppose **u** and **v** are vectors, i.e., each is a collection of directed line segments. To add **u** and **v**, we first select a representative of **u**, say $\overrightarrow{AB}$, as shown in Fig. 14–3(a). Next we take the particular representative of **v** which has its base at the point B, and label it $\overrightarrow{BC}$. We then draw the directed line segment $\overrightarrow{AC}$. The sum **w** of **u** and **v** is the equivalence class of directed line segments of which $\overrightarrow{AC}$ is a representative. We write

$$\mathbf{u} + \mathbf{v} = \mathbf{w}.$$

It is important to note that we could have started with any representative of **u**, say $\overrightarrow{A'B'}$ in Fig. 14–3(b). Then we could have selected the representative of **v** with base at B'. The directed line segments $\overrightarrow{A'C'}$ and $\overrightarrow{AC}$ are representatives of

(a)   (b)

FIGURE 14–3

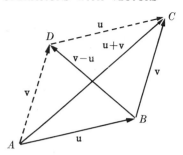

FIGURE 14-4   FIGURE 14-5

the same vector since, by congruent triangles, they have the same length and lie along parallel lines.

Vectors may be multiplied by numbers to yield new vectors. If $\mathbf{v}$ is a vector and c is a positive real number, we say that $c\mathbf{v}$ is a vector with representatives having the same direction and magnitudes c times as long. If c is negative, the magnitudes are multiplied by $|c|$, but the direction is reversed. If c is zero, we get the vector $\mathbf{0}$. Figure 14-4 shows what happens to a representative line segment $\overrightarrow{AB}$ in a number of cases. We write $-\mathbf{v}$ for the vector $(-1) \cdot \mathbf{v}$.

The addition of vectors and the multiplication of vectors by numbers satisfy the following rules of arithmetic:

$$\left. \begin{array}{r} \mathbf{u} + (\mathbf{v} + \mathbf{w}) = (\mathbf{u} + \mathbf{v}) + \mathbf{w} \\ c(d\mathbf{v}) = (cd)\mathbf{v} \end{array} \right\} \quad \text{Associative laws}$$

$$\mathbf{u} + \mathbf{v} = \mathbf{v} + \mathbf{u} \qquad \text{Commutative law}$$

$$\left. \begin{array}{r} (c + d)\mathbf{v} = c\mathbf{v} + d\mathbf{v} \\ c(\mathbf{u} + \mathbf{v}) = c\mathbf{u} + c\mathbf{v} \end{array} \right\} \quad \text{Distributive laws}$$

$$1 \cdot \mathbf{u} = \mathbf{u}, \quad 0 \cdot \mathbf{u} = \mathbf{0}, \quad (-1)\mathbf{v} = -\mathbf{v}.$$

These laws hold for all vectors $\mathbf{u}$, $\mathbf{v}$, $\mathbf{w}$ and all real numbers c and d. It is important to note that multiplication and division of two vectors is not (and will not be) here defined. However, since $(-1)\mathbf{v} = -\mathbf{v}$, we can define *subtraction* of vectors. In terms of representatives, we construct the parallelogram with $\overrightarrow{AB}$ and $\overrightarrow{DC}$ as representatives of a vector $\mathbf{u}$, and $\overrightarrow{AD}$ and $\overrightarrow{BC}$ as representatives of a vector $\mathbf{v}$. Then, as Fig. 14-5 shows, we have $\overrightarrow{AC}$ as the representative of $\mathbf{w}$, where

$$\mathbf{w} = \mathbf{u} + \mathbf{v},$$

and $\overrightarrow{BD}$ as the representative of $\mathbf{z}$ where $\mathbf{z} = \mathbf{v} + (-\mathbf{u})$. In other words,

$$\mathbf{z} = \mathbf{v} - \mathbf{u}.$$

DEFINITION. Suppose that a rectangular coordinate system is given. We define the *vector* $\mathbf{i}$ to be a vector of unit length pointing in the direction of the positive x-axis (Fig. 14-6). We define the *vector* $\mathbf{j}$ to be a vector of unit length pointing in the direction of the positive y-axis.

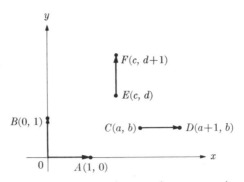

FIG. 14–6. Representatives $\overrightarrow{OA}$ and $\overrightarrow{CD}$ of **i** and $\overrightarrow{OB}$ and $\overrightarrow{EF}$ of **j**.

Theorem 1. *Every vector* **v** *in the plane may be written as a linear combination of* **i** *and* **j**. *That is, there are numbers a and b such that*

$$\mathbf{v} = a\mathbf{i} + b\mathbf{j}.$$

Proof. We select any representative $\overrightarrow{AB}$ of **v**, as shown in Fig. 14–7, and we denote the coordinates of A by (x_A, y_A) and those of B by (x_B, y_B). Draw parallels to the axes, getting the points $C(x_B, y_A)$ and $D(x_A, y_B)$. The directed line segment $\overrightarrow{AC}$ has length $x_B - x_A \equiv a$ and is a representative of the vector $a\mathbf{i}$. The directed line segment $\overrightarrow{AD}$ has length $y_B - y_A \equiv b$ and is a representative of the vector $b\mathbf{j}$, as is also $\overrightarrow{CB}$. According to the rule for addition of vectors, we obtain

$$\mathbf{v} = a\mathbf{i} + b\mathbf{j}.$$

The student should check the signs of a and b as $\overrightarrow{AB}$ points in various directions.

EXAMPLE 1. A vector **v** has one of its representatives going from $A(3, -2)$ to $B(1, 1)$. Express **v** as a linear combination of **i** and **j**. Draw a figure.

Solution. As shown in Fig. 14–8, the points C, D have coordinates $(3, 1)$ and $(1, -2)$, respectively. Therefore the quantities a and b in Theorem 1 have the values -2 and 3, respectively, and we have

$$\mathbf{v} = -2\mathbf{i} + 3\mathbf{j}.$$

FIGURE 14–7

FIGURE 14–8

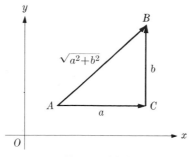

FIGURE 14–9

Corollary. *If a representative $\overrightarrow{AB}$ of a vector* **v** *has for its coordinates* (x_A, y_A) *and* (x_B, y_B), *then we have*

$$\mathbf{v} = (x_B - x_A)\mathbf{i} + (y_B - y_A)\mathbf{j}.$$

This is evident from the way Theorem 1 was proved, and Example 1 shows how it works in actual practice.

Theorem 2. *If* **v** *is any vector which, by Theorem 1, may be written in the form*

$$\mathbf{v} = a\mathbf{i} + b\mathbf{j},$$

then the length of **v**, *which we denote by* $|\mathbf{v}|$, *is given by*

$$|\mathbf{v}| = \sqrt{a^2 + b^2}.$$

Therefore $\mathbf{v} = \mathbf{0}$ *if and only if* $a = b = 0$.

Proof. The length of a vector is the length of any of its representatives. According to Fig. 14–9, $\overrightarrow{AC}$ is of length a, $\overrightarrow{CB}$ is of length b. The Pythagorean Theorem yields the length of $\overrightarrow{AB}$, the representative of **v**.

EXAMPLE 2. Given the vector $\mathbf{v} = 3\mathbf{i} - 4\mathbf{j}$, find the length of **v**.

Solution. $|\mathbf{v}| = \sqrt{3^2 + 4^2} = 5$.

Theorem 3. *If* $\mathbf{v} = a\mathbf{i} + b\mathbf{j}$ *and* $\mathbf{w} = c\mathbf{i} + d\mathbf{j}$,

then

$$\mathbf{v} + \mathbf{w} = (a + c)\mathbf{i} + (b + d)\mathbf{j}.$$

Further, if h *is any number, then* $h\mathbf{v} = ha\mathbf{i} + hb\mathbf{j}$.

Proof. The proof of this result follows from the laws of addition of vectors and multiplication of vectors by numbers, described earlier in this section. As a matter of fact, we now see that these algebraic laws follow at once from the corresponding laws for ordinary numbers. The student should carry out the proof by selecting representatives of each of the vectors and showing how the directed line segments can be added to yield the conclusion.

EXAMPLE 3.   Given the vectors $\mathbf{u} = 2\mathbf{i} - 3\mathbf{j}$, $\mathbf{v} = -4\mathbf{i} + \mathbf{j}$.   Express the vector $2\mathbf{u} - 3\mathbf{v}$ in terms of $\mathbf{i}$ and $\mathbf{j}$.

Solution. $2\mathbf{u} = 4\mathbf{i} - 6\mathbf{j}$ and $-3\mathbf{v} = 12\mathbf{i} - 3\mathbf{j}$.   Adding these vectors, we get $2\mathbf{u} - 3\mathbf{v} = 16\mathbf{i} - 9\mathbf{j}$.

DEFINITION.   Let $\mathbf{v}$ be any vector except $\mathbf{0}$. The unit vector $\mathbf{u}$ in the direction of $\mathbf{v}$ is defined by

$$\mathbf{u} = \left(\frac{1}{|\mathbf{v}|}\right)\mathbf{v}.$$

EXAMPLE 4.   Given the vector $\mathbf{v} = -2\mathbf{i} + 3\mathbf{j}$, find a unit vector in the direction of $\mathbf{v}$.

Solution.   We have $|\mathbf{v}| = \sqrt{4 + 9} = \sqrt{13}$. The desired vector $\mathbf{u}$ is

$$\mathbf{u} = \frac{1}{\sqrt{13}}\mathbf{v} = -\frac{2}{\sqrt{13}}\mathbf{i} + \frac{3}{\sqrt{13}}\mathbf{j}.$$

EXAMPLE 5.   Given the vector $\mathbf{v} = 2\mathbf{i} - 4\mathbf{j}$. Find a representative $\overrightarrow{AB}$ of $\mathbf{v}$, given that A has coordinates $(3, -5)$.

Solution.   Denote the coordinates of B by x_B, y_B. Then we have (by the Corollary)

$$x_B - 3 = 2 \quad \text{and} \quad y_B + 5 = -4.$$

Therefore $x_B = 5$, $y_B = -9$.

EXERCISES

In problems 1 through 7, express $\mathbf{v}$ in terms of $\mathbf{i}$ and $\mathbf{j}$, given that the endpoints A and B of the representative $\overrightarrow{AB}$ of $\mathbf{v}$ have the given coordinates.

1. $A(2, 1)$, $B(-1, -1)$ 2. $A(1, -2)$, $B(-2, 1)$ 3. $A(-3, -2)$, $B(1, 3)$
4. $A(4, -1)$, $B(-1, 2)$ 5. $A(5, 0)$, $B(0, -6)$ 6. $A(5, 1)$, $B(9, 1)$
7. $A(-2, 3)$, $B(-7, 3)$

In problems 8 through 11, in each case find a unit vector $\mathbf{u}$ in the direction of $\mathbf{v}$. Express $\mathbf{u}$ in terms of $\mathbf{i}$ and $\mathbf{j}$.

8. $\mathbf{v} = 4\mathbf{i} + 3\mathbf{j}$ 9. $\mathbf{v} = -5\mathbf{i} - 12\mathbf{j}$
10. $\mathbf{v} = 2\mathbf{i} - 2\sqrt{3}\,\mathbf{j}$ 11. $\mathbf{v} = -2\mathbf{i} + 5\mathbf{j}$

In problems 12 through 17, find the representative $\overrightarrow{AB}$ of the vector $\mathbf{v}$ from the information given.

12. $\mathbf{v} = 7\mathbf{i} - 3\mathbf{j}$, $A(2, -1)$ 13. $\mathbf{v} = -2\mathbf{i} + 4\mathbf{j}$, $A(6, 2)$
14. $\mathbf{v} = 3\mathbf{i} + 2\mathbf{j}$, $B(-2, 1)$ 15. $\mathbf{v} = -4\mathbf{i} - 2\mathbf{j}$, $B(0, 5)$

16. $\mathbf{v} = 3\mathbf{i} + 2\mathbf{j}$, midpoint of segment AB has coordinates $(3, 1)$

17. $\mathbf{v} = -2\mathbf{i} + 3\mathbf{j}$, midpoint of segment AB has coordinates $(-4, 2)$

18. Find a representative of the vector $\mathbf{v}$ of unit length making an angle of 30° with the positive x-direction. Express $\mathbf{v}$ in terms of $\mathbf{i}$ and $\mathbf{j}$.

19. Find the vector $\mathbf{v}$ (in terms of $\mathbf{i}$ and $\mathbf{j}$) which has length $2\sqrt{2}$ and makes an angle of 45° with the positive y-axis (two solutions).

20. Given that $\mathbf{u} = 3\mathbf{i} - 2\mathbf{j}$, $\mathbf{v} = 4\mathbf{i} + 3\mathbf{j}$. Find $\mathbf{u} + \mathbf{v}$ in terms of $\mathbf{i}$ and $\mathbf{j}$. Draw a figure.

21. Given that $\mathbf{u} = -2\mathbf{i} + 3\mathbf{j}$, $\mathbf{v} = \mathbf{i} - 2\mathbf{j}$. Find $\mathbf{u} + \mathbf{v}$ in terms of $\mathbf{i}$ and $\mathbf{j}$. Draw a figure.

22. Given that $\mathbf{u} = -3\mathbf{i} - 2\mathbf{j}$, $\mathbf{v} = 2\mathbf{i} + \mathbf{j}$. Find $3\mathbf{u} - 2\mathbf{v}$ in terms of $\mathbf{i}$ and $\mathbf{j}$. Draw a figure.

23. Show that if $\overrightarrow{AB} \approx \overrightarrow{CD}$ and $\overrightarrow{CD} \approx \overrightarrow{EF}$, then $\overrightarrow{AB} \approx \overrightarrow{EF}$.

24. Show that if $\overrightarrow{AB} \approx \overrightarrow{DE}$ and $\overrightarrow{BC} \approx \overrightarrow{EF}$, then $\overrightarrow{AC} \approx \overrightarrow{DF}$. Draw a figure.

25. Show that if $\overrightarrow{AB} \approx \overrightarrow{DE}$, c is any real number, C is the point c of the way from A to B, and F is the point c of the way from D to E, then $\overrightarrow{AC} \approx \overrightarrow{DF}$. Draw a figure.

26. Show that the vectors $\mathbf{v} = 2\mathbf{i} + 4\mathbf{j}$ and $\mathbf{w} = 10\mathbf{i} - 5\mathbf{j}$ are orthogonal.

27. Show that the vectors $\mathbf{v} = -3\mathbf{i} + \sqrt{2}\,\mathbf{j}$ and $\mathbf{w} = 4\sqrt{2}\,\mathbf{i} + 12\mathbf{j}$ are orthogonal.

3. OPERATIONS WITH VECTORS, CONTINUED

Two vectors $\mathbf{v}$ and $\mathbf{w}$ are said to be *parallel* or *proportional* when each is a scalar multiple of the other (and neither is zero). The representatives of parallel vectors are all parallel directed line segments.

By the *angle between two vectors* $\mathbf{v}$ and $\mathbf{w}$ (neither $= \mathbf{0}$), we mean the measure of the angle between any line containing a representative of $\mathbf{v}$ and any line containing a representative of $\mathbf{w}$ (see Fig. 14–10). Two parallel vectors make an angle either of 0 or of π, depending on whether they are pointing in the same or opposite directions (i.e., whether the scalar multiple is positive or negative).

Suppose that $\mathbf{i}$ and $\mathbf{j}$ are the usual unit vectors pointing in the direction of the x- and y-axes, respectively. Then we have the following theorem.

FIGURE 14–10

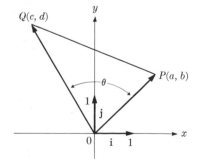

FIGURE 14–11

Theorem 4. *If θ is the angle between the vectors*

$$\mathbf{v} = a\mathbf{i} + b\mathbf{j} \quad and \quad \mathbf{w} = c\mathbf{i} + d\mathbf{j},$$

then

$$\cos \theta = \frac{ac + bd}{|\mathbf{v}| \; |\mathbf{w}|}.$$

Proof. We draw the representatives of $\mathbf{v}$ and $\mathbf{w}$ with base at the origin of the coordinate system, as shown in Fig. 14–11. When we look at the figure, we see that the coordinates of P are (a, b) and those of Q are (c, d). The length of $\mathbf{v}$ is $\overline{OP}$ and the length of $\mathbf{w}$ is $\overline{OQ}$. We apply the law of cosines to $\triangle OPQ$, obtaining

$$\cos \theta = \frac{\overline{OP}^2 + \overline{OQ}^2 - \overline{QP}^2}{2\overline{OP} \cdot \overline{OQ}}.$$

Therefore

$$\cos \theta = \frac{a^2 + b^2 + c^2 + d^2 - (a - c)^2 - (b - d)^2}{2\overline{OP} \cdot \overline{OQ}}$$

$$= \frac{ac + bd}{|\mathbf{v}| \cdot |\mathbf{w}|}.$$

EXAMPLE 1.   Given the vectors $\mathbf{v} = 2\mathbf{i} - 3\mathbf{j}$ and $\mathbf{w} = \mathbf{i} - 4\mathbf{j}$, compute the cosine of the angle between $\mathbf{v}$ and $\mathbf{w}$.

Solution.   We have $|\mathbf{v}| = \sqrt{4 + 9} = \sqrt{13}$, $|\mathbf{w}| = \sqrt{1 + 16} = \sqrt{17}$. Therefore

$$\cos \theta = \frac{2 \cdot 1 + (-3)(-4)}{\sqrt{17}\sqrt{13}} = \frac{14}{\sqrt{221}}.$$

Suppose that we have two directed line segments $\overrightarrow{AB}$ and $\overrightarrow{CD}$, as shown in Fig. 14–12. The *projection of* $\overrightarrow{AB}$ *in the direction* $\overrightarrow{CD}$ is defined as the directed line segment $\overrightarrow{EF}$ obtained by dropping perpendiculars from A and B to the line containing $\overrightarrow{CD}$. We can find the projection of a vector $\mathbf{v}$ along a vector $\mathbf{w}$ by first taking a representative of $\mathbf{v}$ and finding its projection (call it $\overrightarrow{EF}$) in the direction of a representative of $\mathbf{w}$. The vector having $\overrightarrow{EF}$ as a representative is called the *projection of* $\mathbf{v}$ *on* $\mathbf{w}$. It is a vector proportional to $\mathbf{w}$. If θ is the angle between $\mathbf{v}$ and $\mathbf{w}$, we see at once that the length of the projection of $\mathbf{v}$ on $\mathbf{w}$ is

$$|\mathbf{v}| \cos \theta.$$

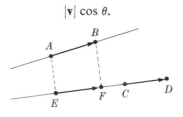

FIGURE 14–12

If $\mathbf{v} = a\mathbf{i} + b\mathbf{j}$ and $\mathbf{w} = c\mathbf{i} + d\mathbf{j}$, then

$$|\mathbf{v}| \cos \theta = \frac{ac + bd}{|\mathbf{w}|}.$$

EXAMPLE 2. Find the vector which is the projection of $\mathbf{v} = 3\mathbf{i} - 2\mathbf{j}$ on $\mathbf{w} = -2\mathbf{i} - 4\mathbf{j}$.

Solution. We obtain the length of the desired vector, which we call $\mathbf{u}$, by using the formula

$$|\mathbf{v}| \cos \theta = \frac{-6 + 8}{\sqrt{20}} = \frac{1}{\sqrt{5}}.$$

Since $\mathbf{u}$ is parallel to $\mathbf{w}$, there is a constant c such that $\mathbf{u} = c\mathbf{w}$. Therefore

$$\mathbf{u} = -2c\mathbf{i} - 4c\mathbf{j}.$$

Since $|\mathbf{u}| = 1/\sqrt{5}$, we get $1/\sqrt{5} = \sqrt{4c^2 + 16c^2}$, or $c = \pm\frac{1}{10}$. Since the angle between $\mathbf{v}$ and $\mathbf{w}$ is between 0 and $\pi/2$, the projection will be in the same direction as $\mathbf{w}$, and we must select $c = +\frac{1}{10}$. The desired vector is

$$\mathbf{u} = -\tfrac{1}{5}\mathbf{i} - \tfrac{2}{5}\mathbf{j}.$$

The *scalar product* of two vectors $\mathbf{v}$ and $\mathbf{w}$, written $\mathbf{v} \cdot \mathbf{w}$, is defined by the formula

$$\mathbf{v} \cdot \mathbf{w} = |\mathbf{v}| |\mathbf{w}| \cos \theta,$$

where θ is the angle between $\mathbf{v}$ and $\mathbf{w}$. The terms *dot product* and *inner product* are also used to designate scalar product. It is evident from the definition that scalar product satisfies the relations

$$\mathbf{v} \cdot \mathbf{w} = \mathbf{w} \cdot \mathbf{v}, \qquad \mathbf{v} \cdot \mathbf{v} = |\mathbf{v}|^2.$$

Furthermore, if $\mathbf{v}$ and $\mathbf{w}$ are orthogonal, then

$$\mathbf{v} \cdot \mathbf{w} = 0,$$

and conversely. If $\mathbf{v}$ and $\mathbf{w}$ are parallel, we have $\mathbf{v} \cdot \mathbf{w} = \pm|\mathbf{v}| |\mathbf{w}|$, and conversely. In terms of the orthogonal unit vectors $\mathbf{i}$ and $\mathbf{j}$, vectors $\mathbf{v} = a\mathbf{i} + b\mathbf{j}$ and $\mathbf{w} = c\mathbf{i} + d\mathbf{j}$ have as their scalar product

$$\mathbf{v} \cdot \mathbf{w} = ac + bd.$$

In addition, it can be verified that the *distributive law*

$$\mathbf{u} \cdot (\mathbf{v} + \mathbf{w}) = \mathbf{u} \cdot \mathbf{v} + \mathbf{u} \cdot \mathbf{w}$$

holds for any three vectors.

EXAMPLE 3. Given the vectors $\mathbf{u} = 3\mathbf{i} + 2\mathbf{j}$ and $\mathbf{v} = 2\mathbf{i} + a\mathbf{j}$. Determine the number a so that $\mathbf{u}$ and $\mathbf{v}$ are orthogonal. Determine a so that $\mathbf{u}$ and $\mathbf{v}$ are parallel. For what value of a will $\mathbf{u}$ and $\mathbf{v}$ make an angle of $\pi/4$?

Solution. If **u** and **v** are orthogonal, we have

$$3 \cdot 2 + 2 \cdot a = 0 \quad \text{and} \quad a = -3.$$

For **u** and **v** to be parallel, we must have

$$\mathbf{u} \cdot \mathbf{v} = \pm |\mathbf{u}|\,|\mathbf{v}|,$$

or

$$6 + 2a = \pm\sqrt{13} \cdot \sqrt{4 + a^2}.$$

Solving, we obtain $a = \frac{4}{3}$. From the formula

$$\tfrac{1}{2}\sqrt{2} = \cos\frac{\pi}{4} = \frac{6 + 2a}{\sqrt{13} \cdot \sqrt{4 + a^2}},$$

we see that **u** and **v** make an angle of $\pi/4$ when

$$a = 10, \ -\tfrac{2}{5}.$$

Because they are geometric quantities which are independent of the coordinate system, vectors are well-suited for establishing certain types of theorems in plane geometry. We give some examples to exhibit the technique.

EXAMPLE 4. Let $\overrightarrow{OA}$ be a representative of **u** and $\overrightarrow{OB}$ a representative of **v**. Let C be the point on the line AB which is $\frac{2}{3}$ of the way from A to B. Express in terms of **u** and **v** the vector **w** which has $\overrightarrow{OC}$ as representative (Fig. 14–13).

Solution. Let **z** be the vector with $\overrightarrow{AC}$ as representative, and **t** the vector with $\overrightarrow{AB}$ as representative. We have

$$\mathbf{w} = \mathbf{u} + \mathbf{z} = \mathbf{u} + \tfrac{2}{3}\mathbf{t}.$$

Also, we know that

$$\mathbf{t} = \mathbf{v} - \mathbf{u},$$

and so

$$\mathbf{w} = \mathbf{u} + \tfrac{2}{3}(\mathbf{v} - \mathbf{u}) = \tfrac{1}{3}\mathbf{u} + \tfrac{2}{3}\mathbf{v}.$$

EXAMPLE 5. Let $ABDC$ be a parallelogram, as shown in Fig. 14–14. Suppose that E is the midpoint of CD and F is $\frac{2}{3}$ of the way from A to E on AE. Show that F is $\frac{2}{3}$ of the way from B to C.

FIGURE 14–13

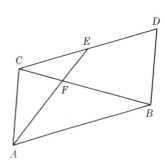

FIGURE 14–14

Solution. Let $\overrightarrow{AB}, \overrightarrow{AC}, \overrightarrow{AF}, \overrightarrow{AE}, \overrightarrow{BF}, \overrightarrow{BC}$, and $\overrightarrow{CE}$ all be representatives of vectors. For convenience we shall use the notation $\mathbf{v}[\overrightarrow{AB}], \mathbf{v}[\overrightarrow{AC}], \mathbf{v}[\overrightarrow{AF}]$, etc., for the vectors which have the directed line segments shown in brackets as representatives. By hypothesis, we have

$$\mathbf{v}[\overrightarrow{AB}] = \mathbf{v}[\overrightarrow{CD}] \quad \text{and} \quad \mathbf{v}[\overrightarrow{CE}] = \tfrac{1}{2}\mathbf{v}[\overrightarrow{CD}].$$

The rule for addition of vectors gives us

$$\mathbf{v}[\overrightarrow{AE}] = \mathbf{v}[\overrightarrow{AC}] + \mathbf{v}[\overrightarrow{CE}] = \mathbf{v}[\overrightarrow{AC}] + \tfrac{1}{2}\mathbf{v}[\overrightarrow{AB}].$$

Also, since $\mathbf{v}[\overrightarrow{AF}] = \tfrac{2}{3}\mathbf{v}[\overrightarrow{AE}]$, we obtain

$$\mathbf{v}[\overrightarrow{AF}] = \tfrac{2}{3}\mathbf{v}[\overrightarrow{AC}] + \tfrac{1}{3}\mathbf{v}[\overrightarrow{AB}].$$

The rule for subtraction of vectors gives us

$$\mathbf{v}[\overrightarrow{BF}] = \mathbf{v}[\overrightarrow{AF}] - \mathbf{v}[\overrightarrow{AB}] = \tfrac{2}{3}\mathbf{v}[\overrightarrow{AC}] - \tfrac{2}{3}\mathbf{v}[\overrightarrow{AB}] = \tfrac{2}{3}(\mathbf{v}[\overrightarrow{AC}] - \mathbf{v}[\overrightarrow{AB}]).$$

Since $\mathbf{v}[\overrightarrow{BC}] = \mathbf{v}[\overrightarrow{AC}] - \mathbf{v}[\overrightarrow{AB}]$, we conclude that

$$\mathbf{v}[\overrightarrow{BF}] = \tfrac{2}{3}\mathbf{v}[\overrightarrow{BC}],$$

which is the desired result.

EXERCISES

In problems 1 through 8, given that θ is the angle between $\mathbf{v}$ and $\mathbf{w}$, find $|\mathbf{v}|$, $|\mathbf{w}|$, $\cos\theta$, and the projection of $\mathbf{v}$ on $\mathbf{w}$.

1. $\mathbf{v} = -3\mathbf{i} + 4\mathbf{j}$, $\mathbf{w} = 4\mathbf{i} + 3\mathbf{j}$
2. $\mathbf{v} = 3\mathbf{i} + 4\mathbf{j}$, $\mathbf{w} = 5\mathbf{i} - 12\mathbf{j}$
3. $\mathbf{v} = 12\mathbf{i} - 5\mathbf{j}$, $\mathbf{w} = 7\mathbf{i} + 24\mathbf{j}$
4. $\mathbf{v} = 7\mathbf{i} + 24\mathbf{j}$, $\mathbf{w} = 4\mathbf{i} + 3\mathbf{j}$
5. $\mathbf{v} = 2\mathbf{i} + 3\mathbf{j}$, $\mathbf{w} = 2\mathbf{i} - 3\mathbf{j}$
6. $\mathbf{v} = \mathbf{i} + 4\mathbf{j}$, $\mathbf{w} = 2\mathbf{i} + 2\mathbf{j}$
7. $\mathbf{v} = 3\mathbf{i} - 2\mathbf{j}$, $\mathbf{w} = 2\mathbf{i} + 5\mathbf{j}$
8. $\mathbf{v} = 7\mathbf{i} + \mathbf{j}$, $\mathbf{w} = -3\mathbf{i} - 4\mathbf{j}$

In problems 9 through 12, find the projection of the vector with representative $\overrightarrow{AB}$ on the vector with representative $\overrightarrow{CD}$. Draw figures.

9. $A(3, 1)$, $B(5, 2)$, $C(-2, -1)$, $D(-1, 3)$
10. $A(2, 4)$, $B(4, 7)$, $C(6, -1)$, $D(2, 2)$
11. $A(2, -1)$, $B(1, 3)$, $C(5, 2)$, $D(9, 3)$
12. $A(1, 6)$, $B(2, 5)$, $C(5, 2)$, $D(9, 3)$

In problems 13 through 17, find $\cos\theta$ and $\cos\alpha$, given that $\theta = \angle ABC$ and $\alpha = \angle BAC$. Use vector methods and draw figures.

13. $A(-1, 1)$, $B(3, -1)$, $C(3, 4)$
14. $A(2, 1)$, $B(-1, 2)$, $C(1, 3)$
15. $A(3, 4)$, $B(5, 1)$, $C(4, 1)$
16. $A(4, 1)$, $B(1, -1)$, $C(3, 3)$
17. $A(0, 0)$, $B(3, -5)$, $C(6, -10)$

In problems 18 through 24, determine the number a (if possible) such that the given condition for $\mathbf{v}$ and $\mathbf{w}$ is satisfied.

18. $\mathbf{v} = 2\mathbf{i} + a\mathbf{j}$, $\mathbf{w} = \mathbf{i} + 3\mathbf{j}$, $\mathbf{v}$ and $\mathbf{w}$ orthogonal
19. $\mathbf{v} = \mathbf{i} - 3\mathbf{j}$, $\mathbf{w} = 2a\mathbf{i} + \mathbf{j}$, $\mathbf{v}$ and $\mathbf{w}$ orthogonal

20. $\mathbf{v} = 3\mathbf{i} - 4\mathbf{j}$, $\mathbf{w} = 2\mathbf{i} + a\mathbf{j}$, $\mathbf{v}$ and $\mathbf{w}$ parallel

21. $\mathbf{v} = a\mathbf{i} + 2\mathbf{j}$, $\mathbf{w} = 2\mathbf{i} - a\mathbf{j}$, $\mathbf{v}$ and $\mathbf{w}$ parallel

22. $\mathbf{v} = a\mathbf{i}$, $\mathbf{w} = 2\mathbf{i} - 3\mathbf{j}$, $\mathbf{v}$ and $\mathbf{w}$ parallel

23. $\mathbf{v} = 5\mathbf{i} + 12\mathbf{j}$, $\mathbf{w} = \mathbf{i} + a\mathbf{j}$, $\mathbf{v}$ and $\mathbf{w}$ make an angle of $\pi/3$

24. $\mathbf{v} = 4\mathbf{i} - 3\mathbf{j}$, $\mathbf{w} = 2\mathbf{i} + a\mathbf{j}$, $\mathbf{v}$ and $\mathbf{w}$ make an angle of $\pi/6$

25. Prove the distributive law for the scalar product.

26. Let $\mathbf{i}$ and $\mathbf{j}$ be the usual unit vectors of one coordinate system, and let $\mathbf{i}_1$ and $\mathbf{j}_1$ be the unit orthogonal vectors corresponding to another rectangular system of coordinates. Given that

$$\mathbf{v} = a\mathbf{i} + b\mathbf{j}, \qquad\qquad \mathbf{w} = c\mathbf{i} + d\mathbf{j},$$
$$\mathbf{v} = a_1\mathbf{i}_1 + b_1\mathbf{j}_1, \qquad \mathbf{w} = c_1\mathbf{i}_1 + d_1\mathbf{j}_1,$$

show that

$$ac + bd = a_1c_1 + b_1d_1.$$

In problems 27 through 30, the quantity $|AB|$ denotes the length of the line segment $\overline{AB}$, the quantity $|AC|$, the length of $\overline{AC}$, etc.

27. Given $\triangle ABC$, in which $\angle A = 120°$, $|AB| = 4$ and $|AC| = 7$. Find $|BC|$ and the projections of $\overrightarrow{AB}$ and $\overrightarrow{AC}$ on $\overrightarrow{BC}$. Draw a figure.

28. Given $\triangle ABC$, with $\angle A = 45°$, $|AB| = 8$, $|AC| = 6\sqrt{2}$. Find $|BC|$ and the projections of $\overrightarrow{AB}$ and $\overrightarrow{AC}$ on $\overrightarrow{BC}$. Draw a figure.

29. Given $\triangle ABC$, with $|AB| = 10$, $|AC| = 9$, $|BC| = 7$. Find the projections of $\overrightarrow{AC}$ and $\overrightarrow{BC}$ on $\overrightarrow{AB}$. Draw a figure.

30. Given $\triangle ABC$, with $|AB| = 5$, $|AC| = 7$, $|BC| = 9$. Find the projections of $\overrightarrow{AB}$ and $\overrightarrow{AC}$ on $\overrightarrow{CB}$. Draw a figure.

In problems 31 through 38, the notation used in Example 5 will be employed.

31. Given the line segments $\overline{AB}$ and $\overline{AC}$, with D on $\overline{AB}$ $\frac{2}{3}$ of the way from A to B. Let E be the midpoint of $\overline{AC}$. Express $\mathbf{v}[\overrightarrow{DE}]$ in terms of $\mathbf{v}[\overrightarrow{AB}]$ and $\mathbf{v}[\overrightarrow{AC}]$. Draw a figure.

32. Suppose that $\mathbf{v}[\overrightarrow{AD}] = \frac{1}{4}\mathbf{v}[\overrightarrow{AB}]$ and $\mathbf{v}[\overrightarrow{BE}] = \frac{1}{2}\mathbf{v}[\overrightarrow{BC}]$. Find $\mathbf{v}[\overrightarrow{DE}]$ in terms of $\mathbf{v}[\overrightarrow{AB}]$ and $\mathbf{v}[\overrightarrow{BC}]$. Draw a figure.

33. Given $\square ABDC$, a parallelogram, with E $\frac{2}{3}$ of the way from B to D, and F as the midpoint of segment $\overline{CD}$. Find $\mathbf{v}[\overrightarrow{EF}]$ in terms of $\mathbf{v}[\overrightarrow{AB}]$ and $\mathbf{v}[\overrightarrow{AC}]$.

34. Given parallelogram $ABDC$, with E $\frac{1}{4}$ of the way from B to C, and F $\frac{1}{4}$ of the way from A to D. Find $\mathbf{v}[\overrightarrow{EF}]$ in terms of $\mathbf{v}[\overrightarrow{AB}]$ and $\mathbf{v}[\overrightarrow{AC}]$.

35. Given parallelogram $ABDC$, with E $\frac{1}{3}$ of the way from B to D, and F $\frac{1}{4}$ of the way from B to C. Show that F is $\frac{3}{4}$ of the way from A to E.

36. Suppose that on the sides of $\triangle ABC$, $\mathbf{v}[\overrightarrow{BD}] = \frac{2}{3}\mathbf{v}[\overrightarrow{BC}]$, $\mathbf{v}[\overrightarrow{CE}] = \frac{2}{3}\mathbf{v}[\overrightarrow{CA}]$, and $\mathbf{v}[\overrightarrow{AF}] = \frac{2}{3}\mathbf{v}[\overrightarrow{AB}]$. Draw a figure and show that

$$\mathbf{v}[\overrightarrow{AD}] + \mathbf{v}[\overrightarrow{BE}] + \mathbf{v}[\overrightarrow{CF}] = \mathbf{0}.$$

37. Show that the conclusion of problem 36 holds when the fraction $\frac{2}{3}$ is replaced by any real number h.

38. Let $\mathbf{a} = \mathbf{v}[\overrightarrow{OA}]$, $\mathbf{b} = \mathbf{v}[\overrightarrow{OB}]$, and $\mathbf{c} = \mathbf{v}[\overrightarrow{OC}]$. Show that the medians of $\triangle ABC$ meet at a point P, and express $\mathbf{v}[\overrightarrow{OP}]$ in terms of $\mathbf{a}$, $\mathbf{b}$, and $\mathbf{c}$. Draw a figure.

4. VECTOR FUNCTIONS AND THEIR DERIVATIVES

A vector function **v** of the real variable t assigns a particular vector to each value of t. More precisely, a *vector function* is a collection of ordered pairs $(t, \mathbf{v})$, in which t is a real number, **v** is a vector, and no two pairs have the same first element. The *domain* consists of all possible values of t in the collection, and the *range* consists of all vectors which occur.

Vector functions are more complicated than ordinary functions, since the elements of the range, namely vectors, are themselves equivalence classes of directed line segments. However, if we concentrate on the representation — the directed line segments — the concept becomes more concrete. Also, many of the properties of ordinary functions extend easily to vector functions when suitably interpreted. We shall use boldface letters such as **f**, **g**, **v**, **F**, **G** to represent vector functions. If the dependence on the independent variable is to be indicated, we shall write $\mathbf{f}(t)$, $\mathbf{g}(s)$, $\mathbf{F}(x)$, and so forth.

DEFINITION. *A vector function* **f** *is continuous at* $t = a$ *if for each* $\epsilon > 0$ *there is a* $\delta > 0$ *such that*

$$|\mathbf{f}(t) - \mathbf{f}(a)| < \epsilon \text{ for all } t \text{ such that } 0 < |t - a| < \delta.$$

We note that the form of the definition of continuity for vector functions is identical with that for ordinary functions. (See p. 108.) We must realize, however, that $\mathbf{f}(t) - \mathbf{f}(a)$ is a vector, and that the symbol $|\mathbf{f}(t) - \mathbf{f}(a)|$ stands for the length of a vector, whereas in the case of ordinary functions, $|f(t) - f(a)|$ is the absolute value of a number. In words, the continuity of a vector function asserts that as $t \to a$ the vector $\mathbf{f}(t)$ approaches $\mathbf{f}(a)$, in both length and direction. When **f** is continuous at a, we also write

$$\lim_{t \to a} \mathbf{f}(t) = \mathbf{f}(a).$$

If **i** and **j** are the customary unit vectors associated with a rectangular coordinate system, a vector function **f** can be written in the form

$$\mathbf{f}(t) = f_1(t)\mathbf{i} + f_2(t)\mathbf{j},$$

where $f_1(t)$ and $f_2(t)$ are functions of t in the ordinary sense. Statements about vector functions **f** may always be interpreted as statements about a pair of functions (f_1, f_2).

Theorem 5. *A function* **f** *is continuous at* $t = a$ *if and only if* f_1 *and* f_2 *are continuous at* $t = a$.

Proof. We have $\mathbf{f}(a) = f_1(a)\mathbf{i} + f_2(a)\mathbf{j}$,

$$|\mathbf{f}(t) - \mathbf{f}(a)| = |(f_1(t) - f_1(a))\mathbf{i} + (f_2(t) - f_2(a))\mathbf{j}|,$$

and (see Fig. 14–15)

$$|\mathbf{f}(t) - \mathbf{f}(a)| = \sqrt{|f_1(t) - f_1(a)|^2 + |f_2(t) - f_2(a)|^2}.$$

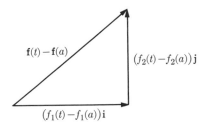

$$f(t) - f(a)$$

$$(f_2(t) - f_2(a))j$$

$$(f_1(t) - f_1(a))i$$

FIGURE 14–15

If $\lim_{t \to a} f_1(t) = f_1(a)$ and $\lim_{t \to a} f_2(t) = f_2(a)$, it follows that $\lim_{t \to a} \mathbf{f}(t) = \mathbf{f}(a)$. On the other hand, the inequalities

$$|f_1(t) - f_1(a)| \le |\mathbf{f}(t) - \mathbf{f}(a)|,$$
$$|f_2(t) - f_2(a)| \le |\mathbf{f}(t) - \mathbf{f}(a)|$$

show that if $\lim_{t \to a} \mathbf{f}(t) = \mathbf{f}(a)$, then *both* $\lim_{t \to a} f_1(t) = f_1(a)$ and $\lim_{t \to a} f_2(t) = f_2(a)$.

If $\mathbf{f}$ is a vector function, we define the *derivative* $\mathbf{f}'$ as

$$\mathbf{f}'(t) = \lim_{h \to 0} \frac{\mathbf{f}(t + h) - \mathbf{f}(t)}{h},$$

whenever it exists. If we have

$$\mathbf{f}(t) = f_1(t)\mathbf{i} + f_2(t)\mathbf{j},$$

then

$$\mathbf{f}'(t) = f_1'(t)\mathbf{i} + f_2'(t)\mathbf{j},$$

where $f_1'(t)$, $f_2'(t)$ are derivatives in the ordinary sense.

EXAMPLE 1. Find the derivative $\mathbf{f}'(t)$ if $\mathbf{f}(t) = (t^2 + 2t - 1)\mathbf{i} + (3t^3 - 2)\mathbf{j}$.

Solution. $\mathbf{f}'(t) = (2t + 2)\mathbf{i} + 9t^2\mathbf{j}$.

EXAMPLE 2. Given that $\mathbf{f}(t) = (\sin t)\mathbf{i} + (3 - 2 \cos t)\mathbf{j}$, find $\mathbf{f}''(t)$.

Solution. $\mathbf{f}'(t) = \cos t\mathbf{i} + 2 \sin t\mathbf{j}$.

$$\mathbf{f}''(t) = -\sin t\mathbf{i} + 2 \cos t\mathbf{j}.$$

EXAMPLE 3. Given $\mathbf{f}(t) = (3t - 2)\mathbf{i} + (2t^2 + 1)\mathbf{j}$. Find the value of $\mathbf{f}'(t) \cdot \mathbf{f}''(t)$.

Solution. $\mathbf{f}'(t) = 3\mathbf{i} + 4t\mathbf{j}$, $\mathbf{f}''(t) = 4\mathbf{j}$, and $\mathbf{f}'(t) \cdot \mathbf{f}''(t) = (3\mathbf{i} + 4t\mathbf{j}) \cdot (4\mathbf{j}) = 16t$.

The derivative of a vector function has a simple geometric interpretation in terms of representatives. Draw the particular representative of $\mathbf{f}(t)$ which has its base at the origin of the coordinate system. Then the head of this representative

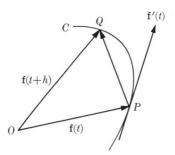

FIGURE 14–16

will trace out a curve C as t takes on all possible values in its domain (Fig. 14–16). The directed line segment $\overrightarrow{OP}$ represents $\mathbf{f}(t)$. Let $\overrightarrow{OQ}$ represent $\mathbf{f}(t + h)$. The difference $\mathbf{f}(t + h) - \mathbf{f}(t)$ has as one of its representatives the directed line segment $\overrightarrow{PQ}$. Multiplying $\mathbf{f}(t + h) - \mathbf{f}(t)$ by $1/h$ gives a vector in the direction of $\overrightarrow{PQ}$, but $1/h$ times as long. As h tends to zero, the quantity

$$\frac{\mathbf{f}(t + h) - \mathbf{f}(t)}{h}$$

tends to a vector, with one of its representatives tangent to the curve C at the point P.

EXERCISES

In problems 1 through 4, calculate $\mathbf{f}'(t)$ and $\mathbf{f}''(t)$.

1. $\mathbf{f}(t) = (3 - 2t)\mathbf{i} + (2t + 1)\mathbf{j}$ 2. $\mathbf{f}(t) = \left(\dfrac{t + 1}{t - 1}\right)\mathbf{i} + \dfrac{2t - 1}{t}\mathbf{j}$

3. $\mathbf{f}(t) = (\sin 2t)\mathbf{i} + (\sec t)\mathbf{j}$ 4. $\mathbf{f}(t) = \sqrt{2t - 1}\,\mathbf{i} + (2t + 1)^2\mathbf{j}$

5. Find $\mathbf{f}(t) \cdot \mathbf{f}'(t)$ if $\mathbf{f}(t) = \dfrac{t^2 + 1}{t^2 + 2}\mathbf{i} + 2t\mathbf{j}$

6. Find $\dfrac{d}{dt}\left(\mathbf{f}(t) \cdot \mathbf{f}'(t)\right)$ if $\mathbf{f}(t) = 2t\mathbf{i} + \dfrac{1}{t + 1}\mathbf{j}$

7. Find $\dfrac{d}{dt}|\mathbf{f}(t)|$ if $\mathbf{f}(t) = \sin 2t\mathbf{i} + \cos 3t\mathbf{j}$

8. Find $\dfrac{d}{dt}|\mathbf{f}(t)|$ if $\mathbf{f}(t) = (t^2 + 1)\mathbf{i} + (3 + 2t^2)\mathbf{j}$

9. Find $\dfrac{d}{dt}|\mathbf{f}(t)|$ if $\mathbf{f}(t) = \cos\dfrac{1}{t}\mathbf{i} + \sin\dfrac{1}{t}\mathbf{j}$

10. Find $\dfrac{d}{dt}\left(\mathbf{f}'(t) \cdot \mathbf{f}''(t)\right)$ if $\mathbf{f}(t) = (3t + 1)\mathbf{i} + (2t^2 - t^3)\mathbf{j}$

11. Find $\dfrac{d}{dt}\left(\mathbf{f}'(t) \cdot \mathbf{f}''(t)\right)$ if $\mathbf{f}(t) = (\log t)\mathbf{i} + \dfrac{2}{t}\mathbf{j}$

12. Find $\dfrac{d}{dt}\,(\mathbf{f}''(t)\cdot\mathbf{f}'''(t))$ if $\mathbf{f}(t) = e^{3t}\mathbf{i} + e^{-3t}\mathbf{j}$

13. Given that $\mathbf{f}(t) = (2t + 1)\mathbf{i} + 3t\mathbf{j}$, $\mathbf{g}(t) = 4t\mathbf{j}$. Find $d\theta/dt$, where $\theta = \theta(t)$ is the angle between $\mathbf{f}$ and $\mathbf{g}$.

14. Prove the formula

$$\frac{d}{dt}\,(F(t)\cdot\mathbf{f}(t)) = F(t)\cdot\mathbf{f}'(t) + F'(t)\cdot\mathbf{f}(t).$$

15. Show that the following chain rule holds:

$$\frac{d}{dt}\,\{\mathbf{f}[g(t)]\} = \mathbf{f}'[g(t)]g'(t).$$

16. Given the vector $\mathbf{f}(t) = (2t + 1)\mathbf{i} + 2t\mathbf{j}$. Describe the curve traced out by the tip of the representative which has its base at the origin.

17. Given the vector $\mathbf{g}(t) = \cos t\mathbf{i} + \sin t\mathbf{j}$. Describe the curve traced out by the tip of the representative which has its base at the origin.

18. Prove that if $\mathbf{f}(t) = \sin 2t\mathbf{i} + \cos 2t\mathbf{j}$, then $\mathbf{f}(t)\cdot\mathbf{f}'(t) = 0$. What is the geometric interpretation of this result?

19. Prove that if

$$\mathbf{f}(t) = \frac{\mathbf{g}(t)}{h(t)}, \qquad \text{then} \qquad \mathbf{f}'(t) = \frac{h(t)\cdot\mathbf{g}'(t) - \mathbf{g}(t)\cdot h'(t)}{h^2(t)}.$$

20. Show that if

$$\mathbf{f}(t) = f_1(t)\mathbf{i} + f_2(t)\mathbf{j}, \qquad \text{then} \qquad \frac{d}{dt}\,(\mathbf{f}(t)\cdot\mathbf{f}(t)) = 2\mathbf{f}(t)\cdot\mathbf{f}'(t).$$

21. Show that

$$\frac{d}{dt}\,(\mathbf{f}(t)\cdot\mathbf{g}(t)) = \mathbf{f}(t)\cdot\mathbf{g}'(t) + \mathbf{f}'(t)\cdot\mathbf{g}(t).$$

(*Hint:* Write $\mathbf{f}(t) = f_1(t)\mathbf{i} + f_2(t)\mathbf{j}$ and $\mathbf{g}(t) = g_1(t)\mathbf{i} + g_2(t)\mathbf{j}$.)

5. VECTOR VELOCITY AND ACCELERATION

The vector function

$$\mathbf{f}(t) = x(t)\mathbf{i} + y(t)\mathbf{j}$$

is equivalent to the pair of parametric equations

$$x = x(t), \qquad y = y(t),$$

since the head of the directed line segment with base at the origin, which represents $\mathbf{f}$, traces out a curve which is identical with the curve given in parametric form by these equations.

We recall that the arc length $s(t)$ of a curve in parametric form satisfies the relation

$$\frac{ds}{dt} = \sqrt{(dx/dt)^2 + (dy/dt)^2},$$

and therefore

$$\frac{ds}{dt} = |\mathbf{f}'(t)|.$$

In our earlier study of the motion of a particle, we were concerned primarily with motion along a straight line. Now we shall take up the motion of a particle along a curve C in the plane given by the parametric equations

$$C: \quad x = x(t), \quad y = y(t).$$

Letting t denote the time, we define the *velocity vector* at the time t as

$$\frac{d\mathbf{f}}{dt} \equiv \mathbf{f}'(t) = x'(t)\mathbf{i} + y'(t)\mathbf{j}.$$

For velocity vector we shall use the symbol $\mathbf{v}(t)$, instead of $\mathbf{f}'(t)$. According to the geometrical interpretation of the derivative of a vector function given in the preceding section, the velocity vector is always tangent to the path describing the motion. We define the *speed* of the particle to be the magnitude of the velocity vector. The speed is

$$|\mathbf{v}(t)| = |\mathbf{f}'(t)| = \sqrt{(dx/dt)^2 + (dy/dt)^2},$$

which tells us that the speed is identical with the quantity ds/dt; in other words, the speed measures the rate of change in arc length s with respect to time t.

The *acceleration vector* $\mathbf{a}(t)$ is defined as the derivative of the velocity vector, or

$$\mathbf{a}(t) = \mathbf{v}'(t) = \mathbf{f}''(t).$$

EXAMPLE 1. Suppose that a particle P moves according to the law

$$\mathbf{f}(t) = (3\cos 2t)\mathbf{i} + (3\sin 2t)\mathbf{j}.$$

Find $\mathbf{v}(t)$, $\mathbf{a}(t)$, $s'(t)$, $s''(t)$, $|\mathbf{a}(t)|$, and $\mathbf{v}(t) \cdot \mathbf{a}(t)$.

Solution. We have

$$\mathbf{v}(t) = \mathbf{f}'(t) = (-6\sin 2t)\mathbf{i} + (6\cos 2t)\mathbf{j},$$
$$\mathbf{a}(t) = (-12\cos 2t)\mathbf{i} - (12\sin 2t)\mathbf{j},$$
$$s'(t) = [(-6\sin 2t)^2 + (6\cos 2t)^2]^{1/2} = 6,$$
$$s''(t) = 0,$$
$$|\mathbf{a}(t)| = [(-12\cos 2t)^2 + (12\sin 2t)^2]^{1/2} = 12,$$
$$\mathbf{v}(t) \cdot \mathbf{a}(t) = 0.$$

Remark. We note that P is moving around a circle with center at O and radius 3, with a constant speed but a changing velocity vector! Since $\mathbf{v}(t) \cdot \mathbf{a}(t) = 0$, we conclude that the acceleration vector is always pointing toward the center of the circle.

EXAMPLE 2. Suppose that a particle P moves according to the law

$$x(t) = t \cos t, \qquad y(t) = t \sin t,$$

or, equivalently,

$$f(t) = (t \cos t)\mathbf{i} + (t \sin t)\mathbf{j}.$$

Find $\mathbf{v}(t)$, $\mathbf{a}(t)$, $s'(t)$, $s''(t)$, and $|\mathbf{a}(t)|$.

Solution.

$$\mathbf{v}(t) = (-t \sin t + \cos t)\mathbf{i} + (t \cos t + \sin t)\mathbf{j},$$
$$\mathbf{a}(t) = (-t \cos t - 2 \sin t)\mathbf{i} + (-t \sin t + 2 \cos t)\mathbf{j}.$$

Therefore

$$s'(t) = |\mathbf{v}(t)| = \sqrt{1 + t^2},$$
$$s''(t) = \tfrac{1}{2}(1 + t^2)^{-1/2}(2t) = \frac{t}{\sqrt{1 + t^2}},$$
$$|\mathbf{a}(t)| = \sqrt{4 + t^2}.$$

EXERCISES

In problems 1 through 10, assume that a particle P moves according to the given law, t being the time. Compute $\mathbf{v}(t)$, $\mathbf{a}(t)$, $s'(t)$, and $s''(t)$.

1. $f(t) = t\mathbf{i} + \tfrac{1}{2}t^2\mathbf{j}$
2. $f(t) = \tfrac{1}{3}t^3\mathbf{i} + \tfrac{1}{4}t^4\mathbf{j}$
3. $f(t) = 12t\mathbf{i} + (4t - 8t^2)\mathbf{j}$
4. $f(t) = \tfrac{4}{3}t^{3/2}\mathbf{i} + (t - \tfrac{1}{2}t^2)\mathbf{j}$
5. $f(t) = t\mathbf{i} + (\ln \sec t)\mathbf{j}$
6. $f(t) = (2e^t)\mathbf{i} + (3e^{-t})\mathbf{j}$
7. $x = 3 \cos t, \ y = 2 \sin t$
8. $x = at, \ y = bt - \tfrac{1}{2}gt^2$
9. $x = e^{-t} \cos t, \ y = e^{-t} \sin t$
10. $x = \dfrac{t}{1 + t^2}, \ y = \dfrac{-2t}{1 + t^2}$

In problems 11 through 15, assume that a particle P moves according to the given law. Find $\mathbf{v}(t)$, $\mathbf{a}(t)$, $s'(t)$, and $s''(t)$ at the given time t.

11. $x = t^2 - t - 1, \ y = t^2 - 2t, \ t = 1$
12. $f(t) = (5 \cos t)\mathbf{i} + (4 \sin t)\mathbf{j}, \ t = 2\pi/3$
13. $x = 3 \sec t, \ y = 2 \tan t, \ t = \pi/6$
14. $f(t) = 4(\pi t - \sin \pi t)\mathbf{i} + 4(1 - \cos \pi t)\mathbf{j}, \ t = \tfrac{3}{4}$
15. $x = \ln (1 + t), \ y = 3/t, \ t = 2$
16. Suppose that P moves according to the law

$$f(t) = (R \cos wt)\mathbf{i} + (R \sin wt)\mathbf{j},$$

where $R > 0$ and w are constants. Find $\mathbf{v}(t)$, $\mathbf{a}(t)$, $s'(t)$, and $s''(t)$. Show that

$$|\mathbf{a}(t)| = \frac{1}{R} |\mathbf{v}(t)|^2.$$

17. Let $T(t)$ be a vector one unit long and parallel to the *velocity vector*. Show that

$$T(t) = \frac{v(t)}{ds/dt} = \frac{x'(t)}{s'(t)} i + \frac{y'(t)}{s'(t)} j.$$

18. Using the formula of problem 17, compute $T(t)$ if the law of motion is

$$f(t) = (3t - 1)i + (t^2 + 2)j.$$

19. Using the formula of problem 17, compute $T(t)$ if the law of motion is

$$f(t) = (4e^{2t})i + (3e^{-2t})j.$$

20. Given that P moves so that

$$f(t) = (c \cosh pt)i + (c \sinh pt)j,$$

find $v(t)$ and $a(t)$, and compare a with f.

6. TANGENTIAL AND NORMAL COMPONENTS

Suppose that we have a motion described by

$$f(t) = x(t)i + y(t)j,$$

with velocity vector $v(t) = f'(t)$. We define the *unit tangent vector* $T(t)$ as the unit vector parallel to $v(t)$ [provided $v(t) \neq 0$]. Then $T(t)$ is given by the formula

$$T(t) = \frac{v(t)}{|v(t)|} = \frac{v(t)}{ds/dt}.$$

We may therefore write

$$T(t) = \frac{df(t)}{dt} \cdot \frac{dt}{ds} = \frac{df}{ds}.$$

We introduce the angle ϕ between the vector T and the positive x-direction. The quantity ϕ is the same angle used in Chapter 12, Section 4, in connection with the curvature of a curve (see Fig. 14–17). We may describe T in terms of i and j by the relation

$$T = (\cos \phi)i + (\sin \phi)j.$$

Of course ϕ depends on t, so that when we differentiate $T(t)$ we obtain

$$T'(t) = [-(\sin \phi)i + (\cos \phi)j] \frac{d\phi}{dt}.$$

The scalar product of $T(t)$ and $T'(t)$ is

$$T(t) \cdot T'(t) = \frac{d\phi}{dt} (\cos \phi i + \sin \phi j)(-\sin \phi i + \cos \phi j) = 0;$$

therefore $T'(t)$ *is orthogonal to* $T(t)$.

FIGURE 14–17   FIGURE 14–18   FIGURE 14–19

The quantity $d\mathbf{T}/ds$ has special significance. We compute

$$\frac{d\mathbf{T}}{ds} = \frac{d\mathbf{T}/dt}{ds/dt} = \frac{d\phi/dt}{ds/dt}\,(-\sin\phi\mathbf{i} + \cos\phi\mathbf{j}),$$

or

$$\frac{d\mathbf{T}}{ds} = \frac{d\phi}{ds}\,(-\sin\phi\mathbf{i} + \cos\phi\mathbf{j}).$$

Recalling from Chapter 12, Section 4, that $d\phi/ds$ is the curvature κ of the curve, and noting that $(-\sin\phi\mathbf{i} + \cos\phi\mathbf{j})$ has length one, we get

$$\left|\frac{d\mathbf{T}}{ds}\right| = \left|\frac{d\phi}{ds}\right| = |\kappa| = \frac{1}{R},$$

where R is the *radius of curvature* as described in Chapter 12, Section 4. We define the *unit normal vector* $\mathbf{N}(t)$ (Fig. 14–18) by the relation,

$$\mathbf{N}(t) = \frac{1}{|\kappa(t)|}\,\frac{d\mathbf{T}}{ds}.$$

Given any vector $\mathbf{u}$, we may find the projections of $\mathbf{u}$ on both $\mathbf{T}$ and $\mathbf{N}$. Denoting these projections by u_T and u_N, respectively, we observe that $\mathbf{u}$ itself (Fig. 14–19) is given by

$$\mathbf{u} = u_T\mathbf{T} + u_N\mathbf{N}.$$

EXAMPLE 1. Given the law of motion

$$\mathbf{f}(t) = t^2\mathbf{i} + \tfrac{2}{3}t^3\mathbf{j}, \qquad t > 0,$$

find $\mathbf{v}(t)$, $s'(t)$, $\mathbf{T}(t)$, $\mathbf{N}$, and $|\kappa|$.

Solution. We have

$$\mathbf{v}(t) = \mathbf{f}'(t) = 2t\mathbf{i} + 2t^2\mathbf{j},$$
$$s'(t) = |\mathbf{v}(t)| = 2t\sqrt{1 + t^2},$$
$$\mathbf{T}(t) = \frac{\mathbf{v}(t)}{|\mathbf{v}(t)|} = \frac{1}{\sqrt{1 + t^2}}\mathbf{i} + \frac{t}{\sqrt{1 + t^2}}\mathbf{j},$$
$$\frac{d\mathbf{T}}{ds} = \frac{\mathbf{T}'(t)}{ds/dt} = -\left(\frac{1}{2(1 + t^2)^2}\right)\mathbf{i} + \frac{1}{2t(1 + t^2)^2}\mathbf{j}.$$

Therefore

$$|\kappa| = \left|\frac{d\mathbf{T}}{ds}\right| = \frac{1}{2t(1 + t^2)^{3/2}},$$

and

$$\mathbf{N} = \frac{1}{|\kappa|} \cdot \frac{d\mathbf{T}}{ds} = \frac{-t}{\sqrt{1 + t^2}}\,\mathbf{i} + \frac{1}{\sqrt{1 + t^2}}\,\mathbf{j}.$$

From the definition of $\mathbf{T}(t)$, we have

$$\mathbf{v}(t) = \frac{ds}{dt}\,\mathbf{T}(t).$$

Since the acceleration $\mathbf{a}(t)$ is defined as $\mathbf{v}'(t)$, we write

$$\mathbf{a}(t) = \frac{d^2s}{dt^2}\,\mathbf{T}(t) + \frac{ds}{dt}\,\mathbf{T}'(t) = \frac{d^2s}{dt^2}\,\mathbf{T}(t) + \left(\frac{ds}{dt}\right)^2 \frac{d\mathbf{T}}{ds}.$$

In terms of the vectors $\mathbf{T}(t)$ and $\mathbf{N}(t)$, we obtain

$$\mathbf{a}(t) = \frac{d^2s}{dt^2}\,\mathbf{T}(t) + \left(\frac{ds}{dt}\right)^2 \cdot |\kappa|\mathbf{N}. \tag{1}$$

Equation (1) shows that the projection of $\mathbf{a}$ on $\mathbf{T}$ is (d^2s/dt^2), and the projection of $\mathbf{a}$ on $\mathbf{N}$ is $(ds/dt)^2|\kappa|$. We have the formulas

$$a_T = \frac{d^2s}{dt^2}, \qquad a_N = \left(\frac{ds}{dt}\right)^2 |\kappa|,$$

$$|\mathbf{a}|^2 = a_T^2 + a_N^2 = \left|\frac{d^2s}{dt^2}\right|^2 + \left(\frac{ds}{dt}\right)^4 \kappa^2.$$

EXAMPLE 2. Find $\mathbf{v}$, $\mathbf{a}$, ds/dt, $\mathbf{T}$, $\mathbf{N}$, a_T, a_N, and κ for a particle moving according to the law

$$\mathbf{f}(t) = t\mathbf{i} + \sqrt{1 + t^2}\,\mathbf{j}.$$

Solution. We have

$$\mathbf{v}(t) = \mathbf{f}'(t) = \mathbf{i} + \frac{t}{\sqrt{1 + t^2}}\,\mathbf{j},$$

$$\mathbf{a}(t) = \frac{1}{(1 + t^2)^{3/2}}\,\mathbf{j},$$

$$\left(\frac{ds}{dt}\right)^2 = |\mathbf{v}(t)|^2 = 2 - \frac{1}{1 + t^2},$$

$$a_T = \frac{d^2s}{dt^2} = \frac{t}{\sqrt{1 + 2t^2}\,(1 + t^2)^{3/2}},$$

$$\mathbf{T} = \frac{\mathbf{v}}{|\mathbf{v}|} = \frac{1}{\sqrt{1 + 2t^2}}\,[\sqrt{1 + t^2}\,\mathbf{i} + t\mathbf{j}].$$

We use the formula

$$\mathbf{a} = \frac{d^2s}{dt^2}\mathbf{T} + \left(\frac{ds}{dt}\right)^2 |\kappa|\mathbf{N},$$

in which we know $\mathbf{a}$ and $\mathbf{T}$, to get a formula for $\mathbf{N}$. Since

$$\mathbf{a} - \frac{d^2s}{dt^2}\mathbf{T} = \frac{1}{(1 + t^2)(1 + 2t^2)}[-t\mathbf{i} + \sqrt{1 + t^2}\,\mathbf{j}],$$

we obtain

$$\mathbf{N} = \frac{1}{\sqrt{1 + 2t^2}}[-t\mathbf{i} + \sqrt{1 + t^2}\,\mathbf{j}],$$

and

$$a_N = \left|\mathbf{a} - \frac{d^2s}{dt^2}\mathbf{T}\right| = \frac{1}{(1 + t^2)\sqrt{1 + 2t^2}} \cdot$$

This gives

$$|\kappa| = (1 + 2t^2)^{-3/2}.$$

EXERCISES

In problems 1 through 7, find $\mathbf{v}$, ds/dt, $\mathbf{T}$, a_T, a_N, R, and $\mathbf{N}$.

1. $\mathbf{f} = \frac{1}{3}(t^3 - 3t)\mathbf{i} + t^2\mathbf{j}$ 　　　　　2. $\mathbf{f} = (t^2 - 2\ln t)\mathbf{i} + 4t\mathbf{j}$, $t > 0$

3. $\mathbf{f} = \frac{1}{2}t^2\mathbf{i} + \frac{1}{3}t^3\mathbf{j}$ 　　　　　　　4. $\mathbf{f} = t\sin t\mathbf{i} - t\cos t\mathbf{j}$

5. $\mathbf{f} = cpt\mathbf{i} + (c\cosh pt)\mathbf{j}$, c, p constants

6. $\mathbf{f} = (t^2 + \frac{1}{3}t^3 + 1)\mathbf{i}$

7. $x = \cos wt$, $y = \sin wt$, w constant

In problems 8 through 12, find $\cos\theta$ where θ is the angle between $\mathbf{v}$ and $\mathbf{a}$; find $\cos\phi$ where ϕ is the angle between $\mathbf{f}$ and $\mathbf{a}$.

8. $\mathbf{f} = t^2\mathbf{i} + 3t\mathbf{j}$ 　　　　　　　　9. $\mathbf{f} = 2t\mathbf{i} + \frac{1}{3}t^3\mathbf{j}$

10. $\mathbf{f} = 3\sin 2t\mathbf{i} + 3\cos 2t\mathbf{j}$ 　　　11. $\mathbf{f} = \sinh 2t\mathbf{i} + t^2\mathbf{j}$

12. $\mathbf{f} = \ln(1 + t)\mathbf{i} + \cos 2t\mathbf{j}$

13. Given that P moves upward along the parabola $y^2 = 2px$ ($p > 0$) with a constant speed v. Find $\mathbf{v}$, $\mathbf{a}$, $\mathbf{T}$, $\mathbf{N}$, ds/dt, a_T, a_N, and R at the instant when P passes through the point $(p/2, p)$.

14. Given that P moves upward along the right branch of the hyperbola $x^2 - y^2 = a^2$, with $dy/dt = c > 0$. Find $\mathbf{v}$, $\mathbf{a}$, $\mathbf{T}$, $\mathbf{N}$, ds/dt, a_T, a_N, and R when P passes through $(2a, a\sqrt{3})$.

CHAPTER 15

Formulas and
Methods of Integration

1. INTEGRATION BY SUBSTITUTION

We saw in Chapter 8 that any function continuous in a closed interval can be integrated. This fact, while it is of theoretical value, gives no hint whatsoever as to ways of actually finding the integral of a function. For example, we know that

$$\int u^n \, du = \frac{u^{n+1}}{n+1} + c, \qquad n \neq -1,$$

but the integral

$$\int (4 - 7x)^{15} \, dx$$

is not quite in the same form. In Section 7 of Chapter 8 we saw that if we let

$$u = 4 - 7x, \qquad du = -7 \, dx,$$

the integral becomes

$$-\tfrac{1}{7} \int u^{15} \, du = -\tfrac{1}{112} u^{16} + c = -\tfrac{1}{112}(4 - 7x)^{16} + c.$$

By making a change of variable we are able to change the integral into a known form, and therefore we can perform the integration. This technique is known as the *method of substitution*.

It is easy to find functions for which there is no way of performing the integration. For example, the integrals

$$\int \frac{dx}{\sqrt{1 + x^3}}, \qquad \int e^{-x^2} \, dx, \qquad \int \frac{\sin x}{x} \, dx$$

cannot be integrated in terms of any of the functions we have studied so far (polynomials, rational functions, trigonometric functions, logarithms, etc.).

Appearances may be deceiving, for while

$$\int e^{-x^2} \, dx$$

443

cannot be integrated, the slightly more complicated integral

$$\int x e^{-x^2} \, dx$$

easily can be.

In this chapter we shall learn a number of methods for performing the integrations in many feasible cases. For ready reference, we collect the formulas for integration which we have already learned:

1. $\displaystyle\int u^n \, du = \frac{u^{n+1}}{n+1} + C, \quad n \neq -1$ 2. $\displaystyle\int \frac{du}{u} = \ln |u| + C$

3. $\displaystyle\int e^u \, du = e^u + C$ 4. $\displaystyle\int a^u \, du = \frac{a^u}{\ln a} + C, \quad a > 0$

The trigonometric formulas are:

5. $\displaystyle\int \sin u \, du = -\cos u + C$ 6. $\displaystyle\int \cos u \, du = \sin u + C$

7. $\displaystyle\int \sec^2 u \, du = \tan u + C$ 8. $\displaystyle\int \csc^2 u \, du = -\cot u + C$

9. $\displaystyle\int \sec u \tan u \, du = \sec u + C$ 10. $\displaystyle\int \csc u \cot u \, du = -\csc u + C$

The hyperbolic formulas are:

11. $\displaystyle\int \sinh u \, du = \cosh u + C$ 12. $\displaystyle\int \cosh u \, du = \sinh u + C$

13. $\displaystyle\int \text{sech}^2 u \, du = \tanh u + C$ 14. $\displaystyle\int \text{csch}^2 u \, du = -\coth u + C$

15. $\displaystyle\int \text{sech } u \tanh u \, du = -\text{sech } u + C$

16. $\displaystyle\int \text{csch } u \coth u \, du = -\text{csch } u + C$

The inverse trigonometric formulas ($a > 0$) are:

17. $\displaystyle\int \frac{du}{\sqrt{a^2 - u^2}} = \arcsin \frac{u}{a} + C$ 18. $\displaystyle\int \frac{du}{a^2 + u^2} = \frac{1}{a} \arctan \frac{u}{a} + C$

19. $\displaystyle\int \frac{du}{u\sqrt{u^2 - a^2}} = \frac{1}{a} \text{arcsec} \frac{u}{a} + C, \quad |u| > a$

The inverse hyperbolic formulas ($a > 0$) are:

20. $\displaystyle\int \frac{du}{\sqrt{a^2 + u^2}} = \text{argsinh} \frac{u}{a} + C$

21. $\displaystyle\int \frac{du}{a^2 - u^2} = \begin{cases} \dfrac{1}{a} \operatorname{argtanh} \dfrac{u}{a} + C, & |u| < a \\[3mm] \dfrac{1}{a} \operatorname{argcoth} \dfrac{u}{a} + C, & |u| > a \end{cases}$

22. $\displaystyle\int \frac{du}{u\sqrt{a^2 - u^2}} = -\frac{1}{a} \operatorname{argsech} \frac{u}{a} + C, \qquad 0 < u < a$

23. $\displaystyle\int \frac{du}{|u|\sqrt{u^2 + a^2}} = -\frac{1}{a} \operatorname{argcsch} \frac{u}{a} + C, \qquad u \neq 0$

24. $\displaystyle\int \frac{du}{\sqrt{u^2 - a^2}} = \operatorname{argcosh} \frac{u}{a} + C, \qquad u > a$

It is evident that Formulas 17 through 19 are derived from the simpler differentiation formulas

$$d \arcsin v = \frac{dv}{\sqrt{1 - v^2}}, \qquad d \arctan v = \frac{dv}{1 + v^2}, \qquad d \operatorname{arcsec} v = \frac{dv}{v\sqrt{v^2 - 1}},$$

using the substitution $v = u/a$. Formulas 20 through 24 are obtained similarly. We shall illustrate the method of substitution with some examples.

EXAMPLE 1. Find $\int xe^{x^2}\,dx$.

Solution. Try $u = x^2$. Then $du = 2x\,dx$, and therefore

$$\int xe^{x^2}\,dx = \tfrac{1}{2}\int e^u\,du = \tfrac{1}{2}e^u + C = \tfrac{1}{2}e^{x^2} + C.$$

EXAMPLE 2. Find

$$\int \frac{\cos 3x\,dx}{1 + \sin 3x}.$$

Solution. Try $u = 1 + \sin 3x$. Then $du = 3 \cos 3x\,dx$, and

$$\int \frac{\cos 3x\,dx}{1 + \sin 3x} = \frac{1}{3}\int \frac{du}{u} = \frac{1}{3}\ln |u| + C = \frac{1}{3}\ln |1 + \sin 3x| + C.$$

EXAMPLE 3. Find

$$\int \frac{dt}{\sqrt{4 - 9t^2}}.$$

Solution. Try $u = 3t$, $du = 3\,dt$. Then

$$\int \frac{dt}{\sqrt{4 - 9t^2}} = \frac{1}{3}\int \frac{du}{\sqrt{4 - u^2}}.$$

This expression is Formula 17 with $a = 2$. Therefore

$$\int \frac{dt}{\sqrt{4 - 9t^2}} = \frac{1}{3}\arcsin \frac{u}{2} + C = \frac{1}{3}\arcsin \frac{3t}{2} + C.$$

EXAMPLE 4. Find

$$\int \frac{t \, dt}{\sqrt{4 - 9t^2}}.$$

Solution. Try $u = 4 - 9t^2$. Then $du = -18t \, dt$, and therefore

$$\int \frac{t \, dt}{\sqrt{4 - 9t^2}} = -\frac{1}{18} \int \frac{du}{u^{1/2}} = -\frac{1}{9} u^{1/2} + C = -\frac{1}{9} \sqrt{4 - 9t^2} + C.$$

Remark. The method of substitution proceeds by trial and error. If a particular substitution does not reduce the integral to a known formula, we should feel no hesitation about abandoning that substitution and trying one of an entirely different nature. Example 4, although it is similar in appearance to Example 3, integrates according to a different substitution.

EXAMPLE 5. Find

$$\int \frac{e^y \, dy}{(1 + e^y)^3}.$$

Solution. Try $u = 1 + e^y$. Then $du = e^y \, dy$, and

$$\int \frac{e^y \, dy}{(1 + e^y)^3} = \int u^{-3} \, du + C = -\frac{1}{2(1 + e^y)^2} + C.$$

Remarks. When an expression such as e^{x^2} or $\sin (\ln x)$ occurs, it is generally worth while to set $u = x^2$ in the first case or $u = \ln x$ in the second case. Such a substitution may reduce the integral to a more recognizable form. It is also fairly easy to spot integrals which are reducible to the forms given in Formulas 17 through 24. But, as Examples 2, 4, and 5 show, it may happen that Formulas 1 and 2 are applicable. Sometimes we must make several substitutions in succession, as the next example shows.

EXAMPLE 6. Find

$$\int \frac{dx}{x[9 + 4 \, (\ln x)^2]}.$$

Solution. Try $u = \ln x$. Then $du = (1/x) \, dx$, and

$$\int \frac{dx}{x[9 + 4 \, (\ln x)^2]} = \int \frac{du}{9 + 4u^2}.$$

Let $v = 2u$. Then $dv = 2 \, du$, and therefore

$$\frac{1}{2} \int \frac{dv}{9 + v^2} = \frac{1}{2} \cdot \frac{1}{3} \arctan \frac{v}{3} + C$$

$$= \frac{1}{6} \arctan \frac{2u}{3} + C = \frac{1}{6} \arctan \frac{2 \ln x}{3} + C.$$

Substitution provides us with a short method for evaluating definite integrals. We shall illustrate the process in the following example.

EXAMPLE 7. Evaluate

$$\int_0^{\pi/4} \tan^2 x \sec^2 x \, dx.$$

Solution. Try $u = \tan x$, $du = \sec^2 x \, dx$. Note that $u(0) = 0$, $u(\pi/4) = 1$. Therefore

$$\int_0^{\pi/4} \tan^2 x \sec^2 x \, dx = \int_0^1 u^2 \, du = \tfrac{1}{3}u^3\big]_0^1 = \tfrac{1}{3}.$$

EXERCISES

In problems 1 through 42, find the indefinite integrals.

1. $\displaystyle \int \frac{dy}{\sqrt[3]{1 - 2y}}$

2. $\displaystyle \int \frac{x^2 \, dx}{x^3 + 1}$

3. $\displaystyle \int \sin 2x \, dx$

4. $\displaystyle \int x \cos (x^2) \, dx$

5. $\displaystyle \int \sec^2 2x \, dx$

6. $\displaystyle \int \csc^2 3x \, dx$

7. $\displaystyle \int \cosh 3x \, dx$

8. $\displaystyle \int \text{sech}^2 2x \, dx$

9. $\displaystyle \int e^{x/2} \, dx$

10. $\displaystyle \int \frac{dx}{\sqrt{9 - 4x^2}}$

11. $\displaystyle \int \frac{dx}{16 + 9x^2}$

12. $\displaystyle \int \frac{dx}{x\sqrt{9x^2 - 4}}$

13. $\displaystyle \int \frac{\sin \sqrt{x} \, dx}{\sqrt{x}}$

14. $\displaystyle \int x \sec^2 (x^2) \, dx$

15. $\displaystyle \int x e^{x^2 + 1} \, dx$

16. $\displaystyle \int \frac{dx}{e^x}$

17. $\displaystyle \int \sin^2 x \cos x \, dx$

18. $\displaystyle \int \tan 2x \sec 2x \, dx$

19. $\displaystyle \int \sinh^3 2x \cosh 2x \, dx$

20. $\displaystyle \int \tan 2x \sec^2 2x \, dx$

21. $\displaystyle \int \frac{\cos (\ln x) \, dx}{x}$

22. $\displaystyle \int \frac{\ln x \, dx}{x[1 + (\ln x)^2]}$

23. $\displaystyle \int \frac{2 \, dx}{x\sqrt{4x^2 - 9}}$

24. $\displaystyle \int \frac{\cos 2x \, dx}{\sin 2x}$

25. $\displaystyle \int \coth x \, dx$

26. $\displaystyle \int \tanh x \, dx$

27. $\displaystyle \int \left(x - \frac{1}{x}\right)^2 dx$

28. $\displaystyle \int (\ln x)^3 \frac{dx}{x}$

29. $\displaystyle \int \frac{dx}{x \ln x}$

30. $\displaystyle \int \frac{e^x \, dx}{(e^x + 2)^2}$

31. $\displaystyle \int \tanh 2x \, \text{sech}^2 2x \, dx$

32. $\displaystyle \int \sec^2 3x \sec 3x \tan 3x \, dx$

33. $\displaystyle\int \sec^7 2x \tan 2x \, dx$

34. $\displaystyle\int \frac{x^2}{x^2 + 1} \, dx$

35. $\displaystyle\int \frac{e^x \, dx}{e^x + 1}$

36. $\displaystyle\int \frac{\sinh x \, dx}{(1 + \cosh x)^2}$

37. $\displaystyle\int \frac{\sqrt{x} \, dx}{4 + x^3}$

38. $\displaystyle\int \frac{\mathrm{sech}^2 x \, dx}{4 - \tanh^2 x}$

39. $\displaystyle\int \frac{dy}{1 + e^y}$

40. $\displaystyle\int \frac{\sinh x \cosh x \, dx}{(1 + \sinh^2 x)^2}$

41. $\displaystyle\int \frac{\mathrm{sech}^2 x \tanh x \, dx}{(1 + \mathrm{sech}^2 x)^2}$

42. $\displaystyle\int \frac{x^5 \, dx}{1 + x^2}$

In problems 43 through 54, evaluate the definite integrals:

43. $\displaystyle\int_0^2 \frac{(2x + 1) \, dx}{\sqrt{x^2 + x + 1}}$

44. $\displaystyle\int_1^3 \frac{\sqrt[3]{\ln x} \, dx}{x}$

45. $\displaystyle\int_0^{\pi/3} \sec^3 x \tan x \, dx$

46. $\displaystyle\int_0^{\pi/4} \tan^3 x \sec^2 x \, dx$

47. $\displaystyle\int_0^{1/\sqrt{2}} \frac{x \, dx}{\sqrt{1 - x^4}}$

48. $\displaystyle\int_0^{\sqrt{2}} \frac{3x \, dx}{4 + x^4}$

49. $\displaystyle\int_0^{\pi/2} \sin^3 x \cos x \, dx$

50. $\displaystyle\int_0^{\pi/2} \frac{\cos x \, dx}{1 + \sin^2 x}$

51. $\displaystyle\int_0^{\pi/3} \frac{\sin x \, dx}{\cos^3 x}$

52. $\displaystyle\int_{\pi/8}^{\pi/4} \cot 2x \csc^2 2x \, dx$

53. $\displaystyle\int_0^1 \frac{\sqrt{1 + e^{-2x}}}{e^{-3x}} \, dx$

54. $\displaystyle\int_0^{1/2} \frac{3 \arcsin x}{\sqrt{1 - x^2}} \, dx$

2. INTEGRATION BY SUBSTITUTION, CONTINUED

If the indicated substitution is simple enough, the reader may shorten the integration process by rewriting the integral so that it is expressed in one of the standard forms. The following examples exhibit the method.

EXAMPLE 1. Find

$$\int \frac{\sin \theta \, d\theta}{\sqrt{1 + \cos \theta}}.$$

Solution. We see that $d(1 + \cos \theta) = -\sin \theta \, d\theta$, and so

$$\int \frac{\sin \theta \, d\theta}{\sqrt{1 + \cos \theta}} = -\int (1 + \cos \theta)^{-1/2} \, d(1 + \cos \theta).$$

This is Formula 1, and we obtain

$$\int \frac{\sin \theta \, d\theta}{\sqrt{1 + \cos \theta}} = -2(1 + \cos \theta)^{1/2} + C.$$

EXAMPLE 2. Find
$$\int \frac{dx}{x \ln x}.$$

Solution. Since $d (\ln x) = (1/x) dx$, we obtain

$$\int \frac{dx}{x \ln x} = \int \frac{d(\ln x)}{\ln x} = \ln (\ln x) + C.$$

EXAMPLE 3. Find
$$\int \frac{\operatorname{sech}^2 2x \, dx}{\tanh^4 2x}.$$

Solution. We note that $d(\tanh 2x) = 2 \operatorname{sech}^2 2x \, dx$, and therefore

$$\int \frac{\operatorname{sech}^2 2x \, dx}{\tanh^4 2x} = \frac{1}{2} \int (\tanh 2x)^{-4} \, d(\tanh 2x) = - \frac{1}{6 \tanh^3 2x} + C.$$

When the integrand consists of a rational function (one polynomial divided by another polynomial) a simplification can be achieved when the degree of the numerator is greater than or equal to the degree of the denominator, simply by performing the division. The succeeding examples illustrate this technique.

EXAMPLE 4. Find
$$\int \frac{x^2 - 2x - 1}{x + 2} \, dx.$$

Solution. We first divide $x^2 - 2x - 1$ by $x + 2$, using ordinary division:

$$
\begin{array}{r}
x - 4 \\
x + 2 \overline{)x^2 - 2x - 1} \\
\underline{x^2 + 2x} \\
-4x - 1 \\
\underline{-4x - 8} \\
+ 7
\end{array}
$$

Then

$$\int \frac{x^2 - 2x - 1}{x + 2} \, dx = \int \left(x - 4 + \frac{7}{x + 2} \right) dx$$

$$= \tfrac{1}{2}x^2 - 4x + 7 \int \frac{d(x + 2)}{x + 2}$$

$$= \tfrac{1}{2}x^2 - 4x + 7 \ln |x + 2| + C.$$

EXAMPLE 5. Find
$$\int \frac{x + 5}{x - 1} \, dx.$$

Solution. Using division, we obtain $(x + 5)/(x - 1) = 1 + 6/(x - 1)$. Therefore

$$\int \frac{x + 5}{x - 1} \, dx = \int \left(1 + \frac{6}{x - 1} \right) dx = x + 6 \ln |x - 1| + C.$$

EXERCISES

In problems 1 through 38, find the indefinite integrals.

1. $\displaystyle\int \frac{(x+1)\,dx}{x^2+2x+2}$ 2. $\displaystyle\int \csc^2\left(\frac{x}{2}\right) dx$ 3. $\displaystyle\int \frac{\sec^2 x\,dx}{1+\tan x}$

4. $\displaystyle\int \frac{e^x\,dx}{1+e^{2x}}$ 5. $\displaystyle\int \coth 2x\,dx$ 6. $\displaystyle\int \frac{dx}{x\sqrt{\ln x}}$

7. $\displaystyle\int \frac{x^2+3x-2}{x+1}\,dx$ 8. $\displaystyle\int \frac{x^3+2x^2-x+1}{x+2}\,dx$

9. $\displaystyle\int \frac{x}{2x-1}\,dx$ 10. $\displaystyle\int \frac{x+1}{2x+3}\,dx$ 11. $\displaystyle\int \frac{dx}{4+3x^2}$

12. $\displaystyle\int xe^{-x^2}\,dx$ 13. $\displaystyle\int \frac{x\,dx}{(x^2+1)^2}$ 14. $\displaystyle\int \cosh 2xe^{\sinh 2x}\,dx$

15. $\displaystyle\int x2^{x^2}\,dx$ 16. $\displaystyle\int \coth^2 \tfrac{1}{3}x\,\operatorname{csch}^2 \tfrac{1}{3}x\,dx$ 17. $\displaystyle\int \frac{x^2+2x-1}{3-x}\,dx$

18. $\displaystyle\int \frac{x^4+x^3-2}{x+5}\,dx$ 19. $\displaystyle\int \frac{x^2+2x+1}{x^2+1}\,dx$ 20. $\displaystyle\int \frac{3x-2}{4x+7}\,dx$

21. $\displaystyle\int \frac{2x^2+6x-2}{x^2+2x-2}\,dx$ 22. $\displaystyle\int \frac{4-5x}{2-3x}\,dx$ 23. $\displaystyle\int e^{\tan x}\sec^2 x\,dx$

24. $\displaystyle\int \frac{e^{\arctan x}}{1+x^2}\,dx$ 25. $\displaystyle\int \frac{e^x\,dx}{\sqrt{3-e^{2x}}}$ 26. $\displaystyle\int \cot 2x\,\csc^3 2x\,dx$

27. $\displaystyle\int x^{-1/2}\sec\sqrt{x}\,\tan\sqrt{x}\,dx$ 28. $\displaystyle\int \frac{\arctan 3x}{1+9x^2}\,dx$

29. $\displaystyle\int \frac{\sinh 2x\,dx}{2+\cosh 2x}$ 30. $\displaystyle\int \frac{2x+1}{x^2+9}\,dx$ 31. $\displaystyle\int \frac{x-2}{\sqrt{5-x^2}}\,dx$

32. $\displaystyle\int \frac{x^2+4}{x\sqrt{x^2-7}}\,dx$ 33. $\displaystyle\int \frac{(2-\sin x)\,dx}{(2x+\cos x)^3}$ 34. $\displaystyle\int \frac{1+e^{2x}}{e^x}\,dx$

35. $\displaystyle\int \frac{\sin 2x\,dx}{3+\cos^2 2x}$ 36. $\displaystyle\int \frac{\cosh x\,dx}{\sqrt{1+\cosh^2 x}}$

3. CERTAIN TRIGONOMETRIC INTEGRALS

We now consider trigonometric integrals of the form

(a) $\displaystyle\int \sin^m u\cos^n u\,du$

(b) $\displaystyle\int \tan^m u\sec^n u\,du$

(c) $\displaystyle\int \cot^m u\csc^n u\,du$

Under type (a) there are two cases:

Case I. Either m or n odd and positive. If m is odd, we factor out $\sin u\, du$ and change the remaining even power of sine to powers of cosine by the identity

$$\sin^2 u + \cos^2 u = 1.$$

If n is odd, we factor out $\cos u\, du$ and change the remaining even power of cosine to powers of sine by the same identity.

EXAMPLE 1. Find $\int \sin^3 x \cos^{-5} x\, dx$.

Solution. Since $m\ (=3)$ is odd and positive, we have

$$\int \sin^3 x \cos^{-5} x\, dx = \int \sin^2 x \cos^{-5} x \sin x\, dx$$

$$= \int (1 - \cos^2 x) \cos^{-5} x \sin x\, dx$$

$$= -\int \cos^{-5} x\, d(\cos x) + \int \cos^{-3} x\, d(\cos x)$$

$$= \frac{1}{4 \cos^4 x} - \frac{1}{2 \cos^2 x} + C.$$

EXAMPLE 2. Find $\int \sin^4 2x \cos^5 2x\, dx$.

Solution. Since $n\ (=5)$ is odd and positive, we write

$$\int \sin^4 2x \cos^5 2x\, dx = \int \sin^4 2x \cos^4 2x \cos 2x\, dx$$

$$= \int \sin^4 2x(1 - \sin^2 2x)^2 \cos 2x\, dx$$

$$= \tfrac{1}{2} \int (\sin^4 2x - 2 \sin^6 2x + \sin^8 2x)\, d(\sin 2x)$$

$$= \tfrac{1}{10} \sin^5 2x - \tfrac{1}{7} \sin^7 2x + \tfrac{1}{18} \sin^9 2x + C.$$

Case II. Both m and n even and positive or zero. In this case, the half-angle formulas are used to lower the degree of the expression. These formulas (which the student should have memorized well) are

$$\sin^2 u = \frac{1 - \cos 2u}{2}, \qquad \cos^2 u = \frac{1 + \cos 2u}{2}.$$

The method of reduction is shown in the following examples.

EXAMPLE 3. Find $\int \sin^2 x \cos^2 x\, dx$.

Solution. By the half-angle formulas, we have

$$\int \sin^2 x \cos^2 x\, dx = \tfrac{1}{4} \int (1 - \cos^2 2x)\, dx = \frac{x}{4} - \frac{1}{4} \int \cos^2 2x\, dx\,.$$

To this last integral we again apply the half-angle formula, and get

$$\int \sin^2 x \cos^2 x \, dx = \frac{x}{4} - \frac{1}{4} \int \frac{1 + \cos 4x}{2} \, dx$$

$$= \frac{x}{4} - \frac{x}{8} - \frac{1}{32} \sin 4x + C$$

$$= \tfrac{1}{8}(x - \tfrac{1}{4}\sin 4x) + C.$$

EXAMPLE 4. Find $\int \sin^4 3u \, du$.

Solution. This is Case II, with $m = 0$, $n = 4$. We have

$$\int \sin^4 3u \, du = \tfrac{1}{4} \int (1 - \cos 6u)^2 \, du$$

$$= \tfrac{1}{4} \int (1 - 2\cos 6u + \cos^2 6u) \, du$$

$$= \frac{u}{4} - \frac{1}{12} \sin 6u + \frac{1}{4} \int \frac{1 + \cos 12u}{2} \, du$$

$$= \frac{3u}{8} - \frac{1}{12} \sin 6u + \frac{1}{96} \sin 12u + C.$$

Under type (b) there are also two cases:

Case I: n is even and positive. We factor out $\sec^2 u \, du$ and change the remaining secants to tangents, using the identity

$$\sec^2 u = 1 + \tan^2 u.$$

EXAMPLE 5. Find

$$\int \frac{\sec^4 u \, du}{\sqrt{\tan u}}.$$

Solution. We write

$$\int (\tan u)^{-1/2} \sec^4 u \, du = \int (\tan u)^{-1/2}(1 + \tan^2 u) \sec^2 u \, du$$

$$= \int (\tan u)^{-1/2} d(\tan u) + \int (\tan u)^{3/2} d(\tan u)$$

$$= 2(\tan u)^{1/2} + \tfrac{2}{5}(\tan u)^{5/2} + C.$$

Case II: m is odd and positive. We factor out $\sec u \tan u \, du$ and change the remaining even power of the tangents to secants, again using the identity $\tan^2 u = \sec^2 u - 1$.

EXAMPLE 6. Find

$$\int \frac{\tan^3 x \, dx}{\sqrt[3]{\sec x}}.$$

Solution. We write

$$\int (\sec x)^{-1/3} \tan^3 x \, dx = \int (\sec x)^{-4/3} \tan^2 x \, (\sec x \tan x \, dx)$$

$$= \int (\sec x)^{-4/3} (\sec^2 x - 1) \, d (\sec x)$$

$$= \int [(\sec x)^{2/3} - (\sec x)^{-4/3}] \, d (\sec x)$$

$$= \tfrac{3}{5} (\sec x)^{5/3} + 3 (\sec x)^{-1/3} + C.$$

Integrals of type (c) are handled similarly to those of (b).

Remark. Integrals which are of type (a), (b), and (c), but which have hyperbolic instead of trigonometric functions, are amenable to the same techniques. The corresponding identities and formulas are

$$\cosh^2 u - \sinh^2 u = 1, \qquad \operatorname{sech}^2 u = 1 - \tanh^2 u,$$

and

$$\sinh^2 u = \frac{\cosh 2u - 1}{2}, \qquad \cosh^2 u = \frac{\cosh 2u + 1}{2}.$$

In dealing with such integrals containing hyperbolic functions, the case-by-case breakdown, according as m and n are even or odd, is identical with that for integrals with trigonometric functions.

EXERCISES

In problems 1 through 14, evaluate the definite integrals.

1. $\displaystyle\int_{-\pi/3}^{\pi/6} \sin^2 x \cos x \, dx$

2. $\displaystyle\int_{-\pi/4}^{\pi/4} \sin^3 2x \, dx$

3. $\displaystyle\int_{\pi/6}^{\pi/2} \frac{\cos^3 x}{\sqrt{\sin x}} \, dx$

4. $\displaystyle\int_{-\pi/4}^{\pi/4} \tan^4 x \sec^2 x \, dx$

5. $\displaystyle\int_{\pi/6}^{\pi/3} \cot^2 2x \csc^2 2x \, dx$

6. $\displaystyle\int_{0}^{\pi/3} \tan^3 x \sec x \, dx$

7. $\displaystyle\int_{0}^{\pi/2} \cos^2 x \, dx$

8. $\displaystyle\int_{0}^{\pi/4} \sin^2 2x \cos^2 2x \, dx$

9. $\displaystyle\int_{0}^{2} \sinh x \cosh^3 x \, dx$

10. $\displaystyle\int_{0}^{1} \tanh^2 2x \operatorname{sech}^4 2x \, dx$

11. $\displaystyle\int_{0}^{\pi/2} \cos^4 x \, dx$

12. $\displaystyle\int_{0}^{\pi/3} \sin^6 x \, dx$

13. $\displaystyle\int_{0}^{1} \sinh^4 x \, dx$

14. $\displaystyle\int_{\pi/6}^{\pi/4} \frac{\sin^3 x \, dx}{\cos^2 x}$

In problems 15 through 36, find the indefinite integrals.

15. $\displaystyle\int \sin^5 (x/2)\, dx$ 16. $\displaystyle\int \sin^3 2x \cos^2 2x\, dx$ 17. $\displaystyle\int \frac{\cos^3 x}{\sin x}\, dx$

18. $\displaystyle\int \frac{\sin^5 3x}{\cos 3x}\, dx$ 19. $\displaystyle\int \tan 2x \sec^2 2x\, dx$ 20. $\displaystyle\int \tan (x/3) \sec^3 (x/3)\, dx$

21. $\displaystyle\int \operatorname{sech}^4 2x\, dx$ 22. $\displaystyle\int \csc^6 x\, dx$ 23. $\displaystyle\int \cot^5 x \csc^3 x\, dx$

24. $\displaystyle\int \tan^2 2x \sec^4 2x\, dx$ 25. $\displaystyle\int \tan^2 x\, dx$ 26. $\displaystyle\int \cot^3 (x/2) \csc^2 (x/2)\, dx$

27. $\displaystyle\int \cot^4 x\, dx$ 28. $\displaystyle\int \coth^3 4x \operatorname{csch}^4 4x\, dx$ 29. $\displaystyle\int x \sin^3 (x^2)\, dx$

30. $\displaystyle\int \frac{\sec^4 x}{\tan^2 x}\, dx$ 31. $\displaystyle\int \frac{\cot x}{\csc^3 x}\, dx$ 32. $\displaystyle\int \frac{\sec^2 \sqrt{x}}{\sqrt{x} \tan \sqrt{x}}\, dx$

33. $\displaystyle\int \frac{\sin^2 x}{\cos^4 x}\, dx$ 34. $\displaystyle\int \tan^2 2x \cos^2 2x\, dx$ 35. $\displaystyle\int \tanh x \cosh^4 x\, dx$

36. $\displaystyle\int \frac{\sin^4 x}{\cos^2 x}\, dx$

4. TRIGONOMETRIC SUBSTITUTION

If the integrand contains expressions of the form $\sqrt{a^2 - x^2}$, $\sqrt{a^2 + x^2}$, or $\sqrt{x^2 - a^2}$, it is frequently possible to transform the integral into one of the forms discussed in Section 3 by means of a *trigonometric substitution*. The way the method works is shown in the succeeding examples.

(a) If an expression of the form $\sqrt{a^2 - x^2}$ occurs, make the substitution $x = a \sin \theta$.

In performing the substitution, the student should sketch a right triangle, as shown in Fig. 15–1. The figure contains all the essential ingredients of the process, and it is evident that $\sqrt{a^2 - x^2} = a \cos \theta$.

EXAMPLE 1. Evaluate

$$\int_{-1}^{\sqrt{3}} \sqrt{4 - x^2}\, dx.$$

Solution. Let $x = 2 \sin \theta$. Then $dx = 2 \cos \theta\, d\theta$ and, according to Fig. 15–1, with $a = 2$ we have $\sqrt{4 - x^2} = 2 \cos \theta$. Therefore

$$\int_{-1}^{\sqrt{3}} \sqrt{4 - x^2}\, dx = 4 \int_{-\pi/6}^{\pi/3} \cos^2 \theta\, d\theta = 2 \int_{-\pi/6}^{\pi/3} (1 + \cos 2\theta)\, d\theta$$

$$= 2\left[\theta + \tfrac{1}{2} \sin 2\theta\right]_{-\pi/6}^{\pi/3} = \pi + \sqrt{3}.$$

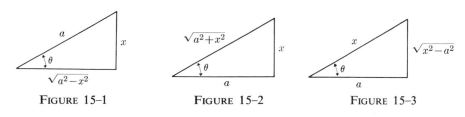

FIGURE 15–1　　　　　　FIGURE 15–2　　　　　　FIGURE 15–3

We note that Fig. 15–1 is only an aid in determining the substitution. In making the change $x = 2 \sin \theta$ or, equivalently, $\theta = \arcsin (x/2)$, the range allowed for θ is $-\pi/2 \le \theta \le \pi/2$.

(b) If an expression of the form $\sqrt{a^2 + x^2}$ occurs, make the substitution $x = a \tan \theta$.

A sketch of this substitution is shown in Fig. 15–2, from which we see that $\sqrt{a^2 + x^2} = a \sec \theta$.

EXAMPLE 2. Find $\int x^3 \sqrt{7 + x^2}\, dx$.

Solution. Let $x = \sqrt{7} \tan \theta$. According to Fig. 15–2, with $a = \sqrt{7}$ we have $\sqrt{7 + x^2} = \sqrt{7} \sec \theta$. Also, $dx = \sqrt{7} \sec^2 \theta\, d\theta$. Therefore

$$\int x^3 \sqrt{7 + x^2}\, dx = \int 7 \sqrt{7} \tan^3 \theta \sqrt{7} \sec \theta \cdot \sqrt{7} \sec^2 \theta\, d\theta$$

$$= 49\sqrt{7} \int \tan^3 \theta \sec^3 \theta\, d\theta.$$

This last integral is of the form (b) of Section 3, with m odd. We obtain

$$\int x^3 \sqrt{7 + x^2}\, dx = 49\sqrt{7} \int (\sec^2 \theta - 1) \sec^2 \theta \cdot (\tan \theta \sec \theta)\, d\theta$$

$$= 49\sqrt{7} \left(\tfrac{1}{5} \sec^5 \theta - \tfrac{1}{3} \sec^3 \theta \right) + C.$$

Referring to Fig. 15–2 again, we now find that $\sec \theta = (1/\sqrt{7}) \sqrt{7 + x^2}$, and so

$$\int x^3 \sqrt{7 + x^2}\, dx = \tfrac{1}{5}(7 + x^2)^{5/2} - \tfrac{7}{3}(7 + x^2)^{3/2} + C.$$

(c) If an expression of the form $\sqrt{x^2 - a^2}$ occurs, make the substitution $x = a \sec \theta$. A sketch of this substitution is shown in Fig. 15–3. It follows that $\sqrt{x^2 - a^2} = a \tan \theta$.

EXAMPLE 3. Evaluate

$$\int_3^6 \frac{\sqrt{x^2 - 9}}{x}\, dx.$$

Solution. We make the substitution $x = 3 \sec \theta$, $dx = 3 \tan \theta \sec \theta\, d\theta$. Further, $\sqrt{x^2 - 9} = 3 \tan \theta$. When $x = 3$, $\sec \theta = 1$ and $\theta = 0$; when $x = 6$, $\sec \theta = 2$ and $\theta = \pi/3$.

Therefore

$$\int_3^6 \frac{\sqrt{x^2 - 9}}{x} \, dx = \int_0^{\pi/3} \frac{3 \tan \theta}{3 \sec \theta} \cdot 3 \tan \theta \sec \theta \, d\theta = 3 \int_0^{\pi/3} \tan^2 \theta \, d\theta$$

$$= 3 \int_0^{\pi/3} (\sec^2 \theta - 1) \, d\theta = 3 \left[\tan \theta - \theta\right]_0^{\pi/3} = 3 \left(\sqrt{3} - \frac{\pi}{3}\right).$$

Remark. When there is an expression of the form $(a^2 - x^2)$, $(a^2 + x^2)$ or $(x^2 - a^2)$, it sometimes helps to make a substitution of type (a), (b), or (c), respectively.

EXERCISES

In problems 1 through 6, evaluate the definite integrals.

1. $\displaystyle\int_0^1 \frac{dx}{\sqrt{4 - x^2}}$

2. $\displaystyle\int_0^2 \frac{x^2 \, dx}{x^2 + 4}$

3. $\displaystyle\int_{-6}^{-2\sqrt{3}} \frac{dx}{x\sqrt{x^2 - 9}}$

4. $\displaystyle\int_0^2 \frac{x^3 \, dx}{\sqrt{16 - x^2}}$

5. $\displaystyle\int_0^{2\sqrt{3}} \frac{x^3 \, dx}{\sqrt{x^2 + 4}}$

6. $\displaystyle\int_0^1 \frac{x^2 \, dx}{\sqrt{4 - x^2}}$

In problems 7 through 20, find the indefinite integrals.

7. $\displaystyle\int \frac{2 \, dx}{x\sqrt{x^2 - 5}}$

8. $\displaystyle\int \frac{\sqrt{2x^2 - 5}}{x} \, dx$

9. $\displaystyle\int \frac{x^3 \, dx}{\sqrt{9 - x^2}}$

10. $\displaystyle\int \frac{x^3 \, dx}{\sqrt{3x^2 - 5}}$

11. $\displaystyle\int \frac{x^3 \, dx}{\sqrt{2x^2 + 7}}$

12. $\displaystyle\int t^3 \sqrt{a^2 t^2 - b^2} \, dt$

13. $\displaystyle\int u^3 \sqrt{a^2 u^2 + b^2} \, du$

14. $\displaystyle\int u^3 \sqrt{a^2 - b^2 u^2} \, du$

15. $\displaystyle\int \frac{\sqrt{x^2 - a^2}}{x} \, dx$

16. $\displaystyle\int \frac{dx}{x^2 \sqrt{a^2 - x^2}}$

17. $\displaystyle\int \frac{dx}{x^2 \sqrt{x^2 + a^2}}$

18. $\displaystyle\int \frac{dx}{(a^2 - x^2)^{3/2}}$

19. $\displaystyle\int \frac{dx}{x^4 \sqrt{a^2 - x^2}}$

20. $\displaystyle\int \frac{dx}{(x^2 + a^2)^2}$

In problems 21 through 28, evaluate the definite integrals.

21. $\displaystyle\int_0^4 \frac{dx}{(16 + x^2)^{3/2}}$

22. $\displaystyle\int_{2/\sqrt{3}}^2 \frac{dx}{(x^2 - 1)^{3/2}}$

23. $\displaystyle\int_0^1 \frac{x^2 \, dx}{(4 - x^2)^{3/2}}$

24. $\displaystyle\int_{2\sqrt{3}}^6 \frac{x^3 \, dx}{(x^2 - 1)^{3/2}}$

25. $\displaystyle\int_{\sqrt{3}}^{3\sqrt{3}} \frac{dx}{x^2 \sqrt{x^2 + 9}}$

26. $\displaystyle\int_{-2}^{2\sqrt{3}} x^3 \sqrt{x^2 + 4} \, dx$

27. $\displaystyle\int_0^{\sqrt{5}} x^2\sqrt{5-x^2}\,dx$

28. $\displaystyle\int_1^3 \frac{dx}{x^4\sqrt{x^2+3}}$

5. INTEGRANDS INVOLVING QUADRATIC FUNCTIONS

When an integrand involves a quadratic function of the form $ax^2 + bx + c$, the integration is usually simplified by completing the square; we write

$$ax^2 + bx + c = a\left(x^2 + \frac{b}{a}x\right) + c$$

$$= a\left(x + \frac{b}{2a}\right)^2 + c - \frac{b^2}{4a}.$$

Then the substitution $y = (x + b/2a)$ changes the quadratic term in the integrand to a form resembling those considered in the previous sections. The next examples show this procedure.

EXAMPLE 1. Find

$$\int \frac{(2x-3)\,dx}{x^2+2x+2}.$$

Solution. We complete the square, obtaining

$$x^2 + 2x + 2 = (x^2 + 2x + 1) + 1 = (x+1)^2 + 1.$$

Let $y = x + 1$, $dy = dx$, and write

$$\int \frac{(2x-3)\,dx}{x^2+2x+2} = \int \frac{2y-5}{y^2+1}\,dy = \int \frac{2y\,dy}{y^2+1} - 5\int \frac{dy}{y^2+1}$$

$$= \ln(y^2+1) - 5\arctan y + C$$

$$= \ln(x^2 + 2x + 2) - 5\arctan(x+1) + C.$$

EXAMPLE 2. Find

$$\int \frac{dx}{\sqrt{2x-x^2}}.$$

Solution. We write

$$2x - x^2 = -(x^2 - 2x + 1) + 1 = -(x-1)^2 + 1.$$

We let $y = x - 1$, $dy = dx$, and so

$$\int \frac{dx}{\sqrt{2x-x^2}} = \int \frac{dy}{\sqrt{1-y^2}} = \arcsin y + C = \arcsin(x-1) + C.$$

EXAMPLE 3. Find

$$\int \frac{2x^3\,dx}{2x^2-4x+3}.$$

Solution. We perform the division, getting

$$\int \frac{2x^3\, dx}{2x^2 - 4x + 3} = \int \left(x + 2 + \frac{5x - 6}{2x^2 - 4x + 3} \right) dx$$

$$= \tfrac{1}{2}x^2 + 2x + \int \frac{5x - 6}{2x^2 - 4x + 3}\, dx.$$

We complete the square to obtain

$$2x^2 - 4x + 3 = 2(x - 1)^2 + 1;$$

therefore the substitution $y = x - 1$ yields

$$\int \frac{2x^3\, dx}{2x^2 - 4x + 3}$$

$$= \tfrac{1}{2}x^2 + 2x + \int \frac{5y - 1}{2y^2 + 1}\, dy$$

$$= \frac{1}{2} x^2 + 2x + \frac{5}{4} \int \frac{d(2y^2 + 1)}{2y^2 + 1} - \frac{1}{2} \int \frac{dy}{y^2 + \tfrac{1}{2}}$$

$$= \tfrac{1}{2}x^2 + 2x + \tfrac{5}{4} \ln (2y^2 + 1) - \tfrac{1}{2}\sqrt{2} \arctan (y\sqrt{2}) + C$$

$$= \tfrac{1}{2}x^2 + 2x + \tfrac{5}{4} \ln (2x^2 - 4x + 3) - \tfrac{1}{2}\sqrt{2} \arctan [\sqrt{2}(x - 1)] + C.$$

EXERCISES

In problems 1 through 22, find the indefinite integrals.

1. $\displaystyle \int \frac{dx}{x^2 + 4x + 5}$

2. $\displaystyle \int \frac{dx}{\sqrt{5 + 4x - x^2}}$

3. $\displaystyle \int \frac{x^2\, dx}{x^2 + 2x + 5}$

4. $\displaystyle \int \frac{x^3 - 2x}{x^2 + x + 3}\, dx$

5. $\displaystyle \int \frac{dx}{(x + 2)\sqrt{x^2 + 4x + 3}}$

6. $\displaystyle \int \frac{dx}{x^2 - x + 1}$

7. $\displaystyle \int \frac{dx}{\sqrt{5 - 2x + x^2}}$

8. $\displaystyle \int \frac{dx}{(x - 1)\sqrt{x^2 - 2x - 3}}$

9. $\displaystyle \int \frac{x + 3}{x^2 + 2x + 5}\, dx$

10. $\displaystyle \int \frac{(2x - 5)\, dx}{\sqrt{4x - x^2}}$

11. $\displaystyle \int \frac{x^4\, dx}{x^2 + 3x + 1}$

12. $\displaystyle \int \frac{4x^3}{2x^2 + 6x + 1}\, dx$

13. $\displaystyle \int \frac{(3x + 4)\, dx}{\sqrt{2x + x^2}}$

14. $\displaystyle \int \frac{\sqrt{x^2 + 2x}}{x + 1}\, dx$

15. $\displaystyle \int \frac{4x + 7}{(x^2 - 2x + 3)^2}\, dx$ 16. $\displaystyle \int \frac{(5x - 3)\, dx}{(x^2 + 4x + 7)^2}$

17. $\displaystyle \int \frac{4x + 5}{(2x^2 + 3x + 4)^2}\, dx$ 18. $\displaystyle \int \frac{(3x - 2)\, dx}{(2x^2 - 5x + 8)^2}$

19. $\displaystyle \int \frac{(4x + 5)\, dx}{(x^2 - 2x + 2)^{3/2}}$ 20. $\displaystyle \int \frac{(x + 2)\, dx}{(3 + 2x - x^2)^{3/2}}$

21. $\displaystyle \int \frac{(2x - 3)\, dx}{(x^2 + 2x - 3)^{3/2}}$ 22. $\displaystyle \int \frac{dx}{(x^2 - 2x - 3)^2}$

6. INTEGRATION BY PARTS

The formula for the differential of a product is

$$d(uv) = u\, dv + v\, du.$$

By integrating both sides, we obtain

$$uv = \int u\, dv + \int v\, du,$$

or

$$\int u\, dv = uv - \int v\, du. \tag{1}$$

Equation (1) is the formula for *integration by parts*. This formula is useful not only for evaluating integrals but also for investigating many theoretical questions.

Any integral can be written in the form $\int u\, dv$. If it happens that $\int v\, du$ is easily calculated, then the integration-by-parts formula allows us to calculate $\int u\, dv$. The following examples show how this method is applied.

———————

EXAMPLE 1. Find $\int xe^x\, dx$.

Solution. Let

$$u = x \quad \text{and} \quad dv = e^x\, dx.$$

Then

$$du = dx \quad \text{and} \quad v = e^x.$$

The integration-by-parts formula yields

$$\int xe^x\, dx = xe^x - \int e^x\, dx = xe^x - e^x + C = e^x(x - 1) + C.$$

EXAMPLE 2. Find $\int \ln x\, dx$.

Solution. We let

$$u = \ln x \quad \text{and} \quad dv = dx.$$

Then

$$du = \frac{1}{x}\, dx \quad \text{and} \quad v = x.$$

Integrating by parts, we get

$$\int \ln x\, dx = x \ln x - \int x \cdot \frac{1}{x}\, dx = x \ln x - x + C.$$

Sometimes integration by parts may be performed several times in succession, as the following example shows.

EXAMPLE 3. Find $\int x^2 e^x \, dx$.

Solution. We let
$$u = x^2 \quad\text{and}\quad dv = e^x \, dx.$$
Then
$$du = 2x \, dx \quad\text{and}\quad v = e^x.$$
Therefore
$$\int x^2 e^x \, dx = x^2 e^x - 2\int xe^x \, dx.$$

The last integral on the right may be found by a second integration by parts, as we saw in Example 1. Taking the result given there, we obtain
$$\int x^2 e^x \, dx = x^2 e^x - 2e^x(x - 1) + C = e^x(x^2 - 2x + 2) + C.$$

Integration by parts may be used to evaluate definite integrals. The appropriate formula is
$$\int_a^b u \, dv = [uv]_a^b - \int_a^b v \, du.$$

EXAMPLE 4. Evaluate $\int_0^{\pi/2} x \cos x \, dx$.

Solution. We let
$$u = x \quad\text{and}\quad dv = \cos x \, dx.$$
Then
$$du = dx \quad\text{and}\quad v = \sin x.$$
We find that
$$\int_0^{\pi/2} x \cos x \, dx = [x \sin x]_0^{\pi/2} - \int_0^{\pi/2} \sin x \, dx$$
$$= \frac{\pi}{2} + [\cos x]_0^{\pi/2} = \frac{\pi}{2} - 1.$$

The next example exhibits an interesting trick which uses integration by parts twice.

EXAMPLE 5. Find $\int e^x \sin x \, dx$.

Solution. We try integration by parts by letting
$$u = e^x, \quad dv = \sin x \, dx, \quad du = e^x \, dx, \quad\text{and}\quad v = -\cos x.$$
Then
$$\int e^x \sin x \, dx = -e^x \cos x + \int e^x \cos x \, dx.$$

The integral on the right appears to be no simpler than the one with which we started. However, we now apply integration by parts to the integral on the right by letting
$$\bar{u} = e^x, \quad d\bar{v} = \cos x \, dx, \quad d\bar{u} = e^x \, dx, \quad\text{and}\quad \bar{v} = \sin x.$$

We then obtain

$$\int e^x \sin x \, dx = -e^x \cos x + e^x \sin x - \int e^x \sin x \, dx.$$

Transposing the integral on the right and dividing by 2, we get

$$\int e^x \sin x \, dx = \tfrac{1}{2} e^x (\sin x - \cos x) + C.$$

Remark. If, in the second integration by parts, we had let $\bar{u} = \cos x$, $d\bar{v} = e^x \, dx$, everything would have canceled out, as this step would have reversed the first integration by parts. The device of Example 5 is rather special, but it is spectacular when it works.

As another illustration of the power of integration by parts, we shall show how certain classes of integrals may be simplified.

EXAMPLE 6. Find $\int \sin^n x \, dx$ where n is a positive integer.

Solution. We let $u = \sin^{n-1} x$ and $dv = \sin x \, dx$. Then

$$du = (n - 1) \sin^{n-2} x \cos x \, dx, \quad v = -\cos x.$$

Consequently

$$\int \sin^n x \, dx = -\cos x \sin^{n-1} x + (n - 1) \int \sin^{n-2} x \cos^2 x \, dx.$$

We now let $\cos^2 x = 1 - \sin^2 x$ in the integral on the right, and we find that

$$\int \sin^n x \, dx = -\cos x \sin^{n-1} x + (n - 1) \int \sin^{n-2} x \, dx - (n - 1) \int \sin^n x \, dx.$$

Transposing the last integral on the right and dividing by n, we obtain

$$\int \sin^n x \, dx = -\frac{\cos x \sin^{n-1} x}{n} + \frac{n - 1}{n} \int \sin^{n-2} x \, dx.$$

Applying the same method to the integral on the right, we get

$$\int \sin^n x \, dx = -\frac{\cos x \sin^{n-1} x}{n} + \frac{n - 1}{n} \left(-\frac{\cos x \sin^{n-3} x}{n - 2} + \frac{n - 3}{n - 2} \int \sin^{n-4} x \, dx \right).$$

We continue this process until all of the integrals are evaluated. As an illustration, let $n = 5$. We have

$$\int \sin^5 x \, dx = -\frac{\cos x \sin^4 x}{5} + \frac{4}{5} \left(-\frac{\cos x \sin^2 x}{3} + \frac{2}{3} \int \sin x \, dx \right)$$

$$= -\frac{\cos x \sin^4 x}{5} - \frac{4 \cos x \sin^2 x}{15} - \frac{8}{15} \cos x + C$$

$$= -\frac{\cos x}{5} (\sin^4 x + \tfrac{4}{3} \sin^2 x + \tfrac{8}{3}) + C.$$

Remark. The integration shown in Example 6 may be performed by the methods of Section 3.

EXAMPLE 7. Given that z and w are functions of x, with $z(0) = 0$, $z'(0) = 1$, $w(0) = 0$, and $w'(0) = 3$. Show that

$$\int_0^a z(x)w''(x)\,dx = z(a)w'(a) - z'(a)w(a) + \int_0^a w(x)z''(x)\,dx.$$

Solution. We let
$$u = z(x) \quad \text{and} \quad dv = w''(x)\,dx.$$
Then
$$du = z'(x)\,dx \quad \text{and} \quad v = w'(x).$$

Then we can write

$$\int_0^a zw''\,dx = [z(x)w'(x)]_0^a - \int_0^a w'(x)z'(x)\,dx$$
$$= z(a)w'(a) - \int_0^a w'(x)z'(x)\,dx.$$

Proceeding to the integral on the right side, we let

$$u = z'(x), \quad dv = w'(x)\,dx, \quad du = z''(x)\,dx, \quad \text{and} \quad v = w(x),$$

which yields

$$\int_0^a zw''\,dx = z(a)w'(a) - \left\{[z'(x)w(x)]_0^a - \int_0^a wz''\,dx\right\}$$
$$= z(a)w'(a) - z'(a)w(a) + \int_0^a wz''\,dx.$$

EXERCISES

In problems 1 through 31, find the indefinite integrals.

1. $\int x \ln x \, dx$ 2. $\int x \sin x \, dx$ 3. $\int x^2 \sin x \, dx$

4. $\int x^2 \ln x \, dx$ 5. $\int (\ln x)^2 \, dx$ 6. $\int x^3 e^{2x} \, dx$

7. $\int \arctan x \, dx$ 8. $\int \arcsin x \, dx$ 9. $\int \operatorname{arcsec} x \, dx$

10. $\int x \arctan x \, dx$ 11. $\int x \arcsin x \, dx$ 12. $\int x \operatorname{arcsec} x \, dx$

13. $\int x \csc^2 \tfrac{1}{2}x \, dx$ 14. $\int (2x\,dx)/(\cos^2 2x)$ 15. $\int 9x \tan^2 3x \, dx$

16. $\int x^m \ln x \, dx, \quad m \neq -1$ 17. $\int 6x^2 \arcsin 2x \, dx$

18. $\int \dfrac{x \ln x \, dx}{\sqrt{x^2 - 4}}$ 19. $\int \sin\sqrt{2x} \, dx$ (*Hint:* let $2x = z^2$.)

20. $\int \arcsin \sqrt{3x} \, dx$ 21. $\int 2x^3 e^{x^2} \, dx$ 22. $\int x^3 \arctan (x^2) \, dx$

23. $\int e^x \sin 2x \, dx$ 24. $\int e^{3x} \sin 2x \, dx$ 25. $\int e^{-x} \cos 3x \, dx$

26. $\int e^{ax} \cos bx \, dx$ 27. $\int e^{ax} \sin bx \, dx$ 28. $\int x^m (\ln x)^2 \, dx$

29. $\int \sin 4x \sin 2x \, dx$ 30. $\int \cos x \sin 3x \, dx$ 31. $\int \sin^6 x \, dx$

In problems 32 through 37, evaluate the definite integrals.

32. $\int_1^2 x^3 \ln x \, dx$ 33. $\int_0^{(1/2)\pi^2} \cos \sqrt{2x} \, dx$ 34. $\int_0^{1/2} x \arcsin 2x \, dx$

35. $\int_0^{\pi/3} x \arctan 2x \, dx$ 36. $\int_0^{\pi/2} \cos^4 x \, dx$ 37. $\int_0^{\pi/4} e^{3x} \sin 4x \, dx$

38. Find a formula for $\int \cos^n x \, dx$ in terms of $\int \cos^{n-4} x \, dx$.

39. Find a formula for $\int \sin^n x \, dx$ in terms of $\int \sin^{n-6} x \, dx$.

40. Given that z and w are functions of x with $z(0) = 1$, $z'(0) = 2$, $z''(0) = 3$, $z(1) = 2$, $z'(1) = -1$, $z''(1) = 2$, $w(0) = -1$, $w'(0) = 2$, $w''(0) = 0$, $w(1) = -1$, $w'(1) = -2$, and $w''(1) = -3$. Express $\int_0^1 zw''' \, dx$ in terms of $\int_0^1 wz''' \, dx$.

41. Given that $f''(x) = -af(x)$ and that $g''(x) = bg(x)$, where a and b are constants. Find the indefinite integral of $\int f(x)g''(x) \, dx$.

7. INTEGRATION OF RATIONAL FUNCTIONS

If P and Q are polynomials, the integration of expressions in the form

$$\int \frac{P(x)}{Q(x)} \, dx$$

can, in theory, always be performed. In practice, however, the actual calculation of the integral depends on whether or not the denominator, $Q(x)$, can be factored. A theorem which is proved in more advanced courses states that every polynomial can be factored into a product of linear factors. That is, when $Q(x)$ is a polynomial of degree r, it may be written as a product of r linear factors:

$$Q(x) = a(x - \alpha_1)(x - \alpha_2) \cdots (x - \alpha_r).$$

In this decomposition some of the numbers $\alpha_1, \alpha_2, \ldots, \alpha_r$ may be complex. In order to be sure that we do not become involved with complex quantities, we shall use the following theorem, which is stated without proof.

Theorem 1. *Every polynomial (with real coefficients) may be decomposed into a product of linear and quadratic factors in such a way that each of the factors has real coefficients.*

For example, the polynomial

$$Q(x) = x^3 - 2x^2 + x - 2$$

can be decomposed into the linear factors

$$Q(x) = (x - 2)(x - i)(x + i).$$

Two of these factors are complex. However, the decomposition

$$Q(x) = (x - 2)(x^2 + 1)$$

into a linear and a quadratic factor has only real quantities.

The basic method of integrating the rational function P/Q consists of two steps: (1) factoring Q into a product of linear and quadratic factors, and (2) writing P/Q as a sum of simpler rational functions, each of which can be integrated by methods which we have already learned.

The student has studied methods of performing step (1) in high-school and college algebra. Finding the factors may be very difficult in specific cases, but we shall assume that this can always be done.

Before discussing step (2) in detail, let us look at some examples of simplifications leading to integrations which can be performed:

$$\frac{2x^2 - 3x + 5}{(x + 2)(x - 1)(x - 3)} = \frac{A}{x + 2} + \frac{B}{x - 1} + \frac{C}{x - 3}$$

$$\frac{x^4 - 2x^2 + 3x + 4}{(x - 1)^3(x^2 + 2x + 2)} = \frac{D}{x - 1} + \frac{E}{(x - 1)^2} + \frac{F}{(x - 1)^3} + \frac{Gx + H}{x^2 + 2x + 2}$$

$$\frac{2x^4 + 3x^3 - x - 1}{(x - 1)(x^2 + 2x + 2)^2} = \frac{J}{(x - 1)} + \frac{Kx + L}{(x^2 + 2x + 2)} + \frac{Mx + N}{(x^2 + 2x + 2)^2}$$

Each of the above equations is an identity in x for properly chosen constants A, B, C, D, etc. We note that every term on the right side is one which we can integrate. For example,

$$\int \frac{A}{x + 2}\, dx = A \ln |x + 2| + C.$$

The integrals

$$\int \frac{dx}{(x - 1)^2}, \qquad \int \frac{dx}{(x - 1)^3}$$

are routine. An expression of the form

$$\int \frac{Gx + H}{x^2 + 2x + 2}\, dx$$

succumbs if we complete the square in the denominator and proceed as described in Section 5, Example 1. The integration of

$$\int \frac{Mx + N}{(x^2 + 2x + 2)^2} \, dx$$

is performed by completing the square in the denominator and then making a trigonometric substitution of the type described in Section 4.

We now turn to the problem of decomposing a rational function P/Q into simpler expressions.

If the degree of P is larger than or equal to the degree of Q, apply long division. Then P/Q will equal a polynomial (quotient) plus a rational function (remainder divided by the divisor) in which the degree of the numerator is definitely less than the degree of the denominator. From now on, we shall always suppose that this simplification has already been performed.

The decomposition of a rational function into the sum of simpler expressions is known as the *method of partial fractions*. We divide the method into four cases, depending on the way the denominator factors.

Case I. The denominator $Q(x)$ can be factored into linear factors, all different. If we can make the decomposition

$$Q(x) = (x - a_1)(x - a_2) \cdots (x - a_r),$$

with no two of the a_i the same, then we can decompose P/Q so that

$$\frac{P(x)}{Q(x)} = \frac{A_1}{x - a_1} + \frac{A_2}{x - a_2} + \frac{A_3}{x - a_3} + \cdots + \frac{A_r}{x - a_r},$$

where $A_1, A_2, \ldots, A_r$ are properly chosen constants.

We shall show by example how the constants may be found.

EXAMPLE 1. Decompose $(x^2 + 2x + 3)/(x^3 - x)$ into partial fractions and integrate.

Solution. $Q(x) = x^3 - x = (x - 0)(x - 1)(x + 1)$. We write

$$\frac{x^2 + 2x + 3}{x(x - 1)(x + 1)} = \frac{A_1}{x} + \frac{A_2}{x - 1} + \frac{A_3}{x + 1},$$

which is an identity for all x ($x \neq 0, 1, -1$) if and only if

$$x^2 + 2x + 3 = A_1(x - 1)(x + 1) + A_2x(x + 1) + A_3x(x - 1). \qquad (1)$$

Multiplying out the right side, we obtain

$$x^2 + 2x + 3 = (A_1 + A_2 + A_3)x^2 + (A_2 - A_3)x - A_1. \qquad (2)$$

In order that these two polynomials be *identical*, every coefficient on the left must equal every coefficient on the right. Then the polynomials are the same for *all values* of x. It is better to work with (1) than with (2). We proceed as follows:

$$\text{If in (1)} \quad x = 0: \qquad 3 = -A_1 \qquad \text{and} \qquad A_1 = -3.$$

$$\text{If in (1)} \quad x = 1: \qquad 6 = 2A_2 \qquad \text{and} \qquad A_2 = 3.$$

$$\text{If in (1)} \quad x = -1: \qquad 2 = 2A_3 \qquad \text{and} \qquad A_3 = 1.$$

We conclude that

$$\int \frac{(x^2 + 2x + 3)\,dx}{x(x - 1)(x + 1)} = \int \left(-\frac{3}{x} + \frac{3}{x - 1} + \frac{1}{x + 1} \right) dx$$

$$= -3 \ln |x| + 3 \ln |x - 1| + \ln |x + 1| + C$$

$$= \ln \left| \frac{(x - 1)^3 (x + 1)}{x^3} \right| + C.$$

In the example above, we made use of the following theorem about polynomials.

Theorem 2. *Suppose that two polynomials*

$$S(x) = a_0 + a_1 x + a_2 x^2 + \cdots + a_n x^n, \quad T(x) = b_0 + b_1 x + \cdots + b_n x^n$$

are equal for all except possibly a finite number of values of x. Then $a_i = b_i$ for all $i = 0, 1, 2, \ldots, n$.

Proof. From the continuity of polynomial functions, $S(x)$ and $T(x)$ must be equal for *all* values of x. We form the expression

$$S(x) - T(x) = (a_0 - b_0) + (a_1 - b_1)x + \cdots + (a_n - b_n)x^n \equiv 0.$$

Setting $x = 0$, we obtain $S(0) - T(0) = a_0 - b_0 = 0$, or $a_0 = b_0$. Then

$$S(x) - T(x) = (a_1 - b_1)x + (a_2 - b_2)x^2 + \cdots + (a_n - b_n)x^n \equiv 0.$$

Dividing through by x and again setting $x = 0$, we obtain $a_1 - b_1 = 0$. Continuing in this way, we get $a_i = b_i$ for each i from 0 to n.

Case II. The denominator $Q(x)$ can be factored into linear factors, some of which are repeated. If we can make the decomposition

$$Q(x) = (x - a_1)^{s_1}(x - a_2)^{s_2} \cdots (x - a_r)^{s_r},$$

then the partial fraction decomposition introduces a number of different types of denominators. For example, a factor such as $(x - 1)^4$ gives rise to the terms

$$\frac{A_1}{(x - 1)} + \frac{A_2}{(x - 1)^2} + \frac{A_3}{(x - 1)^3} + \frac{A_4}{(x - 1)^4},$$

where $A_1, \ldots, A_4$ are properly chosen constants. In general, a factor such as

$(x - a)^q$ gives rise to the terms

$$\frac{A_1}{(x - a)} + \frac{A_2}{(x - a)^2} + \frac{A_3}{(x - a)^3} + \cdots + \frac{A_q}{(x - a)^q}.$$

EXAMPLE 2. Find

$$\int \frac{x + 5}{x^3 - 3x + 2} \, dx.$$

Solution. We factor the denominator, obtaining $x^3 - 3x + 2 = (x - 1)^2(x + 2)$. This falls under Case II, and we write

$$\frac{x + 5}{(x - 1)^2(x + 2)} = \frac{A_1}{(x - 1)} + \frac{A_2}{(x - 1)^2} + \frac{A_3}{x + 2}.$$

Multiplying through by $(x - 1)^2(x + 2)$, we obtain

$$x + 5 = A_1(x - 1)(x + 2) + A_2(x + 2) + A_3(x - 1)^2.$$

We let

$$x = 1: \qquad 6 = 3A_2 \qquad \text{and} \qquad A_2 = 2;$$

$$x = -2: \qquad 3 = 9A_3 \qquad \text{and} \qquad A_3 = \tfrac{1}{3};$$

$$x = 0: \qquad 5 = -2A_1 + 2A_2 + A_3 \qquad \text{and} \qquad A_1 = -\tfrac{1}{3}.$$

Therefore

$$\int \frac{(x + 5) \, dx}{(x - 1)^2(x + 2)} = -\frac{2}{x - 1} - \frac{1}{3} \ln |x - 1| + \frac{1}{3} \ln |x + 2| + C.$$

Case III. The denominator $Q(x)$ can be factored into linear and quadratic factors, and none of the quadratic factors is repeated.

If, for example, the denominator is

$$Q(x) = (x - a_1)(x - a_2)(x - a_3)(x^2 + b_1x + c_1)(x^2 + b_2x + c_2),$$

then

$$\frac{P(x)}{Q(x)} = \frac{A_1}{x - a_1} + \frac{A_2}{x - a_2} + \frac{A_3}{x - a_3} + \frac{A_4x + A_5}{x^2 + b_1x + c_1} + \frac{A_6x + A_7}{x^2 + b_2x + c_2}.$$

In other words, each unrepeated quadratic factor gives rise to a term of the form

$$\frac{Ax + B}{x^2 + bx + c}.$$

EXAMPLE 3. Find

$$\int \frac{3x^2 + x - 2}{(x - 1)(x^2 + 1)} \, dx.$$

Solution. According to Case III, we have

$$\frac{3x^2 + x - 2}{(x - 1)(x^2 + 1)} = \frac{A_1}{x - 1} + \frac{A_2 x + A_3}{x^2 + 1},$$

or

$$3x^2 + x - 2 = A_1(x^2 + 1) + (A_2 x + A_3)(x - 1).$$

We find

$$x = 1: \qquad 2 = 2A_1 \qquad \text{and} \qquad A_1 = 1;$$

$$x = 0: \qquad -2 = A_1 - A_3 \qquad \text{and} \qquad A_3 = 3;$$

$$x = 2: \qquad 12 = 5A_1 + (2A_2 + A_3) \qquad \text{and} \qquad A_2 = 2.$$

Therefore

$$\int \frac{3x^2 + x - 2}{(x - 1)(x^2 + 1)}\, dx = \ln|x - 1| + \ln(x^2 + 1) + 3\arctan x + C.$$

Case IV. The denominator $Q(x)$ can be factored into linear and quadratic factors, and some of the quadratic factors are repeated. If the denominator contains a factor such as $(x^2 + 3x + 5)^3$, it will give rise to the terms

$$\frac{A_1 x + A_2}{x^2 + 3x + 5} + \frac{A_3 x + A_4}{(x^2 + 3x + 5)^2} + \frac{A_5 x + A_6}{(x^2 + 3x + 5)^3}.$$

In general, a factor of the form $(x^2 + bx + c)^q$ will give rise to the terms

$$\frac{A_1 x + A_2}{x^2 + bx + c} + \frac{A_3 x + A_4}{(x^2 + bx + c)^2} + \cdots + \frac{A_{2q-1} x + A_{2q}}{(x^2 + bx + c)^q}.$$

EXAMPLE 4. Find

$$\int \frac{2x^3 + 3x^2 + x - 1}{(x + 1)(x^2 + 2x + 2)^2}\, dx.$$

Solution. This is case IV, and we have

$$\frac{2x^3 + 3x^2 + x - 1}{(x + 1)(x^2 + 2x + 2)^2} = \frac{A_1}{x + 1} + \frac{A_2 x + A_3}{x^2 + 2x + 2} + \frac{A_4 x + A_5}{(x^2 + 2x + 2)^2},$$

or

$$2x^3 + 3x^2 + x - 1 = A_1(x^2 + 2x + 2)^2 + (A_2 x + A_3)(x^2 + 2x + 2)(x + 1)$$
$$+ (A_4 x + A_5)(x + 1).$$

We let

$$x = -1: \quad -1 = A_1 \quad \text{and} \quad A_1 = -1;$$

$$x = 0: \qquad -1 = 4A_1 + 2A_3 + A_5 \quad \text{and} \quad 2A_3 + A_5 = 3;$$

$$x = 1: \quad 5 = 25A_1 + (A_2 + A_3) \cdot (10) + (A_4 + A_5)(2) \quad \text{and}$$
$$5A_2 + 5A_3 + A_4 + A_5 = 15;$$

$$x = 2: \quad 20A_2 + 10A_3 + 2A_4 + A_5 = 43;$$

$$x = -2: \quad 4A_2 - 2A_3 + 2A_4 - A_5 = -3.$$

Solving these four equations for the four unknowns, A_2, A_3, A_4, and A_5, we get $A_2 = 1$, $A_3 = 3, A_4 = -2, A_5 = -3$. Therefore

$$\int \frac{2x^3 + 3x^2 + x - 1}{(x + 1)(x^2 + 2x + 2)^2} \, dx = -\ln|x + 1| + \int \frac{(x + 3) \, dx}{x^2 + 2x + 2} + \int \frac{(-2x - 3) \, dx}{(x^2 + 2x + 2)^2}.$$

We complete the square and set $u = x + 1$, $du = dx$, obtaining

$$\int \frac{(x + 3) \, dx}{x^2 + 2x + 2} = \int \frac{u + 2}{u^2 + 1} \, du = \tfrac{1}{2} \ln|x^2 + 2x + 2| + 2 \arctan(x + 1),$$

and

$$\int \frac{-2x - 3}{(x^2 + 2x + 2)^2} \, dx = \int \frac{-2u - 1}{(u^2 + 1)^2} \, du = + \frac{1}{u^2 + 1} - \int \frac{du}{(u^2 + 1)^2}$$

$$= \frac{1}{x^2 + 2x + 2} - \frac{1}{2} \arctan(x + 1) - \frac{1}{2} \frac{x + 1}{x^2 + 2x + 2}.$$

Combining these integrals, we conclude that

$$\int \frac{2x^3 + 3x^2 + x - 1}{(x + 1)(x^2 + 2x + 2)} \, dx$$

$$= -\ln|x + 1| + \tfrac{1}{2} \ln(x^2 + 2x + 2) + \tfrac{3}{2} \arctan(x + 1) - \frac{1}{2} \frac{x - 1}{x^2 + 2x + 2} + C.$$

EXERCISES

In problems 1 through 34, find the indefinite integrals.

1. $\displaystyle \int \frac{x^2 + 3x + 4}{x - 2} \, dx$

2. $\displaystyle \int \frac{x^3 + x^2 - x - 3}{x + 2} \, dx$

3. $\displaystyle \int \frac{x^3 - x^2 + 2x + 3}{x^2 + 3x + 2} \, dx$

4. $\displaystyle \int \frac{2x^3 + 3x^2 - 4}{x^2 - 4x + 3} \, dx$

5. $\displaystyle \int \frac{x^2 + 2x + 3}{x^2 - 3x + 2} \, dx$

6. $\displaystyle \int \frac{x^4 + 1}{x^3 - x} \, dx$

7. $\displaystyle \int \frac{x^2 - 2x - 1}{x^2 - 4x + 4} \, dx$

8. $\displaystyle \int \frac{x^2 + 2x + 3}{(x + 1)(x - 1)(x - 2)} \, dx$

9. $\displaystyle \int \frac{3x - 2}{(x + 2)(x + 1)(x - 1)} \, dx$

10. $\displaystyle \int \frac{x^3 + 2}{x^2 + 4} \, dx$

11. $\displaystyle\int \frac{2x^2 + 3x - 1}{(x + 3)(x + 2)(x - 1)}\, dx$

12. $\displaystyle\int \frac{x^2 - 2}{(x + 1)(x - 1)^2}\, dx$

13. $\displaystyle\int \frac{x^2 + 3x + 3}{(x + 1)(x^2 + 1)}\, dx$

14. $\displaystyle\int \frac{x^2 - 2x - 3}{(x - 1)(x^2 + 2x + 2)}\, dx$

15. $\displaystyle\int \frac{x - 3}{(x + 1)^2(x - 2)}\, dx$

16. $\displaystyle\int \frac{x^2 + 1}{(x - 1)^3}\, dx$

17. $\displaystyle\int \frac{2x + 3}{(x + 2)(x - 1)^2}\, dx$

18. $\displaystyle\int \frac{2x^2 - 1}{(x + 1)^2(x - 3)}\, dx$

19. $\displaystyle\int \frac{x^3 - 3x + 4}{(x + 1)(x - 1)^3}\, dx$

20. $\displaystyle\int \frac{x^3 + 1}{(x^2 - 1)^2}\, dx$

21. $\displaystyle\int \frac{x^3 + 3x^2 - 2x + 1}{x^4 + 5x^2 + 4}\, dx$

22. $\displaystyle\int \frac{x^2}{x^4 - 5x^2 + 4}\, dx$

23. $\displaystyle\int \frac{x^2 - x + 1}{x^4 - 5x^3 + 5x^2 + 5x - 6}\, dx$

24. $\displaystyle\int \frac{3x\, dx}{x^5 + 2x^4 - 10x^3 - 20x^2 + 9x + 18}$

25. $\displaystyle\int \frac{x^2 - 2x + 3}{(x - 1)^2(x^2 + 4)}\, dx$

26. $\displaystyle\int \frac{x^3 - 2x^2 + 3x - 4}{(x - 1)^2(x^2 + 2x + 2)}\, dx$

27. $\displaystyle\int \frac{x^3 + x^2 - 2x - 3}{(x + 1)^2(x - 2)^2}\, dx$

28. $\displaystyle\int \frac{x^2 - 3x + 5}{x^4 - 8x^2 + 16}\, dx$

29. $\displaystyle\int \frac{4x^3 + 8x^2 - 12}{(x^2 + 4)^2}\, dx$

30. $\displaystyle\int \frac{x^2 + 3x + 5}{x^3 + 8}\, dx$

31. $\displaystyle\int \frac{x^2 + 2x - 1}{x^3 - 27}\, dx$

32. $\displaystyle\int \frac{x^3 - x^2 + 2x + 3}{(x^2 + 2x + 2)^2}\, dx$

33. $\displaystyle\int \frac{x^4 + 1}{(x^2 + 4)^3}\, dx$

34. $\displaystyle\int \frac{2x^5 - 6}{(x^2 + 1)^4}\, dx$

8.   THREE RATIONALIZING SUBSTITUTIONS

I. Whenever an integrand contains a single irrational expression of the form

$$(ax + b)^{p/q}, \qquad p \text{ and } q \text{ integers,}$$

the substitution

$$u = (ax + b)^{1/q}, \quad \text{or} \quad x = \frac{u^q - b}{a}, \quad dx = \frac{q}{a}\, u^{q-1}\, du$$

will convert the given integrand into a rational function of u.

EXAMPLE 1. Find $\displaystyle\int \frac{\sqrt[3]{x + 1}}{x}\, dx.$

Solution. Let $u = (x + 1)^{1/3}$, $x = u^3 - 1$, $dx = 3u^2\, du$. Then

$$\int \frac{\sqrt[3]{x + 1}\, dx}{x} = \int \frac{u\, 3u^2\, du}{u^3 - 1} = \int 3\, du + \int \frac{3\, du}{u^3 - 1}.$$

To evaluate the second integral, we use partial fractions and write

$$\frac{3}{u^3 - 1} = \frac{3}{(u - 1)(u^2 + u + 1)} = \frac{A_1}{u - 1} + \frac{A_2 u + A_3}{u^2 + u + 1},$$

or

$$3 = A_1(u^2 + u + 1) + (A_2 u + A_3)(u - 1).$$

We set

$$u = 1: \quad 3 = 3A_1 \quad \text{and} \quad A_1 = 1;$$

$$u = 0: \quad 3 = A_1 - A_3 \quad \text{and} \quad A_3 = -2;$$

$$u = -1: \quad 3 = A_1 + 2A_2 - 2A_3 \quad \text{and} \quad A_2 = -1.$$

Therefore

$$\int \frac{3\, du}{u^3 - 1} = \int \frac{du}{u - 1} - \int \frac{u + 2}{u^2 + u + 1}\, du$$

$$= \ln |u - 1| - \tfrac{1}{2} \ln (u^2 + u + 1) - \sqrt{3} \arctan \left(\frac{2u + 1}{\sqrt{3}} \right) + C.$$

We finally obtain

$$\int \frac{\sqrt[3]{x + 1}}{x}\, dx = 3(x + 1)^{1/3} + \ln [(x + 1)^{1/3} - 1]$$

$$- \tfrac{1}{2} \ln [(x + 1)^{2/3} + (x + 1)^{1/3} + 1]$$

$$- \sqrt{3} \arctan \left[\frac{2(x + 1)^{1/3} + 1}{\sqrt{3}} \right] + C.$$

II. If a *single* irrational expression of one of the forms

$$\sqrt{a^2 - x^2}, \quad \sqrt{x^2 + a^2}, \quad \sqrt{x^2 - a^2}$$

appears in the integrand, and if x^q (q being an *odd* integer, positive or negative), appears in the integrand, an appropriate substitution will transform the integrand into a rational function. The correct substitution is

$$u = (a^2 - x^2)^{1/2}, \quad \text{or} \quad u = (x^2 + a^2)^{1/2}, \quad \text{or} \quad u = (x^2 - a^2)^{1/2},$$

depending on which expression is involved.

EXAMPLE 2. Find

$$\int \frac{\sqrt{a^2 - x^2}}{x^3}\, dx.$$

Solution. This is of the form II, with $q = -3$.

We let

$$u = (a^2 - x^2)^{1/2}, \quad x^2 = a^2 - u^2, \quad x\,dx = -u\,du.$$

Therefore

$$\int \frac{\sqrt{a^2 - x^2}}{x^3}\,dx = \int \frac{\sqrt{a^2 - x^2}\,x\,dx}{x^4} = -\int \frac{u^2\,du}{(a^2 - u^2)^2}$$

$$= -\int \frac{u^2\,du}{(u + a)^2(u - a)^2}.$$

We proceed by partial fractions and obtain

$$\frac{-u^2}{(u + a)^2(u - a)^2} = \frac{A_1}{u + a} + \frac{A_2}{(u + a)^2} + \frac{A_3}{(u - a)} + \frac{A_4}{(u - a)^2},$$

and

$$-u^2 = A_1(u + a)(u - a)^2 + A_2(u - a)^2 + A_3(u - a)(u + a)^2 + A_4(u + a)^2.$$

We let

$u = a:$ $-a^2 = A_4 4a^2$ and $A_4 = -\tfrac{1}{4};$

$u = -a:$ $-a^2 = A_2 4a^2$ and $A_2 = -\tfrac{1}{4};$

$u = 0:$ $0 = a^3 A_1 + a^2 A_2 - a^3 A_3 + a^2 A_4$ and $A_1 - A_3 = \dfrac{1}{2a};$

$u = 2a:$ $-4a^2 = 3a^3 A_1 + a^2 A_2 + 9a^3 A_3 + 9a^2 A_4$ and $A_1 + 3A_3 = -\dfrac{1}{2a}.$

We get

$$A_1 = \frac{1}{4a}, \qquad A_3 = -\frac{1}{4a},$$

which yields

$$\int \frac{\sqrt{a^2 - x^2}}{x^3}\,dx = \frac{1}{4(u + a)} + \frac{1}{4(u - a)} + \frac{1}{4a}\ln\left|\frac{u + a}{u - a}\right| + C$$

$$= -\frac{\sqrt{a^2 - x^2}}{2x^2} + \frac{1}{2a}\ln\left(a + \sqrt{a^2 - x^2}\right) - \frac{1}{2a}\ln|x| + C.$$

III. An integrand which is a rational function of a trigonometric function, such as

$$\frac{(\cos\theta)^2 + 2\cos\theta - 3}{(\cos\theta)^3 + 2(\cos\theta)},$$

can be transformed into an ordinary rational function by an appropriate substitution. The correct substitution (see Fig. 15–4) is

$$u = \tan\frac{\theta}{2}, \quad \theta = 2\arctan u, \quad d\theta = \frac{2\,du}{1 + u^2}.$$

FIGURE 15–4

Referring again to Fig. 15–4, we see that

$$\sin \tfrac{1}{2}\theta = \frac{u}{\sqrt{1 + u^2}}, \qquad \cos \tfrac{1}{2}\theta = \frac{1}{\sqrt{1 + u^2}}.$$

Since the integrands will contain sines and cosines of θ rather than of $\tfrac{1}{2}\theta$, we use the formulas

$$\sin \theta = 2 \sin \tfrac{1}{2}\theta \cos \tfrac{1}{2}\theta = \frac{2u}{1 + u^2},$$

$$\cos \theta = \cos^2 \frac{\theta}{2} - \sin^2 \frac{\theta}{2} = \frac{1}{1 + u^2} - \frac{u^2}{1 + u^2} = \frac{1 - u^2}{1 + u^2}.$$

EXAMPLE 3. Find

$$\int \frac{d\theta}{5 - 4 \cos \theta}.$$

Solution. Letting $u = \tan \tfrac{1}{2}\theta$, we find that

$$\int \frac{d\theta}{5 - 4 \cos \theta} = \int \frac{2\, du/(1 + u^2)}{5 - 4[(1 - u^2)/(1 + u^2)]} = \int \frac{2\, du}{1 + 9u^2}$$

$$= \tfrac{2}{3} \arctan 3u + C = \tfrac{2}{3} \arctan (3 \tan \tfrac{1}{2}\theta) + C.$$

EXERCISES

In problems 1 through 38, find the indefinite integrals.

1. $\displaystyle\int \frac{(2x + 3)\, dx}{\sqrt{x + 2}}$

2. $\displaystyle\int \frac{3x - 2}{\sqrt{2x - 3}}\, dx$

3. $\displaystyle\int x\sqrt{x + 1}\, dx$

4. $\displaystyle\int \frac{2x + 1}{(x + 2)^{2/3}}\, dx$

5. $\displaystyle\int \frac{x - 2}{(3x - 1)^{2/3}}\, dx$

6. $\displaystyle\int \frac{2x - 1}{(x - 2)^{1/3}}\, dx$

7. $\displaystyle\int \frac{x^2\, dx}{\sqrt[3]{2x + 1}}$

8. $\displaystyle\int (x + 2)\sqrt{x - 1}\, dx$

9. $\displaystyle\int \frac{\sqrt{x + 4}}{x}\, dx$

10. $\displaystyle\int \frac{\sqrt{2x + 3}}{x + 1}\, dx$

11. $\displaystyle\int \frac{\sqrt{x} + 2}{\sqrt{x} - 1}\, dx$

12. $\displaystyle\int \frac{2\sqrt{x + 1} - 3}{3\sqrt{x + 1} - 2}\, dx$

13. $\displaystyle\int \frac{x^3\, dx}{\sqrt{x^2 - 4}}\, dx$

14. $\displaystyle\int \frac{x^3 - x}{\sqrt{9 - x^2}}\, dx$

15. $\displaystyle\int \frac{x^5 + 2x^3}{\sqrt{x^2 + 4}}\, dx$

16. $\int x^3 \sqrt{x^2 + 1}\, dx$ 17. $\int (x^3 - x)\sqrt{16 - x^2}\, dx$

18. $\int x^3 \sqrt{x^2 - a^2}\, dx$ 19. $\int \dfrac{dx}{x\sqrt{a^2 - x^2}}$ 20. $\int \dfrac{dx}{x\sqrt{x^2 + 4}}$

21. $\int \dfrac{\sqrt{a^2 - x^2}}{x}\, dx$ 22. $\int \dfrac{\sqrt{a^2 + x^2}}{x}\, dx$ 23. $\int \dfrac{\sqrt{x^2 - a^2}}{x}\, dx$

24. $\int \dfrac{\sqrt{4 - x}}{x}\, dx$ 25. $\int \dfrac{dx}{x^{1/2} + x^{2/3}}$ 26. $\int \sqrt{2 + \sqrt{x}}\, dx$

27. $\int \dfrac{d\theta}{5 + 4\cos\theta}$ 28. $\int \dfrac{d\theta}{4 - 5\cos\theta}$ 29. $\int \dfrac{d\theta}{2 - \cos\theta}$

30. $\int \dfrac{d\theta}{2 - \sin\theta}$ 31. $\int \dfrac{d\theta}{3 + 2\cos\theta + 2\sin\theta}$ 32. $\int \dfrac{\cos\theta\, d\theta}{5 + 4\cos\theta}$

33. $\int \dfrac{dx}{\tan x - \sin x}$ 34. $\int \dfrac{dx}{3\cos x + 4\sin x}$ 35. $\int \dfrac{d\theta}{\cos\theta + \cot\theta}$

36. $\int \dfrac{dx}{x^3 \sqrt{x^2 + 4}}$ 37. $\int \dfrac{\sqrt{4 - x^2}}{x^3}\, dx$ 38. $\int \dfrac{\sqrt{x^2 + 9}}{x^3}\, dx$

9. SUMMARY

For convenient reference, we list here the methods of integration discussed in this chapter.

(1) Integration by substitution in a formula. (See Sections 1 and 2 and the formulas on pages 444 and 445.)

(2) Integrations of certain integrals involving trigonometric functions. (See Section 3.)

(3) Trigonometric substitutions. (See Section 4.)

(4) Completing the square in quadratic functions. (See Section 5.)

(5) Integration by parts. (See Section 6.)

(6) Integration of rational functions. (See Section 7).

(7) Rationalizing substitutions which reduce problems to the method of (6). (See Section 8.)

The reader should become thoroughly familiar with the methods in this chapter. When one is confronted with an integral, the chances are that it will not be precisely in one of the forms given in the extensive tables of integrals found in various handbooks. The techniques developed in this chapter, however, are invaluable for transforming integrals into "handbook types."

CHAPTER 16

Some Applications
of Integration

---

1. DIFFERENTIAL EQUATIONS

An equation which contains derivatives is called a differential equation. Since we defined velocity and acceleration in terms of derivatives (cf. Chapter 4, Section 5), we can say that any equation involving either of these quantities is a differential equation. In this section we shall present some applications of integration which are related to various physical concepts and the differential equations connecting them. As a starting point, we state Newton's first two laws (axioms) of motion.

FIRST LAW. *A body at rest remains at rest and a body in motion moves in a straight line with unchanging velocity, unless some external force acts on it.*

SECOND LAW. *The rate of change of the momentum of a body is proportional to the resultant external force that acts on the body.*

In our discussions of motion in Chapter 4, Section 5, it was always assumed that the object moved in a straight line. We shall now study the behavior of objects which move along curved paths, with the restriction that *the motion lies in a plane.* The velocity will be a vector quantity (as described in Chapter 14, Section 5), which we denote by $\mathbf{v}$. If m is the mass, the *momentum vector* is defined as the vector $m\mathbf{v}$. If the mass is constant during the motion — the only type of case we shall consider — Newton's second law becomes

$$m \frac{d\mathbf{v}}{dt} = m\mathbf{a} = k\mathbf{F},$$

where $\mathbf{a}$ is the acceleration vector, $\mathbf{F}$ is the force vector, and k is a proportionality constant that depends on the units used. If British engineering units are employed (pounds for mass, seconds for time, feet for distance), we define *one pound of force* as the force exerted by gravity on a body of mass one pound. The constant k in Newton's law is then equal to g, the acceleration due to gravity. The value of g is approximately 32.2 ft/sec^2.

If a rectangular coordinate system (x, y) is introduced, the vector equation $m\mathbf{a} = k\mathbf{F}$ becomes

$$m \frac{d^2x}{dt^2} = kF_X, \qquad m \frac{d^2y}{dt^2} = kF_Y,$$

475

where d^2x/dt^2, d^2y/dt^2 are the components of **a** along the x- and y-axes, and F_X and F_Y are the components of **F** along these axes.

EXAMPLE 1. A ball is thrown vertically upward with a speed of 96 ft/sec from a point 40 ft above level ground. Express its height above the ground as a function of time; neglect air resistance.

Solution. According to Newton's law, the motion will take place in a vertical line. Let m be the mass of the ball. The only force acting on it is that of gravity, which acts directly downward, so that

$$F_Y = -m; \qquad F_X = 0.$$

Then we have

$$m\frac{d^2y}{dt^2} = -32m,$$

with the auxiliary conditions that

$$y = 40 \text{ when } t = 0; \qquad \frac{dy}{dt} = 96 \text{ when } t = 0.$$

Integrating the differential equation $d^2y/dt^2 = -32$, we obtain

$$\frac{dy}{dt} = -32t + C.$$

Inserting the auxiliary condition for the initial velocity, we find that

$$96 = -32(0) + C, \qquad \text{or} \qquad C = 96.$$

The differential equation $dy/dt = -32t + 96$ may be integrated once more to give

$$y = -16t^2 + 96t + k.$$

The auxiliary condition for the initial position of the ball is now used to determine that $k = 40$. We finally obtain

$$y = -16t^2 + 96t + 40.$$

EXAMPLE 2. A projectile is fired from a gun with a velocity of v_0 ft/sec. The barrel of the gun is inclined at an angle α from the horizontal, as in Fig. 16–1. Assuming that

FIGURE 16–1

there is no air resistance and that the motion of the projectile is in the vertical plane through the barrel of the gun, show that the equations of motion are

$$x = (v_0 \cos \alpha)t, \qquad y = (v_0 \sin \alpha)t - \tfrac{1}{2}gt^2,$$

referred to rectangular coordinates with origin at the muzzle of the gun, y-axis vertical and x-axis horizontal. (See Chapter 12, Section 1, Example 3.)

Solution. The components of the velocity vector in the x- and y-directions at time $t = 0$ (*initial velocity vector*) are $v_0 \cos \alpha$ and $v_0 \sin \alpha$, respectively. By hypothesis, the only force acting is that of gravity. Therefore $F_X = 0$, $F_Y = -mg$. The differential equations governing the motion are

$$\frac{d^2x}{dt^2} = 0, \qquad \frac{d^2y}{dt^2} = -g.$$

The auxiliary conditions are

$$x = 0 \quad \text{and} \quad y = 0 \qquad \text{when } t = 0;$$

also,

$$\frac{dx}{dt} = v_0 \cos \alpha \quad \text{and} \quad \frac{dy}{dt} = v_0 \sin \alpha \qquad \text{when } t = 0.$$

Integrating the differential equations, we find that

$$\frac{dx}{dt} = C_1, \qquad \frac{dy}{dt} = -gt + C_2.$$

The auxiliary conditions yield $C_1 = v_0 \cos \alpha$, $C_2 = v_0 \sin \alpha$. Integrating once again, we obtain

$$x = (v_0 \cos \alpha)t + C_3, \qquad y = -\tfrac{1}{2}gt^2 + (v_0 \sin \alpha)t + C_4.$$

Since $x = y = 0$ when $t = 0$, the constants C_3 and C_4 are both zero.

———————————

A large class of problems in physics, chemistry, biology, economics, etc., involves a differential equation of the form

$$\frac{dy}{dt} = ky,$$

in which k is a constant and y is a quantity which is a *positive* function of the time t. The above differential equation expresses the fact that *the rate at which y changes is proportional to y itself.* To solve this equation, we write

$$\frac{dy}{y} = k\,dt$$

and integrate to obtain

$$\ln y = kt + C.$$

From the definition of natural logarithm we get

$$y = e^{kt+C}.$$

From the law of exponents, $e^{kt+C} = e^{kt} \cdot e^{C}$ and, writing A for the (positive) constant e^{C}, we obtain the more convenient form

$$y = Ae^{kt}.$$

The law is completely determined once the constants A and k are known. If k is positive, the law is one of *exponential growth*. If k is negative, the law is that of *exponential decay*. Applications of this law are illustrated by the following examples.

EXAMPLE 3.   In a favorable environment the number of bacteria increases at a rate proportional to the number present. If 1,000,000 bacteria are present at a certain time and 2,000,000 are present an hour later, find the number present four hours later.

Solution. Let y = number of bacteria present at time t. Then

$$\frac{dy}{dt} = ky;$$

integrating this equation, we find that

$$y = Ae^{kt}.$$

Letting $t = 0$ correspond to the time when 1,000,000 bacteria are present, we see that $1,000,000 = Ae^{k \cdot 0}$, and therefore $A = 1,000,000$. Further, at $t = 1$, $y = 2,000,000$, and so

$$2,000,000 = 1,000,000\, e^{k \cdot 1}, \qquad \text{or} \qquad 2 = e^{k}.$$

Taking logarithms, we find that $\ln 2 = k$. The equation for y is

$$y = 1,000,000\, e^{t \ln 2}.$$

Since $t \ln 2 = \ln (2^{t})$ and $e^{\ln(2^{t})} = 2^{t}$, the equation for y may be written

$$y = 1,000,000 \cdot 2^{t}.$$

Letting $t = 4$, we find that $y = 16,000,000$.

EXAMPLE 4.   A radioactive substance decays at a rate proportional to the amount present. If one gram of a radioactive substance reduces to $\frac{1}{4}$ gram in four hours, find how long it will be until $\frac{1}{10}$ gram remains.

Solution. Letting y = amount of substance remaining at time t and using our knowledge of the differential equation $dy/dt = ky$, we write

$$y = Ae^{kt}.$$

The conditions $y = 1$ when $t = 0$ and $y = \frac{1}{4}$ when $t = 4$ yield

$$A = 1 \qquad \text{and} \qquad \tfrac{1}{4} = e^{4k}.$$

Therefore $k = \frac{1}{4} \ln \frac{1}{4} = -\frac{1}{4} \ln 4$, and $y = e^{-(1/4)t \ln 4}$.

Since $-\frac{1}{4}t \ln 4 = \ln (4^{-t/4})$, and $e^{\ln 4^{-t/4}} = 4^{-t/4}$, we obtain y in the form

$$y = 4^{-t/4}.$$

We wish to find t when $y = 0.1$. Upon taking logarithms, we find that $\ln (0.1) = -(t \ln 4)/4$, and that

$$t = -\frac{4 \ln 0.1}{\ln 4} = \frac{4 \ln 10}{\ln 4} = 6.65 \text{ hours, approximately.}$$

EXAMPLE 5. A tank initially contains 600 gal of brine in which 450 lb of salt are dissolved. Pure water is run into the tank at the rate of 15 gal/min, and the mixture, kept uniform by stirring, is withdrawn at the same rate. How many pounds of salt remain after 20 min?

Solution. Let y be the number of pounds of salt remaining after t minutes. At that instant there are $y/600$ lb of salt per gallon in the mixture. Therefore at that instant y is decreasing at the rate of $15(y/600)$ lb/min. The corresponding differential equation is

$$\frac{dy}{dt} = -\frac{15y}{600} = -\frac{1}{40}y.$$

Integrating this equation, we have

$$y = Ae^{-t/40}.$$

Since $y = 450$ when $t = 0$, the resulting expression for y at time t is

$$y = 450e^{-t/40},$$

and when $t = 20$, $y = 450(e^{-1/2}) = 273$ pounds, approximately.

EXERCISES

1. A ball is thrown upward with a speed of 144 ft/sec from a point 80 ft above level ground. Express its height above the ground as a function of time. What is the highest point it reaches? Neglect air resistance.
2. A ball is dropped from a balloon which is stationary at an altitude of 1000 ft. How long does it take for the ball to reach the ground? Neglect air resistance.

In problems 3 through 7, assume that a particle moves along the x-axis with the given value of its acceleration a_X (which may be positive or negative). Find x and $dx/dt = v$ in terms of t, given the stated auxiliary conditions.

3. $a_X = 2$; $v = 12$ and $x = 1$ when $t = 0$
4. $a_X = -t$; $v = 12$ and $x = -2$ when $t = 0$
5. $a_X = 2v$; $v = 5$ and $x = 1$ when $t = 0$
6. $a_X = -kv$; $v = 10$ and $x = 0$ when $t = 0$
7. $a_X = -kv^2$; $v = v_0$ and $x = x_0$ when $t = 0$
8. An automobile traveling in a straight line at a speed of v_0 ft/sec suddenly applies its brakes and stops in T sec after traveling S ft. Assuming that the brakes produce a constant negative acceleration $-k$, find formulas for S and T in terms of v_0 and k.

9. A projectile at an angle of 60° with the horizontal is fired with an initial velocity of 1496 ft/sec. Determine how far the projectile travels and the length of time it takes to strike the ground. Neglect air resistance.

10. An airplane flying horizontally over level ground at an altitude of 3000 ft drops a projectile. If the plane is traveling 600 mi/hr (= 880 ft/sec), find the equation of the trajectory in terms of the time t. What is the horizontal distance traveled by the projectile?

11. An airplane is climbing at an angle of 30° with the horizontal at a speed of 750 mi/hr. At the instant a projectile is dropped, the plane is 6000 ft above level ground. How long does it take for the projectile to strike the ground? Neglect air resistance.

12. A crystalline chemical present in a solution is such that crystals adhere to it at a rate proportional to the amount present. If there are 2 gm initially and 5 gm one hour later, find the amount of crystalline material present at any time t. What is the approximate amount after three hours?

13. The number of bacteria in a certain culture grows at a rate which is exactly equal to $\frac{1}{2}$ the number present. If there are 10,000 bacteria initially, find the number at any time t.

14. The *half-life* of a radioactive substance (see Example 4) is the time it takes for the original amount of material to reduce to one-half that amount. The half-life of radium is 1690 yr. Find the approximate time it would take for 1 gm of radium to reduce to 0.1 gm.

15. Rework problem 14, given that the radioactive substance has a half-life of 3.5 min.

16. If the half-life of a radioactive substance is 1 week, how long does it take to arrive at the point where only 1% of the original amount remains? (See problem 14.)

17. Rework Example 5, given that the tank initially contains 800 gal of brine in which 400 lb of salt are dissolved, and pure water is run in at the rate of 20 gal/min, the solution being drawn off at the same rate.

18. Rework Example 5, given that the tank initially contains the mixture of the preceding problem, but a brine of 0.2 lb of salt per gallon is run in at 20 gal/min, the solution being drawn off at the same rate.

19. Assume that the rate at which a body cools is proportional to the difference between its temperature and that of the surrounding air. A body originally at 120°F cools to 100°F in 10 min in air at 60°. Find an expression for the temperature of the body at any time t.

20. A body cools at a rate (in minutes) which is exactly equal to $\frac{1}{3}$ the difference between its temperature and the temperature of the surrounding air. If the body is originally at 140°F and the air is constantly at 70°F, find the temperature of the body after 20 min. How long will it take (approximately) for the body to reach a temperature of 71°F?

2. FAMILIES OF CURVES AND DIFFERENTIAL EQUATIONS

The differential equation

$$\frac{dy}{dx} = x$$

can be integrated at once. We find that

$$y = \tfrac{1}{2}x^2 + C,$$

which represents a family of curves, specifically a family of parabolas. One parabola of this family passes through each point of the plane. The differential equation asserts that if $P(x, y)$ is any point in the plane, the slope of the curve passing through P has the value x. A particular member of the family is singled out whenever some condition is prescribed. For example, if we seek the curve that passes through the point $(1, 5)$, the constant C is determined. We conclude that

$$y = \tfrac{1}{2}x^2 + \tfrac{9}{2}.$$

EXAMPLE 1. Find the equation of the curve $y = f(x)$ which passes through the point $(-1, 4)$ and is such that the slope of its tangent at (x, y) is $2x^3$.

Solution. We are given that

$$\frac{dy}{dx} = f'(x) = 2x^3, \qquad \text{and} \qquad y = 4 \text{ when } x = -1.$$

Integrating, we obtain

$$y = f(x) = \tfrac{1}{2}x^4 + C.$$

Also,

$$4 = \tfrac{1}{2}(-1)^4 + C, \qquad C = \tfrac{7}{2}.$$

The equation is therefore

$$y = \tfrac{1}{2}x^4 + \tfrac{7}{2}.$$

EXAMPLE 2. Find the equation of the curve $y = f(x)$ which passes through the point $(2, 5)$ and is such that the slope of its tangent at (x, y) is $(x - 1)/y$.

Solution. We have

$$\frac{dy}{dx} = \frac{x - 1}{y}, \qquad \text{and } y = 5 \text{ when } x = 2.$$

To integrate this differential equation, we "separate variables" and get

$$y \, dy = (x - 1) \, dx, \qquad \text{or} \qquad \tfrac{1}{2}y^2 = \tfrac{1}{2}x^2 - x + C.$$

To determine C, we note that $\frac{25}{2} = 2 - 2 + C$, and so

$$y^2 = x^2 - 2x + 25, \qquad \text{or} \quad y = \sqrt{x^2 - 2x + 25},$$

since $y = +5$ when $x = 2$.

EXAMPLE 3. Find the family of curves represented by the differential equation

$$\frac{dy}{dx} = \frac{\cot y}{x}.$$

Solution. We separate variables and obtain

$$\tan y \, dy = \frac{dx}{x}.$$

Integrating, we find that
$$-\ln \cos y = \ln x + C,$$

which we may state in the alternate form (writing $-C = \ln C_1$) as

$$\ln (x \cos y) = \ln C_1,$$

and finally

$$x \cos y = C_1.$$

EXERCISES

In problems 1 through 8, find the equation of the family of curves which satisfies the given differential equation. Locate the particular member of the family which satisfies the given conditions.

1. $dy/dx = 1/x^2$, $y = 3$ when $x = 2$ 2. $dy/dx = 1/x$, $y = 2$ when $x = 1$
3. $dy/dx = 1/\sqrt{4 - x^2}$, $y = 3$ when $x = -1$
4. $dy/dx = \frac{1}{2}y$, $y = 2$ when $x = 1$ 5. $dy/dx = x/y$, $y = -5$ when $x = 4$
6. $dy/dx = y/x$, $y = 2$ when $x = 2$ 7. $dy/dx = 2y^2$, $y = 1$ when $x = 2$

8. $\dfrac{dy}{dx} = \dfrac{x^2 - 2x + 3}{y^2 + 4y - 1}$, $y = -1$ when $x = 2$

In problems 9 through 11, in each case find, in the form $y = f(x)$, the equation of the curve which satisfies the given conditions.

9. $d^2y/dx^2 = 6x - 2$, $y = 3$ and $dy/dx = -2$ when $x = -1$
10. $d^2y/dx^2 = \sec^2 x$, $y = 2$ and $dy/dx = 1$ when $x = 1$
11. $(dy/dx) \cdot (d^2y/dx^2) = 2x^3$, $y = 3$ and $dy/dx = 1$ when $x = 1$. *Hint:* Find

$$\frac{d}{dx}\left[\left(\frac{dy}{dx}\right)^2\right].$$

3. VOLUMES OF SOLIDS OF REVOLUTION. DISC METHOD

In Chapter 8 we developed a method for measuring the area of plane regions. The theory rested on two ideas: (1) the formula for the area of a rectangle, and (2) a method of approximating any region by a combination of rectangular regions.

FIGURE 16–2   FIGURE 16–3

(a)   (b)

FIGURE 16–4

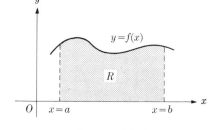

FIGURE 16–5   FIGURE 16–6

It is possible to extend the above process to the measurement of volumes of solids. First, the formula for the volume of a rectangular parallelepiped is length times width times height; next we must find a method for approximating a solid by a combination of rectangular parallelepipeds. (Details of such a procedure are given in Morrey, *University Calculus*, p. 404 ff.)

Let R be a region in the xy-plane (Fig. 16–2), and L a line which does not intersect it (although L may touch the boundary of R). If the region R is revolved about the line L, a solid results which is called a *solid of revolution*. If the region R is a circle, the resulting solid will have the shape of a doughnut (called a *torus*), as seen in Fig. 16–3. A semicircle revolved about its diameter, as shown in Fig. 16–4(a), generates a sphere. A rectangle revolved about one of the edges, as in Fig. 16–4(b), yields a right circular cylinder.

General methods for obtaining the volume of a solid by integration will be developed in the second volume of this text. In this section we shall discuss a method for obtaining the volume of a solid of revolution by the techniques of integration we have already studied. The basis of this method depends on two assumptions. The first is that a right circular cylinder (Fig. 16–5) with radius of base a and altitude h has a volume V given by the formula $V = \pi a^2 h$. The second assumption is that any solid of revolution may be approximated by a combination of right circular cylinders.

Let R be a region in the plane bounded by the curve $y = f(x)$, the lines $x = a$ and $x = b$, and the x-axis, as shown in Fig. 16–6. The following theorem gives the formula for finding the volume of the solid obtained by revolving the region R about the x-axis.

Theorem 1 (Disc Method). *Assume that $f(x) \geq 0$ for $a \leq x \leq b$. Then the solid S obtained by revolving the region*

$$R : a \leq x \leq b, \qquad 0 \leq y \leq f(x),$$

Rectangles $\{r_i\}$

FIGURE 16–7

Rectangles $\{R_i\}$

FIGURE 16–8

about the x-axis has a volume V given by the formula

$$V = \pi \int_a^b [f(x)]^2 \, dx.$$

Proof. Let $\{a = x_0 < x_1 < x_2 < \cdots < x_{n-1} < x_n = b\}$ be any subdivision of the interval $[a, b]$. For each i, let ξ_i and η_i be the values of x where f takes on its minimum and maximum values on the ith interval, $[x_{i-1}, x_i]$, respectively. Denote by r_i and R_i the rectangles

$$r_i : x_{i-1} \leq x \leq x_i, \qquad 0 \leq y \leq f(\xi_i);$$

$$R_i : x_{i-1} \leq x \leq x_i, \qquad 0 \leq y \leq f(\eta_i).$$

Figure 16–7 shows some of the smaller rectangles and Fig. 16–8 some of the larger ones. When the rectangle r_i is revolved about the x-axis, a right circular cylinder is obtained which we denote by s_i. Similarly, revolving R_i yields a cylinder which we denote by S_i. The volumes of these cylinders are designated $V(s_i)$ and $V(S_i)$, respectively. (Figure 16–9 shows one quarter of the desired solid.) We have

$$V(s_1) + V(s_2) + \cdots + V(s_n) \leq V \leq V(S_1) + V(S_2) + \cdots + V(S_n).$$

From the formula for the volume of a right circular cylinder, we obtain

$$\pi[f(\xi_1)]^2 \Delta_1 x + \pi[f(\xi_2)]^2 \Delta_2 x + \cdots$$
$$+ \pi[f(\xi_n)]^2 \Delta_n x \leq V \leq \pi[f(\eta_1)]^2 \Delta_1 x + \cdots + \pi[f(\eta_n)]^2 \Delta_n x,$$

where we recall that $\Delta_i x = x_i - x_{i-1}$. From the properties of integrals as described in Chapter 8, Section 3, we can conclude that the left and right sides of the above inequalities tend to

$$\pi \int_a^b [f(x)]^2 \, dx$$

as the norm of the subdivision, $\|\Delta\|$, tends to zero.*

---

*A precise definition of volume would require a discussion analogous to the one for area. An *inner volume* V^- and an *outer volume* V^+ may be obtained in a way similar to the way in which inner and outer area were obtained. Then we must show that for regions of the type we shall consider here, we have $V^- = V^+$, and this common value, called the *volume*, is given by the integral.

FIGURE 16–9

FIGURE 16–10

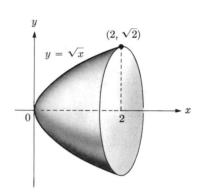

FIGURE 16–11

EXAMPLE 1. Find the volume of the solid generated by revolving the region bounded by the x-axis and one arch of the curve $y = \sin x$ about the x-axis.

Solution. Figure 16–10 shows the region to be revolved. According to the formula in Theorem 1, we have

$$V = \pi \int_0^\pi \sin^2 x \, dx = \frac{\pi}{2} \int_0^\pi (1 - \cos 2x) \, dx = \frac{\pi}{2} \left[x - \tfrac{1}{2} \sin 2x \right]_0^\pi = \frac{\pi^2}{2} \, .$$

EXAMPLE 2. The region bounded by the curve $y = \sqrt{x}$, the x-axis, and the line $x = 2$ is revolved about the x-axis. Find the volume of the solid generated.

Solution. Figure 16–11 is a sketch of the solid of revolution. We have

$$V = \pi \int_0^2 (\sqrt{x})^2 \, dx = \frac{\pi}{2} \left[x^2 \right]_0^2 = 2\pi,$$

and the solid is called a *paraboloid.*

EXAMPLE 3. The region bounded by the line $y = \tfrac{1}{2}x$, the line $x = 3$, and the x-axis is revolved about the x-axis. Find the volume of the solid generated.

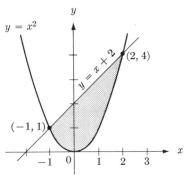

FIGURE 16–12   FIGURE 16–13

Solution. The solid is a right circular cone, as shown in Fig. 16–12. We have

$$V = \pi \int_0^3 (\tfrac{1}{2}x)^2 \, dx = \frac{\pi}{12} [x^3]_0^3 = \tfrac{9}{4}\pi.$$

EXAMPLE 4. The region bounded by the line $y = x + 2$ and the parabola $y = x^2$ is revolved about the x-axis. Find the volume V of the solid S generated (Fig. 16–13).

Solution. We first find the volume V_1 of the solid S_1 generated by revolving the region R_1,

$$R_1 : -1 \le x \le 2, \qquad 0 \le y \le x^2,$$

about the x-axis. Then we subtract it from the volume V_2 of the solid S_2 generated by revolving the region R_2,

$$R_2 : -1 \le x \le 2, \qquad 0 \le y \le x + 2,$$

about the x-axis. We have

$$V = V_2 - V_1 = \pi \int_{-1}^2 (x + 2)^2 \, dx - \pi \int_{-1}^2 x^4 \, dx$$

$$= \pi[\tfrac{1}{3}(x + 2)^3 - \tfrac{1}{5}x^5]_{-1}^2 = \pi[(\tfrac{64}{3} - \tfrac{32}{5}) - (\tfrac{1}{3} + \tfrac{1}{5})] = \tfrac{72}{5}\pi.$$

EXERCISES

In problems 1 through 24, find the volumes of the solids S generated by revolving the described regions R about the x-axis. Draw R and sketch S in each case.

1. R is bounded by $y = 2\sqrt{5x}$, $x = 4$, and the x-axis.
2. R is bounded by $y = 2\sqrt{ax}$, $x = b$, $y = 0$.
3. R is bounded by the x-axis, the y-axis, and the line $2x + 3y = 1$.
4. R is bounded by the x-axis, the y-axis, and the line $(x/h) + (y/r) = 1$. Note that the solid generated is a right circular cone of altitude h and radius of base r.
5. R is bounded by the semicircle $y = \sqrt{a^2 - x^2}$ and the x-axis   (Formula for volume of a sphere of radius a.)

6. R is bounded by $x = a - h$, $x = a$, $y = 0$, $y = \sqrt{a^2 - x^2}$.

7. R is bounded by $y = 0$ and $y = 4 - x^2$.

8. R is bounded by $y = 0$, $y = 2$, $x = 0$, $x = 4 - y^2$.

9. R is bounded by $x = \pi/3$, $y = 0$, $y = \tan x$.

10. R is bounded by $y = x/\sqrt{4 - x}$, $y = 0$, $x = 3$.

11. R is bounded by $y = 0$, $y = \ln x$, $x = 2$.

12. R is bounded by $y = xe^x$, $y = 0$, $x = 1$.

13. R is bounded by $y = 2$, $x = 0$, $x = y^2$.

14. R is bounded by $y = 1$, $y = x$, $xy = 4$.

15. R is bounded by $y = 0$, $y = 2$, $x = 0$, $x = \sqrt{y^2 + 4}$.

16. R is bounded by $x = 0$, and $x + y^2 - 4y = 0$.

17. R is bounded below by $y = 0$ and above by the curves $x = y^2$ and $x = 8 - y^2$.

18. R is bounded by $y = x^2$ and $y^2 = x$.

19. R is bounded by $y = \sqrt{x}$ and $y = x^3$.

20. R is bounded by $x + y = 5$, $xy = 4$.

21. R is bounded by $x = -2$, $x = 2$, $y = 0$, $y = \cosh x$.

22. R is bounded by $x = -b$, $x = b$, $y = 0$, $y = a \cosh (x/a)$.

23. R is bounded by $y = x + 2$ and $y^2 - 3y = 2x$.

24. R is the region to the right of $y = 3x$ and is bounded by $y = 3x$, $y = x^2$, $y = 1$, and $y = 2$.

25. Find the volume of the solid generated by revolving about the x-axis the area bounded by $y = 0$ and one arch of the cycloid $x = a(\theta - \sin \theta)$, $y = a(1 - \cos \theta)$. [*Hint:* $dx = a(1 - \cos \theta)\, d\theta$.]

26. Find the volume of the torus generated by revolving about the x-axis the circle $x^2 + (y - 5)^2 = 16$.

27. Find the volume of the torus generated by revolving about the x-axis the circle $x^2 + (y - b)^2 = a^2$, $b > a > 0$.

4. VOLUMES OF SOLIDS OF REVOLUTION.   SHELL METHOD

A *cylindrical shell* is the solid contained between two concentric cylinders, as in Fig. 16–14.   The volume V of a cylindrical shell with inner radius r_1, outer radius r_2, and height h is

$$V = \pi r_2^2 h - \pi r_1^2 h.$$

We may write the above formula in the form

$$V = \pi(r_2 + r_1)(r_2 - r_1)h = 2\pi \left(\frac{r_2 + r_1}{2} \right) (r_2 - r_1)h.$$

If we define $\bar{r}$ and Δr by the relations

$$\bar{r} = \frac{r_2 + r_1}{2}, \qquad \Delta r = r_2 - r_1,$$

the formula for a cylindrical shell becomes

$$V = 2\pi \bar{r} h\, \Delta r.$$

(a)   (b)

FIGURE 16–14

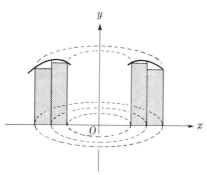

FIGURE 16–15

We note that $2\pi\bar{r}$ is the length of the circumference of a circle of *average* radius, while Δr is the thickness of the shell.

A solid of revolution may be approximated by a combination of cylindrical shells. To see this, let us suppose that a region R of the type we have been considering is revolved about the y-axis, as in Fig. 16–15. We make a subdivision of the x-axis:

$$\{a = x_0 < x_1 < \cdots < x_n = b\}.$$

Let $f(\xi_i)$ and $f(\eta_i)$ be the minimum and maximum values, respectively, of f in the interval $[x_{i-1}, x_i]$. As we did in the disc method, we form the rectangles

$$q_i : x_{i-1} \le x \le x_i, \quad 0 \le y \le f(\xi_i);$$

and

$$Q_i : x_{i-1} \le x \le x_i, \quad 0 \le y \le f(\eta_i).$$

Since the region R is revolved about the y-axis, the rectangles q_i and Q_i will generate cylindrical shells t_i and T_i. We have

$$V(t_i) = 2\pi \left(\frac{x_i + x_{i-1}}{2}\right) \Delta_i x f(\xi_i), \qquad V(T_i) = 2\pi \left(\frac{x_i + x_{i-1}}{2}\right) \Delta_i x f(\eta_i).$$

The volume V of the solid will be between the quantities

$$\sum_{i=1}^{n} V(t_i) \qquad \text{and} \qquad \sum_{i=1}^{n} V(T_i).$$

We thus obtain

$$\sum_{i=1}^{n} V(t_i) = 2\pi \sum_{i=1}^{n} \bar{x}_i f(\xi_i) \Delta_i x \leq V \leq \sum_{i=1}^{n} \bar{x}_i f(\eta_i) \Delta_i x = \sum_{i=1}^{n} V(T_i),$$

where $\bar{x}_i = \frac{1}{2}(x_i + x_{i-1})$. As the norm of the subdivision, $\|\Delta\|$, tends to zero, we get

$$V = 2\pi \int_a^b x f(x)\, dx.$$

When a region formed by the lines $y = c$, $y = d$, $x = g(y)$, $(g(y) \geq 0)$, and $x = 0$ is revolved about the x-axis, the volume V of the resulting solid is given by the formula

$$V = 2\pi \int_c^d y g(y)\, dy.$$

_____

EXAMPLE 1. The region bounded by $y = x^2$ and the lines $y = 0$ and $x = 3$ is revolved about the y-axis. Find the volume of the solid generated.

Solution. Figure 16–16 shows the situation. According to the shell method we have

$$V = 2\pi \int_0^3 x \cdot x^2\, dx = \frac{2\pi}{4} [x^4]_0^3 = \frac{81\pi}{2}.$$

EXAMPLE 2. The region bounded by the positive x-axis, the y-axis, and the curve $y = \sqrt{a^2 - x^2}$ is revolved about the y-axis. Find the volume of the solid generated.

Solution. The solid generated is a hemisphere, as shown in Fig. 16–17. Applying the method of shells, we have

$$V = 2\pi \int_0^a x\sqrt{a^2 - x^2}\, dx.$$

To integrate the above expression, we let $u = a^2 - x^2$, $du = -2x\, dx$ and obtain

$$V = -\frac{2\pi}{2} \int_{a^2}^0 \sqrt{u}\, du = -\pi[\tfrac{2}{3}u^{3/2}]_{a^2}^0 = \tfrac{2}{3}\pi a^3.$$

EXAMPLE 3. The region R, bounded by the x-axis, the y-axis, the line $y = 2$, and the parabola

$$y^2 = 12 - 4x,$$

is revolved about the x-axis. Find the volume of the solid generated.

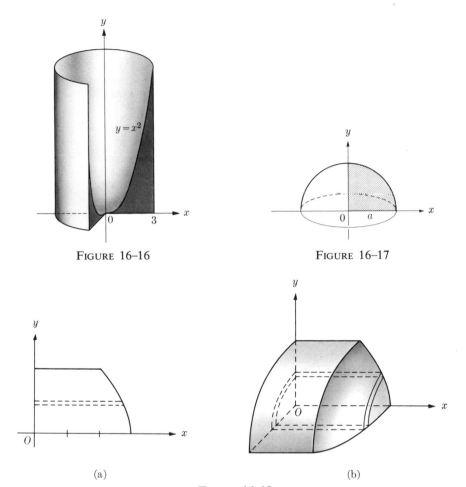

FIGURE 16–16   FIGURE 16–17

(a)   (b)

FIGURE 16–18

Solution. The region R is shown in Fig. 16–18(a), and one quarter of the solid generated is illustrated in Fig. 16–18(b). We apply the shell method, which leads to an integration along the y-axis. We have $g(y) = 3 - \frac{1}{4}y^2$, and therefore

$$V = 2\pi \int_0^2 y(3 - \tfrac{1}{4}y^2)\, dy = 2\pi\left[\tfrac{3}{2}y^2 - \tfrac{1}{16}y^4\right]_0^2 = 10\pi.$$

EXERCISES

In problems 1 through 11, the region R is revolved about the given axis. Use the method of shells to find the volume of the solid generated.

1. R is bounded by $y = \sqrt{x}$, $x = 0$, and $y = 2$; R is revolved about the y-axis.
2. R is bounded by $y = x^3$, $y = 0$, and $x = 1$; R is revolved about the y-axis.

3. R is the same as in problem 2, but the region is revolved about the x-axis.

4. R is bounded by $y = 0$, $y = \ln x$, $x = 2$; R is revolved about the y-axis.

5. R is the same as in problem 4, but the region is revolved about the x-axis.

6. R is bounded by the x-axis, the y-axis, the line $y = 2$, and the curve $x = \sqrt{y^2 + 4}$; R is revolved about the y-axis.

7. R is bounded by $y = 0$ and one arch of $y = \sin x$; R is revolved about the y-axis.

8. R is bounded by $y = 0$, $x = 3$, $y = x/\sqrt{4 - x}$; R is revolved about the y-axis.

9. R is bounded below by $y = 0$ and above by the curves $x = y^2$ and $x = 8 - y^2$; R is revolved about the y-axis.

10. R is bounded by $x = 0$ and $x + y^2 - 4y = 0$; R is revolved about the y-axis.

11. R is bounded by $y = \sqrt{x}$ and $y = x^3$; R is revolved about the y-axis.

12. A cylindrical hole of radius a and axis the y-axis is bored through a sphere of radius $b > a$ with center at the origin. Find the volume remaining.

13. The region R bounded by the x-axis, the y-axis, and the line $x + y = 1$ is revolved about the line $y = -1$. Find the volume of the solid generated.

14. The region R bounded by $y = 0$ and $y = 4 - x^2$ is revolved about the line $y = -1$. Find the volume of the solid generated.

15. Find the volume of the solid generated when the region of problem 14 is revolved about the line $x = -2$.

16. Find the volume of the solid generated when the region R, bounded by $y = 0$ and the arch of $y = \sin x$ between 0 and π, is revolved about the line $y = -1$.

17. Find the volume of the solid generated when the region R of problem 16 is revolved about the line $x = -1$.

5. IMPROPER INTEGRALS

The integral of e^{-x} in the interval $[0, a]$ is easily obtained. We have

$$\int_0^a e^{-x}\, dx = -e^{-x}\big]_0^a = -e^{-a} + 1.$$

The quantity e^{-a} tends to zero as a tends to infinity (Fig. 16–19). Letting a tend to infinity in the above equation, we obtain

$$\lim_{a \to \infty} \int_0^a e^{-x}\, dx = \lim_{a \to \infty} (-e^{-a} + 1) = 1.$$

FIGURE 16–19

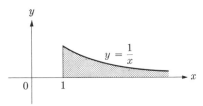

FIGURE 16–20

In other words, the area of the shaded region in Fig. 16–19 tends to the value 1 as a tends to infinity. It is natural to define

$$\int_0^\infty e^{-x}\, dx = \lim_{a \to \infty} \int_0^a e^{-x}\, dx$$

and assign the value 1 to the area of the region under the curve $y = e^{-x}$ situated to the right of the y-axis.

As a second illustration, we shall consider the integral

$$\int_1^a \frac{1}{x}\, dx = [\ln x]_1^a = \ln a.$$

Since $\lim_{a \to \infty} [\ln a]$ does not exist, we see that

$$\lim_{a \to \infty} \int_1^a \frac{1}{x}\, dx \qquad \text{does not exist.}$$

There is no way of assigning a value to the shaded region under the curve in Fig. 16–20. We say that $\int_1^\infty (1/x)\, dx$ does not exist.

DEFINITIONS. Suppose that f is continuous for all $x \geq x_0$. If

$$\lim_{a \to \infty} \int_{x_0}^a f(x)\, dx$$

exists, we say that

$$\int_{x_0}^\infty f(x)\, dx$$

is *convergent* to the value given by the above limit. If the limit does not exist, we say that $\int_{x_0}^\infty f(x)\, dx$ is *divergent*, and the integral is not defined.

EXAMPLE 1.   Determine whether the following integral is convergent or divergent, and if it is convergent, determine its value:

$$\int_0^\infty \frac{dx}{1 + x^2}.$$

Solution.

$$\int_0^a \frac{dx}{1 + x^2} = \arctan a, \qquad \lim_{a \to \infty} (\arctan a) = \frac{\pi}{2},$$

and therefore

$$\int_0^\infty \frac{dx}{1 + x^2} = \frac{\pi}{2}.$$

EXAMPLE 2. Determine whether the following integral is convergent or divergent; if it is convergent, determine its value:

$$\int_0^\infty \frac{x^2}{1 + x^2}\, dx.$$

Solution. By division, we have

$$\int_0^a \frac{x^2}{1 + x^2}\, dx = \int_0^a \left(1 - \frac{1}{1 + x^2}\right) dx = [x - \arctan x]_0^a = a - \arctan a.$$

Therefore

$$\lim_{a \to \infty} \int_0^a \frac{x^2}{1 + x^2}\, dx = \lim_{a \to \infty} [a - \arctan a].$$

The limit on the right does not exist and the integral is divergent.

––––––––––

The above definitions and examples extend the notion of integral to unbounded intervals. The functions being integrated in these cases were continuous throughout. It may happen, however, that we wish to integrate a function which is not bounded within the interval of integration. For example, the integral

$$\int_1^3 \frac{1}{\sqrt{x - 1}}\, dx$$

is not defined, since the function $f(x) = 1/\sqrt{x - 1}$ tends to infinity as $x \to 1$. The interval of integration is finite, but the function being integrated is not continuous in $[1, 3]$, and in fact is unbounded there. The expression

$$\int_a^3 \frac{1}{\sqrt{x - 1}}\, dx$$

is defined for every $a > 1$, and we have

$$\int_a^3 \frac{1}{\sqrt{x - 1}}\, dx = 2\sqrt{x - 1}\,]_a^3 = 2\sqrt{2} - 2\sqrt{a - 1}, \qquad a > 1.$$

Furthermore,

$$\lim_{a \to 1} \int_a^3 \frac{1}{\sqrt{x - 1}}\, dx = \lim_{a \to 1} [2\sqrt{2} - 2\sqrt{a - 1}\,] = 2\sqrt{2}.$$

We assign the value $2\sqrt{2}$ to the area of the shaded region in Fig. 16–21.

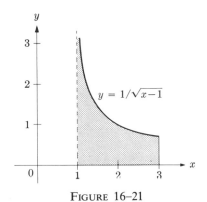

FIGURE 16–21

DEFINITIONS. Suppose that $f(x)$ is continuous for $a < x \leq b$ but is not continuous at a. Then $\int_a^b f(x)\, dx$ is *convergent* if

$$\lim_{\epsilon \to 0} \int_{a+\epsilon}^b f(x)\, dx$$

exists, where ϵ approaches zero through positive values. The *value* of $\int_a^b f(x)\, dx$ is the value of the limit. If the limit does not exist, the integral is said to be *divergent*. A similar definition is given for the case in which $f(x)$ is continuous for $a \leq x < b$ but not at b.

EXAMPLE 3. Determine whether

$$\int_0^1 \frac{dx}{1 - x}$$

is convergent and, if so, find its value.

Solution. $f(x) = 1/(1 - x)$ and tends to infinity as $x \to 1$. We write

$$\int_0^{1-\epsilon} \frac{dx}{1 - x}$$

and let $u = 1 - x$. Then $du = -dx$ and

$$\int_0^{1-\epsilon} \frac{dx}{1 - x} = -\int_1^\epsilon \frac{du}{u} = -\ln u \big]_1^\epsilon = -\ln \epsilon.$$

However, $-\ln \epsilon \to \infty$ as $\epsilon \to 0$, and the integral is divergent.

EXAMPLE 4. Determine whether

$$\int_0^3 \frac{dx}{(3 - x)^{2/3}}$$

is convergent and, if so, find its value.

Solution. $f(x) = (3 - x)^{-2/3}$ and tends to infinity as $x \to 3$. Letting $u = 3 - x$, $du = -dx$, we have

$$\int_0^{3-\epsilon} \frac{dx}{(3 - x)^{2/3}} = -\int_3^\epsilon \frac{du}{u^{2/3}} = -3[u^{1/3}]_3^\epsilon = 3\sqrt[3]{3} - 3\sqrt[3]{\epsilon}.$$

As ϵ tends to zero, we obtain

$$\int_0^3 \frac{dx}{(3 - x)^{2/3}} = 3\sqrt[3]{3}.$$

It may happen that the integrand $f(x)$ is unbounded somewhere in the interior of the interval of integration. In such cases, the next definition is employed.

DEFINITION. Suppose that $f(x)$ is continuous for $a \le x \le b$, except for $x = c$, where $a < c < b$. Then we say that $\int_a^b f(x)\, dx$ is *convergent* if *both* of the integrals $\int_a^c f(x)\, dx$ and $\int_c^b f(x)\, dx$ are convergent. We define

$$\int_a^b f(x)\, dx = \int_a^c f(x)\, dx + \int_c^b f(x)\, dx.$$

EXAMPLE 5. Determine whether

$$\int_{-1}^1 \frac{1}{x^2}\, dx$$

is convergent and, if so, find its value.

Solution. $f(x) = 1/x^2$ tends to infinity as $x \to 0$. We consider

$$\int_{-1}^{-\epsilon} \frac{1}{x^2}\, dx \quad \text{and} \quad \int_\epsilon^1 \frac{1}{x^2}\, dx, \qquad \epsilon > 0.$$

The second of these yields, upon integration,

$$\int_\epsilon^1 \frac{1}{x^2}\, dx = \left[-\frac{1}{x} \right]_\epsilon^1 = \frac{1}{\epsilon} - 1.$$

The limit as $\epsilon \to 0$ does not exist, and the integral is divergent.

Remark. If we had not noted that $f(x) = 1/x^2$ tends to infinity as $x \to 0$, and if we had gone blindly ahead with the integration, we would have obtained

$$\int_{-1}^1 \frac{1}{x^2}\, dx = \left[-\frac{1}{x} \right]_{-1}^1 = -1 - \left(-\frac{1}{-1} \right) = -2.$$

This result is obviously erroneous, since $f(x) = 1/x^2$ is positive everywhere and could never yield a negative value for the integral.

EXAMPLE 6.   Determine whether

$$\int_{-2}^{3} x^{-1/3}\, dx$$

is convergent and, if so, find its value.

Solution. $f(x) = (1/x^{1/3}) \to \infty$ as $x \to 0$. Therefore we evaluate

$$\int_{\epsilon}^{3} x^{-1/3}\, dx = \tfrac{3}{2}x^{2/3}\big]_{\epsilon}^{3} = \tfrac{3}{2}\sqrt[3]{9} - \tfrac{3}{2}\sqrt[3]{\epsilon^2}, \qquad \epsilon > 0,$$

getting

$$\int_{0}^{3} x^{-1/3}\, dx = \tfrac{3}{2}\sqrt[3]{9}.$$

Similarly,

$$\int_{-2}^{-\epsilon} x^{-1/3}\, dx = \tfrac{3}{2}x^{2/3}\big]_{-2}^{-\epsilon} = \tfrac{3}{2}\sqrt[3]{\epsilon^2} - \tfrac{3}{2}\sqrt[3]{4}, \qquad \epsilon > 0,$$

and

$$\int_{-2}^{0} x^{-1/3}\, dx = -\tfrac{3}{2}\sqrt[3]{4}.$$

The integral is convergent, and

$$\int_{-2}^{3} x^{-1/3}\, dx = \tfrac{3}{2}(\sqrt[3]{9} - \sqrt[3]{4}).$$

Remarks. The extended integrals defined in this section are called *improper integrals*. Improper integrals may be defined, in more general cases, where f may become infinite at several points in the interval of integration, which may itself be infinite. In such a case, we then divide that interval into smaller intervals of two types: In the first type, the interval is finite and f becomes infinite at one end while, in the second type, f remains continuous but the interval is infinite in one direction only. Then the original improper integral converges if and only if each of the component parts converges. The *value* is the sum of the values of the integrals taken over the smaller intervals.

EXERCISES

In problems 1 through 30, determine whether or not each of the improper integrals is convergent, and compute its value if it is.

1. $\displaystyle\int_{1}^{\infty} \frac{dx}{x^2}$

2. $\displaystyle\int_{1}^{\infty} \frac{dx}{x^3}$

3. $\displaystyle\int_{0}^{\infty} \frac{1}{(x+1)^{3/2}}\, dx$

4. $\displaystyle\int_{1}^{\infty} \frac{1}{x^p}\, dx, \quad p > 1$

5. $\displaystyle\int_{1}^{\infty} \frac{1}{x}\, dx$

6. $\displaystyle\int_{1}^{\infty} \frac{1}{x^p}\, dx, \quad p < 1$

7. $\displaystyle\int_{0}^{1} \frac{1}{x^p}\, dx, \quad p < 1$

8. $\displaystyle\int_{0}^{1} \frac{1}{x}\, dx$

9. $\displaystyle\int_{0}^{1} \frac{1}{x^p}\, dx, \quad p > 1$

10. $\displaystyle\int_0^\infty \frac{dx}{(x^2+1)^2}$

11. $\displaystyle\int_0^1 \frac{dx}{\sqrt{1-x}}$

12. $\displaystyle\int_0^2 \frac{dx}{\sqrt{4-x^2}}$

13. $\displaystyle\int_0^\infty xe^{-x}\,dx$

14. $\displaystyle\int_{-\infty}^0 x^2e^x\,dx$

15. $\displaystyle\int_{-8}^1 x^{-2/3}\,dx$

16. $\displaystyle\int_{-1}^1 x^{-3}\,dx$

17. $\displaystyle\int_{-2}^0 \frac{dx}{\sqrt[3]{x+1}}$

18. $\displaystyle\int_0^\infty \frac{e^{-\sqrt{x}}}{\sqrt{x}}\,dx$

19. $\displaystyle\int_0^\infty xe^{-x^2}\,dx$

20. $\displaystyle\int_0^\infty x^p e^{-x^{p+1}}\,dx,\quad p>0$

21. $\displaystyle\int_0^{\pi/2} \cot\theta\,d\theta$

22. $\displaystyle\int_0^{\pi/4} \frac{\sec^2 x\,dx}{\sqrt{\tan x}}$

23. $\displaystyle\int_0^4 \frac{x\,dx}{\sqrt{16-x^2}}$

24. $\displaystyle\int_0^\infty \frac{dx}{\sqrt{x}\,(x+4)}$

25. $\displaystyle\int_{-1}^1 \sqrt{1+x^{-2/3}}\,dx$

26. $\displaystyle\int_0^4 \frac{(2-x)\,dx}{\sqrt{4x-x^2}}$

27. $\displaystyle\int_0^4 \frac{dx}{\sqrt{4x-x^2}}$

28. $\displaystyle\int_{-4}^\infty \frac{dx}{x\sqrt{x+4}}$

29. $\displaystyle\int_{-\infty}^\infty x^2 e^{-x^3}\,dx$

30. $\displaystyle\int_{-\infty}^\infty x^3 e^{-x^4}\,dx$

In problems 31 through 34, use the substitution $t = \tan\theta/2$, if necessary, to evaluate each integral.

31. $\displaystyle\int_0^\pi \frac{\sin\theta\,d\theta}{\sqrt{1+\cos\theta}}$

32. $\displaystyle\int_0^\pi \frac{d\theta}{5+4\cos\theta}$

33. $\displaystyle\int_0^\pi \frac{d\theta}{2-\sin\theta}$

34. $\displaystyle\int_0^\pi \frac{\cos\theta\,d\theta}{5+4\cos\theta}$

35. The region bounded by $f(x) = 1/x$, the x-axis, and the line $x = 1$, and situated to the right of $x = 1$, is revolved about the x-axis. Evaluate the improper integral and assign a value to the volume of the solid generated. Note that the plane region does not have a finite area.

36. Rework problem 35, with $f(x) = 1/x^p$, $p > 0$. For what values of p does the solid have a finite value?

6. ARC LENGTH

In Chapter 12, Section 3, the length of an arc was defined, and formulas for computing such lengths were obtained. When an arc C is given in the parametric form

$$x = x(t), \qquad y = y(t), \qquad a \leq t \leq b,$$

with $x'(t)$ and $y'(t)$ continuous functions, then the length of C is given by the formula

$$l(C) = \int_a^b \sqrt{[x'(t)]^2 + [y'(t)]^2}\, dt.$$

If the curve is given in either of the nonparametric forms $y = f(x)$ or $x = g(y)$, the formula is

$$l = \int \sqrt{1 + (dy/dx)^2}\, dx \quad \text{or} \quad l = \int \sqrt{1 + (dx/dy)^2}\, dy.$$

In Chapter 13, Section 5, we derived the formula for arc length when the equation of the arc is given in polar coordinates. We found that if the equation is of the form

$$r = f(\theta), \quad a \le \theta \le b,$$

then

$$l = \int_a^b \sqrt{[f(\theta)]^2 + [f'(\theta)]^2}\, d\theta.$$

By employing the powerful methods of integration which we learned in Chapter 15, we are now able to integrate many types of expressions which were beyond our grasp when we first studied arc length. Furthermore, some of the most interesting integrals for arc length lead to improper integrals. The following examples show how arc lengths may be obtained by evaluation of improper and difficult integrals.

———————

EXAMPLE 1. Find the length of the semicircle

$$C : y = \sqrt{a^2 - x^2}, \quad -a \le x \le a.$$

Solution. We have

$$\frac{dy}{dx} = -\frac{x}{\sqrt{a^2 - x^2}}, \quad 1 + \left(\frac{dy}{dx}\right)^2 = \frac{a^2}{a^2 - x^2},$$

and

$$l(C) = a \int_{-a}^{a} \frac{dx}{\sqrt{a^2 - x^2}}.$$

The integrand becomes infinite at $-a$ and at a. We decompose it into two parts, obtaining

$$l(C) = a \int_{-a}^{0} \frac{dx}{\sqrt{a^2 - x^2}} + a \int_{0}^{a} \frac{dx}{\sqrt{a^2 - x^2}}.$$

Evaluating each improper integral, we get

$$a \int_{-a+\epsilon}^{0} \frac{dx}{\sqrt{a^2 - x^2}} = a \left[\arcsin \frac{x}{a} \right]_{-a+\epsilon}^{0} = a \left[0 - \arcsin \left(\frac{-a + \epsilon}{a} \right) \right].$$

This integral tends to $a[0 - (-\pi/2)]$ as $\epsilon \to 0$. Similarly, we have

$$a \int_0^{a-\epsilon} \frac{dx}{\sqrt{a^2 - x^2}} = a \left[\arcsin \frac{x}{a} \right]_0^{a-\epsilon} \to a \cdot \arcsin 1 = \frac{\pi a}{2}.$$

Therefore $l(C) = \pi a$, a familiar result.

EXAMPLE 2. Find $l(C)$, given that

$$x = t, \qquad y = \ln t, \qquad 0 \le t \le 1.$$

Solution. We have $x'^2 = 1$, $y'^2 = 1/t^2$ and

$$l(C) = \int_0^1 \sqrt{1 + 1/t^2} \, dt = \int_0^1 \sqrt{1 + t^2}/t \, dt,$$

which is an improper integral. To evaluate it we first make the substitution $t = \tan \theta$, $dt = \sec^2 \theta \, d\theta$. We obtain

$$l(C) = \int_0^{\pi/4} \frac{\sec \theta \cdot \sec^2 \theta \, d\theta}{\tan \theta} = \int_0^{\pi/4} \frac{\cos^2 \theta}{\sin \theta} \, d\theta.$$

We now integrate between the limits ϵ and $\pi/4$, and find that

$$\int_\epsilon^{\pi/4} [\csc \theta - \sin \theta] \, d\theta = \left[\ln|\csc \theta - \cot \theta| - \cos \theta \right]_\epsilon^{\pi/4}.$$

Since

$$\csc \epsilon - \cot \epsilon = \frac{1 - \cos \epsilon}{\sin \epsilon} \to 0 \quad \text{as} \quad \epsilon \to 0,$$

the integral diverges and the length of arc is not finite.

EXAMPLE 3. Find $l(C)$, if C is the arc

$$l(C) : r = \theta, \qquad 0 \le \theta \le 2\pi.$$

Solution. $f(\theta) = \theta$ and $[f(\theta)]^2 + [f'(\theta)]^2 = \theta^2 + 1$. Therefore

$$l(C) = \int_0^{2\pi} \sqrt{1 + \theta^2} \, d\theta.$$

To evaluate this integral, set

$$\theta = \sinh u, \quad d\theta = \cosh u \, du;$$

then

$$l(C) = \int_0^b \cosh^2 u \, du = \tfrac{1}{2} \int_0^b (1 + \cosh 2u) \, du$$

$$= \tfrac{1}{2}(b + \sinh b \cosh b) = \tfrac{1}{2}(\operatorname{argsinh} 2\pi + 2\pi\sqrt{1 + 4\pi^2}),$$

where $b = \operatorname{argsinh} 2\pi$.

EXERCISES

Find $l(C)$ in each of the following problems. Note any improper integrals.

1. $y = x^2, 0 \leq x \leq 1$ 2. $y = a \cosh(x/a), 0 \leq x \leq b$

3. $x = (a^{2/3} - y^{2/3})^{3/2}, -a \leq y \leq a$ 4. $y = \ln \sec x, 0 \leq x \leq \pi/3$

5. $x = \ln \sin y, \pi/4 \leq y \leq 3\pi/4$ 6. $x = \frac{1}{3}(y - 3)\sqrt{y}, 0 \leq y \leq 3$

7. $y = x^{2/3}, -8 \leq x \leq 1$ 8. $x = \frac{1}{3}t^3, y = \frac{1}{2}t^2, 1 \leq t \leq 3$

9. $x = \frac{1}{2}t^2, y = \frac{1}{4}t^4, 1 \leq t \leq 2$ 10. $r = 2(1 - \cos \theta), 0 \leq \theta \leq 2\pi$

11. $r = 2(1 + \cos \theta), 0 \leq \theta \leq \pi$ 12. $r = 2(1 + \cos \theta), 0 \leq \theta \leq 2\pi$

13. $r = 2 \sec \theta, -\pi/4 \leq \theta \leq \pi/4$ 14. $x = u \cos u, y = u \sin u, 0 \leq u \leq \pi$

15. $y = \sqrt{x}, 0 \leq x \leq 1$ 16. $x = \cos^3 t, y = \sin^3 t, 0 \leq t \leq \pi/3$

17. $y = \sin^{-1}(e^{-x}), 0 \leq x \leq \ln \sqrt{3}$

7. AREA OF A SURFACE OF REVOLUTION

When an arc situated above the x-axis in the xy-plane is revolved about the x-axis, a *surface of revolution* is generated. We shall define the area of such a surface and show how to calculate it by integration. In defining the area of a plane region, we saw that the fundamental quantity is the area of a rectangle. For the volume of a solid of revolution, the fundamental quantity is the volume of a right circular cylinder. *For determining the area of a surface of revolution, the fundamental quantity is the lateral area of the frustum of a cone.*

The lateral surface area S of a right circular cone with radius of base r and slant height l, as in Fig. 16–22(a), is given by the formula

$$S = \pi rl,$$

which may be seen intuitively by cutting the cone along a generator, l, and flattening the surface onto a plane. The result is a circular sector, as shown in Fig. 16–22(b), whose area is exactly πrl.

A frustum of a cone is shown in Fig. 16–23. The smaller radius is r_1, the larger is r_2, and the slant height is l. The surface area of such a frustum is

$$\pi r_2(l_1 + l) - \pi r_1 l_1.$$

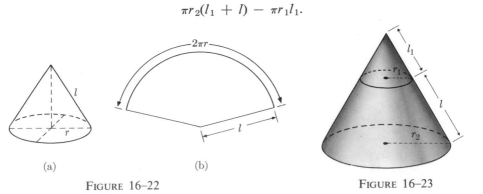

(a)   (b)

FIGURE 16–22   FIGURE 16–23

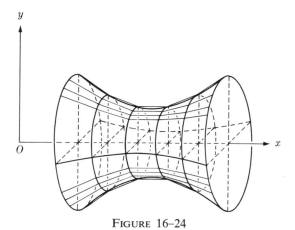

FIGURE 16–24

We use the proportion $l_1/r_1 = l/(r_2 - r_1)$ to eliminate l_1 in the above formula, and obtain, for the *lateral surface area F of a frustum of a cone,*

$$F = \pi(r_1 + r_2)l.$$

We write this formula in the more suggestive form

$$F = 2\pi \bar{r} l,$$

where $\bar{r} = \frac{1}{2}(r_1 + r_2)$ is the average radius.

Suppose that an arc C, situated entirely above the x-axis, is given in the parametric form

$$x = x(t), \qquad y = y(t), \qquad a \leq t \leq b.$$

We revolve C about the x-axis, obtaining a surface of revolution. We let $\{a = t_0 < t_1 < t_2 < \cdots < t_n = b\}$ be a subdivision of $[a, b]$, and we construct the inscribed polygon to C exactly as we did in defining arc length. When this inscribed polygon is revolved about the x-axis, we obtain a collection of frustums of cones, as in Fig. 16–24. The sum of the lateral surface areas of these frustums will be an approximate measure of the (as yet undefined) area of the surface S generated by the arc C. We argue intuitively that the "closer" the inscribed polygon is to the curve C, the more accurate will be the approximation to the surface area.

DEFINITION. Assume that $C : x = x(t), y = y(t), a \leq t \leq b$ is situated in the upper half-plane [that is, $y(t) \geq 0$]. Let $x_i = x(t_i), y_i = y(t_i), i = 0, 1, 2, \ldots, n$; define S as the surface of revolution obtained by revolving C about the x-axis. Then the *area $A(S)$* is defined as the limit approached by the sums

$$\sum_{i=1}^{n} 2\pi \bar{y}_i \sqrt{(x_i - x_{i-1})^2 + (y_i - y_{i-1})^2}, \quad \text{where} \quad \bar{y}_i = \frac{y_i + y_{i-1}}{2},$$

$$l = \sqrt{(x_i - x_{i-1})^2 + (y_i - y_{i-1})^2}$$

$$F = 2\pi \left(\frac{y_i + y_{i-1}}{2} \right) l$$

FIGURE 16–25

as the norms of the subdivisions tend to zero, provided the limit exists. Each term in the above sum is the lateral surface area of the inscribed frustum of a cone (Fig. 16–25).

We now state without proof the formula for evaluating the area $A(S)$. (A proof is given in Morrey, *University Calculus*, p. 422.) *If an arc*

$$C : x = x(t), \qquad y = y(t), \qquad a \leq t \leq b,$$

is in the upper half-plane, then the area $A(S)$ of the surface generated by revolving C about the x-axis is given by the formula

$$A(S) = 2\pi \int_a^b y(t)\sqrt{(dx/dt)^2 + (dy/dt)^2}\, dt.$$

If the arc C is located to the right of the y-axis and is revolved about the y-axis, the area $A(S)$ of the surface generated is given by the formula

$$A(S) = 2\pi \int_a^b x(t)\sqrt{(dx/dt)^2 + (dy/dt)^2}\, dt.$$

The above formulas can be written in a simpler, more useful form. For revolution about the x-axis, we write

$$A(S) = 2\pi \int_a^b y\, ds,$$

while for revolution about the y-axis, we write

$$A(S) = 2\pi \int_a^b x\, ds.$$

Then any particular form for x, y, and ds is usable in these formulas. For example, if C is given in the form $y = f(x)$ and C is revolved about the x-axis, we have

$$ds = \sqrt{1 + [f'(x)]^2}\, dx, \qquad \text{and} \qquad A(S) = 2\pi \int_a^b f(x)\sqrt{1 + [f'(x)]^2}\, dx,$$

while if $y = f(x)$ and C is revolved about the y-axis, we get

$$A(S) = 2\pi \int_a^b x\sqrt{1 + [f'(x)]^2}\, dx.$$

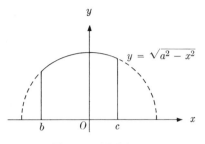

FIGURE 16–26

EXAMPLE 1. Find the surface area of a zone of a sphere obtained by revolving about the x-axis the part of the semicircle

$$y = \sqrt{a^2 - x^2}, \quad b \le x \le c, \quad (\text{where } -a \le b < c \le a).$$

Solution. We draw the graph (Fig. 16–26) and use the formula

$$A = 2\pi \int_b^c y \, ds,$$

with $ds = \sqrt{1 + (dy/dx)^2} \, dx$ and $y = \sqrt{a^2 - x^2}$. We have

$$\frac{dy}{dx} = -\frac{x}{\sqrt{a^2 - x^2}}, \quad \text{and} \quad ds = \frac{a}{\sqrt{a^2 - x^2}} \, dx.$$

Therefore

$$A = 2\pi \int_b^c \sqrt{a^2 - x^2} \cdot \frac{a}{\sqrt{a^2 - x^2}} \, dx = 2\pi a(c - b).$$

EXAMPLE 2. Find the area of the surface generated by revolving about the y-axis the arc $y = x^2, 0 \le x \le 1$.

Solution. We use the formula

$$A = 2\pi \int_0^1 x \, ds,$$

with $ds = \sqrt{1 + (dy/dx)^2} \, dx = \sqrt{1 + 4x^2} \, dx$. Therefore

$$A = 2\pi \int_0^1 x\sqrt{1 + 4x^2} \, dx = \frac{\pi}{6} [(1 + 4x^2)^{3/2}]_0^1 = \frac{\pi}{6} (5\sqrt{5} - 1).$$

EXAMPLE 3. Find the area of the surface generated by revolving about the x-axis the arc $x = t^3, y = \frac{3}{2}t^2, 1 \le t \le 3$.

Solution. We use the formula

$$A = 2\pi \int_1^3 y \, ds,$$

with $ds = \sqrt{(dx/dt)^2 + (dy/dt)^2} \, dt$, and $y = \frac{3}{2}t^2$. Therefore

$$A = 3\pi \int_1^3 t^2\sqrt{9t^4 + 9t^2} \, dt = 9\pi \int_1^3 t^3\sqrt{1 + t^2} \, dt.$$

We make the substitution $u = 1 + t^2$, $du = 2t\,dt$, and obtain

$$A = \frac{9\pi}{2} \int_2^{10} (u - 1)\sqrt{u}\,du = \tfrac{9}{2}\pi[\tfrac{2}{5}u^{5/2} - \tfrac{2}{3}u^{3/2}]_2^{10} = 3\pi(50\sqrt{10} - \tfrac{2}{5}\sqrt{2}).$$

EXERCISES

In problems 1 through 20, find the area of each surface S obtained by revolving about the x-axis the part of the given locus where $y \geq 0$.

1. $y = \tfrac{1}{3}x^3$, $0 \leq x \leq 2$
2. $y = x^3/6 + 1/2x$, $1 \leq x \leq 2$
3. $x = t^2$, $y = 2t$, $1 \leq t \leq 2$
4. $y^2 = 6x$, $0 \leq x \leq 6$
5. $y^2 = 2 - x$, $0 \leq x \leq 2$
6. $18y^2 = x(6 - x)^2$, $0 \leq x \leq 6$
7. $y = x^4/8 + 1/4x^2$, $1 \leq x \leq 2$
8. $y = (x^2/4) - \tfrac{1}{2}\ln x$, $1 \leq x \leq 2$
9. $y = a \cosh(x/a)$, $0 \leq x \leq a$
10. $x = (y^2/4) - \tfrac{1}{2}\ln y$, $1 \leq y \leq 2$
11. $x = (y^3/6) + (1/2y)$, $1 \leq y \leq 2$
12. $y = e^x$, $0 \leq x \leq 1$
13. $x^{2/3} + y^{2/3} = a^{2/3}$
14. $y = \sin x$, $0 \leq x \leq \pi$
15. $y = \tfrac{3}{2}x^{2/3}$, $0 \leq x \leq 1$
16. $r = a(1 - \cos\theta)$
17. $x = a(\theta - \sin\theta)$, $y = a(1 - \cos\theta)$, $0 \leq \theta \leq 2\pi$
18. $r = 4 + 3\cos\theta$
19. $(x^2/a^2) + (y^2/b^2) = 1$
20. $y = e^{-x}$, $0 \leq x < \infty$

In problems 21 through 26, find the area of each surface S generated by revolving about the y-axis the part of the given locus where $x \geq 0$.

21. $x = b + a\cos\phi$, $y = a\sin\phi$, $0 \leq \phi \leq 2\pi$, $b > a > 0$
22. $y = (x^2/4) - \tfrac{1}{2}\ln x$, $1 \leq x \leq 3$
23. $y = (x^3/6) + (1/2x)$, $1 \leq x \leq 2$
24. $y = a\cosh(x/a)$, $0 \leq x \leq a$
25. $y = \tfrac{1}{3}x^3$, $0 \leq x \leq 2$
26. $r = a(1 - \cos\theta)$

8. MEAN VALUE OF A FUNCTION

The *average* of a set of n numbers $y_1, y_2, \ldots, y_n$ is defined by

$$\frac{y_1 + y_2 + y_3 + \cdots + y_n}{n}.$$

The term "mean" of a set of n numbers is synonymous with "average."

DEFINITION.   The *mean value of a function f over the interval* $[a, b]$ is defined by

$$f_m = \frac{1}{b - a} \int_a^b f(x)\,dx.$$

We connect this definition of the mean value of a function with the average (or mean) of a set of numbers in the following way. We divide the interval $[a, b]$

into n *equal* parts, each of length $(b - a)/n$, of course:

$$x_0 = a \quad x_1 \quad x_2 \quad x_3 \quad \cdots \quad x_{n-1} \quad x_n = b.$$

Then we select a point ξ_i in the ith interval $[x_{i-1}, x_i]$ and form the average

$$\frac{f(\xi_1) + f(\xi_2) + \cdots + f(\xi_n)}{n}.$$

Denoting the length of each subinterval $x_i - x_{i-1}$ by Δx, we obtain

$$\frac{1}{n\,\Delta x} \sum_{i=1}^{n} f(\xi_i)\,\Delta x.$$

However, $n\,\Delta x = b - a$ and, from the Fundamental Theorem of Integration, we know that

$$\frac{1}{b-a} \sum_{i=1}^{n} f(\xi_i)\,\Delta x \to \frac{1}{b-a} \int_a^b f(x)\,dx \quad \text{as} \quad n \to \infty.$$

We conclude that the mean value f_m of a function over an interval is the limit of a sequence of averages of the same function.

In Chapter 8, Section 6, we established the Theorem of the Mean for Integrals, which stated that *if f is continuous on a closed interval $[a, b]$ there is a number ξ between a and b such that*

$$\int_a^b f(x)\,dx = f(\xi)(b - a).$$

The ξ of the theorem is such that

$$f(\xi) = f_m.$$

If $f(x) \geq 0$ for $a \leq x \leq b$, then f_m is the altitude of the rectangle which has $[a, b]$ as base and an area equal to that under the curve $y = f(x)$ between $x = a$ and $x = b$ (Fig. 16–27).

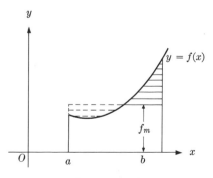

FIGURE 16–27

EXAMPLE 1. Find the mean value of the function $f(x) = x^2$ over the interval $[0, 2]$.

Solution.

$$f_m = \frac{1}{2 - 0} \int_0^2 x^2 \, dx = \left[\frac{x^3}{6}\right]_0^2 = \frac{4}{3}.$$

Often, in certain applications, we want to find the average value of one quantity with respect to another. Suppose the quantities are v and u, respectively, and $v = f(u)$, with u varying steadily from a to b.

DEFINITION. The average of v with respect to u is defined as equal to

$$\frac{1}{b - a} \int_a^b f(u) \, du.$$

As an illustration, let us suppose that v is the velocity of a particle moving along the x-axis according to some law. Then the average velocity of the particle with respect to the time t (*the time average*) between the times t_1 and t_2 is

$$\frac{1}{t_2 - t_1} \int_{t_1}^{t_2} v(t) \, dt = \frac{1}{t_2 - t_1} \int_{t_1}^{t_2} \frac{dx}{dt} \, dt = \frac{x(t_2) - x(t_1)}{t_2 - t_1}.$$

If we wish to obtain the average of v with respect to u, we must evaluate

$$\frac{1}{b - a} \int_a^b v \, du.$$

When both v and u are functions of another variable, say x (that is, if $v = v(x)$ and $u = u(x)$), we may write $u'(x) \, dx$ for du in the above integral. Furthermore, if $u(c) = a$ and $u(d) = b$, then the new limits are inserted and the average for v with respect to u becomes

$$\frac{1}{u(d) - u(c)} \int_c^d v(x)u'(x) \, dx.$$

EXAMPLE 2. Find the average ordinate with respect to the arc length along the semi-circle $y = \sqrt{a^2 - x^2}$.

Solution. We wish to find the average of y with respect to s, where $y = \sqrt{a^2 - x^2}$ and s is the arc length from $x = -a$ to $x = x$ (Fig. 16–28). That is, we seek

$$\frac{1}{\pi a} \int_0^{\pi a} y \, ds,$$

where πa is the length of a semicircle of radius a. Since

$$ds = \sqrt{1 + (dy/dx)^2} \, dx = \frac{a \, dx}{\sqrt{a^2 - x^2}},$$

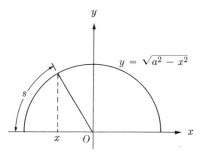

FIGURE 16–28

we have, upon writing $\mathrm{av}_s\, y$ for the average of y with respect to s,

$$\mathrm{av}_s\, y \;=\; \frac{1}{\pi a}\int_{-a}^{a}\sqrt{a^2 - x^2}\ \frac{a\,dx}{\sqrt{a^2 - x^2}} \;=\; \frac{2a^2}{\pi a} \;=\; \frac{2a}{\pi}.$$

EXAMPLE 3. A particle is dropped from a balloon, and the distance s it falls is given by $s = 16t^2$, s in feet and t in seconds. Find the average velocity v with respect to the distance s traveled after the particle has fallen 256 ft. What is the time average of the velocity during this interval?

Solution. The quantity $\mathrm{av}_s\, v$ is given by

$$\frac{1}{256 - 0}\int_{0}^{256} v\,ds.$$

Since $v = 32t$ and $s = 16t^2$, $ds = 32t\,dt$, we have

$$\mathrm{av}_s\, v \;=\; \frac{1}{256}\int_{0}^{4} 32t \cdot 32t\,dt \;=\; \left[\tfrac{4}{3}t^3\right]_0^4 \;=\; \tfrac{256}{3}.$$

The time average of the velocity is

$$\mathrm{av}_t\, v \;=\; \frac{1}{4 - 0}\int_{0}^{4} v\,dt \;=\; \tfrac{1}{4}\int_{0}^{4} 32t\,dt \;=\; 4\left[t^2\right]_0^4 \;=\; 64.$$

EXERCISES

In problems 1 through 10, find the mean value of each given function over the given interval. Draw the graph of $y = f(x)$. Note any improper integrals.

1. $f(x) = x^2 - 2x + 1,\ 0 \le x \le 1$ 2. $f(x) = x\sqrt{a^2 - x^2},\ -a \le x \le a$

3. $f(x) = e^x,\ 0 \le x \le b$ 4. $f(x) = \sqrt{a^2 - x^2},\ -a \le x \le a$

5. $f(x) = \sin x,\ 0 \le x \le \pi$ 6. $f(x) = \sec^2 x,\ 0 \le x \le \pi/4$

7. $f(x) = \ln x,\ 1 \le x \le 3$ 8. $f(x) = \tan x,\ 0 \le x \le \pi/4$

9. $f(x) = \sin^2 x,\ 0 \le x \le \pi$ 10. $f(x) = x^2/\sqrt{a^2 - x^2},\ 0 \le x \le a$

11. Find the mean value f_m of $f(x) = 1/x^2$ in $[1, a]$. What is the value of $\lim_{a \to \infty} f_m$?

12. Find the mean value f_m of $f(x) = e^{-x}$ in $[0, a]$. Find the value of $\lim_{a \to \infty} f_m$.

13. Find the average of the lengths of the radius vectors of the cardioid $r = a(1 - \cos \theta)$, $0 \le \theta \le 2\pi$: (a) with respect to θ, and (b) with respect to arc length.

14. Find the average of the ordinates (y-values) of one arch of the cycloid $x = a(\theta - \sin \theta)$, $y = a(1 - \cos \theta)$, $0 \le \theta \le 2\pi$: (a) with respect to x, and (b) with respect to arc length.

15. Find the average of the ordinates (y-values) along the upper half of the cardioid $r = a(1 - \cos \theta)$: (a) with respect to θ, and (b) with respect to arc length.

16. Find the average of the ordinates along the upper half of the curve $x^{2/3} + y^{2/3} = a^{2/3}$: (a) with respect to arc length, and (b) with respect to x.

17. A particle moves along the x-axis according to the law $x = \frac{1}{3}t^3 + t$. Find (a) the time average of its velocity v for t between 1 and 3, and (b) the average of v with respect to x for values of x corresponding to these t.

18. A particle is falling with a speed $v = v_0 + at$, $a > 0$. Suppose that $s(0) = 0$, $s(t_1) = s_1$, where s is the distance fallen. (a) Find the time average of v over the interval $0 \le t \le t_1$. (b) Show that $v = \sqrt{v_0^2 + 2as}$. (c) Use the result of (b) to find the average of v with respect to s for $0 \le s \le s_1$.

9. CENTER OF MASS

Suppose that four masses are situated on a line, as shown in Fig. 16–29. Let the distance of m_i ($i = 1, 2, 3, 4$) from the origin O be x_i (x_i is positive if m_i is

FIGURE 16–29

to the right of O, negative if m_i is to the left). We define the *moment of m_i with respect to O* as the product $m_i x_i$. For the system of four masses, we define the quantity

$$\bar{x} = \frac{m_1 x_1 + m_2 x_2 + m_3 x_3 + m_4 x_4}{m_1 + m_2 + m_3 + m_4},$$

and call it the *center of mass* of the system. This definition is easily extendable to a system of n particles on a line, the center of mass being located at

$$\bar{x} = \frac{m_1 x_1 + m_2 x_2 + \cdots + m_n x_n}{m_1 + m_2 + \cdots + m_n}.$$

The center of mass is the point where the system will balance if a knife-edge is put at $\bar{x}$ and the line itself is considered weightless. Furthermore, each mass is assumed to occupy exactly one point. An important fact is that the location of $\bar{x}$ does not depend on the position of the origin O. (See problem 5 of the exercises at the end of this section.)

FIGURE 16–30

EXAMPLE 1. Weights of 2, 3, 5, and 4 oz are located on the x-axis at the points $(4, 0)$, $(2, 0)$, $(-6, 0)$, and $(-4, 0)$, respectively. Find the center of mass of the system.

Solution.

$$\bar{x} = \frac{2(4) + 2(3) + 5(-6) + 4(-4)}{2 + 3 + 5 + 4} = -\frac{16}{7}.$$

Suppose that a number of masses, say five, are located at various points in the xy-plane. We wish to find the center of mass of this system. From the point of view of mechanics, we imagine the masses supported by a weightless tray and assume that each mass occupies a single point. The center of mass is the point where the tray will balance when supported by a sharp nail (Fig. 16–30). To locate this point, we suppose that the mass m_i is situated at the point (x_i, y_i). The *moment of m_i with respect to the y-axis* is the product $m_i x_i$. The *moment of m_i with respect to the x-axis* is the product $m_i y_i$. The *center of mass $(\bar{x}, \bar{y})$ of a system of n masses located at the points (x_i, y_i), $i = 1, 2, \ldots, n$ is defined by the formulas*

$$\bar{x} = \frac{m_1 x_1 + m_2 x_2 + \cdots + m_n x_n}{m_1 + m_2 + \cdots + m_n},$$

$$\bar{y} = \frac{m_1 y_1 + m_2 y_2 + \cdots + m_n y_n}{m_1 + m_2 + \cdots + m_n}.$$

EXAMPLE 2. Find the center of mass of the system consisting of masses of 4, 2, and 3 oz located at the points $(1, 3)$, $(-2, 1)$, and $(4, -2)$, respectively.

Solution.

$$\bar{x} = \frac{4(1) + 2(-2) + 3(4)}{4 + 2 + 3} = \frac{4}{3},$$

$$\bar{y} = \frac{4(3) + 2(1) + 3(-2)}{4 + 2 + 3} = \frac{8}{9}.$$

An important fact is that the center of mass is independent of the location of the coordinate axes. (See problem 10.)

A thin piece of metal of uniform density has its center of mass at the place where it will balance horizontally when supported on the point of a nail. We idealize the situation by imagining the metal as two-dimensional and think of it

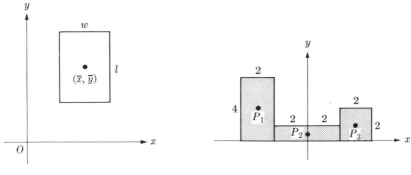

FIGURE 16–31   FIGURE 16–32

as a region located in the *xy*-plane. If the metal is uniform (and we always assume that it is) the density is constant, and the total mass of the piece of metal is proportional to the area of the region. For example, a rectangular piece of length *l* and width *w* made up of material of constant density ρ has total mass $\rho l w$. The center of mass of a rectangular region is at the center of the rectangle (Fig. 16–31). *The moment of a rectangle with respect to the y-axis* is

$$\rho l w \cdot \bar{x},$$

where $\bar{x}$ is the *x*-coordinate of the center of mass of the rectangle. Similarly, *the moment of a rectangle with respect to the x-axis* is

$$\rho l w \cdot \bar{y}.$$

With these definitions, it is possible to find the center of mass of regions composed of a combination of rectangles. Each rectangle may be treated as if its mass were concentrated at the center of the rectangle. We shall illustrate by an example.

EXAMPLE 3. A region is made up of a combination of rectangles of uniform density ρ, as shown in Fig. 16–32. Find the center of mass.

Solution. The centers of mass of the three rectangles are at $P_1(-3, 2)$, $P_2(0, \frac{1}{2})$, and $P_3(3, 1)$. The total masses of the rectangles are 8ρ, 4ρ, and 4ρ, respectively. We may treat the region as a system of three point masses located at the centers of mass. We obtain

$$\bar{x} = \frac{[8(-3) + 4(0) + 4(3)]\rho}{16\rho} = -\frac{3}{4},$$

$$\bar{y} = \frac{[8(2) + 4(\frac{1}{2}) + 4(1)]\rho}{16\rho} = \frac{11}{8}.$$

Remarks. The numerator of the expression for $\bar{x}$ is the sum of the moments of the rectangles with respect to the *y*-axis and, correspondingly, the one for $\bar{y}$ is the sum of the moments of the rectangles with respect to the *x*-axis. In each case the denominator is the total mass.

So long as the region is of uniform density, the actual value of the density plays no part in the location of the center of mass. The above example shows how the factor ρ cancels in the computation of $\bar{x}$ and $\bar{y}$. Therefore, *we always assume that the density has the value* 1; then the total mass of a region is its area.

EXERCISES

In problems 1 through 4, the masses m_i are located at the points P_i on the x-axis; find the center of mass.

1. $m_1 = 3$, $m_2 = 4$, $m_3 = 1$; $P_1(2, 0)$, $P_2(6, 0)$, $P_3(-4, 0)$

2. $m_1 = 7$, $m_2 = 1$, $m_3 = 5$, $m_4 = 12$; $P_1(-4, 0)$, $P_2(1, 0)$, $P_3(5, 0)$, $P_4(-7, 0)$

3. $m_1 = 2$, $m_2 = 1$, $m_3 = 5$, $m_4 = 6$, $m_5 = 1$; $P_1(0, 0)$, $P_2(1, 0)$, $P_3(-1, 0)$ $P_4(2, 0)$, $P_5(-2, 0)$

4. $m_1 = 1$, $m_2 = 2$, $m_3 = 1$, $m_4 = 1$, $m_5 = 2$; $P_1(1, 0)$, $P_2(2, 0)$, $P_3(3, 0)$, $P_4(4, 0)$, $P_5(5, 0)$

5. (a) Find the center of mass $\bar{x}$ of the system $m_1 = 7$, $m_2 = 5$, $m_3 = 4$, $m_4 = 2$, located on the x-axis at the points $P_1(5, 0)$, $P_2(-5, 0)$, $P_3(4, 0)$, $P_4(-2, 0)$. (b) Show that when the origin is shifted a distance h to the right, the location of the center of mass relative to the masses does not change.

In problems 6 through 9, the masses m_i are located in the xy-plane at the points P_i; find the centers of mass.

6. $m_1 = 1$, $m_2 = 3$, $m_3 = 2$; $P_1(2, 1)$, $P_2(-1, 3)$, $P_3(1, 2)$

7. $m_1 = 3$, $m_2 = 1$, $m_3 = 4$; $P_1(1, 0)$, $P_2(0, 3)$, $P_3(1, 2)$

8. $m_1 = 4$, $m_2 = 5$, $m_3 = 1$, $m_4 = 6$; $P_1(1, 1)$, $P_2(5, 0)$, $P_3(-4, 0)$, $P_4(0, 5)$

9. $m_1 = 2$, $m_2 = 8$, $m_3 = 5$, $m_4 = 2$; $P_1(0, 0)$, $P_2(0, 4)$, $P_3(5, 1)$, $P_4(-1, -1)$

10. (a) Find the center of mass $(\bar{x}, \bar{y})$ of the system $m_1 = 3$, $m_2 = 4$, $m_3 = 2$, located at the points $P_1(1, 1)$, $P_2(3, 0)$, $P_3(-1, 1)$. (b) Show that if the coordinate axes are translated so that the origin is at the point (h, k), the location of the center of mass relative to the masses does not change. Can the computation of the center of mass be simplified in this manner?

In problems 11 through 14, introduce a convenient rectangular coordinate system and find the coordinates of the center of mass in that coordinate system.

11. A plane region of uniform density has the shape shown in Fig. 16-33. Find the center of mass.

FIGURE 16-33

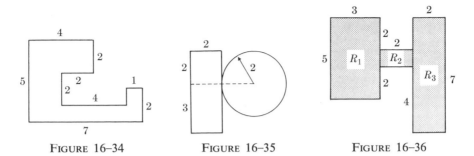

FIGURE 16–34   FIGURE 16–35   FIGURE 16–36

12. A plane region of uniform density has the shape shown in Fig. 16–34. Find the center of mass.

13. A plane region of uniform density has the shape shown in Fig. 16–35. Find the center of mass.

14. A plane region is composed of the regions R_1, R_2, and R_3, as shown in Fig. 16–36. The density of R_2 is twice that of R_1, and the density of R_3 is three times that of R_2. Find the center of mass.

10. CENTERS OF MASS OF PLANE REGIONS

In the preceding section we showed how to find the center of mass of a plane region composed of a collection of rectangles, each of uniform density. We now establish methods for finding the center of mass $(\bar{x}, \bar{y})$ of more general plane figures. *We always assume that the density is constant.* It is convenient to take the density equal to 1, since then the total mass of a region is its area. The results rest on the following two principles, proofs of which may be found in Morrey, *University Calculus*, Sections 21–6 and 21–11.

PRINCIPLE 1. *The center of mass of a plane region lies on any axis of symmetry of that region.*

PRINCIPLE 2. *Suppose that a plane region R with center of mass $(\bar{x}, \bar{y})$ is divided into regions R_1, R_2, . . . , R_n (no two of which overlap), having areas A_1, A_2, . . . , A_n, and centers of mass at $(\bar{x}_1, \bar{y}_1)$, $(\bar{x}_2, \bar{y}_2)$, . . . , $(\bar{x}_n, \bar{y}_n)$. Then*

$$\bar{x} = \frac{A_1\bar{x}_1 + A_2\bar{x}_2 + \cdots + A_n\bar{x}_n}{A_1 + A_2 + \cdots + A_n},$$

$$\bar{y} = \frac{A_1\bar{y}_1 + A_2\bar{y}_2 + \cdots + A_n\bar{y}_n}{A_1 + A_2 + \cdots + A_n}.$$

Let R be the region bounded by the graph of a nonnegative function $y = f(x)$ and the lines $x = a$, $x = b$, and $y = 0$, as shown in Fig. 16–37. We make a subdivision of the interval $[a, b]$ into n parts: $\{a = x_0 < x_1 < x_2 < \cdots < x_n = b\}$. We erect ordinates at the subdivision points, thereby dividing R into n nonoverlapping regions R_1, R_2, . . . , R_n. According to Principle 2, the center of mass

FIGURE 16–37

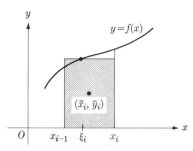

FIGURE 16–38

of R can be found if the center of mass and the area of each of the regions R_1, $R_2, \ldots, R_n$ are known. The procedure is similar to that used in defining integrals. For each i we select a point ξ_i in $[x_{i-1}, x_i]$ and erect a rectangle of height $f(\xi_i)$ and width $\Delta_i x = x_i - x_{i-1}$, as shown in Fig. 16–38. This rectangle approximates the area R_i, and the center of mass of the rectangle approximates the center of mass of R_i. According to Principle 1, the center of mass $(\bar{x}_i, \bar{y}_i)$ of the rectangle is at

$$\bar{x}_i = \tfrac{1}{2}(x_{i-1} + x_i),$$

$$\bar{y}_i = \tfrac{1}{2}f(\xi_i).$$

The area of the rectangle is $f(\xi_i)\,\Delta_i x$. Therefore the center of mass $(\bar{x}, \bar{y})$ of R is approximated (according to Principle 2) by the expressions

$$\frac{(f(\xi_1)\,\Delta_1 x)\bar{x}_1 + (f(\xi_2)\,\Delta_2 x)\bar{x}_2 + \cdots + (f(\xi_n)\,\Delta_n x)\bar{x}_n}{f(\xi_1)\,\Delta_1 x + f(\xi_2)\,\Delta_2 x + \cdots + f(\xi_n)\,\Delta_n x},$$

$$\frac{(f(\xi_1)\,\Delta_1 x)\bar{y}_1 + (f(\xi_2)\,\Delta_2 x)\bar{y}_2 + \cdots + (f(\xi_n)\,\Delta_n x)\bar{y}_n}{f(\xi_1)\,\Delta_1 x + f(\xi_2)\,\Delta_2 x + \cdots + f(\xi_n)\,\Delta_n x}.$$

We made the above computation for one subdivision. We now make a sequence of such subdivisions, with the norms of the subdivisions tending to zero. We can show, in the same way that we developed the integration formulas for area, that if f is a continuous function the above expressions tend to the center of mass of R, and that $\bar{x}$ and $\bar{y}$ are given by

$$\bar{x} = \frac{\displaystyle\int_a^b x f(x)\, dx}{\displaystyle\int_a^b f(x)\, dx}, \qquad \bar{y} = \frac{\tfrac{1}{2}\displaystyle\int_a^b [f(x)]^2\, dx}{\displaystyle\int_a^b f(x)\, dx}.$$

We observe that the denominator in each case is the area of the region R.

EXAMPLE 1. Compute the center of mass of the region R bounded by $y = x^2$, $x = 1$, $x = 3$, and $y = 0$ (Fig. 16–39).

FIGURE 16-39

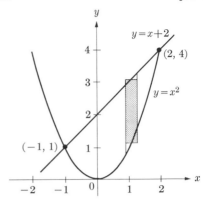

FIGURE 16-40

Solution. The region is of the type discussed above, and therefore

$$\bar{x} = \frac{\int_1^3 x^3 \, dx}{A}, \qquad \bar{y} = \frac{\frac{1}{2}\int_1^3 x^4 \, dx}{A},$$

where A is the area of R. We have

$$A = \int_1^3 x^2 \, dx = \tfrac{26}{3},$$

and so

$$\bar{x} = \tfrac{30}{13}, \qquad \bar{y} = \tfrac{363}{130}.$$

Rather than memorize the above formulas for the center of mass of a region of a particular type, the student should learn the method for deriving such formulas. The steps in the method are as follows: (1) Make a subdivision of the interval on the x-axis (or y-axis, if that appears more convenient). The region R is approximated by erecting rectangles at the subdivision points. (2) Find the center of mass of each rectangle by Principle 1. (3) Use Principle 2 to obtain an approximate expression for $(\bar{x}, \bar{y})$, the center of mass of R. (4) Proceed to the limit by writing the appropriate integrals. (5) Evaluate the integrals.

The next example illustrates this technique.

EXAMPLE 2. Find the center of mass of the region bounded by the curves $y = x^2$ and $y = x + 2$.

Solution. As Fig. 16-40 shows, the curves intersect at $(-1, 1)$ and $(2, 4)$. We make a subdivision of the interval $[-1, 2]$ and erect rectangles at the subdivision points. (A typical one is shown in Fig. 16-40.) The center of mass $(\bar{x}_i, \bar{y}_i)$ of this rectangle is at

$$\bar{x}_i = \tfrac{1}{2}(x_{i-1} + x_i), \qquad \bar{y}_i = \tfrac{1}{2}[(\xi_i + 2) + \xi_i^2],$$

where ξ_i is some number in the interval $[x_{i-1}, x_i]$.

Remark. Since we shall always be dealing with a typical rectangle (or other typical shape), it pays to abbreviate the notation in the following way. We drop the subscript i and instead of $\frac{1}{2}(x_{i-1} + x_i)$, we write x. Since ξ_i is between x_{i-1} and x_i, we can also use x for this quantity. We then have

$$\bar{x}_i = x, \qquad \bar{y}_i = \tfrac{1}{2}[(x + 2) + x^2].$$

Although it may appear that such sloppiness will lead to errors, we need not worry, since we shall eventually proceed to the limit and replace sums by integrals. (Of course, if there is any doubt in the reader's mind in a specific case, the longer notation should be kept.)

The area of a typical rectangle (in abbreviated notation) is

$$[(x + 2) - x^2]\Delta x.$$

Using Principle 2, we obtain as approximate expressions for $\bar{x}$ ahd $\bar{y}$

$$\frac{\sum\{[(x + 2) - x^2]\Delta x\}x}{\sum[(x + 2) - x^2]\Delta x}, \qquad \frac{\sum\{[(x + 2) - x^2]\Delta x\}\tfrac{1}{2}[(x + 2) + x^2]}{\sum[(x + 2) - x^2]\Delta x}.$$

These sums extend from 1 to n. Proceeding to the limit, we find that

$$\bar{x} = \frac{\int_{-1}^{2} x[(x + 2) - x^2]\,dx}{A}, \qquad \bar{y} = \frac{\tfrac{1}{2}\int_{-1}^{2} [(x + 2) + x^2][(x + 2) - x^2]\,dx}{A},$$

where A is the area of the entire region. We get A in the usual way from the formula

$$A = \int_{-1}^{2} [(x + 2) - x^2]\,dx.$$

Evaluating the various integrals, we obtain

$$\bar{x} = \tfrac{1}{2}, \qquad \bar{y} = \tfrac{8}{5}.$$

EXAMPLE 3. Find the center of mass of the triangular region with vertices at $(0, 0)$, $(a, 0)$, and (b, c).

Solution. We first concentrate on finding $\bar{y}$. It is convenient to subdivide the interval $[0, c]$ along the y-axis. A typical rectangle is shown in Fig. 16–41. We suppose that its height is y. Then the y-coordinate of its center of mass is simply y. Let l be the length

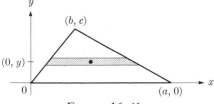

FIGURE 16–41

and Δy the width of this rectangle. By similar triangles, we have the proportion

$$\frac{l}{a} = \frac{c - y}{c};$$

therefore the area of a typical rectangle is

$$l\,\Delta y = \frac{a}{c}(c - y)\,\Delta y.$$

According to Principle 2, $\bar{y}$ is approximated by

$$\frac{\sum (a/c)(c - y)\,\Delta y \cdot y}{\sum (a/c)(c - y)\,\Delta y}.$$

We conclude that

$$\bar{y} = \frac{(a/c)\int_0^c (c - y)y\,dy}{\frac{1}{2}ac} = \frac{\frac{1}{6}ac^2}{\frac{1}{2}ac} = \frac{1}{3}c.$$

The center of mass is one-third of the distance from the base to the vertex. Since any side could have been chosen as base, we deduce that the center of mass of any triangle is at the point of intersection of its medians.

EXERCISES

In problems 1 through 11, find the center of mass of each of the plane regions R.

1. R is bounded by $y = \sqrt{4x}$, the x-axis, and the line $x = 6$.
2. R is bounded by $y = x^2$ and $y = x$.
3. R is bounded by one arch of $y = \sin x$ and the x-axis.
4. R is bounded by $y = \sin x$, and the lines $x = 0$, $x = \pi/2$, $y = 0$.
5. R is the semicircular region bounded by $y = \sqrt{a^2 - x^2}$, $-a \le x \le a$, and the x-axis.
6. R is the quarter-circle bounded by $y = \sqrt{a^2 - x^2}$ and the lines $x = 0$, $y = 0$.
7. R is the region to the right of $y = 3x$, and bounded by $y = 3x$, $y = x^2$, $y = 1$, and $y = 2$.
8. R is bounded by $y = \sec^2 x$ and the lines $x = 0$, $x = \pi/4$, and $y = 0$.
9. R is bounded by $y = \ln x$ and the lines $x = 2$, $x = 4$, and $y = 0$.
10. R is bounded by $y = x^3$ and $y = x$ (the portion in the first quadrant).
11. R is the region above $y = x^2$ and below $y = x - x^2$.

11. CENTERS OF MASS OF SOLIDS OF REVOLUTION

The methods we have developed enable us now to find the centers of mass of certain solids of revolution. As before, we shall assume that the object is made of uniform material of constant density. For convenience we shall select the density equal to 1, so that the total mass of an object is its volume.

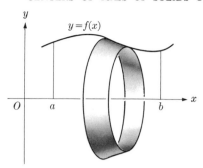

FIGURE 16–42

PRINCIPLE 1′. *A solid of revolution will have its center of mass on the axis of revolution.* If the axis of revolution is taken as the x-axis, then only the coordinate $\bar{x}$ has to be determined. The principle we use in locating this value is the analogue of Principle 2 of the last section.

PRINCIPLE 2′. *Suppose that a solid F is divided into solids* $F_1, F_2, \ldots, F_n$ *(no two of which overlap), having volumes* $V_1, V_2, \ldots, V_n$. *Let* $\bar{x}_1, \bar{x}_2, \ldots, \bar{x}_n$ *be the x-values of the centers of mass of* $F_1, F_2, \ldots, F_n$, *respectively. Then*

$$\bar{x} = \frac{V_1\bar{x}_1 + V_2\bar{x}_2 + \cdots + V_n\bar{x}_n}{V_1 + V_2 + \cdots + V_n}.$$

Let R be a region bounded by the nonnegative function $y = f(x)$ and the lines $x = a$, $x = b$, and $y = 0$. We revolve this region about the x-axis, obtaining a solid of revolution F (Fig. 16–42). The center of mass of F will be on the x-axis, according to Principle 1′, and we shall show how to locate it. We make a subdivision of the interval $[a, b]$: $\{a = x_0 < x_1 \cdots < x_n = b\}$, and slice the solid F into domains $F_1, F_2, \ldots, F_n$, by planes through the subdivision points. We approximate each F_i by a disc of thickness $\Delta_i x = x_i - x_{i-1}$ and radius $f(\xi_i)$, where $x_{i-1} \le \xi_i \le x_i$. Then the volume of the disc is

$$\pi[f(\xi_i)]^2 \, \Delta x,$$

and the center of mass of the disc is on the x-axis at $\frac{1}{2}(x_{i-1} + x_i)$. We use the abbreviated notation described in Example 2 of the preceding section and obtain (by Principle 2′) the approximation to $\bar{x}$,

$$\frac{\sum(\pi[f(x)]^2 \, \Delta x)x}{\sum \pi[f(x)]^2 \, \Delta x}.$$

Proceeding to the limit, we then find

$$\bar{x} = \frac{\pi \int_a^b x[f(x)]^2 \, dx}{\pi \int_a^b [f(x)]^2 \, dx}.$$

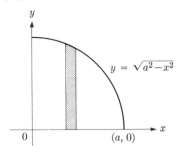

FIGURE 16–43

EXAMPLE 1. Find the center of mass of the hemisphere of radius a, center at the origin, and axis along the positive x-axis.

Solution. The solid is generated by revolving about the x-axis the quadrant of the circle $0 \leq x \leq a$, $0 \leq y \leq \sqrt{a^2 - x^2}$ (Fig. 16–43). We divide the solid into thin slabs by planes through subdivision points. According to the above description of the method, we then have

$$\bar{x} = \frac{\int_0^a x(a^2 - x^2)\, dx}{\int_0^a (a^2 - x^2)\, dx} = \frac{3a}{8}.$$

EXERCISES

In problems 1 through 8, in each case find the center of mass of the solid generated by revolving about the x-axis the plane figure bounded by the curves whose equations are given.

1. $y = 0$, $x = h$, $y = (a/h)x$. (Note that the solid is a cone of altitude h and radius of base a.)

2. $y = 0$, $y = \sqrt{2px}$, $x = b$ 3. $y = 0$, $y = (b/a)\sqrt{a^2 - x^2}$, $x \geq 0$

4. $x = 0$, $x = \pi/3$, $y = 0$, $y = \sec^2 x$ 5. $y = 0$, $x = 3$, $y = x/\sqrt{4 - x}$

6. $y = 0$, $y = \ln x$, $x = 2$ 7. $y = 0$, $y = \sin x$, $0 \leq x \leq \pi$

8. $x = 0$, $x = a$, $y = 0$, $y = a \cosh (x/a)$

9. $y = x^2$, $y^2 = x$

10. $x + y = 5$, $xy = 4$

11. $y = x^2$, $y = x + 2$

In problems 12 through 15, in each case find the center of mass of the solid generated by revolving about the y-axis the plane figure bounded by the curves whose equations are given.

12. $y = 1$, $y = 3$, $x = 0$, $x = y^2$ 13. $y = 0$, $y = 1$, $x = 0$, $x = \sqrt{y^2 + 1}$

14. $x = 0$, $x + y^2 - 6y = 0$ 15. $x = 1/(y + 1)$, $y = 0$, $y = 3$, $x = 0$

16. A cylindrical hole of radius 4 in. is bored through a solid hemisphere of radius 5 in. in such a way that the axis of the hole coincides with that of the hemisphere. Locate the center of mass of the remaining solid.

17. Using the principles stated and the result of Example 1, find the center of mass of a solid in the form of a right circular cylinder of altitude h and radius a, capped by a hemisphere of the same radius.

18. Using the principles stated and the results of Example 1 and problem 1, find the center of mass of a solid "top" in the form of a cone of altitude h and base of radius a, with vertex downward, surmounted by a hemisphere of radius a.

12. CENTERS OF MASS OF WIRES AND SURFACES

Continuing the development of the problem of finding the centers of mass of various kinds of objects, we now consider the question of locating the center of mass of a thin wire. As usual, we assume that the material is uniform and the density constant and equal to 1; we idealize the problem further by supposing that the wire is one-dimensional. The total mass will then be equal to the length of the curve.

Suppose that the wire is described by the equation $y = f(x)$ between the points $A(a, f(a))$ and $B(b, f(b))$. We make a decomposition of the arc

$$\{A = P_0, P_1, P_2, \ldots, P_{n-1}, P_n = B\}$$

and approximate each arc by a straight-line segment (Fig. 16–44). The center of mass of a straight-line segment is at its midpoint. We use the analogue of Principle 2 to approximate the center of mass $(\bar{x}, \bar{y})$ by

$$\frac{\sum (\Delta s) \cdot x}{\sum (\Delta s)}, \qquad \frac{\sum (\Delta s) f(x)}{\sum (\Delta s)},$$

where Δs is the length of $\overline{P_{i-1}P_i}$, and abbreviated notation has been used (Fig. 16–45). Proceeding to the limit, we obtain

$$\bar{x} = \frac{\int_a^b x \, ds}{\int_a^b ds}, \qquad \bar{y} = \frac{\int_a^b f(x) \, ds}{\int_a^b ds}.$$

EXAMPLE 1. Find the center of mass of the arc of the circle $x^2 + y^2 = a^2$ which is in the first quadrant.

FIGURE 16–44

FIGURE 16–45

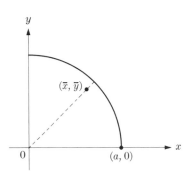

FIGURE 16–46   FIGURE 16–47

Solution. The line $y = x$ is a line of symmetry, and therefore $\bar{x} = \bar{y}$. We have

$$ds = \sqrt{1 + (dy/dx)^2}\, dx = \frac{a}{\sqrt{a^2 - x^2}}\, dx,$$

and therefore

$$\bar{x} = \frac{\int_0^a x(a/\sqrt{a^2 - x^2})\, dx}{\frac{1}{2}\pi a} = \frac{2a}{\pi} = \bar{y}.$$

In Fig. 16–46, note that the center of mass is not on the arc.

EXAMPLE 2. Find the center of mass of the arc in Fig. 16–47:

$$y = \frac{1}{6}x^3 + \frac{1}{2x}, \qquad 1 \le x \le 2.$$

Solution. We subdivide the x-interval. A typical section will have mass Δs, and its center of mass will be at $(x, \frac{1}{6}x^3 + 1/2x)$. As an approximation to $(\bar{x}, \bar{y})$, we obtain

$$\frac{\sum (\Delta s) \cdot x}{\sum \Delta s}, \qquad \frac{\sum (\Delta s)\left(\dfrac{x^3}{6} + \dfrac{1}{2x}\right)}{\sum (\Delta s)}.$$

Therefore

$$\bar{x} = \frac{\int_1^2 x\, ds}{\int_1^2 ds}, \qquad \bar{y} = \frac{\int_1^2 f(x)\, ds}{\int_1^2 ds}.$$

We also have

$$ds = \sqrt{1 + (dy/dx)^2}\, dx = \frac{1}{2}\left(x^2 + \frac{1}{x^2}\right) dx,$$

and so

$$\bar{x} = \frac{\frac{1}{2}\int_1^2 [x^3 + (1/x)]\, dx}{\frac{1}{2}\int_1^2 [x^2 + (1/x^2)]\, dx}, \qquad \bar{y} = \frac{\frac{1}{2}\int_1^2 [\frac{1}{6}x^3 + (1/2x)][x^2 + (1/x^2)]\, dx}{\frac{1}{2}\int_1^2 [x^2 + (1/x^2)]\, dx}.$$

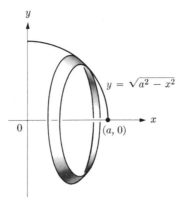

$$y = \sqrt{a^2 - x^2}$$

$$(a, 0)$$

FIGURE 16–48

Computing the various integrals, we find

$$\bar{x} = \tfrac{45}{34} + \tfrac{6}{17} \ln 2, \qquad \bar{y} = \tfrac{141}{136}.$$

When a thin wire is revolved about an axis, a shell of revolution is obtained. If we consider this as a two-dimensional object, the center of mass may sometimes be found by simple integrations. As usual, the density is assumed constant and equal to 1. Since the method follows the usual pattern, we shall limit the discussion to working examples.

EXAMPLE 3. Find the center of mass of the surface of a hemisphere of radius a.

Solution. The hemisphere is obtained by revolving about the x-axis the quarter circle $y = \sqrt{a^2 - x^2}$, $0 \le x \le a$, and the center of mass is on the x-axis (Fig. 16–48). To locate it we divide the interval $[0, a]$ into thin slices. The surface area of each slice is

$$2\pi f(x)\, \Delta s$$

(using abbreviated notation). Using the analogue of Principle 2', we now obtain, as an approximation for $\bar{x}$,

$$\frac{2\pi \sum [f(x)\, \Delta s] \cdot x}{2\pi \sum [f(x)\, \Delta s]}.$$

Proceeding to the limit, we find that

$$\bar{x} = \frac{2\pi \int_0^a x f(x)\, ds}{2\pi \int_0^a f(x)\, ds}.$$

The denominator is simply the surface area of the hemisphere, which we know is $2\pi a^2$. Therefore

$$\bar{x} = \frac{1}{a^2} \int_0^a x \sqrt{a^2 - x^2}\ \frac{a}{\sqrt{a^2 - x^2}}\, dx = \frac{1}{2}\, a.$$

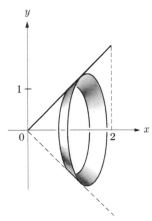

FIGURE 16–49

EXAMPLE 4. The line $y = x$, $0 \leq x \leq 2$, is revolved about the x-axis, generating the surface of a cone. Find the center of mass of this surface (Fig. 16–49).

Solution. We have the formula for $\bar{x}$:

$$\bar{x} = \frac{2\pi \int_0^2 x f(x)\, ds}{2\pi \int_0^2 f(x)\, ds}.$$

Therefore

$$\bar{x} = \frac{\int_0^2 x^2 \sqrt{2}\, dx}{2\sqrt{2}} = \tfrac{1}{2}[\tfrac{1}{3}x^3]_0^2 = \tfrac{4}{3}.$$

EXERCISES

In problems 1 through 7, find the centers of mass of the given arcs.

1. $8y = x^4 + 2x^{-2}$, $1 \leq x \leq 2$ 2. $y = \cosh x$, $0 \leq x \leq 1$

3. $x^{2/3} + y^{2/3} = a^{2/3}$, $x \geq 0, y \geq 0$ 4. $y = \sqrt{a^2 - x^2}$, $-a \leq x \leq a$

5. $y = x^2$, $0 \leq x \leq 2$ 6. $r = a(1 - \cos \theta)$, $0 \leq \theta \leq \pi$

7. $4x = y^2 - 2 \ln y$, $1 \leq y \leq 2$

In problems 8 through 14, in each case find the center of mass of the surface obtained by revolving about the x-axis the part of the locus of the equation given for which $y \geq 0$.

8. $y = ax/h$, $0 \leq x \leq h$ 9. $y^2 = 4x$, $0 \leq x \leq 4$

10. $y = a \cosh (x/a)$, $0 \leq x \leq a$ 11. $y^2 = 3 - x$, $0 \leq x \leq 3$

12. $r = a(1 - \cos \theta)$ 13. $4x^2 + 9y^2 = 36$

14. $4y = x^2 - 2 \ln x$, $1 \leq x \leq 2$

In problems 15 through 17, in each case find the center of mass of the surface obtained by revolving about the y-axis the part of the locus where $x \geq 0$.

15. $y = x^2, \quad 0 \leq x \leq 2$ 16. $6y = x^3 + 3x^{-1}, \quad 1 \leq x \leq 2$

17. $y = a \cosh (x/a), \quad 0 \leq x \leq a$

13. THEOREMS OF PAPPUS

The two theorems given in this section are useful tools for finding volumes of solids of revolution and areas of surfaces of revolution. They provide interesting applications of the material on finding the center of mass.

Theorem 2 (First Theorem of Pappus). *If a region R lies on one side of a line l in its plane, the volume of the solid generated by revolving R about l is equal to the product of the area A of R and the length of the path described by the center of mass of R.*

Theorem 3 (Second Theorem of Pappus). *If an arc C in a plane lies on one side of a line l in the plane, the area of the surface generated by revolving C about l is the product of the length of C and the length of the path described by the center of mass of C.*

The proofs of these theorems may be found in Morrey, *University Calculus,* Sections 16–11 and 21–8.

EXAMPLE 1. Find the volume of the solid generated by revolving about the y-axis the region bounded by $y = 0$ and $y = 4x - x^2$ (Fig. 16–50).

Solution. Since $y = 4x - x^2$ is a parabola with the line $x = 2$ as a line of symmetry, we have $\bar{x} = 2$. The area of the region is

$$A = \int_0^4 (4x - x^2)\, dx = \tfrac{32}{3}.$$

Therefore the volume is

$$\frac{32}{3} \cdot 2\pi \cdot 2 = \frac{128\pi}{3}.$$

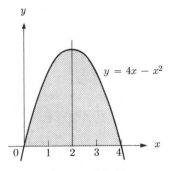

FIGURE 16–50

EXAMPLE 2. The arc $y = 4x - x^2$ from $x = 0$ to $x = 4$ is revolved about the y-axis. Find the surface area generated.

Solution. By symmetry we have $\bar{x} = 2$. The length of the arc is

$$\int_0^4 \sqrt{1 + (4 - 2x)^2} \, dx = 8\sqrt{17} + 2 \ln (4 + \sqrt{17}).$$

The total surface area is

$$2\pi 2 \, [8\sqrt{17} + 2 \ln (4 + \sqrt{17})].$$

EXERCISES

In each of problems 1 through 4, the region R is revolved about the given axis. Use the first theorem of Pappus to find the volumes generated.

1. R is bounded by $y = \sqrt{x}$ and the lines $x = 2$, $y = 0$. R is revolved about the x-axis.
2. R is bounded by $y = \sin x$, $0 \leq x \leq \pi$, and the line $y = 0$. R is revolved about the y-axis.
3. R is the same region as in problem 2 but is revolved about the x-axis.
4. R is bounded by the lines $y = ax/h$, $y = 0$, and $x = h$. R is revolved about the x-axis. (Use result of Example 3 of Section 10.)
5. The region of Example 1, Section 10, is revolved about the x-axis. Find the volume generated.
6. The region of Example 2, Section 10, is revolved about the line $y = -3$. Find the volume generated.
7. R is bounded by $y = x^3$ and $y = x$. The region is revolved about the x-axis. Find the volume generated.
8. Find the volume and the surface area of a sphere of radius a by using the Theorems of Pappus.
9. Find the volume and surface area of the torus obtained by revolving about the y-axis the circle $(x - b)^2 + y^2 = a^2$, where $a < b$.
10. Use the First Theorem of Pappus to find the volume of the solid generated by revolving about the x-axis the figure bounded by $y = x^2$ and $y = 8 - x^2$.

14. APPROXIMATE INTEGRATION

In the preceding sections and in Chapter 8, we saw how many physical and geometrical quantities can be computed by evaluating definite integrals. The familiar antiderivative rule for the evaluation of definite integrals may be used if an antiderivative can be found. Unfortunately, there are still many functions for which an antiderivative cannot be found by any known method. But if a function is continuous on an interval $[a, b]$, we know that its definite integral has a specific value. In Chapter 4, Section 6 and Chapter 8, Section 5, we showed how to

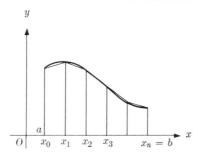

FIGURE 16–51

compute a definite integral approximately by means of sums of the type used in its definition; the midpoint rule (Chapter 8, Section 5) is often quite accurate. In most numerical work it is convenient to use values of all the functions involved only at certain equally spaced points. In this section we shall introduce two new methods which involve the values of the integrand at such points.

Method I (The Trapezoidal Rule). Suppose that $f(x)$ is continuous for $a \le x \le b$, and let $\{a = x_0 < x_1 < x_2 < \cdots < x_n = b\}$ be a subdivision of $[a, b]$ into n equal intervals of length $h = (b - a)/n$. Then, approximately,

$$\int_a^b f(x)\, dx = \frac{h}{2}[f(x_0) + 2f(x_1) + 2f(x_2) + \cdots + 2f(x_{n-1}) + f(x_n)].$$

In case $f(x) \ge 0$ on $[a, b]$, the expression on the right above denotes the sum of the areas of the trapezoids indicated in Fig. 16–51. In general, it represents the integral of the "polygonal function" having its vertices on the locus of $y = f(x)$ "above" or "below" the points x_i.

EXAMPLE 1. Compute

$$\int_0^1 \frac{dx}{1 + x^2},$$

using the Trapezoidal Rule with $n = 5$. Check your result by integrating and finding the exact value. Keep four decimals in computing each term, and round off the result to three.

Solution.

$$\frac{b - a}{n} = \frac{1 - 0}{5} = 0.2 = h.$$

$$
\begin{aligned}
f(0) &= 1.0000 \\
2f(0.2) &= 1.9231 \\
2f(0.4) &= 1.7241 \\
2f(0.6) &= 1.4706 \\
2f(0.8) &= 1.2195 \\
f(1) &= 0.5000 \\
\hline
\text{Sum} &= 7.8373
\end{aligned}
$$

Therefore $\displaystyle\int_0^1 \frac{dx}{1+x^2} = \frac{0.2}{2}$ (7.8373) = 0.784 (approximately).

The exact value is obtained from

$$\int_0^1 \frac{dx}{1+x^2} = \arctan x\big]_0^1 = \frac{\pi}{4} = 0.7854^-.$$

Before introducing the second method, we establish the *Prismoidal Formula*.

Theorem 4 (Prismoidal Formula). *If $f(x)$ is a polynomial of degree three or less, then*

$$\int_a^{a+2h} f(x)\,dx = \frac{h}{3}[f(a) + 4f(a+h) + f(a+2h)]$$

exactly.

Proof. Let $f(x)$ be any polynomial of degree 3 or less, say

$$f(x) = a + bx + cx^2 + dx^3.$$

When we make the substitution $x = a + h + u$, we have

$$f(a + h + u) = g(u),$$

where $g(u)$ is still a polynomial of the same degree as f. We write

$$g(u) = A + Bu + Cu^2 + Du^3.$$

Then

$$\int_a^{a+2h} f(x)\,dx = \int_{-h}^{h} g(u)\,du = Au + \frac{Bu^2}{2} + \frac{Cu^3}{3} + \frac{Du^4}{4}\bigg]_{-h}^{h}$$

$$= 2Ah + \frac{2Ch^3}{3}.$$

From the expression for $g(u)$, we have

$$g(0) = A, \qquad g(h) + g(-h) = 2A + 2Ch^2,$$

and therefore

$$C = \frac{g(h) + g(-h) - 2g(0)}{2h^2}.$$

We conclude that

$$\int_a^{a+2h} f(x)\,dx = 2g(0)h + \frac{h}{3}[g(h) + g(-h) - 2g(0)].$$

We now have $g(0) = f(a + h)$, $g(h) = f(a + 2h)$, $g(-h) = f(a)$ and, substituting these values in the last equation, we obtain the Prismoidal Formula.

EXAMPLE 2. Evaluate $\int_1^3 x^3 \, dx$, using the Prismoidal Formula. Check by integration.

Solution. $a = 1$, $a + 2h = 3$, $h = 1$, $a + h = 2$. Therefore

$$\int_1^3 x^3 \, dx = \tfrac{1}{3}[1^3 + 4 \cdot 2^3 + 3^3] = 20.$$

On the other hand,

$$\int_1^3 x^3 \, dx = [\tfrac{1}{4}x^4]_1^3 = \tfrac{81}{4} - \tfrac{1}{4} = 20.$$

Method II (Simpson's Rule). Suppose that $f(x)$ is continuous for $a \le x \le b$ and $\{a = x_0 < x_1 < x_2 < \cdots < x_{2n-1} < x_{2n} = b\}$ is a subdivision of $[a, b]$ into $2n$ intervals of length $h = (b - a)/2n$. Then, approximately,

$$\int_a^b f(x) \, dx = \frac{h}{3} [f(x_0) + 4f(x_1) + 2f(x_2) + 4f(x_3) + 2f(x_4) + \cdots$$

$$+ 2f(x_{2n-2}) + 4f(x_{2n-1}) + f(x_{2n})].$$

Applying the Prismoidal Formula to the first two intervals, we obtain

$$\frac{h}{3} [f(x_0) + 4f(x_1) + f(x_2)].$$

Adding to this the result of applying the Prismoidal Formula to the third and fourth intervals, we get

$$\frac{h}{3} [f(x_0) + 4f(x_1) + 2f(x_2) + 4f(x_3) + f(x_4)].$$

Simpson's Rule results from a continuation of the process to include all n pairs of intervals.

EXAMPLE 3. Compute

$$\int_0^1 \frac{dx}{1 + x^2},$$

using Simpson's Rule with $n = 2$. Keep five decimal places in each term and round off the result to four decimals.

Solution. $(b - a)/2n = (1 - 0)/4 = 0.25$. We have

$$\begin{aligned}
f(0) &= 1 = 1.00000 \\
4f(\tfrac{1}{4}) &= \tfrac{64}{17} = 3.76471 \\
2f(\tfrac{1}{2}) &= \tfrac{8}{5} = 1.60000 \\
4f(\tfrac{3}{4}) &= \tfrac{64}{25} = 2.56000 \\
f(1) &= \tfrac{1}{2} = 0.50000 \\
\hline
\text{Sum} &= 9.42471
\end{aligned}$$

$$\tfrac{1}{12}(9.42471) = 0.78539+$$

Therefore

$$\int_0^1 \frac{dx}{1 + x^2} = 0.7854^-$$

The following theorem, stated without proof, gives a method for estimating the error committed in numerical integration. (A proof is given in Morrey, *University Calculus*, Section A–5.)

Theorem 5. *Suppose that ϵ_T is the error (i.e., the difference between the true value of the integral and the value obtained from the numerical process) in the Trapezoidal Rule, and that ϵ_S is the error in Simpson's Rule. (a) If f, f', and f'' are continuous on $[a, b]$, there is a ξ in $[a, b]$ such that*

$$\epsilon_T = -\frac{(b - a)h^2}{12} f''(\xi),$$

$$h = \frac{b - a}{n} .$$

(b) *If also f''' and $f^{(4)}$ are continuous on $[a, b]$, there is an η in $[a, b]$ such that*

$$\epsilon_S = -\frac{(b - a)h^4}{180} f^{(4)}(\eta).$$

EXAMPLE 4. Find the minimum and maximum values of $f''(x)$ for $0 \le x \le 1$, and obtain bounds for the error in the result of Example 1.

Solution.

$$f'(x) = -2x(1 + x^2)^{-2};$$

$$f''(x) = 8x^2(1 + x^2)^{-3} - 2(1 + x^2)^{-2} = \frac{6x^2 - 2}{(1 + x^2)^3};$$

$$f'''(x) = -6x(6x^2 - 2)(1 + x^2)^{-4} + 12x(1 + x^2)^{-3} = 24x(1 + x^2)^{-4}(1 - x^2).$$

Therefore, since $f''' > 0$ for $0 < x < 1$, we have for the minimum m and maximum M of f'',

$$m = f''(0) = -2,$$
$$M = f''(1) = \tfrac{1}{2}.$$

Thus, in Example 1,

$$\frac{-2}{300} \le -\epsilon_T \le \frac{1}{600},$$

or

$$-\frac{1}{600} \le \epsilon_T \le \frac{1}{150}.$$

EXERCISES

In problems 1 through 6, use the Trapezoidal Rule with the given values of n to compute the approximate values of the given integrals. Keep the number of decimal places indicated in each term and round off to one less. Compute the exact values by integration.

1. $\int_1^4 x^2\,dx,\ n = 6,\ 2\ \text{dec}$

2. $\int_0^3 x\sqrt{16 + x^2}\,dx,\ n = 6,\ 2\ \text{dec}$

3. $\int_1^2 dx/x,\ n = 5,\ 4\ \text{dec}$

4. $\int_0^{1/2} dx/\sqrt{1 - x^2},\ n = 5,\ 4\ \text{dec}$

5. $\int_0^1 dx/\sqrt{1 + x^2},\ n = 5,\ 4\ \text{dec}$

6. $\int_0^{\pi/2} \sin x\,dx,\ n = 10,\ 4\ \text{dec}$

In problems 7 through 10, compute the exact value of each integral by the Prismoidal Formula.

7. $\int_1^3 x^2\,dx$

8. $\int_1^3 (x^3 - 2x^2 + 3x - 4)\,dx$

9. $\int_{-2}^0 (x^3 + x^2 - 3x + 4)\,dx$

10. $\int_{-1}^3 (2x^3 + 3x^2 - 4x - 5)\,dx$

In problems 11 through 16, use Simpson's Rule with the given values of $2n$ to compute the approximate values of the given integrals. Keep the number of decimal places indicated in each term and round off to one less. Compute the exact values by integration.

11. $\int_1^2 dx/x,\ 2n = 4,\ 5\ \text{dec}$

12. $\int_0^{1/2} dx/\sqrt{1 - x^2},\ 2n = 4,\ 6\ \text{dec}$

13. $\int_0^1 dx/\sqrt{1 + x^2},\ 2n = 4,\ 5\ \text{dec}$

14. $\int_0^{\pi/2} \sin x\,dx,\ 2n = 10,\ 5\ \text{dec}$

15. $\int_0^1 dx/(x^2 + x + 1),\ 2n = 4,\ 5\ \text{dec}$

16. $\int_0^2 x\,dx/(x^2 + 1),\ 2n = 10,\ 5\ \text{dec}$

In problems 17 through 22, compute approximate values for the integrals, using Simpson's Rule, as in problems 11 through 16.

17. $\int_0^1 dx/(1 + x^3),\ 2n = 4,\ 5\ \text{dec}$

18. $\int_0^1 dx/\sqrt{1 + x^3},\ 2n = 4,\ 5\ \text{dec}$

19. $\int_0^1 \sqrt[3]{1 + x^2}\,dx,\ 2n = 4,\ 5\ \text{dec}$

20. $\int_0^1 e^{-x^2}\,dx,\ 2n = 4,\ 5\ \text{dec}$

21. $\int_0^1 x\,dx/\sqrt{1 + x^3},\ 2n = 4,\ 5\ \text{dec}$

22. $\int_0^{\pi/2} dx/\sqrt{1 - \tfrac{1}{2}\sin^2 x},\ 2n = 4,\ 5\ \text{dec}$

In problems 23 through 28, find the minimum and maximum values of $f''(x)$ or $f^{(4)}(x)$, and obtain bounds for the error in the computation of the problem indicated.

23. Problem 1   24. Problem 2   25. Problem 4

26. Problem 5   27. Problems 3 and 11 28. Problems 6 and 14

15.   NUMERICAL INTEGRATION AND COMPUTING MACHINES

The Trapezoidal Formula and Simpson's Rule are well adapted for use with electronic computers. The formulas are simple and require only the elementary processes of arithmetic. The use of computers, however, raises certain mathematical questions which are best described in terms of an example. Suppose that we wish to evaluate the integral

$$\int_0^a x^{3/2} e^{-x^2/2}\, dx,$$

and it is known that the integration cannot be performed by elementary methods. This can easily be done numerically by, say, the Trapezoidal Formula. Furthermore, suppose that the problem is such that the upper limit of integration a is not known in advance but is the result of a long series of computations carried out by the machine. The entire process of performing the numerical integration can be done by machine also, if only the values of the function

$$f(x) = x^{3/2} e^{-x^2/2}$$

are known at the appropriate subdivision points. Since the subdivision points depend on a, they are not known in advance. Therefore, unless the machine has a complete table of various powers of e in its memory, the process breaks down. Such tables would tax the capacity of even the largest machines. We can surmount the problem by finding approximations of $e^{-x^2/2}$ in terms of rational functions. For example,* we have the approximation

$$e^{-x^2/2} \approx \sqrt{2\pi}\ \frac{1}{b_0 + b_1 x^2 + b_2 x^4 + b_3 x^6 + b_4 x^8},$$

where

$$b_0 = 2.51126, \quad b_1 = 1.17280, \quad b_2 = 0.49462, \quad b_3 = -0.06342, \quad b_4 = 0.02946.$$

The expression on the right, involving only additions, subtractions, multiplications, and divisions, is easy for the machine to compute. Only a few items of its memory are used. In addition, the error made in employing such a formula instead of the true value of $e^{-x^2/2}$ is known in advance to a great degree of precision.† This example shows the special mathematical treatment needed when dealing with

---

*Hastings, *Approximations for Digital Computers*, Princeton University Press (1955), p. 152.

†Hastings, *op. cit.*, p. 138.

machine techniques. It also exhibits the way that machines give rise to purely mathematical questions. The values of functions such as $\log x$, $\sin x$, $\arctan x$, are all determined by tables. For machine purposes, tables are awkward and cumbersome. The purely mathematical problem of finding formulas using only the elementary processes of arithmetic and approximating these functions to a given degree of precision turns out to be an interesting and challenging one.

A second problem pertaining to numerical integration concerns the form of the integral. We again describe the process by giving an example. Suppose we wish to evaluate

$$\int_0^{\pi/4} \frac{\cos x}{\sqrt{x}}\, dx.$$

This integral is a convergent improper integral. Furthermore, an antiderivative cannot be found by elementary means. The integrand

$$f(x) = \frac{\cos x}{\sqrt{x}}$$

tends to infinity as x tends to zero. Using, say, Simpson's Rule with a large number of subdivisions, we see that at the subdivision points near zero the function $f(x)$ is very large. These values tend to swamp the effect of $f(x)$ near the upper limit of integration, where the values of f are moderate in size. Unless we calculate each quantity with a great deal of accuracy, the process of multiplying very large numbers by very small numbers leads to enormous errors in the computation.

In the above integral the problem is easily avoided. An integration by parts yields

$$\int_0^{\pi/4} \frac{\cos x}{\sqrt{x}}\, dx = \sqrt{\pi/2} + 2\int_0^{\pi/4} \sqrt{x}\, \sin x\, dx.$$

The integral on the right is not an improper integral, and its evaluation is routine. If the integration is carried out by machine, the function $\sin x$ would have an approximation such as*

$$\sin \frac{\pi}{2} x \approx c_1 x + c_2 x^3 + c_3 x^5 \qquad \begin{cases} c_1 = 1.5706268, \\ c_2 = -0.6432292, \\ c_3 = 0.0727102, \end{cases}$$

valid for $-1 \leq x \leq 1$ with an error smaller than ± 0.00012.

As the two examples show, care and ingenuity are required in the application of computing-machine techniques to the performance of apparently routine mathematical problems. The presence of the electronic computer has indeed revolutionized many areas of pure and applied mathematics. The sword is two-edged, however. On the one hand, computers have helped solve many problems, but on the other, their presence has helped pose serious and difficult mathematical questions as yet unanswered.

---

*Hastings, *op. cit.*, p. 138.

CHAPTER 17

Solid Analytic Geometry

1. COORDINATES. THE DISTANCE FORMULA

In three-dimensional space, consider three mutually perpendicular lines which intersect in a point O. We designate these lines the *coordinate axes* and, starting from O, we set up number scales along each of them. If the positive directions of the x, y, and z axes are labeled x, y, and z, as shown in Fig. 17–1, we say the axes form a *right-handed system*. Figure 17–2 illustrates the axes in a *left-handed system*. We shall use a right-handed coordinate system throughout.

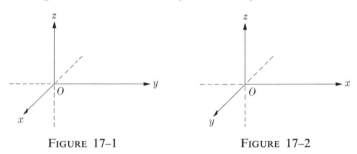

FIGURE 17–1   FIGURE 17–2

Any two intersecting lines in space determine a plane. A plane containing two of the coordinate axes is called a *coordinate plane*. Clearly, there are three such planes.

To each point P in three-dimensional space we can assign an ordered triple of numbers in the following way. Through P construct three planes, each parallel to one of the coordinate planes as shown in Fig. 17–3. We label the intersections of the planes through P with the coordinate axes Q, R, and S, as shown. Then,

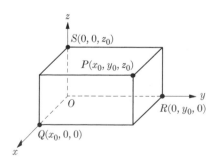

FIGURE 17–3

532

if Q is x_0 units from the origin O, R is y_0 units from O, and S is z_0 units from O, we assign to P the number triple (x_0, y_0, z_0) and say that the point P has *rectangular coordinates* (x_0, y_0, z_0). To each point in space there corresponds exactly one ordered number triple and, conversely, to each ordered number triple there is associated exactly one point in three-dimensional space. We have just described a *rectangular* or *cartesian* coordinate system. In Section 9 we shall discuss other coordinate systems.

In studying plane analytic geometry we saw that an equation such as

$$y = 3$$

represents all points lying on a line parallel to the x-axis and three units above it (Fig. 17-4). The equation

$$y = 3$$

FIGURE 17-4

in the context of three-dimensional geometry represents something entirely different. The locus of points satisfying this equation is a plane parallel to the xz-plane (the xz-plane is the coordinate plane determined by the x-axis and the z-axis) and three units from it (Fig. 17-5). The plane represented by $y = 3$ is perpendicular to the y-axis and passes through the point $(0, 3, 0)$. Since there is exactly one plane which is perpendicular to a given line and which passes through a given point, we see that the locus of the equation $y = 3$ consists of one and only one such plane. Conversely, from the very definition of a rectangular coordinate system every point with y-coordinate 3 must lie in this plane. Equations such as $x = a$ or $y = b$ or $z = c$ always represent planes parallel to the coordinate planes.

We recall from Euclidean solid geometry that *any two nonparallel planes intersect in a straight line*. Therefore, the locus of all points which simultaneously satisfy the equations

$$x = a \qquad \text{and} \qquad y = b$$

is a line parallel to (or coincident with) the z-axis. Conversely, any such line is the locus of a pair of equations of the above form. Since the plane $x = a$ is parallel to the z-axis, and the plane $y = b$ is parallel to the z-axis, the line of intersection must be parallel to the z-axis also. (Corresponding statements hold with the axes interchanged.)

A plane separates three-dimensional space into two parts, each of which is called a *half-space*. The inequality

$$x > 5$$

represents all points with x-coordinate greater

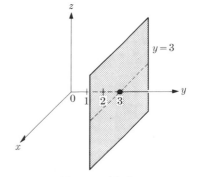

FIGURE 17-5

than 5. The set of such points comprises a half-space. Two intersecting planes divide three-space into 4 regions which we call *infinite wedges*. Three intersecting planes divide space into 8 regions (or possibly fewer), four planes into 16 regions (or possibly fewer), and so on. The inequality

$$|y| \leq 4$$

represents all points between (and on) the planes $y = -4$ and $y = 4$. Regions in space defined by inequalities are more difficult to visualize than those in the plane. However, *polyhedral domains*—i.e., those determined by the intersection of a number of planes—are frequently simple enough to be sketched. A polyhedron with six faces in which opposite faces are congruent parallelograms is called a *parallelepiped*. Cubes and rectangular bins are particular cases of parallelepipeds.

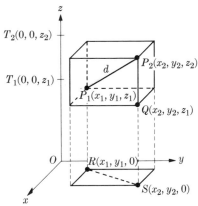

FIGURE 17–6

Theorem 1. *The distance d between the points $P_1(x_1, y_1, z_1)$ and $P_2(x_2, y_2, z_2)$ is*

$$d = \sqrt{(x_2 - x_1)^2 + (y_2 - y_1)^2 + (z_2 - z_1)^2}.$$

Proof. We make the construction shown in Fig. 17–6. By the Pythagorean theorem we have

$$d^2 = \overline{P_1 Q}^2 + \overline{QP_2}^2.$$

Noting that $\overline{P_1 Q} = \overline{RS}$, we use the formula for distance in the xy-plane to get

$$\overline{P_1 Q}^2 = \overline{RS}^2 = (x_2 - x_1)^2 + (y_2 - y_1)^2.$$

Furthermore, since P_2 and Q are on a line parallel to the z-axis, we see that

$$\overline{QP_2}^2 = \overline{T_1 T_2}^2 = (z_2 - z_1)^2.$$

Therefore

$$d^2 = (x_2 - x_1)^2 + (y_2 - y_1)^2 + (z_2 - z_1)^2.$$

The midpoint P of the line segment connecting the point $P_1(x_1, y_1, z_1)$ and $P_2(x_2, y_2, z_2)$ has coordinates $P(\bar{x}, \bar{y}, \bar{z})$ given by the formula

$$\bar{x} = \frac{x_1 + x_2}{2}, \qquad \bar{y} = \frac{y_1 + y_2}{2}, \qquad \bar{z} = \frac{z_1 + z_2}{2}.$$

If P_1 and P_2 lie in the xy-plane—i.e., if $z_1 = 0$ and $z_2 = 0$—then so does the midpoint, and we recognize the formula as the one we learned in plane analytic geometry. To establish the above formula we set up proportional triangles in complete analogy with the two-dimensional case. (See Exercise 24 at the end of this section.)

EXAMPLE 1. Find the coordinates of the point Q which divides the line segment from $P_1(1, 4, -2)$ to $P_2(-3, 6, 7)$ in the proportion 3 to 1.

Solution. The midpoint P of the segment P_1P_2 has coordinates $P(-1, 5, \frac{5}{2})$. When we find the midpoint of PP_2 we get $Q(-2, \frac{11}{2}, \frac{19}{4})$.

EXAMPLE 2. One endpoint of a segment P_1P_2 has coordinates $P_1(-1, 2, 5)$. The midpoint P is known to lie in the xz-plane, while the other endpoint is known to lie on the intersection of the planes $x = 5$ and $z = 8$. Find the coordinates of P and P_2.

Solution. For $P(\bar{x}, \bar{y}, \bar{z})$ we note that $\bar{y} = 0$, since P is in the xz-plane. Similarly, for $P_2(x_2, y_2, z_2)$ we have $x_2 = 5$ and $z_2 = 8$. From the midpoint formula we get

$$\bar{x} = \frac{-1 + 5}{2}, \qquad 0 = \bar{y} = \frac{2 + y_2}{2}, \qquad \bar{z} = \frac{5 + 8}{2}.$$

Therefore the points have coordinates $P(2, 0, \frac{13}{2})$, $P_2(5, -2, 8)$.

EXERCISES

In problems 1 through 5, find the lengths of the sides of triangle ABC and state whether the triangle is a right triangle, an isosceles triangle, or both.

1. $A(2, 1, 3)$, $B(3, -1, -2)$, $C(0, 2, -1)$ 2. $A(4, 3, 1)$, $B(2, 1, 2)$, $C(0, 2, 4)$
3. $A(3, -1, -1)$, $B(1, 2, 1)$, $C(6, -1, 2)$ 4. $A(1, 2, -3)$, $B(4, 3, -1)$, $C(3, 1, 2)$
5. $A(0, 0, 0)$, $B(4, 1, 2)$, $C(-5, -5, -1)$

In problems 6 through 9, find the midpoint of the segment joining the given points A, B.

6. $A(2, 1, 3)$, $B(-4, -1, 2)$ 7. $A(4, 6, 1)$, $B(2, -1, 3)$
8. $A(0, 2, -3)$, $B(1, 4, 6)$ 9. $A(-2, 0, 0)$, $B(0, 4, -1)$

In problems 10 through 13, find the lengths of the medians of the given triangles ABC.

10. $A(2, 1, 3)$, $B(3, -1, -2)$, $C(0, 2, -1)$ 11. $A(4, 3, 1)$, $B(2, 1, 2)$, $C(0, 2, 4)$
12. $A(3, -1, -1)$, $B(1, 2, 1)$, $C(6, -1, 2)$ 13. $A(1, 2, -3)$, $B(4, 3, -1)$, $C(3, 1, 2)$

14. One endpoint of a line segment is at $P(4, 6, -3)$ and the midpoint is at $Q(2, 1, 6)$. Find the other endpoint.

15. One endpoint of a line segment is at $P_1(-2, 1, 6)$ and the midpoint Q lies in the plane $y = 3$. The other endpoint, P_2, lies on the intersection of the planes $x = 4$ and $z = -6$. Find the coordinates of P_2 and Q.

In problems 16 through 19, determine whether or not the three given points lie on a line.

16. $A(1, -1, 2)$, $B(-1, -4, 3)$, $C(3, 2, 1)$ 17. $A(2, 3, 1)$, $B(4, 6, 5)$, $C(-2, -2, -7)$

18. $A(1, -1, 2)$, $B(3, 3, 4)$, $C(-2, -6, -1)$

19. $A(-4, 5, -6)$, $B(-1, 2, -1)$, $C(3, -3, 6)$

20. Describe the locus of points in space which satisfy the inequalities $-2 \leq x < 3$.

21. Describe the locus of points in space which satisfy the relations $x = 2$, $z = -4$.

22. Describe the locus of points in space which satisfy the inequalities $x \geq 0$, $y \geq 0$, $z \geq 0$.

23. Describe the locus of points in space which satisfy the inequalities $x \geq 0$, $y > 0$, $z < 0$.

24. Derive the formula for determining the midpoint of a line segment.

25. The formula for the coordinates of a point $Q(x_0, y_0, z_0)$ which divides the line segment from $P_1(x_1, y_1, z_1)$ to $P_2(x_2, y_2, z_2)$ in the ratio p to q is

$$x_0 = \frac{px_2 + qx_1}{p + q}, \qquad y_0 = \frac{py_2 + qy_1}{p + q}, \qquad z_0 = \frac{pz_2 + qz_1}{p + q}.$$

Derive this formula.

26. Find the equation of the locus of all points equidistant from the points $(2, -1, 3)$ and $(3, 1, -1)$. Can you describe the locus?

27. Find the equation of the locus of all points equidistant from the points $(5, 1, 0)$ and $(2, -1, 4)$. Can you describe the locus?

28. The points $A(0, 0, 0)$, $B(1, 0, 0)$, $C(\frac{1}{2}, \frac{1}{2}, 1/\sqrt{2})$, $D(0, 1, 0)$ are the vertices of a four-sided figure. Show that $\overline{AB} = \overline{BC} = \overline{CD} = \overline{DA} = 1$. Prove that the figure is not a rhombus.

29. Prove that the diagonals joining opposite vertices of a rectangular parallelepiped (there are four of them which are interior to the parallelepiped) bisect each other.

2. DIRECTION COSINES AND NUMBERS

Consider a line L passing through the origin and place an arrow on it so that one of the two possible directions is distinguished (Fig. 17–7). We call such a line a *directed line*. If no arrow is placed, then L is called an *undirected line*. Denote by α, β, and γ the angles made by the directed line L and the positive directions of the x-, y-, and z-axes, respectively. We define these angles to be the *direction angles* of the directed line L. The undirected line L will have two possible sets of direction angles according as the arrow points in one direction or the other. The two sets are

$$\alpha, \beta, \gamma \qquad \text{and} \qquad 180 - \alpha, \quad 180 - \beta, \quad 180 - \gamma,$$

where α, β, γ are the direction angles of the directed line.

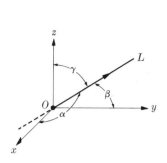

FIGURE 17–7   FIGURE 17–8

DEFINITION. If α, β, γ are direction angles of a line L, then $\cos \alpha$, $\cos \beta$, $\cos \gamma$ are called the *direction cosines* of the line L.

Since $\cos (180 - \theta) = -\cos \theta$, we see that if λ, μ, ν are direction cosines of a directed line L, then λ, μ, ν and $-\lambda$, $-\mu$, $-\nu$ are the two sets of direction cosines of the undirected line L.

We shall show that the direction cosines of any line L satisfy the relation

$$\cos^2 \alpha + \cos^2 \beta + \cos^2 \gamma = 1.$$

Let $P(x_0, y_0, z_0)$ be a point on a line L which goes through the origin. Then the distance d of P from the origin is

$$d = \sqrt{x_0^2 + y_0^2 + z_0^2},$$

and (see Fig. 17–8) we have

$$\cos \alpha = \frac{x_0}{d}, \qquad \cos \beta = \frac{y_0}{d}, \qquad \cos \gamma = \frac{z_0}{d}.$$

Squaring and adding, we get the desired result.

To define the direction cosines of any line L in space, we simply consider the line L' parallel to L which passes through the origin, and assert that *by definition L has the same direction cosines as L'.* Thus *all parallel lines in space have the same direction cosines.*

DEFINITION. Two sets of number triples, a, b, c and a', b', c', neither all zero, are said to be *proportional* if there is a number k such that

$$a' = ka, \qquad b' = kb, \qquad c' = kc.$$

Remark. The number k may be positive or negative but not zero, since by hypothesis neither of the number triples is $0, 0, 0$. If none of the numbers a, b, and c is zero, we may write the proportionality relations as

$$\frac{a'}{a} = k, \qquad \frac{b'}{b} = k, \qquad \frac{c'}{c} = k$$

or, more simply,

$$\frac{a'}{a} = \frac{b'}{b} = \frac{c'}{c}.$$

DEFINITION. Suppose that a line L has direction cosines λ, μ, ν. Then a set of numbers a, b, c is called a *set of direction numbers* for L if a, b, c and λ, μ, ν are proportional.

A line L has unlimited sets of direction numbers.

Theorem 2. *If $P_1(x_1, y_1, z_1)$ and $P_2(x_2, y_2, z_2)$ are two points on a line L, then*

$$\lambda = \frac{x_2 - x_1}{d}, \qquad \mu = \frac{y_2 - y_1}{d}, \qquad \nu = \frac{z_2 - z_1}{d}$$

is a set of direction cosines of L where d is the distance from P_1 to P_2.

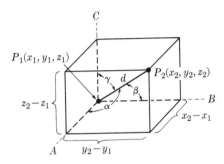

FIGURE 17–9

Proof. In Fig. 17–9 we note that the angles α, β, and γ are equal to the direction angles, since the lines P_1A, P_1B, P_1C are parallel to the coordinate axes. We read off from the figure that

$$\cos \alpha = \frac{x_2 - x_1}{d}, \qquad \cos \beta = \frac{y_2 - y_1}{d}, \qquad \cos \gamma = \frac{z_2 - z_1}{d},$$

which is the desired result.

Corollary 1. *If $P_1(x_1, y_1, z_1)$ and $P_2(x_2, y_2, z_2)$ are two points on a line L, then*

$$x_2 - x_1, \qquad y_2 - y_1, \qquad z_2 - z_1$$

is a set of direction numbers for L.

Multiplying λ, μ, ν of Theorem 2 by the constant d, we obtain the result of the Corollary.

EXAMPLE 1. Find direction numbers and direction cosines for the line L passing through the points $P_1(1, 5, 2)$ and $P_2(3, 7, -4)$.

Solution. From the Corollary, 2, 2, −6 is a set of direction numbers. We compute

$$d = \overline{P_1 P_2} = \sqrt{4 + 4 + 36} = \sqrt{44} = 2\sqrt{11},$$

and so

$$\frac{1}{\sqrt{11}}, \quad \frac{1}{\sqrt{11}}, \quad -\frac{3}{\sqrt{11}}$$

is a set of direction cosines. Since L is undirected, it has two such sets, the other being

$$-\frac{1}{\sqrt{11}}, \quad -\frac{1}{\sqrt{11}}, \quad \frac{3}{\sqrt{11}}.$$

EXAMPLE 2. Do the three points $P_1(3, -1, 4)$, $P_2(1, 6, 8)$, and $P_3(9, -22, -8)$ lie on the same straight line?

Solution. A set of direction numbers for the line L_1 through P_1 and P_2 is $-2, 7, 4$. A set of direction numbers for the line L_2 through P_2 and P_3 is $8, -28, -16$. Since the second set is proportional to the first (with $k = -4$), we conclude that L_1 and L_2 have the same direction cosines. Therefore the two lines are parallel. However, they have the point P_2 in common and so must coincide.

From Theorem 2 and the statements in Example 2, we easily obtain the next result.

Corollary 2. *A line L_1 is parallel to a line L_2 if and only if a set of direction numbers of L_1 is proportional to a set of direction numbers of L_2.*

The angle between two intersecting lines in space is defined in the same way as the angle between two lines in the plane. It may happen that two lines L_1 and L_2 in space are neither parallel nor intersecting. Such lines are said to be *skew* to each other. Nevertheless, the angle between L_1 and L_2 can still be defined. Denote by L_1' and L_2' the lines passing through the origin and parallel to L_1 and L_2, respectively. *The angle between L_1 and L_2 is defined to be the angle between the intersecting lines L_1' and L_2'.*

Theorem 3. *If L_1 and L_2 have direction cosines λ_1, μ_1, ν_1 and λ_2, μ_2, ν_2, respectively, and if θ is the angle between L_1 and L_2, then*

$$\cos \theta = \lambda_1 \lambda_2 + \mu_1 \mu_2 + \nu_1 \nu_2.$$

Proof. From the way we defined the angle between two lines we may consider L_1 and L_2 as lines passing through the origin. Let $P_1(x_1, y_1, z_1)$ be a point on L_1 and $P_2(x_2, y_2, z_2)$ a point on L_2 (see Fig. 17–10). Denote by d_1 the distance of P_1 from O, by d_2 the distance of P_2 from O; let $d = \overline{P_1 P_2}$. We apply the Law

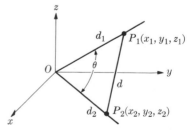

FIGURE 17–10

of Cosines to triangle OP_1P_2, getting

$$d^2 = d_1^2 + d_2^2 - 2d_1d_2 \cos \theta,$$

or

$$\cos \theta = \frac{d_1^2 + d_2^2 - d^2}{2d_1d_2}$$

and

$$\cos \theta = \frac{x_1^2 + y_1^2 + z_1^2 + x_2^2 + y_2^2 + z_2^2 - (x_2 - x_1)^2 - (y_2 - y_1)^2 - (z_2 - z_1)^2}{2d_1d_2}.$$

After simplification we get

$$\cos \theta = \frac{x_1x_2 + y_1y_2 + z_1z_2}{d_1d_2} = \frac{x_1}{d_1} \cdot \frac{x_2}{d_2} + \frac{y_1}{d_1} \cdot \frac{y_2}{d_2} + \frac{z_1}{d_1} \cdot \frac{z_2}{d_2}$$

$$= \lambda_1\lambda_2 + \mu_1\mu_2 + \nu_1\nu_2.$$

Corollary. *Two lines L_1 and L_2 with direction numbers a_1, b_1, c_1 and a_2, b_2, c_2, respectively, are perpendicular if and only if*

$$a_1a_2 + b_1b_2 + c_1c_2 = 0.$$

EXAMPLE 3. Find the cosine of the angle between the line L_1, passing through the points $P_1(1, 4, 2)$ and $P_2(3, -1, 3)$, and the line L_2, passing through the points $Q_1(3, 1, 2)$ and $Q_2(2, 1, 3)$.

Solution. A set of direction numbers for L_1 is $2, -5, 1$. A set for L_2 is $-1, 0, 1$. Therefore direction cosines for the two lines are

$$L_1: \frac{2}{\sqrt{30}}, \frac{-5}{\sqrt{30}}, \frac{1}{\sqrt{30}}; \quad L_2: \frac{-1}{\sqrt{2}}, 0, \frac{1}{\sqrt{2}}.$$

We obtain

$$\cos \theta = -\frac{1}{\sqrt{15}} + 0 + \frac{1}{2\sqrt{15}} = -\frac{1}{2\sqrt{15}}.$$

We observe that two lines always have two possible supplementary angles of intersection. If $\cos \theta$ is negative, we have obtained the obtuse angle and, if it is positive, the acute angle of intersection.

EXERCISES

In problems 1 through 4, find a set of direction numbers and a set of direction cosines for the line passing through the given points.

1. $P_1(3, 1, 2), P_2(2, 6, 0)$ 2. $P_1(4, 1, 0), P_2(0, 1, 2)$
3. $P_1(-5, -1, 4), P_2(2, 0, 6)$ 4. $P_1(-1, 5, 5), P_2(3, 5, 5)$

In each of problems 5 through 8, a point P_1 and a set of direction numbers are given. Find another point which is on the line passing through P_1 and having the given set of direction numbers.

  5. $P_1(2, 5, 1)$, direction numbers 3, 2, 5

  6. $P_1(3, 0, -5)$, direction numbers 2, -1, 0

  7. $P_1(0, 4, -3)$, direction numbers 0, 0, 5

  8. $P_1(0, 0, 0)$, direction numbers 2, -4, 0

In each of problems 9 through 12, determine whether or not the three given points lie on a line.

  9. $A(3, 1, 0)$, $B(2, 2, 2)$, $C(0, 4, 6)$

  10. $A(2, -1, 1)$, $B(4, 1, -3)$, $C(7, 4, -9)$

  11. $A(4, 2, -1)$, $B(2, 1, 1)$, $C(0, 0, 2)$

  12. $A(5, 8, 6)$, $B(-2, -3, 1)$, $C(4, 2, 8)$

In each of problems 13 through 15, determine whether or not the line through the points P_1, P_2 is parallel to the line through the points Q_1, Q_2.

  13. $P_1(4, 8, 0)$, $P_2(1, 2, 3)$; $Q_1(0, 5, 0)$, $Q_2(-3, -1, 3)$

  14. $P_1(2, 1, 1)$, $P_2(3, 2, -1)$; $Q_1(0, 1, 4)$, $Q_2(2, 3, 0)$

  15. $P_1(3, 1, 4)$, $P_2(-3, 2, 5)$; $Q_1(4, 6, 1)$, $Q_2(0, 5, 8)$

In each of problems 16 through 18, determine whether or not the line through the points P_1, P_2 is perpendicular to the line through the points Q_1, Q_2.

  16. $P_1(2, 1, 3)$, $P_2(4, 0, 5)$; $Q_1(3, 1, 2)$, $Q_2(2, 1, 6)$

  17. $P_1(2, -1, 0)$, $P_2(3, 1, 2)$; $Q_1(2, 1, 4)$, $Q_2(4, 0, 4)$

  18. $P_1(0, -4, 2)$, $P_2(5, -1, 0)$; $Q_1(3, 0, 2)$, $Q_2(2, 1, 1)$

In each of problems 19 through 21, find $\cos \theta$ where θ is the angle between the line L_1 passing through P_1, P_2 and L_2 passing through Q_1, Q_2.

  19. $P_1(2, 1, 4)$, $P_2(-1, 4, 1)$; $Q_1(0, 5, 1)$, $Q_2(3, -1, -2)$

  20. $P_1(4, 0, 5)$, $P_2(-1, -3, -2)$; $Q_1(2, 1, 4)$, $Q_2(2, -5, 1)$

  21. $P_1(0, 0, 5)$, $P_2(4, -2, 0)$; $Q_1(0, 0, 6)$, $Q_2(3, -2, 1)$

  22. A *regular tetrahedron* is a 4-sided figure each side of which is an equilateral triangle. Find 4 points in space which are the vertices of a regular tetrahedron with each edge of length 2 units.

  23. A *regular pyramid* is a 5-sided figure with a square base and sides consisting of 4 congruent isosceles triangles. If the base has a side of length 4 and if the height of the pyramid is 6 units, find the area of each of the triangular faces.

  24. The points $P_1(1, 2, 3)$, $P_2(2, 1, 2)$, $P_3(3, 0, 1)$, $P_4(5, 2, 7)$ are the vertices of a plane quadrilateral. Find the coordinates of the midpoints of the sides. What kind of quadrilateral do these four midpoints form?

  25. Prove that the four interior diagonals of a parallelepiped bisect each other.

3. EQUATIONS OF A LINE

In plane analytic geometry a single equation of the first degree,

$$Ax + By + C = 0,$$

is the equation of a line (so long as A and B are not both zero). *In the geometry of three dimensions such an equation represents a plane.* Although we shall postpone a systematic study of planes until the next section, we assert now that in three-dimensional geometry it is not possible to represent a line by a single first-degree equation.

A line in space is determined by two points. If $P_0(x_0, y_0, z_0)$ and $P_1(x_1, y_1, z_1)$ are given points, we seek an analytic method of representing the line L determined by these points. The result is obtained by solving a locus problem. A point $P(x, y, z)$ is on L if and only if the direction numbers determined by P and P_0 are proportional to those determined by P_1 and P_0 (Fig. 17–11). Calling the proportionality constant t, we see that the conditions are

$$x - x_0 = t(x_1 - x_0),$$
$$y - y_0 = t(y_1 - y_0),$$
$$z - z_0 = t(z_1 - z_0).$$

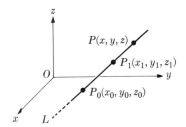

FIGURE 17–11

Thus we obtain the *two-point form of the parametric equations of a line*:

$$x = x_0 + (x_1 - x_0)t,$$
$$y = y_0 + (y_1 - y_0)t, \qquad (1)$$
$$z = z_0 + (z_1 - z_0)t.$$

EXAMPLE 1. Find the parametric equations of the line through the points $A(3, 2, -1)$ and $B(4, 4, 6)$. Locate three additional points on the line.

Solution. Substituting in (1) we obtain

$$x = 3 + t, \qquad y = 2 + 2t, \qquad z = -1 + 7t.$$

To get an additional point on the line we let $t = 2$ and obtain $P_1(5, 6, 13)$; $t = -1$ yields $P_2(2, 0, -8)$ and $t = 3$ gives $P_3(6, 8, 20)$.

Theorem 4. *The parametric equations of a line L through the point $P_0(x_0, y_0, z_0)$ with direction numbers a, b, c are given by*

$$x = x_0 + at, \qquad y = y_0 + bt, \qquad z = z_0 + ct. \qquad (2)$$

Proof. The point $P_1(x_0 + a, y_0 + b, z_0 + c)$ must be on L, since the direction numbers formed by P_0 and P_1 are just a, b, c. Using the two-point form (1) for the equations of a line through P_0 and P_1, we get (2) precisely.

EXAMPLE 2. Find the parametric equations of the line L through the point $A(3, -2, 5)$ with direction numbers 4, 0, -2. What is the relation of L to the coordinate planes?

Solution. Substituting in (2), we obtain

$$x = 3 + 4t, \qquad y = -2, \qquad z = 5 - 2t.$$

Since all points on the line must satisfy all three of the above equations, L must lie in the plane $y = -2$. This plane is parallel to the xz-plane. Therefore L is parallel to the xz-plane.

If none of the direction numbers is zero, the parameter t may be eliminated from the system of equations (2). We may write

$$\frac{x - x_0}{a} = \frac{y - y_0}{b} = \frac{z - z_0}{c} \tag{3}$$

for the equations of a line. For any value of t in (2) the ratios in (3) are equal. Conversely, if the ratios in (3) are all equal we may set the common value equal to t and (2) is satisfied.

If one of the direction numbers is zero, the form (3) may still be used if the zero in the denominator is interpreted properly. The equations

$$\frac{x - x_0}{a} = \frac{y - y_0}{b} = \frac{z - z_0}{0}$$

are understood to stand for the equations

$$\frac{x - x_0}{a} = \frac{y - y_0}{b} \qquad \text{and} \qquad z = z_0.$$

The system

$$\frac{x - x_0}{0} = \frac{y - y_0}{b} = \frac{z - z_0}{0}$$

stands for

$$x = x_0 \qquad \text{and} \qquad z = z_0.$$

We recognize these last two equations as those of planes parallel to coordinate planes. In other words, *a line is represented as the intersection of two planes.* This point will be discussed further in the next section.

The two-point form for the equations of a line also may be written *symmetrically.* We have

$$\frac{x - x_0}{x_1 - x_0} = \frac{y - y_0}{y_1 - y_0} = \frac{z - z_0}{z_1 - z_0}.$$

EXERCISES

In each of problems 1 through 4, find the equations of the line going through the given points. Find two additional points on each line.

1. $P_1(2, 3, 4)$, $P_2(-1, -3, 2)$ 2. $P_1(1, -1, 3)$, $P_2(2, 1, 5)$

3. $P_1(1, 2, -1)$, $P_2(3, -1, 2)$ 4. $P_1(-1, 2, 1)$, $P_2(3, 1, -1)$

In each of problems 5 through 9, find the equations of the line passing through the given point with the given direction numbers.

5. $P_1(1, 0, -1)$, direction numbers 2, 1, -3
6. $P_1(-2, 1, 3)$, direction numbers 3, -1, -2
7. $P_1(4, 0, 0)$, direction numbers 2, -1, -3
8. $P_1(1, 2, 0)$, direction numbers 0, 1, 3
9. $P_1(3, -1, -2)$, direction numbers 2, 0, 0

In each of problems 10 through 14, decide whether or not L_1 and L_2 are perpendicular.

10. $L_1: \dfrac{x-2}{2} = \dfrac{y+1}{-3} = \dfrac{z-1}{4}$; $L_2: \dfrac{x-2}{-3} = \dfrac{y+1}{2} = \dfrac{z-1}{3}$

11. $L_1: \dfrac{x}{1} = \dfrac{y+1}{2} = \dfrac{z+1}{3}$; $L_2: \dfrac{x-3}{0} = \dfrac{y+1}{-3} = \dfrac{z+4}{2}$

12. $L_1: \dfrac{x+2}{-1} = \dfrac{y-2}{2} = \dfrac{z+3}{3}$; $L_2: \dfrac{x+2}{1} = \dfrac{y-2}{2} = \dfrac{z+3}{-1}$

13. $L_1: \dfrac{x+5}{4} = \dfrac{y-1}{3} = \dfrac{z+8}{5}$; $L_2: \dfrac{x-4}{3} = \dfrac{y+7}{2} = \dfrac{z+4}{1}$

14. $L_1: \dfrac{x+1}{0} = \dfrac{y-2}{1} = \dfrac{z+8}{0}$; $L_2: \dfrac{x-3}{1} = \dfrac{y+2}{0} = \dfrac{z-1}{0}$

15. Find the equations of the medians of the triangle with vertices at $A(4, 0, 2)$, $B(3, 1, 4)$, $C(2, 5, 0)$.

16. Find the points of intersection of the line

$$x = 3 + 2t, \qquad y = 7 + 8t, \qquad z = -2 + t$$

with each of the coordinate planes.

17. Find the points of intersection of the line

$$\frac{x+1}{-2} = \frac{y+1}{3} = \frac{z-2}{7}$$

with each of the coordinate planes.

18. Show that the following lines are coincident:

$$\frac{x-1}{2} = \frac{y+1}{-3} = \frac{z}{4}; \qquad \frac{x-5}{2} = \frac{y+7}{-3} = \frac{z-8}{4}.$$

19. Find the equations of the line through $(3, 1, 5)$ which is parallel to the line

$$x = 4 - t, \qquad y = 2 + 3t, \qquad z = -4 + t.$$

20. Find the equations of the line through $(3, 1, -2)$ which is perpendicular and intersects the line

$$\frac{x+1}{1} = \frac{y+2}{1} = \frac{z+1}{1}.$$

[*Hint:* Let (x_0, y_0, z_0) be the point of intersection and determine its coordinates.]

21. A triangle has vertices at $A(2, 1, 6)$, $B(-3, 2, 4)$ and $C(5, 8, 7)$. Perpendiculars are drawn from these vertices to the xz-plane. Locate the points A', B', and C' which are the intersections of the perpendiculars through A, B, C and the xz-plane. Find the equations of the sides of the triangle $A'B'C'$.

4. THE PLANE

Any three points not on a straight line determine a plane. While this characterization of a plane is quite simple, it is not convenient for beginning the study of planes. Instead we use the fact that *there is exactly one plane which passes through a given point and is perpendicular to a given line.*

Let $P_0(x_0, y_0, z_0)$ be a given point, and suppose that a given line L goes through the point $P_1(x_1, y_1, z_1)$ and has direction numbers A, B, C.

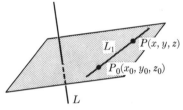

FIGURE 17–12

Theorem 5. *The equation of the plane passing through P_0 and perpendicular to L is*

$$A(x - x_0) + B(y - y_0) + C(z - z_0) = 0.$$

Proof. We establish the result by solving a locus problem. Let $P(x, y, z)$ be a point on the locus (Fig. 17–12). From Euclidean geometry we recall that if a line L_1 through P_0 and P is perpendicular to L, then P must be in the desired plane. A set of direction numbers for the line L_1 is

$$x - x_0, \quad y - y_0, \quad z - z_0.$$

Since L has direction numbers A, B, C, we conclude that the two lines L and L_1 are perpendicular if and only if their direction numbers satisfy the relation

$$A(x - x_0) + B(y - y_0) + C(z - z_0) = 0,$$

which is the equation we seek.

Remark. Note that only the direction of L—and not the coordinates of P_1— enters the above equation. We obtain the same plane and the same equation if any line parallel to L is used in its stead.

EXAMPLE 1. Find the equation of the plane through the point $P_0(5, 2, -3)$ which is perpendicular to the line through the points $P_1(5, 4, 3)$ and $P_2(-6, 1, 7)$.

Solution. The line through the points P_1 and P_2 has direction numbers $-11, -3, 4$. The equation of the plane is

$$-11(x - 5) - 3(y - 2) + 4(z + 3) = 0$$

or

$$11x + 3y - 4z - 73 = 0.$$

All lines perpendicular to the same plane are parallel and therefore have proportional direction numbers.

DEFINITION. A set of *attitude numbers* of a plane is any set of direction numbers of a line perpendicular to the plane.

In Example 1 above, $11, 3, -4$ form a set of attitude numbers of the plane.

EXAMPLE 2. What are sets of attitude numbers for planes parallel to the coordinate planes?

Solution. A plane parallel to the yz-plane has an equation of the form

$$x - c = 0,$$

where c is a constant. A set of attitude numbers for this plane is $1, 0, 0$. A plane parallel to the xz-plane has attitude numbers $0, 1, 0$, and any plane parallel to the xy-plane has attitude numbers $0, 0, 1$.

Since lines perpendicular to the same or parallel planes are themselves parallel, we get at once the next theorem.

Theorem 6. *Two planes are parallel if and only if their attitude numbers are proportional.*

Theorem 7. *If A, B, and C are not all zero, the locus of an equation of the form*

$$Ax + By + Cz + D = 0 \tag{1}$$

is a plane.

Proof. Suppose that $C \neq 0$, for example. Then the point $P_0(0, 0, -D/C)$ is on the locus, as its coordinates satisfy the above equation. Therefore we may write

$$A(x - 0) + B(y - 0) + C\left(z + \frac{D}{C}\right) = 0,$$

and the locus is the plane passing through P_0 perpendicular to any line with direction numbers A, B, C.

An equation of the plane through three points not on a line can be found by assuming that the plane has an equation of the form (1), substituting in turn the coordinates of the points, and solving simultaneously the three resulting equations. The fact that there are four constants, A, B, C, D, and only three equations is illusory, since we may divide through by one of them (say D) and obtain three equations in the unknowns A/D, B/D, C/D. This is equivalent to setting D (or one of the other constants) equal to some convenient value. An example illustrates the procedure.

EXAMPLE 3. Find an equation of the plane passing through the points $(2, 1, 3)$, $(1, 3, 2)$, $(-1, 2, 4)$.

Solution. Since the three points lie in the plane, each of them satisfies equation (1). We have

$$(2, 1, 3): \qquad 2A + B + 3C + D = 0,$$
$$(1, 3, 2): \qquad A + 3B + 2C + D = 0,$$
$$(-1, 2, 4): \qquad -A + 2B + 4C + D = 0.$$

Solving for A, B, C in terms of D, we obtain

$$A = -\tfrac{3}{25}D, \qquad B = -\tfrac{4}{25}D, \qquad C = -\tfrac{5}{25}D.$$

Setting $D = -25$, we get the equation

$$3x + 4y + 5z - 25 = 0.$$

EXERCISES

In each of problems 1 through 4, find the equation of the plane which passes through the given point P and has the given attitude numbers.

1. $P(0, 5, 6)$; 4, 2, -1 2. $P(-3, 1, 4)$; 0, 2, 5

3. $P(1, -2, -3)$; 4, 0, -1 4. $P(2, 0, 6)$; 0, 0, -5

In each of problems 5 through 8, find the equation of the plane which passes through the three points.

5. $(1, -2, 1)$, $(2, 0, 3)$, $(0, 1, -1)$ 6. $(2, 2, 1)$, $(-1, 2, 3)$, $(3, -5, -2)$

7. $(3, -1, 2)$, $(1, 2, -1)$, $(2, 3, 1)$ 8. $(-1, 3, 1)$, $(2, 1, 2)$, $(4, 2, -1)$

In each of problems 9 through 12, find the equation of the plane passing through P_1 and perpendicular to the line L_1.

9. $P_1(2, -1, 3)$; L_1: $x = -1 + 2t$, $y = 1 + 3t$, $z = -4t$

10. $P_1(1, 2, -3)$; L_1: $x = t$, $y = -2 - 2t$, $z = 1 + 3t$

11. $P_1(2, -1, -2)$; L_1: $x = 2 + 3t$, $y = 0$, $z = -1 - 2t$

12. $P_1(-1, 2, -3)$; L_1: $x = -1 + 5t$, $y = 1 + 2t$, $z = -1 + 3t$

In each of problems 13 through 16, find the equations of the line through P_1 and perpendicular to the given plane M_1.

13. $P_1(-2, 3, 1)$; $M_1: 2x + 3y + z - 3 = 0$
14. $P_1(1, -2, -3)$; $M_1: 3x - y - 2z + 4 = 0$
15. $P_1(-1, 0, -2)$; $M_1: x + 2z + 3 = 0$
16. $P_1(2, -1, -3)$; $M_1: x = 4$

In each of problems 17 through 20, find an equation of the plane through P_1 and parallel to the plane Φ.

17. $P_1(1, -2, -1)$; $\Phi: 3x + 2y - z + 4 = 0$
18. $P_1(-1, 3, 2)$; $\Phi: 2x + y - 3z + 5 = 0$
19. $P_1(2, -1, 3)$; $\Phi: x - 2y - 3z + 6 = 0$
20. $P_1(3, 0, 2)$; $\Phi: x + 2y + 1 = 0$

In each of problems 21 through 23, find equations of the line through P_1 parallel to the given line L.

21. $P_1(2, -1, 3)$; $L: \dfrac{x - 1}{3} = \dfrac{y + 2}{-2} = \dfrac{z - 2}{4}$

22. $P_1(0, 0, 1)$; $L: \dfrac{x + 2}{1} = \dfrac{y - 1}{3} = \dfrac{z + 1}{-2}$

23. $P_1(1, -2, 0)$; $L: \dfrac{x - 2}{2} = \dfrac{y + 2}{-1} = \dfrac{z - 3}{4}$

In each of problems 24 through 28, find the equation of the plane containing L_1 and L_2.

24. $L_1: \dfrac{x + 1}{2} = \dfrac{y - 2}{3} = \dfrac{z - 1}{1}$; $L_2: \dfrac{x + 1}{1} = \dfrac{y - 2}{-1} = \dfrac{z - 1}{2}$

25. $L_1: \dfrac{x - 1}{3} = \dfrac{y + 2}{2} = \dfrac{z - 2}{2}$; $L_2: \dfrac{x - 1}{1} = \dfrac{y + 2}{1} = \dfrac{z - 2}{0}$

26. $L_1: \dfrac{x + 2}{1} = \dfrac{y}{0} = \dfrac{z + 1}{2}$; $L_2: \dfrac{x + 2}{2} = \dfrac{y}{3} = \dfrac{z + 1}{1}$

27. $L_1: \dfrac{x}{2} = \dfrac{y - 1}{3} = \dfrac{z + 2}{-1}$; $L_2: \dfrac{x - 2}{2} = \dfrac{y + 1}{3} = \dfrac{z}{-1}$ $(L_1 \parallel L_2)$

28. $L_1: \dfrac{x - 2}{2} = \dfrac{y + 1}{-1} = \dfrac{z}{3}$; $L_2: \dfrac{x + 1}{2} = \dfrac{y}{-1} = \dfrac{z + 2}{3}$ $(L_1 \parallel L_2)$

In problems 29 and 30, find the equation of the plane through P_1 and the given line L.

29. $P_1(3, -1, 2)$; $L: \dfrac{x - 2}{2} = \dfrac{y + 1}{3} = \dfrac{z}{-2}$

30. $P_1(1, -2, 3)$; $L: x = -1 + t, \quad y = 2 + 2t, \quad z = 2 - 2t$

31. Show that the plane $2x - 3y + z - 2 = 0$ is parallel to the line

$$\frac{x-2}{1} = \frac{y+2}{1} = \frac{z+1}{1}.$$

32. Show that the plane $5x - 3y - z - 6 = 0$ contains the line

$$x = 1 + 2t, \qquad y = -1 + 3t, \qquad z = 2 + t.$$

33. A plane has attitude numbers A, B, C, and a line has direction numbers a, b, c. What condition must be satisfied in order that the plane and line be parallel?

5. ANGLES. DISTANCE FROM A POINT TO A PLANE

The angle between two lines was defined in Section 2. We recall that if line L_1 has direction cosines λ_1, μ_1, ν_1 and line L_2 has direction cosines λ_2, μ_2, ν_2, then

$$\cos \theta = \lambda_1\lambda_2 + \mu_1\mu_2 + \nu_1\nu_2,$$

where θ is the angle between L_1 and L_2.

DEFINITION. Let Φ_1 and Φ_2 be two planes, and let L_1 and L_2 be two lines which are perpendicular to Φ_1 and Φ_2, respectively. Then the *angle between Φ_1 and Φ_2* is, by definition, the angle between L_1 and L_2. Furthermore, we make the convention that we always select the acute angle between these lines as the angle between Φ_1 and Φ_2.

Theorem 8. *The angle θ between the planes $A_1x + B_1y + C_1z + D_1 = 0$ and $A_2x + B_2y + C_2z + D_2 = 0$ is given by*

$$\cos \theta = \frac{|A_1A_2 + B_1B_2 + C_1C_2|}{\sqrt{A_1^2 + B_1^2 + C_1^2}\,\sqrt{A_2^2 + B_2^2 + C_2^2}}.$$

Proof. From the definition of attitude numbers for a plane, we know that they are direction numbers of any line perpendicular to the plane. Converting to direction cosines, we get the above formula.

Corollary. *Two planes with attitude numbers A_1, B_1, C_1 and A_2, B_2, C_2 are perpendicular if and only if*

$$A_1A_2 + B_1B_2 + C_1C_2 = 0.$$

EXAMPLE 1. Find $\cos \theta$ where θ is the angle between the planes $3x - 2y + z = 4$ and $x + 4y - 3z - 2 = 0$.

Solution. Substituting in the formula of Theorem 8, we have

$$\cos \theta = \frac{|3 - 8 - 3|}{\sqrt{9 + 4 + 1}\sqrt{1 + 16 + 9}} = \frac{4}{\sqrt{91}}.$$

Two nonparallel planes intersect in a line. Every point on the line satisfies the equations of both planes and, conversely, every point which satisfies the equations of both planes must be on the line. *Therefore we may characterize any line in space by finding two planes which contain it.* Since every line has an unlimited number of planes which pass through it and since *any* two of them are sufficient to determine the line uniquely, we see that there is an unlimited number of ways of writing the equations of a line. The next example shows how to transform one representation into another.

EXAMPLE 2. The two planes

$$2x + 3y - 4z - 6 = 0 \quad \text{and} \quad 3x - y + 2z + 4 = 0$$

intersect in a line. (That is, the points which satisfy *both* equations determine the line.) Find a set of parametric equations of the line of intersection.

Solution. We solve the above equations for x and y in terms of z, getting

$$x = -\tfrac{2}{11}z - \tfrac{6}{11}, \quad y = \tfrac{16}{11}z + \tfrac{26}{11}$$

and

$$\frac{x + \tfrac{6}{11}}{-\tfrac{2}{11}} = \frac{y - \tfrac{26}{11}}{\tfrac{16}{11}} = \frac{z}{1}.$$

We can therefore write

$$x = -\tfrac{6}{11} - \tfrac{2}{11}t, \quad y = \tfrac{26}{11} + \tfrac{16}{11}t, \quad z = t,$$

which are the desired parametric equations.

Three planes may be parallel, may pass through a common line, may have no common points, or may have a unique point of intersection. If they have a unique point of intersection, the intersection point may be found by solving simultaneously the three equations of the planes. If they have no common point, an attempt to solve simultaneously will fail. A further examination will show whether or not two or more of the planes are parallel.

EXAMPLE 3. Determine whether or not the planes Φ_1: $3x - y + z - 2 = 0$; Φ_2: $x + 2y - z + 1 = 0$; Φ_3: $2x + 2y + z - 4 = 0$ intersect. If so, find the point of intersection.

Solution. Eliminating z between Φ_1 and Φ_2, we have

$$4x + y - 1 = 0. \tag{1}$$

Eliminating z between Φ_2 and Φ_3, we find

$$3x + 4y - 3 = 0. \tag{2}$$

We solve equations (1) and (2) simultaneously to get

$$x = \tfrac{1}{13}, \qquad y = \tfrac{9}{13}.$$

Substituting in the equation for Φ_1, we obtain $z = \tfrac{32}{13}$. Therefore the single point of intersection of the three planes is $(\tfrac{1}{13}, \tfrac{9}{13}, \tfrac{32}{13})$.

EXAMPLE 4.   Find the point of intersection of the plane $3x - y + 2z - 3 = 0$ and the line

$$\frac{x + 1}{3} = \frac{y + 1}{2} = \frac{z - 1}{-2}.$$

Solution. We write the equations of the line in parametric form:

$$x = -1 + 3t, \qquad y = -1 + 2t, \qquad z = 1 - 2t.$$

The point of intersection is given by a value of t; call it t_0. This point must satisfy the equation of the plane. We have

$$3(-1 + 3t_0) - (-1 + 2t_0) + 2(1 - 2t_0) - 3 = 0,$$

or

$$t_0 = 1.$$

The desired point is $(2, 1, -1)$.

Theorem 9. *The distance d from the point $P_1(x_1, y_1, z_1)$ to the plane*

$$Ax + By + Cz + D = 0$$

is given by

$$d = \frac{|Ax_1 + By_1 + Cz_1 + D|}{\sqrt{A^2 + B^2 + C^2}}.$$

Proof. We write the equations of the line L through P_1 which is perpendicular to the plane. They are

$$L: x = x_1 + At, \qquad y = y_1 + Bt, \qquad z = z_1 + Ct.$$

Denote by (x_0, y_0, z_0) the intersection of L and the plane. Then

$$d^2 = (x_1 - x_0)^2 + (y_1 - y_0)^2 + (z_1 - z_0)^2. \tag{3}$$

Also (x_0, y_0, z_0) is on both the line and the plane. Therefore, we have for some value t_0

$$x_0 = x_1 + At_0,$$
$$y_0 = y_1 + Bt_0,   \tag{4}$$
$$z_0 = z_1 + Ct_0$$

and

$$Ax_0 + By_0 + Cz_0 + D = 0$$
$$= A(x_1 + At_0) + B(y_1 + Bt_0) + C(z_1 + Ct_0) + D.$$

Thus, from (3) and (4), we write

$$d = \sqrt{A^2 + B^2 + C^2}\, |t_0|,$$

and now, inserting the relation

$$t_0 = \frac{-(Ax_1 + By_1 + Cz_1 + D)}{A^2 + B^2 + C^2}$$

in the preceding expression for d, we obtain the desired formula.

EXAMPLE 5. Find the distance from the point $(2, -1, 5)$ to the plane

$$3x + 2y - 2z - 7 = 0.$$

Solution.

$$d = \frac{|6 - 2 - 10 - 7|}{\sqrt{9 + 4 + 4}} = \frac{13}{\sqrt{17}}.$$

EXERCISES

In each of problems 1 through 4, find $\cos \theta$ where θ is the angle between the given planes.

1. $2x - y + 2z - 3 = 0,$ $3x + 2y - 6z - 11 = 0$
2. $x + 2y - 3z + 6 = 0,$ $x + y + z - 4 = 0$
3. $2x - y + 3z - 5 = 0,$ $3x - 2y + 2z - 7 = 0$
4. $x + 4z - 2 = 0,$ $y + 2z - 6 = 0$

In each of problems 5 through 8, find the equations in parametric form of the line of intersection of the given planes.

5. $3x + 2y - z + 5 = 0,$ $2x + y + 2z - 3 = 0$
6. $x + 2y + 2z - 4 = 0,$ $2x + y - 3z + 5 = 0$
7. $x + 2y - z + 4 = 0,$ $2x + 4y + 3z - 7 = 0$
8. $2x + 3y - 4z + 7 = 0,$ $3x - 2y + 3z - 6 = 0$

In each of problems 9 through 12, find the point of intersection of the given line and the given plane.

9. $3x - y + 2z - 5 = 0,$ $\dfrac{x-1}{2} = \dfrac{y+1}{3} = \dfrac{z-1}{-2}$

10. $2x + 3y - 4z + 15 = 0,$ $\dfrac{x+3}{2} = \dfrac{y-1}{-2} = \dfrac{z+4}{3}$

11. $x + 2z + 3 = 0,$ $\dfrac{x+1}{1} = \dfrac{y}{0} = \dfrac{z+2}{2}$

12. $2x + 3y + z - 3 = 0,$ $\dfrac{x+2}{2} = \dfrac{y-3}{3} = \dfrac{z-1}{1}$

In each of problems 13 through 16, find the distance from the given point to the given plane.

13. $(2, 1, -1),$ $x - 2y + 2z + 5 = 0$

14. $(3, -1, 2),$ $3x + 2y - 6z - 9 = 0$

15. $(-1, 3, 2),$ $2x - 3y + 4z - 5 = 0$

16. $(0, 4, -3),$ $3y + 2z - 7 = 0$

17. Find the equation of the plane through the line

$$\frac{x+1}{3} = \frac{y-1}{2} = \frac{z-2}{4}$$

which is perpendicular to the plane

$$2x + y - 3z + 4 = 0.$$

18. Find the equation of the plane through the line

$$\frac{x-2}{2} = \frac{y-2}{3} = \frac{z-1}{-2}$$

which is parallel to the line

$$\frac{x+1}{3} = \frac{y-1}{2} = \frac{z+1}{1}.$$

19. Find the equation of the plane through the line

$$\frac{x+2}{3} = \frac{y}{-2} = \frac{z+1}{2}$$

which is parallel to the line

$$\frac{x-1}{2} = \frac{y+1}{3} = \frac{z-1}{4}.$$

20. Find the equations of any line through the point $(1, 4, 2)$ which is parallel to the plane

$$2x + y + z - 4 = 0.$$

21. Find the equation of the plane through $(3, 2, -1)$ and $(1, -1, 2)$ which is parallel to the line

$$\frac{x - 1}{3} = \frac{y + 1}{2} = \frac{z}{-2}.$$

In each of problems 22 through 26, find all the points of intersection of the three given planes. If the three planes pass through a line, find the equations of the line in parametric form.

22. $2x + y - 2z - 1 = 0,\quad 3x + 2y + z - 10 = 0,\quad x + 2y - 3z + 2 = 0$
23. $x + 2y + 3z - 4 = 0,\quad 2x - 3y + z - 2 = 0,\quad 3x + 2y - 2z - 5 = 0$
24. $3x - y + 2z - 4 = 0,\quad x + 2y - z - 3 = 0,\quad 3x - 8y + 7z + 1 = 0$
25. $2x + y - 2z - 3 = 0,\quad x - y + z + 1 = 0,\quad x + 5y - 7z - 3 = 0$
26. $x + 2y + 3z - 5 = 0,\quad 2x - y - 2z - 2 = 0,\quad x - 8y - 13z + 11 = 0.$

In each of problems 27 through 29, find the equations in parametric form of the line through the given point P_1 which intersects and is perpendicular to the given line L.

27. $P_1(3, -1, 2);\quad L: \dfrac{x - 1}{2} = \dfrac{y + 1}{-1} = \dfrac{z}{3}$

28. $P_1(-1, 2, 3);\quad L: \dfrac{x}{2} = \dfrac{y - 2}{0} = \dfrac{z + 3}{-3}$

29. $P_1(0, 2, 4);\quad L: \dfrac{x - 1}{3} = \dfrac{y - 2}{1} = \dfrac{z - 3}{4}$

30. (a) If $A_1x + B_1y + C_1z + D_1 = 0$ and $A_2x + B_2y + C_2z + D_2 = 0$ are two intersecting planes, what is the locus of all points which satisfy

$$A_1x + B_1y + C_1z + D_1 + k(A_2x + B_2y + C_2z + D_2) = 0,$$

where k is a constant? (b) Find the equation of the plane passing through the point $(2, 1, -3)$ and the intersection of the planes $3x + y - z - 2 = 0$, $2x + y + 4z - 1 = 0$.

6. THE SPHERE. CYLINDERS

A *sphere* is the locus of all points at a given distance from a fixed point. The fixed point is called the *center* and the fixed distance is called the radius.

If the center is at the point (h, k, l), the radius is r, and (x, y, z) is any point on the sphere, then, from the formula for the distance between two points, we obtain the relation

$$(x - h)^2 + (y - k)^2 + (z - l)^2 = r^2. \tag{1}$$

Equation (1) is the *equation of a sphere*. If it is multiplied out and the terms collected we have the equivalent form

$$x^2 + y^2 + z^2 + Dx + Ey + Fz + G = 0. \tag{2}$$

EXAMPLE 1. Find the center and radius of the sphere with equation

$$x^2 + y^2 + z^2 + 4x - 6y + 9z - 6 = 0.$$

Solution. We complete the square by first writing

$$x^2 + 4x \quad + y^2 - 6y \quad + z^2 + 9z \quad = 6;$$

then, adding the appropriate quantities to both sides, we have

$$x^2 + 4x + 4 + y^2 - 6y + 9 + z^2 + 9z + \tfrac{81}{4} = 6 + 4 + 9 + \tfrac{81}{4}$$

and

$$(x + 2)^2 + (y - 3)^2 + (z + \tfrac{9}{2})^2 = \tfrac{157}{4}.$$

The center is at $(-2, 3, -\tfrac{9}{2})$ and the radius is $\tfrac{1}{2}\sqrt{157}$.

EXAMPLE 2. Find the equation of the sphere which passes through $(2, 1, 3)$, $(3, 2, 1)$, $(1, -2, -3)$, $(-1, 1, 2)$.

Solution. Substituting these points in the form (2) above for the equation of a sphere, we obtain

$$
\begin{aligned}
(2, 1, 3): \quad & 2D + E + 3F + G = -14, \\
(3, 2, 1): \quad & 3D + 2E + F + G = -14, \\
(1, -2, -3): \quad & D - 2E - 3F + G = -14, \\
(-1, 1, 2): \quad & -D + E + 2F + G = -6.
\end{aligned}
$$

Solving these by elimination (first G, then D, then F) we obtain, successively,

$$D + E - 2F = 0, \quad D + 3E + 6F = 0, \quad 3D + F = -8,$$

and

$$2E + 8F = 0, \quad -3E + 7F = -8; \quad \text{and so} \quad -38E = -64.$$

Therefore

$$E = \tfrac{32}{19}, \quad F = -\tfrac{8}{19}, \quad D = -\tfrac{48}{19}, \quad G = -\tfrac{178}{19}.$$

The desired equation is

$$x^2 + y^2 + z^2 - \tfrac{48}{19}x + \tfrac{32}{19}y - \tfrac{8}{19}z - \tfrac{178}{19} = 0.$$

FIGURE 17–13

A *cylindrical surface* is a surface which consists of a collection of parallel lines. Each of the parallel lines is called a *generator* of the *cylinder* or cylindrical surface.

The customary right circular cylinder of elementary geometry is clearly a special case of the type of cylinder we are considering. Figure 17–13 shows some examples of cylindrical surfaces. Note that a plane is a cylinder.

Theorem 10. *An equation of the form*

$$f(x, y) = 0$$

is a cylindrical surface with generators all parallel to the z-axis. The surface intersects the xy-plane in the curve

$$f(x, y) = 0, \qquad z = 0.$$

A similar result holds with axes interchanged.

Proof. Suppose that x_0, y_0 satisfies $f(x_0, y_0) = 0$. Then any point (x_0, y_0, z) for $-\infty < z < \infty$ satisfies the same equation, since z is absent. Therefore the line parallel to the z-axis through $(x_0, y_0, 0)$ is a generator.

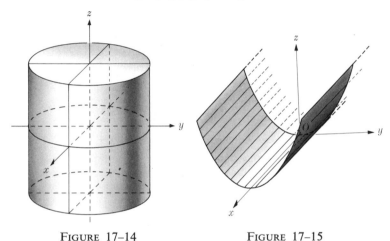

FIGURE 17–14   FIGURE 17–15

EXAMPLE 3. Describe and sketch the locus of the equation $x^2 + y^2 = 9$.

Solution. The locus is a right circular cylinder with generators parallel to the z-axis (Theorem 10). It is sketched in Fig. 17–14.

EXAMPLE 4. Describe and sketch the locus of the equation

$$y^2 = 4z.$$

Solution. According to Theorem 10 the locus is a cylinder with generators parallel to the x-axis. The intersection with the yz-plane is a parabola. The locus, called a parabolic cylinder, is sketched in Fig. 17–15.

EXERCISES

In each of problems 1 through 4, find the equation of the sphere with center C and radius r.

1. $C(2, 0, 1)$, $r = 4$ 2. $C(3, -2, 1)$, $r = 6$
3. $C(3, -2, 6)$, $r = 7$ 4. $C(2, 1, -4)$, $r = 3$

In each of problems 5 through 9, determine the locus of the equation. If it is a sphere find its center and radius.

5. $x^2 + y^2 + z^2 + 2x - 4z + 1 = 0$

6. $x^2 + y^2 + z^2 - 4x + 2y + 6z - 2 = 0$

7. $x^2 + y^2 + z^2 - 2x + 4y - 2z + 7 = 0$

8. $x^2 + y^2 + z^2 + 4x - 2y + 4z + 9 = 0$

9. $x^2 + y^2 + z^2 - 6x + 4y + 2z + 10 = 0$

10. Find the equation of the locus of all points which are twice as far from $A(3, -1, 2)$ as from $B(0, 2, -1)$.

11. Find the equation of the locus of all points which are three times as far from $A(2, 1, -3)$ as from $B(-2, -3, 5)$.

12. Find the equation of the locus of all points whose distances from the point $(0, 0, 4)$ are equal to their perpendicular distances from the xy-plane.

In each of problems 13 through 24, describe and sketch the locus of the given equation.

13. $x = 3$ 14. $x^2 + y^2 = 16$ 15. $2x + y = 3$

16. $x + 2z = 4$ 17. $x^2 = 4z$ 18. $z = 2 - y^2$

19. $4x^2 + y^2 = 16$ 20. $4x^2 - y^2 = 16$ 21. $y^2 + x^2 = 9$

22. $z^2 = 2 - 2x$ 23. $x^2 + y^2 - 2x = 0$ 24. $z^2 = y^2 + 4$

In each of problems 25 through 28, describe the curve of intersection, if any, of the given surface S and the given plane Φ.

25. $S: x^2 + y^2 + z^2 = 25$; $\Phi: z = 3$

26. $S: 4x = y^2 + z^2$; $\Phi: x = 4$

27. $S: x^2 + 2y^2 + 3z^2 = 12$; $\Phi: y = 4$

28. $S: x^2 + y^2 = z^2$; $\Phi: 2x + z = 4$

7. QUADRIC SURFACES

In the plane any equation of the form

$$Ax^2 + Bxy + Cy^2 + Dx + Ey + F = 0$$

is the representation of a curve. More specifically, we have found that circles, parabolas, ellipses, and hyperbolas, i.e., all conic sections, are represented by such second-degree equations.

In three-space the most general equation of the second degree in x, y, and z has the form

$$ax^2 + by^2 + cz^2 + dxy + exz + fyz + gx + hy + kz + l = 0, \qquad (1)$$

where the quantities $a, b, c, \ldots, l$ are positive or negative numbers or zero. The points in space satisfying such an equation all lie on a surface. Certain special cases, such as spheres and cylinders, were discussed in Section 6. Any second-degree equation which does not reduce to a cylinder, plane, line, or point corresponds to a surface which we call *quadric*. Quadric surfaces are classified into six types, and it can be shown that every second-degree equation which does not degenerate into a cylinder, a plane, etc., corresponds to one of these six types. The proof of this result involves the study of translation and rotation of coordinates in three-dimensional space, a topic beyond the scope of this book.

DEFINITIONS. The *x-, y-, and z-intercepts* of a surface are, respectively, the *x-*, *y-*, and *z*-coordinates of the points of intersection of the surface with the respective axes. When we are given an equation of a surface, we get the *x*-intercept by setting *y* and *z* equal to zero and solving for *x*. We proceed analogously for the *y-* and *z*-intercepts.

The *traces* of a surface on the coordinate planes are the curves of intersections of the surface with the coordinate planes. When we are given a surface, we obtain the trace on the *xz*-plane by first setting *y* equal to zero and then considering the resulting equation in *x* and *z* as the equation of a curve in the plane, as in plane analytic geometry. A *section of a surface by a plane* is the curve of intersection of the surface with the plane.

_____

EXAMPLE 1. Find the *x-, y-,* and *z*-intercepts of the surface

$$3x^2 + 2y^2 + 4z^2 = 12.$$

Describe the traces of this surface. Find the section of this surface by the plane $z = 1$ and by the plane $x = 3$.

Solution. We set $y = z = 0$, getting $3x^2 = 12$; the *x*-intercepts are at 2 and -2. Similarly, the *y*-intercepts are at $\pm\sqrt{6}$, the *z*-intercepts at $\pm\sqrt{3}$. To find the trace on the *xy*-plane, we set $z = 0$, getting

$$3x^2 + 2y^2 = 12 \quad \text{or} \quad \frac{x^2}{4} + \frac{y^2}{6} = 1.$$

We recognize this curve as an ellipse, with major semi-axis $\sqrt{6}$, minor semi-axis 2, foci at $(0, \sqrt{2}, 0)$, $(0, -\sqrt{2}, 0)$. Similarly, the trace on the *xz*-plane is the ellipse

$$\frac{x^2}{4} + \frac{z^2}{3} = 1,$$

and the trace on the *yz*-plane is the ellipse

$$\frac{y^2}{6} + \frac{z^2}{3} = 1.$$

The section of the surface by the plane $z = 1$ is the curve

$$3x^2 + 2y^2 + 4 = 12 \quad \text{or} \quad \frac{x^2}{8/3} + \frac{y^2}{4} = 1,$$

which we recognize as an ellipse. The section by the plane $x = 3$ is the curve

$$27 + 2y^2 + 4z^2 = 12 \quad \text{or} \quad 2y^2 + 4z^2 + 15 = 0.$$

Since the sum of three positive quantities can never be zero, we conclude that the plane $x = 3$ does not intersect the surface. The section is void.

DEFINITIONS. A surface is *symmetric with respect to the xy-plane* if and only if the point $(x, y, -z)$ lies on the surface whenever (x, y, z) does; *it is symmetric with respect to the x-axis* if and only if the point $(x, -y, -z)$ is on the locus whenever (x, y, z) is. Similar definitions are easily formulated for symmetry with respect to the remaining coordinate planes and axes.

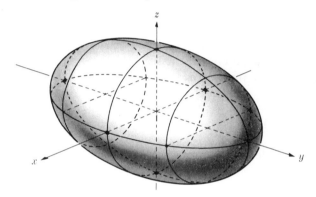

FIGURE 17–16

The notions of intercepts, traces, and symmetry are useful in the following description of the six types of quadric surfaces.

(i) An *ellipsoid* is the locus of an equation of the form

$$\frac{x^2}{A^2} + \frac{y^2}{B^2} + \frac{z^2}{C^2} = 1.$$

The surface is sketched in Fig. 17–16. The x-, y-, and z-intercepts are the numbers $\pm A$, $\pm B$, $\pm C$, respectively, and the traces on the xy-, xz-, and yz-planes are, respectively, the ellipses

$$\frac{x^2}{A^2} + \frac{y^2}{B^2} = 1, \quad \frac{x^2}{A^2} + \frac{z^2}{C^2} = 1, \quad \frac{y^2}{B^2} + \frac{z^2}{C^2} = 1.$$

Sections made by the planes $y = k$ (k a constant) are the similar ellipses

$$\frac{x^2}{A^2(1 - k^2/B^2)} + \frac{z^2}{C^2(1 - k^2/B^2)} = 1, \quad y = k, \quad -B < k < B.$$

Several such ellipses are drawn in Fig. 17–16.

If $A = B = C$, we obtain a sphere while, if two of the three numbers are equal, the surface is an *ellipsoid of revolution*, also called a *spheroid*. If, for example, $A = B$ and $C > A$, the surface is called a *prolate spheroid*, exemplified by a football. On the other hand, if $A = B$ and $C < A$, we have an *oblate spheroid*. The earth is approximately the shape of an oblate spheroid, with the section at the equator being circular and the distance between the North and South poles being smaller than the diameter of the equatorial circle.

(ii) An *elliptic hyperboloid of one sheet* is the locus of an equation of the form

$$\frac{x^2}{A^2} + \frac{y^2}{B^2} - \frac{z^2}{C^2} = 1.$$

A locus of such a surface is sketched in Fig. 17–17. The x-intercepts are at $\pm A$ and the y-intercepts at $\pm B$. As for the z-intercepts, we must solve the equation $-z^2/C^2 = 1$, which has no real solutions. Therefore the surface does not intersect the z-axis. The trace on the xy-plane is an ellipse, while the traces on the yz- and xz-planes are hyperbolas. The sections made by any plane $z = k$ are the ellipses

$$\frac{x^2}{A^2(1 + k^2/C^2)} + \frac{y^2}{B^2(1 + k^2/C^2)} = 1,$$

and the sections made by the planes $y = k$ are the hyperbolas

$$\frac{x^2}{A^2(1 - k^2/B^2)} - \frac{z^2}{C^2(1 - k^2/B^2)} = 1.$$

(iii) An *elliptic hyperboloid of two sheets* is the locus of an equation of the form

$$\frac{x^2}{A^2} - \frac{y^2}{B^2} - \frac{z^2}{C^2} = 1.$$

FIGURE 17–17

Such a locus is sketched in Fig. 17–18. We observe that we must have $|x| \geq A$, for otherwise the quantity $(x^2/A^2) < 1$ and the left side of the above equation will always be less than the right side. The x-intercepts are at $x = \pm A$. There are no y- and z-intercepts. The traces on the xz- and xy-planes are hyperbolas; there is no trace on the yz-plane. The sections made by the planes $x = k$ are the ellipses

$$\frac{y^2}{B^2(k^2/A^2 - 1)} + \frac{z^2}{C^2(k^2/A^2 - 1)} = 1, \qquad \text{if } |k| > A,$$

while the trace is void if $|k| < A$. The sections by the planes $y = k$ and $z = k$ are hyperbolas.

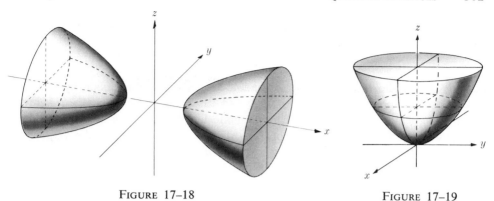

FIGURE 17–18   FIGURE 17–19

(iv) An *elliptic paraboloid* is the locus of an equation of the form

$$\frac{x^2}{A^2} + \frac{y^2}{B^2} = z.$$

A typical elliptic paraboloid is sketched in Fig. 17–19.

All three intercepts are 0; the traces on the yz- and xz-planes are parabolas, while the trace on the xy-plane consists of a single point, the origin. Sections made by planes $z = k$ are ellipses if $k > 0$, void if $k < 0$. Sections made by planes $x = k$ and $y = k$ are parabolas.

If $A = B$, we have a *paraboloid of revolution*, and the sections made by the planes $z = k, k > 0$ are circles. The reflecting surfaces of telescopes, automobile headlights, etc., are always paraboloids of revolution. (See Chapter 10, Section 2.)

(v) A *hyperbolic paraboloid* is the locus of an equation of the form

$$\frac{x^2}{A^2} - \frac{y^2}{B^2} = z.$$

Such a locus is sketched in Fig. 1–20. As in the elliptic paraboloid, all intercepts are zero. The trace on the xz-plane is a parabola opening upward; the trace

FIGURE 17–20

on the yz-plane is a parabola opening downward; and the trace on the xy-plane is the pair of intersecting straight lines

$$y = \pm(B/A)\,x.$$

As Fig. 17–20 shows, the surface is "saddle-shaped"; sections made by planes $x = k$ are parabolas opening downward and those made by planes $y = k$ are parabolas opening upward. The sections made by planes $z = k$ are hyperbolas facing one way if $k < 0$ and the other way if $k > 0$. The trace on the xy-plane corresponds to $k = 0$ and, as we saw, consists of two intersecting lines.

(vi) An *elliptic cone* is the locus of an equation of the form

$$\frac{x^2}{A^2} + \frac{y^2}{B^2} = \frac{z^2}{C^2}.$$

A typical cone of this type is shown in Fig. 17–21. Once again all intercepts are zero. The traces on the xz- and yz-planes are pairs of intersecting straight lines, while the trace on the xy-plane is a single point, the origin. Planes parallel to the coordinate planes yield sections which are the familiar conic sections of plane analytic geometry.

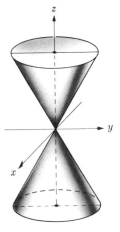

EXAMPLE 2.   Name and sketch the locus of

$$4x^2 - 9y^2 + 8z^2 = 72.$$

Indicate a few sections parallel to the coordinate plane.

Solution.   We divide by 72, getting

$$\frac{x^2}{18} - \frac{y^2}{8} + \frac{z^2}{9} = 1,$$

FIGURE 17–21

which is an elliptic hyperboloid of one sheet. The x-intercepts are $\pm 3\sqrt{2}$, the z-intercepts are ± 3, and there are no y-intercepts. The trace on the xy-plane is the hyperbola

$$\frac{x^2}{18} - \frac{y^2}{8} = 1,$$

the trace on the xz-plane is the ellipse

$$\frac{x^2}{18} + \frac{z^2}{9} = 1,$$

and the trace on the yz-plane is the hyperbola

$$\frac{z^2}{9} - \frac{y^2}{8} = 1.$$

The surface is sketched in Fig. 17–22.

FIGURE 17–22

EXERCISES

Name and sketch the locus of each of the following equations.

1. $\dfrac{x^2}{16} + \dfrac{y^2}{9} + \dfrac{z^2}{4} = 1$

2. $\dfrac{x^2}{9} + \dfrac{y^2}{12} + \dfrac{z^2}{9} = 1$

3. $\dfrac{x^2}{16} + \dfrac{y^2}{20} + \dfrac{z^2}{20} = 1$

4. $\dfrac{x^2}{16} + \dfrac{y^2}{9} - \dfrac{z^2}{4} = 1$

5. $\dfrac{x^2}{16} - \dfrac{y^2}{9} - \dfrac{z^2}{4} = 1$

6. $\dfrac{x^2}{16} - \dfrac{y^2}{9} + \dfrac{z^2}{4} = 1$

7. $\dfrac{y^2}{9} + \dfrac{z^2}{4} = 1 + \dfrac{x^2}{16}$

8. $-\dfrac{x^2}{16} - \dfrac{y^2}{9} + \dfrac{z^2}{4} = 1$

9. $\dfrac{x}{4} = \dfrac{y^2}{4} + \dfrac{z^2}{9}$

10. $z = \dfrac{y^2}{4} - \dfrac{x^2}{9}$

11. $y = \dfrac{x^2}{8} + \dfrac{z^2}{8}$

12. $z^2 = 4x^2 + 4y^2$

13. $y^2 = x^2 + z^2$

14. $z^2 = x^2 - y^2$

15. $2x^2 + 6y^2 - 3z^2 = 8$

16. $4x^2 - 3y^2 + 2z^2 = 0$

17. $3x = 2y^2 - 5z^2$

18. $\dfrac{y}{5} = 8z^2 - 2x^2$

8. TRANSLATION OF AXES

Figure 17–23(a) shows a rectangular coordinate system in three dimensions. Suppose we introduce a second rectangular coordinate system, with axes x', y', and z' so located that the x'-axis is parallel to the x-axis and h units from it, the y'-axis is parallel to the y-axis and k units from it, and the z'-axis is parallel to the z-axis and l units from it (Fig. 17–23b). A point P in space will have coordinates in both systems. If its coordinates are (x, y, z) in the original system and (x', y', z') in the second system, the equations

$$x' = x - h,$$
$$y' = y - k,$$
$$z' = z - l$$

(a)   (b)

FIGURE 17–23

hold. Two coordinate systems, xyz and $x'y'z'$, which satisfy these equations are said to be related by a *translation of axes*.

As in the case of plane analytic geometry (Chapter 10, Section 7), the method of translation of axes may be used to simplify second-degree equations, thereby making evident the nature of certain quadric surfaces. *The principal tool in this process is "completing the square."* We illustrate the method with several examples.

EXAMPLE 1. Use a translation of coordinates to identify the quadric surface

$$x^2 + 4y^2 + 3z^2 + 2x - 8y + 9z = 10.$$

Sketch.

Solution. We write

$$x^2 + 2x \qquad + 4(y^2 - 2y \qquad) + 3(z^2 + 3z \qquad) = 10.$$

Completing the square, we obtain

$$(x + 1)^2 + 4(y - 1)^2 + 3(z + \tfrac{3}{2})^2$$
$$= 10 + 1 + 4 + \tfrac{27}{4}.$$

Introducing the translation of coordinates

$$x' = x + 1,$$
$$y' = y - 1,$$
$$z' = z + \tfrac{3}{2},$$

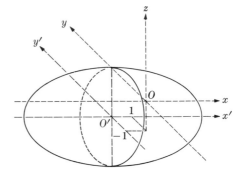

FIGURE 17–24

we find, for the equation of the surface,

$$x'^2 + 4y'^2 + 3z'^2 = \tfrac{87}{4},$$

which we recognize as an ellipsoid. The surface and both coordinate systems are sketched in Fig. 17–24.

EXAMPLE 2. Use a translation of coordinates to identify the surface

$$2x^2 - 3y^2 + 6x - 12y - 4z = 0.$$

Sketch.

Solution. We write the equation in the form

$$2(x^2 + 3x \qquad) - 3(y^2 + 4y \qquad) = 4z$$

and complete the square, getting

$$2(x + \tfrac{3}{2})^2 - 3(y + 2)^2 = 4z + \tfrac{9}{2} - 12$$
$$= 4(z - \tfrac{15}{8}).$$

The translation of axes

$$x' = x + \tfrac{3}{2}, \qquad y' = y + 2, \qquad z' = z - \tfrac{15}{8},$$

yields the equation

$$2x'^2 - 3y'^2 = 4z'.$$

Dividing by 4, we get

$$\frac{x'^2}{2} - \frac{y'^2}{4/3} = z',$$

which we see is a hyperbolic paraboloid. The surface and both coordinate systems are sketched in Fig. 17–25.

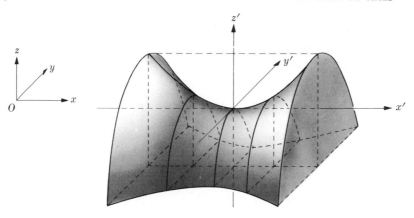

FIGURE 17–25

EXAMPLE 3. Use a translation of coordinates to identify the surface

$$4x^2 - 3y^2 + 2z^2 + 8x + 18y - 8z = 15.$$

Sketch.

Solution. We write

$$4(x^2 + 2x \qquad) - 3(y^2 - 6y \qquad) + 2(z^2 - 4z \qquad) = 15.$$

Completing the square, we obtain

$$4(x + 1)^2 - 3(y - 3)^2 + 2(z - 2)^2 = 15 + 4 - 27 + 8 = 0.$$

The translation of axes,

$$x' = x + 1, \qquad y' = y - 3, \qquad z' = z - 2,$$

shows that the surface is an elliptic cone with equation

$$4x'^2 + 2z'^2 = 3y'^2.$$

The surface and coordinate systems are shown in Fig. 17–26.

FIGURE 17–26

EXERCISES

In each of problems 1 through 12, employ a translation of coordinates to identify the locus. Sketch the surface, showing both coordinate systems.

1. $x^2 + y^2 + z^2 - 3x + 4y - 8z = 0$
2. $2x^2 + 4y^2 + 6z^2 - 2x + 4y - 15z = 10$
3. $x^2 + 2y^2 - z^2 + 2x + 4y - 6z = 18$
4. $x^2 + 4y^2 + z^2 - 3x + 2y - 4z + 9 = 0$
5. $x^2 + 8z^2 + 2x - 3y + 16z = 0$
6. $2x^2 + 3y^2 + 4x + 2z = 5$
7. $2y^2 - 3z^2 + 4x - 3y + 2z = 0$
8. $x^2 + y^2 - z^2 + 2x + 4y - 2z = 0$
9. $x^2 + y^2 - z^2 + 4x + 8y + 6z + 11 = 0$
10. $2x^2 - 5z^2 + 3x - 4y + 10z = 4$
11. $x^2 - y^2 + 2x - 3y + 4z = 0$
12. $x^2 - 2y^2 - 3z^2 + 4x - 6y + 8z = 2$
13. Use the rotation of coordinates in the plane

$$x = x' \cos\theta - y' \sin\theta, \qquad y = x' \sin\theta + y' \cos\theta,$$

(see Chapter 10, Section 8) to eliminate the xy-term in the equation of the surface

$$8x^2 - 4xy + 5y^2 + z^2 = 36.$$

Identify the surface and sketch.
14. Use the method of problem 13 to eliminate the xz-term in the equation

$$2x^2 + y^2 - 2z^2 + 3xz = 25.$$

Identify the surface and sketch.
15. Use a rotation of coordinates, as in problem 13, and a translation of coordinates to simplify and identify the surface

$$x^2 - 4xz + 2y^2 + 4z^2 - 3x + 2y - 4z = 5.$$

Sketch.
16. Use a rotation of coordinates, as in problem 13, to show that the equation

$$3x^2 = 2y + 2z$$

represents a parabolic cylinder.

9. OTHER COORDINATE SYSTEMS

In plane analytic geometry we employed a rectangular coordinate system for certain types of problems and a polar coordinate system for others. We saw that there are circumstances in which one system is more convenient than the other.

A similar situation prevails in three-dimensional geometry, and we now take up systems of coordinates other than the rectangular one which we have studied exclusively so far. One such system, known as *cylindrical coordinates*, is described in the following way. A point P in space with rectangular coordinates (x, y, z) may also be located by replacing the x- and y-values with the corresponding polar coordinates r, θ and by allowing the z-value to remain unchanged. In other words, to each ordered number triple of the form (r, θ, z), there is associated a point in space. The transformation from cylindrical to rectangular coordinates is given by the equations

$$x = r \cos \theta,$$

$$y = r \sin \theta,$$

$$z = z.$$

The transformation from rectangular to cylindrical coordinates is given by

$$r^2 = x^2 + y^2,$$

$$\tan \theta = \frac{y}{x},$$

$$z = z.$$

FIGURE 17–27

If the coordinates of a point are given in one system, the above equations show how to get the coordinates in the other. Figure 17–27 exhibits the relation between the two systems. It is always assumed that the origins of the systems coincide and that $\theta = 0$ corresponds to the xz-plane. We see that the locus $\theta = \text{const}$ consists of all points in a plane containing the z-axis. The locus $r = \text{const}$ consists of all points on a right circular cylinder with the z-axis as its central axis. (The term "cylindrical coordinates" comes from this fact.) The locus $z = \text{const}$ consists of all points in a plane parallel to the xy-plane.

EXAMPLE 1. Find the cylindrical coordinates of the points whose rectangular coordinates are $P(3, 3, 5)$, $Q(2, 0, -1)$, $R(0, 4, 4)$, $S(0, 0, 5)$, $T(2, 2\sqrt{3}, 1)$.

Solution. For the point P we have $r = \sqrt{9 + 9} = 3\sqrt{2}$, $\tan \theta = 1$, $\theta = \pi/4$, $z = 5$. Therefore the coordinates are $(3\sqrt{2}, \pi/4, 5)$. For Q we have $r = 2$, $\theta = 0$, $z = -1$. The coordinates are $(2, 0, -1)$. For R we get $r = 4$, $\theta = \pi/2$, $z = 4$. The result is $(4, \pi/2, 4)$. For S we see at once that the coordinates are $(0, \theta, 5)$ for any θ. For T we get $r = \sqrt{4 + 12} = 4$, $\tan \theta = \sqrt{3}$, $\theta = \pi/3$. The answer is $(4, \pi/3, 1)$.

Remark. Just as polar coordinates do not give a one-to-one correspondence between ordered number pairs and points in the plane, so cylindrical coordinates do not give a one-to-one correspondence between ordered number triples and points in space.

A *spherical coordinate system* is defined in the following way. A point P with rectangular coordinates (x, y, z) has spherical coordinates (ρ, θ, ϕ) where ρ is the distance of the point P from the origin, θ is the same quantity as in cylindrical coordinates, and ϕ is the angle that the line $\overline{OP}$ makes with the positive z-direction. Figure 17–28 exhibits the relation between rectangular and spherical coordinates. The transformation from spherical to rectangular coordinates is given by the equations

$$x = \rho \sin \phi \cos \theta,$$
$$y = \rho \sin \phi \sin \theta,$$
$$z = \rho \cos \phi.$$

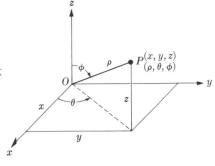

The transformation from rectangular to spherical coordinates is given by

$$\rho^2 = x^2 + y^2 + z^2,$$
$$\tan \theta = \frac{y}{x},$$
$$\cos \phi = \frac{z}{\sqrt{x^2 + y^2 + z^2}}.$$

FIGURE 17–28

We note that the locus $\rho = $ const is a sphere with center at the origin (from which is derived the term "spherical coordinates"). The locus $\theta = $ const is a plane through the z-axis, as in cylindrical coordinates. The locus $\phi = $ const is a cone with vertex at the origin and angle opening 2ϕ (see Fig. 17–29).

EXAMPLE 2. Find an equation in spherical coordinates of the sphere

$$x^2 + y^2 + z^2 - 2z = 0.$$

Sketch the locus.

Solution. We have $\rho^2 = x^2 + y^2 + z^2$ and $z = \rho \cos \phi$. Therefore

$$\rho^2 - 2\rho \cos \phi = 0 \equiv \rho(\rho - 2 \cos \phi) = 0.$$

The locus of this equation is the locus of $\rho = 0$ and $\rho - 2 \cos \phi = 0$. The locus of

FIGURE 17–29

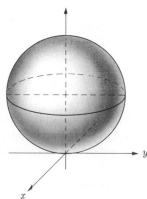

FIGURE 17–30

$\rho = 0$ is on the locus of $\rho - 2 \cos \phi = 0$ (with $\phi = \pi/2$). Plotting the surface

$$\rho = 2 \cos \phi,$$

we get the surface shown in Fig. 17–30.

If ρ is constant, then the quantities (θ, ϕ) form a coordinate system on the surface of a sphere. Latitude and longitude on the surface of the earth also form a coordinate system. If we restrict θ so that $-\pi < \theta \leq \pi$, then θ is called the *longitude* of the point in spherical coordinates. If ϕ is restricted so that $0 \leq \phi \leq \pi$, then ϕ is called the *colatitude* of the point. That is, ϕ is $(\pi/2) -$ latitude, where latitude is taken in the ordinary sense—i.e., positive north of the equator and negative south of it.

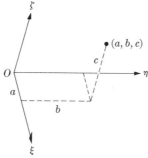

FIGURE 17–31

Any three lines in space which do not lie in a plane and which intersect in a point may be used as the axes of a coordinate system. Taking the point of intersection as origin, we mark off scales on each axis and so obtain an oblique system of coordinates (see Fig. 17–31). Calling the axes ξ, η, and ζ, we locate a point (a, b, c) by starting at the origin, proceeding a distance a along the ξ-axis, then going parallel to the η-axis a distance b, and finally traversing c units in a direction parallel to the ζ-axis.

EXERCISES

1. Find a set of cylindrical coordinates for each of the points whose rectangular coordinates are

   (a) $(3, 3, 7)$,   (b) $(4, 8, 2)$,   (c) $(-2, 3, 1)$.

2. Find the rectangular coordinates of the points whose cylindrical coordinates are

   (a) $(2, \pi/3, 1)$,   (b) $(3, -\pi/4, 2)$,   (c) $(7, 2\pi/3, -4)$.

3. Find a set of spherical coordinates for each of the points whose rectangular coordinates are

   (a) $(2, 2, 2)$,   (b) $(2, -2, -2)$,   (c) $(-1, \sqrt{3}, 2)$.

4. Find the rectangular coordinates of the points whose spherical coordinates are

(a) $(4, \pi/6, \pi/4)$,   (b) $(6, 2\pi/3, \pi/3)$,   (c) $(8, \pi/3, 2\pi/3)$.

5. Find a set of cylindrical coordinates for each of the points whose spherical co-ordinates are

(a) $(4, \pi/3, \pi/2)$,   (b) $(2, 2\pi/3, 5\pi/6)$,   (c) $(7, \pi/2, \pi/6)$.

6. Find a set of spherical coordinates for each of the points whose cylindrical co-ordinates are

(a) $(2, \pi/4, 1)$,   (b) $(3, \pi/2, 2)$,   (c) $(1, 5\pi/6, -2)$.

In each of problems 7 through 16, find an equation in cylindrical coordinates of the locus whose (x, y, z) equation is given. Sketch.

7. $x^2 + y^2 + z^2 = 9$ 8. $x^2 + y^2 + 2z^2 = 8$

9. $x^2 + y^2 = 4z$ 10. $x^2 + y^2 - 2x = 0$

11. $x^2 + y^2 = z^2$ 12. $x^2 + y^2 + 2z^2 + 2z = 0$

13. $x^2 - y^2 = 4$ 14. $xy + z^2 = 5$

15. $x^2 + y^2 - 4y = 0$ 16. $x^2 + y^2 + z^2 - 2x + 3y - 4z = 0$

In each of problems 17 through 22, find an equation in spherical coordinates of the locus whose (x, y, z) equation is given. Sketch.

17. $x^2 + y^2 + z^2 - 4z = 0$ 18. $x^2 + y^2 + z^2 + 2z = 0$

19. $x^2 + y^2 = z^2$ 20. $x^2 + y^2 = 4$

21. $x^2 + y^2 = 4z + 4$ (Solve for ρ in terms of ϕ.)

22. $x^2 + y^2 - z^2 + z - y = 0$

10. LINEAR INEQUALITIES

Every plane divides three-dimensional space into two regions. If a plane is represented by the equation

$$Ax + By + Cz + D = 0,$$

then all points on one side of the plane satisfy the inequality

$$Ax + By + Cz + D > 0,$$

and all points on the other side satisfy the opposite inequality.

Two intersecting planes divide three-space into four regions, each of which may be described by a pair of linear inequalities. For example, the intersecting planes

$$\Phi_1: x - y + 2z - 4 = 0, \qquad \Phi_2: x + 2y - z + 2 = 0,$$

separate three-space into four regions which we label R_1, R_2, R_3, and R_4. Every point in R_1 satisfies the pair of inequalities

$$x - y + 2z - 4 > 0, \qquad x + 2y - z + 2 > 0;$$

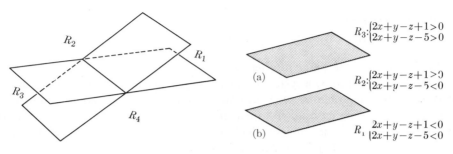

$$R_3: \begin{cases} 2x+y-z+1>0 \\ 2x+y-z-5>0 \end{cases}$$

(a)

$$R_2: \begin{cases} 2x+y-z+1>0 \\ 2x+y-z-5<0 \end{cases}$$

$$R_1 \quad \begin{matrix} 2x+y-z+1<0 \\ 2x+y-z-5<0 \end{matrix}$$

(b)

FIGURE 17–32   FIGURE 17–33

every point in R_2 satisfies the pair of inequalities

$$x - y + 2z - 4 > 0, \qquad x + 2y - z + 2 < 0,$$

and so forth. Figure 17–32 shows, in a schematic way, how Φ_1 and Φ_2 divide space into four regions.

Two parallel planes divide three-dimensional space into three regions. For example, the parallel planes

$$2x + y - z + 1 = 0, \qquad 2x + y - z - 5 = 0,$$

separate space into three regions, R_1, R_2, and R_3, as shown in Fig. 17–33. Note that it is impossible for the two inequalities

$$2x + y - z < -1, \qquad 2x + y - z > 5,$$

to hold simultaneously, and so there is no region corresponding to this pair of inequalities.

Three planes divide three-dimensional space into at most eight regions. If the planes are parallel or have a line in common, then the division is into fewer than eight regions. In fact, it is not difficult to see that three distinct planes always decompose the entire space into 4, 6, 7, or 8 regions, depending on the circumstances.

An enumeration of all possible types of regions into which four planes may separate space is lengthy and tedious. The student can verify that there can be at *most* $2^4 = 16$ regions. Similarly, it is not difficult to show that n planes can divide space into at most 2^n regions.

Rather than attempt to describe in a general way the manner in which a system of inequalities determines a region, we shall consider several special cases which are of particular interest.

The system of inequalities

$$x > 0, \qquad y > 0, \qquad z > 0$$

determines a region which we call the first octant. We recognize that $x = 0$ is the equation of the yz-plane. Similarly, $y = 0$ and $z = 0$ are the equations of the other two coordinate planes.

The four inequalities

$$x > 0, \qquad y > 0, \qquad z > 0, \qquad 2x + 2y + z - 2 < 0$$

enclose a region in the shape of a tetrahedron (Fig. 17–34).

A region determined by a system of linear inequalities has a boundary consisting of three parts. First, there are the parts we call *faces*, which are composed of portions of planes, such as triangles, quadrilaterals, etc. Two adjoining faces have in common a straight line segment which we call an *edge*. Finally, the points which are the intersections of edges are called *vertices*.

In the example of the tetrahedron in Fig. 17–34, the four vertices are at $A(1, 0, 0)$, $B(0, 1, 0)$, $C(0, 0, 2)$, and the origin O.

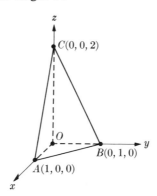

FIGURE 17–34

To determine the vertices of the boundary of a region defined by a system of linear inequalities, we may proceed by a method which is an extension of the one described in Chapter 3, Section 5. We do so by finding the vertices in a particular example.

———————

EXAMPLE. Determine the region in three-space (if any) which satisfies all the inequalities

$$L_1: x \geq 0, \qquad L_2: y \geq 0, \qquad L_3: z \geq 0,$$
$$L_4: -x - y - 2z + 4 \geq 0, \qquad L_5: -x - y - 4z + 6 \geq 0.$$

Solution. We have a system of five linear inequalities, and we find all possible points of intersections of the five corresponding equations. Since three planes determine a point, there are $5 \cdot 4 \cdot 3 / 1 \cdot 2 \cdot 3 = 10$ possible points of intersection. We find for these points of intersection:

$$P_1(0, 0, 0), \qquad P_2(0, 0, 2), \qquad P_3(0, 0, \tfrac{3}{2}), \qquad P_4(0, 4, 0),$$
$$P_5(0, 6, 0), \qquad P_6(0, 2, 1), \qquad P_7(4, 0, 0), \qquad P_8(6, 0, 0),$$
$$P_9(2, 0, 1), \qquad P_{10}(\text{no solution}).$$

The point P_1 was obtained by solving simultaneously L_1, L_2, and L_3; the point P_2 by solving simultaneously L_1, L_2, and L_4; the point P_3 by solving L_1, L_2, and L_5; and so forth.

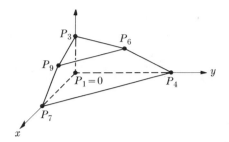

FIGURE 17–35

The coordinates of P_1 satisfy all five inequalities and, therefore, P_1 is a vertex of the region to be determined. The coordinates of P_2 do not satisfy L_5 and this point is rejected. Continuing, we see that the vertices of the region are the points P_1, P_3, P_4, P_6, P_7, and P_9 (see Fig. 17–35). To determine an edge of the boundary, we check the vertices by pairs. The vertices P_1 and P_7 connect an edge, since P_1 was obtained from L_1, L_2, and L_3, while P_7 was obtained from L_2, L_3, and L_4. In general, if two vertices have in common two of the planes determining their intersection, then the line segment joining them is an edge. The edges of the region are shown in Fig. 17–35. We also see why P_{10} could not be obtained. The planes $z = 0$, $x + y + 2z - 4 = 0$, and $x + y + 4z - 6 = 0$ intersect in parallel lines. (Note that the line through P_6 and P_9 is parallel to the line through P_4 and P_7.)

EXERCISES

In each of the following problems, determine the region, if any, which satisfies the given system of inequalities.

1. $x \geq 0$, $y \geq 0$, $z \geq 0$, $x + y + 2z - 4 \leq 0$

2. $x \geq 0$, $y > 0$, $z \geq 0$, $3x + 2y - 7 \leq 0$

3. $x > 0$, $y > 0$, $z < 0$, $x + 2y - 2z - 4 \leq 0$

4. $x \geq 0$, $y \geq 0$, $z \geq 0$, $2x + y - 5 \leq 0$, $z - 5 \leq 0$

5. $x \geq 0$, $y \geq 0$, $z \geq 0$, $3x + 2y - 9 \leq 0$, $x \leq 2$, $y \leq 2$

6. $x \geq 0$, $y \geq 0$, $z \geq 0$, $x + y + 3z - 9 \leq 0$, $x + y + 6z - 12 \leq 0$, $y \leq 15$

7. $x \leq 5$, $z \geq -2$, $y \leq 4$, $x - y \leq 1$, $z + x \geq 1$, $y + z \geq 2$

8. $x \geq 0$, $y \geq 0$, $z \geq 0$, $x + y + 2z - 1 \leq 0$, $3x + y \geq 12$

CHAPTER 18

Vectors in Three Dimensions

1. OPERATIONS WITH VECTORS

The development of vectors in three-dimensional space parallels the development in the plane, as given in Chapter 14. The student should review the material in that chapter, since the same notation and terminology will be employed here.

A *directed line segment* $\overrightarrow{AB}$ is defined as before, except that now the *base A* and the *head B* may be situated anywhere in three-space.

DEFINITION. A *vector* is the collection of all directed line segments having a given magnitude and a given direction.

Boldface letters will be used throughout for vectors. Any directed line segment in a collection forming a vector **v** is called a *representative* of the vector. The collection of directed line segments which defines a vector is called an *equivalence class* of directed line segments.

DEFINITIONS. The *length* of a vector is the common length of all its representative directed line segments. A *unit vector* is a vector of length one. Two vectors are said to be orthogonal (or perpendicular) if any representative of one vector is perpendicular to any representative of the other. The *zero vector*, denoted by **0**, is the class of directed line segments of zero length (i.e., simply points). We make the convention that the zero vector is orthogonal to all vectors.

FIGURE 18–1

Vectors may be added to yield other vectors. Suppose **u** and **v** are vectors. To add **u** and **v**, we first select a representative of **u**, say $\overrightarrow{AB}$ as shown in Fig. 18–1. Next we take the particular representative of **v** which has its base at the point B and label it $\overrightarrow{BC}$. We then draw the directed line segment $\overrightarrow{AC}$. The sum **w** of **u** and **v** is the equivalence class of directed line segments of which $\overrightarrow{AC}$ is a representative. We write

$$\mathbf{u} + \mathbf{v} = \mathbf{w}.$$

It is important to note that we could have started with any representative of **u**, say $\overrightarrow{A'B'}$, in Fig. 18–1. Then we could have selected the representative of **v** with base at B'. The directed line segments $\overrightarrow{AC}$ and $\overrightarrow{A'C'}$ are representatives of the same vector, as is evident from elementary geometry.

The addition of vectors and the multiplication of vectors by numbers satisfy the same rules of arithmetic as do vectors in the plane. (See p. 422.) These rules are:

$$\left.\begin{array}{r} \mathbf{u} + (\mathbf{v} + \mathbf{w}) = (\mathbf{u} + \mathbf{v}) + \mathbf{w} \\ c(d\mathbf{v}) = (cd)\mathbf{v} \end{array}\right\} \quad \text{Associative laws}$$

$$\mathbf{u} + \mathbf{v} = \mathbf{v} + \mathbf{u} \quad\quad \text{Commutative law}$$

$$\left.\begin{array}{r} (c + d)\mathbf{v} = c\mathbf{v} + d\mathbf{v} \\ c(\mathbf{u} + \mathbf{v}) = c\mathbf{u} + c\mathbf{v} \end{array}\right\} \quad \text{Distributive laws}$$

$$1 \cdot \mathbf{u} = \mathbf{u}, \quad 0 \cdot \mathbf{u} = \mathbf{0}, \quad (-1)\mathbf{u} = -\mathbf{u}.$$

Since $(-1)\mathbf{u} = -\mathbf{u}$, we can define *subtraction* of vectors in such a way that it is completely analogous to subtraction of vectors in the plane. In terms of representatives we construct the parallelogram, with $\overrightarrow{AB}$ and $\overrightarrow{DC}$ as two representatives of a vector **u** and $\overrightarrow{AD}$ and $\overrightarrow{BC}$ as representatives of a vector **v**. Then, as Fig. 18–2 shows, $\overrightarrow{AC}$ is a representative of the vector **w**, where

$$\mathbf{w} = \mathbf{u} + \mathbf{v},$$

and $\overrightarrow{BD}$ is a representative of the vector **t**, where

$$\mathbf{t} = \mathbf{v} + (-\mathbf{u}).$$

In other words,

$$\mathbf{t} = \mathbf{v} - \mathbf{u}.$$

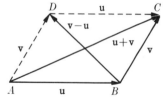

FIGURE 18–2

DEFINITIONS. Suppose that a rectangular coordinate system is given. We define the *vector* **i** to be a vector of unit length pointing in the direction of the positive x-axis. We define the *vector* **j** to be a vector of unit length pointing in the direction of the positive y-axis. We define the *vector* **k** to be a vector of unit length pointing in the direction of the positive z-axis.

Figure 18–3 shows a number of representatives of the vectors **i**, **j**, and **k**. The directed line segments $\overrightarrow{OA}$ and $\overrightarrow{DE}$ are representatives of **i**; the segments $\overrightarrow{OB}$ and $\overrightarrow{FG}$ are representatives of **j**; and the segments $\overrightarrow{OC}$ and $\overrightarrow{HJ}$ are representatives of **k**.

Theorem 1. *Every vector* **v** *in three-dimensional space may be written as a linear combination of* **i**, **j**, *and* **k**. *That is, there are numbers a, b, and c such that*

$$\mathbf{v} = a\mathbf{i} + b\mathbf{j} + c\mathbf{k}.$$

Proof. Select the representative $\overrightarrow{OA}$ of **v** which has its base at the origin (Fig. 18–4). Denote by $a\mathbf{i}$ the vector which has $\overrightarrow{OB}$ as representative, by $b\mathbf{j}$ the

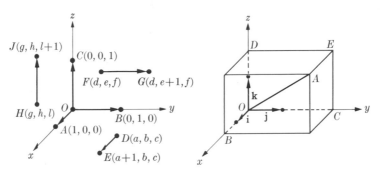

FIGURE 18–3   FIGURE 18–4

vector which has $\overrightarrow{OC}$ as representative, and by $c\mathbf{k}$ the vector which has $\overrightarrow{OD}$ as representative. Then, according to the law of addition of vectors, we see that $\mathbf{v} = a\mathbf{i} + b\mathbf{j} + c\mathbf{k}$.

Remark. The student should verify the result by taking a representative $\overrightarrow{FG}$ of $\mathbf{v}$ located in some general position in space.

———————

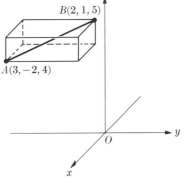

EXAMPLE 1. A vector $\mathbf{v}$ has the directed line segment $\overrightarrow{AB}$ as one of its representatives. Express $\mathbf{v}$ as a linear combination of $\mathbf{i}$, $\mathbf{j}$, and $\mathbf{k}$, if A has coordinates $(3, -2, 4)$ and B has coordinates $(2, 1, 5)$.

Solution. As shown in Fig. 18–5, the required quantities are $a = 2 - 3 = -1$, $b = 1 - (-2) = 3$, $c = 5 - 4 = 1$. Therefore,

$$\mathbf{v} = -\mathbf{i} + 3\mathbf{j} + \mathbf{k}.$$

———————

FIGURE 18–5

Corollary. *If a representative $\overrightarrow{AB}$ of a vector $\mathbf{v}$ has for its coordinates (x_A, y_A, z_A) and (x_B, y_B, z_B), then we have*

$$\mathbf{v} = (x_B - x_A)\mathbf{i} + (y_B - y_A)\mathbf{j} + (z_B - z_A)\mathbf{k}.$$

The result is evident from the way in which Theorem 1 was proved, and Example 1 shows how it works in practice.

Theorem 2. *If $\mathbf{v}$ is any vector which, by Theorem 1, may be written in the form*

$$\mathbf{v} = a\mathbf{i} + b\mathbf{j} + c\mathbf{k},$$

then the length of $\mathbf{v}$, which we denote by $|\mathbf{v}|$, is given by

$$|\mathbf{v}| = \sqrt{a^2 + b^2 + c^2}.$$

Therefore, $\mathbf{v} = \mathbf{0}$ if and only if $a = b = c = 0$.

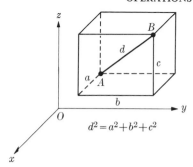

$$d^2 = a^2 + b^2 + c^2$$

FIGURE 18–6

Proof. If $\overrightarrow{AB}$ is a representative of **v**, the result follows (Fig. 18–6) from the formula for the distance between two points in three-dimensional space.

EXAMPLE 2. Find the length of the vector **v** = 2**i** − 3**j** + 4**k**.

Solution. $|\mathbf{v}| = \sqrt{2^2 + 3^2 + 4^2} = \sqrt{29}$.

The next theorem is obtained at once from the laws of addition of vectors and multiplication of vectors by numbers.

Theorem 3. *If* **v** = a**i** + b**j** + c**k** *and* **w** = d**i** + e**j** + f**k**, *then*

$$\mathbf{v} + \mathbf{w} = (a + d)\mathbf{i} + (b + e)\mathbf{j} + (c + f)\mathbf{k}.$$

Further, if h is any number, then

$$h\mathbf{v} = ha\mathbf{i} + hb\mathbf{j} + hc\mathbf{k}.$$

EXAMPLE 3. Given the vectors **u** = 3**i** − 2**j** + 4**k** and **v** = 6**i** − 4**j** − 2**k**, express the vector 3**u** − 2**v** in terms of **i**, **j**, and **k**.

Solution. 3**u** = 9**i** − 6**j** + 12**k** and −2**v** = −12**i** + 8**j** + 4**k**. Adding these vectors, we get 3**u** − 2**v** = −3**i** + 2**j** + 16**k**.

DEFINITION. Let **v** be any vector except **0**. The *unit vector* **u** *in the direction of* **v** is defined by

$$\mathbf{u} = \left(\frac{1}{|\mathbf{v}|}\right)\mathbf{v}.$$

EXAMPLE 4. Given the vector **v** = 2**i** − 3**j** + **k**, find a unit vector in the direction of **v**.

Solution. We have $|\mathbf{v}| = \sqrt{4 + 9 + 1} = \sqrt{14}$. The desired vector $\mathbf{u}$ is

$$\mathbf{u} = \frac{1}{\sqrt{14}}\mathbf{v} = \frac{2}{\sqrt{14}}\mathbf{i} - \frac{3}{\sqrt{14}}\mathbf{j} + \frac{1}{\sqrt{14}}\mathbf{k}.$$

EXAMPLE 5.   Given the vector $\mathbf{v} = 2\mathbf{i} + 4\mathbf{j} - 3\mathbf{k}$, find the representative $\overrightarrow{AB}$ of $\mathbf{v}$ if the point A has coordinates $(2, 1, -5)$.

Solution. Denote the coordinates of B by x_B, y_B, z_B. Then we have

$$x_B - 2 = 2, \qquad y_B - 1 = 4, \qquad z_B + 5 = -3.$$

Therefore, $x_B = 4, y_B = 5, z_B = -8$.

EXERCISES

In problems 1 through 6, express $\mathbf{v}$ in terms of $\mathbf{i}$, $\mathbf{j}$, and $\mathbf{k}$, given that the endpoints A and B of the representative $\overrightarrow{AB}$ of $\mathbf{v}$ have the given coordinates:

1. $A(3, 1, 0)$, $B(2, -1, 4)$ 2. $A(0, 1, 5)$, $B(-2, 1, 4)$
3. $A(1, 6, 2)$, $B(1, -4, -5)$ 4. $A(2, 2, 2)$, $B(0, 5, -1)$
5. $A(0, 0, 4)$, $B(4, 0, 0)$ 6. $A(-1, -3, 5)$, $B(2, 1, -4)$

In problems 7 through 10, in each case find a unit vector $\mathbf{u}$ in the direction of $\mathbf{v}$. Express $\mathbf{u}$ in terms of $\mathbf{i}$, $\mathbf{j}$, and $\mathbf{k}$.

7. $\mathbf{v} = 3\mathbf{i} + 2\mathbf{j} - 4\mathbf{k}$ 8. $\mathbf{v} = \mathbf{i} - \mathbf{j} + \mathbf{k}$
9. $\mathbf{v} = 2\mathbf{i} - 4\mathbf{j} - \mathbf{k}$ 10. $\mathbf{v} = -2\mathbf{i} + 3\mathbf{j} + 5\mathbf{k}$

In problems 11 through 17, find the representative $\overrightarrow{AB}$ of the vector $\mathbf{v}$ from the information given.

11. $\mathbf{v} = 2\mathbf{i} + \mathbf{j} - 3\mathbf{k}$, $A(1, 2, -1)$
12. $\mathbf{v} = -\mathbf{i} + 3\mathbf{j} - 2\mathbf{k}$, $A(2, 0, 4)$
13. $\mathbf{v} = 3\mathbf{i} + 2\mathbf{j} - 4\mathbf{k}$, $B(2, 0, -4)$
14. $\mathbf{v} = -2\mathbf{i} + 4\mathbf{j} + \mathbf{k}$, $B(0, 0, -5)$
15. $\mathbf{v} = \mathbf{i} - 2\mathbf{j} + 2\mathbf{k}$; the midpoint of the segment AB has coordinates $(2, -1, 4)$.
16. $\mathbf{v} = 3\mathbf{i} + 4\mathbf{k}$; the midpoint of the segment AB has coordinates $(1, 2, -5)$.
17. $\mathbf{v} = -\mathbf{i} + \mathbf{j} - 2\mathbf{k}$; the point three-fourths of the distance from A to B has coordinates $(1, 0, 2)$.
18. Find a vector $\mathbf{u}$ in the direction of $\mathbf{v} = -\mathbf{i} + \mathbf{j} - \mathbf{k}$ and having half the length of $\mathbf{v}$.
19. Given $\mathbf{u} = \mathbf{i} + 2\mathbf{j} - 4\mathbf{k}$, $\mathbf{v} = 3\mathbf{i} - 7\mathbf{j} + 5\mathbf{k}$, find $\mathbf{u} + \mathbf{v}$ in terms of $\mathbf{i}$, $\mathbf{j}$, and $\mathbf{k}$. Sketch a figure.
20. Given that $\mathbf{u} = -3\mathbf{i} + 7\mathbf{j} - 4\mathbf{k}$, $\mathbf{v} = 2\mathbf{i} + \mathbf{j} - 6\mathbf{k}$, find $3\mathbf{u} - 7\mathbf{v}$ in terms of $\mathbf{i}$, $\mathbf{j}$, and $\mathbf{k}$.
21. Let a and b be any real numbers. Show that the vector $\mathbf{k}$ is orthogonal to $a\mathbf{i} + b\mathbf{j}$.

2. THE INNER (SCALAR OR DOT) PRODUCT

Two vectors are said to be *parallel* or *proportional* when each is a scalar multiple of the other (and neither is zero). The representatives of parallel vectors are all parallel directed line segments.

By the *angle between two vectors* **v** *and* **w** (neither $=$ **0**), we mean the measure of the angle between any line containing a representative of **v** and an intersecting line containing a representative of **w** (Fig. 18–7). Two parallel vectors make an angle of 0 or π, depending on whether they are pointing in the same or opposite directions.

Theorem 4. *If θ is the angle between the vectors*

$$\mathbf{v} = a_1\mathbf{i} + a_2\mathbf{j} + a_3\mathbf{k}$$

and

$$\mathbf{w} = b_1\mathbf{i} + b_2\mathbf{j} + b_3\mathbf{k},$$

then

$$\cos\theta = \frac{a_1b_1 + a_2b_2 + a_3b_3}{|\mathbf{v}| \cdot |\mathbf{w}|}.$$

Representative of **w**

Representative of **v**

FIGURE 18–7

The proof is a straightforward extension of the proof of the analogous theorem in the plane (Theorem 4, p. 428) and will therefore be omitted. The proof is also a direct consequence of Theorem 3 of Chapter 17.

EXAMPLE 1. Given the vectors $\mathbf{v} = 2\mathbf{i} + \mathbf{j} - 3\mathbf{k}$ and $\mathbf{w} = -\mathbf{i} + 4\mathbf{j} - 2\mathbf{k}$, find the cosine of the angle between **v** and **w**.

Solution.   We have $|\mathbf{v}| = \sqrt{4 + 1 + 9} = \sqrt{14}$, $|\mathbf{w}| = \sqrt{1 + 16 + 4} = \sqrt{21}$.

Therefore

$$\cos\theta = \frac{-2 + 4 + 6}{\sqrt{14} \cdot \sqrt{21}} = \frac{8}{7\sqrt{6}}.$$

DEFINITIONS. Given the vectors **u** and **v**, we define the *inner (scalar or dot)* *product*

$$\mathbf{u} \cdot \mathbf{v}$$

by the formula

$$\mathbf{u} \cdot \mathbf{v} = |\mathbf{u}|\,|\mathbf{v}|\cos\theta,$$

where θ is the angle between the vectors. If either **u** or **v** is **0**, we define $\mathbf{u} \cdot \mathbf{v} = 0$. Two vectors **u** and **v** are *orthogonal* if and only if $\mathbf{u} \cdot \mathbf{v} = 0$.

Theorem 5. *The scalar product satisfies the laws*

(a) $\mathbf{u} \cdot \mathbf{v} = \mathbf{v} \cdot \mathbf{u}$;   (b) $\mathbf{u} \cdot \mathbf{u} = |\mathbf{u}|^2$.

(c) *If* $\mathbf{u} = a_1\mathbf{i} + b_1\mathbf{j} + c_1\mathbf{k}$ *and* $\mathbf{v} = a_2\mathbf{i} + b_2\mathbf{j} + c_2\mathbf{k}$,   *then*

$$\mathbf{u} \cdot \mathbf{v} = a_1a_2 + b_1b_2 + c_1c_2.$$

Proof. Parts (a) and (b) are direct consequences of the definition; part (c) follows from Theorem 4, since

$$\mathbf{u} \cdot \mathbf{v} = |\mathbf{u}| \cdot |\mathbf{v}| \cos\theta = |\mathbf{u}| \cdot |\mathbf{v}| \frac{a_1a_2 + b_1b_2 + c_1c_2}{|\mathbf{u}| \cdot |\mathbf{v}|}.$$

Corollary. (a) *If c and d are any numbers and if* $\mathbf{u}$, $\mathbf{v}$, $\mathbf{w}$ *are any vectors, then*

$$\mathbf{u} \cdot (c\mathbf{v} + d\mathbf{w}) = c(\mathbf{u} \cdot \mathbf{v}) + d(\mathbf{u} \cdot \mathbf{w}).$$

(b) *We have*

$$\mathbf{i} \cdot \mathbf{i} = \mathbf{j} \cdot \mathbf{j} = \mathbf{k} \cdot \mathbf{k} = 1, \qquad \mathbf{i} \cdot \mathbf{j} = \mathbf{i} \cdot \mathbf{k} = \mathbf{j} \cdot \mathbf{k} = 0.$$

EXAMPLE 1. Find the scalar product of the vectors

$$\mathbf{u} = 3\mathbf{i} + 2\mathbf{j} - 4\mathbf{k} \qquad \text{and} \qquad \mathbf{v} = -2\mathbf{i} + \mathbf{j} + 5\mathbf{k}.$$

Solution. $\mathbf{u} \cdot \mathbf{v} = 3(-2) + 2 \cdot 1 + (-4)(5) = -24.$

EXAMPLE 2. Express $|3\mathbf{u} + 5\mathbf{v}|^2$ in terms of $|\mathbf{u}|^2$, $|\mathbf{v}|^2$, and $\mathbf{u} \cdot \mathbf{v}$.

Solution.
$$\begin{aligned}
|3\mathbf{u} + 5\mathbf{v}|^2 &= (3\mathbf{u} + 5\mathbf{v}) \cdot (3\mathbf{u} + 5\mathbf{v}) \\
&= 9(\mathbf{u} \cdot \mathbf{u}) + 15(\mathbf{u} \cdot \mathbf{v}) + 15(\mathbf{v} \cdot \mathbf{u}) + 25(\mathbf{v} \cdot \mathbf{v}) \\
&= 9|\mathbf{u}|^2 + 30(\mathbf{u} \cdot \mathbf{v}) + 25|\mathbf{v}|^2.
\end{aligned}$$

DEFINITION. Let $\mathbf{v}$ and $\mathbf{w}$ be two vectors which make an angle θ. We denote by $|\mathbf{v}| \cos\theta$ the *projection of* $\mathbf{v}$ *along* $\mathbf{w}$. We also call this quantity the *component of* $\mathbf{v}$ *along* $\mathbf{w}$.

From the formula for $\cos\theta$, we may also write

$$|\mathbf{v}| \cos\theta = |\mathbf{v}| \frac{\mathbf{v} \cdot \mathbf{w}}{|\mathbf{v}| \cdot |\mathbf{w}|} = \frac{\mathbf{v} \cdot \mathbf{w}}{|\mathbf{w}|}.$$

EXAMPLE 3. Find the projection of $\mathbf{v} = -\mathbf{i} + 2\mathbf{j} + 3\mathbf{k}$ along $\mathbf{w} = 2\mathbf{i} - \mathbf{j} - 4\mathbf{k}$.

Solution. $\mathbf{v} \cdot \mathbf{w} = (-1)(2) + (2)(-1) + (3)(-4) = -16$; $|\mathbf{w}| = \sqrt{21}$. Therefore, the projection of $\mathbf{v}$ along $\mathbf{w} = -16/\sqrt{21}$.

An application of scalar product to mechanics occurs in the calculation of work done by a constant force $\mathbf{F}$ when its point of application moves along a segment from A to B. The *work done* in this case is defined as the product of the distance from A to B and the projection of $\mathbf{F}$ along $\mathbf{v}$ $(\overrightarrow{AB})$. We have

$$\text{Projection of } \mathbf{F} \text{ along } \mathbf{v} = \frac{\mathbf{F} \cdot \mathbf{v}}{|\mathbf{v}|};$$

since the distance from A to B is exactly $|\mathbf{v}|$, we conclude that

$$\text{Work done by } \mathbf{F} = \mathbf{F} \cdot \mathbf{v}.$$

EXAMPLE 4. Find the work done by the force

$$\mathbf{F} = 5\mathbf{i} - 3\mathbf{j} + 2\mathbf{k}$$

as its point of application moves from the point $A(2, 1, 3)$ to $B(4, -1, 5)$.

Solution. We have $\mathbf{v}(\overrightarrow{AB}) = (4 - 2)\mathbf{i} + (-1 - 1)\mathbf{j} + (5 - 3)\mathbf{k} = 2\mathbf{i} - 2\mathbf{j} + 2\mathbf{k}$. Therefore, work done $= 5 \cdot 2 + 3 \cdot 2 + 2 \cdot 2 = 20$.

Theorem 6. *If* $\mathbf{u}$ *and* $\mathbf{v}$ *are not* $\mathbf{0}$, *there is a unique number* k *such that* $\mathbf{v} - k\mathbf{u}$ *is orthogonal to* $\mathbf{u}$. *In fact,* k *can be found from the formula*

$$k = \frac{\mathbf{u} \cdot \mathbf{v}}{|\mathbf{u}|^2}.$$

Proof. $(\mathbf{v} - k\mathbf{u})$ is orthogonal to $\mathbf{u}$ if and only if $\mathbf{u} \cdot (\mathbf{v} - k\mathbf{u}) = 0$. But

$$\mathbf{u} \cdot (\mathbf{v} - k\mathbf{u}) = \mathbf{u} \cdot \mathbf{v} - k|\mathbf{u}|^2 = 0.$$

Therefore, selection of $k = \mathbf{u} \cdot \mathbf{v}/|\mathbf{u}|^2$ yields the result.

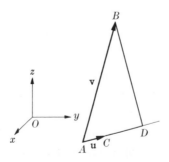

FIGURE 18–8

Figure 18–8 shows geometrically how k is to be selected. We drop a perpendicular from the head of $\mathbf{v}$ (point B) to the line containing $\mathbf{u}$ (point D). The directed segment $\overrightarrow{AD}$ gives the proper multiple of $\mathbf{u}(\overrightarrow{AC})$, and the directed segment $\overrightarrow{BD}$ represents the orthogonal vector.

EXAMPLE 5. Find a linear combination of $\mathbf{u} = 2\mathbf{i} + 3\mathbf{j} - \mathbf{k}$ and $\mathbf{v} = \mathbf{i} + 2\mathbf{j} + \mathbf{k}$ which is orthogonal to $\mathbf{u}$.

Solution. We select $k = (2 + 6 - 1)/14 = \frac{1}{2}$, and the desired vector is $\frac{1}{2}\mathbf{j} + \frac{3}{2}\mathbf{k}$.

EXERCISES

In problems 1 through 5, find $\cos\theta$ where θ is the angle between the vectors $\mathbf{u}$ and $\mathbf{v}$.

1. $\mathbf{u} = 2\mathbf{i} - 3\mathbf{j} + \mathbf{k}$, $\mathbf{v} = -\mathbf{i} + 2\mathbf{j} + \mathbf{k}$
2. $\mathbf{u} = \mathbf{i} + \mathbf{j} - 4\mathbf{k}$, $\mathbf{v} = -2\mathbf{i} + 3\mathbf{j} - 4\mathbf{k}$
3. $\mathbf{u} = 2\mathbf{i} + \mathbf{j} + 5\mathbf{k}$, $\mathbf{v} = -6\mathbf{i} + 2\mathbf{j} - 4\mathbf{k}$
4. $\mathbf{u} = \mathbf{i} + 2\mathbf{j} - 3\mathbf{k}$, $\mathbf{v} = -2\mathbf{i} - 4\mathbf{j} + 6\mathbf{k}$
5. $\mathbf{u} = 2\mathbf{i} + 3\mathbf{j} + \mathbf{k}$, $\mathbf{v} = 2\mathbf{i} + 4\mathbf{j} - 12\mathbf{k}$

In each of problems 6 through 10, find the projection of the vector $\mathbf{v}$ along $\mathbf{u}$.

6. $\mathbf{u} = 2\mathbf{i} - 6\mathbf{j} + 3\mathbf{k}$, $\mathbf{v} = \mathbf{i} + 2\mathbf{j} - 2\mathbf{k}$
7. $\mathbf{u} = 6\mathbf{i} + 2\mathbf{j} - 3\mathbf{k}$, $\mathbf{v} = -\mathbf{i} + 8\mathbf{j} + 4\mathbf{k}$
8. $\mathbf{u} = 12\mathbf{i} + 3\mathbf{j} + 4\mathbf{k}$, $\mathbf{v} = 4\mathbf{i} + 8\mathbf{j} + \mathbf{k}$
9. $\mathbf{u} = 3\mathbf{i} + 5\mathbf{j} - 4\mathbf{k}$, $\mathbf{v} = 4\mathbf{i} - 3\mathbf{j} + 5\mathbf{k}$
10. $\mathbf{u} = 2\mathbf{i} - 5\mathbf{j} + 3\mathbf{k}$, $\mathbf{v} = -\mathbf{i} + 2\mathbf{j} + 7\mathbf{k}$

In each of problems 11 through 14, find the work done by the force $\mathbf{F}$ when its point of application moves from A to B.

11. $\mathbf{F} = -32\mathbf{k}$, A: $(-1, 1, 2)$, B: $(3, 2, -1)$
12. $\mathbf{F} = 5\mathbf{i} - 2\mathbf{j} + 3\mathbf{k}$, A: $(1, -2, 2)$, B: $(3, 1, -1)$
13. $\mathbf{F} = -2\mathbf{i} + 3\mathbf{j} + 4\mathbf{k}$, A: $(2, -1, -2)$, B: $(-1, 2, 3)$
14. $\mathbf{F} = 3\mathbf{i} - 2\mathbf{j} - 3\mathbf{k}$, A: $(-1, 2, 3)$, B: $(2, 1, -1)$

In each of problems 15 through 17, find a unit vector in the direction of $\mathbf{u}$.

15. $\mathbf{u} = 2\mathbf{i} - 6\mathbf{j} + 3\mathbf{k}$ 16. $\mathbf{u} = -\mathbf{i} + 2\mathbf{k}$ 17. $\mathbf{u} = 3\mathbf{i} - 2\mathbf{j} + 7\mathbf{k}$

In each of problems 18 through 21, find the value of k so that $\mathbf{v} - k\mathbf{u}$ is orthogonal to $\mathbf{u}$. Also, find the value h so that $\mathbf{u} - h\mathbf{v}$ is orthogonal to $\mathbf{v}$.

18. $\mathbf{u} = 2\mathbf{i} - \mathbf{j} + 2\mathbf{k}$, $\mathbf{v} = 3\mathbf{i} + \mathbf{j} + 2\mathbf{k}$
19. $\mathbf{u} = 2\mathbf{i} - 3\mathbf{j} + 6\mathbf{k}$, $\mathbf{v} = 7\mathbf{i} + 14\mathbf{k}$
20. $\mathbf{u} = 3\mathbf{i} + 4\mathbf{j} - 5\mathbf{k}$, $\mathbf{v} = 9\mathbf{i} + 12\mathbf{j} - 5\mathbf{k}$
21. $\mathbf{u} = \mathbf{i} + 3\mathbf{j} - 2\mathbf{k}$, $\mathbf{v} = 6\mathbf{i} + 10\mathbf{j} - 3\mathbf{k}$
22. Write a detailed proof of Theorem 4.
23. Show that if $\mathbf{u}$ and $\mathbf{v}$ are any vectors ($\neq \mathbf{0}$), then $\mathbf{u}$ and $\mathbf{v}$ make equal angles with $\mathbf{w}$ if

$$\mathbf{w} = \left(\frac{|\mathbf{v}|}{|\mathbf{u}| + |\mathbf{v}|}\right)\mathbf{u} + \left(\frac{|\mathbf{u}|}{|\mathbf{u}| + |\mathbf{v}|}\right)\mathbf{v}.$$

24. Show that if **u** and **v** are any vectors, the vectors $|{\bf v}|{\bf u} + |{\bf u}|{\bf v}$ and $|{\bf v}|{\bf u} - |{\bf u}|{\bf v}$ are orthogonal.

In each of problems 25 through 27, determine the relation between g and h so that $g{\bf u} + h{\bf v}$ is orthogonal to **w**.

25. $\mathbf{u} = 3\mathbf{i} - 2\mathbf{j} + \mathbf{k}$, $\mathbf{v} = \mathbf{i} + 2\mathbf{j} - 3\mathbf{k}$, $\mathbf{w} = -\mathbf{i} + \mathbf{j} + 2\mathbf{k}$

26. $\mathbf{u} = 2\mathbf{i} + \mathbf{j} - 2\mathbf{k}$, $\mathbf{v} = \mathbf{i} - \mathbf{j} + \mathbf{k}$, $\mathbf{w} = -\mathbf{i} + 2\mathbf{j} + 3\mathbf{k}$

27. $\mathbf{u} = \mathbf{i} + 2\mathbf{j} - 3\mathbf{k}$, $\mathbf{v} = 3\mathbf{i} + \mathbf{j} - \mathbf{k}$, $\mathbf{w} = 4\mathbf{i} - \mathbf{j} + 2\mathbf{k}$

In each of problems 28 through 30, determine g and h so that $\mathbf{w} - g\mathbf{u} - h\mathbf{v}$ is orthogonal to both **u** and **v**.

28. $\mathbf{u} = 2\mathbf{i} - \mathbf{j} + \mathbf{k}$, $\mathbf{v} = \mathbf{i} + \mathbf{j} + 2\mathbf{k}$, $\mathbf{w} = 2\mathbf{i} - \mathbf{j} + 4\mathbf{k}$

29. $\mathbf{u} = \mathbf{i} + \mathbf{j} - 2\mathbf{k}$, $\mathbf{v} = -\mathbf{i} + 2\mathbf{j} + 3\mathbf{k}$, $\mathbf{w} = 5\mathbf{i} + 8\mathbf{k}$

30. $\mathbf{u} = 3\mathbf{i} - 2\mathbf{j}$, $\mathbf{v} = 2\mathbf{i} - \mathbf{k}$, $\mathbf{w} = 4\mathbf{i} - 2\mathbf{k}$

3. THE VECTOR OR CROSS PRODUCT

We saw in Section 2 that the scalar product of two vectors **u** and **v** is an operation which associates an ordinary number, or scalar, with each pair of vectors. The vector or cross product, on the other hand, is an operation which associates a vector with each ordered pair of vectors. However, before defining this operation, we shall discuss the notion of *right-handed* and *left-handed* triples of vectors.

Let **u** and **v** be two vectors (neither zero) which are not proportional. Then any two intersecting representatives determine a plane. Let **w** be a vector which is perpendicular to any such plane determined by **u** and **v**. We say that the triple, **u**, **v**, and **w**, forms a *right-handed triple* if the vectors are as shown in Fig. 18–9. They form a *left-handed triple* if they appear as in Fig. 18–10. A right-handed triple may be thought of as corresponding to a right-handed coordinate system with **u**, **v**, **w** corresponding to the x-, y-, and z-axes in orientation. A left-handed triple corresponds to a left-handed coordinate system.

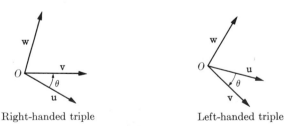

Right-handed triple   Left-handed triple

FIGURE 18–9   FIGURE 18–10

DEFINITION. Given the vectors **u** and **v**, we define the *vector or cross product* **u** $\times$ **v** as follows:

(i) If either **u** or **v** is **0**,

$$\mathbf{u} \times \mathbf{v} = \mathbf{0}.$$

(ii) If **u** is proportional to **v**,

$$\mathbf{u} \times \mathbf{v} = \mathbf{0}.$$

(iii) If otherwise,

$$\mathbf{u} \times \mathbf{v} = \mathbf{w},$$

where **w** is a vector perpendicular to a plane determined by **u** and **v**; the magnitude of **w** is

$$|\mathbf{w}| = |\mathbf{u}|\,|\mathbf{v}| \sin \theta,$$

where θ is the angle between **u** and **v**; finally, the direction of **w** is selected so that **u**, **v**, and **w** form a right-handed triple.

Remark. We shall always select the unit vectors **i**, **j**, and **k** so as to form a right-handed triple. (We have done so up to now without pointing out this fact specifically.)

We obtain at once from the definition of vector product the simple relations:

$$\mathbf{i} \times \mathbf{i} = \mathbf{j} \times \mathbf{j} = \mathbf{k} \times \mathbf{k} = 0;$$
$$\mathbf{i} \times \mathbf{j} = -\mathbf{j} \times \mathbf{i} = \mathbf{k};$$
$$\mathbf{j} \times \mathbf{k} = -\mathbf{k} \times \mathbf{j} = \mathbf{i};$$
$$\mathbf{k} \times \mathbf{i} = -\mathbf{i} \times \mathbf{k} = \mathbf{j}.$$

Theorem 7. *If*

$$\mathbf{u} = a_1\mathbf{i} + a_2\mathbf{j} + a_3\mathbf{k} \qquad and \qquad \mathbf{v} = b_1\mathbf{i} + b_2\mathbf{j} + b_3\mathbf{k},$$

then

$$\mathbf{u} \times \mathbf{v} = (a_2b_3 - a_3b_2)\mathbf{i} + (a_3b_1 - a_1b_3)\mathbf{j} + (a_1b_2 - a_2b_1)\mathbf{k}. \qquad (1)$$

The proof will be omitted. (It may be found in Morrey, *University Calculus*, p. 531.)

Corollary. *If* **u** *and* **v** *are any vectors, then*

(i) $\mathbf{u} \times \mathbf{v} = -\mathbf{v} \times \mathbf{u}$

(ii) $\mathbf{u} \times (\mathbf{v} + \mathbf{w}) = \mathbf{u} \times \mathbf{v} + \mathbf{u} \times \mathbf{w}.$

The results of this corollary are obtained by writing $\mathbf{u} = a_1\mathbf{i} + a_2\mathbf{j} + a_3\mathbf{k}$, $\mathbf{v} = b_1\mathbf{i} + b_2\mathbf{j} + b_3\mathbf{k}$, $\mathbf{w} = c_1\mathbf{i} + c_2\mathbf{j} + c_3\mathbf{k}$, and then applying the formula (1) for the cross product of two vectors.

EXAMPLE 1. Find the vector product $\mathbf{u} \times \mathbf{v}$ of $\mathbf{u} = 2\mathbf{i} - 3\mathbf{j} + \mathbf{k}$ and $\mathbf{v} = \mathbf{i} + \mathbf{j} - 2\mathbf{k}$.

Solution. Since $a_1 = 2$, $a_2 = -3$, $a_3 = 1$, $b_1 = 1$, $b_2 = 1$, $b_3 = -2$, we have

$$\mathbf{u} \times \mathbf{v} = (6 - 1)\mathbf{i} + (1 + 4)\mathbf{j} + (2 + 3)\mathbf{k} = 5\mathbf{i} + 5\mathbf{j} + 5\mathbf{k}.$$

Theorem 8. *The area of a parallelogram with adjacent sides $\overrightarrow{AB}$ and $\overrightarrow{AC}$ is given by*

$$|\mathbf{v}(\overrightarrow{AB}) \times \mathbf{v}(\overrightarrow{AC})|.$$

The area of $\triangle ABC$ is then $\frac{1}{2}|\mathbf{v}(\overrightarrow{AB}) \times \mathbf{v}(\overrightarrow{AC})|$.

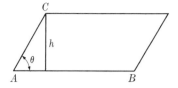

FIGURE 18-11

Proof. From Fig. 18-11, we see that the area of the parallelogram is $|AB| \cdot h = |AB| \cdot |AC| \sin \theta$. The result then follows from the definition of cross product.

EXAMPLE 2. Find the area of $\triangle ABC$ with $A(-2, 1, 3)$, $B(1, -1, 1)$, $C(3, -2, 4)$.

Solution. We have $\mathbf{v}(\overrightarrow{AB}) = 3\mathbf{i} - 2\mathbf{j} - 2\mathbf{k}$, $\mathbf{v}(\overrightarrow{AC}) = 5\mathbf{i} - 3\mathbf{j} + \mathbf{k}$. From Theorem 8 we obtain

$$\mathbf{v}(\overrightarrow{AB}) \times \mathbf{v}(\overrightarrow{AC}) = -8\mathbf{i} - 13\mathbf{j} + \mathbf{k}$$

and

$$\tfrac{1}{2}|-8\mathbf{i} - 13\mathbf{j} + \mathbf{k}| = \tfrac{1}{2}\sqrt{64 + 169 + 1} = \tfrac{3}{2}\sqrt{26}.$$

The vector product may be used to find the equation of a plane through three points. The next example illustrates the technique.

EXAMPLE 3. Find the equation of the plane through the points $A(-1, 1, 2)$, $B(1, -2, 1)$, $C(2, 2, 4)$.

Solution. A vector normal to the plane will be perpendicular to both the vectors

$$\mathbf{v}(\overrightarrow{AB}) = 2\mathbf{i} - 3\mathbf{j} - \mathbf{k}$$

and

$$\mathbf{v}(\overrightarrow{AC}) = 3\mathbf{i} + \mathbf{j} + 2\mathbf{k}.$$

One such vector is the cross product

$$\mathbf{v}(\overrightarrow{AB}) \times \mathbf{v}(\overrightarrow{AC}) = -5\mathbf{i} - 7\mathbf{j} + 11\mathbf{k}.$$

Therefore the numbers $-5, -7, 11$ form a set of *attitude numbers* (see Chapter 17, Section 4) of the desired plane. Using $A(-1, 1, 2)$ as a point on the plane, we get for the equation

$$-5(x + 1) - 7(y - 1) + 11(z - 2) = 0$$

or

$$5x + 7y - 11z + 20 = 0.$$

EXAMPLE 4. Find the perpendicular distance between the skew lines

$$L_1: \frac{x + 2}{2} = \frac{y - 1}{3} = \frac{z + 1}{-1}, \qquad L_2: \frac{x - 1}{-1} = \frac{y + 1}{2} = \frac{z - 2}{4}.$$

Solution. The vector $\mathbf{v}_1 = 2\mathbf{i} + 3\mathbf{j} - \mathbf{k}$ is a vector along L_1. The vector $\mathbf{v}_2 = -\mathbf{i} + 2\mathbf{j} + 4\mathbf{k}$ is a vector along L_2. A vector perpendicular to both $\mathbf{v}_1$ and $\mathbf{v}_2$ (i.e., to both L_1 and L_2) is

$$\mathbf{v}_1 \times \mathbf{v}_2 = 14\mathbf{i} - 7\mathbf{j} + 7\mathbf{k}.$$

Call this common perpendicular $\mathbf{w}$. The desired length may be obtained as a *projection*. Select any point on L_1 (call it P_1) and any point on L_2 (call it P_2). Then the desired length is the projection of the vector $\mathbf{v}(\overrightarrow{P_1P_2})$ along $\mathbf{w}$. To get this, we select $P_1(-2, 1, -1)$ on L_1 and $P_2(1, -1, 2)$ on L_2; and so

$$\mathbf{v}(\overrightarrow{P_1P_2}) = 3\mathbf{i} - 2\mathbf{j} + 3\mathbf{k}.$$

Therefore,

$$\text{Projection of } \mathbf{v}(\overrightarrow{P_1P_2}) \text{ along } \mathbf{w} = \frac{\mathbf{v}(\overrightarrow{P_1P_2}) \cdot \mathbf{w}}{|\mathbf{w}|}$$

$$= \frac{3 \cdot 14 + (-2)(-7) + 3(7)}{7\sqrt{6}} = \frac{11}{\sqrt{6}}.$$

EXERCISES

In each of problems 1 through 6, find the cross product $\mathbf{u} \times \mathbf{v}$.

1. $\mathbf{u} = 2\mathbf{i} + \mathbf{j} + \mathbf{k}$, $\mathbf{v} = -\mathbf{i} + 2\mathbf{j} + 3\mathbf{k}$
2. $\mathbf{u} = 2\mathbf{i} + \mathbf{j} - 3\mathbf{k}$, $\mathbf{v} = 2\mathbf{i} + 2\mathbf{j} - 4\mathbf{k}$
3. $\mathbf{u} = \mathbf{i} + 3\mathbf{j}$, $\mathbf{v} = 2\mathbf{i} - 5\mathbf{k}$
4. $\mathbf{u} = 3\mathbf{i} - 2\mathbf{j} + \mathbf{k}$, $\mathbf{v} = 3\mathbf{j} + 4\mathbf{k}$
5. $\mathbf{u} = 2\mathbf{i} + 4\mathbf{j} - 3\mathbf{k}$, $\mathbf{v} = -4\mathbf{i} - 8\mathbf{j} + 6\mathbf{k}$
6. $\mathbf{u} = 3\mathbf{i}$, $\mathbf{v} = 2\mathbf{j} + \mathbf{k}$

In problems 7 through 11, find in each case the area of $\triangle ABC$ and the equation of the plane through A, B, and C.

7. $A(1, -2, 3)$, $B(3, 1, 2)$, $C(2, 3, -1)$
8. $A(3, 2, -2)$, $B(4, 1, 2)$, $C(1, 2, 3)$
9. $A(2, -1, 1)$, $B(3, 2, -1)$, $C(-1, 3, 2)$
10. $A(1, -2, 3)$, $B(2, -1, 1)$, $C(4, 2, -1)$
11. $A(-2, 3, 1)$, $B(4, 2, -2)$, $C(2, 0, 1)$

In problems 12 through 14, find in each case the perpendicular distance between the given lines.

12. $\dfrac{x+1}{2} = \dfrac{y-3}{-3} = \dfrac{z+2}{4}$; $\dfrac{x-2}{3} = \dfrac{y+1}{2} = \dfrac{z-1}{5}$

13. $\dfrac{x-1}{3} = \dfrac{y+1}{2} = \dfrac{z-1}{5}$; $\dfrac{x+2}{4} = \dfrac{y-1}{3} = \dfrac{z+1}{-2}$

14. $\dfrac{x+1}{2} = \dfrac{y-1}{-4} = \dfrac{z+2}{3}$; $\dfrac{x}{3} = \dfrac{y}{5} = \dfrac{z-2}{-2}$

In problems 15 through 19, use vector methods to find, in each case, the equations in symmetric form of the line through the given point P and parallel to the two given planes.

15. $P(-1, 3, 2)$, $3x - 2y + 4z + 2 = 0$, $2x + y - z = 0$

16. $P(2, 3, -1)$, $x + 2y + 2z - 4 = 0$, $2x + y - 3z + 5 = 0$

17. $P(1, -2, 3)$, $3x + y - 2z + 3 = 0$, $2x + 3y + z - 6 = 0$

18. $P(-1, 0, -2)$, $2x + 3y - z + 4 = 0$, $3x - 2y + 2z - 5 = 0$

19. $P(3, 0, 1)$, $x + 2y = 0$, $3y - z = 0$

In problems 20 and 21, find in each case equations in symmetric form of the line of intersection of the given planes. Use the method of vector products.

20. $2(x - 1) + 3(y + 1) - 4(z - 2) = 0$

     $3(x - 1) - 4(y + 1) + 2(z - 2) = 0$

21. $3(x + 2) - 2(y - 1) + 2(z + 1) = 0$

     $(x + 2) + 2(y - 1) - 3(z + 1) = 0$

In each of problems 22 through 26, find an equation of the plane through the given point or points and parallel to the given line or lines.

22. $(1, 3, 2)$; $\dfrac{x + 1}{2} = \dfrac{y - 2}{-1} = \dfrac{z + 3}{3}$; $\dfrac{x - 2}{1} = \dfrac{y + 1}{-2} = \dfrac{z + 2}{2}$

23. $(2, -1, -3)$; $\dfrac{x - 1}{3} = \dfrac{y + 2}{2} = \dfrac{z}{-4}$; $\dfrac{x}{2} = \dfrac{y - 1}{-3} = \dfrac{z - 2}{2}$

24. $(2, 1, -2)$; $(1, -1, 3)$; $\dfrac{x + 1}{3} = \dfrac{y - 1}{2} = \dfrac{z - 2}{2}$

25. $(1, -2, 3)$; $(-1, 2, -1)$; $\dfrac{x - 2}{2} = \dfrac{y + 1}{3} = \dfrac{z - 1}{4}$

26. $(0, 1, 2)$; $(2, 0, 1)$; $\dfrac{x - 1}{3} = \dfrac{y + 1}{0} = \dfrac{z + 1}{1}$

In problems 27 through 29, find in each case the equation of the plane through the line L_1 which also satisfies the additional condition.

27. L_1: $\dfrac{x - 1}{2} = \dfrac{y + 1}{3} = \dfrac{z - 2}{1}$;   through $(2, 1, 1)$

28. L_1: $\dfrac{x - 2}{2} = \dfrac{y - 2}{3} = \dfrac{z - 1}{-2}$;   parallel to $\dfrac{x + 1}{3} = \dfrac{y - 1}{2} = \dfrac{z + 1}{1}$

29. L_1: $\dfrac{x + 1}{1} = \dfrac{y - 1}{2} = \dfrac{z - 2}{-2}$;   perpendicular to $2x + 3y - z + 4 = 0$

In problems 30 and 31, find the equation of the plane through the given points and perpendicular to the given planes.

30. $(1, 2, -1)$; $2x - 3y + 5z - 1 = 0$; $3x + 2y + 4z + 6 = 0$

31. $(-1, 3, 2)$; $(1, 6, 1)$; $3x - y + 4z - 7 = 0$

In problems 32 and 33, find equations in symmetric form of the line through the given point which is perpendicular to and intersects the given line. Use the cross product.

32. $(3, 3, -1);$ $\dfrac{x}{-1} = \dfrac{y-3}{1} = \dfrac{z+1}{1}$

33. $(3, -2, 0);$ $\dfrac{x-4}{3} = \dfrac{y-4}{-4} = \dfrac{z-5}{-1}$

34. Assuming Theorem 7, write out the details of the proof that

$$\mathbf{u} \times \mathbf{v} = -\mathbf{v} \times \mathbf{u}.$$

35. Assuming Theorem 7, write out the details of the proof that

$$\mathbf{u} \times (\mathbf{v} + \mathbf{w}) = \mathbf{u} \times \mathbf{v} + \mathbf{u} \times \mathbf{w}.$$

36. Show that if $\mathbf{u}$, $\mathbf{v}$, and $\mathbf{w}$ are any three vectors, then

$$(\mathbf{u} \times \mathbf{v}) \cdot \mathbf{w} = \mathbf{u} \cdot (\mathbf{v} \times \mathbf{w}).$$

4. DERIVATIVES OF VECTOR FUNCTIONS. SPACE CURVES. TANGENTS AND ARC LENGTH

In Chapter 14, Section 4, we discussed two-dimensional vector functions and their derivatives. We now extend these definitions to vectors in space. The following theorem can be established in the same way as was the corresponding theorem in the two-dimensional case.

Theorem 9. *Suppose that*

$$\mathbf{f}(t) = f_1(t)\mathbf{i} + f_2(t)\mathbf{j} + f_3(t)\mathbf{k}$$

is a vector function and that the vector $\mathbf{c} = c_1\mathbf{i} + c_2\mathbf{j} + c_3\mathbf{k}$ *is a constant. Then*

(a) $\mathbf{f}(t) \to \mathbf{c}$ *as* $t \to a$ *if and only if*

$$f_1(t) \to c_1 \quad and \quad f_2(t) \to c_2 \quad and \quad f_3(t) \to c_3.$$

(b) $\mathbf{f}$ *is continuous at* a *if and only if* $f_1, f_2,$ *and* f_3 *are.*

(c) $\mathbf{f}'(t)$ *exists if and only if* $f_1'(t), f_2'(t),$ *and* $f_3'(t)$ *do.*

(d) *We have the formulas*

$$\mathbf{f}'(t) = f_1'(t)\mathbf{i} + f_2'(t)\mathbf{j} + f_3'(t)\mathbf{k}.$$

(e) *If* $\mathbf{v}(t) = a\mathbf{w}(t),$ *then* $\mathbf{v}'(t) = a\mathbf{w}'(t)$ *where* a *is a constant.*

(f) *If* $\mathbf{v}(t) = c(t)\mathbf{w}(t),$ *then*

$$\mathbf{v}'(t) = c(t)\mathbf{w}'(t) + c'(t)\mathbf{w}(t).$$

(g) *If* $\mathbf{v}(t) = \mathbf{w}(t)/c(t)$, *then*

$$\mathbf{v}'(t) = \frac{c(t)\mathbf{w}'(t) - c'(t)\mathbf{w}(t)}{[c(t)]^2}.$$

EXAMPLE 1. Given $\mathbf{f}(t) = 3t^2\mathbf{i} - 2t^3\mathbf{j} + (t^2 + 3)\mathbf{k}$, find $\mathbf{f}'(t)$, $\mathbf{f}''(t)$, $\mathbf{f}'''(t)$.

Solution. $\mathbf{f}'(t) = 6t\mathbf{i} - 6t^2\mathbf{j} + 2t\mathbf{k}$,
$\quad\quad\mathbf{f}''(t) = 6\mathbf{i} - 12t\mathbf{j} + 2\mathbf{k}$,
$\quad\quad\mathbf{f}'''(t) = -12\mathbf{j}$.

The next theorem shows how to differentiate functions involving scalar and vector products.

Theorem 10. *If* $\mathbf{u}(t)$ *and* $\mathbf{v}(t)$ *are differentiable, then the derivative of* $f(t) =$ $\mathbf{u}(t) \cdot \mathbf{v}(t)$ *is given by the formula*

$$f'(t) = \mathbf{u}(t) \cdot \mathbf{v}'(t) + \mathbf{u}'(t) \cdot \mathbf{v}(t). \tag{2}$$

The derivative of $\mathbf{w}(t) = \mathbf{u}(t) \times \mathbf{v}(t)$ *is given by the formula*

$$\mathbf{w}'(t) = \mathbf{u}(t) \times \mathbf{v}'(t) + \mathbf{u}'(t) \times \mathbf{v}(t). \tag{3}$$

The proofs of formulas (2) and (3) follow from the corresponding differentiation formulas for ordinary functions. Note that in formula (3) it is essential to retain the order of the factors in each vector product.

EXAMPLE 2. Find the derivative

$$f'(t) \text{ of } f(t) = \mathbf{u}(t) \cdot \mathbf{v}(t) \quad\quad \text{and} \quad\quad \mathbf{w}'(t) \text{ of } \mathbf{w}(t) = \mathbf{u}(t) \times \mathbf{v}(t)$$

if

$$\mathbf{u}(t) = (t + 3)\mathbf{i} + t^2\mathbf{j} + (t^3 - 1)\mathbf{k} \quad\quad \text{and} \quad\quad \mathbf{v}(t) = 2t\mathbf{i} + (t^4 - 1)\mathbf{j} + (2t + 3)\mathbf{k}.$$

Solution. By formula (2) we have

$$\begin{aligned}
f'(t) &= [(t + 3)\mathbf{i} + t^2\mathbf{j} + (t^3 - 1)\mathbf{k}] \cdot (2\mathbf{i} + 4t^3\mathbf{j} + 2\mathbf{k}) \\
&\quad + (\mathbf{i} + 2t\mathbf{j} + 3t^2\mathbf{k}) \cdot [2t\mathbf{i} + (t^4 - 1)\mathbf{j} + (2t + 3)\mathbf{k}] \\
&= (2t + 6) + 4t^5 + 2t^3 - 2 + 2t + 2t^5 - 2t + 6t^3 + 9t^2 \\
&= 6t^5 + 8t^3 + 9t^2 + 2t + 4.
\end{aligned}$$

According to (3), we have

$$\begin{aligned}
\mathbf{w}'(t) &= [(t + 3)\mathbf{i} + t^2\mathbf{j} + (t^3 - 1)\mathbf{k}] \times (2\mathbf{i} + 4t^3\mathbf{j} + 2\mathbf{k}) \\
&\quad + (\mathbf{i} + 2t\mathbf{j} + 3t^2\mathbf{k}) \times [2t\mathbf{i} + (t^4 - 1)\mathbf{j} + (2t + 3)\mathbf{k}].
\end{aligned}$$

Computing the two cross products on the right, we get

$$\mathbf{w}'(t) = (-7t^6 + 4t^3 + 9t^2 + 6t)\mathbf{i} + (8t^3 - 4t - 11)\mathbf{j} + (5t^4 + 12t^3 - 6t^2 - 1)\mathbf{k}.$$

Consider a rectangular coordinate system and a directed line segment from the origin O to a point P in space. As in two dimensions, we denote the vector $\mathbf{v}(\overrightarrow{OP})$ by $\mathbf{r}$. We define an *arc* C in space in a way completely analogous to that in which an arc in the plane was defined. (See page 388.) The vector equation

$$\mathbf{r}(t) = x(t)\mathbf{i} + y(t)\mathbf{j} + z(t)\mathbf{k}$$

is considered to be equivalent to the parametric equations

$$x = x(t), \qquad y = y(t), \qquad z = z(t),$$

which represent an arc C in space.

The definition of *length* of an arc C in three-space is identical with its definition in the plane. If we denote the length of an arc by $l(C)$ we get, in a way that is similar to the two-dimensional analysis, the formulas

$$l(C) = \int_a^b \sqrt{[x'(t)]^2 + [y'(t)]^2 + [z'(t)]^2}\, dt \qquad (4)$$

and

$$s'(t) = \sqrt{[x'(t)]^2 + [y'(t)]^2 + [z'(t)]^2} \qquad (5)$$

where $s(t)$ is an arc length function. We could also write the above formulas (4) and (5) in the vector form

$$l(C) = \int_a^b |\mathbf{r}'(t)|\, dt, \qquad s'(t) = |\mathbf{r}'(t)|.$$

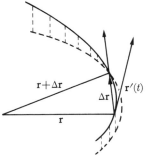

FIGURE 18–12

DEFINITIONS. If $\mathbf{r}'(t) \neq \mathbf{0}$, we define the vector $\mathbf{T}(t) = \mathbf{r}'(t)/|\mathbf{r}'(t)|$ as the *unit tangent vector* to the path corresponding to the value t. The line through the point P_0 corresponding to $\mathbf{r}(t_0)$ and parallel to $\mathbf{T}(t_0)$ is called the *tangent line to the arc* at t_0; the line directed in the same way as $\mathbf{T}(t_0)$ is called the *directed tangent line* at t_0 (Fig. 18–12).

EXAMPLE 3. The locus of the equations

$$x = a \cos t, \qquad y = a \sin t, \qquad z = bt \qquad (6)$$

is called a *helix*.

(a) Find $s'(t)$. (b) Find the length of that part of the helix for which $0 \le t \le 2\pi$. (c) Show that the unit tangent vector makes a constant angle with the z-axis.

Solution. (See Fig. 18–13 for the graph.)

(a) $x'(t) = -a \sin t$, $y'(t) = a \cos t$, $z'(t) = b$. Therefore, (a) $s'(t) = \sqrt{a^2 + b^2}$.

(b) $l(C) = 2\pi\sqrt{a^2 + b^2}$.

(c) $\mathbf{T}(t) = \dfrac{-y\mathbf{i} + x\mathbf{j} + b\mathbf{k}}{\sqrt{a^2 + b^2}}$.

Letting ϕ be the angle between $\mathbf{T}$ and $\mathbf{k}$, we get

$$\cos \phi = b/\sqrt{a^2 + b^2}.$$

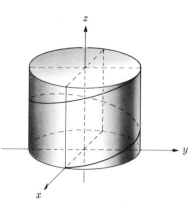

FIGURE 18–13

Remark. We note that the helix (6) winds around the cylinder $x^2 + y^2 = a^2$.

DEFINITIONS. If t denotes time in the parametric equations of an arc $\mathbf{r}(t)$, then $\mathbf{r}'(t)$ is the *velocity vector* $\mathbf{v}(t)$, and $\mathbf{r}''(t) = \mathbf{v}'(t)$ is called the *acceleration vector*. The quantity $s'(t)$ (a scalar) is called the *speed* of the particle moving according to the law

$$\mathbf{r}(t) = x(t)\mathbf{i} + y(t)\mathbf{j} + z(t)\mathbf{k}.$$

EXERCISES

In problems 1 through 6, find in each case the derivatives $\mathbf{f}'(t)$ and $\mathbf{f}''(t)$.

1. $\mathbf{f}(t) = (2t + 1)\mathbf{i} + t^2\mathbf{j} + (3t - 2)\mathbf{k}$

2. $\mathbf{f}(t) = (\cos t)\mathbf{i} + (2 \sin t)\mathbf{j} + (3t)\mathbf{k}$

3. $\mathbf{f}(t) = e^{2t}\mathbf{i} + e^{-2t}\mathbf{j} + 2\mathbf{k}$

4. $\mathbf{f}(t) = \dfrac{t}{t + 2}\mathbf{i} + \dfrac{t^2}{1 + t}\mathbf{j} + 3t^2\mathbf{k}$

5. $\mathbf{f}(t) = (\cos 2t)\mathbf{i} + \dfrac{1}{t}\mathbf{j} + (\sin 2t)\mathbf{k}$

6. $\mathbf{f}(t) = (\ln t)\mathbf{i} + e^{-t}\mathbf{j} + (t \ln t)\mathbf{k}$

In problems 7 through 9, find in each case either $f'(t)$ or $\mathbf{f}'(t)$, whichever is appropriate.

7. $f(t) = \mathbf{u}(t) \cdot \mathbf{v}(t)$, where

$$\mathbf{u}(t) = 3t\mathbf{i} + 2t^2\mathbf{j} + \frac{1}{t}\mathbf{k}, \qquad \mathbf{v} = t^2\mathbf{i} + \frac{1}{t}\mathbf{j} + t^3\mathbf{k}.$$

8. $\mathbf{f}(t) = \mathbf{u}(t) \times \mathbf{v}(t)$, where
$$\mathbf{u}(t) = (\cos t)\mathbf{i} + (\sin t)\mathbf{j} + t\mathbf{k}, \qquad \mathbf{v}(t) = (\sin t)\mathbf{i} + (\cos t)\mathbf{j} + t^2\mathbf{k}.$$

9. $f(t) = \mathbf{u}(t) \cdot [\mathbf{v}(t) \times \mathbf{w}(t)]$, where

$$\mathbf{u}(t) = t\mathbf{i} + (t + 1)\mathbf{k}, \qquad \mathbf{v}(t) = t^2\mathbf{j}, \qquad \mathbf{w}(t) = \frac{1}{t^2}\mathbf{k}.$$

In problems 10 through 13, find $l(C)$.

10. C: $x = t$, $y = t^2/\sqrt{2}$, $z = t^3/3$; $0 \le t \le 2$

11. C: $x = t$, $y = 3t^2/2$, $z = 3t^3/2$; $0 \le t \le 2$

12. C: $x = t$, $y = \ln(\sec t + \tan t)$, $z = \ln \sec t$; $0 \le t \le \pi/4$

13. C: $x = t \cos t$, $y = t \sin t$, $z = t$; $0 \le t \le \pi/2$

In problems 14 through 16, the parameter t is the time in seconds. Taking s to be the length in feet, in each case find the velocity, speed, and acceleration.

14. $\mathbf{r}(t) = t^2\mathbf{i} + 2t\mathbf{j} + (t^3 - 1)\mathbf{k}$

15. $\mathbf{r}(t) = (t \sin t)\mathbf{i} + (t \cos t)\mathbf{j} + t\mathbf{k}$

16. $\mathbf{r}(t) = e^{3t}\mathbf{i} + e^{-3t}\mathbf{j} + te^{3t}\mathbf{k}$

5. TANGENTIAL AND NORMAL COMPONENTS. THE MOVING TRIHEDRAL

We consider the locus of the equation

$$\mathbf{r} = \mathbf{r}(t)$$

or

$$\mathbf{r}(t) = x(t)\mathbf{i} + y(t)\mathbf{j} + z(t)\mathbf{k}.$$

In the last section, we defined the *unit tangent vector* $\mathbf{T}(t)$ by the relation

$$\mathbf{T}(t) = \frac{\mathbf{r}'(t)}{|\mathbf{r}'(t)|},$$

which we could also write

$$\mathbf{T}(t) = \frac{\mathbf{r}'(t)}{s'(t)} = \frac{d\mathbf{r}}{ds}.$$

Now, since $\mathbf{T} \cdot \mathbf{T} = 1$ for all t, we differentiate this relation with respect to t to obtain

$$\mathbf{T}(t) \cdot \mathbf{T}'(t) + \mathbf{T}'(t) \cdot \mathbf{T}(t) = 2\mathbf{T}(t) \cdot \mathbf{T}'(t) = 0.$$

Therefore, the vector $\mathbf{T}'(t)$ is orthogonal to $\mathbf{T}(t)$. We define the vector $\kappa(t)$ by the relation

$$\kappa(t) = \frac{d\mathbf{T}}{ds} = \frac{\mathbf{T}'(t)}{s'(t)}.$$

Taking the scalar product of κ and $\mathbf{T}$, we see that

$$\kappa(t) \cdot \mathbf{T}(t) = \frac{1}{s'(t)} \mathbf{T}'(t) \cdot \mathbf{T}(t) = 0,$$

and so κ is orthogonal to $\mathbf{T}$. The vector κ is the vector rate of change of direction of the curve with respect to arc length. Bearing in mind the definition of curvature of a plane curve (see Chapter 12, Section 4, and Chapter 14, Section 6), we make the following definitions.

DEFINITIONS. The vector $\kappa(t)$, defined above, is called the *curvature vector* of the curve $\mathbf{r} = \mathbf{r}(t)$. The magnitude $|\kappa(t)| = \kappa(t)$ is called the curvature. If $\kappa(t) \neq 0$, we define the *principal normal vector* $\mathbf{N}(t)$ and the *binormal vector* $\mathbf{B}(t)$ by the relations

$$\mathbf{N}(t) = \frac{\kappa(t)}{|\kappa(t)|}, \qquad \mathbf{B}(t) = \mathbf{T}(t) \times \mathbf{N}(t).$$

The *center of curvature* $C(t)$ is defined by the equation

$$\mathbf{v}[\overrightarrow{OC}(t)] = \mathbf{r}(t) + \frac{1}{\kappa(t)} \mathbf{N}(t).$$

The *radius of curvature* is $R(t) = 1/\kappa(t)$. The *osculating plane* corresponding to t is the plane which contains the tangent line to the path and the center of curvature at t; it is defined only for those values of t for which $\kappa(t) \neq 0$.

EXAMPLE 1. Given the curve

$$x = t, \qquad y = t^2, \qquad z = 1 + t^2,$$

find $\mathbf{T}(t)$ and $\kappa(t)$.

Solution. We may write

$$\mathbf{r}(t) = t\mathbf{i} + t^2\mathbf{j} + (1 + t^2)\mathbf{k}.$$

Therefore

$$\mathbf{r}'(t) = \mathbf{i} + 2t\mathbf{j} + 2t\mathbf{k}$$

and

$$|\mathbf{r}'(t)| = \sqrt{1 + 8t^2} = s'(t).$$

Since $\mathbf{T} = \mathbf{r}'(t)/|\mathbf{r}'(t)|$, we have

$$\mathbf{T}(t) = \frac{1}{\sqrt{1 + 8t^2}} (\mathbf{i} + 2t\mathbf{j} + 2t\mathbf{k}).$$

We may differentiate to get

$$\mathbf{T}'(t) = \frac{-8t}{(1 + 8t^2)^{3/2}} (\mathbf{i} + 2t\mathbf{j} + 2t\mathbf{k}) + \frac{1}{\sqrt{1 + 8t^2}} (2\mathbf{j} + 2\mathbf{k}).$$

Hence

$$\kappa(t) = \frac{\mathbf{T}'(t)}{s'(t)} = \frac{-8t}{(1 + 8t^2)^2} (\mathbf{i} + 2t\mathbf{j} + 2t\mathbf{k}) + \frac{1}{1 + 8t^2} (2\mathbf{j} + 2\mathbf{k})$$

$$= \frac{-8t}{(1 + 8t^2)^2} \mathbf{i} + \frac{2}{(1 + 8t^2)^2} \mathbf{j} + \frac{2}{(1 + 8t^2)^2} \mathbf{k}.$$

It is clear from the definitions of $\mathbf{T}$ and $\mathbf{N}$ that they are unit vectors which are orthogonal. From the definition of cross product, we see at once that $\mathbf{B}$ is a unit vector orthogonal to both $\mathbf{T}$ and $\mathbf{N}$. The triple $\mathbf{T}(t)$, $\mathbf{N}(t)$, $\mathbf{B}(t)$ form a mutually orthogonal triple of unit vectors at each point, the *trihedral* at the point. (It is assumed that $\kappa(t) \neq 0$.) We may also write the formulas

$$\frac{d\mathbf{T}}{ds} = \kappa\mathbf{N} \quad \text{or} \quad \mathbf{T}'(t) = \kappa(t)s'(t)\,\mathbf{N}(t).$$

The equation of the osculating plane at $t = t_0$ is given by

$$b_1(x - x_0) + b_2(y - y_0) + b_3(z - z_0) = 0,$$

where (x_0, y_0, z_0) is the point on the curve corresponding to $t = t_0$ and $\mathbf{B}(t_0) = b_1\mathbf{i} + b_2\mathbf{j} + b_3\mathbf{k}$.

EXAMPLE 2. Given the helix

$$x = 4\cos t, \quad y = 4\sin t, \quad z = 2t$$

or, equivalently,

$$\mathbf{r}(t) = (4\cos t)\mathbf{i} + (4\sin t)\mathbf{j} + (2t)\mathbf{k},$$

find **T**, **N**, and **B** for $t = 2\pi/3$. Also find κ, the equation of the osculating plane, and the equations of the tangent line.

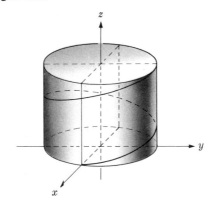

FIGURE 18–14

Solution. The curve is shown in Fig. 18–14. We have

$$x' = -4\sin t, \quad y' = 4\cos t, \quad z' = 2, \quad s' = 2\sqrt{5},$$

$$\mathbf{T} = \frac{1}{2\sqrt{5}}(-y\mathbf{i} + x\mathbf{j} + 2\mathbf{k}), \quad \mathbf{T}'(t) = \frac{1}{2\sqrt{5}}(-x\mathbf{i} - y\mathbf{j}).$$

We compute

$$\kappa(t) = \frac{|\mathbf{T}'(t)|}{s'(t)} = \frac{1}{5}$$

and, using the formula $\mathbf{T}'(t) = \kappa(t)s'(t)\mathbf{N}(t)$, we get

$$\mathbf{N}(t) = -(\cos t)\mathbf{i} - (\sin t)\mathbf{j}.$$

For $t = 2\pi/3$, $x_0 = -2$, $y_0 = 2\sqrt{3}$, $z_0 = 4\pi/3$, we obtain

$$\mathbf{T} = \frac{1}{\sqrt{5}}(-\sqrt{3}\,\mathbf{i} - \mathbf{j} + \mathbf{k}), \qquad \mathbf{N} = \frac{1}{2}\mathbf{i} - \frac{\sqrt{3}}{2}\mathbf{j},$$

$$\mathbf{B} = \frac{1}{2\sqrt{5}}(\sqrt{3}\,\mathbf{i} + \mathbf{j} + 4\mathbf{k}), \qquad \kappa\left(\frac{2\pi}{3}\right) = \frac{1}{5}.$$

The tangent line is

$$\frac{x+2}{\sqrt{3}} = \frac{y - 2\sqrt{3}}{1} = \frac{z - 4\pi/3}{-1},$$

and the equation of the osculating plane is

$$\sqrt{3}\,(x+2) + (y - 2\sqrt{3}) + 4(z - 4\pi/3) = 0.$$

DEFINITIONS. *If a particle moves according to the law* $\mathbf{r} = \mathbf{r}(t)$, *the tangential* and *normal components* of any vector are its components along $\mathbf{T}$ and $\mathbf{N}$, respectively.

Theorem 11. *If a particle moves according to the law* $\mathbf{r} = \mathbf{r}(t)$, *with* t *the time and* $\mathbf{T}(t)$, $\mathbf{N}(t)$, $R(t)$ *defined as above, then the acceleration vector* $\mathbf{a}(t) = \mathbf{v}'(t)$ *satisfies the equation*

$$\mathbf{a}(t) = s''(t)\mathbf{T}(t) + \frac{|\mathbf{v}(t)|^2}{R(t)}\mathbf{N}(t). \tag{1}$$

Proof. Since $\mathbf{v}(t) = \mathbf{r}'(t)$, we have, from the definition of $\mathbf{T}(t)$, that

$$\mathbf{v}(t) = s'(t)\mathbf{T}(t).$$

We differentiate this equation and obtain

$$\mathbf{a}(t) = s''(t)\mathbf{T}(t) + s'(t)\mathbf{T}'(t).$$

The relation $\mathbf{T}'(t) = \kappa(t)s'(t)\mathbf{N}(t)$ yields

$$\mathbf{a}(t) = s''(t)\mathbf{T}(t) + \kappa(t)[s'(t)]^2\mathbf{N}(t).$$

We observe that $|\mathbf{v}(t)| = s'(t)$ and $\kappa(t) = 1/R(t)$, and the proof is complete.

Remark. Since $\mathbf{T}$, $\mathbf{N}$, and $\mathbf{B}$ are mutually orthogonal vectors, formula (1) shows that $s''(t)$ and $|\mathbf{v}(t)|^2/R(t)$ are the tangential and normal components, respectively, of $\mathbf{a}(t)$.

EXAMPLE 3. A particle moves according to the law

$$x = t, \qquad y = t^2, \qquad z = t^3.$$

Find its vector velocity and acceleration, its speed, the unit vectors **T** and **N**, and the normal and tangential components of the acceleration vector, all at $t = 1$.

Solution. Since $\mathbf{r}(t) = t\mathbf{i} + t^2\mathbf{j} + t^3\mathbf{k}$, we have

$$\mathbf{v}(t) = \mathbf{r}'(t) = \mathbf{i} + 2t\mathbf{j} + 3t^2\mathbf{k},$$
$$\mathbf{a}(t) = \mathbf{v}'(t) = 2\mathbf{j} + 6t\mathbf{k}.$$

Also,

$$s'(t) = (1 + 4t^2 + 9t^4)^{1/2};$$
$$s''(t) = \frac{4t + 18t^3}{(1 + 4t^2 + 9t^4)^{1/2}}.$$

The path of the particle is sketched in Fig. 18–15. For $t = 1$,

$$\mathbf{v} = \mathbf{i} + 2\mathbf{j} + 3\mathbf{k},$$
$$\mathbf{a} = 2\mathbf{j} + 6\mathbf{k}.$$

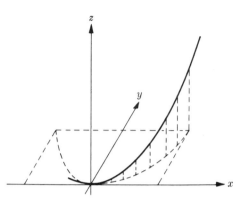

FIGURE 18–15

The speed is $s'(1) = \sqrt{14}$. We obtain

$$s''(1) = \frac{22}{\sqrt{14}}; \qquad \mathbf{T} = \frac{1}{\sqrt{14}}(\mathbf{i} + 2\mathbf{j} + 3\mathbf{k});$$

$$\mathbf{a} - s''\mathbf{T} = \frac{(s')^2}{R}\mathbf{N} = 2\mathbf{j} + 6\mathbf{k} - \frac{11}{7}(\mathbf{i} + 2\mathbf{j} + 3\mathbf{k})$$

$$= \frac{1}{7}(-11\mathbf{i} - 8\mathbf{j} + 9\mathbf{k}).$$

Therefore

$$|\mathbf{a} - s''\mathbf{T}| = \frac{1}{7}\sqrt{266} = \frac{14}{R};$$

$$\mathbf{N} = \frac{1}{\sqrt{266}}(-11\mathbf{i} - 8\mathbf{j} + 9\mathbf{k});$$

$$R = \frac{98}{\sqrt{266}}.$$

So far in this section we have shown how to obtain certain properties of curves in space by using tools of the calculus. The general study of the geometric properties of curves and surfaces in which methods of the calculus are employed is a branch of the subject known as *differential geometry*. The next theorem introduces a quantity τ known as the *torsion* of a curve. It is a remarkable fact that the curvature and torsion of a space curve describe it completely except for its position in space.

Theorem 12. *If* $\kappa(t) \neq 0$, *a quantity* $\tau(t)$ *exists such that*

$$\frac{d\mathbf{T}}{ds} = \kappa\mathbf{N}, \qquad \frac{d\mathbf{N}}{ds} = -\kappa\mathbf{T} - \tau\mathbf{B}, \qquad \frac{d\mathbf{B}}{ds} = \tau\mathbf{N}.$$

A proof is given in Morrey, *University Calculus*, p. 544.

EXERCISES

In each of problems 1 through 6, find the unit tangent vector $\mathbf{T}(t)$.

1. $\mathbf{r}(t) = t^3\mathbf{i} + (1 - t)\mathbf{j} + (2t + 1)\mathbf{k}$

2. $\mathbf{r}(t) = (\sin t)\mathbf{i} + (\cos t)\mathbf{j} + 3t^4\mathbf{k}$

3. $x(t) = e^{-2t}, \qquad y(t) = e^{2t}, \qquad z(t) = 1 + t^2$

4. $\mathbf{r}(t) = \dfrac{t}{1 + t}\mathbf{i} + \dfrac{t^2}{1 + t}\mathbf{j} + \dfrac{1 - t}{1 + t}\mathbf{k}$

5. $x(t) = e^t \sin t, \quad y(t) = e^{2t} \cos t, \quad z(t) = e^{-t}$

6. $\mathbf{r}(t) = \ln(1 + t)\mathbf{i} + \dfrac{t}{1 + t^2}\mathbf{j} - 2t^3\mathbf{k}$

In each of problems 7 through 11, for the particular value of t given, find the vectors $\mathbf{T}$, $\mathbf{N}$, and $\mathbf{B}$; the curvature κ; the equations of the tangent line; and the equation of the osculating plane to the curves given.

7. $x = 1 + t, \qquad y = 3 - t, \qquad z = 2t + 4, \qquad t = 3$

8. $\mathbf{r}(t) = t\mathbf{i} + t^2\mathbf{j} + \frac{1}{3}t^3\mathbf{k}, \qquad t = 0$

9. $x = e^t \cos t, \qquad y = e^t \sin t, \qquad z = e^t, \qquad t = 0$

10. $x = \frac{1}{3}t^3, \qquad y = 2t, \qquad z = 2/t, \qquad t = 2$

11. $x = 2 \cosh(t/2), \qquad y = 2 \sinh(t/2), \qquad z = 2t, \qquad t = 0$

12. Given the path $x = e^t \cos t$, $y = e^t \sin t$, $z = e^t$, show that the path lies on the upper half of the cone $z^2 = x^2 + y^2$, and that the tangent vector $\mathbf{T}(t)$ cuts the generators of the cone at a constant angle and makes a constant angle with the z-axis for all t. Also, find $\mathbf{N}$ and κ in terms of t.

In problems 13 through 16, a particle moves according to the law given. In each case, find its vector velocity and acceleration, its speed, the radius of curvature of its path, the unit vectors $\mathbf{T}$ and $\mathbf{N}$, and the tangential and normal components of acceleration at the given time.

13. $x = t, \qquad y = \frac{3}{2}t^2, \qquad z = \frac{3}{2}t^3, \qquad t = 2$

14. $x = t, \qquad y = \ln(\sec t + \tan t), \qquad z = \ln \sec t, \qquad t = \pi/3$

15. $x = t^3/3, \qquad y = 2t, \qquad z = 2/t, \qquad t = 1$

16. $x = t \cos t, \qquad y = t \sin t, \qquad z = t, \qquad t = 0$

CHAPTER **19**

Elements of Infinite Series

1. INDETERMINATE FORMS

If $f(x)$ and $F(x)$ both approach 0 as x tends to a value a, the quotient

$$\frac{f(x)}{F(x)}$$

may approach a limit, may become infinite, or may fail to have any limit. We saw in the definition of derivative that it is the evaluation of just such expressions that leads to the usual differentiation formulas. We are aware that the expression

$$\frac{f(a)}{F(a)} = \frac{0}{0}$$

is in itself a meaningless one, and we use the term *indeterminate form* for the ratio $0/0$.

If $f(x)$ and $F(x)$ both tend to infinity as x tends to a, the ratio $f(x)/F(x)$ may or may not tend to a limit. We use the same term, *indeterminate form*, for the expression ∞/∞, obtained by direct substitution of $x = a$ into the quotient $f(x)/F(x)$.

We recall the Theorem of the Mean, which we established (Chapter 7, p. 154).

Theorem 1. (Theorem of the Mean.) *Suppose that f is continuous for $a \le x \le b$ and that $f'(x)$ exists for each x between a and b. Then there is an x_0 between a and b (that is, $a < x_0 < b$) such that*

$$\frac{f(b) - f(a)}{b - a} = f'(x_0).$$

Remark. Rolle's Theorem (p. 153) is the special case $f(a) = f(b) = 0$.

The evaluation of indeterminate forms requires an extension of the Theorem of the Mean which we now prove.

Theorem 2. (Generalized Theorem of the Mean.) *Suppose that f and F are continuous for $a \le x \le b$, and $f'(x)$ and $F'(x)$ exist for $a < x < b$ with $F'(x) \ne 0$ there. Then $F(b) - F(a) \ne 0$ and there is a number ξ with $a < \xi < b$ such that*

$$\frac{f(b) - f(a)}{F(b) - F(a)} = \frac{f'(\xi)}{F'(\xi)}. \tag{1}$$

598

Proof. The fact that $F(b) - F(a) \neq 0$ is obtained by applying the Theorem of the Mean (Theorem 1) to F. For then, $F(b) - F(a) = F'(x_0)(b - a)$ for some x_0 such that $a < x_0 < b$. By hypothesis, the right side is different from zero.

To prove the main part of the theorem, we define the function $\phi(x)$ by the formula

$$\phi(x) = f(x) - f(a) - \frac{f(b) - f(a)}{F(b) - F(a)}[F(x) - F(a)].$$

We compute $\phi(a)$, $\phi(b)$, and $\phi'(x)$, getting

$$\phi(a) = f(a) - f(a) - \frac{f(b) - f(a)}{F(b) - F(a)}[F(a) - F(a)] = 0,$$

$$\phi(b) = f(b) - f(a) - \frac{f(b) - f(a)}{F(b) - F(a)}[F(b) - F(a)] = 0,$$

$$\phi'(x) = f'(x) - \frac{f(b) - f(a)}{F(b) - F(a)}F'(x).$$

Applying the Theorem of the Mean (i.e., in the special form of Rolle's Theorem) to $\phi(x)$ in the interval (a, b), we find

$$\frac{\phi(b) - \phi(a)}{b - a} = 0 = \phi'(\xi) = f'(\xi) - \frac{f(b) - f(a)}{F(b) - F(a)}F'(\xi)$$

for some ξ between a and b. Dividing by $F'(\xi)$, we obtain formula (1).

The next theorem, known as *l'Hôpital's Rule*, is useful in the evaluation of indeterminate forms.

Theorem 3. (l'Hôpital's Rule.) *Suppose that*

$$\lim_{x \to a} f(x) = 0, \qquad \lim_{x \to a} F(x) = 0, \qquad and \qquad \lim_{x \to a} \frac{f'(x)}{F'(x)} = L,$$

and that the hypotheses of Theorem 2 hold in some deleted interval about a. Then

$$\lim_{x \to a} \frac{f(x)}{F(x)} = \lim_{x \to a} \frac{f'(x)}{F'(x)} = L.$$

Proof. For some h we apply Theorem 2 in the interval $a < x < a + h$. Then

$$\frac{f(a + h) - f(a)}{F(a + h) - F(a)} = \frac{f(a + h)}{F(a + h)} = \frac{f'(\xi)}{F'(\xi)}, \qquad a < \xi < a + h,$$

where we have taken $f(a) = F(a) = 0$. As h tends to 0, ξ tends to a, and so

$$\lim_{h \to 0} \frac{f(a + h)}{F(a + h)} = \lim_{\xi \to a} \frac{f'(\xi)}{F'(\xi)} = L.$$

A similar proof is valid for x on the interval $(a - h) < x < a$.

EXAMPLE 1. Evaluate

$$\lim_{x \to 3} \frac{x^3 - 2x^2 - 2x - 3}{x^2 - 9}.$$

Solution. We set $f(x) = x^3 - 2x^2 - 2x - 3$ and $F(x) = x^2 - 9$. We see at once that $f(3) = 0$ and $F(3) = 0$, and we have an indeterminate form. We calculate

$$f'(x) = 3x^2 - 4x - 2, \qquad F'(x) = 2x.$$

By Theorem 3 (l'Hôpital's Rule):

$$\lim_{x \to 3} \frac{f(x)}{F(x)} = \lim_{x \to 3} \frac{f'(x)}{F'(x)} = \frac{3(9) - 4(3) - 2}{2(3)} = \frac{13}{6}.$$

Remarks. It is essential that $f(x)$ and $F(x)$ *both* tend to zero as x tends to a before applying l'Hôpital's Rule. If either or both functions tend to finite limits $\neq 0$, or if one tends to zero and the other does not, then the limit of the quotient is found by the method of direct substitution as given in Chapter 5.

It may happen that $f'(x)/F'(x)$ is an indeterminate form as $x \to a$. Then l'Hôpital's Rule may be applied again, and the limit $f''(x)/F''(x)$ may exist as x tends to a. In fact, for some problems l'Hôpital's Rule may be required a number of times before the limit is actually determined. Example 3 below exhibits this point.

EXAMPLE 2. Evaluate

$$\lim_{x \to a} \frac{x^p - a^p}{x^q - a^q}, \qquad a \neq 0.$$

Solution. We set $f(x) = x^p - a^p$, $F(x) = x^q - a^q$. Then $f(a) = 0$, $F(a) = 0$. We compute $f'(x) = px^{p-1}$, $F'(x) = qx^{q-1}$. Therefore

$$\lim_{x \to a} \frac{f(x)}{F(x)} = \lim_{x \to a} \frac{f'(x)}{F'(x)} = \lim_{x \to a} \frac{px^{p-1}}{qx^{q-1}} = \frac{p}{q} a^{p-q}.$$

EXAMPLE 3. Evaluate

$$\lim_{x \to 0} \frac{x - \sin x}{x^3}.$$

Solution. We set $f(x) = x - \sin x$, $F(x) = x^3$. Since $f(0) = 0$, $F(0) = 0$, we apply l'Hôpital's Rule and get

$$\lim_{x \to 0} \frac{f(x)}{F(x)} = \lim_{x \to 0} \frac{1 - \cos x}{3x^2}.$$

But we note that $f'(0) = 0$, $F'(0) = 0$, and so we apply l'Hôpital's Rule again:

$$f''(x) = \sin x, \qquad F''(x) = 6x.$$

Hence

$$\lim_{x\to 0}\frac{f(x)}{F(x)} = \lim_{x\to 0}\frac{f''(x)}{F''(x)}.$$

Again we have an indeterminate form: $f''(0) = 0$, $F''(0) = 0$. We continue, to obtain $f'''(x) = \cos x$, $F'''(x) = 6$. Now we find that

$$\lim_{x\to 0}\frac{f(x)}{F(x)} = \lim_{x\to 0}\frac{f'''(x)}{F'''(x)} = \frac{\cos 0}{6} = \frac{1}{6}.$$

L'Hôpital's Rule can be extended to the case where *both* $f(x) \to \infty$ and $F(x) \to \infty$ as $x \to a$.

Theorem 4. (l'Hôpital's Rule.) *Suppose that*

$$\lim_{x\to a} f(x) = \infty, \qquad \lim_{x\to a} F(x) = \infty, \qquad and \qquad \lim_{x\to a}\frac{f'(x)}{F'(x)} = L.$$

Then

$$\lim_{x\to a}\frac{f(x)}{F(x)} = \lim_{x\to a}\frac{f'(x)}{F'(x)} = L.$$

This theorem is proved in Morrey, *University Calculus*, p. 338.

EXAMPLE 4. Evaluate

$$\lim_{x\to 0}\frac{\ln x}{\operatorname{csch} x}.$$

Solution. We first note that x must tend to zero through positive values. In fact, all the theorems we have stated hold for one-sided limits as well as for ordinary limits. We set

$$f(x) = \ln x, \qquad F(x) = \operatorname{csch} x.$$

Then $f(x) \to -\infty$ and $F(x) \to +\infty$ as $x \to 0+$. Therefore

$$\lim_{x\to 0}\frac{f(x)}{F(x)} = \lim_{x\to 0}\frac{1/x}{-\operatorname{csch} x \coth x} = \lim_{x\to 0}\frac{-\sinh^2 x}{x\cosh x}.$$

We still have an indeterminate form, and we take derivatives again. Hence

$$\lim_{x\to 0}\frac{\ln x}{\operatorname{csch} x} = \lim_{x\to 0}\frac{-2\sinh x \cosh x}{\cosh x + x\sinh x} = \frac{0}{1} = 0.$$

Remark. Theorems 3 and 4 are valid if $a = +\infty$ or $-\infty$. That is, if $f(\infty)/F(\infty)$ is indeterminate, then

$$\lim_{x\to\infty}\frac{f(x)}{F(x)} = \lim_{x\to\infty}\frac{f'(x)}{F'(x)}.$$

The next example exhibits this type of indeterminate form.

EXAMPLE 5. Evaluate

$$\lim_{x \to +\infty} \frac{8x}{e^x}.$$

Solution.

$$\lim_{x \to +\infty} \frac{8x}{e^x} = \lim_{x \to +\infty} \frac{8}{e^x} = 0.$$

Remarks. Indeterminate forms of the type $0 \cdot \infty$ or $\infty - \infty$ can often be evaluated by transforming the expression into a quotient of the form $0/0$ or ∞/∞. Limits involving exponential expressions may often be evaluated by taking logarithms. Of course, algebraic or trigonometric reductions may be made at any step. The next examples illustrate the procedure.

EXAMPLE 6. Evaluate

$$\lim_{x \to \pi/2} (\sec x - \tan x).$$

Solution. We employ trigonometric reduction to change $\infty - \infty$ into a standard form. We have

$$\lim_{x \to \pi/2} (\sec x - \tan x) = \lim_{x \to \pi/2} \frac{1 - \sin x}{\cos x} = \lim_{x \to \pi/2} \frac{-\cos x}{-\sin x} = 0.$$

EXAMPLE 7. Evaluate

$$\lim_{x \to 0} (1 + x)^{1/x}.$$

Solution. We have 1^∞, which is indeterminate. Set $y = (1 + x)^{1/x}$ and take logarithms. Then

$$\ln y = \ln (1 + x)^{1/x} = \frac{\ln (1 + x)}{x}.$$

By l'Hôpital's Rule,

$$\lim_{x \to 0} \frac{\ln (1 + x)}{x} = \lim_{x \to 0} \frac{1}{1 + x} = 1.$$

Therefore, $\lim_{x \to 0} \ln y = 1$, and we conclude that

$$\lim_{x \to 0} y = \lim_{x \to 0} (1 + x)^{1/x} = e.$$

EXERCISES

Evaluate the following limits:

1. $\displaystyle \lim_{x \to -2} \frac{2x^2 + 5x + 2}{x^2 - 4}$

2. $\displaystyle \lim_{x \to 2} \frac{x^3 - x^2 - x - 2}{x^3 - 8}$

3. $\displaystyle \lim_{x \to 1} \frac{x^3 - 3x + 2}{x^3 - x^2 - x + 1}$

4. $\displaystyle \lim_{x \to 2} \frac{x^4 - 3x^2 - 4}{x^3 + 2x^2 - 4x - 8}$

5. $\lim\limits_{x\to\infty}\dfrac{2x^3 - x^2 + 3x + 1}{3x^3 + 2x^2 - x - 1}$

6. $\lim\limits_{x\to 4}\dfrac{x^3 - 8x^2 + 2x + 1}{x^4 - x^2 + 2x - 3}$

7. $\lim\limits_{x\to\infty}\dfrac{x^3 - 3x + 1}{2x^4 - x^2 + 2}$

8. $\lim\limits_{x\to\infty}\dfrac{x^4 - 2x^2 - 1}{2x^3 - 3x^2 + 3}$

9. $\lim\limits_{x\to 0}\dfrac{\tan 3x}{\sin x}$

10. $\lim\limits_{x\to 0}\dfrac{\sin 7x}{x}$

11. $\lim\limits_{x\to 0}\dfrac{e^{2x} - 2x - 1}{1 - \cos x}$

12. $\lim\limits_{x\to 0}\dfrac{e^{3x} - 1}{1 - \cos x}$

13. $\lim\limits_{x\to 0}\dfrac{x - \sinh x}{(1 - \cosh x)^2}$

14. $\lim\limits_{x\to 0}\dfrac{\ln x}{e^x}$

15. $\lim\limits_{x\to\infty}\dfrac{\ln x}{x^h},\quad h>0$

16. $\lim\limits_{x\to 0}\dfrac{\ln(1 + 2x)}{3x}$

17. $\lim\limits_{x\to 0}\dfrac{3^x - 2^x}{x}$

18. $\lim\limits_{x\to 0}\dfrac{3^x - 2^x}{x^2}$

19. $\lim\limits_{x\to 0}\dfrac{3^x - 2^x}{\sqrt{x}}$

20. $\lim\limits_{\theta\to 0}\dfrac{\tanh 2\theta - 2\theta}{3\theta - \sinh 3\theta}$

21. $\lim\limits_{x\to\pi/2}\dfrac{1 - \sin x}{\cos x}$

22. $\lim\limits_{x\to 2}\dfrac{\sqrt{2x} - 2}{\ln(x - 1)}$

23. $\lim\limits_{x\to\pi/2}\dfrac{\ln \sin x}{1 - \sin x}$

24. $\lim\limits_{x\to\pi/2}\dfrac{\cos x}{\sin^2 x}$

25. $\lim\limits_{x\to\infty}\dfrac{x^3}{e^x}$

26. $\lim\limits_{x\to\pi/2}\dfrac{\tan x}{\ln \cos x}$

27. $\lim\limits_{x\to\infty}\dfrac{\sin x}{x}$

28. $\lim\limits_{x\to\pi/2}\dfrac{\sin x}{x}$

29. $\lim\limits_{x\to 0}\dfrac{x - \arctan x}{x - \sin x}$

30. $\lim\limits_{x\to 0}\sqrt{x}\,\ln x$

31. $\lim\limits_{x\to 0} x \cot x$

32. $\lim\limits_{x\to\pi/2}(x - \pi/2)\sec x$

33. $\lim\limits_{x\to\infty}\dfrac{\arctan x}{x}$

34. $\lim\limits_{\theta\to 0}\left(\csc\theta - \dfrac{1}{\theta}\right)$

35. $\lim\limits_{x\to 0}(\operatorname{csch} x - \coth x)$

36. $\lim\limits_{x\to 0}\left(\cot^2 x - \dfrac{1}{x^2}\right)$

37. $\lim\limits_{x\to 0} x^x$

38. $\lim\limits_{x\to 0} x^{4x}$

39. $\lim\limits_{x\to 0}(\sinh x)^{\tan x}$

40. $\lim\limits_{x\to\infty}\left(1 + \dfrac{k}{x}\right)^x$

41. $\lim\limits_{x\to 0} x^{(x^2)}$

42. $\lim\limits_{x\to 0}(\cot x)^x$

43. $\lim\limits_{x\to 0} x^{(1/\ln x)}$

44. $\lim\limits_{x\to\infty}\dfrac{x^p}{e^x},\quad p>0$

2. CONVERGENT AND DIVERGENT SERIES

In Chapter 5, Section 5, p. 119, the idea of a sequence of numbers was introduced. We begin by repeating some of the material presented there. The numbers

$$b_1, b_2, b_3, \ldots, b_{12}, b_{13}, b_{14}$$

form a sequence of fourteen numbers. Since this set contains both a first and last element, the sequence is termed *finite*. In all other circumstances it is called *infinite*. The subscripts not only identify the location of each element but also serve to associate a positive integer with each member of the sequence. In other words, *a sequence is a function* with *domain* a portion (or all) of the positive integers and with *range* in the collection of real numbers.

If the domain is an infinite collection of positive integers, e.g., all positive integers, we write

$$a_1, a_2, \ldots, a_n, \ldots,$$

the final dots indicating the never-ending character of the sequence. Simple examples of infinite sequences are

$$1, \frac{1}{2}, \frac{1}{3}, \frac{1}{4}, \ldots, \frac{1}{n}, \ldots \tag{1}$$

$$\frac{1}{2}, \frac{2}{3}, \frac{3}{4}, \ldots, \frac{n}{n+1}, \ldots \tag{2}$$

$$2, 4, 6, \ldots, 2n, \ldots \tag{3}$$

DEFINITION. Given the infinite sequence

$$a_1, a_2, \ldots, a_n, \ldots,$$

we say that this *sequence has the limit c* if, for each $\epsilon > 0$, there is a positive integer N (the size of N depending on ϵ) such that

$$|a_n - c| < \epsilon \qquad \text{for all } n > N.$$

We also write $a_n \to c$ as $n \to \infty$ and, equivalently,

$$\lim_{n \to \infty} a_n = c.$$

In the sequence (1), we have

$$a_1 = 1, \quad a_2 = \frac{1}{2}, \quad \ldots, \quad a_n = \frac{1}{n}, \quad \ldots$$

and $\lim_{n \to \infty} a_n = 0$. The sequence (2) has the form

$$a_1 = \frac{1}{2}, \quad a_2 = \frac{2}{3}, \quad \ldots, \quad a_n = \frac{n}{n+1}, \quad \ldots$$

and $\lim_{n \to \infty} a_n = 1$. The sequence (3) does not tend to a limit.

An expression such as

$$u_1 + u_2 + u_3 + \cdots + u_{24}$$

is called a *finite series*. The *sum* of such a series is obtained by adding the 24 terms. We now extend the notion of a finite series by considering an expression of the form

$$u_1 + u_2 + u_3 + \cdots + u_n + \cdots$$

which is nonterminating and which we call an *infinite series*. Our first task is to give a meaning, if possible, to such an infinite succession of additions.

DEFINITION. Given the infinite series $u_1 + u_2 + u_3 + \cdots + u_n + \cdots$, the quantity $s_k = u_1 + u_2 + \cdots + u_k$ is called the *kth partial sum* of the series. That is,

$$s_1 = u_1, \qquad s_2 = u_1 + u_2, \qquad s_3 = u_1 + u_2 + u_3,$$

etc. Each partial sum is obtained simply by a *finite* number of additions.

DEFINITION. Given the series

$$u_1 + u_2 + u_3 + \cdots + u_n + \cdots \qquad (4)$$

with the sequence of partial sums

$$s_1, s_2, s_3, \ldots, s_n, \ldots,$$

we define the *sum of the series* (4) to be

$$\lim_{n \to \infty} s_n \qquad (5)$$

whenever the limit exists.

Using the $\sum$-notation for sum, we can also write

$$\sum_{n=1}^{\infty} u_n = \lim_{n \to \infty} s_n.$$

If the limit (5) does not exist, then the sum (4) *is not defined.*

DEFINITIONS. If the limit (5) exists, the series $\sum_{n=1}^{\infty} u_n$ is said to *converge* to that limit; otherwise the series is said to *diverge.*

The sequence of terms

$$a, ar, ar^2, ar^3, \ldots, ar^{n-1}, ar^n, \ldots$$

forms a *geometric progression*. Each term (except the first) is obtained by multiplication of the preceding term by r, the *common ratio*. The partial sums of the *geometric series*

$$a + ar + ar^2 + ar^3 + \cdots + ar^n + \cdots$$

are

$$s_1 = a,$$
$$s_2 = a + ar,$$
$$s_3 = a + ar + ar^2,$$
$$s_4 = a + ar + ar^2 + ar^3,$$

and, in general,

$$s_n = a(1 + r + r^2 + \cdots + r^{n-1}).$$

For example, with $a = 2$ and $r = \frac{1}{2}$,

$$s_n = 2\left(1 + \frac{1}{2} + \frac{1}{4} + \cdots + \frac{1}{2^{n-1}}\right).$$

The identity

$$(1 + r + r^2 + \cdots + r^{n-1})(1 - r) = 1 - r^n,$$

which may be verified by straightforward multiplication, leads to the formula

$$s_n = a\frac{1 - r^n}{1 - r}$$

for the nth partial sum. The example $a = 2$, $r = \frac{1}{2}$ gives

$$s_n = 2\frac{1 - 2^{-n}}{\frac{1}{2}} = 4 - \frac{1}{2^{n-2}}.$$

In general, we may write

$$s_n = a\frac{1 - r^n}{1 - r} = \frac{a}{1 - r} - \frac{a}{1 - r}r^n, \qquad r \neq 1. \tag{6}$$

The next theorem is a direct consequence of formula (6).

Theorem 5. *A geometric series*

$$a + ar + ar^2 + \cdots + ar^n + \cdots$$

converges if $-1 < r < 1$ and diverges if $|r| \geq 1$. In the convergent case we have

$$\sum_{n=1}^{\infty} ar^{n-1} = \frac{a}{1 - r}. \tag{7}$$

Proof. From (6) we see that $r^n \to 0$ if $|r| < 1$, yielding (7); also, $r^n \to \infty$ if $|r| > 1$. For $r = 1$, the partial sum s_n is na, and s_n does not tend to a limit as $n \to \infty$. If $r = -1$, the partial sum s_n is a if n is odd and 0 if n is even.

The next theorem is useful in that it exhibits a limitation on the behavior of the terms of a convergent series.

Theorem 6. *If the series*

$$\sum_{k=1}^{\infty} u_k = u_1 + u_2 + u_3 + \cdots + u_n + \cdots \tag{8}$$

converges, then

$$\lim_{n \to \infty} u_n = 0.$$

Proof. Writing

$$s_n = u_1 + u_2 + \cdots + u_n,$$
$$s_{n-1} = u_1 + u_2 + \cdots + u_{n-1},$$

we have, by subtraction, $u_n = s_n - s_{n-1}$. Letting c denote the sum of the series, we see that $s_n \to c$ as $n \to \infty$; also, $s_{n-1} \to c$ as $n \to \infty$. Therefore

$$\lim_{n \to \infty} u_n = \lim_{n \to \infty} (s_n - s_{n-1}) = \lim_{n \to \infty} s_n - \lim_{n \to \infty} s_{n-1} = c - c = 0.$$

Remark. The converse of Theorem 6 is not necessarily true. Later we shall show (by example) that it is possible both for u_n to tend to 0 and for the series to diverge.

Corollary. *If u_n does not tend to zero as $n \to \infty$, then the series $\sum_{n=1}^{\infty} u_n$ is divergent.*

Convergent series may be added, subtracted, and multiplied by constants, as the next theorem shows.

Theorem 7. *If $\sum_{n=1}^{\infty} u_n$ and $\sum_{n=1}^{\infty} v_n$ both converge and c is any number, then the series*

$$\sum_{n=1}^{\infty} (cu_n), \qquad \sum_{n=1}^{\infty} (u_n + v_n), \qquad \sum_{n=1}^{\infty} (u_n - v_n)$$

all converge, and

$$\sum_{n=1}^{\infty} (cu_n) = c \sum_{n=1}^{\infty} u_n,$$

$$\sum_{n=1}^{\infty} (u_n \pm v_n) = \sum_{n=1}^{\infty} u_n \pm \sum_{n=1}^{\infty} v_n.$$

Proof. For each n, we have the following equalities for the partial sums:

$$\sum_{j=1}^{n} (cu_j) = c \sum_{j=1}^{n} u_j; \qquad \sum_{j=1}^{n} (u_j \pm v_j) = \sum_{j=1}^{n} u_j \pm \sum_{j=1}^{n} v_j.$$

The results follow from the theorems on limits of sequences, as given in Chapter 5.

EXAMPLE. Express the repeating decimal $A = 0.151515\ldots$ as the ratio of two integers.

Solution. We write A in the form of a geometric series:

$$A = 0.15(1 + 0.01 + (0.01)^2 + (0.01)^3 + \cdots),$$

in which $a = 0.15$ and $r = 0.01$. This series is convergent and has sum

$$s = \frac{0.15}{1 - 0.01} = \frac{0.15}{0.99} = \frac{5}{33} = A.$$

EXERCISES

In problems 1 through 6, express each repeating decimal as the ratio of two integers.

1. $0.535353\ldots$
2. $0.012012012\ldots$
3. $463.546354635463\ldots$
4. $22.818181\ldots$
5. $3.7217217217\ldots$
6. $27.5431313131\ldots$
7. Find the sum of the geometric series if $a = 3$, $r = -\frac{1}{3}$.
8. The first term of a geometric series is 3 and the fifth term is $\frac{16}{27}$. Find the sum of the infinite series.

In problems 9 through 12, write the first five terms of each of the series given. Use the Corollary to Theorem 6 to show that the series is divergent.

9. $\displaystyle\sum_{n=1}^{\infty} \frac{2n}{3n + 5}$
10. $\displaystyle\sum_{n=1}^{\infty} \frac{n^2 - 2n + 3}{2n^2 + n + 1}$

11. $\displaystyle\sum_{n=1}^{\infty} (-1)^{n+1} \frac{e^n}{n^3}$
12. $\displaystyle\sum_{n=1}^{\infty} \frac{n^2 + n + 2}{\log (n + 1)}$

In problems 13 through 16, *assume* that the series

$$\sum_{n=1}^{\infty} \frac{1}{n^2}, \quad \sum_{n=1}^{\infty} \frac{1}{n^3}, \quad \sum_{n=1}^{\infty} \frac{1}{n^4}$$

all converge. In each case use Theorem 7 to show that the given series is convergent.

13. $\displaystyle\sum_{n=1}^{\infty} \frac{3n + 2}{n^3}$
14. $\displaystyle\sum_{n=1}^{\infty} \frac{n - 2}{n^3}$

15. $\displaystyle\sum_{n=1}^{\infty} \frac{3n^2 + 4}{n^4}$
16. $\displaystyle\sum_{n=1}^{\infty} \frac{3n^2 - 2n + 4}{n^4}$

17. Suppose that the series $\sum_{k=1}^{\infty} u_k$ converges. Show that any series obtained from this one by deleting a finite number of terms also converges. [*Hint:* Since $s_n = \sum_{k=1}^{n} u_k$ converges to a limit, find the value to which S_n, the partial sums of the deleted series, must tend.]

3. SERIES OF POSITIVE TERMS

Except in very special cases, it is not possible to tell if a series converges by finding whether or not s_n, the nth partial sum, tends to a limit. (The geometric series, however, is one of the special cases where it *is* possible.) In this section, we present some *indirect* tests for convergence and divergence which apply only to series with positive (or at least nonnegative) terms. That is, we assume throughout this section that $u_n \geq 0$ for $n = 1, 2, \ldots$. Tests for series with terms which may be positive or negative will be discussed in the following sections.

Theorem 8.   *Suppose that $u_n \geq 0$, $n = 1, 2, \ldots$ and $s_n = \sum_{k=1}^{n} u_k$ is the nth partial sum. Then, either (a), there is a number M such that all the $s_n \leq M$, in which case the series $\sum_{k=1}^{\infty} u_k$ converges to a value $s \leq M$, or else (b), $s_n \to +\infty$ and the series diverges.*

Proof. By subtraction, we have

$$u_n = s_n - s_{n-1} \geq 0,$$

and so the s_n form an increasing (or at least nondecreasing) sequence. If all $s_n \leq M$, then by Axiom C (p. 122), which says that a nondecreasing bounded sequence has a limit, we conclude that $s_n \to s \leq M$. Thus part (a) of the theorem is established. If there is no such M, then for each number E, no matter how large, there must be an $s_n > E$; and all s_m with $m > n$ are greater than or equal to s_n. This is another way of saying $s_n \to +\infty$.

The next theorem is one of the most useful tests for deciding convergence and divergence of series.

Theorem 9.   (Comparison Test.) *Suppose that all $u_n \geq 0$. (a) If $\sum_{n=1}^{\infty} a_n$ is a convergent series and $u_n \leq a_n$ for all n, then $\sum_{n=1}^{\infty} u_n$ is convergent and*

$$\sum_{n=1}^{\infty} u_n \leq \sum_{n=1}^{\infty} a_n.$$

(b) *If $\sum_{n=1}^{\infty} a_n$ is a divergent series of nonnegative terms and $u_n \geq a_n$ for all n, then $\sum_{n=1}^{\infty} u_n$ diverges.*

Proof. We let

$$s_n = u_1 + u_2 + \cdots + u_n, \qquad S_n = a_1 + a_2 + \cdots + a_n$$

be the nth partial sums. The s_n, S_n are both nondecreasing sequences. In case (a), we let S be the limit of S_n and, since

$$s_n \leq S_n \leq S$$

for every n, we apply Theorem 8 to conclude that s_n converges. In case (b), we have $S_n \to +\infty$ and $s_n \geq S_n$ for every n. Hence, $s_n \to +\infty$.

Remarks. In order to apply the Comparison Test, the student must show either (a), that the terms u_n of the given series are $\leq a_n$ where $\sum_{n=1}^{\infty} a_n$ is a *known* convergent series or (b), that each $u_n \geq a_n$ where $\sum_{n=1}^{\infty} a_n$ is a *known* divergent series. In all other cases, no conclusion can be drawn.

For the Comparison Test to be useful, we must have at hand as large a number as possible of series (of positive terms) about whose convergence and divergence we are fully informed. Then, when confronted with a new series of positive terms, we shall have available a body of series for comparison purposes. So far, the only series which we have shown to be convergent are the geometric series with $r < 1$, and the only series which we have shown to be divergent are those in which u_n does not tend to zero. We now study the convergence and divergence of a few special types of series in order to obtain material which can be used for the Comparison Test.

DEFINITION. *If n is a positive integer, we define $n!$ (read n factorial) $= 1 \cdot 2 \cdots n$; it is convenient to define $0! = 1$.*

For example, $5! = 1 \cdot 2 \cdot 3 \cdot 4 \cdot 5 = 120$, etc. We see that

$$(n+1)! = (n+1) \cdot n!, \qquad n \geq 0.$$

EXAMPLE 1. Test the series

$$\sum_{n=1}^{\infty} \frac{1}{n!}$$

for convergence or divergence.

Solution. Writing the first few terms, we obtain

$$\frac{1}{1!} = \frac{1}{1}, \qquad \frac{1}{2!} = \frac{1}{1 \cdot 2}, \qquad \frac{1}{3!} = \frac{1}{1 \cdot 2 \cdot 3}, \qquad \frac{1}{4!} = \frac{1}{1 \cdot 2 \cdot 3 \cdot 4}.$$

Since each factor except 1 and 2 in $n!$ is larger than 2, we have the inequalities

$$n! \geq 2^{n-1} \qquad \text{and} \qquad \frac{1}{n!} \leq \frac{1}{2^{n-1}}.$$

The series $\sum_{n=1}^{\infty} a_n$ with $a_n = 1/2^{n-1}$ is a geometric series with $r = \frac{1}{2}$, and is therefore convergent. Hence, by the Comparison Test, $\sum_{n=1}^{\infty} 1/n!$ converges.

Remark. Since any *finite* number of terms at the beginning of a series does not affect convergence or divergence, the comparison between u_n and a_n in Theorem 9 is not required for all n. It is required for all n *except a finite number.*

The next theorem gives us an entire collection of series useful for comparison purposes.

Theorem 10. (The *p*-series.) *The series*

$$\sum_{n=1}^{\infty} \frac{1}{n^p},$$

known as the p-series, is convergent if $p > 1$ and divergent if $p \leq 1$.

The proof of this theorem is deferred until later in the section. We note that it is not necessary that p be an integer.

EXAMPLE 2. Test the series

$$\sum_{n=1}^{\infty} \frac{1}{n(n+1)}$$

for convergence or divergence.

Solution. For each n we have

$$\frac{1}{n(n+1)} \leq \frac{1}{n^2}.$$

Since $\sum_{n=1}^{\infty} 1/n^2$ is a *p*-series with $p = 2$ and so converges, we are in a position to use the Comparison Test. Therefore, the series

$$\sum_{n=1}^{\infty} \frac{1}{n(n+1)}$$

converges.

EXAMPLE 3. Test the series

$$\sum_{n=1}^{\infty} \frac{1}{n+10}$$

for convergence or divergence.

Solution 1. Writing out a few terms, we have

$$\tfrac{1}{11} + \tfrac{1}{12} + \tfrac{1}{13} + \tfrac{1}{14} + \cdots,$$

and we see that the series is just like $\sum_{n=1}^{\infty} 1/n$, except that the first ten terms are missing. According to the Remark before Theorem 10, we may compare the given series with the *p*-series for $p = 1$. The comparison establishes divergence.

Solution 2. We have, for every $n \geq 1$,

$$n + 10 \leq 11n,$$

and so

$$\frac{1}{n+10} \geq \frac{1}{11n}.$$

The series

$$\sum_{n=1}^{\infty} \frac{1}{11n} = \frac{1}{11} \sum_{n=1}^{\infty} \frac{1}{n}$$

is divergent (*p*-series with $p = 1$) and, therefore, the given series diverges.

The next theorem yields another test which is used frequently in conjunction with the Comparison Test.

Theorem 11.   (Integral Test.)   *Assume that f is a continuous, nonnegative, and nonincreasing function defined for all $x \geq 1$. That is, we suppose that*

$$f(x) \geq 0, \text{ (nonnegative)}$$

and

$$f(x) \geq f(y) \quad \text{for } x \leq y \text{ (nonincreasing).}$$

Suppose that $\sum_{n=1}^{\infty} u_n$ is a series with

$$u_n = f(n) \quad \text{for each } n \geq 1.$$

Then (a) $\sum_{n=1}^{\infty} u_n$ is convergent if the improper integral $\int_1^{\infty} f(x)\, dx$ is convergent and, conversely (b), the improper integral converges if the series does.

FIGURE 19–1

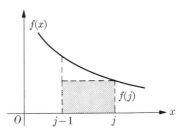

FIGURE 19–2

Proof. (See Fig. 19–1.)   (a) Suppose first that the improper integral is convergent. Then, since $f(x) \geq f(j)$ for $x \leq j$, we see that

$$\int_{j-1}^{j} f(x)\, dx \geq f(j), \tag{1}$$

a fact verified by noting in Fig. 19–2 that $f(j)$ is the shaded area and the integral is the area under the curve. We define

$$a_j = \int_{j-1}^{j} f(x)\, dx,$$

and then

$$a_1 + \int_{1}^{n} f(x)\, dx = a_1 + a_2 + \cdots + a_n,$$

where we have set $a_1 = f(1) = u_1$. By hypothesis, $\int_1^{\infty} f(x)\, dx$ is finite, and so the series $\sum_{n=1}^{\infty} a_n$ is convergent. Since $f(j) = u_j$, the inequality $a_j \geq u_j$ is a restatement of (1), and now the comparison theorem applies to yield the result.

(b) Suppose now that $\sum_{n=1}^{\infty} u_n$ converges. Let

$$v_n = \int_n^{n+1} f(x)\, dx \le f(n) = u_n, \qquad n = 1, 2, \dots,$$

the inequality holding since $f(x) \le f(n)$ for $n \le x$ (Fig. 19–3).   Because $f(x) \ge 0$, each $v_n \ge 0$, and so $\sum_{n=1}^{\infty} v_n$ converges to some number S.   That is,

$$\sum_{k=1}^{n} v_k = \int_1^{n+1} f(x)\, dx \le S$$

for every n. Let ϵ be any positive number. There is an N such that

$$S - \epsilon < \int_1^{n+1} f(x)\, dx \le S \qquad \text{for all} \quad n \ge N.$$

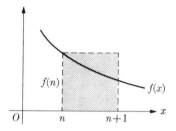

$f(n)$

$f(x)$

0 n $n+1$ x

FIGURE 19–3

Since $f(x) \ge 0$, we see that

$$S - \epsilon < \int_1^{n+1} f(x)\, dx \le \int_1^{X} f(x)\, dx \le S \qquad \text{if} \quad X \ge N + 1.$$

Hence the improper integral converges.

We shall now employ the Integral Test to establish the convergence and divergence of the p-series.

Proof of Theorem 10. We define the function $f(x) = 1/x^p$, which satisfies all the conditions of the integral test if $p > 0$. We have

$$\int_1^{\infty} \frac{dx}{x^p} = \lim_{t \to \infty} \int_1^{t} \frac{dx}{x^p} = \lim_{t \to \infty} \left(\frac{t^{1-p} - 1}{1 - p} \right) \qquad \text{for} \quad p \ne 1.$$

The limit exists for $p > 1$ and fails to exist for $p < 1$. As for the case $p = 1$, we have

$$\int_1^{t} \frac{dx}{x} = \ln t,$$

which tends to ∞ as $t \to \infty$. Thus Theorem 10 is established.

EXAMPLE 4. Test the series

$$\sum_{n=1}^{\infty} \frac{1}{(n+1)\ln(n+1)}$$

for convergence or divergence.

Solution. Let

$$f(x) = \frac{1}{(x+1)\ln(x+1)}$$

and note that all conditions for the Integral Test are fulfilled. We obtain

$$\int_{1}^{t} \frac{dx}{(x+1)\ln(x+1)} = \int_{2}^{t+1} \frac{du}{u\ln u} = \int_{2}^{t+1} \frac{d(\ln u)}{\ln u}$$

$$= \ln[\ln(t+1)] - \ln(\ln 2).$$

The expression on the right diverges as $t \to \infty$ and, therefore, the given series is divergent.

The particular p-series with $p = 1$, known as the *harmonic series*, is interesting, as it appears to be on the borderline between convergence and divergence of the various p-series. It is an example of a series in which the general term u_n tends to zero while the series diverges. (See p. 607.) We can prove divergence of the harmonic series without recourse to the Integral Test. To do so, we write

$$\tfrac{1}{1} + \tfrac{1}{2} + (\tfrac{1}{3} + \tfrac{1}{4}) + (\tfrac{1}{5} + \tfrac{1}{6} + \tfrac{1}{7} + \tfrac{1}{8})$$

$$+ (\tfrac{1}{9} + \tfrac{1}{10} + \tfrac{1}{11} + \tfrac{1}{12} + \tfrac{1}{13} + \tfrac{1}{14} + \tfrac{1}{15} + \tfrac{1}{16}) + (\text{next 16 terms}) + \cdots.$$

$$(2)$$

We have the obvious inequalities

$$\tfrac{1}{3} + \tfrac{1}{4} > \tfrac{1}{4} + \tfrac{1}{4} = \tfrac{1}{2},$$

$$\tfrac{1}{5} + \tfrac{1}{6} + \tfrac{1}{7} + \tfrac{1}{8} > \tfrac{1}{8} + \tfrac{1}{8} + \tfrac{1}{8} + \tfrac{1}{8} = \tfrac{1}{2},$$

$$\tfrac{1}{9} + \tfrac{1}{10} + \tfrac{1}{11} + \tfrac{1}{12} + \tfrac{1}{13} + \tfrac{1}{14} + \tfrac{1}{15} + \tfrac{1}{16}$$

$$> \tfrac{1}{16} + \tfrac{1}{16} + \tfrac{1}{16} + \tfrac{1}{16} + \tfrac{1}{16} + \tfrac{1}{16} + \tfrac{1}{16} + \tfrac{1}{16} = \tfrac{1}{2},$$

and so forth.

In other words, each set of terms in a set of parentheses in series (2) is larger than $\tfrac{1}{2}$. By taking a sufficient number of parentheses, we can make the partial sum s_n of the harmonic series as large as we please. Therefore the series diverges.

EXAMPLE 5. Show that the series

$$\sum_{n=1}^{\infty} \frac{1}{3n-2}$$

diverges.

Solution. We may use the Integral Test, or observe that

$$\sum_{n=1}^{\infty} \frac{1}{3n - 2} = \frac{1}{3} \sum_{n=1}^{\infty} \frac{1}{(n - \frac{2}{3})} \quad \text{and} \quad \frac{1}{n - \frac{2}{3}} \geq \frac{1}{n} \quad \text{for all} \quad n \geq 1.$$

The comparison test shows divergence. The divergence may also be shown directly by recombination of terms, as in the harmonic series.

EXERCISES

Test the following series for convergence or divergence.

1. $\displaystyle\sum_{n=1}^{\infty} \frac{1}{n\sqrt{n}}$

2. $\displaystyle\sum_{n=1}^{\infty} \frac{1}{\sqrt{n}}$

3. $\displaystyle\sum_{n=1}^{\infty} \frac{1}{(n + 1)(n + 2)}$

4. $\displaystyle\sum_{n=1}^{\infty} \frac{n + 1}{n\sqrt{n}}$

5. $\displaystyle\sum_{n=1}^{\infty} \frac{2n + 3}{n^2 + 3n + 2}$

6. $\displaystyle\sum_{n=1}^{\infty} \frac{1}{n \cdot 2^n}$

7. $\displaystyle\sum_{n=1}^{\infty} \frac{n - 1}{n^3}$

8. $\displaystyle\sum_{n=1}^{\infty} \frac{n^2 + 3n - 6}{n^4}$

9. $\displaystyle\sum_{n=1}^{\infty} \frac{1}{\sqrt{n(n + 1)}}$

10. $\displaystyle\sum_{n=1}^{\infty} \frac{1}{2n + 3}$

11. $\displaystyle\sum_{n=1}^{\infty} \frac{1}{n + 100}$

12. $\displaystyle\sum_{n=1}^{\infty} \frac{2}{2^n + 3}$

13. $\displaystyle\sum_{n=1}^{\infty} \frac{1}{n^2 + 2}$

14. $\displaystyle\sum_{n=1}^{\infty} \frac{2^n}{1000}$

15. $\displaystyle\sum_{n=1}^{\infty} \frac{2n + 5}{n^3}$

16. $\displaystyle\sum_{n=1}^{\infty} \frac{n - 1}{n^2}$

17. $\displaystyle\sum_{n=1}^{\infty} \frac{\ln n}{n}$

18. $\displaystyle\sum_{n=1}^{\infty} \frac{1}{(n + 1)[\ln (n + 1)]^2}$

19. $\displaystyle\sum_{n=1}^{\infty} \frac{\ln (n + 1)}{(n + 1)^3}$

20. $\displaystyle\sum_{n=1}^{\infty} \frac{n!}{1 \cdot 3 \cdot 5 \cdot 7 \ldots (2n - 1)}$

21. $\displaystyle\sum_{n=1}^{\infty} \frac{n}{e^n}$

22. $\displaystyle\sum_{n=1}^{\infty} \frac{1}{\sqrt{n^2 + 1}}$

23. $\displaystyle\sum_{n=1}^{\infty} \frac{n + 1}{n \cdot 2^n}$

24. $\displaystyle\sum_{n=1}^{\infty} \frac{n^4}{e^n}$

25. $\displaystyle\sum_{n=1}^{\infty} \frac{n}{2^n}$

26. $\displaystyle\sum_{n=1}^{\infty} \frac{n^2}{2^n}$

27. $\displaystyle\sum_{n=1}^{\infty} \frac{\ln n}{n^2}$

28. $\displaystyle\sum_{n=1}^{\infty} \frac{\ln n}{n\sqrt{n}}$

29. $\displaystyle\sum_{n=1}^{\infty} \frac{n^4}{n!}$

30. $\displaystyle\sum_{n=1}^{\infty} \frac{(2n)!}{(3n)!}$

4. SERIES OF POSITIVE AND NEGATIVE TERMS

In this section we establish three theorems which serve as important tests for the convergence and divergence of series whose terms are not necessarily positive.

Theorem 12. *If* $\sum_{n=1}^{\infty} |u_n|$ *converges, then* $\sum_{n=1}^{\infty} u_n$ *converges, and*

$$\left| \sum_{n=1}^{\infty} u_n \right| \leq \sum_{n=1}^{\infty} |u_n|.$$

Proof. We define the numbers $v_1, v_2, \ldots, v_n, \ldots$ by the relations

$$v_n = \begin{cases} u_n & \text{if} \quad u_n \quad \text{is nonnegative,} \\ 0 & \text{if} \quad u_n \quad \text{is negative.} \end{cases}$$

In other words, the series $\sum_{n=1}^{\infty} v_n$ consists of all the nonnegative entries in $\sum_{n=1}^{\infty} u_n$. Similarly, we define the sequence w_n by

$$w_n = \begin{cases} 0 & \text{if} \quad u_n \quad \text{is nonnegative,} \\ -u_n & \text{if} \quad u_n \quad \text{is negative.} \end{cases}$$

The w_n are all positive, and we have

$$v_n + w_n = |u_n|, \qquad v_n - w_n = u_n \tag{1}$$

for each n. Since $v_n \leq |u_n|$ and $w_n \leq |u_n|$, and since, by hypothesis, $\sum_{n=1}^{\infty} |u_n|$ converges, we may apply the comparison test to conclude that the series

$$\sum_{n=1}^{\infty} v_n, \qquad \sum_{n=1}^{\infty} w_n$$

converge. Also,

$$\left| \sum_{n=1}^{\infty} u_n \right| = \left| \left(\sum_{n=1}^{\infty} v_n \right) - \left(\sum_{n=1}^{\infty} w_n \right) \right|$$

$$\leq \sum_{n=1}^{\infty} v_n + \sum_{n=1}^{\infty} w_n = \sum_{n=1}^{\infty} |u_n|.$$

Remark. Theorem 12 shows that if the series of absolute values $\sum_{n=1}^{\infty} |u_n|$ is convergent, then the series itself also converges. The converse is not necessarily true. We give an example below (page 618) in which $\sum_{n=1}^{\infty} u_n$ converges while $\sum_{n=1}^{\infty} |u_n|$ diverges.

DEFINITIONS. A series $\sum_{n=1}^{\infty} u_n$ which is such that $\sum_{n=1}^{\infty} |u_n|$ converges is said to be *absolutely convergent*. However, if $\sum_{n=1}^{\infty} u_n$ converges and $\sum_{n=1}^{\infty} |u_n|$ diverges, then the series $\sum_{n=1}^{\infty} u_n$ is said to be *conditionally convergent*.

The next theorem yields a test for series whose terms are alternately positive and negative. Since the hypotheses are rather stringent, the test can be used only under special circumstances.

Theorem 13. (Alternating Series Theorem.) *Suppose that the numbers $u_1, u_2, \ldots$, $u_n, \ldots$ satisfy the hypotheses:*

(i)   *the u_n are alternately positive and negative,*

(ii) $|u_{n+1}| < |u_n|$ *for every n, and*

(iii) $\lim_{n \to \infty} u_n = 0$.

Then $\sum_{n=1}^{\infty} u_n$ is convergent. Furthermore, if the sum is denoted by s, then s lies between the partial sums s_n and s_{n+1} for each n.

Proof. Assume that u_1 is positive. (If it is not, we can consider the series beginning with u_2, since discarding a finite number of terms does not affect convergence.) Therefore, all u_k with odd subscripts are positive and all u_k with even subscripts are negative. We state this fact in the form

$$u_{2n-1} > 0, \qquad u_{2n} < 0$$

for each n. We now write

$$s_{2n} = (u_1 + u_2) + (u_3 + u_4) + (u_5 + u_6) + \cdots + (u_{2n-1} + u_{2n}).$$

Since $|u_{2k}| < u_{2k-1}$ for each k, we know that each quantity in the parentheses is positive. Hence s_{2n} increases for all n. On the other hand,

$$s_{2n} = u_1 + (u_2 + u_3) + (u_4 + u_5) + \cdots + (u_{2n-2} + u_{2n-1}) + u_{2n}.$$

Each quantity in parentheses in the above expression is negative, and so is u_{2n}. Therefore $s_{2n} < u_1$ for all n. We conclude that s_{2n} is an increasing sequence bounded by the number u_1. It must tend to a limit (Axiom C).

We apply similar reasoning to s_{2n-1}. We have

$$s_{2n-1} + u_{2n} = s_{2n}$$

and, since $u_{2n} < 0$, we have $s_{2n-1} > s_{2n}$ for every n. Therefore for $n > 1$, s_{2n-1} is bounded from below by $s_2 = u_1 + u_2$. Also,

$$s_{2n+1} = s_{2n-1} + (u_{2n} + u_{2n+1}).$$

Since the quantity in parentheses on the right is negative,

$$s_{2n-1} > s_{2n+1};$$

FIGURE 19-4

in other words, the partial sums with odd subscripts form a decreasing bounded sequence (Fig. 19-4). The limits approached by s_{2n} and s_{2n-1} must be the same, since by hypothesis (iii),

$$u_{2n} = s_{2n} - s_{2n-1} \to 0.$$

If s is the limit, we see that any even sum is less than or equal to s, while any odd sum is greater than or equal to s.

EXAMPLE 1. Test the series

$$\sum_{n=1}^{\infty} \frac{(-1)^{n+1}}{n}$$

for convergence or divergence. If it is convergent, determine whether it is conditionally convergent or absolutely convergent.

Solution. We set $u_n = (-1)^{n+1}/n$ and observe that the three hypotheses of Theorem 13 hold; i.e., the terms alternate in sign, $1/(n+1) < 1/n$ for each n, and $\lim_{n \to \infty} (-1)^n/n = 0$. Therefore the given series converges. However, the series $\sum_{n=1}^{\infty} |u_n|$ is the harmonic series

$$\sum_{n=1}^{\infty} \frac{1}{n},$$

which is divergent. Therefore the original series is conditionally convergent.

The next test is one of the most useful for determining absolute convergence of series.

Theorem 14. (Ratio Test.) *Suppose that in the series $\sum_{n=1}^{\infty} u_n$ every $u_n \neq 0$ and that*

$$\lim_{n \to \infty} \left| \frac{u_{n+1}}{u_n} \right| = \rho \quad or \quad \left| \frac{u_{n+1}}{u_n} \right| \to +\infty.$$

Then

(i) *if $\rho < 1$, the series $\sum_{n=1}^{\infty} u_n$ converges absolutely;*

(ii) *if $\rho > 1$, or if $|u_{n+1}/u_n| \to +\infty$, the series diverges;*

(iii) *if $\rho = 1$, the test gives no information.*

Proof. (i) Suppose that $\rho < 1$. Choose any ρ' such that $\rho < \rho' < 1$. Then, since

$$\lim_{n \to \infty} \left| \frac{u_{n+1}}{u_n} \right| = \rho,$$

there must be a sufficiently large N for which

$$\left|\frac{u_{n+1}}{u_n}\right| < \rho', \qquad \text{for all} \quad n \geq N.$$

Then we obtain

$$|u_{N+1}| < \rho'|u_N|, \qquad |u_{N+2}| < \rho'|u_{N+1}|, \qquad |u_{N+3}| < \rho'|u_{N+2}|, \qquad \text{etc.}$$

By substitution we find

$$|u_{N+2}| < \rho'^2|u_N|, \qquad |u_{N+3}| < \rho'^3|u_N|, \qquad |u_{N+4}| < \rho'^4|u_N|, \qquad \text{etc.}$$

and, in general,

$$|u_{N+k}| < (\rho')^k|u_N| \qquad \text{for } k = 1, 2, \ldots. \tag{2}$$

The series

$$\sum_{k=1}^{\infty} |u_N|(\rho')^k = |u_N| \sum_{k=1}^{\infty} (\rho')^k$$

is a geometric series with ratio less than 1 and hence convergent. From (2) and the Comparison Test, we conclude that

$$\sum_{k=1}^{\infty} |u_{N+k}| \tag{3}$$

converges. Since (3) differs from the series

$$\sum_{n=1}^{\infty} |u_n|$$

in only a finite number of terms (N, to be exact), statement (i) of the theorem is established.

(ii) Suppose that $\rho > 1$ or $|u_{n+1}/u_n| \to +\infty$. There is an N such that

$$\frac{|u_{n+1}|}{|u_n|} > 1 \qquad \text{for all} \quad n \geq N.$$

By induction $|u_n| > |u_N|$ for all $n > N$. Therefore u_n does not tend to zero, and the series diverges.

To establish (iii), we exhibit two cases in which $\rho = 1$, one of them corresponding to a divergent series, the other to a convergent series. The p-series

$$\sum_{n=1}^{\infty} \frac{1}{n^p}$$

has $u_n = 1/n^p$. Therefore

$$\left|\frac{u_{n+1}}{u_n}\right| = \frac{n^p}{(n+1)^p} = 1 \bigg/ \left(1 + \frac{1}{n}\right)^p.$$

Since for any p

$$\lim_{n \to \infty} 1 \Big/ \left(1 + \frac{1}{n}\right)^p = 1 = \rho,$$

we see that if $p > 1$ the series converges (and $\rho = 1$), while if $p \leq 1$, the series diverges (and $\rho = 1$).

Remarks. A good working procedure for a student is to try first the ratio test for convergence or divergence. If the limit ρ turns out to be 1, some other test must then be tried. The integral test is one possibility. (We observe that the integral test establishes convergence and divergence for the p-series, while the ratio test fails.) When the terms have alternating signs, the Alternating Series Theorem is suggested. In addition, we may also try comparison theorems.

In the statement of Theorem 14, it may appear at first glance that all possible situations for ρ have been considered. That is not the case, since it may happen that

$$\left| \frac{u_{n+1}}{u_n} \right|$$

does not tend to any limit and does not tend to $+\infty$. In such circumstances, more sophisticated ratio tests are available—ones which, however, are beyond the scope of this course.

EXAMPLE 2. Test for absolute convergence:

$$\sum_{n=1}^{\infty} \frac{2^n}{n!} .$$

Solution. Applying the ratio test, we have

$$u_{n+1} = \frac{2^{n+1}}{(n+1)!}, \qquad u_n = \frac{2^n}{n!},$$

and

$$\left| \frac{u_{n+1}}{u_n} \right| = \frac{2^{n+1}}{(n+1)!} \cdot \frac{n!}{2^n} = \frac{2}{n+1} .$$

Therefore

$$\lim_{n \to \infty} \left| \frac{u_{n+1}}{u_n} \right| = 0 = \rho.$$

The series converges absolutely.

EXAMPLE 3. Test for absolute and conditional convergence:

$$\sum_{n=1}^{\infty} \frac{(-1)^n n}{2^n} .$$

Solution. We have

$$u_{n+1} = (-1)^{n+1} \frac{n+1}{2^{n+1}}, \qquad u_n = \frac{(-1)^n n}{2^n},$$

and therefore

$$\left|\frac{u_{n+1}}{u_n}\right| = \frac{n+1}{2^{n+1}} \cdot \frac{2^n}{n} = \frac{1}{2}\left(\frac{n+1}{n}\right) = \frac{1}{2}\left(\frac{1+1/n}{1}\right).$$

Hence

$$\lim_{n\to\infty}\left|\frac{u_{n+1}}{u_n}\right| = \frac{1}{2} = \rho.$$

The series converges absolutely.

EXAMPLE 4. Test for absolute convergence:

$$\sum_{n=1}^{\infty}\frac{(2n)!}{n^{100}}.$$

Solution. We have

$$u_n = \frac{(2n)!}{n^{100}} \qquad \text{and} \qquad u_{n+1} = \frac{[2(n+1)]!}{(n+1)^{100}}.$$

Therefore

$$\left|\frac{u_{n+1}}{u_n}\right| = \frac{(2n+2)!}{(n+1)^{100}} \cdot \frac{n^{100}}{(2n)!} = (2n+1)(2n+2)\left(\frac{n}{1+n}\right)^{100}$$

$$= (2n+1)(2n+2)\left(\frac{1}{1+1/n}\right)^{100}.$$

Hence

$$\lim_{n\to\infty}\left|\frac{u_{n+1}}{u_n}\right| = +\infty,$$

and the series is divergent.

EXERCISES

Test each of the following series for convergence or divergence. If the series is convergent, determine whether it is absolutely or conditionally so.

1. $\displaystyle\sum_{n=1}^{\infty}\frac{n!}{10^n}$

2. $\displaystyle\sum_{n=1}^{\infty}\frac{10^n}{n!}$

3. $\displaystyle\sum_{n=1}^{\infty}\frac{(-1)^{n-1}n!}{10^n}$

4. $\displaystyle\sum_{n=1}^{\infty}\frac{(-1)^{n-1}10^n}{n!}$

5. $\displaystyle\sum_{n=1}^{\infty}n\left(\frac{3}{4}\right)^n$

6. $\displaystyle\sum_{n=1}^{\infty}n^2\left(\frac{3}{4}\right)^n$

7. $\displaystyle\sum_{n=1}^{\infty}\frac{(-1)^n}{\sqrt{n}}$

8. $\displaystyle\sum_{n=1}^{\infty}\frac{(-1)^n}{n^p}, \quad 0 < p < 1$

9. $\displaystyle\sum_{n=1}^{\infty}\frac{(-1)^n}{n\sqrt{n}}$

10. $\displaystyle\sum_{n=1}^{\infty}\frac{(-1)^{n+1}(n-1)}{n^2+1}$

11. $\displaystyle\sum_{n=1}^{\infty}\frac{(-1)^n n^2}{2^n}$

12. $\displaystyle\sum_{n=1}^{\infty}\frac{(-1)^{n+1}(n-1)^2}{n^3}$

13. $\displaystyle\sum_{n=1}^{\infty} \frac{(-1)^{n-1}(4/3)^n}{n^2}$

14. $\displaystyle\sum_{n=1}^{\infty} \frac{(-1)^n(3/2)^2}{n^4}$

15. $\displaystyle\sum_{n=1}^{\infty} \frac{(-5)^{n-1}}{n \cdot n!}$

16. $\displaystyle\sum_{n=1}^{\infty} \frac{(-2)^{n-1} \cdot (n+1)}{(2n)!}$

17. $\displaystyle\sum_{n=1}^{\infty} \frac{(-1)^{n-1}n!}{1 \cdot 3 \cdot 5 \cdots (2n-1)}$

18. $\displaystyle\sum_{n=1}^{\infty} \frac{(-1)^{n-1}(n!)^2 \cdot 2^n}{(2n)!}$

19. $\displaystyle\sum_{n=1}^{\infty} \frac{(-1)^{n-1}(n+1)}{n\sqrt{n}}$

20. $\displaystyle\sum_{n=1}^{\infty} \frac{(n!)^2 5^n}{(2n)!}$

21. $\displaystyle\sum_{n=1}^{\infty} \frac{(-1)^n 2 \cdot 4 \cdot 6 \cdots (2n)}{1 \cdot 4 \cdot 7 \cdots (3n-2)}$

22. $\displaystyle\sum_{n=1}^{\infty} \frac{(-1)^{n+1} 3^{n+1}}{2^{4n}}$

23. $\displaystyle\sum_{n=1}^{\infty} \frac{(-1)^{n-1}n}{n+1}$

24. $\displaystyle\sum_{n=1}^{\infty} \frac{(-1)^n(n-2)}{n^{7/4}}$

25. $\displaystyle\sum_{n=1}^{\infty} \frac{(-1)^n(6n^2-9n+4)}{n^3}$

26. $\displaystyle\sum_{n=1}^{\infty} \frac{(-1)^{n+1}}{(n+1)\ln(n+1)}$

27. $\displaystyle\sum_{n=1}^{\infty} \frac{(-1)^{n+1}\ln(n+1)}{n+1}$

28. $\displaystyle\sum_{n=1}^{\infty} \frac{(-1)^{n-1}\ln n}{n^2}$

5. POWER SERIES

A *power series* is a series of the form

$$c_0 + c_1(x-a) + c_2(x-a)^2 + \cdots + c_n(x-a)^n + \cdots,$$

in which a and the c_i, $i = 0, 1, 2, \ldots$, are constants. If a particular value is given to x, we then obtain an infinite series of numbers of the type we have been considering. The special case $a = 0$ occurs frequently, in which case the series becomes

$$c_0 + c_1 x + c_2 x^2 + c_3 x^3 + \cdots + c_n x^n + \cdots.$$

Most often, we use the $\sum$-notation, writing

$$\sum_{n=0}^{\infty} c_n(x-a)^n \qquad \text{and} \qquad \sum_{n=0}^{\infty} c_n x^n.$$

If a power series converges for certain values of x, we may define a function of x by setting

$$f(x) = \sum_{n=0}^{\infty} c_n(x-a)^n \qquad \text{or} \qquad g(x) = \sum_{n=0}^{\infty} c_n x^n$$

for those values of x. We shall see that all the functions we have studied can be represented by convergent power series (with certain exceptions for the value a).

The Ratio Test may be used to determine when a power series converges. We begin with several examples.

EXAMPLE 1. Find the values of x for which the series

$$\sum_{n=1}^{\infty} \frac{1}{n} x^n$$

converges.

Solution. We apply the Ratio Test, noting that

$$u_n = \frac{1}{n} x^n, \qquad u_{n+1} = \frac{1}{n+1} x^{n+1}.$$

Then

$$\left| \frac{u_{n+1}}{u_n} \right| = \frac{|x|^{n+1}}{n+1} \cdot \frac{n}{|x|^n} = |x| \frac{n}{n+1}.$$

It is important to observe that x remains *unaffected* as $n \to \infty$. Hence

$$\lim_{n \to \infty} \left| \frac{u_{n+1}}{u_n} \right| = \lim_{n \to \infty} |x| \frac{n}{n+1} = |x| \lim_{n \to \infty} \frac{1}{1+1/n} = |x|.$$

That is, $\rho = |x|$ in the Ratio Test.

We conclude: (a) the series converges if $|x| < 1$; (b) the series diverges if $|x| > 1$; (c) if $|x| = 1$, the Ratio Test gives no information. The last case corresponds to $x = \pm 1$, and we may try other methods for these two series, which are

$$\sum_{n=1}^{\infty} \frac{1}{n} \quad (\text{if } x = 1) \qquad \text{and} \qquad \sum_{n=1}^{\infty} \frac{(-1)^n}{n} \quad (\text{if } x = -1).$$

The first series above is the divergent harmonic series. The second series converges by the Alternating Series Theorem. Therefore the given series converges for $-1 \le x < 1$.

EXAMPLE 2. Find the values of x for which the series

$$\sum_{n=1}^{\infty} \frac{(-1)^n (x+1)^n}{2^n n^2}$$

converges.

Solution. We have

$$u_n = \frac{(-1)^n (x+1)^n}{2^n n^2}, \qquad u_{n+1} = \frac{(-1)^{n+1}(x+1)^{n+1}}{2^{n+1}(n+1)^2}.$$

Therefore

$$\left| \frac{u_{n+1}}{u_n} \right| = \frac{|x+1|^{n+1}}{2^{n+1}(n+1)^2} \cdot \frac{2^n n^2}{|x+1|^n} = \frac{1}{2} |x+1| \left(\frac{n}{n+1} \right)^2$$

and

$$\lim_{n \to \infty} \frac{|u_{n+1}|}{|u_n|} = \frac{1}{2} |x+1| \lim_{n \to \infty} \left(\frac{1}{1+1/n} \right)^2 = \frac{|x+1|}{2}.$$

According to the Ratio Test: (a) the series converges if $\frac{1}{2}|x + 1| < 1$; (b) the series diverges if $\frac{1}{2}|x + 1| > 1$; (c) if $|x + 1| = 2$, the test fails.

The inequality $|x + 1| < 2$ may be written

$$-2 < x + 1 < 2 \quad \text{or} \quad -3 < x < 1,$$

and the series converges in this interval, while it diverges for x outside this interval. The values $x = -3$ and $x = 1$ remain for consideration. The corresponding series are

$$\sum_{n=1}^{\infty} \frac{(-1)^n(-2)^n}{2^n n^2} = \sum_{n=1}^{\infty} \frac{1}{n^2} \quad \text{and} \quad \sum_{n=1}^{\infty} \frac{(-1)^n 2^n}{2^n n^2} = \sum_{n=1}^{\infty} \frac{(-1)^n}{n^2}.$$

Both series converge absolutely by the p-series test. The original series converges for x in the interval $-3 \le x \le 1$.

EXAMPLE 3. Find the values of x for which the series

$$\sum_{n=0}^{\infty} \frac{(-1)^n x^n}{n!}$$

converges.

Solution. We have

$$u_n = \frac{(-1)^n x^n}{n!}, \qquad u_{n+1} = \frac{(-1)^{n+1} x^{n+1}}{(n+1)!},$$

and

$$\left| \frac{u_{n+1}}{u_n} \right| = \frac{|x|^{n+1}}{(n+1)!} \cdot \frac{n!}{|x|^n} = |x| \frac{1}{n+1}.$$

Hence $\rho = 0$, regardless of the value of $|x|$. The series converges for all values of x; that is, $-\infty < x < \infty$.

EXAMPLE 4. Find the values of x for which the series

$$\sum_{n=0}^{\infty} \frac{(-1)^n n! x^n}{10^n}$$

converges.

Solution. We have

$$u_n = \frac{(-1)^n n! x^n}{10^n}, \qquad u_{n+1} = \frac{(-1)^{n+1}(n+1)! x^{n+1}}{10^{n+1}},$$

and, if $x \ne 0$,

$$\left| \frac{u_{n+1}}{u_n} \right| = \frac{|x|^{n+1}(n+1)!}{10^{n+1}} \cdot \frac{10^n}{|x|^n n!} = |x| \cdot \frac{n+1}{10}.$$

Therefore, if $x \ne 0$, $|u_{n+1}/u_n| \to \infty$ and the series diverges. The series converges only for $x = 0$.

The convergence properties of the most general power series are illustrated in the examples above. However, the proof of the theorem which states this fact (given below in Theorem 16) is beyond the scope of this text. In all the examples above we see that it always happened that $|u_{n+1}/u_n|$ tended to a limit or to $+\infty$. The examples are deceptive, since there are cases in which $|u_{n+1}/u_n|$ may neither tend to a limit nor tend to $+\infty$.

Lemma. *If the series $\sum_{n=0}^{\infty} u_n$ converges, there is a number M such that $|u_n| \leq M$ for every n.*

Proof. By Theorem 6 we know that $\lim_{n \to \infty} u_n = 0$. From the definition of a limit, there must be a number N such that

$$|u_n| < 1 \qquad \text{for all} \qquad n > N$$

(by taking $\epsilon = 1$ in the definition of limit). We define M to be the largest of the numbers

$$|u_0|, \quad |u_1|, \quad |u_2|, \quad \ldots, \quad |u_N|, \quad 1,$$

and the result is established.

Theorem 15. *If the series $\sum_{n=0}^{\infty} a_n x^n$ converges for some $x_1 \neq 0$, then the series converges absolutely for all x for which $|x| < |x_1|$, and there is a number M such that*

$$|a_n x^n| \leq M \left| \frac{x}{x_1} \right|^n$$

for all n.

Proof. Since the series $\sum_{n=0}^{\infty} a_n x_1^n$ converges, we know from the Lemma above that there is a number M such that

$$|a_n x_1^n| \leq M \qquad \text{for all } n.$$

Then

$$|a_n x^n| = \left| a_n x_1^n \frac{x^n}{x_1^n} \right| = |a_n x_1^n| \cdot \left| \frac{x}{x_1} \right|^n \leq M \left| \frac{x}{x_1} \right|^n.$$

The series

$$\sum_{n=0}^{\infty} M \left| \frac{x}{x_1} \right|^n$$

is a geometric series with ratio less than 1, and so convergent. Hence, by the Comparison Test, the series

$$\sum_{n=0}^{\infty} a_n x^n$$

converges absolutely.

Remark. Theorem 15 may be established for series of the form $\sum_{n=0}^{\infty} a_n(x-a)^n$ in a completely analogous manner.

Theorem 16. *Let $\sum_{n=0}^{\infty} a_n(x - a)^n$ be any given power series. Then either*

(i)   *the series converges only for $x = a$;*
(ii) *the series converges for all values of x; or*
(iii) *there is a number $R > 0$ such that the series converges for all x for which $|x - a| < R$ and diverges for all x for which $|x - a| > R$.*

We omit the proof. (See, however, Morrey, *University Calculus*, page 464.) The consequence (iii) in Theorem 16 states that there is an *interval of convergence* $-R < x - a < R$ or $a - R < x < a + R$. Nothing is stated about what happens when $x = a - R$ or $a + R$. These *endpoint* problems must be settled on a case-by-case basis. The alternatives (i) and (ii) correspond to $R = 0$ and $R = +\infty$, respectively.

EXERCISES

In problems 1 through 27, find the values of x for which the following power series converge. Include a discussion of the endpoints.

1. $\displaystyle\sum_{n=0}^{\infty} x^n$

2. $\displaystyle\sum_{n=0}^{\infty} (-1)^n x^n$

3. $\displaystyle\sum_{n=0}^{\infty} (2x)^n$

4. $\displaystyle\sum_{n=0}^{\infty} \left(\frac{1}{4}x\right)^n$

5. $\displaystyle\sum_{n=0}^{\infty} (-1)^n(n + 1)x^n$

6. $\displaystyle\sum_{n=1}^{\infty} \frac{(x - 1)^n}{3^n n^2}$

7. $\displaystyle\sum_{n=1}^{\infty} \frac{(x - 1)^n}{2^n n^3}$

8. $\displaystyle\sum_{n=1}^{\infty} \frac{(-1)^{n+1}(x - 2)^n}{n\sqrt{n}}$

9. $\displaystyle\sum_{n=1}^{\infty} \frac{(x + 2)^n}{\sqrt{n}}$

10. $\displaystyle\sum_{n=0}^{\infty} \frac{(10x)^n}{n!}$

11. $\displaystyle\sum_{n=0}^{\infty} \frac{x^n}{(2n)!}$

12. $\displaystyle\sum_{n=0}^{\infty} \frac{n!(x + 1)^n}{5^n}$

13. $\displaystyle\sum_{n=0}^{\infty} \frac{(-1)^n(3/2)^n x^n}{n + 1}$

14. $\displaystyle\sum_{n=0}^{\infty} \frac{(2n)!x^n}{n!}$

15. $\displaystyle\sum_{n=1}^{\infty} n^2(x - 1)^n$

16. $\displaystyle\sum_{n=1}^{\infty} \frac{n(x + 2)^n}{2^n}$

17. $\displaystyle\sum_{n=1}^{\infty} \frac{(-1)^{n-1}(x + 4)^n}{3^n \cdot n^2}$

18. $\displaystyle\sum_{n=1}^{\infty} \frac{n!(x - 3)^n}{1 \cdot 3 \cdot 5 \cdots (2n - 1)}$

19. $\displaystyle\sum_{n=1}^{\infty} \frac{(-1)^{n+1}(n!)^2(x - 2)^n}{2^n(2n)!}$

20. $\displaystyle\sum_{n=1}^{\infty} \frac{n!(x - 1)^n}{4^n \cdot 1 \cdot 3 \cdot 5 \cdots (2n - 1)}$

21. $\displaystyle\sum_{n=1}^{\infty} \frac{(-1)^{n-1} n!(3/2)^n x^n}{1 \cdot 3 \cdot 5 \cdots (2n-1)}$

22. $\displaystyle\sum_{n=0}^{\infty} \frac{(-1)^n 3^{n+1} x^n}{2^{3n}}$

23. $\displaystyle\sum_{n=1}^{\infty} \frac{(n-2)x^n}{n^2}$

24. $\displaystyle\sum_{n=0}^{\infty} \frac{(6n^2 + 3n + 1)x^n}{2^n(n+1)^3}$

25. $\displaystyle\sum_{n=1}^{\infty} \frac{(-1)^{n-1} x^n}{(n+1)\ln(n+1)}$

26. $\displaystyle\sum_{n=1}^{\infty} \frac{\ln(n+1)3^n(x-1)^n}{n+1}$

27. $\displaystyle\sum_{n=1}^{\infty} \frac{(-1)^{n-1}(\ln n)2^n x^n}{3^n n^2}$

28. Prove Theorem 15 for series of the form

$$\sum_{n=0}^{\infty} a_n(x-a)^n.$$

29. (a) Find the interval of convergence of the series

$$\sum_{n=1}^{\infty} \frac{1 \cdot 3 \cdot 5 \cdots (2n-1)}{2 \cdot 4 \cdot 6 \cdots (2n)} x^n.$$

(b) Show that the series in (a) is identical with the series

$$\sum_{n=1}^{\infty} \frac{(2n)!}{2^{2n}(n!)^2} x^n.$$

30. Find the interval of convergence of the series

$$\sum_{n=1}^{\infty} \frac{1 \cdot 3 \cdot 5 \cdots (2n-1)(x-2)^n}{2^n \cdot 1 \cdot 4 \cdot 7 \cdots (3n-2)}.$$

31. Find the interval of convergence of the binomial series

$$1 + \sum_{n=1}^{\infty} \frac{m(m-1) \cdots (m-n+1)}{n!} x^n; \qquad m \text{ fixed.}$$

6. TAYLOR'S SERIES

Suppose that a power series

$$\sum_{n=0}^{\infty} a_n(x-a)^n$$

converges in some interval $-R < x - a < R$ $(R > 0)$. Then the sum of the series has a value for each x in this interval and so defines a function of x. We can therefore write

$$f(x) = a_0 + a_1(x-a) + a_2(x-a)^2 + a_3(x-a)^3 + \cdots,$$
$$a - R < x < a + R. \tag{1}$$

We ask the question: What is the relationship between the coefficients a_1, a_2, $a_3, \ldots, a_n, \ldots$ and the function f?

We shall proceed naïvely, as if the right side of (1) were a polynomial. Setting $x = a$, we find at once that

$$f(a) = a_0.$$

We differentiate (1) (as if the right side were a polynomial) and get

$$f'(x) = a_1 + 2a_2(x - a) + 3a_3(x - a)^2 + 4a_4(x - a)^3 + \cdots.$$

For $x = a$, we find that

$$f'(a) = a_1.$$

We continue both differentiating and setting $x = a$, to obtain

$$f''(x) = 2a_2 + 3 \cdot 2a_3(x - a) + 4 \cdot 3a_4(x - a)^2 + 5 \cdot 4a_5(x - a)^3 + \cdots,$$

$$f''(a) = 2a_2 \quad \text{or} \quad a_2 = \frac{f''(a)}{2!},$$

$$f'''(x) = 3 \cdot 2a_3 + 4 \cdot 3 \cdot 2a_4(x - a) + 5 \cdot 4 \cdot 3a_5(x - a)^2$$
$$+ 6 \cdot 5 \cdot 4a_6(x - a)^3 + \cdots,$$

$$f'''(a) = 3 \cdot 2a_3 \quad \text{or} \quad a_3 = \frac{f'''(a)}{3!},$$

and so forth. The pattern is now clear. The general formula for the coefficients $a_0, a_1, a_2, \ldots, a_n, \ldots$ is

$$a_n = \frac{f^{(n)}(a)}{n!}.$$

In Section 8, it will be shown that all of the above steps are legitimate so long as the series is convergent in some positive interval. Substituting the formulas for the coefficients a_n into the power series, we obtain

$$f(x) = \sum_{n=0}^{\infty} \frac{f^{(n)}(a)}{n!} (x - a)^n. \tag{2}$$

DEFINITION. The right side of Eq. (2) is called the *Taylor series for f about the point a* or the *expansion of f into a power series about a*.

For the special case $a = 0$, the Taylor series is

$$f(x) = \sum_{n=0}^{\infty} \frac{f^{(n)}(0)}{n!} x^n. \tag{3}$$

The right side of (3) is called the *Maclaurin series for f*.

———————

EXAMPLE 1.   Assuming that $f(x) = \sin x$ is given by its Maclaurin series, expand $\sin x$ into such a series.

Solution. We have

$$f(x) = \sin x, \qquad f(0) = 0,$$
$$f'(x) = \cos x, \qquad f'(0) = 1,$$
$$f''(x) = -\sin x, \qquad f''(0) = 0,$$
$$f^{(3)}(x) = -\cos x, \qquad f^{(3)}(0) = -1,$$
$$f^{(4)}(x) = \sin x, \qquad f^{(4)}(0) = 0.$$

It is clear that $f^{(5)} = f', f^{(6)} = f''$, etc., so that the sequence $0, 1, 0, -1, 0, 1, 0, -1, \ldots$ repeats itself indefinitely. Therefore, from (3) we obtain

$$\sin x = x - \frac{x^3}{3!} + \frac{x^5}{5!} - \frac{x^7}{7!} + \frac{x^9}{9!} \cdots$$
$$= \sum_{k=0}^{\infty} \frac{(-1)^k x^{2k+1}}{(2k+1)!}. \tag{4}$$

Remark. It may be verified (by the Ratio Test, for example) that the series (4) converges for all values of x.

EXAMPLE 2. Expand the function

$$f(x) = \frac{1}{x}$$

into a Taylor series about $x = 1$, assuming that such an expansion is valid.

Solution. We have

$$f(x) = x^{-1} \qquad\qquad f(1) = 1$$
$$f'(x) = (-1)x^{-2} \qquad\qquad f'(1) = -1$$
$$f''(x) = (-1)(-2)x^{-3} \qquad\qquad f''(1) = (-1)^2 \cdot 2!$$
$$f^{(3)}(x) = (-1)(-2)(-3)x^{-4} \qquad\qquad f^{(3)}(1) = (-1)^3 \cdot 3!$$
$$f^{(n)}(x) = (-1)(-2)\cdots(-n)x^{-n-1} \qquad f^{(n)}(1) = (-1)^n \cdot n!$$

Therefore from (2) with $a = 1$, we obtain

$$f(x) = \frac{1}{x} = \sum_{n=0}^{\infty} (-1)^n (x-1)^n. \tag{5}$$

Remark. The series (5) converges for $|x - 1| < 1$ or $0 < x < 2$, as may be confirmed by the Ratio Test.

Examples 1 and 2 have meaning only if it is known that the functions are representable by means of power series. There are examples of functions for which it is possible to compute all the quantities $f^{(n)}(x)$ at a given value a, and yet the Taylor series about a will not represent the function. (See Morrey, *University Calculus*, p. 467. See also Exercise 33 below.)

EXAMPLE 3. Compute the first six terms of the Maclaurin expansion of the function

$$f(x) = \tan x,$$

assuming that such an expansion is valid.

Solution. We have

$$f(x) = \tan x, \qquad f(0) = 0$$
$$f'(x) = \sec^2 x, \qquad f'(0) = 1$$
$$f''(x) = 2 \sec^2 x \tan x, \qquad f''(0) = 0$$
$$f^{(3)}(x) = 2 \sec^4 x + 4 \sec^2 x \tan^2 x, \qquad f^{(3)}(0) = 2$$
$$f^{(4)}(x) = 8 \tan x \sec^2 x (2 + 3 \tan^2 x), \qquad f^{(4)}(0) = 0$$
$$f^{(5)}(x) = 48 \tan^2 x \sec^4 x + 8 \sec^2 x (2 + 3 \tan^2 x)(\sec^2 x + 2 \tan^2 x), \qquad f^{(5)}(0) = 16$$

Therefore

$$f(x) = \tan x = x + \frac{x^3}{3} + \frac{2x^5}{15} + \cdots.$$

Remark. Example 3 shows that the general pattern for the successive derivatives may not always be readily discernible. Examples 1 and 2, on the other hand, show how the general formula for the nth derivative may be arrived at simply.

EXERCISES

In problems 1 through 16, find the Taylor (Maclaurin if $a = 0$) series for each function f about the given value of a.

1. $f(x) = e^x, \quad a = 0$

2. $f(x) = \cos x, \quad a = 0$

3. $f(x) = \ln (1 + x), \quad a = 0$

4. $f(x) = \ln (1 + x), \quad a = 1$

5. $f(x) = (1 - x)^{-2}, \quad a = 0$

6. $f(x) = (1 - x)^{-1/2}, \quad a = 0$

7. $f(x) = (1 + x)^{1/2}, \quad a = 0$

8. $f(x) = e^x, \quad a = 1$

9. $f(x) = \ln x, \quad a = 3$

10. $f(x) = \sin x, \quad a = \pi/4$

11. $f(x) = \cos x, \quad a = \pi/3$

12. $f(x) = \sin x, \quad a = 2\pi/3$

13. $f(x) = \sqrt{x}, \quad a = 4$

14. $f(x) = \sin (x + \frac{1}{2}), \quad a = 0$

15. $f(x) = \cos (x + \frac{1}{2}), \quad a = 0$

16. $f(x) = x^m, \quad a = 1$

In each of problems 17 through 31, find the first few terms of the Taylor expansion about the given value of a. Carry out the process to include the term $(x - a)^n$ for the given integer n.

17. $f(x) = e^{-x^2}, \quad a = 0, \quad n = 4$

18. $f(x) = xe^x, \quad a = 0, \quad n = 4$

19. $f(x) = \dfrac{1}{1 + x^2}, \quad a = 0, \quad n = 4$

20. $f(x) = \arctan x, \quad a = 0, \quad n = 5$

21. $f(x) = e^x \cos x, \quad a = 0, \quad n = 4$

22. $f(x) = \dfrac{1}{\sqrt{1 - x^2}}, \quad a = 0, \quad n = 4$

23. $f(x) = \arcsin x$, $a = 0$, $n = 5$ 24. $f(x) = \tanh x$, $a = 0$, $n = 5$
25. $f(x) = \ln \sec x$, $a = 0$, $n = 6$ 26. $f(x) = \sec x$, $a = 0$, $n = 4$
27. $f(x) = \operatorname{sech} x$, $a = 0$, $n = 4$ 28. $f(x) = \csc x$, $a = \pi/2$, $n = 4$
29. $f(x) = \sec x$, $a = \pi/3$, $n = 3$ 30. $f(x) = \ln \sin x$, $a = \pi/4$, $n = 4$
31. $f(x) = \tan x$, $a = 0$, $n = 8$ (See Example 3.)

32. (a) Given the polynomial

$$f(x) = 3 + 2x - x^2 + 4x^3 - 2x^4, \tag{6}$$

show that f may be written in the form

$$f(x) = a_0 + a_1(x - 1) + a_2(x - 1)^2 + a_3(x - 1)^3 + a_4(x - 1)^4.$$

[*Hint:* Use the Taylor expansion (2) and (6) to get each a_i.]

*(b) Given the same polynomial in two forms,

$$f(x) = \sum_{k=0}^{N} a_k(x - a)^k, \qquad f(x) = \sum_{k=0}^{n} b_k(x - b)^k,$$

express each b_i in terms of a, b, and the a_i.

*33. (a) Given the function (see Fig. 19–5)

$$F(x) = \begin{cases} e^{-1/x^2}, & x \neq 0, \\ 0, & x = 0, \end{cases}$$

use l'Hôpital's Rule to show that

$$F'(0) = 0.$$

FIGURE 19–5

(b) Show that $F^{(n)}(0) = 0$ for every positive integer n.

(c) What can be said about the Taylor series for F?

7. TAYLOR'S THEOREM WITH REMAINDER

If a function f possesses only a finite number—say n—of derivatives, then it is clear that it is not possible to represent it by a Taylor series, since the coefficients $a_k = f^{(k)}(a)/k!$ cannot be computed beyond a_n. In such cases it is still possible to obtain a *finite version* of a Taylor expansion.

Suppose that $f(x)$ possesses n continuous derivatives in some interval about the value a. Then it is always possible to write

$$f(x) = f(a) + \frac{f'(a)}{1!}(x - a) + \frac{f^{(2)}(a)}{2!}(x - a)^2 + \cdots$$

$$+ \frac{f^{(n)}(a)}{n!}(x - a)^n + R_n \tag{1}$$

for x in this interval. The right side consists of a polynomial in x of degree n and a *remainder* R_n about which, as yet, we have no knowledge. The content of *Taylor's Theorem* concerns the character of R_n. This theorem is not only of great theoretical value but may also be used in approximations and numerical computations.

Theorem 17. (Taylor's Theorem with Derivative Form of Remainder.) *Suppose that $f, f', f^{(2)}, \ldots, f^{(n)}, f^{(n+1)}$ are all continuous in some interval containing a and b. Then there is a number ξ between a and b such that*

$$f(b) = f(a) + \frac{f'(a)}{1!}(b-a) + \frac{f^{(2)}(a)}{2!}(b-a)^2 + \cdots + \frac{f^{(n)}(a)}{n!}(b-a)^n$$
$$+ \frac{f^{(n+1)}(\xi)(b-a)^{n+1}}{(n+1)!}.$$

That is, the remainder R_n is given by the formula

$$R_n = \frac{f^{(n+1)}(\xi)(b-a)^{n+1}}{(n+1)!}. \tag{2}$$

Remarks. (i) We see that R_n depends on both b and a, and we write, in general, $R_n = R_n(a, b)$, a function of two variables.

(ii) If we take the special case $n = 0$, we obtain $f(b) = f(a) + f'(\xi)(b-a)$, which we recognize as the Theorem of the Mean.

Proof. The proof makes use of Rolle's Theorem. We create a function $\phi(x)$ which is zero at a and b and so, by Rolle's Theorem, there must be a number ξ between a and b where $\phi'(\xi) = 0$. The algebra is lengthy, and the student should write out the details for the cases $n = 1, 2, 3$ in order to grasp the essence of the proof. We use the form (1) for $x = b$ and write

$$f(b) = f(a) + \frac{f'(a)}{1!}(b-a) + \frac{f^{(2)}(a)(b-a)^2}{2!} + \cdots$$
$$+ \frac{f^{(n)}(a)(b-a)^n}{n!} + R_n(a, b);$$

we wish to find $R_n(a, b)$. We define the function

$$\phi(x) = f(b) - f(x) - \frac{f'(x)(b-x)}{1!} - \frac{f^{(2)}(x)(b-x)^2}{2!} - \frac{f^{(3)}(x)(b-x)^3}{3!}$$
$$- \cdots - \frac{f^{(n-1)}(x)(b-x)^{n-1}}{(n-1)!} - \frac{f^{(n)}(x)(b-x)^n}{n!} - R_n(a, b)\frac{(b-x)^{n+1}}{(b-a)^{n+1}}.$$

The function ϕ was concocted in such a way that $\phi(a) = 0$ and $\phi(b) = 0$, facts which are easily checked by straight substitution. We compute the derivative

$\phi'(x)$ (using the formula for the derivative of a product wherever necessary):

$$\phi'(x) = -f'(x) + f'(x) - \frac{f^{(2)}(x)(b-x)}{1!} + \frac{2f^{(2)}(x)(b-x)}{2!}$$
$$- \frac{f^{(3)}(x)(b-x)^2}{2!} + \frac{3f^{(3)}(x)(b-x)^2}{3!} - \frac{f^{(4)}(x)(b-x)^3}{3!} + \cdots$$
$$- \frac{f^{(n+1)}(x)(b-x)^n}{n!} + \frac{R_n(a,b)(n+1)(b-x)^n}{(b-a)^{n+1}}.$$

Amazingly, all the terms cancel except the last two, and we find

$$\phi'(x) = -\frac{f^{(n+1)}(x)(b-x)^n}{n!} + R_n(a,b)(n+1)\frac{(b-x)^n}{(b-a)^{n+1}}.$$

Using Rolle's Theorem, we know there must be a value ξ between a and b such that $\phi'(\xi) = 0$. Therefore we get

$$0 = -\frac{f^{(n+1)}(\xi)(b-\xi)^n}{n!} + R_n(a,b)(n+1)\frac{(b-\xi)^n}{(b-a)^{n+1}}$$

or, upon solving for $R_n(a, b)$, the formula (2) exactly.

Remarks. (i) If we know that $f(x)$ has continuous derivatives of all orders and if $R_n(a, b) \to 0$ as $n \to \infty$, then we can establish the validity of the Taylor series.

(ii) In any case, R_n is a measure of how much f differs from a certain polynomial of degree n. If R_n is small, then the polynomial may be used for approximations.

When we use Taylor's Theorem in the computation of functions from the approximating polynomial, errors may arise from two sources: the error R_n, made above by neglecting the powers of $(b - a)$ beyond the nth; and the "round-off error" made by expressing each term in decimal form. If we wish to compute the value of some function $f(b)$ to an accuracy of four decimal places, it is essential to be able to say for certain that $f(b)$ is between some decimal fraction with four decimals -0.00005 and the same decimal fraction $+0.00005$. Time is saved by computing each term to two decimals more than are required. Frequently R_n is close to the value of the first term in the series omitted, and this fact can be used as a guide in choosing the number of terms. Although we do not know R_n exactly, we can often show that there are two numbers m and M with

$$m \le f^{(n+1)}(x) \le M \qquad \text{for } all \ x \text{ between } a \text{ and } b.$$

Then we get for $R_n(a, b)$ the inequality

$$\frac{m(b-a)^{n+1}}{(n+1)!} \le R_n(a,b) \le \frac{M(b-a)^{n+1}}{(n+1)!}.$$

EXAMPLE 1. Compute $(1.1)^{1/5}$ to an accuracy of four decimal places.

Solution. The key to the solution, using Taylor's Theorem, is the fact that we can set

$$f(x) = (1 + x)^{1/5}, \quad a = 0, \quad b = 0.1.$$

Then

$f(x) = (1 + x)^{1/5},$	$f(a) = 1$	$=$	1.0000 00
$f'(x) = \dfrac{1}{5}(1 + x)^{-4/5},$	$f'(a)(b - a) = \dfrac{1}{5}(0.1)^1$	$=$	0.0200 00
$f''(x) = -\dfrac{4}{25}(1 + x)^{-9/5},$	$\dfrac{f''(a)(b - a)^2}{2!} = -\dfrac{2}{25}(0.1)^2$	$=$	-0.0008 00
$f'''(x) = \dfrac{36}{125}(1 + x)^{-14/5},$	$\dfrac{f'''(a)(b - a)^3}{3!} = \dfrac{6}{125}(0.1)^3$	$=$	0.0000 48

For all x between 0 and 1 we have

$$0 < (1 + x)^{-14/5} < 1.$$

Therefore we can estimate R_n for $n = 2$:

$$0 < R_2 = \frac{36}{125}(1 + \xi)^{-14/5}\frac{(b - a)^3}{3!} < \frac{6}{125}(0.1)^3 = 0.0000 \quad 48.$$

Adding the terms in the Taylor expansion through $n = 2$, we get

$$(1.1)^{1/5} = 1.0192, \text{ approximately};$$

in fact, a more precise statement is

$$1.0192 < (1.1)^{1/5} < 1.0192 \quad 48.$$

Remark. In Example 1, we could have selected $f(x) = x^{1/5}$ with $a = 1, b = 1.1$. The result is the same.

EXAMPLE 2. Compute $\sqrt[3]{7}$ to an accuracy of four decimal places.

Solution. Set
$$f(x) = x^{1/3}, \quad a = 8, \quad b = 7.$$

Then $b - a = -1$ and

$f(x) = x^{1/3},$	$f(a) = 2$	$=$	2.0000 00
$f'(x) = \dfrac{1}{3}x^{-2/3},$	$f'(a)(b - a) = -\dfrac{1}{12}$	$=$	-0.0833 33
$f''(x) = -\dfrac{2}{9}x^{-5/3},$	$\dfrac{f''(a)(b - a)^2}{2!} = -\dfrac{1}{9 \cdot 2^5}$	$=$	-0.0034 72
$f^{(3)}(x) = \dfrac{10}{27}x^{-8/3},$	$\dfrac{f'''(a)(b - a)^3}{3!} = -\dfrac{5}{81 \cdot 2^8}$	$=$	-0.0002 41
$f^{(4)}(x) = \dfrac{-80}{81}x^{-11/3},$	$\dfrac{f^{(4)}(a)(b - a)^4}{4!} = -\dfrac{5}{243 \cdot 2^{10}}$	$=$	-0.0000 20

It would appear to be sufficient to use only the terms through $(b - a)^3$. However, by computing the sum of the decimal fractions given, we obtain 1.9129   54. But the next term is -0.0000 20 which, if included, would reduce the value to 1.9129   34. If we stopped with the $(b - a)^3$ term and rounded off, we would obtain 1.9130 whereas, if we keep the next term and round off, we obtain 1.9129. So the term in $(b - a)^4$ should be retained, and the remainder R_4 must be estimated. We have

$$f^{(5)}(x) = \frac{880}{243} x^{-14/3} = \frac{880 x^{1/3}}{243 x^5}.$$

Since we are concerned with the interval $7 < x < 8$, we see that $x^{1/3} < 2$ and $x^5 > (49)(343)$. Hence

$$0 < \frac{f^{(5)}(x)}{5!} < \frac{1760}{(243)(49)(343)(120)} < \frac{1}{270{,}000} < 0.000004.$$

Since $(b - a)^5 = -1$, we conclude that

$$-0.000004 < R_4 < 0$$

and that

$$\sqrt[3]{7} = 1.9129$$

to the required accuracy. Actually, if we merely keep an extra decimal in each term retained, we see that

$$\sqrt[3]{7} = 1.91293$$

to five decimals.

Remarks. In Example 1 there was no round-off error, since each decimal fraction gave the exact value of the corresponding term. This was not true in Example 2, however. In general, the round-off error in each term may be as much as $\frac{1}{2}$ in the last decimal place retained. Round-off errors may tend to cancel each other if there is a large number of computations in a given problem.

One may ask why two additional decimal places were kept in the above examples. Why not one or four or seven? It is clear that if several thousand additions are made the round-off error may be much larger. In computations with high-speed electronic computers the round-off error may be serious, since computations frequently run into the millions. The study of how such questions are handled is a part of the subject known as numerical analysis, a topic which has come under intensive examination because of the capabilities of high-speed computers. We have here an example of how the presence of computing machines has given rise to an entire complex of purely mathematical questions—some of which have been answered while many are still unsolved.

The remainder $R_n(a, b)$ in Taylor's Theorem may be given in many forms. The next theorem, stated without proof, gives the remainder in the form of an integral.

Theorem 18. (Taylor's Theorem with Integral Form of Remainder.) *Suppose that $f, f', f^{(2)}, \ldots, f^{(n)}, f^{(n+1)}$ are all continuous in some interval containing a*

and b. Then f(x) may be written in the form

$$f(b) = f(a) + \frac{f'(a)}{1!}(b - a) + \frac{f^{(2)}(a)(b - a)^2}{2!} + \cdots$$

$$+ \frac{f^{(n)}(a)(b - a)^n}{n!} + R_n$$

where

$$R_n = \frac{1}{n!} \int_a^b f^{(n+1)}(t)(b - t)^n \, dt.$$

EXAMPLE 3. Write $\ln(1 + x)$ as a polynomial of the third degree, and estimate the remainder R_n for $0 < x < \frac{1}{2}$.

Solution. We select

$$f(x) = \ln(1 + x), \qquad a = 0, \qquad b = x.$$

Then

$$f'(x) = \frac{1}{1 + x}, \qquad\qquad f'(0) = 1,$$

$$f''(x) = -\frac{1}{(1 + x)^2}, \qquad f''(0) = -1,$$

$$f^{(3)}(x) = \frac{2}{(1 + x)^3}, \qquad f^{(3)}(0) = 2,$$

$$f^{(4)}(x) = -\frac{6}{(1 + x)^4}.$$

Therefore

$$\ln(1 + x) = x - \frac{x^2}{2} + \frac{x^3}{3} + R_n,$$

with

$$R_n = -\frac{6}{6} \int_0^x \frac{1}{(1 + t)^4}(x - t)^3 \, dt.$$

A simple estimate replaces $(1 + t)^{-4}$ by its smallest value 1, and we find

$$|R_n| < \int_0^{1/2} \left(\frac{1}{2} - t\right)^3 dt = \frac{1}{64}.$$

EXERCISES

In each of problems 1 through 20, compute the given quantities to the specified number of decimal places. Make sure of your accuracy by using Taylor's Theorem with Remainder. Use the fact that $2 < e < 4$ wherever necessary.

1. $e^{-0.2}$,   5 decimals   2. $e^{-0.4}$,   4 decimals

3. $e^{0.2}$,   5 decimals   4. $\sin(0.5)$,   5 decimals

5. $\cos(0.5)$,   5 decimals   6. $\tan(0.1)$,   3 decimals

7. ln (1.2), 4 decimals   8. ln (0.9), 5 decimals

9. e^{-1}, 5 decimals   10. e, 5 decimals

11. $(1.08)^{1/4}$, 5 decimals   12. $(0.92)^{1/4}$, 5 decimals

13. $(0.91)^{1/3}$, 5 decimals   14. $(0.90)^{1/5}$, 5 decimals

15. $(30)^{1/5}$, 5 decimals   16. $(15)^{1/4}$, 5 decimals

17. $(0.8)^{1/5}$, 5 decimals   18. $(65)^{1/6}$, 5 decimals

19. ln (0.8), 5 decimals   20. ln (0.6), 3 decimals

Given that $1° = \pi/180$ radians $= 0.0174533$ radians and $5° = \pi/36$ radians $= 0.0872655$ radians, compute each of the fol'owing to the number of decimal places required.

21. sin 1°, 6 decimals   22. sin 5°, 5 decimals   23. cos 5°, 5 decimals

8. DIFFERENTIATION AND INTEGRATION OF SERIES

In Section 6 we developed the formula for the Taylor series of a function and, in so doing, we ignored the validity of the manipulations which were performed. Now we shall establish the theorems which verify the correctness of the results already obtained.

Theorem 19. *If $R > 0$ and the series*

$$\sum_{n=0}^{\infty} a_n x^n \tag{1}$$

converges for $|x| < R$, then the series obtained from (1) by term-by-term differentiation converges absolutely for $|x| < R$.

Proof. Term-by-term differentiation of (1) yields

$$\sum_{n=1}^{\infty} n a_n x^{n-1}. \tag{2}$$

Choose any value x such that $|x| < R$ and choose x_1 so that $|x| < |x_1| < R$. According to the Lemma of Section 5 (page 625), there is a positive number M with the property that

$$|a_n x_1^n| \leq M \qquad \text{for all } n.$$

We have the relation

$$|n a_n x^{n-1}| = \left| n a_n \frac{x^{n-1}}{x_1^n} \cdot x_1^n \right| \leq n \frac{M}{x_1} \left| \frac{x}{x_1} \right|^{n-1},$$

and now we can apply the comparison test to the series (2). The series

$$\frac{M}{x_1} \sum_{n=1}^{\infty} n \left| \frac{x}{x_1} \right|^{n-1}$$

converges by the Ratio Test, since $\rho = |x/x_1| < 1$; hence, so does the series (2). Since x was any number in the interval $(-R, R)$, the interval of convergence of (2) is the same as that of (1).

Corollary. *Under the hypotheses of Theorem* 19, *the series* (1) *may be differentiated any number of times and each of the differentiated series converges for* $|x| < R$.

Remarks. (i) The Corollary is obtained by induction, since each differentiated series has the same radius of convergence as the one before. (ii) The results of Theorem 19 and the Corollary are valid for a series of the form

$$\sum_{n=0}^{\infty} a_n(x - a)^n,$$

which converges for $|x - a| < R$ so long as $R > 0$. The proof is the same. (iii) The quantity R may be $+\infty$, in which case the series and its derived ones converge for all values of x.

Theorem 20. *If* $R > 0$ *and* f *is defined by*

$$f(x) = \sum_{n=0}^{\infty} a_n x^n \qquad for \ |x| < R,$$

then f *is continuous for* $|x| < R$.

Proof. Let x_0 be any number such that $-R < x_0 < R$; we wish to show that f is continuous at x_0. In other words we must show that

$$f(x) \to f(x_0) \quad as \quad x \to x_0.$$

We have

$$|f(x) - f(x_0)| = \left| \sum_{n=0}^{\infty} a_n(x^n - x_0^n) \right|$$

$$\leq \sum_{n=0}^{\infty} |a_n| \, |x^n - x_0^n|.$$

We apply the Theorem of the Mean to the function $g(x) = x^n$; that is, the relation

$$g(x) - g(x_0) = g'(\xi)(x - x_0), \qquad (\xi \text{ is between } x \text{ and } x_0),$$

applied to the function $g(x) = x^n$, is

$$x^n - x_0^n = n\xi_n^{n-1}(x - x_0), \qquad (\xi_n \text{ between } x \text{ and } x_0).$$

The subscript n has been put on ξ to identify the particular exponent of the function x^n. We may also write

$$|x^n - x_0^n| = n|\xi_n|^{n-1}|x - x_0|.$$

Thus we find

$$|f(x) - f(x_0)| \leq \sum_{n=0}^{\infty} n|a_n| \, |\xi_n|^{n-1}|x - x_0|.$$

So long as x is in the interval of convergence there is an x_1 such that $|\xi_n| < x_1$ for all n. We deduce that

$$|f(x) - f(x_0)| \leq |x - x_0| \sum_{n=0}^{\infty} n|a_n| x_1^{n-1}.$$

Now we apply Theorem 19 to conclude that the series on the right converges; call its sum K. Then

$$|f(x) - f(x_0)| \leq |x - x_0| \cdot K.$$

As x tends to x_0 the quantity on the right tends to zero, and so $f(x)$ tends to $f(x_0)$. That is, $f(x)$ is continuous at x_0.

Theorem 21. (Term-by-term integration of power series.) *Suppose that $R > 0$ and*

$$f(x) = \sum_{n=0}^{\infty} a_n x^n \tag{3}$$

converges for $|x| < R$. We define

$$F(x) = \int_0^x f(t) \, dt.$$

Then

$$F(x) = \sum_{n=0}^{\infty} a_n \frac{x^{n+1}}{n+1} \tag{4}$$

holds for $|x| < R$.

Proof. Let x be any number such that $-R < x < R$. Choose x_1 so that $|x| < |x_1| < R$. We note that for any n

$$\int_0^x a_n t^n \, dt = \frac{a_n x^{n+1}}{n+1}.$$

Therefore

$$F(x) - \sum_{n=0}^{N} a_n \frac{x^{n+1}}{n+1} = \int_0^x \left[f(t) - \sum_{n=0}^{N} a_n t^n \right] dt. \tag{5}$$

But now

$$f(t) - \sum_{n=0}^{N} a_n t^n = \sum_{n=0}^{\infty} a_n t^n - \sum_{n=0}^{N} a_n t^n = \sum_{n=N+1}^{\infty} a_n t^n,$$

and for all t such that $|\xi_n| < x_1 < R$,

$$\left| f(t) - \sum_{n=0}^{N} a_n t^n \right| \leq \sum_{n=N+1}^{\infty} |a_n| \, |x|^n. \tag{6}$$

Since the series (3) converges absolutely at x, the right side of (6)—being the remainder—tends to zero as $N \to \infty$. We conclude from (5) that

$$\left| F(x) - \sum_{n=0}^{N} a_n \frac{x^{n+1}}{n+1} \right| \leq \int_0^x \left(\sum_{n=N+1}^{\infty} |a_n| \, |x|^n \right) dt = \left(\sum_{n=N+1}^{\infty} |a_n| \, |x|^n \right) \cdot x.$$

If N tends to ∞, the right side above tends to zero and the left side above yields (4).

EXAMPLE 1. Assuming that the function $f(x) = \sin x$ is given by the series

$$\sin x = x - \frac{x^3}{3!} + \frac{x^5}{5!} - \cdots + \frac{(-1)^n x^{2n+1}}{(2n+1)!} + \cdots,$$

find the Taylor series for $\cos x$.

Solution. Applying the Ratio Test to the series

$$\sum_{n=0}^{\infty} \frac{(-1)^n x^{2n+1}}{(2n+1)!},$$

we see that it converges for all values of x. We define

$$F(x) = \int_0^x \sin t \, dt = -\cos x + 1.$$

Integrating the above series for $\sin x$ term by term, we obtain

$$F(x) = 1 - \cos x = \sum_{n=0}^{\infty} \frac{(-1)^n x^{2n+2}}{(2n+2)!}$$

or

$$\cos x = 1 - \frac{x^2}{2!} + \frac{x^4}{4!} - \frac{x^6}{6!} + \cdots + \frac{(-1)^n x^{2n}}{(2n)!} + \cdots = \sum_{n=0}^{\infty} \frac{(-1)^n x^{2n}}{(2n)!}.$$

The next theorem relates the derivative of a function given by a series with the term-by-term differentiation of the series.

Theorem 22. *If $R > 0$ and*

$$f(x) = \sum_{n=0}^{\infty} a_n x^n \qquad \text{for } |x| < R, \tag{7}$$

then $f(x)$ has continuous derivatives of all orders for $|x| < R$ which are given there by series obtained by successive term-by-term differentiations of (7).

Proof. The fact that

$$\sum_{n=1}^{\infty} n a_n \, x^{n-1} \tag{8}$$

converges for $|x| < R$ was shown in Theorem 19. We must show that $g(x) = \sum_{n=1}^{\infty} n a_n x^{n-1}$ is the derivative of f. Theorem 20 establishes the fact that g is continuous. Then, integrating the series (8) term by term we get, on the one hand,

$$a_0 + \int_0^x g(t)\, dt$$

and, on the other, the series for $f(x)$. That is,

$$f(x) = a_0 + \int_0^x g(t)\, dt.$$

The Fundamental Theorem of the Calculus then asserts that

$$f'(x) = g(x),$$

which is the result we wished to establish.

Remark. The result of Theorem 22 holds equally well for functions f given by series of the form

$$f(x) = \sum_{n=0}^{\infty} a_n (x - a)^n,$$

which converge for $|x - a| < R$ with $R > 0$.

EXAMPLE 2. Assuming that the expansion of $f(x) = \sinh x$ is given by

$$\sinh x = x + \frac{x^3}{3!} + \frac{x^5}{5!} + \cdots + \frac{x^{2n-1}}{(2n-1)!} + \cdots,$$

valid for all x, obtain an expansion for $\cosh x$.

Solution. Differentiating term by term, we find

$$\cosh x = 1 + \frac{x^2}{2!} + \frac{x^4}{4!} + \cdots + \frac{x^{2n}}{(2n)!} + \cdots.$$

We now make use of the above theorems and the fact that the function $1/(1 + x)$ may be expanded in the simple geometric series

$$\frac{1}{1 + x} = \sum_{n=0}^{\infty} (-1)^n x^n, \qquad |x| < 1$$

to obtain additional series expansions.

Theorem 23.

$$\ln(1 + x) = \sum_{n=1}^{\infty} \frac{(-1)^{n-1} x^n}{n} \qquad for\ |x| < 1.$$

Proof. Letting $F(x) = \ln(1 + x)$ and differentiating, we find

$$F'(x) = f(x) = \frac{1}{1 + x} = \sum_{n=0}^{\infty} (-1)^n x^n, \qquad |x| < 1.$$

Now, by Theorem 21, we may integrate term by term and get

$$F(x) = \int_0^x f(t)\,dt = \sum_{n=0}^{\infty} \frac{(-1)^n x^{n+1}}{n+1},$$

which is identical with the statement of the theorem.

EXAMPLE 3. Find the Maclaurin series for

$$f(x) = \frac{1}{(1-x)^2}.$$

Solution. If we define $F(x) = (1-x)^{-1}$, we see that $F'(x) = f(x)$.

Now

$$F(x) = \sum_{n=0}^{\infty} x^n, \qquad |x| < 1$$

[which we can obtain from the expansion for $(1 + x)^{-1}$ if we replace x by $-x$]. Therefore

$$f(x) = \frac{1}{(1-x)^2} = \sum_{n=1}^{\infty} n x^{n-1} = \sum_{k=0}^{\infty} (k+1)x^k, \qquad |x| < 1.$$

EXAMPLE 4. Find the Maclaurin expansion for $f(x) = (1 + x^2)^{-1}$.

Solution. The geometric series

$$\frac{1}{1+u} = \sum_{n=0}^{\infty} (-1)^n u^n, \qquad |u| < 1$$

after substitution of x^2 for u, becomes

$$\frac{1}{1+x^2} = \sum_{n=0}^{\infty} (-1)^n x^{2n},$$

valid for $x^2 < 1$. The inequality $x^2 < 1$ is equivalent to the inequality $|x| < 1$.

EXERCISES

In each of problems 1 through 13, find the Taylor or Maclaurin series for the functions f, assuming that the Taylor or Maclaurin series for the functions given in Sections 6 and 7 are known.

1. $f(x) = \begin{cases} (\sin x)/x, & x \neq 0 \\ 1, & x = 0 \end{cases}$

2. $f(x) = \begin{cases} (e^x - 1)/x, & x \neq 0 \\ 1, & x = 0 \end{cases}$

3. $f(x) = \begin{cases} (1 - \cos x)/x, & x \neq 0 \\ 0, & x = 0 \end{cases}$

4. $f(x) = \ln (x + \sqrt{1 + x^2}) = \operatorname{argsinh} x$

5. $f(x) = \arcsin x$

6. $f(x) = \arctan x$

7. $f(x) = \operatorname{argtanh} x$

8. $f(x) = (1 + x)^{-2}$

9. $f(x) = \ln \dfrac{1 + x}{1 - x}$

10. $f(x) = (1 - x)^{-3}$

11. $f(x) = x(1 + x^2)^{-2}$

12. $f(x) = x \ln (1 + x^2)$

13. $f(x) = \sin^2 x$

9. VALIDITY OF TAYLOR EXPANSIONS AND COMPUTATIONS WITH SERIES

The theorems of this section state that certain functions are truly represented by their Taylor series.

Theorem 24. *For any values of a and x, we have*

$$e^x = e^a \sum_{n=0}^{\infty} \frac{(x - a)^n}{n!};$$ (1)

i.e., *the Taylor series for e^x about $x = a$ converges to e^x for any a and x.*

Proof. For simplicity, set $a = 0$, the proof being analogous when $a \neq 0$. If we let $f(x) = e^x$, then $f^{(n)}(x) = e^x$ for all n. Now, using Taylor's Theorem with Remainder, we have

$$e^x = \sum_{k=0}^{n} \frac{x^k}{k!} + R_n,$$

where

$$R_n = \frac{e^{\xi} x^{n+1}}{(n + 1)!},$$

with ξ between 0 and x. If x is positive, then $e^{\xi} < e^x$ while, if x is negative, then $e^{\xi} < e^0 = 1$. In either case,

$$R_n \leq C \frac{|x|^{n+1}}{(n + 1)!},$$ (2)

where C is the larger of 1 and e^x but is *independent of n.* If the right side of (2) is the general term of a series then, by the Ratio Test, that series is convergent for all x. The general term of any convergent series must tend to zero, and so

$$C \frac{|x|^{n+1}}{(n + 1)!} \to 0 \quad \text{as} \quad n \to \infty \text{ for each } x.$$

We conclude that $R_n \to 0$ as $n \to \infty$, and so (1) is established.

Theorem 25. *The following functions are given by their Maclaurin series:*

$$\sin x = \sum_{n=0}^{\infty} \frac{(-1)^n x^{2n+1}}{(2n+1)!},$$

$$\cos x = \sum_{n=0}^{\infty} \frac{(-1)^n x^{2n}}{(2n)!},$$

$$\sinh x = \sum_{n=0}^{\infty} \frac{x^{2n+1}}{(2n+1)!},$$

$$\cosh x = \sum_{n=0}^{\infty} \frac{x^{2n}}{(2n)!}.$$

The proofs of these results follow the same outline as the proof of Theorem 24 and are left as exercises for the student at the end of this section.

Theorem 26. (Binomial Theorem.) *For each real number m, we have*

$$(1+x)^m = 1 + \sum_{n=1}^{\infty} \frac{m(m-1)(m-2)\cdots(m-n+1)}{n!} x^n \quad \text{for } |x| < 1.$$

Proof. To show that the series on the right converges absolutely for $|x| < 1$, we apply the Ratio Test:

$$\left| \frac{u_{n+1}}{u_n} \right|$$

$$= \left| \frac{m(m-1)\cdots(m-n+1)(m-n)}{(n+1)!} \cdot \frac{n!}{m(m-1)\cdots(m-n+1)} \cdot \frac{x^{n+1}}{x^n} \right|$$

$$= \frac{|m-n|}{n+1} |x| = \frac{|1 - m/n|}{1 + 1/n} |x|.$$

The quantity on the right tends to $|x|$ as $n \to \infty$, and so the series converges for $|x| < 1$. We define

$$f(x) = 1 + \sum_{n=1}^{\infty} \frac{m(m-1)\cdots(m-n+1)}{n!} x^n,$$

and we wish to show that $f(x) = (1+x)^m$ if $|x| < 1$. Employing Theorem 22, we get $f'(x)$ by term-by-term differentiation of the series for f. We have

$$f'(x) = m + \sum_{n=2}^{\infty} \frac{m(m-1)\cdots(m-n+1)}{(n-1)!} x^{n-1}. \tag{3}$$

Multiplying both sides of (3) by x, we get

$$xf'(x) = \sum_{n=1}^{\infty} n \frac{m(m-1)\cdots(m-n+1)}{n!} x^n. \tag{4}$$

We add (3) and (4) to obtain

$$(1 + x)f'(x) = m\left\{1 + \sum_{n=1}^{\infty} \frac{m(m - 1) \cdots (m - n + 1)}{n!} x^n\right\} = mf(x).$$

The derivative of $\ln f(x)$ is given by

$$\frac{d}{dx} \ln f(x) = \frac{f'(x)}{f(x)} = \frac{m}{1 + x}.$$

On the other hand,

$$\frac{d}{dx} \ln (1 + x)^m = m \frac{d}{dx} \ln (1 + x) = \frac{m}{1 + x}.$$

Since $f(x)$ and $(1 + x)^m$ have the same derivative, and since $f(0) = 1$, we conclude finally that

$$f(x) = (1 + x)^m, \qquad |x| < 1.$$

EXAMPLE 1. Write the first 5 terms of the series expansion for $(1 + x)^{3/2}$.

Solution. We have $m = \frac{3}{2}$, and therefore

$$(1 + x)^{3/2} = 1 + \frac{\frac{3}{2}}{1!}x + \frac{(\frac{3}{2})(\frac{1}{2})}{2!} x^2 + \frac{(\frac{3}{2})(\frac{1}{2})(-\frac{1}{2})}{3!} x^3 + \frac{(\frac{3}{2})(\frac{1}{2})(-\frac{1}{2})(-\frac{3}{2})}{4!} x^4$$

$$= 1 + \frac{3}{2}x + \frac{3}{8}x^2 - \frac{3}{2^3 \cdot 3!}x^3 + \frac{3^2}{2^4 \cdot 4!}x^4 - \cdots.$$

EXAMPLE 2. Write the binomial series for $(1 + x)^7$.

Solution. We have

$$(1 + x)^7 = 1 + \sum_{n=1}^{\infty} \frac{7(6) \cdots (7 - n + 1)}{n!} x^n.$$

We now observe that beginning with $n = 8$ all the terms have a zero in the numerator. Therefore,

$$(1 + x)^7 = 1 + \sum_{n=1}^{7} \frac{7(6) \cdots (7 - n + 1)}{n!} x^n$$

$$= 1 + 7x + \frac{7 \cdot 6}{2!}x^2 + \frac{7 \cdot 6 \cdot 5}{3!}x^3 + \cdots + \frac{7!}{7!}x^7.$$

For m a positive integer, the binomial series always terminates after a finite number of terms.

EXAMPLE 3. Compute

$$\int_0^{0.5} e^{x^2}\, dx$$

to an accuracy of five decimal places.

Solution. We have

$$e^u = \sum_{n=0}^{\infty} \frac{u^n}{n!} \qquad \text{for all } u,$$

and so

$$e^{x^2} = \sum_{n=0}^{\infty} \frac{x^{2n}}{n!} \qquad \text{for all } x.$$

By Theorem 21 we can integrate term by term to get

$$\int_0^x e^{x^2}\, dx = \sum_{n=0}^{\infty} \frac{x^{2n+1}}{n!(2n+1)}.$$

For $x = 0.5$, we now compute

$$x \quad = \quad 0.5 \quad = \quad \frac{1}{2} \quad = 0.50000 \quad 00,$$

$$\frac{x^3}{1!\cdot 3} = \frac{(0.5)^3}{3} = \frac{1}{24} \quad = 0.04166 \quad 67^-,$$

$$\frac{x^5}{2!\cdot 5} = \frac{(0.5)^5}{10} = \frac{1}{320} \quad = 0.00312 \quad 50,$$

$$\frac{x^7}{3!\cdot 7} = \frac{(0.5)^7}{42} = \frac{1}{5376} \quad = 0.00018 \quad 60^+,$$

$$\frac{x^9}{4!\cdot 9} = \frac{(0.5)^9}{216} = \frac{1}{110{,}592} = 0.00000 \quad 90^+,$$

Sum of the right-hand column $= 0.54498 \quad 67.$

If we wish to stop at this point we must estimate the error made by neglecting all the remaining terms. The remainder is

$$\sum_{n=5}^{\infty} \frac{x^{2n+1}}{n!(2n+1)} \le \frac{x^{11}}{5!\cdot 11}\left(1 + \frac{x^2}{6} + \frac{x^4}{6^2} + \frac{x^6}{6^3} + \cdots\right)$$

$$\le \frac{x^{11}}{1320}\,\frac{1}{(1 - x^2/6)} = \frac{24}{23}\cdot\frac{1}{1320}\cdot\frac{1}{2048}$$

$$\le 0.00000 \quad 04.$$

Therefore

$$\int_0^{0.5} e^{x^2}\, dx = \begin{cases} 0.54499 \text{ to an accuracy of 5 decimals} \\ 0.544987 \text{ to an accuracy of 6 decimals} \end{cases}$$

EXERCISES

In each of problems 1 through 7, write the beginning of the binomial series for the given expression to the required number of terms.

1. $(1 + x)^{-3/2}$, 5 terms
2. $(1 - x)^{1/2}$, 4 terms
3. $(1 + x^2)^{-2/3}$, 5 terms
4. $(1 - x^2)^{-1/2}$, 6 terms

5. $(1 + x^3)^7$, all terms   6. $(5 + x)^{1/2}$, 4 terms   7. $(3 + \sqrt{x})^{-3}$, 5 terms

In each of problems 8 through 17, compute the value of the definite integral to the number of decimal places specified. Estimate the remainder.

8. $\displaystyle\int_0^1 \sin (x^2)\, dx$, 5 decimals

9. $\displaystyle\int_0^1 \cos (x^2)\, dx$, 5 decimals

10. $\displaystyle\int_0^1 e^{-x^2}\, dx$, 5 decimals

11. $\displaystyle\int_0^{0.5} \frac{dx}{1 + x^3}$, 5 decimals

12. $\displaystyle\int_0^1 \frac{\sin x}{x}\, dx$, 5 decimals

13. $\displaystyle\int_0^1 \frac{e^x - 1}{x}\, dx$, 5 decimals

14. $\displaystyle\int_0^{0.5} \frac{dx}{\sqrt{1 + x^3}}$, 5 decimals

15. $\displaystyle\int_0^{1/3} \frac{dx}{\sqrt[3]{1 + x^2}}$, 5 decimals

16. $\displaystyle\int_0^{1/3} \frac{dx}{\sqrt[3]{1 - x^2}}$, 5 decimals

17. $\displaystyle\int_0^{0.5} \frac{dx}{\sqrt{1 - x^3}}$, 5 decimals

18. Use the series for $\ln \dfrac{1 + x}{1 - x}$ to find $\ln 1.5$ to 5 decimals of accuracy.

19. Same as Problem 18, to find $\ln 2$.

20. Prove that
$$\sin x = \sum_{n=0}^{\infty} \frac{(-1)^n x^{2n+1}}{(2n + 1)!}$$

21. Prove that
$$\cos x = \sum_{n=0}^{\infty} \frac{(-1)^n x^{2n}}{(2n)!}$$

22. Prove that
$$\sinh x = \sum_{n=0}^{\infty} \frac{x^{2n+1}}{(2n + 1)!}$$

23. Prove that
$$\cosh x = \sum_{n=0}^{\infty} \frac{x^{2n}}{(2n)!}$$

24. If $f(x) = \sin x$ show, by induction, that $f^{(k)}(x) = \sin (x + \tfrac{1}{2}k\pi)$.

25. Use the result of Problem 24 to show that for all a and x the Taylor series for $\sin x$ is given by
$$\sin x = \sum_{n=0}^{\infty} \frac{\sin (a + \tfrac{1}{2}n\pi)}{n!} (x - a)^n.$$

26. If $f(x) = \cos x$ show, by induction, that $f^{(k)}(x) = \cos (x + \tfrac{1}{2}k\pi)$.

27. Use the result of Problem 26 to show that for all a and x the Taylor series for $\cos x$ is given by
$$\cos x = \sum_{n=0}^{\infty} \frac{\cos (a + \tfrac{1}{2}n\pi)}{n!} (x - a)^n.$$

10. ALGEBRAIC OPERATIONS WITH SERIES

In previous sections we discussed the question of term-by-term differentiation and integration of series. Now we turn to the question of multiplication and division of power series.

Suppose we are given two power series

$$\sum_{n=0}^{\infty} a_n x^n = a_0 + a_1 x + a_2 x^2 + \cdots + a_n x^n + \cdots,$$

$$\sum_{n=0}^{\infty} b_n x^n = b_0 + b_1 x + b_2 x^2 + \cdots + b_n x^n + \cdots.$$

Without considering questions of convergence, we multiply the two series by following the rules for multiplying two polynomials. We obtain the successive lines, each obtained by multiplying an element of the second series with all the terms of the first series:

b_0: $\quad a_0 b_0 + a_1 b_0 x + a_2 b_0 x^2 + \cdots + a_n b_0 x^n + \cdots,$

$b_1 x$: $\quad\quad a_0 b_1 x + a_1 b_1 x^2 + \cdots + a_{n-1} b_1 x^n + a_n b_1 x^{n+1} + \cdots,$

$b_2 x^2$: $\quad\quad\quad a_0 b_2 x^2 + \cdots + a_{n-2} b_2 x^n + a_{n-1} b_2 x^{n+1} + a_n b_2 x^{n+2} + \cdots,$

$\quad\quad \vdots$

$b_n x^n$: $\quad\quad\quad\quad a_0 b_n x^n \quad + a_1 b_n x^{n+1} \quad + a_2 b_n x^{n+2} + \cdots.$

Adding the columns, we obtain the power series

$$a_0 b_0 + (a_1 b_0 + a_0 b_1) x + (a_2 b_0 + a_1 b_1 + a_0 b_2) x^2$$
$$+ (a_3 b_0 + a_2 b_1 + a_1 b_2 + a_0 b_3) x^3 + \cdots$$
$$+ (a_n b_0 + a_{n-1} b_1 + \cdots + a_0 b_n) x^n + \cdots.$$

The technique for computing the coefficients of any term is easy to determine. The subscripts of the a's decrease by one as the subscripts of the b's increase, the total always remaining the same.

DEFINITION. Given the series

$$\sum_{n=0}^{\infty} a_n x^n, \quad \sum_{n=0}^{\infty} b_n x^n,$$

we define the *Cauchy Product* to be the series

$$c_0 + c_1 x + c_2 x^2 + \cdots + c_n x^n + \cdots$$

where

$$c_n = a_n b_0 + a_{n-1} b_1 + \cdots + a_0 b_n = \sum_{k=0}^{n} a_{n-k} b_k.$$

EXAMPLE 1. Given the Maclaurin series for e^x and $\cos x$, find the first seven terms of the Cauchy Product of these two series—i.e., the terms through x^6.

Solution. We have

$$e^x = 1 + x + \frac{x^2}{2} + \frac{x^3}{6} + \frac{x^4}{24} + \frac{x^5}{120} + \frac{x^6}{720} + \cdots,$$

$$\cos x = 1 \qquad - \frac{x^2}{2} \qquad + \frac{x^4}{24} \qquad - \frac{x^6}{720} + \cdots.$$

We multiply term by term to obtain

$$1 + x + \frac{x^2}{2} + \frac{x^3}{6} + \frac{x^4}{24} + \frac{x^5}{120} + \frac{x^6}{720}$$

$$- \frac{x^2}{2} - \frac{x^3}{2} - \frac{x^4}{4} - \frac{x^5}{12} - \frac{x^6}{48}$$

$$+ \frac{x^4}{24} + \frac{x^5}{24} + \frac{x^6}{48}$$

$$- \frac{x^6}{720}$$

$$\text{Cauchy Product} = 1 + x - \frac{x^3}{3} - \frac{x^4}{6} - \frac{x^5}{30} + 0 \cdot x^6 + \cdots.$$

Theorem 27. *If*

$$f(x) = \sum_{n=0}^{\infty} a_n x^n, \qquad g(x) = \sum_{n=0}^{\infty} b_n x^n,$$

both converge for $|x| < R$; then the Cauchy Product of the two series converges to $f(x) \cdot g(x)$ for $|x| < R$.

The proof of this theorem is given in Morrey, *University Calculus*, p. 711.

On the basis of Theorem 27, we see that, in Example 1 above, the Cauchy Product is actually the Maclaurin expansion of the function $e^x \cos x$, valid for all x.

Now we apply the process of long division to two series as if they were polynomials. We write

$$
\begin{array}{r}
c_0 + \quad c_1 x \qquad\qquad\qquad\qquad\qquad\\
\hline
b_0 + b_1 x + b_2 x^2 + \cdots \,) a_0 + \quad a_1 x + \quad a_2 x^2 + \cdots\\
c_0 b_0 + c_0 b_1 x + c_0 b_2 x^2 + \cdots\\
\hline
+ (a_1 - c_0 b_1)x + (a_2 - c_0 b_2)x^2 + \cdots\\
c_1 b_0\, x + \qquad\quad c_1 b_1\, x^2 + \cdots\\
\hline
+ (a_2 - c_0 b_2 - c_1 b_1)x^2 + \cdots\\
c_2 b_0\, x^2 + \cdots
\end{array}
$$

In order for the division process to proceed, we must have (assuming $b_0 \neq 0$)

$$a_0 = c_0 b_0 \quad \text{or} \quad c_0 = a_0/b_0,$$
$$a_1 - c_0 b_1 = c_1 b_0 \quad \text{or} \quad c_1 = (a_1 - c_0 b_1)/b_0,$$
$$a_2 - c_0 b_2 - c_1 b_1 = c_2 b_0 \quad \text{or} \quad c_2 = (a_2 - c_0 b_2 - c_1 b_1)/b_0,$$

etc. By induction it can be established that the Cauchy Product of the quotient series with the divisor series yields the dividend series.

Theorem 28. *Under the hypotheses of Theorem 27, the quotient series converges to $f(x)/g(x)$ for $|x| < T$ for some $T > 0$ so long as $b_0 \neq 0$.*

The proof is omitted.

————————

EXAMPLE 2. By division of the Maclaurin series for $\sin x$ by the one for $\cos x$, find the terms up to x^5 in the Maclaurin series for $\tan x$.

Solution. We have

$$
\begin{array}{r}
x + \dfrac{x^3}{3} + \dfrac{2x^5}{15} \\[1.5ex]
\left(1 - \dfrac{x^2}{2} + \dfrac{x^4}{24} - \cdots\right) \overline{\Big)\, x - \dfrac{x^3}{6} + \dfrac{x^5}{120} - \cdots} \\[1.5ex]
\underline{x - \dfrac{x^3}{2} + \dfrac{x^5}{24} - \cdots} \\[1.5ex]
+ \dfrac{x^3}{3} - \dfrac{x^5}{30} + \cdots \\[1.5ex]
\underline{+ \dfrac{x^3}{3} - \dfrac{x^5}{6} + \cdots} \\[1.5ex]
\dfrac{2x^5}{15} + \cdots
\end{array}
$$

EXERCISES

In each of problems 1 through 20, find the Maclaurin series to the number of terms given by the index n.

1. $\dfrac{\sin x}{1 + x}$, $\quad n = 5$

2. $\dfrac{\sin x}{1 - x}$, $\quad n = 5$

3. $\dfrac{\cos x}{1 + x}$, $\quad n = 5$

4. $\dfrac{\cos x}{1 - x}$, $\quad n = 5$

5. $\sqrt{1 + x}\ \ln(1 + x)$, $\quad n = 5$

6. $\sqrt{1 - x}\ \ln(1 - x)$, $\quad n = 5$

7. $\dfrac{\ln(1 + x)}{\sqrt{1 + x}}$, $\quad n = 5$

8. $\dfrac{\ln(1 - x)}{\sqrt{1 + x}}$, $\quad n = 5$

9. $e^x \sec x$, $n = 5$

10. $e^{-x} \tan x$, $n = 3$

11. $\dfrac{e^x}{\sqrt{1 + x^2}}$, $n = 5$

12. $\dfrac{e^{-x}}{\sqrt{1 + x^2}}$, $n = 5$

13. $\dfrac{\arctan x}{1 + x}$, $n = 5$

14. $\dfrac{1 - x}{1 - x^3} = \dfrac{1}{1 + x + x^2}$, all n

15. $\dfrac{\arcsin x}{\cosh x}$, $n = 5$

16. $\operatorname{sech} x$, $n = 6$

17. $(1 + x)^{1/3}(1 + x^2)^{4/3}$, $n = 4$

18. $\sin^2 x \cos x$, $n = 4$

19. $(1 + x^2)^{3/2}(1 - x^3)^{-1/2}$, $n = 4$

20. $\tanh^2 x$, $n = 5$

CHAPTER 20

Partial Differentiation

---

1. LIMITS AND CONTINUITY. PARTIAL DERIVATIVES

A symbolic expression of the form

$$z = F(x, y),$$

where x and y are independent variables, indicates that the dependent variable z is a function of *both* the independent variables. A function of three variables is written

$$w = G(x, y, z),$$

where x, y, and z are independent variables and w is the dependent variable. We can go on and consider functions of four, of five, or of any number of independent variables. If the exact number of independent variables is n, we usually write

$$y = f(x_1, x_2, \ldots, x_n),$$

in which $x_1, x_2, \ldots, x_n$ are n independent variables and y is the dependent variable.

We now give a precise definition of a function of two variables. (See page 184.)

DEFINITION. Consider a collection of ordered pairs (A, w) where the elements A are themselves ordered pairs of real numbers and the elements w are real numbers. If no two members of the collection have the same item A as a first element —i.e., if it can never happen that there are two members (A_1, w_1) and (A_1, w_2) with $w_1 \neq w_2$—then we call this collection *a function of two variables.* The totality of possible ordered pairs A is called the *domain* of the function. The totality of possible values for w is called the *range* of the function.

Remark. The definition of a *function of three variables* is precisely the same as that for a function of two variables except that the elements A are ordered triples rather than ordered pairs. A *function of n variables* is defined by considering the elements A to be ordered n-tuples of real numbers.

We are now ready to define a limit of a function of two variables. Let f be a function of the two independent variables x, y. We wish to examine the behavior of f as $(x, y) \rightarrow (a, b)$—i.e., as $x \rightarrow a$ and $y \rightarrow b$.

DEFINITION. We say that $f(x, y)$ *tends to the number L as (x, y) tends to (a, b)*, and we write

$$f(x, y) \to L \quad \text{as} \quad (x, y) \to (a, b)$$

if and only if for each $\epsilon > 0$ there is a $\delta > 0$ such that

$$|f(x, y) - L| < \epsilon$$

whenever

$$|x - a| < \delta \quad \text{and} \quad |y - b| < \delta \quad \text{and} \quad (x, y) \neq (a, b).$$

A geometric interpretation of this definition is exhibited in Fig. 20–1. The definition asserts that whenever (x, y) are in the shaded square, as shown, then the function values, which we represent by z, must lie in the rectangular box of height 2ϵ between the values $L - \epsilon$ and $L + \epsilon$. This interpretation is an extension of the one given in Chapter 5 (page 97) for functions of one variable.

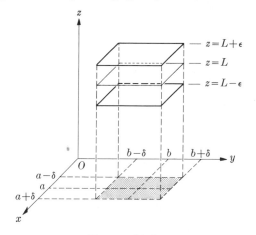

FIGURE 20–1

Remark. It is not necessary that (a, b) be in the domain of f. That is, a limit may exist with $f(a, b)$ being undefined.

DEFINITION. We say that *f is continuous at (a, b)* if and only if
(i) $f(a, b)$ is defined, and
(ii) $f(x, y) \to f(a, b)$ as $(x, y) \to (a, b)$.

Definitions of limits and continuity for functions of three, four, and more variables are completely similar.

Functions of two or more variables do not have ordinary derivatives of the type we studied for functions of one variable. If f is a function of two variables, say x and y, then for each *fixed* value of y, f is a function of a single variable x. The derivative with respect to x (keeping y fixed) is then called the partial derivative with respect to x. For x fixed and y varying, we also obtain a partial derivative with respect to y.

DEFINITIONS. We define *the partial derivatives of a function f of the variables x and y* by

$$f_{,1}(x, y) = \lim_{h \to 0} \frac{f(x + h, y) - f(x, y)}{h},$$

$$f_{,2}(x, y) = \lim_{h \to 0} \frac{f(x, y + h) - f(x, y)}{h},$$

where y is kept fixed in the first limit and x is kept fixed in the second. If F is a function of the three variables x, y, and z, we define the *partial derivatives* $F_{,1}$, $F_{,2}$, and $F_{,3}$ by

$$F_{,1}(x, y, z) = \lim_{h \to 0} \frac{F(x + h, y, z) - F(x, y, z)}{h}, \quad (y, z \text{ fixed})$$

$$F_{,2}(x, y, z) = \lim_{h \to 0} \frac{F(x, y + h, z) - F(x, y, z)}{h}, \quad (x, z \text{ fixed})$$

$$F_{,3}(x, y, z) = \lim_{h \to 0} \frac{F(x, y, z + h) - F(x, y, z)}{h}, \quad (x, y \text{ fixed}).$$

In other words, *to find the partial derivative $F_{,1}$ of a function of three variables, regard y and z as constants and find the usual derivative with respect to x; the derivatives $F_{,2}$ and $F_{,3}$ are found correspondingly. The same procedure applies for functions of any number of variables.*

EXAMPLE 1. Given $f(x, y) = x^3 + 7x^2y + 8y^3 + 3x - 2y + 7$, find $f_{,1}$ and $f_{,2}$.

Solution. Keeping y fixed and differentiating with respect to x, we find that

$$f_{,1} = 3x^2 + 14xy + 3.$$

Similarly, keeping x fixed, we get

$$f_{,2} = 7x^2 + 24y^2 - 2.$$

EXAMPLE 2. Given $f(x, y, z) = x^3 + y^3 + z^3 + 3xyz$, find $f_{,1}(x, y, z)$, $f_{,2}(x, y, z)$, and $f_{,3}(x, y, z)$.

Solution.

$$f_{,1}(x, y, z) = 3x^2 + 3yz, \qquad f_{,2}(x, y, z) = 3y^2 + 3xz, \qquad f_{,3}(x, y, z) = 3z^2 + 3xy.$$

Remarks on notation. The notation presented here is not classical, although it is coming into use more and more. The chief advantage of our notation is that it is independent of the letters used. A more common notation for $f_{,1}$ is

$$f_x.$$

It has the disadvantage of implying that the independent variable must be the letter x. Another common symbol is

$$\frac{\partial f}{\partial x}$$

(read partial of f with respect to x). This notation has the double disadvantage of using the letter x and of giving the impression (incorrectly) that the derivative is a fraction with ∂f and ∂x having independent meanings (which they do not). If we write $z = f(x, y)$, still another symbol for partial derivative is the expression

$$\frac{\partial z}{\partial x}.$$

Because of the multiplicity of symbols for partial derivatives used in texts on mathematics and various related branches of technology, it is important that the student familiarize himself with all of them.

EXAMPLE 3. Given $f(x, y) = e^{xy} \cos x \sin y$, find $f_x(x, y)$ and $f_y(x, y)$.

Solution. We have

$$f_x(x, y) = e^{xy} \sin y(-\sin x) + \cos x \sin y e^{xy} \cdot y$$
$$= e^{xy} \sin y(y \cos x - \sin x),$$

and

$$f_y(x, y) = e^{xy} \cos x(x \sin y + \cos y).$$

EXAMPLE 4. Given that $z = x \arctan (y/x)$, find $\partial z/\partial x$ and $\partial z/\partial y$.

Solution. We have

$$\frac{\partial z}{\partial x} = x \cdot \frac{-(y/x^2)}{1 + (y^2/x^2)} + \arctan (y/x)$$
$$= \arctan (y/x) - \frac{xy}{x^2 + y^2},$$

and

$$\frac{\partial z}{\partial y} = x \frac{1/x}{1 + (y^2/x^2)}$$
$$= \frac{x^2}{x^2 + y^2}.$$

EXAMPLE 5. Given $f(x, y) = x^2 - 3xy + 2x - 3y + 5$, find $f_{,1}(2, 3)$.

Solution. We have

$$f_{,1}(x, y) = 2x - 3y + 2, \qquad f_{,1}(2, 3) = -3.$$

EXERCISES

In each of problems 1 through 12, find $f_{,1}(x, y)$ and $f_{,2}(x, y)$.

1. $f(x, y) = x^2 + 2xy^2 - 2x$

2. $f(x, y) = x^3y^2 + x^2y^3 + 3$

3. $f(x, y) = x^3y - 3x^2y^2 + 2xy$

4. $f(x, y) = \sqrt{x^2 + 1} + y^3$

5. $f(x, y) = \sqrt{x^2 + y^2}$

6. $f(x, y) = \dfrac{xy}{x^2 + y^2}$

7. $f(x, y) = \ln (x^2 + y^2)$

8. $f(x, y) = \ln \sqrt{x^2 + y^2}$

9. $f(x, y) = \arctan \dfrac{y}{x}$

10. $f(x, y) = \arcsin \dfrac{x}{1 + y}$

11. $f(x, y) = xye^{x^2 + y^2}$

12. $f(x, y) = \cos (xe^y)$

In each of problems 13 through 18, find $f_{,1}$ and $f_{,2}$ at the values indicated.

13. $f(x, y) = x \arcsin (x - y)$, $x = 1$, $y = 2$

14. $f(u, v) = e^{uv} \sec \left(\dfrac{u}{v}\right)$, $u = v = 3$

15. $f(x, z) = e^{\sin z} \tan xz$, $x = \dfrac{\pi}{4}$, $z = 1$

16. $f(t, u) = \dfrac{\cos 2tu}{t^2 + u^2}$, $t = 0$, $u = 1$

17. $f(y, x) = x^{xy}$, $x = y = 2$

18. $f(s, t) = s^t + t^s$, $s = t = 3$

In each of problems 19 through 22, find $f_{,1}(x, y, z)$, $f_{,2}(x, y, z)$ and $f_{,3}(x, y, z)$.

19. $f(x, y, z) = x^2y - 2x^2z + 3xyz - y^2z + 2xz^2$

20. $f(x, y, z) = \dfrac{xyz}{x^2 + y^2 + z^2}$

21. $f(x, y, z) = e^{xyz} \sin xy \cos 2xz$

22. $f(x, y, z) = x^2 + z^2 + y^3 + 2x - 3y + 4z$

In problems 23 through 26 find in each case the indicated partial derivative.

23. $w = \ln \left(\dfrac{xy}{x^2 + y^2}\right)$; $\dfrac{\partial w}{\partial x}$, $\dfrac{\partial w}{\partial y}$

24. $w = (r^2 + s^2 + t^2) \cosh rst$; $\dfrac{\partial w}{\partial r}$, $\dfrac{\partial w}{\partial t}$

25. $w = e^{\sin(y/x)}$; $\dfrac{\partial w}{\partial y}$, $\dfrac{\partial w}{\partial x}$

26. $w = (\sec tu) \arcsin tv$; $\dfrac{\partial w}{\partial t}$, $\dfrac{\partial w}{\partial u}$, $\dfrac{\partial w}{\partial v}$

2. IMPLICIT DIFFERENTIATION

An equation involving x, y, and z establishes a relation among the variables. If we can solve for z in terms of x and y, then we may have one or more functions determined by the relation. For example, the equation

$$2x^2 + y^2 + z^2 - 16 = 0 \tag{1}$$

may be solved for z to give

$$z = \pm\sqrt{16 - 2x^2 - y^2}. \tag{2}$$

If one or more functions are determined by a relation, it is possible to compute partial derivatives implicitly in a way that is completely similar to the methods used for ordinary derivatives. (See Chapter 6, page 142.)

For example, in Equation (1) above, considering x and y as independent variables with z as the dependent variable, we can compute $\partial z/\partial x$ directly from (1) without resorting to (2). We keep y fixed and, in (1), differentiate implicitly with respect to x, getting

$$4x + 2z\frac{\partial z}{\partial x} = 0 \quad \text{and} \quad \frac{\partial z}{\partial x} = -\frac{2x}{z}.$$

Further examples exhibit the method.

EXAMPLE 1. Suppose that x, y, and z are variables and that z is a function of x and y which satisfies

$$x^3 + y^3 + z^3 + 3xyz = 5.$$

Find $\partial z/\partial x$ and $\partial z/\partial y$.

Solution. Holding y constant and differentiating z with respect to x implicitly, we obtain

$$3x^2 + 3z^2\frac{\partial z}{\partial x} + 3xy\frac{\partial z}{\partial x} + 3yz = 0.$$

Therefore

$$\frac{\partial z}{\partial x} = -\frac{x^2 + yz}{xy + z^2}.$$

Holding x constant and differentiating with respect to y, we get

$$3y^2 + 3z^2\frac{\partial z}{\partial y} + 3xy\frac{\partial z}{\partial y} + 3xz = 0$$

and

$$\frac{\partial z}{\partial y} = -\frac{y^2 + xz}{xy + z^2}.$$

The same technique works with equations relating four or more variables, as the next example shows.

EXAMPLE 2. If r, s, t, and w are variables and if w is a function of r, s, and t which satisfies

$$e^{rt} - 2se^w + wt - 3w^2r = 5,$$

find $\partial w/\partial r$, $\partial w/\partial s$, and $\partial w/\partial t$.

Solution. To find $\partial w/\partial r$, we keep s and t fixed and differentiate implicitly with respect to r. The result is

$$te^{rt} - 2se^w \frac{\partial w}{\partial r} + t \frac{\partial w}{\partial r} - 3w^2 - 6rw \frac{\partial w}{\partial r} = 0$$

or

$$\frac{\partial w}{\partial r} = \frac{3w^2 - te^{rt}}{t - 2se^w - 6rw}.$$

Keeping r and t fixed, we obtain

$$-2e^w - 2se^w \frac{\partial w}{\partial s} + t \frac{\partial w}{\partial s} - 6rw \frac{\partial w}{\partial s} = 0$$

and

$$\frac{\partial w}{\partial s} = \frac{2e^w}{t - 2se^w - 6rw}.$$

Similarly, with r and s fixed the result is

$$re^{rt} - 2se^w \frac{\partial w}{\partial t} + w + t \frac{\partial w}{\partial t} - 6rw \frac{\partial w}{\partial t} = 0$$

or

$$\frac{\partial w}{\partial t} = \frac{w + re^{rt}}{2se^w - t + 6rw}.$$

EXERCISES

In each of problems 1 through 12, assume that w is a function of all other variables. Find the partial derivatives as indicated in each case.

1. $3x^2 + 2y^2 + 6w^2 - x + y - 12 = 0;$ $\dfrac{\partial w}{\partial x}, \dfrac{\partial w}{\partial y}$

2. $x^2 + y^2 + w^2 + 3xy - 2xw + 3yw = 36;$ $\dfrac{\partial w}{\partial x}, \dfrac{\partial w}{\partial y}$

3. $x^2 - 2xy + 2xw + 3y^2 + w^2 = 21;$ $\dfrac{\partial w}{\partial x}, \dfrac{\partial w}{\partial y}$

4. $x^2y - x^2w - 2xy^2 - yw^2 + w^3 = 7;$ $\dfrac{\partial w}{\partial x}, \dfrac{\partial w}{\partial y}$

5. $w - (r^2 + s^2) \cosh rw = 0;$ $\dfrac{\partial w}{\partial r}, \dfrac{\partial w}{\partial s}$

6. $w - e^{w \, \sin(y/x)} = 1;$ $\dfrac{\partial w}{\partial x}, \dfrac{\partial w}{\partial y}$

7. $e^{xyw} \sin xy \cos 2xw - 4 = 0;$ $\dfrac{\partial w}{\partial x}, \dfrac{\partial w}{\partial y}$

8. $w^2 - 3xw - \ln \left(\dfrac{xy}{x^2 + y^2} \right) = 0;$ $\dfrac{\partial w}{\partial x}, \dfrac{\partial w}{\partial y}$

9. $xyz + x^2z + xzw - yzw + yz^2 - w^3 = 3;$ $\dfrac{\partial w}{\partial x}, \dfrac{\partial w}{\partial y}, \dfrac{\partial w}{\partial z}$

10. $r^2 + 3s^2 - 2t^2 + 6tw - 8w^2 + 12sw^3 = 4;$ $\dfrac{\partial w}{\partial r}, \dfrac{\partial w}{\partial s}, \dfrac{\partial w}{\partial t}$

11. $we^{xw} - ye^{yw} + e^{xy} = 1;$ $\dfrac{\partial w}{\partial x}, \dfrac{\partial w}{\partial y}$

12. $x^3 + 3x^2y + 2z^2t - 4zt^3 + 7xw - 8yw^2 + w^4 = 5;$ $\dfrac{\partial w}{\partial x}, \dfrac{\partial w}{\partial y}, \dfrac{\partial w}{\partial z}, \dfrac{\partial w}{\partial t}$

3. THE CHAIN RULE

The Chain Rule is one of the most effective devices for calculating ordinary derivatives. (See Chapter 6, page 133.) In this section we show how to extend the Chain Rule for the computation of partial derivatives. The basis of the Rule in the case of functions of one variable is the Fundamental Lemma on Differentiation, which we now recall.

Theorem 1. *If F has a derivative at a value a so that F'(a) exists, then*

$$F(a + h) - F(a) = [F'(a) + G(h)]h$$

where G(h) tends to zero as h tends to zero and G(0) = 0.

The proof of this theorem is on page 133.
The above theorem has a natural generalization for functions of two variables.

Theorem 2. (Fundamental Lemma on Differentiation.) *Suppose that f is a continuous function of two variables (say x and y) and that $f_{,1}$ and $f_{,2}$ are continuous at (x_0, y_0). Then there are two functions, $G_1(h, k)$ and $G_2(h, k)$ continuous at $(0, 0)$ with $G_1(0, 0) = G_2(0, 0) = 0$, such that*

$$f(x_0 + h, y_0 + k) - f(x_0, y_0) = f_{,1}(x_0, y_0)h + f_{,2}(x_0, y_0)k$$
$$+ G_1(h, k)h + G_2(h, k)k. \quad (1)$$

Proof. The proof depends on writing the left side of (1) in a more complicated way:

$$f(x_0 + h, y_0 + k) - f(x_0, y_0) = [f(x_0 + h, y_0 + k) - f(x_0 + h, y_0)]$$
$$+ [f(x_0 + h, y_0) - f(x_0, y_0)]. \quad (2)$$

Figure 20–2 shows the points at which f is evaluated in (2) (h and k are taken to be positive in the figure). We apply the Theorem of the Mean to each of the quantities in brackets in (2) above. The results are

$$\frac{f(x_0 + h, y_0 + k) - f(x_0 + h, y_0)}{(y_0 + k) - y_0} = f_{,2}(x_0 + h, \eta) \quad (3)$$

and

$$\frac{f(x_0 + h, y_0) - f(x_0, y_0)}{(x_0 + h) - x_0} = f_{,1}(\xi, y_0), \quad (4)$$

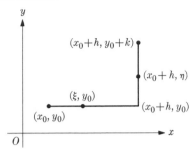

FIGURE 20–2

where η is between y_0 and $y_0 + k$ and ξ is between x_0 and $x_0 + h$. Typical locations for ξ and η are shown in Fig. 20–2. Substituting (3) and (4) into the right side of (2), we find

$$f(x_0 + h, y_0 + k) - f(x_0, y_0) = f_{,1}(\xi, y_0)h + f_{,2}(x_0 + h, \eta)k. \qquad (5)$$

The quantities G_1 and G_2 are defined by

$$G_1 = f_{,1}(\xi, y_0) - f_{,1}(x_0, y_0),$$
$$G_2 = f_{,2}(x_0 + h, \eta) - f_{,2}(x_0, y_0).$$

Multiplying the expression for G_1 by h and that for G_2 by k and inserting the result in the right side of (5), we obtain the statement of the theorem. Since $\xi \rightarrow x_0$ as $h \rightarrow 0$ and $\eta \rightarrow y_0$ as $k \rightarrow 0$, it follows (since $f_{,1}$ and $f_{,2}$ are continuous) that G_1 and G_2 tend to zero as h and k tend to zero. Thus G_1 and G_2 are continuous at $(0, 0)$ if we define them as being equal to zero there.

Theorem 3. (Chain Rule.) *Suppose that* $z = f(x, y)$ *is continuous and that* $f_{,1}$, $f_{,2}$ *are continuous. Assume that* $x = x(r, s)$ *and* $y = y(r, s)$ *are functions of* r *and* s *such that* $x_{,1}$, $x_{,2}$, $y_{,1}$, $y_{,2}$ *all exist. Then* z *is a function of* r *and* s *and the following formulas hold:*

$$\left.\begin{aligned}\frac{\partial f}{\partial r} &= \left(\frac{\partial f}{\partial x}\right)\left(\frac{\partial x}{\partial r}\right) + \left(\frac{\partial f}{\partial y}\right)\left(\frac{\partial y}{\partial r}\right) \\ \frac{\partial f}{\partial s} &= \left(\frac{\partial f}{\partial x}\right)\left(\frac{\partial x}{\partial s}\right) + \left(\frac{\partial f}{\partial y}\right)\left(\frac{\partial y}{\partial s}\right)\end{aligned}\right\} \qquad (6)$$

Proof. The first formula will be established; the second is proved similarly. We use the Δ notation. A change Δr in r induces a change Δx in x and a change Δy in y. That is,

$$\Delta x = x(r + \Delta r, s) - x(r, s), \qquad \Delta y = y(r + \Delta r, s) - y(r, s).$$

The function f, thought of as a function of r and s, has the partial derivatives

$$\frac{\partial f}{\partial r} = \lim_{\Delta r \to 0} \frac{\Delta f}{\Delta r}$$

where Δf, the change in f due to the change Δr in r, is given by

$$\Delta f = f(x + \Delta x, y + \Delta y) - f(x, y).$$

The Fundamental Lemma on differentiation with $h = \Delta x$ and $k = \Delta y$ reads

$$\Delta f = \frac{\partial f}{\partial x} \Delta x + \frac{\partial f}{\partial y} \Delta y + G_1 \Delta x + G_2 \Delta y,$$

where we have changed notation by using $\partial f / \partial x$ in place of $f_{,1}(x, y)$ and $\partial f / \partial y$ for $f_{,2}(x, y)$. We divide the equation above by Δr:

$$\frac{\Delta f}{\Delta r} = \frac{\partial f}{\partial x} \frac{\Delta x}{\Delta r} + \frac{\partial f}{\partial y} \frac{\Delta y}{\Delta r} + G_1 \frac{\Delta x}{\Delta r} + G_2 \frac{\Delta y}{\Delta r}.$$

Letting Δr tend to zero and remembering that $G_1 \to 0$, $G_2 \to 0$, we obtain the desired formula.

Remarks. (i) The formulas (6) may be written in various notations. Two common expressions are

$$\left. \begin{aligned} \frac{\partial z}{\partial r} &= \left(\frac{\partial z}{\partial x}\right)\left(\frac{\partial x}{\partial r}\right) + \left(\frac{\partial z}{\partial y}\right)\left(\frac{\partial y}{\partial r}\right) \\ \frac{\partial z}{\partial s} &= \left(\frac{\partial z}{\partial x}\right)\left(\frac{\partial x}{\partial s}\right) + \left(\frac{\partial z}{\partial y}\right)\left(\frac{\partial y}{\partial s}\right) \end{aligned} \right\} \tag{7}$$

and

$$\left. \begin{aligned} f_r &= f_x x_r + f_y y_r \\ f_s &= f_x x_s + f_y y_s \end{aligned} \right\} \tag{8}$$

(ii) To use our preferred notation we introduce the symbol $g(r, s)$ to represent the function f considered as a function of r and s. The formulas expressing the Chain Rule are then

$$\left. \begin{aligned} g_{,1}(r, s) &= f_{,1}(x, y) x_{,1}(r, s) + f_{,2}(x, y) y_{,1}(r, s) \\ g_{,2}(r, s) &= f_{,1}(x, y) x_{,2}(r, s) + f_{,2}(x, y) y_{,2}(r, s) \end{aligned} \right\} \tag{9}$$

(iii) For functions of one variable, the Chain Rule is easily remembered as the rule which allows us to think of derivatives as fractions. The formula

$$\frac{dy}{dx} = \frac{dy}{du} \cdot \frac{du}{dx}$$

is an example. The symbol du has a meaning of its own. To attempt to draw such an analogy with the Chain Rule for Partial Derivatives leads to disaster. Formulas (6) are the ones we usually employ in the applications. The parentheses around the individual terms are used to indicate the inseparable nature of each item. Actually, the forms (8) and (9) for the same formulas avoid the danger of treating partial derivatives as fractions.

EXAMPLE 1.   Suppose that $f(x, y) = x^3 + y^3$, $x = 2r + s$, $y = 3r - 2s$.   Find $\partial f/\partial r$ and $\partial f/\partial s$.

Solution. We can employ the Chain Rule and obtain

$$\frac{\partial f}{\partial x} = 3x^2, \qquad \frac{\partial f}{\partial y} = 3y^2$$

$$\frac{\partial x}{\partial r} = 2, \qquad \frac{\partial x}{\partial s} = 1, \qquad \frac{\partial y}{\partial r} = 3, \qquad \frac{\partial y}{\partial s} = -2.$$

Therefore

$$\frac{\partial f}{\partial r} = (3x^2)(2) + (3y^2)(3) = 6x^2 + 9y^2 = 6(2r + s)^2 + 9(3r - 2s)^2,$$

$$\frac{\partial f}{\partial s} = (3x^2)(1) + (3y^2)(-2) = 3x^2 - 6y^2 = 3(2r + s)^2 - 6(3r - 2s)^2.$$

In Theorem 3 (the Chain Rule), the variables r and s are independent variables; we denote the variables x and y *intermediate variables* and, of course, z is the dependent variable.   The formulas we derived extend easily to any number of independent variables and any number of intermediate variables.   For example, if

$$w = f(x, y, z)$$

and if

$$x = x(r, s), \quad y = y(r, s), \quad z = z(r, s),$$

then

$$\frac{\partial f}{\partial r} = \left(\frac{\partial f}{\partial x}\right)\left(\frac{\partial x}{\partial r}\right) + \left(\frac{\partial f}{\partial y}\right)\left(\frac{\partial y}{\partial r}\right) + \left(\frac{\partial f}{\partial z}\right)\left(\frac{\partial z}{\partial r}\right),$$

and there is a similar formula for $\partial f/\partial s$.   The case of four intermediate variables and one independent variable—that is,

$$w = f(x, y, u, v), \quad x = x(t), \quad y = y(t), \quad u = u(t), \quad v = v(t)$$

—leads to the formula

$$\frac{df}{dt} = \frac{\partial f}{\partial x}\frac{dx}{dt} + \frac{\partial f}{\partial y}\frac{dy}{dt} + \frac{\partial f}{\partial u}\frac{du}{dt} + \frac{\partial f}{\partial v}\frac{dv}{dt}.$$

The ordinary d is used for derivatives with respect to t, since w, x, y, u, and v are all functions of the single variable t.

Remark. As an aid in remembering the Chain Rule, we note that *there are as many terms in the formula as there are intermediate variables.*

EXAMPLE 2.   If $z = 2x^2 + xy - y^2 + 2x - 3y + 5$, $x = 2s - t$, $y = s + t$, find $\partial z/\partial t$.

Solution. We use the Chain Rule:

$$\frac{\partial z}{\partial x} = 4x + y + 2, \quad \frac{\partial z}{\partial y} = x - 2y - 3, \quad \frac{\partial x}{\partial t} = -1, \quad \frac{\partial y}{\partial t} = 1.$$

Therefore

$$\frac{\partial z}{\partial t} = (4x + y + 2)(-1) + (x - 2y - 3)(1) = -3x - 3y - 5$$

$$= -3(2s - t) - 3(s + t) - 5$$

$$= -9s - 5.$$

EXAMPLE 3. Given $w = x^2 + 3y^2 - 2z^2 + 4x - y + 3z - 1$, $x = t^2 - 2t + 1$, $y = 3t - 2$, $z = t^2 + 4t - 3$, find dw/dt when $t = 2$.

Solution. Employing the Chain Rule, we find

$$\frac{\partial w}{\partial x} = 2x + 4, \quad \frac{\partial w}{\partial y} = 6y - 1, \quad \frac{\partial w}{\partial z} = -4z + 3,$$

$$\frac{dx}{dt} = 2t - 2, \quad \frac{dy}{dt} = 3, \quad \frac{dz}{dt} = 2t + 4.$$

Therefore

$$\frac{dw}{dt} = (2x + 4)(2t - 2) + (6y - 1)(3) + (-4z + 3)(2t + 4).$$

When $t = 2$, we have $x = 1$, $y = 4$, $z = 9$, and so

$$\frac{dw}{dt} = (6)(2) + (23)(3) + (-33)(8) = -183.$$

EXERCISES

In each of problems 1 through 12, use the Chain Rule to obtain the indicated partial derivative.

1. $f(x, y) = x^2 + y^2$; $x = s - 2t$, $y = 2s + t$; $\dfrac{\partial f}{\partial s}, \dfrac{\partial f}{\partial t}$

2. $f(x, y) = x^2 - xy - y^2$; $x = s + t$, $y = -s + t$; $\dfrac{\partial f}{\partial s}, \dfrac{\partial f}{\partial t}$

3. $f(x, y) = x^2 + y^2$; $x = s^2 - t^2$, $y = 2st$; $\dfrac{\partial f}{\partial s}, \dfrac{\partial f}{\partial t}$

4. $f(x, y) = \dfrac{x}{x^2 + y^2}$; $x = s \cos t$, $y = s \sin t$; $\dfrac{\partial f}{\partial s}, \dfrac{\partial f}{\partial t}$

5. $f(x, y) = \dfrac{x}{\sqrt{x^2 + y^2}}$; $x = 2s - t$, $y = s + 2t$; $\dfrac{\partial f}{\partial s}, \dfrac{\partial f}{\partial t}$

6. $f(x, y) = e^x \cos y$; $x = s^2 - t^2$, $y = 2st$; $\dfrac{\partial f}{\partial s}, \dfrac{\partial f}{\partial t}$

7. $f(x, y, z) = x^2 + y^2 + z^2 + 3xy - 2xz + 4$; $x = 3s + t$, $y = 2s - t$, $z = s + 2t$; $\dfrac{\partial f}{\partial s}, \dfrac{\partial f}{\partial t}$

8. $f(x, y, z) = x^3 + 2y^3 + z^3$; $x = s^2 - t^2$, $y = s^2 + t^2$, $z = 2st$; $\dfrac{\partial f}{\partial s}, \dfrac{\partial f}{\partial t}$

9. $f(x, y, z) = x^2 - y^2 + 2z^2$; $x = r^2 + 1$, $y = r^2 - 2r + 1$, $z = r^2 - 2$; $\dfrac{df}{dr}$

10. $f(x, y) = \dfrac{x - y}{1 + x^2 + y^2}$; $x = r + 3s - t$, $y = r - 2s + 3t$; $\dfrac{\partial f}{\partial r}, \dfrac{\partial f}{\partial s}, \dfrac{\partial f}{\partial t}$

11. $f(u) = u^3 + 2u^2 - 3u + 1$; $u = r^2 - s^2 + t^2$; $\dfrac{\partial f}{\partial r}, \dfrac{\partial f}{\partial s}, \dfrac{\partial f}{\partial t}$

12. $f(x, y, u, v) = x^2 + y^2 - u^2 - v^2 + 3x - 2y + u - v$;

$x = 2r + s - t$, $y = r - 2s + t$, $u = 3r - 2s + t$, $v = r - s - t$;

$\dfrac{\partial f}{\partial r}, \dfrac{\partial f}{\partial s}, \dfrac{\partial f}{\partial t}$

In problems 13 through 20, use the Chain Rule to find the indicated derivatives at the values given.

13. $z = x^2 - y^2$; $x = r \cos \theta$, $y = r \sin \theta$; $\dfrac{\partial z}{\partial r}, \dfrac{\partial z}{\partial \theta}$ where $r = \sqrt{2}, \theta = \dfrac{\pi}{4}$

14. $w = x^2 + y^2 - z^2$; $x = 1 - t^2$, $y = 2t + 3$, $z = t^2 + t$, $\dfrac{dw}{dt}$ where $t = -1$

15. $w = xy + yz + zx$; $x = t \cos t$, $y = t \sin t$, $z = t$; $\dfrac{dw}{dt}$ where $t = \dfrac{\pi}{4}$

16. $z = u^3 + 2u - 3$; $u = s^2 + t^2 - 4$; $\dfrac{\partial z}{\partial s}, \dfrac{\partial z}{\partial t}$ where $s = 1$ and $t = 2$

17. $z = \dfrac{xy}{x^2 + y^2}$; $x = r \cos \theta$, $y = r \sin \theta$; $\dfrac{\partial z}{\partial r}, \dfrac{\partial z}{\partial \theta}$ where $r = 3, \theta = \dfrac{\pi}{6}$

18. $f = e^{xyz} \cos xyz$; $x = r^2 + t^2$, $y = t^2 + r$, $z = r + t$;

$\dfrac{\partial f}{\partial x}, \dfrac{\partial f}{\partial y}, \dfrac{\partial f}{\partial z}, r = 2, t = -2$

19. $w = x^3 + y^3 + z^3 - u^2 - v^2$; $x = r^2 + s^2 + t^2$, $y = r^2 + s^2 - t^2$,

$z = r^2 - s^2 - t^2$, $u = r^2 + t^2$, $v = r^2 - s^2$;

$\dfrac{\partial w}{\partial s}, \dfrac{\partial w}{\partial t}$, where $r = 1, s = 0, t = -1$

20. $w = x^4 - y^4 - z^4$; $x = 5r + 3s - 2t + u - v$,

$y = 2r - 4s + t - u^2 + v^2$; $z = s^3 - 2t^2 + 3v^2$;

$\dfrac{\partial w}{\partial s}, \dfrac{\partial w}{\partial v}$ where $r = 1, s = -1, t = 0, u = 3, v = -2$

4. APPLICATIONS OF THE CHAIN RULE

The Chain Rule may be employed profitably in many types of applications. These are best illustrated with examples, and we shall begin with two problems in related rates, a topic discussed in Chapter 7, page 193.

EXAMPLE 1. At a certain instant the altitude of a right circular cone is 30 in. and is increasing at the rate of 2 in./sec. At the same instant, the radius of the base is 20 in. and is increasing at the rate of 1 in./sec. At what rate is the volume increasing at that instant? (See Fig. 20–3.)

Solution. The volume V is given by

$$V = \tfrac{1}{3}\pi r^2 h,$$

with r and h functions of the time t. We can apply the Chain Rule to obtain

$$\frac{dV}{dt} = \frac{\partial V}{\partial r}\frac{dr}{dt} + \frac{\partial V}{\partial h}\frac{dh}{dt}$$

$$= \frac{2}{3}\pi r h \frac{dr}{dt} + \frac{1}{3}\pi r^2 \frac{dh}{dt}.$$

FIGURE 20–3

At the given instant,

$$\frac{dV}{dt} = \frac{2}{3}\pi(20)(30)(1) + \frac{1}{3}\pi(20)^2(2) = \frac{2000\pi}{3}\ \text{in}^3/\text{sec}.$$

EXAMPLE 2. The base B of a trapezoid increases in length at the rate of 2 in./sec and the base b decreases in length at the rate of 1 in./sec. If the altitude h is increasing at the rate of 3 in./sec, how rapidly is the area A changing when $B = 30$ in., $b = 50$ in., and $h = 10$ in.? (See Fig. 20–4.)

Solution. The area A is given by

$$A = \tfrac{1}{2}(B + b)h,$$

with B, b, and h functions of time. We apply the Chain Rule to get

$$\frac{dA}{dt} = \frac{\partial A}{\partial B}\frac{dB}{dt} + \frac{\partial A}{\partial b}\frac{db}{dt} + \frac{\partial A}{\partial h}\frac{dh}{dt}$$

$$= \frac{1}{2}h\frac{dB}{dt} + \frac{1}{2}h\frac{db}{dt} + \frac{1}{2}(B + b)\frac{dh}{dt}$$

$$= (5)(2) + (5)(-1) + (40)(3) = 125\ \text{in}^2/\text{sec}.$$

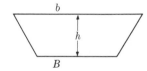

FIGURE 20–4

Note that since b is decreasing, db/dt is negative.

————————

The next example shows that a clear understanding of the symbolism in partial differentiation is required in many applications.

————————

EXAMPLE 3. Suppose that $z = f(x + at)$ and a is constant. Show that

$$\frac{\partial z}{\partial t} = a\frac{\partial z}{\partial x}.$$

Solution. We observe that f is a function of *one argument* (in which, however, two variables occur in a particular combination). We let

$$u = x + at$$

and, if we now write

$$z = f(u), \quad u = x + at,$$

we recognize the applicability of the Chain Rule. Therefore

$$\frac{\partial z}{\partial x} = \frac{dz}{du}\frac{\partial u}{\partial x} = f'(u)\cdot 1,$$

$$\frac{\partial z}{\partial t} = \frac{dz}{du}\frac{\partial u}{\partial t} = f'(u)\cdot a.$$

We conclude that

$$\frac{\partial z}{\partial t} = a\,\frac{\partial z}{\partial x}.$$

EXAMPLE 4. An airplane is traveling directly east at 300 mi/hr and is climbing at the rate of 600 ft/min. At a certain instant, the airplane is 12,000 ft above ground and 5 mi directly west of an observer on the ground. How fast is the distance changing between the airplane and the observer at this instant?

Solution. Referring to Fig. 20–5, with the observer at O and the airplane at A, we see that x, y, and s are functions of the time t. The distance s between the airplane and the observer is given by

$$s = (x^2 + y^2)^{1/2},$$

and we wish to find ds/dt. Using the Chain Rule, we get

$$\frac{ds}{dt} = \frac{\partial s}{\partial x}\frac{dx}{dt} + \frac{\partial s}{\partial y}\frac{dy}{dt}$$

$$= \frac{x}{\sqrt{x^2 + y^2}}\frac{dx}{dt} + \frac{y}{\sqrt{x^2 + y^2}}\frac{dy}{dt}.$$

FIGURE 20–5

From the given data we see that, at the instant in question,

$$y = 12{,}000, \ x = 26{,}400, \ \frac{dx}{dt} = -440 \text{ ft/sec and } \frac{dy}{dt} = +10 \text{ ft/sec.}$$

Therefore

$$\frac{ds}{dt} = \frac{26{,}400}{1000\sqrt{840.96}}\,(-440) + \frac{12{,}000}{1000\sqrt{840.96}}\,(10)$$

$$= -\frac{(264)(44)}{\sqrt{840.96}} + \frac{120}{\sqrt{840.96}} = -396^{+} \text{ ft/sec.}$$

The negative sign indicates that the airplane is approaching the observer.

EXERCISES

1. Find the rate at which the lateral area of the cone in Example 1 is increasing at the given instant.

2. At a certain instant a right circular cylinder has radius of base 10 in. and altitude 15 in. At this instant the radius is decreasing at the rate of 5 in./sec and the altitude is increasing at the rate of 4 in./sec. How rapidly is the volume changing at this moment?

3. A gas obeys the law $pv = RT (R = \text{const})$. At a certain instant while the gas is being compressed, $v = 15 \text{ ft}^3$, $p = 25 \text{ lb/in}^2$, v is decreasing at the rate of $3 \text{ ft}^3/\text{min}$, and p is increasing at the rate of $6\frac{2}{3} \text{ lb/in}^2/\text{min}$. Find dT/dt. (Answer in terms of R.)

4. (a) In problem 2, find how rapidly the lateral surface area of the cylinder is changing at the same instant. (b) What would the result be for the area A consisting of the top and bottom of the cylinder as well as the lateral surface?

5. At a certain instant of time, the angle A of a triangle ABC is 60° and increasing at the rate of 5°/sec, the side $\overline{AB}$ is 10 in. and increasing at the rate of 1 in./sec, and side $\overline{AC}$ is 16 in. and decreasing at the rate of $\frac{1}{2}$ in./sec. Find the rate of change of side $\overline{BC}$.

6. A point moves along the surface

$$z = x^2 + 2y^2 - 3x + y$$

in such a way that $dx/dt = 3$ and $dy/dt = 2$. Find how z changes with time when $x = 1, y = 4$.

7. Water is leaking out of a conical tank at the rate of $0.5 \text{ ft}^3/\text{min}$. The tank is also stretching in such a way that, while it remains conical, the distance across the top at the water surface is increasing at the rate of 0.2 ft/min. How fast is the height h of water changing at the instant when $h = 10$ and the volume of water is 75 cu. ft?

8. A rectangular bin is changing in size in such a way that its length is increasing at the rate of 3 in./sec, its width is decreasing at the rate of 2 in./sec, and its height is increasing at the rate of 1 in./sec. (a) How fast is the volume changing at the instant when the length is 15, the width is 10, and the height is 8? (b) How fast is the total surface area changing at the same instant?

9. (a) Given $z = f(y/x)$. Find $\partial z/\partial x$ and $\partial z/\partial y$ in terms of $f'(y/x)$ and x and y. [*Hint.* Let $u = y/x$.] (b) Show that $x\,(\partial z/\partial x) + y\,(\partial z/\partial y) = 0$.

10. (a) Given that $w = f(y - x - t,\ z - y + t)$. By letting $u = y - x - t$, $v = z - y + t$, find $\partial w/\partial x, \partial w/\partial y, \partial w/\partial z, \partial w/\partial t$ in terms of $f_{,1}$ and $f_{,2}$. (b) Show that

$$\frac{\partial w}{\partial x} + 2\,\frac{\partial w}{\partial y} + \frac{\partial w}{\partial z} + \frac{\partial w}{\partial t} = 0.$$

11. Suppose that $z = f(x, y)$ and $x = r \cos \theta,\ y = r \sin \theta$. (a) Express $\partial z/\partial r$ and $\partial z/\partial \theta$ in terms of $\partial z/\partial x$ and $\partial z/\partial y$. (b) Show that

$$\left(\frac{\partial z}{\partial r}\right)^2 + \frac{1}{r^2}\left(\frac{\partial z}{\partial \theta}\right)^2 = \left(\frac{\partial z}{\partial x}\right)^2 + \left(\frac{\partial z}{\partial y}\right)^2.$$

12. Suppose that $z = f(x, y)$, $x = e^s \cos t$, $y = e^s \sin t$. Show that

$$\left(\frac{\partial z}{\partial s}\right)^2 + \left(\frac{\partial z}{\partial t}\right)^2 = e^{2s}\left[\left(\frac{\partial z}{\partial x}\right)^2 + \left(\frac{\partial z}{\partial y}\right)^2\right].$$

13. Suppose that $u = f(x + at, y + bt)$, with a and b constants. Show that

$$\frac{\partial u}{\partial t} = a\frac{\partial u}{\partial x} + b\frac{\partial u}{\partial y}.$$

14. Given that

$$f(x, y) = \frac{x + y}{x^2 - xy + y^2},$$

show that

$$xf_{,1} + yf_{,2} = -f.$$

15. Given that $f(x, y) = x^2 - y^2 + xy \ln (y/x)$, show that $xf_{,1} + yf_{,2} = 2f$.

16. If in Example 4 a second observer is situated at a point O', 12 miles west of the one at O, find the rate of change of the distance between A and O' at the same instant.

17. If in Example 2 one of the acute angles is held constant at 60°, find the rate of change of the perimeter of the trapezoid at the instant in question.

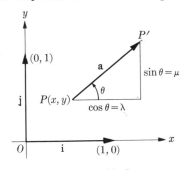

FIGURE 20–6

5. DIRECTIONAL DERIVATIVES. GRADIENT

The partial derivative of a function with respect to x may be considered as the derivative in the x-direction; the partial derivative with respect to y is the derivative in the y-direction. We now show how we may define the derivative in *any direction*. To see this, we consider a function $f(x, y)$ and a point $P(x, y)$ in the xy-plane. A particular direction is singled out by specifying the angle θ which a line through P makes with the positive x-axis (Fig. 20–6). We may also prescribe the direction by drawing the directed line segment $\overrightarrow{PP'}$ of *unit* length, as shown, and defining the vector $\mathbf{a}$ by the relation

$$\mathbf{a} = \lambda\mathbf{i} + \mu\mathbf{j},$$

with $\lambda = \cos \theta$, $\mu = \sin \theta$, and $\mathbf{i}$ and $\mathbf{j}$ the customary unit vectors. We note that $\mathbf{a}$ is a vector of unit length. The vector $\mathbf{a}$ determines the same direction as the angle θ.

DEFINITION. Let f be a function of two variables. We define the *directional derivative $D_a f$ of f in the direction of* **a** by

$$D_a f(x, y) = \lim_{h \to 0} \frac{f(x + \lambda h, y + \mu h) - f(x, y)}{h}$$

whenever the limit exists.

Remark. We note that, when $\theta = 0$, then $\lambda = 1$, $\mu = 0$, and the direction is the positive x-direction. The directional derivative is exactly $\partial f/\partial x$. Similarly, if $\theta = \pi/2$, we have $\lambda = 0$, $\mu = 1$, and the directional derivative is $\partial f/\partial y$.

The working formula for directional derivatives is established in the next theorem.

Theorem 4. *If $f(x, y)$ and its partial derivatives are continuous and*

$$\mathbf{a} = (\cos \theta)\mathbf{i} + (\sin \theta)\mathbf{j},$$

then

$$D_a f(x, y) = f_{,1}(x, y) \cos \theta + f_{,2}(x, y) \sin \theta.$$

Proof. We define the function $g(s)$ by

$$g(s) = f(x + s \cos \theta, y + s \sin \theta),$$

in which we keep x, y, and θ fixed and allow s to vary. The Chain Rule now yields
$g'(s) = f_{,1}(x + s \cos \theta, y + s \sin \theta) \cos \theta + f_{,2}(x + s \cos \theta, y + s \sin \theta) \sin \theta$
and

$$g'(0) = f_{,1}(x, y) \cos \theta + f_{,2}(x, y) \sin \theta.$$

Since, by definition, $g'(0)$ is precisely $D_a f(x, y)$, the result is established.

EXAMPLE 1. Given $f(x, y) = x^2 + 2y^2 - 3x + 2y$, find the directional derivative of f in the direction $\theta = \pi/6$. What is the value of this derivative at the point $(2, -1)$?

Solution. We compute
$$f_{,1} = 2x - 3, \qquad f_{,2} = 4y + 2.$$
Therefore
$$D_a f = (2x - 3) \cdot \tfrac{1}{2}\sqrt{3} + (4y + 2) \cdot \tfrac{1}{2}.$$
In particular, when $x = 2$ and $y = -1$, we obtain
$$D_a f = \tfrac{1}{2}\sqrt{3} - 1.$$

An alternate notation for directional derivative for functions of two variables is the symbol

$$d_\theta f(x, y),$$

in which θ is the angle the direction makes with the x-axis. For a fixed value of

x and y, the directional derivative is a function of θ. It is an ordinary problem in maxima and minima to find the value of θ which makes the directional derivative at a given point the largest or the smallest. The next example shows the method.

EXAMPLE 2.   Given $f(x, y) = x^2 - xy - y^2$, find $d_\theta f(x, y)$ at the point $(2, -3)$. For what value of θ does $d_\theta(2, -3)$ take on its maximum value?

Solution. We have

$$f_{,1}(x, y) = 2x - y, \qquad f_{,2}(x, y) = -x - 2y.$$

Therefore for $x = 2$, $y = -3$,

$$d_\theta f(2, -3) = 7 \cos \theta + 4 \sin \theta.$$

To find the maximum of this function of θ we differentiate

$$k(\theta) = 7 \cos \theta + 4 \sin \theta$$

and set the derivative equal to zero. We get

$$k'(\theta) = -7 \sin \theta + 4 \cos \theta = 0 \quad \text{or} \quad \tan \theta = \tfrac{4}{7}.$$

The result is $\cos \theta = \pm 7/\sqrt{65}$, $\sin \theta = \pm 4/\sqrt{65}$, and

$$\tan \theta = \tfrac{4}{7}, \qquad \theta = \begin{cases} 29°45' \text{ approximately,} \\ 209°45' \text{ approximately.} \end{cases}$$

It is clear by substitution that the first choice for θ makes $k(\theta)$ a maximum, while the second makes it a minimum.

The definition of directional derivative for functions of two variables has a natural extension to functions of three variables. In three dimensions, a direction is determined by a set of direction cosines λ, μ, ν or, equivalently, a vector

$$\mathbf{a} = \lambda \mathbf{i} + \mu \mathbf{j} + \nu \mathbf{k}.$$

We recall that $\lambda^2 + \mu^2 + \nu^2 = 1$, and so $\mathbf{a}$ is a *unit* vector.

DEFINITION.   We define the *directional derivative $D_\mathbf{a} f$ of $f(x, y, z)$ in the direction of $\mathbf{a}$* by

$$D_\mathbf{a} f(x, y, z) = \lim_{h \to 0} \frac{f(x + \lambda h, y + \mu h, z + \nu h) - f(x, y, z)}{h}$$

whenever the limit exists.

The proof of the next theorem is entirely analogous to the proof of Theorem 4.

Theorem 5. *If $f(x, y, z)$ and its partial derivatives are continuous and* $\mathbf{a} = \lambda \mathbf{i} + \mu \mathbf{j} + \nu \mathbf{k}$ *is a unit vector, then*

$$D_{\mathbf{a}}f(x, y, z) = \lambda f_{,1}(x, y, z) + \mu f_{,2}(x, y, z) + \nu f_{,3}(x, y, z).$$

EXAMPLE 3. Find the directional derivative of $f(x, y, z) = x^2 + y^2 + z^2 - 3xy + 2xz - yz$ at the point $(1, 2, -1)$.

Solution. We have

$$f_{,1}(x, y, z) = 2x - 3y + 2z; \quad f_{,2}(x, y, z) = 2y - 3x - z; \quad f_{,3}(x, y, z) = 2z + 2x - y.$$

Denoting the direction by $\mathbf{a} = \lambda \mathbf{i} + \mu \mathbf{j} + \nu \mathbf{k}$, we get

$$D_{\mathbf{a}}f(1, 2, -1) = -6\lambda + 2\mu - 2\nu.$$

EXAMPLE 4. Given the function

$$f(x, y, z) = xe^{yz} + ye^{xz} + ze^{xy},$$

find the directional derivative at $P(1, 0, 2)$ in the direction going from P to $P'(5, 3, 3)$.

Solution. A set of direction numbers for the line through P and P' is 4, 3, 1. The corresponding direction cosines are $4/\sqrt{26}, 3/\sqrt{26}, 1/\sqrt{26}$, which we denote by λ, μ, ν. The direction $\mathbf{a}$ is given by

$$\mathbf{a} = \frac{4}{\sqrt{26}} \mathbf{i} + \frac{3}{\sqrt{26}} \mathbf{j} + \frac{1}{\sqrt{26}} \mathbf{k}.$$

We find that

$$
\begin{aligned}
f_{,1}(x, y, z) &= e^{yz} + yze^{xz} + zye^{xy} & \text{and} && f_{,1}(1, 0, 2) &= 1, \\
f_{,2}(x, y, z) &= xze^{yz} + e^{xz} + xze^{xy} & \text{and} && f_{,2}(1, 0, 2) &= 4 + e^2, \\
f_{,3}(x, y, z) &= xye^{yz} + xye^{xz} + e^{xy} & \text{and} && f_{,3}(1, 0, 2) &= 1.
\end{aligned}
$$

Therefore

$$D_{\mathbf{a}}f(1, 0, 2) = \frac{4}{\sqrt{26}} + (4 + e^2)\frac{3}{\sqrt{26}} + \frac{1}{\sqrt{26}} = \frac{17 + 3e^2}{\sqrt{26}}.$$

As the next definition shows, the *gradient* of a function is a vector containing the partial derivatives of the function.

DEFINITIONS. (i) If $f(x, y)$ has partial derivatives, we define the *gradient vector*

$$\text{grad } f(x, y) = f_{,1}(x, y)\mathbf{i} + f_{,2}(x, y)\mathbf{j}.$$

(ii) If $g(x, y, z)$ has partial derivatives, we define

$$\text{grad } g(x, y, z) = g_{,1}(x, y, z)\mathbf{i} + g_{,2}(x, y, z)\mathbf{j} + g_{,3}(x, y, z)\mathbf{k}.$$

The symbol ∇, an inverted delta, is called "del" and is a common one used to denote the gradient. We will frequently write ∇f for grad f.

If $\mathbf{b}$ and $\mathbf{c}$ are two vectors, we recall that the scalar product $\mathbf{b} \cdot \mathbf{c}$ of $\mathbf{b} = b_1\mathbf{i} + b_2\mathbf{j} + b_3\mathbf{k}$ and $\mathbf{c} = c_1\mathbf{i} + c_2\mathbf{j} + c_3\mathbf{k}$ is given by

$$\mathbf{b} \cdot \mathbf{c} = b_1c_1 + b_2c_2 + b_3c_3.$$

For two-dimensional vectors the result is the same, with $b_3 = c_3 = 0$.

We recognize that if $\mathbf{a}$ is a *unit* vector so that $\mathbf{a} = \lambda\mathbf{i} + \mu\mathbf{j} + \nu\mathbf{k}$, then we have the formula

$$D_{\mathbf{a}}f = \lambda f_{,1} + \mu f_{,2} + \nu f_{,3} = \mathbf{a} \cdot \nabla f.$$

Looked at another way, the scalar product of $\mathbf{a}$ and ∇f is given by

$$\mathbf{a} \cdot \nabla f = |\mathbf{a}|\,|\nabla f|\cos\phi = D_{\mathbf{a}}f,$$

where ϕ is the angle between $\mathbf{a}$ and ∇f.

From the above formula we can conclude that $D_{\mathbf{a}}f$ *is a maximum when ϕ is zero*—i.e., when $\mathbf{a}$ *is in the direction of* the grad f.

EXAMPLE 5. Given the function

$$f(x, y, z) = x^3 + 2y^3 + z^3 - 4xyz,$$

find the maximum value of $D_{\mathbf{a}}f$ at the point $P = (-1, 1, 2)$.

Solution. We have

$$f_{,1} = 3x^2 - 4yz; \qquad f_{,2} = 6y^2 - 4xz; \qquad f_{,3} = 3z^2 - 4xy.$$

Therefore

$$\nabla f(-1, 1, 2) = -5\mathbf{i} + 14\mathbf{j} + 16\mathbf{k},$$

and a unit vector $\mathbf{a}$ in the direction of ∇f is

$$\mathbf{a} = -\frac{5}{3\sqrt{53}}\mathbf{i} + \frac{14}{3\sqrt{53}}\mathbf{j} + \frac{16}{3\sqrt{53}}\mathbf{k}.$$

The maximum value of $D_{\mathbf{a}}f$ is given by

$$D_{\mathbf{a}}f = -5\left(\frac{-5}{3\sqrt{53}}\right) + 14\left(\frac{14}{3\sqrt{53}}\right) + 16\left(\frac{16}{3\sqrt{53}}\right) = 3\sqrt{53}.$$

EXERCISES

In problems 1 through 6, find in each case $d_\theta f(x, y)$ at the given point.

1. $f(x, y) = x^2 + y^2$; $(3, 4)$
2. $f(x, y) = x^3 + y^3 - 3x^2y - 3xy^2$; $(1, -2)$

3. $f(x, y) = \arctan (y/x)$; $(4, 3)$ 4. $f(x, y) = \sin xy$; $(2, \pi/4)$

5. $f(x, y) = e^x \cos y$; $(0, \pi/3)$ 6. $f(x, y) = (\sin x)^{xy}$; $(\pi/2, 0)$

In each of problems 7 through 10 find the value of $d_\theta f(x, y)$ at the given point. Also, find the value of θ which makes $d_\theta f$ a maximum at this point. Express your answer in terms of $\sin \theta$ and $\cos \theta$.

7. $f(x, y) = x^2 + y^2 - 2x + 3y$; $(2, -1)$ 8. $f(x, y) = \arctan (x/y)$; $(3, 4)$

9. $f(x, y) = e^x \sin y$; $(0, \pi/6)$ 10. $f(x, y) = (\sin y)^{xy}$; $(0, \pi/2)$

In each of problems 11 through 14, find $D_\mathbf{a} f$ at the given point.

11. $f(x, y, z) = x^2 + xy - xz + y^2 - z^2$; $(2, 1, -2)$

12. $f(x, y, z) = x^2 y + xze^y - xye^z$; $(-2, 3, 0)$

13. $f(x, y, z) = \cos xy + \sin xz$; $(0, 2, -1)$

14. $f(x, y, z) = \ln (x + y + z) - xyz$; $(-1, 2, 1)$

In problems 15 through 18, in each case find $D_\mathbf{a} f$ at the given point P when $\mathbf{a}$ is the given unit vector.

15. $f(x, y, z) = x^2 + 2xy - y^2 + xz + z^2$; $P(2, 1, 1)$; $\mathbf{a} = \frac{1}{3}\mathbf{i} - \frac{2}{3}\mathbf{j} + \frac{2}{3}\mathbf{k}$

16. $f(x, y, z) = x^2 y + xye^z - 2xze^y$; $P(1, 2, 0)$; $\mathbf{a} = \frac{2}{7}\mathbf{i} - \frac{3}{7}\mathbf{j} + \frac{6}{7}\mathbf{k}$

17. $f(x, y, z) = \sin xz + \cos xy$; $P(0, -1, 2)$; $\mathbf{a} = \dfrac{1}{\sqrt{6}}\mathbf{i} - \dfrac{1}{\sqrt{6}}\mathbf{j} + \dfrac{2}{\sqrt{6}}\mathbf{k}$

18. $f(x, y, z) = \tan xyz + \sin xy - \cos xz$; $P(0, 1, 1)$;

$$\mathbf{a} = \dfrac{1}{\sqrt{26}}\mathbf{i} + \dfrac{3}{\sqrt{26}}\mathbf{j} + \dfrac{4}{\sqrt{26}}\mathbf{k}$$

19. The temperature at any point of a rectangular plate in the xy-plane is given by the formula $T = 50(x^2 - y^2)$ (in degrees centigrade). Find $d_\theta T(4, 3)$, and find $\tan \theta$ when $d_\theta T(4, 3) = 0$. Find also the slope of the curve $T = $ const which passes through that point.

In each of problems 20 through 23, find ∇f at the given point.

20. $f(x, y) = x^3 - 2x^2 y + xy^2 - y^3$; $P(3, -2)$

21. $f(x, y) = \ln (x^2 + y^2 + 1) + e^{2xy}$; $P(0, -2)$

22. $f(x, y, z) = \sin xy + \sin xz + \sin yz$; $P(1, 2, -1)$

23. $f(x, y, z) = xze^{xy} + yze^{xz} + xye^{yz}$; $P(-1, 2, 1)$

In each of problems 24 through 27, find $D_\mathbf{a} f$ at the given point P where $\mathbf{a}$ is a unit vector in the direction $\overrightarrow{PP'}$. Also, find at P the value of $D_{\bar{\mathbf{a}}} f$ where $\bar{\mathbf{a}}$ is a unit vector such that $D_{\bar{\mathbf{a}}} f$ is a maximum.

24. $f(x, y, z) = x^2 + 3xy + y^2 + z^2$; $P(1, 0, 2)$; $P'(-1, 3, 4)$

25. $f(x, y, z) = e^x \cos y + e^y \sin z$; $P(2, 1, 0)$; $P'(-1, 2, 2)$

26. $f(x, y, z) = \ln (x^2 + y^2) + e^z$; $P(0, 1, 0)$; $P'(-4, 2, 3)$

27. $f(x, y, z) = x \cos y + y \cos z + z \cos x$; $P(2, 1, 0)$; $P'(1, 4, 2)$

FIGURE 20-7

FIGURE 20-8

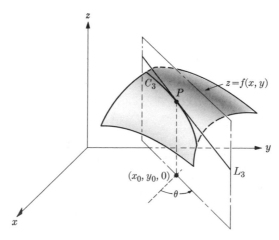

FIGURE 20-9

6. GEOMETRIC INTERPRETATION OF PARTIAL DERIVATIVES. TANGENT PLANES

From the geometric point of view, a function of one variable represents a curve in the plane. The derivative at a point on the curve is the slope of the line tangent to the curve at this point. A function of two variables $z = f(x, y)$ represents a surface in three-dimensional space. If x_0, y_0 are the coordinates of a point in the xy-plane, then $P(x_0, y_0, z_0)$, with $z_0 = f(x_0, y_0)$, is a point on the surface. Consider the vertical plane $y = y_0$, as shown in Fig. 20–7. This plane cuts the surface $z = f(x, y)$ in a curve C_1 which contains the point P. From the definition of partial derivative we see that

$$f_x(x_0, y_0)$$

is the slope of the line tangent to the curve C_1 at the point P. This line is labeled L_1 in Fig. 20–7 and, of course, is in the plane $y = y_0$. In a completely analogous way we construct a plane $x = x_0$ intersecting the surface with equation $z = f(x, y)$ in a curve C_2. The partial derivative

$$f_y(x_0, y_0)$$

is the slope of the line tangent to C_2 at the point P. The line is denoted L_2 in Fig. 20–8, and its slope is the tangent of the angle β, as shown.

The directional derivative $d_\theta f(x_0, y_0)$ has a similar interpretation. We construct the vertical plane through $(x_0, y_0, 0)$ which makes an angle θ with the positive x-direction. Such a plane is shown in Fig. 20–9. The curve C_3 is the intersection of this plane with the surface, and the line L_3 is the line tangent to C_3 at P. Then $d_\theta f(x_0, y_0)$ is the slope of L_3.

According to Theorem 2, we may write the formula

$$f(x, y) - f(x_0, y_0) = f_{,1}(x_0, y_0)(x - x_0) + f_{,2}(x_0, y_0)(y - y_0)$$
$$+ G_1 \cdot (x - x_0) + G_2 \cdot (y - y_0),$$

in which we take

$$x - x_0 = h \quad \text{and} \quad y - y_0 = k.$$

Since G_1 and G_2 tend to zero as $(x, y) \to (x_0, y_0)$, the next definition has an intuitive geometric meaning.

DEFINITION. The plane whose equation is

$$z - z_0 = m_1(x - x_0) + m_2(y - y_0)$$

where

$$z_0 = f(x_0, y_0), \quad m_1 = f_{,1}(x_0, y_0), \quad m_2 = f_{,2}(x_0, y_0)$$

is called the *tangent plane* to the surface $z = f(x, y)$ at (x_0, y_0).

Remarks. (i) According to the geometric interpretation of partial derivative which we gave, it is easy to verify that the tangent plane contains the lines L_1

and L_2, tangents to C_1 and C_2, respectively. (ii) From the definition of tangent plane we observe at once that

$$f_{,1}(x_0, y_0), \qquad f_{,2}(x_0, y_0), \qquad -1$$

is a set of attitude numbers for the plane. (Attitude numbers were defined on page 546.) The relation between attitude numbers and direction numbers leads to the next definition.

DEFINITION. The line with equations

$$\frac{x - x_0}{m_1} = \frac{y - y_0}{m_2} = \frac{z - z_0}{-1},$$

with $z_0 = f(x_0, y_0)$, $m_1 = f_{,1}(x_0, y_0)$, $m_2 = f_{,2}(x_0, y_0)$, is called the *normal line* to the surface at the point $P(x_0, y_0, z_0)$. Clearly, the normal line is perpendicular to the tangent plane.

Remarks. In addition to $f_{,1}(x_0, y_0)$ we shall use the symbols

$$f_x(x_0, y_0), \qquad \frac{\partial f(x_0, y_0)}{\partial x}, \qquad \text{and} \qquad \frac{\partial z}{\partial x}\bigg|_{\substack{x=x_0 \\ y=y_0}}$$

for m_1, and analogous notations for m_2.

EXAMPLE 1. Find the equation of the tangent plane and the equations of the normal line to the surface

$$z = x^2 + xy - y^2$$

at the point where $x = 2$, $y = -1$.

Solution. We have $z_0 = f(2, -1) = 1$; $f_{,1}(x, y) = 2x + y$, $f_{,2}(x, y) = x - 2y$. Therefore $m_1 = 3$, $m_2 = 4$, and the desired equation for the tangent plane is

$$z - 1 = 3(x - 2) + 4(y + 1).$$

The equations of the normal line are

$$\frac{x - 2}{3} = \frac{y + 1}{4} = \frac{z - 1}{-1}.$$

If the equation of the surface is given in implicit form it is possible to use the methods of Section 2 to find $\partial z/\partial x$ and $\partial z/\partial y$ at the desired point. The next example shows how we obtain the equations of the tangent plane and normal line under such circumstances.

EXAMPLE 2. Find the equations of the tangent plane and normal line at $(3, -1, 2)$ to the locus of

$$xy + yz + xz - 1 = 0.$$

Solution. Holding y constant and differentiating with respect to x, we get

$$y + y\frac{\partial z}{\partial x} + z + x\frac{\partial z}{\partial x} = 0 \quad \text{and} \quad \frac{\partial z}{\partial x} = -\frac{y+z}{y+x} = -\frac{1}{2} = m_1.$$

Similarly, holding x constant, we obtain

$$x + y\frac{\partial z}{\partial y} + z + x\frac{\partial z}{\partial y} = 0, \quad \frac{\partial z}{\partial y} = -\frac{x+z}{x+y} = -\frac{5}{2} = m_2.$$

The equation of the tangent plane is

$$z - 2 = -\tfrac{1}{2}(x - 3) - \tfrac{5}{2}(y + 1) \quad \text{or} \quad x + 5y + 2z - 2 = 0.$$

The normal line has equations

$$\frac{x-3}{-1/2} = \frac{y+1}{-5/2} = \frac{z-2}{-1} \quad \text{or} \quad \frac{x-3}{1} = \frac{y+1}{5} = \frac{z-2}{2}.$$

The methods of the calculus of functions of several variables enable us to establish purely geometric facts, as the next example shows.

EXAMPLE 3. Show that any line normal to the sphere

$$x^2 + y^2 + z^2 = a^2$$

always passes through the center of the sphere.

Solution. Since the sphere has center at $(0, 0, 0)$, we must show that the equations of the line are satisfied for $x = y = z = 0$. Let (x_0, y_0, z_0) be a point on the sphere. Differentiating implicitly, we find

$$\frac{\partial z}{\partial x} = -\frac{x}{z}, \quad \frac{\partial z}{\partial y} = -\frac{y}{z}.$$

The normal line to the sphere at (x_0, y_0, z_0) has equations

$$\frac{x - x_0}{-x_0/z_0} = \frac{y - y_0}{-y_0/z_0} = \frac{z - z_0}{-1}. \tag{1}$$

Letting $x = y = z = 0$, we get an identity for (1); hence the line passes through the origin.

Let the equations

$$z = f(x, y) \quad \text{and} \quad z = g(x, y)$$

represent surfaces which intersect in a curve C. The *tangent line* to the intersection at a point P on C is by definition the line of intersection of the tangent planes to f and g at P (Fig. 20–10).

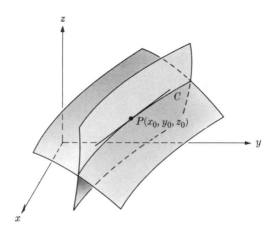

FIGURE 20–10

We can use vector algebra in the following way to find the equations of this tangent line. If P has coordinates (x_0, y_0, z_0), then

$$\mathbf{u} = f_x(x_0, y_0)\mathbf{i} + f_y(x_0, y_0)\mathbf{j} + (-1)\mathbf{k}$$

is a vector perpendicular to the plane tangent to f at P. Similarly, we have

$$\mathbf{v} = g_x(x_0, y_0)\mathbf{i} + g_y(x_0, y_0)\mathbf{j} + (-1)\mathbf{k}$$

is a vector perpendicular to the plane tangent to g at P. The line of intersection of these tangent planes is perpendicular to both $\mathbf{u}$ and $\mathbf{v}$. We recall from the study of vectors that, if $\mathbf{u}$ and $\mathbf{v}$ are nonparallel vectors, the vector $\mathbf{u} \times \mathbf{v}$ is perpendicular to both $\mathbf{u}$ and $\mathbf{v}$. Defining the vector $\mathbf{w} = a\mathbf{i} + b\mathbf{j} + c\mathbf{k}$ by the relation

$$\mathbf{w} = \mathbf{u} \times \mathbf{v},$$

we see that the equations of the line of intersection of the tangent plane are

$$\frac{x - x_0}{a} = \frac{y - y_0}{b} = \frac{z - z_0}{c}.$$

The next example shows how the method works.

EXAMPLE 4. Find the equations of the line tangent to the intersection of the surfaces

$$z = f(x, y) = x^2 + 2y^2, \qquad z = g(x, y) = 2x^2 - 3y^2 + 1$$

at the point $(2, 1, 6)$.

Solution. We have

$$f_x = 2x, \quad f_y = 4y; \qquad g_x = 4x, \quad g_y = -6y.$$

Therefore

$$\mathbf{u} = 4\mathbf{i} + 4\mathbf{j} - \mathbf{k}; \qquad \mathbf{v} = 8\mathbf{i} - 6\mathbf{j} - \mathbf{k}; \qquad \mathbf{u} \times \mathbf{v} = -10\mathbf{i} - 4\mathbf{j} - 56\mathbf{k}.$$

The desired equations are

$$\frac{x - 2}{10} = \frac{y - 1}{4} = \frac{z - 6}{56}.$$

EXERCISES

In problems 1 through 14, find in each case the equation of the tangent plane and the equations of the normal line to the given surface at the given point.

1. $z = x^2 + 2y^2$; $(2, -1, 6)$
2. $z = 3x^2 - y^2 - 2$; $(-1, 2, -3)$
3. $z = xy$; $(2, -1, -2)$
4. $z = x^2 y^2$; $(-2, 2, 16)$
5. $z = e^x \sin y$; $(1, \pi/2, e)$
6. $z = e^{2x} \cos 3y$; $(1, \pi/3, -e^2)$
7. $z = \ln \sqrt{x^2 + y^2}$; $(-3, 4, \ln 5)$
8. $x^2 + 2y^2 + 3z^2 = 6$; $(1, 1, -1)$
9. $x^2 + 2y^2 - 3z^2 = 3$; $(2, 1, -1)$
10. $x^2 + 3y^2 - z^2 = 0$; $(2, -2, 4)$
11. $x^2 + z^2 = 25$; $(4, -2, -3)$
12. $xy + yz + xz = 1$; $(2, 3, -1)$
13. $x^{1/2} + y^{1/2} + z^{1/2} = 6$; $(4, 1, 9)$
14. $y^{1/2} + z^{1/2} = 7$; $(3, 16, 9)$

15. Show that the equation of the plane tangent at (x_1, y_1, z_1) to the ellipsoid

$$\frac{x^2}{A^2} + \frac{y^2}{B^2} + \frac{z^2}{C^2} = 1 \qquad \text{is} \qquad \frac{x_1 x}{A^2} + \frac{y_1 y}{B^2} + \frac{z_1 z}{C^2} = 1.$$

16. Show that every plane tangent to the cone

$$x^2 + y^2 = z^2$$

passes through the origin.

17. Show that every line normal to the cone

$$z^2 = 3x^2 + 3y^2$$

intersects the z-axis.

18. Show that the sum of the squares of the intercepts of any plane tangent to the surface

$$x^{2/3} + y^{2/3} + z^{2/3} = a^{2/3}$$

is constant.

In problems 19 through 22, find the equations of the line tangent to the intersection of the two surfaces at the given point.

19. $z = x^2 + y^2$, $z = 2x + 4y + 20$; $(4, -2, 20)$
20. $z = \sqrt{x^2 + y^2}$, $z = 2x - 3y - 13$; $(3, -4, 5)$
21. $z = x^2$, $z = 25 - y^2$; $(4, -3, 16)$
22. $z = \sqrt{25 - 9x^2}$, $z = e^{xy} + 3$; $(1, 0, 4)$

7. THE TOTAL DIFFERENTIAL. APPROXIMATION

The differential of a function of one variable is a function of two variables selected in a special way. We recall that if $y = f(x)$, then the quantity df, called the differential of f, is defined by the relation

$$df = f'(x)h,$$

where h and x are independent variables. (See Chapter 7, page 184.)

Let f be a function of several variables; the next definition is the appropriate one for generalizing the notion of differential to such functions.

DEFINITIONS. The *total differential* of $f(x, y)$ is the function df of four variables x, y, h, k given by the formula

$$df(x, y, h, k) = f_{,1}(x, y)h + f_{,2}(x, y)k.$$

If F is a function of three variables—say x, y, and z—we define the *total differential* as the function of six variables x, y, z, h, k, l given by

$$dF(x, y, z, h, k, l) = F_{,1}(x, y, z)h + F_{,2}(x, y, z)k + F_{,3}(x, y, z)l.$$

A quantity related to the total differential is the difference of a function at two nearby values. As is customary, we use Δ notation and, for functions of two variables, we define the quantity Δf by the relation

$$\Delta f \equiv \Delta f(x, y, h, k) = f(x + h, y + k) - f(x, y).$$

Here Δf is a function of four variables, as is df. If f depends on x, y, and z, then Δf is a function of six variables defined by

$$\Delta f \equiv \Delta f(x, y, z, h, k, l) = f(x + h, y + k, z + l) - f(x, y, z).$$

———————————

EXAMPLE 1. Given the function

$$f(x, y) = x^2 + xy - 2y^2 - 3x + 2y + 4,$$

find $df(a, b, h, k)$ and $\Delta f(a, b, h, k)$ with $a = 3$, $b = 1$.

Solution. We have

$$f(3, 1) = 7; \qquad f_{,1}(x, y) = 2x + y - 3; \qquad f_{,2}(x, y) = x - 4y + 2;$$
$$f_{,1}(3, 1) = 4; \qquad f_{,2}(3, 1) = 1.$$

Also

$$f(3 + h, 1 + k) = (3 + h)^2 + (3 + h)(1 + k) - 2(1 + k)^2 - 3(3 + h)$$
$$+ 2(1 + k) + 4 = h^2 + hk - 2k^2 + 4h + k + 7.$$

Therefore

$$df(3, 1, h, k) = 4h + k; \qquad \Delta f(3, 1, h, k) = 4h + k + h^2 + hk - 2k^2.$$

The close relationship between df and Δf is exhibited in Theorem 2. Equation (1) of that theorem may be written in the form

$$\Delta f(x_0, y_0, h, k) = df(x_0, y_0, h, k) + G_1(h, k)h + G_2(h, k)k.$$

The conclusion of the theorem implies that

$$\frac{\Delta f - df}{|h| + |k|} \rightarrow 0 \quad \text{as} \quad h, k \rightarrow 0,$$

since both G_1 and G_2 tend to zero with h and k. In many problems Δf is difficult to calculate, while df is easy. If h and k are both "small," we can use df as an approximation to Δf. The next example shows the technique.

EXAMPLE 2. Find, approximately, the value of $\sqrt{(5.98)^2 + (8.01)^2}$.

Solution. We consider the function

$$z = f(x, y) = \sqrt{x^2 + y^2},$$

and we wish to find $f(5.98, 8.01)$. We see at once that $f(6, 8) = 10$; hence we may write

$$f(5.98, 8.01) = f(6, 8) + \Delta f,$$

where Δf is defined as above with $x_0 = 6$, $y_0 = 8$, $h = -0.02$, $k = 0.01$. The approximation consists of replacing Δf by df. We have

$$\frac{\partial z}{\partial x} = \frac{x}{\sqrt{x^2 + y^2}}, \qquad \frac{\partial z}{\partial y} = \frac{y}{\sqrt{x^2 + y^2}},$$

and so

$$df(6, 8, -0.02, 0.01) = \tfrac{6}{10}(-0.02) + \tfrac{8}{10}(0.01) = -0.004.$$

We conclude that $\sqrt{(5.98)^2 + (8.01)^2} = 10 - 0.004 = 9.996$, approximately. The true value is $9.9959992+$.

As in the case of functions of one variable, the symbolism for the total differential may be used as an aid in differentiation. We let $z = f(x, y)$ and employ the symbols

$$dz \quad \text{for} \quad df, \qquad dx \quad \text{for} \quad h, \qquad \text{and} \qquad dy \quad \text{for} \quad k.$$

As in the case of one variable, there is a certain ambiguity, since dz has a precise definition as the total differential, while dx and dy are used as independent variables. The next theorem shows how the Chain Rule comes to our rescue and removes all difficulties when dx and dy are in turn functions of other variables (i.e., dx and dy are what we call intermediate variables).

Theorem 6. *Suppose that* $z = f(x, y)$, *and* x *and* y *are functions of some other variables. Then*

$$dz = \frac{\partial z}{\partial x} dx + \frac{\partial z}{\partial y} dy.$$

The result for $w = F(x, y, z)$ *is similar. That is, the formula*

$$dw = \frac{\partial w}{\partial x} dx + \frac{\partial w}{\partial y} dy + \frac{\partial w}{\partial z} dz$$

holds when x, y, *and* z *are either independent or intermediate variables.*

Proof. We establish the result for $z = f(x, y)$ with x and y functions of two variables, say r and s. The proof in all other cases is analogous. We may write

$$x = x(r, s), \qquad y = y(r, s),$$

and then

$$z = f(x, y) = f[x(r, s), y(r, s)] = g(r, s).$$

The definition of total differential yields

$$dz = g_{,1}(r, s)h + g_{,2}(r, s)k,$$
$$dx = x_{,1}(r, s)h + x_{,2}(r, s)k,$$
$$dy = y_{,1}(r, s)h + y_{,2}(r, s)k.$$

According to the Chain Rule, we have

$$g_{,1}(r, s) = \frac{\partial f}{\partial r} = \frac{\partial f}{\partial x}\frac{\partial x}{\partial r} + \frac{\partial f}{\partial y}\frac{\partial y}{\partial r}$$
$$= f_{,1}(x, y)x_{,1}(r, s) + f_{,2}(x, y)y_{,1}(r, s);$$
$$g_{,2}(r, s) = \frac{\partial f}{\partial s} = \frac{\partial f}{\partial x}\frac{\partial x}{\partial s} + \frac{\partial f}{\partial y}\frac{\partial y}{\partial s}$$
$$= f_{,1}(x, y)x_{,2}(r, s) + f_{,2}(x, y)y_{,2}(r, s).$$

Substituting the above expressions for $g_{,1}$ and $g_{,2}$ into that for dz, we obtain

$$dz = \frac{\partial f}{\partial x}[x_{,1}(r, s)h + x_{,2}(r, s)k] + \frac{\partial f}{\partial y}[y_{,1}(r, s)h + y_{,2}(r, s)k]$$

or

$$dz = \frac{\partial f}{\partial x} dx + \frac{\partial f}{\partial y} dy.$$

We recognize this last formula as the statement of the theorem.

———————

EXAMPLE 3. Given

$$z = e^x \cos y + e^y \sin x, \qquad x = r^2 - t^2, \qquad y = 2rt,$$

find $dz(r, t, h, k)$ in two ways and verify that the results coincide.

Solution. We have, by one method,

$$dz = \frac{\partial z}{\partial x}\,dx + \frac{\partial z}{\partial y}\,dy$$

$$= (e^x \cos y + e^y \cos x)\,dx + (-e^x \sin y + e^y \sin x)\,dy;$$

$$dx = 2rh - 2tk;$$

$$dy = 2th + 2rk.$$

Therefore

$$dz = (e^x \cos y + e^y \cos x)(2rh - 2tk) + (-e^x \sin y + e^y \sin x)(2th + 2rk)$$

$$= 2[e^x \cos y + e^y \cos x)r + (e^y \sin x - e^x \sin y)t]h$$

$$+ 2[(-e^x \cos y - e^y \cos x)t + (e^y \sin x - e^x \sin y)r]k. \tag{1}$$

On the other hand,

$$dz = \frac{\partial z}{\partial r}\,h + \frac{\partial z}{\partial t}\,k \tag{2}$$

and, using the Chain Rule,

$$\frac{\partial z}{\partial r} = \frac{\partial z}{\partial x}\frac{\partial x}{\partial r} + \frac{\partial z}{\partial y}\frac{\partial y}{\partial r}, \qquad \frac{\partial z}{\partial t} = \frac{\partial z}{\partial x}\frac{\partial x}{\partial t} + \frac{\partial z}{\partial y}\frac{\partial y}{\partial t}.$$

We compute the various quantities in the two formulas above and find that

$$\frac{\partial z}{\partial r} = (e^x \cos y + e^y \cos x)(2r) + (e^y \sin x - e^x \sin y)(2t),$$

$$\frac{\partial z}{\partial t} = (e^x \cos y + e^y \cos x)(-2t) + (e^y \sin x - e^x \sin y)(2r).$$

Substituting these expressions in (2), we get (1) precisely.

EXERCISES

In each of problems 1 through 6, find $df(x, y, h, k)$ and $\Delta f(x, y, h, k)$ for the given values of x, y, h, and k.

1. $f(x, y) = x^2 - xy + 2y^2$, $x = 2$, $y = -1$, $h = -0.01$, $k = 0.02$

2. $f(x, y) = 2x^2 + 3xy - y^2$, $x = 1$, $y = 2$, $h = 0.02$, $k = -0.01$

3. $f(x, y) = \sin xy + \cos (x + y)$, $x = \pi/6$, $y = 0$, $h = 2\pi$, $k = 3\pi$

4. $f(x, y) = e^{xy} \sin (x + y)$, $x = \pi/4$, $y = 0$, $h = -\pi/2$, $k = 4\pi$

5. $f(x, y) = x^3 - 3xy + y^3$, $x = -2$, $y = 1$, $h = -0.03$, $k = -0.02$

6. $f(x, y) = x^2y - 2xy^2 + 3x$, $x = 1$, $y = 1$, $h = 0.02$, $k = 0.01$

In each of problems 7 through 10, find $df(x, y, z, h, k, l)$ and $\Delta f(x, y, z, h, k, l)$ for the given values of x, y, z, h, k, and l.

7. $f(x, y, z) = x^2 - 2y^2 + z^2 - xz$; $(x, y, z) = (2, -1, 3)$; $(h, k, l) = (0.01, -0.02, 0.03)$

8. $f(x, y, z) = xy - xz + yz + 2x - 3y + 1$; $(x, y, z) = (2, 0, -3)$;
   $(h, k, l) = (0.1, -0.2, 0.1)$

9. $f(x, y, z) = x^2y - xyz + z^3$; $(x, y, z) = (1, 2, -1)$;
   $(h, k, l) = (-0.02, 0.01, 0.02)$

10. $f(x, y, z) = \sin (x + y) - \cos (x - z) + \sin (y + 2z)$;
    $(x, y, z) = (\pi/3, \pi/6, 0)$; $(h, k, l) = (\pi/4, \pi/2, 2\pi)$

11. We define the *approximate percentage error* of a function f (see page 188) by the relation

$$\text{Approximate percentage error} = 100 \frac{df}{f}.$$

Find the approximate percentage error if $f(x, y, z) = 3x^3y^7z^4$.

12. Find the approximate percentage error (see problem 11) if $f = kx^my^nz^p$
    $(k = \text{const})$.

13. A crate has square ends, 11.98 in. on each side, and has a length of 30.03 in. Find its approximate volume, using differentials.

14. Use differentials to find the approximate value of $\sqrt{(5.02)^2 + (11.97)^2}$.

15. The legs of a right triangle are measured and found to be 6.0 and 8.0 in., with a possible error of 0.1 in. Find approximately the maximum possible value of the error in computing the hypotenuse. What is the maximum approximate percentage error? (See problem 11.)

16. Find in degrees the maximum possible approximate error in the computed value of the smaller acute angle in the triangle of problem 15.

17. The diameter and height of a right circular cylinder are found by measurement to be 8.0 and 12.5 in., respectively, with possible errors of 0.05 in. in each measurement. Find the maximum possible approximate error in the computed volume.

18. A right circular cone is measured, and the radius of the base is 12.0 in. with the height 16.0 in. If the possible error in each measurement is 0.06, find the maximum possible error in the computed volume. What is the maximum possible approximate error in the lateral surface area?

19. By measurement, a triangle is found to have two sides of length 50 in. and 70 in.; the angle between them is 30°. If there are possible errors of $\frac{1}{2}\%$ in the measurements of the sides and $\frac{1}{2}$ degree in that of the angle, find the maximum approximate percentage error in the measurement of the area. (See problem 11.)

20. Use differentials to find the approximate value of

$$\sqrt{(3.02)^2 + (1.99)^2 + (5.97)^2}.$$

21. Use differentials to find the approximate value of

$$[(3.01)^2 + (3.98)^2 + (6.02)^2 + 5(1.97)^2]^{-1/2}.$$

In each of problems 22 through 26, find dz in two ways in terms of the independent variables.

22. $z = x^2 + xy - y^2$; $x = r^2 + 2s^2$, $y = rs + 2$

23. $z = 2x^2 + 3xy + y^2$; $x = t^3 + 2t - 1$, $y = t^2 + t - 3$

24. $z = x^3 + y^3 - x^2y$; $x = r + 2s - t$, $y = r - 3s + 2t$

25. $z = u^2 + 2v^2 - x^2 + 3y^2$; $u = r^2 - s^2$, $v = r^2 + s^2$, $x = 2rs$, $y = 2r/s$

26. $z = u^3 + v^3 + w^3$; $u = r^2 + s^2 + t^2$, $v = r^2 - s^2 + t^2$, $w = r^2 + s^2 - t^2$

8. APPLICATIONS OF THE TOTAL DIFFERENTIAL

Once we clearly understand the concept of function we are able to use the notation of the total differential to obtain a number of useful differentiation formulas.

One of the simplest formulas, which we now develop, uses the fact that *the total differential of a constant is zero.* Suppose that x and y are related by some equation such as

$$f(x, y) = 0.$$

If we think of y as a function of x, we can compute the derivative dy/dx by implicit methods in the usual way. However, we may also use an alternate procedure. Since $f = 0$, the differential df also vanishes. Therefore we can write

$$df = \frac{\partial f}{\partial x} dx + \frac{\partial f}{\partial y} dy = 0$$

or

$$\frac{dy}{dx} = -\frac{\partial f/\partial x}{\partial f/\partial y} \quad \left(\text{if } \frac{\partial f}{\partial y} \neq 0\right). \tag{1}$$

EXAMPLE 1. Use the methods of partial differentiation to compute dy/dx if

$$x^4 + 3x^2y^2 - y^4 + 2x - 3y = 5.$$

Solution. Setting

$$f(x, y) = x^4 + 3x^2y^2 - y^4 + 2x - 3y - 5 = 0,$$

we find

$$f_x = 4x^3 + 6xy^2 + 2, \qquad f_y = 6x^2y - 4y^3 - 3.$$

Therefore, using (1) above,

$$\frac{dy}{dx} = -\frac{4x^3 + 6xy^2 + 2}{6x^2y - 4y^3 - 3}.$$

Of course, the same result is obtained by the customary process of implicit differentiation.

The above method for ordinary differentiation may be extended to yield partial derivatives. Suppose x, y, and z are connected by a relation of the form

$$F(x, y, z) = 0,$$

and we imagine that z is a function of x and y. That is, we make the assumption that it is possible to solve for z in terms of x and y even though we have no intention of doing so; in fact, we may find it exceptionally difficult (if not down-right impossible) to perform the necessary steps. If z is a function of x and y, then we have the formula for the total differential:

$$dz = \frac{\partial z}{\partial x} dx + \frac{\partial z}{\partial y} dy. \tag{2}$$

On the other hand, since $F = 0$, the differential dF is also. Therefore

$$dF = F_x \, dx + F_y \, dy + F_z \, dz = 0.$$

Solving for dz, we get

$$dz = \left(-\frac{F_x}{F_z}\right) dx + \left(-\frac{F_y}{F_z}\right) dy, \tag{3}$$

assuming that $F_z \neq 0$. Comparing Eq. (2) and (3), it is possible to conclude that

$$\frac{\partial z}{\partial x} = -\frac{F_x}{F_z} \quad \text{and} \quad \frac{\partial z}{\partial y} = -\frac{F_y}{F_z}. \tag{4}$$

(The validity of this conclusion is established in Morrey, *University Calculus*, page 568.) We exhibit the technique in the next example.

EXAMPLE 2. Use formulas (4) to find $\partial z/\partial x$ and $\partial z/\partial y$ if

$$e^{xy} \cos z + e^{-xz} \sin y + e^{yz} \cos x = 0.$$

Solution. We set

$$F(x, y, z) = e^{xy} \cos z + e^{-xz} \sin y + e^{yz} \cos x,$$

and compute

$$F_x = ye^{xy} \cos z - ze^{-xz} \sin y - e^{yz} \sin x,$$
$$F_y = xe^{xy} \cos z + e^{-xz} \cos y + ze^{yz} \cos x,$$
$$F_z = -e^{xy} \sin z - xe^{-xz} \sin y + ye^{yz} \cos x.$$

Therefore

$$\frac{\partial z}{\partial x} = -\frac{ye^{xy} \cos z - ze^{-xz} \sin y - e^{yz} \sin x}{-e^{xy} \sin z - xe^{-xz} \sin y + ye^{yz} \cos x},$$

$$\frac{\partial z}{\partial y} = -\frac{xe^{xy} \cos z + e^{-xz} \cos y + ze^{yz} \cos x}{-e^{xy} \sin z - xe^{-xz} \sin y + ye^{yz} \cos x}.$$

Remarks. (i) Note that we also could have found the derivatives by the implicit methods described in Section 2. (ii) Formulas similar to (4) may be established for a single relation with any number of variables. For example, if we are given $G(x, y, u, v, w) = 0$ and we assume w is a function of the remaining variables with $G_w \neq 0$, then

$$\frac{\partial w}{\partial x} = -\frac{G_x}{G_w}, \quad \frac{\partial w}{\partial y} = -\frac{G_y}{G_w}, \quad \frac{\partial w}{\partial u} = -\frac{G_u}{G_w}, \quad \frac{\partial w}{\partial v} = -\frac{G_v}{G_w}.$$

A more complicated application of differentials is exhibited in the derivation of the next set of formulas. Suppose, for example, that x, y, u, v are related by *two* equations, so that

$$F(x, y, u, v) = 0 \quad \text{and} \quad G(x, y, u, v) = 0.$$

If we could solve one of them for, say u, and substitute in the other, we would get a single equation for x, y, v. Then, solving for v, we would find that v is a function of x and y. Similarly, we might find u as a function of x and y. Of course, all this work is purely fictitious, since we have no intention of carrying out such a process. In fact, it may be impossible. The main point is that we know that under appropriate circumstances the process is *theoretically feasible*. (This fact is usually proved in a course in advanced calculus.) Therefore it makes sense to write the symbols

$$\frac{\partial u}{\partial x}, \quad \frac{\partial u}{\partial y}, \quad \frac{\partial v}{\partial x}, \quad \frac{\partial v}{\partial y} \tag{5}$$

whenever $u = u(x, y)$ and $v = v(x, y)$. Furthermore, the selection of u and v in terms of x and y is arbitrary. We could equally well attempt to solve for v and x in terms of u and y or for any two of the variables in terms of the remaining two variables.

The problem we pose is one of determining the quantities in (5) without actually finding the functions $u(x, y)$ and $v(x, y)$. We use the total differential. Since $F = 0$ and $G = 0$, so are dF and dG. We have

$$dF = F_x\, dx + F_y\, dy + F_u\, du + F_v\, dv = 0,$$
$$dG = G_x\, dx + G_y\, dy + G_u\, du + G_v\, dv = 0.$$

We write these equations,

$$F_u\, du + F_v\, dv = -F_x\, dx - F_y\, dy, \qquad G_u\, du + G_v\, dv = -G_x\, dx - G_y\, dy,$$

and consider du and dv as unknowns with everything else known. Solving two equations in two unknowns is easy. We obtain

$$du = \frac{G_x F_v - G_v F_x}{F_u G_v - F_v G_u}\, dx + \frac{G_y F_v - G_v F_y}{F_u G_v - F_v G_u}\, dy, \tag{6}$$

$$dv = \frac{G_u F_x - G_x F_u}{F_u G_v - F_v G_u}\, dx + \frac{G_u F_y - G_y F_u}{F_u G_v - F_v G_u}\, dy. \tag{7}$$

(It is assumed that $F_u G_v - F_v G_u \neq 0$.) On the other hand, we know that if $u = u(x, y)$, $v = v(x, y)$, then

$$du = \frac{\partial u}{\partial x}\, dx + \frac{\partial u}{\partial y}\, dy, \tag{8}$$

$$dv = \frac{\partial v}{\partial x}\, dx + \frac{\partial v}{\partial y}\, dy. \tag{9}$$

Therefore, comparing (6) with (8) and (7) with (9), we find

$$\frac{\partial u}{\partial x} = \frac{G_x F_v - G_v F_x}{F_u G_v - F_v G_u},$$

(10)

and similar formulas for $\partial u/\partial y$, $\partial v/\partial x$, and $\partial v/\partial y$. If F and G are given, the right side of (10) is computable.

EXAMPLE 3. Given the relations for x, y, u, v:

$$u^2 - uv - v^2 + x^2 + y^2 - xy = 0,$$
$$uv - x^2 + y^2 = 0,$$

and assuming that $u = u(x, y)$, $v = v(x, y)$, find $\partial u/\partial x$, $\partial u/\partial y$, $\partial v/\partial x$, and $\partial v/\partial y$.

Solution. We could find F_x, F_y, ..., G_u, G_v and then substitute for the coefficients in (6) and (7) to obtain the result. Instead we make use of the fact that we can treat differentials both as independent variables and as total differentials, with no fear of difficulty (because of the Chain Rule). Taking such differentials in each of the equations given, we get

$$2u\,du - u\,dv - v\,du - 2v\,dv + 2x\,dx + 2y\,dy - x\,dy - y\,dx = 0,$$
$$v\,du + u\,dv - 2x\,dx + 2y\,dy = 0.$$

Solving the two equations simultaneously for du and dv in terms of dx and dy, we obtain

$$du = \frac{uy + 4xv}{2(u^2 + v^2)}\,dx + \frac{ux - 4y(u + v)}{2(u^2 + v^2)}\,dy,$$

$$dv = \frac{4xu - yv}{2(u^2 + v^2)}\,dx + \frac{4y(v - u) - xv}{2(u^2 + v^2)}\,dy.$$

From these equations we read off the results. For example,

$$\frac{\partial u}{\partial y} = \frac{ux - 4y(u + v)}{2(u^2 + v^2)},$$

and there are corresponding expressions for $\partial u/\partial x$, $\partial v/\partial x$, $\partial v/\partial y$.

EXERCISES

In each of problems 1 through 7, find the derivative dy/dx by the methods of partial differentiation.

1. $x^2 + 3xy - 4y^2 + 2x - 6y + 7 = 0$
2. $x^3 + 3x^2y - 4xy^2 + y^3 - x^2 + 2y - 1 = 0$
3. $\ln(1 + x^2 + y^2) + e^{xy} = 5$
4. $x^4 - 3x^2y^2 + y^4 - x^2y + 2xy^2 = 3$ 5. $e^{xy} + \sin xy + 1 = 0$
6. $xe^y + ye^x + \sin(x + y) - 2 = 0$ 7. $\arctan(y/x) + (x^2 + y^2)^{3/2} = 2$

In each of problems 8 through 12, assume that w is a function of the remaining variables. Find the partial derivatives as indicated by the method of Example 2.

8. $x^2 + y^2 + w^2 - 3xyw - 4 = 0$; $\dfrac{\partial w}{\partial y}$

9. $x^3 + 3x^2w - y^2w + 2yw^2 - 3w + 2x = 8$; $\dfrac{\partial w}{\partial x}$

10. $e^{xy} + e^{yw} - e^{xw} + xyw = 4$; $\dfrac{\partial w}{\partial y}$

11. $\sin(xyw) + x^2 + y^2 + w^2 = 3$; $\dfrac{\partial w}{\partial x}$

12. $(w^2 - y^2)(w^2 + x^2)(x^2 - y^2) = 1$; $\dfrac{\partial w}{\partial y}$

In problems 13 and 14, use the methods of this section to find the partial derivatives as indicated.

13. $x^2 + y^2 - z^2 - w^2 + 3xy - 2xz + 4xw - 3zw + 2x - 3y = 0$; $\dfrac{\partial w}{\partial y}$

14. $x^2y^2z^2w^2 + x^2z^2w^4 - y^4w^4 + x^6w^2 - 2y^3w^3 = 8$; $\dfrac{\partial w}{\partial z}$

If $F(x, y, z) = 0$ and $G(x, y, z) = 0$, then we may consider z and y as functions of the single variable x; that is, $z = z(x)$, $y = y(x)$. Using differentials, we obtain

$$F_x\,dx + F_y\,dy + F_z\,dz = 0, \qquad G_x\,dx + G_y\,dy + G_z\,dz = 0,$$

and so we can get the ordinary derivatives dz/dx and dy/dx. Use this method in problems 15 through 18 to obtain these derivatives.

15. $z = x^2 + y^2$, $y^2 = 4x + 2z$
16. $x^2 - y^2 + z^2 = 7$, $2x + 3y + 4z = 15$
17. $2x^2 + 3y^2 + 4z^2 = 12$, $x = yz$
18. $xyz = 5$, $x^2 + y^2 - z^2 = 16$

In each of problems 19 through 23, find $\partial u/\partial x$, $\partial u/\partial y$, $\partial v/\partial x$, and $\partial v/\partial y$ by the method of differentials.

19. $x = u^2 - v^2$, $y = 2uv$
20. $x = u + v$, $y = uv$
21. $u + v - x^2 = 0$, $u^2 - v^2 - y = 0$
22. $u^3 + xv^2 - xy = 0$, $u^2y + v^3 + x^2 - y^2 = 0$
23. $u^2 + v^2 + x^2 - y^2 = 4$, $u^2 - v^2 - x^2 - y^2 = 1$
24. Given that $F(x, y, z) = 0$, show that by considering each of the variables in turn as the dependent variable, the relation

$$\frac{\partial x}{\partial y} \cdot \frac{\partial y}{\partial z} \cdot \frac{\partial z}{\partial x} = -1$$

holds.

25. Given that $x = f(u, v)$, $y = g(u, v)$, find $\partial u/\partial x$, $\partial u/\partial y$, $\partial v/\partial x$, $\partial v/\partial y$ in terms of u and v and the derivatives of f and g.

26. Given that $F(u, v, x, y, z) = 0$ and $G(u, v, x, y, z) = 0$, assume that $u = u(x, y, z)$ and $v = v(x, y, z)$ and find formulas for $\partial u/\partial x$, $\partial v/\partial x$, $\ldots$, $\partial v/\partial z$ in terms of the derivatives of F and G.

9. SECOND AND HIGHER DERIVATIVES

If f is a function of two variables—say x and y—then $f_{,1}$ and $f_{,2}$ are also functions of the same two variables. When we differentiate $f_{,1}$ and $f_{,2}$, we obtain second partial derivatives. The *second partial derivatives of* $f_{,1}$ are defined by the formulas

$$f_{1,1}(x, y) = \lim_{h \to 0} \frac{f_{,1}(x + h, y) - f_{,1}(x, y)}{h},$$

$$f_{1,2}(x, y) = \lim_{k \to 0} \frac{f_{,1}(x, y + k) - f_{,1}(x, y)}{k}.$$

The derivatives of $f_{,2}$ are defined by similar expressions. We observe that, if f is a function of two variables, there are four second partial derivatives.

There is a multiplicity of notations for partial derivatives which at times may lead to confusion. For example, if we write $z = f(x, y)$, then the following five symbols all have the same meaning:

$$f_{,1,1}; \qquad \frac{\partial^2 z}{\partial x^2}; \qquad \frac{\partial^2 f}{\partial x^2}; \qquad f_{xx}; \qquad z_{xx}.$$

For other partial derivatives we have the variety of expressions:

$$f_{,1,2} = f_{xy} = \frac{\partial}{\partial y}\left(\frac{\partial z}{\partial x}\right) = \frac{\partial^2 z}{\partial y\, \partial x} = \frac{\partial^2 f}{\partial y\, \partial x} = z_{xy},$$

$$f_{,2,1} = f_{yx} = \frac{\partial}{\partial x}\left(\frac{\partial z}{\partial y}\right) = \frac{\partial^2 z}{\partial x\, \partial y} = \frac{\partial^2 f}{\partial x\, \partial y} = z_{yx},$$

$$f_{,1,2,1} = \frac{\partial}{\partial x}\left(\frac{\partial^2 z}{\partial y\, \partial x}\right) = \frac{\partial^3 z}{\partial x\, \partial y\, \partial x} = \frac{\partial^3 f}{\partial x\, \partial y\, \partial x} = f_{xyx} = z_{xyx},$$

and so forth. Note that, in the subscript notation, symbols such as f_{xyy} or z_{xyy} mean that the order of partial differentiation is taken from left to right—that is, first with respect to x and then twice with respect to y. On the other hand, the symbol

$$\frac{\partial^3 z}{\partial x\, \partial y\, \partial y}$$

asserts that we first take two derivatives with respect to y and then one with respect to x. The denominator symbol and the subscript symbol are the reverse of each other.

EXAMPLE 1. Given $z = x^3 + 3x^2y - 2x^2y^2 - y^4 + 3xy$, find

$$\frac{\partial z}{\partial x}, \quad \frac{\partial z}{\partial y}, \quad \frac{\partial^2 z}{\partial x^2}, \quad \frac{\partial^2 z}{\partial x\, \partial y}, \quad \frac{\partial^2 z}{\partial y\, \partial x}, \quad \frac{\partial^2 z}{\partial y^2}.$$

Solution. We have

$$\frac{\partial z}{\partial x} = 3x^2 + 6xy - 4xy^2 + 3y; \qquad \frac{\partial z}{\partial y} = 3x^2 - 4x^2y - 4y^3 + 3x;$$

$$\frac{\partial^2 z}{\partial x^2} = 6x + 6y - 4y^2; \qquad \frac{\partial^2 z}{\partial y^2} = -4x^2 - 12y^2;$$

$$\frac{\partial^2 z}{\partial y\, \partial x} = 6x - 8xy + 3; \qquad \frac{\partial^2 z}{\partial x\, \partial y} = 6x - 8xy + 3.$$

In the example above, it is not accidental that $\partial^2 z/\partial y\, \partial x = \partial^2 z/\partial x\, \partial y$, as the next theorem shows.

Theorem 7. *Assume that $f(x, y)$, $f_{,1}$, $f_{,2}$, $f_{,1,2}$, and $f_{,2,1}$ are all continuous at (x_0, y_0). Then*

$$f_{,1,2}(x_0, y_0) = f_{,2,1}(x_0, y_0).$$

In traditional notation, the formula reads

$$f_{xy}(x_0, y_0) = f_{yx}(x_0, y_0).$$

(*The order of partial differentiation may be reversed without affecting the result.*)

Proof. The result is obtained by use of a quantity we call the *double difference*, denoted by $\Delta_2 f$, and defined by the formula

$$\Delta_2 f = [f(x_0 + h, y_0 + h) - f(x_0 + h, y_0)] - [f(x_0, y_0 + h) - f(x_0, y_0)]. \quad (1)$$

We shall show that, as h tends to zero, the quantity $\Delta_2 f/h^2$ tends to $f_{xy}(x_0, y_0)$. On the other hand, we shall also show that the same quantity tends to $f_{yx}(x_0, y_0)$. The principal tool is the repeated application of the Theorem of the Mean. (See page 598.) We may write $\Delta_2 f$ in a more transparent way by defining

$$\phi(s) = f(x_0 + s, y_0 + h) - f(x_0 + s, y_0), \quad (2)$$
$$\chi(t) = f(x_0 + h, y_0 + t) - f(x_0, y_0 + t). \quad (3)$$

(The quantities x_0, y_0, h are considered fixed in the definition of ϕ and χ.) Then straight substitution in (1) shows that

$$\Delta_2 f = \phi(h) - \phi(0) \quad (4)$$

and

$$\Delta_2 f = \chi(h) - \chi(0). \quad (5)$$

We apply the Theorem of the Mean in (4) and (5), getting two expressions for $\Delta_2 f$. They are

$$\Delta_2 f = \phi'(s_1) \cdot h \qquad \text{with} \quad 0 < s_1 < h,$$
$$\Delta_2 f = \chi'(t_1) \cdot h \qquad \text{with} \quad 0 < t_1 < h.$$

The derivatives $\phi'(s_1)$ and $\chi'(t_1)$ are easily computed from (2) and (3). We obtain

$$\phi'(s_1) = f_{,1}(x_0 + s_1, y_0 + h) - f_{,1}(x_0 + s_1, y_0),$$
$$\chi'(t_1) = f_{,2}(x_0 + h, y_0 + t_1) - f_{,2}(x_0, y_0 + t_1),$$

and the two expressions for $\Delta_2 f$ yield

$$\frac{1}{h} \Delta_2 f = [f_{,1}(x_0 + s_1, y_0 + h) - f_{,1}(x_0 + s_1, y_0)], \tag{6}$$

$$\frac{1}{h} \Delta_2 f = [f_{,2}(x_0 + h, y_0 + t_1) - f_{,2}(x_0, y_0 + t_1)]. \tag{7}$$

In (6) the Theorem of the Mean may be applied to the expression on the right with respect to $y_0 + h$ and y_0. We get

$$\frac{1}{h} \Delta_2 f = f_{,1,2}(x_0 + s_1, y_0 + t_2)h \qquad \text{with} \qquad 0 < t_2 < h. \tag{8}$$

Similarly, the Theorem of the Mean may be applied in (7) to the expression on the right with respect to $x_0 + h$ and x_0. The result is

$$\frac{1}{h} \Delta_2 f = f_{,2,1}(x_0 + s_2, y_0 + t_1)h \qquad \text{with} \qquad 0 < s_2 < h. \tag{9}$$

Dividing by h in (8) and (9), we find that

$$\frac{1}{h^2} \Delta_2 f = f_{,1,2}(x_0 + s_1, y_0 + t_2) = f_{,2,1}(x_0 + s_2, y_0 + t_1).$$

Letting h tend to zero and noticing that s_1, s_2, t_1, and t_2 all tend to zero with h, we obtain the result.

Corollary 1. *If f is a function of any number of variables and s and t are any two of them, then*

$$f_{st} = f_{ts}.$$

For example, if the function is $f(x, y, s, t, u, v)$, then

$$f_{xt} = f_{tx}, \qquad f_{yu} = f_{uy}, \qquad f_{yv} = f_{vy}, \qquad \text{etc.}$$

The proof of the corollary is identical with the proof of the theorem.

Corollary 2. *For derivatives of the third, fourth, or any order, it does not matter in what order the differentiations with respect to the various variables are performed. For instance,*

$$\frac{\partial^4 z}{\partial x\, \partial x\, \partial y\, \partial y} = \frac{\partial^4 z}{\partial x\, \partial y\, \partial x\, \partial y} = \frac{\partial^4 z}{\partial x\, \partial y\, \partial y\, \partial x}$$

$$= \frac{\partial^4 z}{\partial y\, \partial x\, \partial x\, \partial y} = \frac{\partial^4 z}{\partial y\, \partial x\, \partial y\, \partial x} = \frac{\partial^4 z}{\partial y\, \partial y\, \partial x\, \partial x}.$$

Remarks. (i) It is true that there are functions for which f_{xy} is not equal to f_{yx}. Of course, the hypotheses of Theorem 7 are violated for such functions. (ii) All the functions we have considered thus far and all the functions we shall consider from now on will always satisfy the hypotheses of Theorem 7. Therefore the order of differentiation will be reversible throughout.

EXAMPLE 2.　Given $u = e^x \cos y + e^y \sin z$, find all first partial derivatives and verify that

$$\frac{\partial^2 u}{\partial x\, \partial y} = \frac{\partial^2 u}{\partial y\, \partial x}, \qquad \frac{\partial^2 u}{\partial x\, \partial z} = \frac{\partial^2 u}{\partial z\, \partial x}, \qquad \frac{\partial^2 u}{\partial y\, \partial z} = \frac{\partial^2 u}{\partial z\, \partial y}.$$

Solution.　We have

$$\frac{\partial u}{\partial x} = e^x \cos y; \qquad \frac{\partial u}{\partial y} = -e^x \sin y + e^y \sin z; \qquad \frac{\partial u}{\partial z} = e^y \cos z.$$

Therefore

$$\frac{\partial^2 u}{\partial y\, \partial x} = -e^x \sin y = \frac{\partial^2 u}{\partial x\, \partial y},$$

$$\frac{\partial^2 u}{\partial z\, \partial x} = 0 \qquad = \frac{\partial^2 u}{\partial x\, \partial z},$$

$$\frac{\partial^2 u}{\partial z\, \partial y} = e^y \cos z \qquad = \frac{\partial^2 u}{\partial y\, \partial z}.$$

EXAMPLE 3.　Suppose that $u = F(x, y, z)$ and $z = f(x, y)$. Obtain a formula for $\partial^2 u/\partial x^2$ in terms of the derivatives of F (that is, F_x, F_y, F_z, F_{xx}, etc.) and the derivatives of f (or, equivalently, z). That is, in the expression for F we consider x, y, z *intermediate variables*, while in the expression for f we consider x and y *independent variables*.

Solution.　We apply the Chain Rule to F to obtain $\partial u/\partial x$ with x and y as independent variables.　We get

$$\frac{\partial u}{\partial x} = F_x \frac{\partial x}{\partial x} + F_y \frac{\partial y}{\partial x} + F_z \frac{\partial z}{\partial x}.$$

Since x and y are independent, $\partial y/\partial x = 0$; also, $\partial x/\partial x = 1$. Therefore

$$\frac{\partial u}{\partial x} = F_x + F_z \frac{\partial z}{\partial x}.$$

In order to differentiate a second time, we must recognize that F_x and F_z are again functions of the three intermediate variables. We find that

$$\frac{\partial^2 u}{\partial x^2} = F_{xx} \frac{\partial x}{\partial x} + F_{xy} \frac{\partial y}{\partial x} + F_{xz} \frac{\partial z}{\partial x} + \frac{\partial z}{\partial x} \left(F_{zx} \frac{\partial x}{\partial x} + F_{zy} \frac{\partial y}{\partial x} + F_{zz} \frac{\partial z}{\partial x} \right) + F_z \frac{\partial^2 z}{\partial x^2}.$$

The result is

$$\frac{\partial^2 u}{\partial x^2} = F_{xx} + 2F_{xz} \frac{\partial z}{\partial x} + F_{zz} \left(\frac{\partial z}{\partial x} \right)^2 + F_z \frac{\partial^2 z}{\partial x^2}.$$

EXERCISES

In each of problems 1 through 8, verify that $f_{,1,2} = f_{,2,1}$.

1. $f(x, y) = x^2 - 2xy - 3y^2$
2. $f(x, y) = 3x^2 + 4xy + 2y^2 - 3x + 7y - 6$
3. $f(x, y) = x^3 - x^2y + 2xy^2$
4. $f(x, y) = x^4 + 4x^3y - 3x^2y^2 + 6xy^3 + 9y^4$
5. $f(r, s) = e^{rs} \sin r \cos s$
6. $f(u, v) = e^{2u} \cos v + e^{3v} \sin u$
7. $f(s, t) = \arctan (t/s)$
8. $f(x, z) = \ln \dfrac{1 + x}{1 + z} - e^{xz}$

In each of problems 9 through 13, verify that $u_{xy} = u_{yx}$ and $u_{xz} = u_{zx}$.

9. $u = \ln \sqrt{x^2 + y^2 + z^2}$ 10. $u = \ln (x + \sqrt{y^2 + z^2})$
11. $u = x^3 + y^3 + z^3 - 3xyz$
12. $u = e^{xy} + e^{2xz} - e^{3yz}$
13. $u = e^{xy}/\sqrt{x^2 + z^2}$
14. Given that $u = 1/\sqrt{x^2 + y^2 + z^2}$, verify that

$$\frac{\partial^2 u}{\partial x^2} + \frac{\partial^2 u}{\partial y^2} + \frac{\partial^2 u}{\partial z^2} = 0.$$

15. Given that $u = xe^x \cos y$, verify that

$$\frac{\partial^4 u}{\partial x^4} + 2 \frac{\partial^4 u}{\partial x^2 \partial y^2} + \frac{\partial^4 u}{\partial y^4} = 0.$$

In each of problems 16 through 19, r and s are independent variables. Find $\partial^2 z/\partial r^2$ by (a) the Chain Rule and by (b) finding z in terms of r and s first.

16. $z = x^2 - xy - y^2$, $x = r + s$, $y = s - r$
17. $z = x^2 - y^2$, $x = r \cos s$, $y = r \sin s$
18. $z = x^3 - y^3$, $x = 2r - s$, $y = s + 2r$
19. $z = x^2 - 2xy - y^2$, $x = r^2 - s^2$, $y = 2rs$

20. Given that $u = F(x, y, z)$ and $z = f(x, y)$, find $\partial^2 u/\partial y\, \partial x$ with all variables as in Example 3.

21. Given that $u = F(x, y, z)$ and $z = f(x, y)$, find $\partial^2 u/\partial y^2$ with all variables as in Example 3.

22. If $u = F(x, y)$, $y = f(x)$, find $d^2 u/dx^2$.

23. Given that $u = f(x + 2y) + g(x - 2y)$, show that

$$u_{xx} - \tfrac{1}{4} u_{yy} = 0.$$

24. Given that $u = F(x, y)$, $x = r \cos \theta$, $y = r \sin \theta$, find $\partial^2 u/\partial r^2$, r and θ being independent variables.

25. Given $u = F(x, y)$, $x = f(r, s)$, $y = g(r, s)$, find $\partial^2 u/\partial r\, \partial s$, r and s being independent variables.

26. If $F(x, y) = 0$, find $d^2 y/dx^2$ in terms of partial derivatives of F.

27. Given that $u = F(x, y)$, $x = e^s \cos t$, $y = e^s \sin t$, use the Chain Rule to show that

$$\frac{\partial^2 u}{\partial s^2} + \frac{\partial^2 u}{\partial t^2} = e^{2s} \left(\frac{\partial^2 u}{\partial x^2} + \frac{\partial^2 u}{\partial y^2} \right),$$

where s and t are independent variables and x and y are intermediate variables.

28. Given $V = F(x, y)$, $x = \tfrac{1}{2} r(e^s + e^{-s})$, $y = \tfrac{1}{2} r(e^s - e^{-s})$, show that

$$V_{xx} - V_{yy} = V_{rr} + \frac{1}{r} V_r + \frac{1}{r^2} V_{ss}.$$

*29. If $u = f(x - ut)$, show that $u_t + u u_x = 0$.

10. TAYLOR'S THEOREM WITH REMAINDER

Taylor's theorem for functions of one variable was established in Chapter 19 on page 632.   There we found that if $F(x)$ has $n + 1$ derivatives in an interval containing a value x_0, then we can obtain the expansion

$$F(x) = F(x_0) + F'(x_0)(x - x_0) + \cdots + \frac{F^{(n)}(x_0)(x - x_0)^n}{n!} + R_n, \quad (1)$$

where the remainder R_n is given by the formula

$$R_n = \frac{F^{(n+1)}(\xi)(x - x_0)^{n+1}}{(n + 1)!},$$

with ξ some number between x_0 and x.

Taylor's theorem in several variables is a generalization of the expansion (1). We carry out the procedure for a function of two variables $f(x, y)$, the process for functions of more variables being completely analogous. Consider the function

$$\phi(t) = f(x + \lambda t, y + \mu$$

in which the quantities x, y, λ, and μ are temporarily kept constant. Then ϕ is a function of the single variable t, and we may compute its derivative. Using the Chain Rule, we obtain

$$\phi'(t) = f_{,1}(x + \lambda t, y + \mu t)\lambda + f_{,2}(x + \lambda t, y + \mu t)\mu.$$

It is convenient to use the more suggestive notation

$$\phi'(t) = f_x(x + \lambda t, y + \mu t)\lambda + f_y(x + \lambda t, y + \mu t)\mu.$$

In fact, we will simplify matters further by omitting the arguments in f. We write

$$\phi'(t) = f_x\lambda + f_y\mu.$$

It is important to compute second, third, fourth, etc., derivatives of ϕ. We do so by applying the Chain Rule repeatedly. The result is

$$\phi''(t) = \lambda^2 f_{xx} + 2\lambda\mu f_{xy} + \mu^2 f_{yy},$$
$$\phi^{(3)}(t) = \lambda^3 f_{xxx} + 3\lambda^2\mu f_{xxy} + 3\lambda\mu^2 f_{xyy} + \mu^3 f_{yyy},$$
$$\phi^{(4)}(t) = \lambda^4 f_{xxxx} + 4\lambda^3\mu f_{xxxy} + 6\lambda^2\mu^2 f_{xxyy} + 4\lambda\mu^3 f_{xyyy} + \mu^4 f_{yyyy}.$$

Examining the pattern in each of the above derivatives, we see that the coefficients in ϕ'' are formed by the *symbolic* expression

$$\left(\lambda \frac{\partial}{\partial x} + \mu \frac{\partial}{\partial y}\right)^2 f,$$

provided that the exponent applied to a partial derivative is interpreted as repeated differentiation instead of multiplication. Using this new symbolism we can easily write any derivative of ϕ. The kth derivative is

$$\phi^{(k)}(t) = \left(\lambda \frac{\partial}{\partial x} + \mu \frac{\partial}{\partial y}\right)^k f. \tag{2}$$

For instance, with $k = 7$ we obtain

$$\phi^{(7)}(t) = \lambda^7 f_{xxxxxxx} + 7\lambda^6\mu f_{xxxxxxy} + \frac{7 \cdot 6}{1 \cdot 2}\lambda^5\mu^2 f_{xxxxxyy} + \cdots + \mu^7 f_{yyyyyyy}.$$

Of course all derivatives are evaluated at $(x + \lambda t, y + \mu t)$. The validity of (2) may be established by induction. (See Morrey, *University Calculus*, pp. 574 and 695.)

Before stating Taylor's theorem for functions of two variables, we must introduce still more symbols. The quantity

$$\sum_{1 \leq r+s \leq p} (\quad)$$

means that the sum of the terms in parentheses is taken over all possible combinations of r and s which add up to a number between 1 and p. Neither r nor s is allowed to be negative. For example, if $p = 3$ the combinations are

$$(r = 0, s = 1), \qquad (r = 0, s = 2), \qquad (r = 0, s = 3)$$
$$(r = 1, s = 0), \qquad (r = 1, s = 1), \qquad (r = 1, s = 2)$$
$$(r = 2, s = 0), \qquad (r = 2, s = 1)$$
$$(r = 3, s = 0).$$

The symbol

$$\sum_{r+s=p} (\quad)$$

means that the sum is taken over all possible nonnegative combinations of r and s which add up to p exactly. For instance, if $p = 3$, then the combinations are

$$(r = 0, s = 3), \qquad (r = 1, s = 2), \qquad (r = 2, s = 1), \qquad (r = 3, s = 0).$$

Theorem 8. (Taylor's Theorem.) *Suppose that f is a function of two variables and that f and all of its partial derivatives of order up to $p + 1$ are continuous in a neighborhood of the point (a, b). Then we have the expansion*

$$f(x, y) = f(a, b) + \sum_{1 \leq r+s \leq p} \frac{\partial^{r+s} f(a, b)}{\partial x^r \, \partial y^s} \frac{(x - a)^r}{r!} \cdot \frac{(y - b)^s}{s!} + R_p, \qquad (3)$$

where the remainder R_p is given by the formula

$$R_p = \sum_{r+s=p+1} \frac{\partial^{r+s} f(\xi, \eta)}{\partial x^r \, \partial y^s} \frac{(x - a)^r}{r!} \frac{(y - b)^s}{s!},$$

with the value (ξ, η) situated on the line segment join-ing the points (a, b) to (x, y). (See Fig. 20–11.)

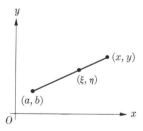

Proof. We let $d = \sqrt{(x - a)^2 + (y - b)^2}$ and define

$$\lambda = \frac{x - a}{d}, \qquad \mu = \frac{y - b}{d}.$$

The function

$$\phi(t) = f(a + \lambda t, b + \mu t), \qquad 0 \leq t \leq d$$

FIGURE 20–11

may be differentiated according to the rules described at the beginning of the sec-tion. Taylor's theorem for $\phi(t)$ (a function of *one* variable) taken about $t = 0$ and evaluated at d yields

$$\phi(d) = \phi(0) + \phi'(0)d + \phi''(0)\frac{d^2}{2!} + \cdots$$

$$+ \frac{\phi^{(p)}(0) \, d^p}{p!} + \frac{\phi^{(p+1)}(\tau) \, d^{p+1}}{(p + 1)!}.$$

$$(4)$$

The kth derivative of ϕ evaluated at 0 is given by

$$\phi^k(0) = \left(\lambda \frac{\partial}{\partial x} + \mu \frac{\partial}{\partial y}\right)^k f(a, b).$$

We now recall the binomial formula:

$$(A + B)^k = A^k + \frac{k}{1} A^{k-1}B + \frac{k(k-1)}{1 \cdot 2} A^{k-2}B^2 + \cdots + B^k$$

$$= \sum_{q=0}^{k} \frac{k!}{q!(k-q)!} A^{k-q} B^q.$$

Applying the binomial formula to the symbolic expression for $\phi^{(k)}(0)$, we obtain

$$\phi^{(k)}(0) = \sum_{q=0}^{k} \frac{k!}{q!(k-q)!} \frac{\partial^k f(a, b)}{\partial x^{k-q} \partial y^q} \lambda^{k-q} \mu^q. \tag{5}$$

Noting that $\phi(d) = f(a + \lambda d, b + \mu d) = f(x, y)$ and that $\phi(0) = f(a, b)$, we find, upon substitution of (5) into (4):

$$f(x, y) = f(a, b) + \frac{\partial f(a, b)}{\partial x} (x - a) + \frac{\partial f(a, b)}{\partial y} (y - b)$$

$$+ \frac{\partial^2 f(a, b)}{\partial x^2} \frac{(x - a)^2}{2!} + \frac{\partial^2 f(a, b)}{\partial x \, \partial y} (x - a)(y - b)$$

$$+ \frac{\partial^2 f(a, b)}{\partial y^2} \frac{(y - b)^2}{2!} + \cdots,$$

which is precisely the formula in the statement of the theorem. The remainder term shows that if $0 < \tau < d$, then

$$\xi = a + \frac{(x - a)}{d} \tau,$$

$$\eta = b + \frac{(y - b)}{d} \tau,$$

which places (ξ, η) on the line segment joining (a, b) and (x, y).

  Remarks. (i) Taylor's formula [as (3) is usually called] is also often written in the form

$$f(x, y) = f(a, b)$$
$$+ \sum_{q=1}^{p} \frac{1}{q!} \left[\sum_{r=0}^{q} \frac{q!}{(q-r)!r!} \frac{\partial^q f(a, b)}{\partial x^{q-r} \partial y^r} (x - a)^{q-r}(y - b)^r \right] + R_p.$$

(ii) For some functions f, if we let p tend to infinity we may find that $R_p \to 0$. We thereby obtain a representation of f as an infinite series in x and y. Such a series is called a *double series*, and we say that f is *expanded about the point* (a, b).

For functions of three variables we obtain a triple sum, the Taylor formula in this case being

$$f(x, y, z) = f(a, b, c)$$

$$+ \sum_{1 \le r+s+t \le p} \frac{\partial^{r+s+t} f(a, b, c)}{\partial x^r \, \partial y^s \, \partial z^t} \frac{(x-a)^r}{r!} \frac{(y-b)^s}{s!} \frac{(z-c)^t}{t!} + R_p,$$

with

$$R_p = \sum_{r+s+t=p+1} \frac{\partial^{p+1} f(\xi, \eta, \zeta)}{\partial x^r \, \partial y^s \, \partial z^t} \frac{(x-a)^r}{r!} \frac{(y-b)^s}{s!} \frac{(z-x)^t}{t!},$$

where (ξ, η, ζ) is on the line segment joining (a, b, c) and (x, y, z).

EXAMPLE 1. Expand $x^2 y$ about the point $(1, -2)$ out to and including the terms of the second degree. Find R_2.

Solution. Setting $f(x, y) = x^2 y$, we obtain

$$f_x = 2xy, \qquad f_y = x^2, \qquad f_{xx} = 2y, \qquad f_{xy} = 2x, \qquad f_{yy} = 0,$$
$$f_{xxx} = 0, \qquad f_{xxy} = 2, \qquad f_{xyy} = f_{yyy} = 0.$$

Noting that $f(1, -2) = -2$, we find

$$x^2 y = -2 - 4(x-1) + (y+2) + \frac{1}{2!}[-4(x-1)^2 + 4(x-1)(y+2)] + R_2,$$

with

$$R_2 = \frac{1}{3!} 3 \cdot 2(x-1)^2(y+2) = (x-1)^2(y+2).$$

EXAMPLE 2.   Given $f(x, y, z) = e^x \cos y + e^y \cos z + e^z \cos x$.   Define

$$\phi(t) = f(x + \lambda t, y + \mu t, z + \nu t).$$

Find $\phi'(0)$ and $\phi''(0)$ in terms of $x, y, z, \lambda, \mu, \nu$.

Solution. We have

$$\phi'(0) = f_{,1}(x, y, z)\lambda + f_{,2}(x, y, z)\mu + f_{,3}(x, y, z)\nu.$$

Computing the derivatives, we obtain

$$\phi'(0) = (e^x \cos y - e^z \sin x)\lambda + (e^y \cos z - e^x \sin y)\mu + (e^z \cos x - e^y \sin z)\nu.$$

The formula for $\phi''(0)$ is

$$\phi''(0) = \left(\lambda \frac{\partial}{\partial x} + \mu \frac{\partial}{\partial y} + \nu \frac{\partial}{\partial z}\right)^2 f$$
$$= \lambda^2(e^x \cos y - e^z \cos x) + \mu^2(e^y \cos z - e^x \cos y)$$
$$+ \nu^2(e^z \cos x - e^y \cos z) + 2\lambda\mu(-e^x \sin y)$$
$$+ 2\lambda\nu(-e^z \sin x) + 2\mu\nu(-e^y \sin z).$$

EXERCISES

1. Expand $x^3 + xy^2$ about the point $(2, 1)$.

2. Expand $x^4 + x^2y^2 - y^4$ about the point $(1, 1)$ out to terms of the second degree. Find the form of R_2.

3. Find the expansion of $\sin(x + y)$ about $(0, 0)$ out to and including the terms of the third degree in (x, y). Compare the result with that which you get by writing $\sin u \approx u - \frac{1}{6}u^3$ and setting $u = x + y$.

4. Find the expansion of $\cos(x + y)$ about $(0, 0)$ out to and including terms of the fourth degree in (x, y). Compare the result with that which you get by writing $\cos u = 1 - \frac{1}{2}u^2 + \frac{1}{24}u^4$ and setting $u = x + y$.

5. Find the expansion of e^{x+y} about $(0, 0)$ out to and including the terms of the third degree in (x, y). Compare the result with that which you get by setting $e^u \approx 1 + u + \frac{1}{2}u^2 + \frac{1}{6}u^3$, and then setting $u = x + y$. Next compare the result with that obtained by multiplying the series for e^x by that for e^y and keeping terms up to and including the third degree.

6. Find the expansion of $\sin x \sin y$ about $(0, 0)$ out to and including the terms of the fourth degree in (x, y). Compare the result with that which you get by multiplying the series for $\sin x$ and $\sin y$.

7. Do the same as problem 6 for $\cos x \cos y$.

8. Expand $e^x \arctan y$ about $(1, 1)$ out to and including the terms of the second degree in $(x - 1)$ and $(y - 1)$.

9. Expand $x^2 + 2xy + yz + z^2$ about $(1, 1, 0)$.

10. Expand $x^3 + x^2y - yz^2 + z^3$ about $(1, 0, 1)$ out to and including the terms of the second degree in $(x - 1)$, y, and $(z - 1)$.

11. If $f(x, y) = x^2 + 4xy + y^2 - 6x$ and $\phi(t) = f(x + \lambda t, y + \mu t)$, find $\phi''(0)$ when $x = -1$ and $y = 2$. Is $\phi''(0) > 0$ when $(x, y) = (-1, 2)$ if λ and μ are related so that $\lambda^2 + \mu^2 = 1$?

12. If $f(x, y) = x^3 + 3xy^2 - 3x^2 - 3y^2 + 4$ and $\phi(t) = f(x + \lambda t, y + \mu t)$, find $\phi''(0)$ for $(x, y) = (2, 0)$. Show that $\phi''(0) > 0$ for all λ and μ such that $\lambda^2 + \mu^2 = 1$.

*13. (a) Write the appropriate expansion formula using binomial coefficients for

$$(A + B + C)^k,$$

with k a positive integer. (b) If $f(x, y, z)$ and $\phi(t) = f(x + \lambda t, y + \mu t, z + \nu t)$ are sufficiently differentiable, show the relationship between the symbolic expression

$$\left(\lambda \frac{\partial}{\partial x} + \mu \frac{\partial}{\partial y} + \nu \frac{\partial}{\partial z} \right)^k f(x + \lambda t, y + \mu t, z + \nu t) \qquad \text{and} \qquad \phi^{(k)}(t).$$

14. Write Taylor's formula for a function $f(x, y, u, v)$ of four variables expanded about the point a, b, c, d. How many second derivative terms are there? Third derivative terms?

11. MAXIMA AND MINIMA

One of the principal applications of differentiation of functions of one variable occurs in the study of maxima and minima. In Chapter 7 we derived various tests using first and second derivatives which enable us to determine relative maxima and minima of functions of a single variable. These tests are useful for graphing functions, for solving problems involving related rates, and for attacking a variety of geometrical and physical problems. (See Chapter 7, Sections 3, 4, 6, and 7.)

The study of maxima and minima for functions of two, three, or more variables has its basis in the following theorem, which is stated without proof.

Theorem 9. *Let R be a region in the xy-plane with the boundary curve of R considered as part of R also (Fig. 20–12). If f is a function of two variables defined and continuous in R, then there is (at least) one point in R where f takes on a maximum value and there is (at least) one point in R where f takes on a minimum value.*

FIGURE 20–12

Remarks. (i) Theorem 9 is a straightforward generalization of Theorem 1 given on page 147 (Extreme Value Theorem). (ii) Analogous theorems may be stated for functions of three, four, or more variables. (iii) The maximum and minimum may occur on the boundary of R. Thus, as in the case of one variable where the interval must be *closed*, the region R *must contain its boundary* in order to ensure the validity of the result.

DEFINITION. A function $f(x, y)$ is said to have a *relative maximum* at (x_0, y_0) if there is some region containing (x_0, y_0) *in its interior* such that

$$f(x, y) \leq f(x_0, y_0)$$

for all (x, y) in this region. More precisely, there must be some positive number δ (which may be "small") such that the above inequality holds for all (x, y) in the square

$$|x - x_0| < \delta, \qquad |y - y_0| < \delta.$$

A similar definition holds for *relative minimum* when the inequality $f(x, y) \geq f(x_0, y_0)$ is satisfied in a square about (x_0, y_0). The above definitions are easily extended to functions of three, four, or more variables.

Theorem 10. *Suppose that $f(x, y)$ is defined in a region R containing (x_0, y_0) in its interior. Suppose that $f_{,1}(x_0, y_0)$ and $f_{,2}(x_0, y_0)$ are defined and that*

$$f(x, y) \leq f(x_0, y_0)$$

for all (x, y) in R; that is, $f(x_0, y_0)$ is a relative maximum. Then

$$f_{,1}(x_0, y_0) = f_{,2}(x_0, y_0) = 0.$$

Proof. We show that $f_{,1}(x_0, y_0) = 0$, the proof for $f_{,2}$ being analogous. By definition,

$$f_{,1}(x_0, y_0) = \lim_{h \to 0} \frac{f(x_0 + h, y_0) - f(x_0, y_0)}{h}.$$

By hypothesis,

$$f(x_0 + h, y_0) - f(x_0, y_0) \leq 0$$

for all h sufficiently small so that $(x_0 + h, y_0)$ is in R. If h is positive, then

$$\frac{f(x_0 + h, y_0) - f(x_0, y_0)}{h} \leq 0,$$

and as $h \to 0$ we conclude that $f_{,1}$ must be nonpositive. On the other hand, if $h < 0$, then

$$\frac{f(x_0 + h, y_0) - f(x_0, y_0)}{h} \geq 0,$$

since division of both sides of an inequality by a negative number reverses its direction. Letting $h \to 0$, we conclude that $f_{,1}$ is nonnegative. A quantity which is both nonnegative and nonpositive vanishes.

Corollary. *The same result holds at a relative minimum.*

DEFINITION. A value (x_0, y_0) at which both $f_{,1}$ and $f_{,2}$ vanish is called a *critical point of f*.

Discussion. The conditions that $f_{,1}$ and $f_{,2}$ vanish at a point are *necessary* conditions for a relative maximum or a relative minimum. It is easy to find a function for which $f_{,1}$ and $f_{,2}$ vanish at a point, with the function having neither a relative maximum nor a relative minimum at that point. A critical point at which f is neither a maximum nor a minimum may be a "*saddle point.*" A simple example of a function which has such a point is given by

$$f(x, y) = x^2 - y^2.$$

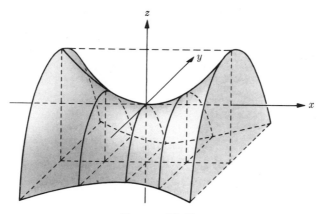

FIGURE 20–13

We see that $f_{,1} = 2x$, $f_{,2} = 2y$, and $(0, 0)$ is a critical point. However, as Fig. 20–13 shows, the function is "saddle-shaped" in a neighborhood of $(0, 0)$.

While we shall develop a test which, under certain conditions, guarantees that a function has a maximum or minimum at a critical point, it is sometimes possible to make this decision from the nature of the problem itself. We exhibit such an example.

EXAMPLE 1. In three-dimensional space find the point on the plane

$$S: 2x + 3y - z = 1$$

which is closest to the origin.

Solution. The function $d = \sqrt{x^2 + y^2 + z^2}$ represents a distance function which has a specific value at each point on the plane S. The minimum of the function

$$f = x^2 + y^2 + z^2$$

occurs at the same point as the minimum of d, and f is simpler to handle. We substitute for z from the equation of the plane, and so we must minimize

$$f(x, y) = x^2 + y^2 + (1 - 2x - 3y)^2$$
$$= 5x^2 + 10y^2 + 12xy - 4x - 6y + 1.$$

A critical point must be a solution of the equations

$$f_{,1} = 10x + 12y - 4 = 0, \qquad f_{,2} = 20y + 12x - 6 = 0.$$

Solving these equations simultaneously, we find

$$x = \tfrac{1}{7}, \qquad y = \tfrac{3}{14}.$$

From the geometric character of the problem we know that $(\tfrac{1}{7}, \tfrac{3}{14})$ corresponds to a minimum. The point on S corresponding to $x = \tfrac{1}{7}$, $y = \tfrac{3}{14}$ is found by substitution in the equation for S. The answer is $(\tfrac{1}{7}, \tfrac{3}{14}, -\tfrac{1}{14})$.

The basic criterion for finding maxima and minima for functions of two variables is the so-called Second Derivative Test, which we now establish.

Theorem 11. (Second Derivative Test.) *Suppose that f and its partial derivatives up to and including the third order are continuous near the point (a, b), and suppose that*

$$f_x(a, b) = f_y(a, b) = 0;$$

that is, (a, b) is a critical point. Then we have

(i) *a local minimum if*

$$f_{xx}(a, b)f_{yy}(a, b) - f_{xy}^2(a, b) > 0 \qquad \text{and} \qquad f_{xx}(a, b) > 0;$$

(ii) *a local maximum if*

$$f_{xx}(a, b)f_{yy}(a, b) - f_{xy}^2(a, b) > 0 \qquad \text{and} \qquad f_{xx}(a, b) < 0;$$

(iii) *a saddle point if*

$$f_{xx}(a, b)f_{yy}(a, b) - f_{xy}^2(a, b) < 0;$$

(iv) *no information if*

$$f_{xx}(a, b)f_{yy}(a, b) - f_{xy}^2(a, b) = 0.$$

Proof. For convenience, we define

$$A = f_{xx}(a, b), \qquad B = f_{xy}(a, b), \qquad C = f_{yy}(a, b).$$

From the Taylor expansion of $f(x, y)$ about the point (a, b), we find

$$f(x, y) = f(a, b) + \tfrac{1}{2}[A(x - a)^2 + 2B(x - a)(y - b) + C(y - b)^2] + R_2. \tag{1}$$

The first derivative terms are absent because (a, b) is a critical point. The term R_2 is given by

$$R_2 = \frac{1}{6}\left[\frac{\partial^3 f(\xi, \eta)}{\partial x^3}(x - a)^3 + 3\frac{\partial^3 f}{\partial x^2 \, dy}(x - a)^2(y - b) \right.$$

$$+ 3\frac{\partial^3 f(\xi, \eta)}{\partial x \, dy^2}(x - a)(y - b)^2$$

$$\left. + \frac{\partial^3 f(\xi, \eta)}{\partial y^3}(y - b)^3 \right].$$

We define $r = \sqrt{(x - a)^2 + (y - b)^2}$ and the quantities λ, μ by the relations

$$\lambda = \frac{x - a}{r}, \qquad \mu = \frac{y - b}{r}.$$

Note that for any x, y, a, b the relation $\lambda^2 + \mu^2 = 1$ prevails. The Taylor expansion (1) now becomes

$$f(x, y) - f(a, b) = \tfrac{1}{2}r^2(A\lambda^2 + 2B\lambda\mu + C\mu^2 + r\rho), \qquad (2)$$

where

$$\rho = \frac{1}{3}\left(\frac{\partial^3 f}{\partial x^3}\lambda^3 + 3\frac{\partial^3 f}{\partial x^2\,\partial y}\lambda^2\mu + 3\frac{\partial^2 f}{\partial x\,\partial y^2}\lambda\mu^2 + \frac{\partial^3 f}{\partial y^3}\mu^3\right)_{\substack{x=\xi \\ y=\eta}}.$$

The quantity ρ is bounded since, by hypothesis, f has continuous third derivatives. The behavior of $f(x, y) - f(a, b)$ is determined completely by the size of $r\rho$ and the size of the quadratic expression

$$A\lambda^2 + 2B\lambda\mu + C\mu^2, \qquad (3)$$

with $\lambda^2 + \mu^2 = 1$. If

$$B^2 - AC < 0 \qquad \text{and} \qquad A > 0,$$

then there are no real roots to (3) and it has a positive minimum value. (Call it m.) Now, selecting r so small that $r\rho$ is negligible compared with m, we deduce that the right side of (2) is always positive if (x, y) is sufficiently close to (a, b). Hence

$$f(x, y) - f(a, b) > 0$$

and f is a minimum at (a, b). We have just established part (i) of the theorem. By the same argument, if

$$B^2 - AC < 0 \qquad \text{and} \qquad A < 0,$$

then (3) is always negative and

$$f(x, y) - f(a, b) < 0$$

for (x, y) near (a, b). Thus the statement of (ii) follows. Part (iii) results when $B^2 - AC > 0$, in which case (3) (and therefore (2)) is sometimes positive and sometimes negative. Then f can have neither a maximum nor a minimum at (a, b) and the surface $z = f(x, y)$ can be shown to be saddle-shaped near (a, b). Part (iv) is provided for completeness.

———————

EXAMPLE 2. Test for relative maxima and minima the function f defined by

$$f(x, y) = x^3 + 3xy^2 - 3x^2 - 3y^2 + 4.$$

Solution. We have

$$f_{,1} = 3x^2 + 3y^2 - 6x \qquad \text{and} \qquad f_{,2} = 6xy - 6y.$$

We set these equations equal to zero and solve simultaneously. Writing

$$x^2 + y^2 - 2x = 0, \qquad y(x - 1) = 0,$$

we see that the second equation vanishes only when $y = 0$ or $x = 1$. If $y = 0$, the first equation gives $x = 0$ and 2; if $x = 1$, the first equation gives $y = \pm 1$. The critical points are

$$(0, 0), \quad (2, 0), \quad (1, 1), \quad (1, -1).$$

To apply the Second Derivative Test, we compute

$$A = f_{,1,1} = 6x - 6, \qquad B = f_{,1,2} = 6y, \qquad C = f_{,2,2} = 6x - 6.$$

At $(0, 0)$: $\quad AC - B^2 > 0 \quad$ and $\quad A < 0$, a maximum.

At $(2, 0)$: $\quad AC - B^2 > 0 \quad$ and $\quad A > 0$, a minimum.

At $(1, 1)$: $\quad AC - B^2 < 0$, saddle point.

At $(1, -1)$: $\quad AC - B^2 < 0$, saddle point.

EXAMPLE 3. Find the dimensions of the rectangular box, open at the top, which has maximum volume if the surface area is 12.

Solution. Let V be the volume of the box; let (x, y) be the horizontal directions and z the height. Then

$$V = xyz,$$

and the surface area is given by

$$xy + 2xz + 2yz = 12.$$

Solving this equation for z and substituting its value in the expression for V, we get

$$V = \frac{xy(12 - xy)}{2(x + y)} = \frac{12xy - x^2 y^2}{2(x + y)}.$$

The domains for x, y, z are restricted by the inequalities

$$x > 0, \qquad y > 0, \qquad xy < 12.$$

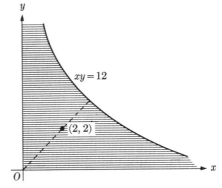

FIGURE 20–14

In other words, x and y must lie in the shaded region shown in Fig. 20–14. To find the critical points, we compute

$$V_x = \frac{y^2(12 - x^2 - 2xy)}{2(x + y)^2}, \qquad V_y = \frac{x^2(12 - y^2 - 2xy)}{2(x + y)^2}$$

and set these expressions equal to zero. We obtain (excluding $x = y = 0$)

$$x^2 + 2xy = 12, \qquad y^2 + 2xy = 12.$$

Subtracting, we find that $x = \pm y$. If $x = y$, then the positive solution is $x = y = 2$. We reject $x = -y$, since both quantities must be positive. From the formula for surface area we conclude that $z = 1$ when $x = y = 2$. From geometrical considerations, we conclude that these are the dimensions which give a maximum volume.

———

Remarks. (i) The determination of maxima and minima hinges on our ability to solve the two simultaneous equations in two unknowns resulting when we set

$f_x = 0$ and $f_y = 0$. In Example 1 these equations are linear and so quite easy
to solve. In Examples 2 and 3, however, the equations are nonlinear, and there
are no routine methods for solving nonlinear simultaneous equations. Elementary
courses in algebra usually avoid such topics, and the student is left to his own devices. The only general rule we can state is: try to solve one of the equations for
one of the unknowns in terms of the other. Substitute this value in the second
equation and try to find all solutions of the second equation. Otherwise use
trickery and guesswork. In actual practice, systems of nonlinear equations may
be solved by a variety of numerical techniques. The remarkable achievements of
the electronic computer come to the fore in such problems. (ii) Definitions of
critical point, relative maximum and minimum, etc., for functions of three, four,
and more variables are simple extensions of the two-variable case. If $f(x, y, z)$
has first derivatives, then a point where

$$f_x = 0, \qquad f_y = 0, \qquad f_z = 0$$

is a *critical point*. We obtain such points by solving simultaneously three equations
in three unknowns. To obtain the critical points for functions of n variables, we
set all n first derivatives equal to zero and solve simultaneously the n equations in
n unknowns. (iii) Extensions of the Second Derivative Test for functions of three
or more variables are given in advanced courses.

EXERCISES

In each of problems 1 through 13, test the functions f for relative maxima and minima.

1. $f(x, y) = x^2 + 2y^2 - 4x + 4y - 3$
2. $f(x, y) = x^2 - y^2 + 2x - 4y - 2$
3. $f(x, y) = x^2 + 2xy + 3y^2 + 2x + 10y + 9$
4. $f(x, y) = x^2 - 3xy + y^2 + 13x - 12y + 13$
5. $f(x, y) = y^3 + x^2 - 6xy + 3x + 6y - 7$
6. $f(x, y) = x^3 + y^2 + 2xy + 4x - 3y - 5$
7. $f(x, y) = 3x^2y + x^2 - 6x - 3y - 2$
8. $f(x, y) = xy + 4/x + 2/y$ 9. $f(x, y) = \sin x + \sin y + \sin (x + y)$
10. $f(x, y) = x^3 - 6xy + y^3$ 11. $f(x, y) = 8^{2/3} - x^{2/3} - y^{2/3}$
12. $f(x, y) = e^x \cos y$ 13. $f(x, y) = e^{-x} \sin^2 y$

In each of problems 14 through 17, find the critical points.

14. $f(x, y, z) = x^2 + 2y^2 + z^2 - 6x + 3y - 2z - 5$
15. $f(x, y, z) = x^2 + y^2 - 2z^2 + 3x + y - z - 2$
16. $f(x, y, z) = x^2 + y^2 + z^2 + 2xy - 3xz + 2yz - x + 3y - 2z - 5$
17. $f(x, y, z, t) = x^2 + y^2 + z^2 - t^2 - 2xy + 4xz + 3xt - 2yt + 4x - 5y - 3$
18. In three-dimensional space find the minimum distance from the origin to the plane

$$3x + 4y + 2z = 6.$$

19. In the plane find the minimum distance from the point $(-1, -3)$ to the line $x + 3y = 7$.

20. In three-dimensional space find the minimum distance from the point $(-1, 3, 2)$ to the plane

$$x + 3y - 2z = 8.$$

21. In three-dimensional space find the minimum distance from the origin to the cone

$$z^2 = (x - 1)^2 + (y - 2)^2.$$

22. For a package to go by parcel post, the sum of the length and girth (perimeter of cross-section) must not exceed 100 in. Find the dimensions of the package of largest volume which can be sent; assume the package has the shape of a rectangular box.

23. Find the dimensions of the rectangular parallelepiped of maximum volume with edges parallel to the axes which can be inscribed in the ellipsoid

$$\frac{x^2}{9} + \frac{y^2}{4} + \frac{z^2}{16} = 1.$$

24. Find the shape of the closed rectangular box of largest volume with a surface area of 16 sq in.

25. The base of an open rectangular box costs half as much per square foot as the sides. Find the dimensions of the box of largest volume which can be made for D dollars.

*26. The cross-section of a trough is an isosceles trapezoid (see Fig. 20–15). If the trough is made by bending up the sides of a strip of metal 18 in. wide, what should the dimensions be in order for the area of the cross-section to be a maximum? Choose h and l as independent variables.

FIGURE 20–15   FIGURE 20–16

*27. A pentagon is composed of a rectangle surmounted by an isosceles triangle (see Fig. 20–16). If the pentagon has a given perimeter P, find the dimensions for maximum area. Choose variables as indicated in Fig. 20–16.

12.   MAXIMA AND MINIMA; LAGRANGE MULTIPLIERS

In Example 2 of Section 11 (page 705), we solved the problem of finding the relative maxima and minima of the function

$$f(x, y) = x^3 + 3xy^2 - 3x^2 - 3y^2 + 4. \tag{1}$$

In Example 1 of the same section (page 703), we solved the problem of finding the minimum of the function

$$f(x, y, z) = x^2 + y^2 + z^2, \tag{2}$$

subject to the condition that (x, y, z) is on the plane

$$2x + 3y - z - 1 = 0. \tag{3}$$

The problem of finding the critical points of (1) is quite different from that of finding those of (2) because, in the latter case, the additional condition (3) is attached. This distinction leads to the following definitions.

DEFINITIONS. The problem of finding maxima and minima of a function of several variables [such as (1) above] without added conditions is called a problem in *free maxima and minima*. When a condition such as (3) is imposed on a function such as (2) above, the problem of determining the maximum and minimum of that function is called a problem in *constrained maxima and minima*. The added condition is called a *side condition*. Problems in maxima and minima may have one or more side conditions. When side conditions occur, they are usually crucial. For example, the minimum of the function f given by (2) without a side condition is obviously zero.

While the problem of minimizing (2) with the side condition (3) has already been solved, we shall do it again by a new and interesting method. This method, due to Lagrange, changes a problem in constrained maxima and minima to a problem in free maxima and minima.

We first introduce a new variable, traditionally denoted by λ, and form the function

$$F(x, y, z, \lambda) = (x^2 + y^2 + z^2) + \lambda(2x + 3y - z - 1).$$

The problem of finding the critical points of (2) with side condition (3) can be shown to be equivalent (under rather general circumstances) to that of finding the critical points of F considered as a function of the *four* variables x, y, z, λ. (See the end of this section.) We proceed by computing F_x, F_y, F_z, and F_λ and setting each of these expressions equal to zero. We obtain

$$F_x = 2x + 2\lambda = 0, \qquad F_y = 2y + 3\lambda = 0,$$
$$F_z = 2z - \lambda = 0, \qquad F_\lambda = 2x + 3y - z - 1 = 0.$$

Note that the equation $F_\lambda = 0$ is precisely the side condition (3). That is, any solution to the problem will automatically satisfy the side condition. We solve these equations simultaneously by writing

$$x = -\lambda, \qquad y = -\tfrac{3}{2}\lambda, \qquad z = \tfrac{1}{2}\lambda,$$
$$2(-\lambda) + 3(-\tfrac{3}{2}\lambda) - (\tfrac{1}{2}\lambda) - 1 = 0,$$

and we get $\lambda = -\frac{1}{7}$, $x = \frac{1}{7}$, $y = \frac{3}{14}$, $z = -\frac{1}{14}$. The solution satisfies $F_\lambda = 0$ and so is on the plane (2).

The general method, known as the *method of Lagrange multipliers*, may be stated as follows: In order to find the critical points of a function

$$f(x, y, z)$$

subject to the side condition

$$\phi(x, y, z) = 0,$$

form the function

$$F(x, y, z, \lambda) = f(x, y, z) + \lambda\phi(x, y, z)$$

and find the critical points of F considered as a function of the four variables x, y, z, λ.

The method is quite general in that several "multipliers" may be introduced if there are several side conditions. To find the critical points of

$$f(x, y, z),$$

subject to the conditions

$$\phi_1(x, y, z) = 0 \quad \text{and} \quad \phi_2(x, y, z) = 0. \tag{4}$$

form the function

$$F(x, y, z, \lambda_1, \lambda_2) = f(x, y, z) + \lambda_1\phi_1(x, y, z) + \lambda_2\phi_2(x, y, z)$$

and find the critical points of F as a function of the five variables x, y, z, λ_1, and λ_2.

We shall exhibit the method by working several examples.

———————

EXAMPLE 1. Find the minimum of the function

$$f(x, y) = x^2 + 2y^2 + 2xy + 2x + 3y,$$

subject to the condition that x and y satisfy the equation

$$x^2 - y = 1.$$

Solution. We form the function

$$F(x, y, \lambda) = (x^2 + 2y^2 + 2xy + 2x + 3y) + \lambda(x^2 - y - 1).$$

Then

$$F_x = 2x + 2y + 2 + 2x\lambda = 0,$$
$$F_y = 4y + 2x + 3 - \lambda = 0,$$
$$F_\lambda = x^2 - y - 1 = 0.$$

Substituting $y = x^2 - 1$ in the first two equations, we get

$$x + x^2 - 1 + 1 + \lambda x = 0, \qquad 4x^2 - 4 + 2x + 3 = \lambda.$$

Solving, we obtain

$$x = 0, \qquad y = -1, \qquad \lambda = -1,$$

and

$$x = -\tfrac{3}{4}, \qquad y = -\tfrac{7}{16}, \qquad \lambda = -\tfrac{1}{4}.$$

Evaluating f at these points, we find that a lower value occurs when $x = -\tfrac{3}{4}, y = -\tfrac{7}{16}$. From geometrical considerations we conclude that f is a minimum at this value.

Remarks. We could have solved this problem as a simple maximum and minimum problem by substituting $y = x^2 - 1$ in the equation for f and finding the critical points of the resulting function of the single variable x. However, in some problems the side condition may be so complicated that we cannot easily solve for one of the variables in terms of the others, although it may be possible to do so theoretically. It is in such cases that the power of the method of Lagrange multipliers becomes apparent. The system of equations obtained by setting the first derivatives equal to zero may be solvable even though the side condition alone may not be. The next example illustrates this point.

EXAMPLE 2. Find the critical values of

$$f(x, y) = x^2 + y^2, \tag{5}$$

subject to the condition that

$$x^3 + y^3 - 6xy = 0. \tag{6}$$

Solution. We form the function

$$F(x, y, \lambda) = x^2 + y^2 + \lambda(x^3 + y^3 - 6xy)$$

and obtain the derivatives

$$F_x = 2x + 3x^2\lambda - 6y\lambda = 0,$$
$$F_y = 2y + 3y^2\lambda - 6x\lambda = 0,$$
$$F_\lambda = x^3 + y^3 - 6xy = 0.$$

Solving simultaneously, we find from the first two equations that

$$\lambda = \frac{-2x}{3x^2 - 6y}, \qquad \lambda = \frac{-2y}{3y^2 - 6x}, \qquad \text{and} \qquad x(3y^2 - 6x) = y(3x^2 - 6y).$$

The equations

$$x^2y - xy^2 + 2x^2 - 2y^2 = 0,$$
$$x^3 + y^3 - 6xy = 0$$

may be solved simultaneously by a trick. Factoring the first equation, we see that

$$(x - y)(2x + 2y + xy) = 0$$

and $x = y$ is a solution. When $x = y$, the second equation yields

$$2x^3 - 6x^2 = 0, \qquad x = 0, 3.$$

We discard the complex solutions obtained by setting $2x + 2y + xy = 0$. The values $x = 0$, $y = 0$ clearly yield a minimum, while from geometric considerations (Fig. 20–17), the point $x = 3$, $y = 3$ corresponds to a relative maximum. There is no true maximum of f, since $x^2 + y^2$ (the distance from the origin to the curve) grows without bound if either x or y does.

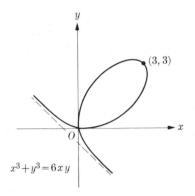

FIGURE 20–17

Note that it is not easy to solve Eq. (6) for either x or y and substitute in (5) to get a function of one variable. Therefore the methods of one-dimensional calculus are not readily usable in this problem.

The next example illustrates the technique when there are two side conditions.

EXAMPLE 3. Find the minimum of the function

$$f(x, y, z, t) = x^2 + 2y^2 + z^2 + t^2,$$

subject to the conditions

$$x + 3y - z + \ t = 2, \tag{7}$$
$$2x - \ y + z + 2t = 4. \tag{8}$$

Solution. We form the function

$$F(x, y, z, t, \lambda_1, \lambda_2) = (x^2 + 2y^2 + z^2 + t^2) + \lambda_1(x + 3y - z + t - 2)$$
$$+ \lambda_2(2x - y + z + 2t - 4).$$

We have

$$F_x = 2x + \lambda_1 + 2\lambda_2 = 0, \qquad F_t = 2t + \lambda_1 + 2\lambda_2 = 0,$$
$$F_y = 4y + 3\lambda_1 - \lambda_2 = 0, \qquad F_{\lambda_1} = x + 3y - z + t - 2 = 0,$$
$$F_z = 2z - \lambda_1 + \lambda_2 = 0, \qquad F_{\lambda_2} = 2x - y + z + 2t - 4 = 0.$$

Solving these six linear equations in six unknowns is tedious but routine. We obtain

$$x = \tfrac{67}{69}, \qquad y = \tfrac{6}{69}, \qquad z = \tfrac{14}{69}, \qquad t = \tfrac{67}{69}.$$

The corresponding values of λ_1 and λ_2 are: $\lambda_1 = -26/69$, $\lambda_2 = -54/69$.

The validity of the method of Lagrange multipliers hinges on the ability to solve an equation for a side condition such as

$$\phi(x, y, z) = 0 \tag{9}$$

for one of the unknowns in terms of the other two. Theorems which state when such a process can be performed (theoretically, that is, not actually) are called *implicit function theorems* and are studied in advanced calculus. Suppose we wish to find the critical values of

$$f(x, y, z)$$

with the side condition

$$\phi(x, y, z) = 0.$$

If we assume that (x_0, y_0, z_0) is the point where f has its critical value, and if we assume that $\phi_z(x_0, y_0, z_0) \neq 0$, then it is possible to establish the validity of the method of Lagrange multipliers. It can be shown that if

$$\phi_z(x_0, y_0, z_0) \neq 0,$$

then we may solve the equation $\phi(x, y, z) = 0$ for z in terms of x and y, so that $z = g(x, y)$. We now set

$$H(x, y) = f[x, y, g(x, y)],$$

and we note that H has a critical point at (x_0, y_0). Therefore

$$H_x = f_x + f_z g_x = 0, \qquad H_y = f_y + f_z g_y = 0. \tag{10}$$

But, by differentiating (9) implicitly, we obtain

$$\frac{\partial z}{\partial x} = g_x = -\frac{\phi_x}{\phi_z}, \qquad \frac{\partial z}{\partial y} = g_y = -\frac{\phi_y}{\phi_z}, \tag{11}$$

$$[\text{since } \phi_z \neq 0 \text{ near } (x_0, y_0, z_0)].$$

Substituting (11) into (10), we find

$$f_x - \frac{f_z}{\phi_z} \phi_x = 0 \qquad \text{and} \qquad f_y - \frac{f_z}{\phi_z} \phi_y = 0.$$

We add to these equations the obvious identity

$$f_z - \frac{f_z}{\phi_z} \phi_z = 0,$$

and then we set $\lambda_0 = -f_z(x_0, y_0, z_0)/\phi_z(x_0, y_0, z_0)$. In this way we obtain the equations

$$f_x + \lambda_0\phi_x = 0, \qquad f_y + \lambda_0\phi_y = 0, \qquad f_z + \lambda_0\phi_z = 0, \qquad \phi = 0,$$

which are just the equations satisfied at a critical point of $F = f + \lambda\phi$. The proof when there are more side conditions is similar but somewhat more complicated.

EXERCISES

Solve the following problems by the method of Lagrange multipliers.

1. Find the minimum of $f(x, y, z) = x^2 + y^2 + z^2$ subject to the condition that $x + 3y - 2z = 4$.

2. Find the minimum of $f(x, y, z) = 3x^2 + 2y^2 + 4z^2$ subject to the condition that $2x + 4y - 6z + 5 = 0$.

3. Find the minimum of $f(x, y, z) = x^2 + y^2 + z^2$ subject to the condition that $ax + by + cz = d$.

4. Find the minimum of $f(x, y, z) = ax^2 + by^2 + cz^2$ subject to the condition that $dx + ey + gz + h = 0$ $(a, b, c$ positive$)$.

5. Find the minimum of $f(x, y, z) = x^2 + y^2 + z^2$ if (x, y, z) is on the line of intersection of the planes

$$x + 2y + z - 1 = 0, \qquad 2x - y - 3z - 4 = 0.$$

6. Find the minimum of $f(x, y, z) = 2x^2 + y^2 + 3z^2$ if (x, y, z) is on the line of intersection of the planes

$$2x + y - 3z = 4, \qquad x - y + 2z = 6.$$

7. Find the point on the curve $x^2 + 2xy + 2y^2 = 100$ which is closest to the origin.

8. Find the relative maxima and minima of the function $f(x, y, z) = x^3 + y^3 + z^3$ where (x, y, z) is on the plane $x + y + z = 4$.

9. Find the dimensions of the rectangular box, open at the top, which has maximum volume if the surface area is 12. (Compare with Example 3, page 706.)

10. A tent is made in the form of a cylinder surmounted by a cone (Fig. 20–18). If the cylinder has radius 5 and the total surface area is 100, find the height H of the cylinder and the height h of the cone which make the volume a maximum.

11. A container is made of a right circular cylinder with radius 5 and with a conical cap at each end. If the volume is given, find the height H of the cylinder and the height h of each of the conical caps which together make the total surface area as small as possible.

FIGURE 20–18

12. Find the minimum of the function

$$f(x, y, z, t) = x^2 + y^2 + z^2 + t^2$$

subject to the condition $3x + 2y - 4z + t = 2$.

13. Find the minimum of the function

$$f(x, y, z, t) = x^2 + y^2 + z^2 + t^2$$

subject to the conditions

$$x + y - z + 2t = 2, \qquad 2x - y + z + 3t = 3.$$

14. Find the minimum of the function

$$f(x, y, z, t) = 2x^2 + y^2 + z^2 + 2t^2$$

subject to the conditions

$$x + y + z + 2t = 1, \qquad 2x + y - z + 4t = 2, \qquad x - y + z - t = 4.$$

15. Find the points on the curve $x^4 + y^4 + 3xy = 2$ which are closest to the origin; find those which are farthest from the origin.

16. Find three critical points of the function $x^4 + y^4 + z^4 + 3xyz$ subject to the condition that (x, y, z) is on the plane $x + y + z = 3$. Can you identify these points?

17. Work Exercise 22 of Section 11 by the method of Lagrange multipliers.

18. Find the dimensions of the rectangular parallelepiped of maximum volume with edges parallel to the axes which can be inscribed in the ellipsoid

$$\frac{x^2}{a^2} + \frac{y^2}{b^2} + \frac{z^2}{c^2} = 1.$$

19. If the base of an open rectangular box costs three times as much per square foot as the sides, find the dimensions of the box of largest volume which can be made for D dollars.

20. Find and identify the critical points of the function

$$f(x, y, z) = 2x^2 + y^2 + z^2$$

subject to the condition that (x, y, z) is on the surface $x^2 yz = 1$.

21. Find the critical points of the function $f(x, y, z) = x^a y^b z^c$ if $x + y + z = A$, where a, b, c, A are given positive numbers.

13. EXACT DIFFERENTIALS

In Section 7 we saw that the differential of a function $f(x, y)$ is given by

$$df = \frac{\partial f}{\partial x} dx + \frac{\partial f}{\partial y} dy. \tag{1}$$

The quantity df is a function of four variables, since $\partial f/\partial x$ and $\partial f/\partial y$ are functions of x and y and dx and dy are additional independent variables. It turns out that expressions of the form

$$P(x, y)\, dx + Q(x, y)\, dy$$

occur frequently in problems in engineering and physics. It is natural to ask when such an expression is the total differential of a function f. For example, if we are given

$$(3x^2 + 2y)\, dx + (2x - 3y^2)\, dy,$$

we may guess (correctly) that the function $f(x, y) = x^3 + 2xy - y^3$ has the above expression as its total differential, df. On the other hand, if we are given

$$(2x^2 - 3y)\, dx + (2x - y^3)\, dy, \tag{2}$$

then it can be shown that *there is no function f whose total differential is the expression* (2).

DEFINITION. If there is a function $f(x, y)$ such that

$$df = P(x, y)\, dx + Q(x, y)\, dy$$

for all (x, y) in some region and for all values of dx and dy, we say that

$$P(x, y)\, dx + Q(x, y)\, dy$$

is an *exact differential*. If there is a function $F(x, y, z)$ such that

$$dF = P(x, y, z)\, dx + Q(x, y, z)\, dy + R(x, y, z)\, dz$$

for all (x, y, z) in some region and for all values of dx, dy, and dz, we say that $P\, dx + Q\, dy + R\, dz$ is an *exact differential*. For functions with any number of variables the extension is immediate.

The next theorem gives a precise criterion for determining when a differential expression is an exact differential.

Theorem 12. *Suppose that $P(x, y)$, $Q(x, y)$, $\partial P/\partial y$, $\partial Q/\partial x$ are continuous in a rectangle S. Then the expression*

$$P(x, y)\, dx + Q(x, y)\, dy \tag{3}$$

is an exact differential for (x, y) in the region S if and only if

$$\frac{\partial P}{\partial y} = \frac{\partial Q}{\partial x} \qquad for\ all \qquad (x, y)\ in\ S. \tag{4}$$

Proof. The theorem has two parts: we must show (a), that if (3) is an exact differential, then (4) holds; and (b), that if (4) holds, then the expression (3) is an exact differential.

To establish (a) we start with the assumption that there is a function f such that

$$df = P\,dx + Q\,dy,$$

and so $\partial f/\partial x = P(x, y)$ and $\partial f/\partial y = Q(x, y)$. We differentiate and obtain

$$\frac{\partial^2 f}{\partial y\,\partial x} = \frac{\partial P}{\partial y}$$

and

$$\frac{\partial^2 f}{\partial x\,\partial y} = \frac{\partial Q}{\partial x}.$$

Now Theorem 7 of Section 9, which states that the order of differentiation is immaterial, may be invoked to conclude that (4) holds.

To prove (b) we assume that (4) holds, and we must construct a function f such that df is equal to the differential expression (3). That is, we must find a function f such that

$$\frac{\partial f}{\partial x} = P(x, y) \qquad \text{and} \qquad \frac{\partial f}{\partial y} = Q(x, y). \tag{5}$$

Let (a, b) be a point of S; suppose we try to solve these two partial differential equations for the function f. We integrate the first with respect to x, getting

$$f(x, y) = C(y) + \int_a^x P(\xi, y)\,d\xi$$

where, instead of a "constant" of integration, we get a function of the remaining variable. Letting $x = a$, we find that $f(a, y) = C(y)$, and we can write

$$f(x, y) = f(a, y) + \int_a^x P(\xi, y)\,d\xi. \tag{6}$$

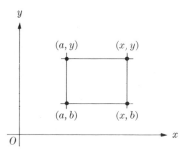

Setting $x = a$ in the second equation of (5) and integrating with respect to y, we obtain

$$f(a, y) = C_1 + \int_b^y Q(a, \eta)\,d\eta;$$

letting $y = b$, we conclude that

$$f(a, y) = f(a, b) + \int_b^y Q(a, \eta)\,d\eta.$$

FIGURE 20–19

Substitution of this expression for $f(a, y)$ into the equation (6) yields (Fig. 20–19)

$$f(x, y) = f(a, b) + \int_b^y Q(a, \eta)\,d\eta + \int_a^x P(\xi, y)\,d\xi. \tag{7}$$

We may repeat the entire process by integrating with respect to y first and with respect to x second. The three equations are

$$f(x, y) = f(x, b) + \int_b^y Q(x, \eta)\, d\eta, \qquad f(x, b) = f(a, b) + \int_a^x P(\xi, b)\, d\xi,$$

and

$$f(x, y) = f(a, b) + \int_a^x P(\xi, b)\, d\xi + \int_b^y Q(x, \eta)\, d\eta. \tag{8}$$

The two expressions for f given by (7) and (8) will be identical if and only if (after subtraction) the equation

$$\int_a^x [P(\xi, y) - P(\xi, b)]\, d\xi = \int_b^y [Q(x, \eta) - Q(a, \eta)]\, d\eta \tag{9}$$

holds. To establish (9), we start with the observation that

$$P(\xi, y) - P(\xi, b) = \int_b^y \frac{\partial P(\xi, \eta)}{\partial y}\, d\eta = \int_b^y \frac{\partial Q(\xi, \eta)}{\partial x}\, d\eta,$$

where, for the first time, we have used the hypothesis that $\partial P/\partial y = \partial Q/\partial x$. Therefore, upon integration,

$$\int_a^x [P(\xi, y) - P(\xi, b)]\, d\xi = \int_a^x \left[\int_b^y \frac{\partial Q(\xi, \eta)}{\partial x}\, d\eta \right] d\xi.$$

It will be shown in Chapter 21, Section 2 that the order of integrations in the term on the right may be interchanged, so that

$$\int_a^x [P(\xi, y) - P(\xi, b)]\, d\xi = \int_b^y \left[\int_a^x \frac{\partial Q(\xi, \eta)}{\partial x}\, d\xi \right] d\eta$$

$$= \int_b^y [Q(x, \eta) - Q(a, \eta)]\, d\eta.$$

But this equality is (9) precisely; the theorem is established when we observe that as a result of (7) or (8), the relations

$$\frac{\partial f}{\partial x} = P \qquad \text{and} \qquad \frac{\partial f}{\partial y} = Q$$

hold.

The proof of Theorem 12 contains in it the method for finding the function f when it exists. Examples illustrate the technique.

———————

EXAMPLE 1. Show that

$$(3x^2 + 6y)\, dx + (3y^2 + 6x)\, dy$$

is an exact differential, and find the function f of which it is the total differential.

Solution. Setting $P = 3x^2 + 6y$, $Q = 3y^2 + 6x$, we obtain

$$Q_x = 6, \qquad P_y = 6,$$

so that $P \, dx + Q \, dy$ is an exact differential. We write (as in the proof of the theorem)

$$f_x = 3x^2 + 6y$$

and integrate to get

$$f = x^3 + 6xy + C(y).$$

We differentiate with respect to y. We find

$$f_y = 6x + C'(y),$$

and this expression must be equal to Q. Therefore

$$6x + C'(y) = 3y^2 + 6x$$

or

$$C'(y) = 3y^2, \quad C(y) = y^3 + C_1.$$

Thus

$$f(x, y) = x^3 + 6xy + y^3 + C_1.$$

A constant of integration will always appear in the integration of exact differentials.

EXAMPLE 2. Show that

$$(e^x \cos y - e^y \sin x) \, dx + (e^y \cos x - e^x \sin y) \, dy$$

is an exact differential, and find the function f of which it is the differential.

Solution. Setting $P = e^x \cos y - e^y \sin x$, $Q = e^y \cos x - e^x \sin y$, we have

$$\frac{\partial P}{\partial y} = -e^x \sin y - e^y \sin x = \frac{\partial Q}{\partial x},$$

and the differential is exact. Integrating $f_x = P$, we get

$$f(x, y) = e^x \cos y + e^y \cos x + C(y).$$

Differentiating with respect to y, we find

$$f_y = -e^x \sin y + e^y \cos x + C'(y) = Q = e^y \cos x - e^x \sin y.$$

Therefore, $C'(y) = 0$ and C is a constant. The function f is given by

$$f(x, y) = e^x \cos y + e^y \cos x + C.$$

The next theorem is an extension of Theorem 12 to functions of three variables.

Theorem 13. *Suppose that $P(x, y, z)$, $Q(x, y, z)$, $R(x, y, z)$ are continuous in some rectangular parallelepiped S. Then*

$$P(x, y, z)\,dx + Q(x, y, z)\,dy + R(x, y, z)\,dz$$

is an exact differential on S if and only if

$$\frac{\partial P}{\partial y} = \frac{\partial Q}{\partial x}, \qquad \frac{\partial P}{\partial z} = \frac{\partial R}{\partial x}, \qquad \frac{\partial Q}{\partial z} = \frac{\partial R}{\partial y}.$$

It is assumed that all the above partial derivatives are continuous functions of (x, y, z) on S.

The proof of this theorem follows the lines (and uses the proof) of Theorem 12. It may be found in Morrey, *University Calculus*, page 586.

The next example shows how to integrate an exact differential in three variables.

———————

EXAMPLE 3. Determine whether or not

$$(3x^2 - 4xy + z^2 + yz - 2)\,dx + (xz - 6y^2 - 2x^2)\,dy + (9z^2 + 2xz + xy + 6z)\,dz$$

is an exact differential and, if so, find the function f of which it is the total differential.

Solution. Setting P, Q, R equal to the coefficients of dx, dy, and dz, respectively, we obtain

$$P_y = -4x + z = Q_x, \qquad P_z = 2z + y = R_x, \qquad Q_z = x = R_y.$$

Therefore $P\,dx + Q\,dy + R\,dz$ is an exact differential, and we proceed to find f. Writing $f_x = P$, we integrate to get

$$f(x, y, z) = x^3 - 2x^2y + xz^2 + xyz - 2x + C(y, z).$$

We differentiate with respect to y:

$$f_y(x, y, z) = -2x^2 + xz + C_y(y, z) = Q = xz - 6y^2 - 2x^2.$$

Hence

$$C_y(y, z) = -6y^2$$

and, upon integration with respect to y,

$$C(y, z) = -2y^3 + C_1(z).$$

We may write

$$f(x, y, z) = x^3 - 2x^2y + xz^2 + xyz - 2x - 2y^3 + C_1(z),$$

and we wish to find $C_1(z)$. We differentiate f with respect to z:

$$f_z = 2xz + xy + C_1'(z) = R = 9z^2 + 2xz + xy + 6z.$$

We obtain

$$C_1'(z) = 9z^2 + 6z \qquad \text{and} \qquad C_1(z) = 3z^3 + 3z^2 + C_2.$$

Therefore

$$f(x, y, z) = x^3 - 2y^3 + 3z^3 - 2x^2y + xz^2 + xyz + 3z^2 - 2x + C_2.$$

EXERCISES

In each of problems 1 through 18, determine which of the differentials are exact. In case a differential is exact, find the functions of which it is the total differential.

1. $(x^3 + 3x^2y) dx + (x^3 + y^3) dy$

2. $(2x + 3y) dx + (3x + 2y) dy$

3. $\left(2y - \dfrac{1}{x}\right) dx + \left(2x + \dfrac{1}{y}\right) dy$

4. $(x^2 + 2xy) dx + (y^3 - x^2) dy$

5. $x^2 \sin y \, dx + x^2 \cos y \, dy$

6. $\dfrac{x^2 + y^2}{2y^2} dx - \dfrac{x^3}{3y^3} dy$

7. $2xe^{x^2} \sin y \, dx + e^{x^2} \cos y \, dy$

8. $(ye^{xy} + 3x^2) dx + (xe^{xy} - \cos y) dy$

9. $\dfrac{x \, dy - y \, dx}{x^2 + y^2}, \; x > 0$

10. $(2x \ln y) dx + \dfrac{x^2}{y} dy$

11. $(x + \cos x \tan y) dx + (y + \tan x \cos y) dy$

12. $\dfrac{1}{y} e^{2x/y} dx - \dfrac{1}{y^3} e^{2x/y}(y + 2x) dy$

13. $(3x^2 \ln y - x^3) dx + \dfrac{3x^2}{y} dy$

14. $\dfrac{x \, dx}{\sqrt{x^2 + y^2}} + \left(\dfrac{y}{\sqrt{x^2 + y^2}} - 2\right) dy$

15. $(2x - y + 3z) dx + (3y + 2z - x) dy + (2x + 3y - z) dz$

16. $(2xy + z^2) dx + (2yz + x^2) dy + (2xz + y^2) dz$

17. $(e^x \sin y \cos z) dx + (e^x \cos y \cos z) dy - (e^x \sin y \sin z) dz$

18. $\left(\dfrac{1}{y^2} - \dfrac{y}{x^2z} - \dfrac{z}{x^2y}\right) dx + \left(\dfrac{1}{xz} - \dfrac{x}{y^2z} - \dfrac{z}{xy^2}\right) dy + \left(\dfrac{1}{xy} - \dfrac{x}{yz^2} - \dfrac{y}{xz^2}\right) dz$

*19. (a) Given the differential expression

$$P \, dx + Q \, dy + R \, dz + S \, dt,$$

where P, Q, R, S are functions of x, y, z, t, state a theorem which is a plausible generalization of Theorem 13 in order to decide when the above expression is exact. (b) Use the result of part (a) to show that the following expression is exact. Find the function f of which it is the total differential.

$$(3x^2 + 2z + 3) dx + (2y - t - 2) dy + (3z^2 + 2x) dz + (4 - 3t^2 - y) dt.$$

14. DEFINITION OF A LINE INTEGRAL

Let C be an arc in the plane extending from the point $A(a, b)$ to the point $B(c, d)$, as shown in Fig. 20–20. Suppose that $f(x, y)$ is a continuous function defined in a region which contains the arc C in its interior. We make a decomposition of the arc C by introducing $n - 1$ points between A and B along C. We label these points $P_1, P_2, \ldots, P_{n-2}, P_{n-1}$, and set $A = P_0, B = P_n$. Denote the coordinates of the point P_i by (x_i, y_i), $i = 0, 1, 2, \ldots, n$. (See Fig. 20–21). Between each two successive points of the subdivision we select a point on the curve. Call these points $Q_1, Q_2, \ldots, Q_n$, and denote the coordinates of Q_i by (ξ_i, η_i), $i = 1, 2,$ $\ldots, n$. This selection may be made in any manner whatsoever so long as Q_i is on the part of C between P_{i-1} and P_i (Fig. 20–22).

FIGURE 20–20

FIGURE 20–21   FIGURE 20–22

We form the sum

$$f(\xi_1, \eta_1)(x_1 - x_0) + f(\xi_2, \eta_2)(x_2 - x_1) + \cdots + f(\xi_n, \eta_n)(x_n - x_{n-1}),$$

or, written more compactly,

$$\sum_{i=1}^{n} f(\xi_i, \eta_i)(x_i - x_{i-1}) = \sum_{i=1}^{n} f(\xi_i, \eta_i)\,\Delta_i x. \tag{1}$$

As in the case of subdivisions of an interval along the x-axis (see page 213), we define the *norm of the subdivision* $P_0, P_1, P_2, \ldots, P_n$ of the curve C to be the maximum distance between any two successive points of the subdivision. We denote the norm by $\|\Delta\|$.

DEFINITION. Suppose there is a number L with the following property: for each $\epsilon > 0$ there is a $\delta > 0$ such that

$$\left| \sum_{i=1}^{n} f(\xi_i, \eta_i)(x_i - x_{i-1}) - L \right| < \epsilon$$

for every subdivision with $\|\Delta\| < \delta$ and for any choices of the (ξ_i, η_i) as described above. Then we say that *the line integral of f with respect to x along the curve C exists and its value is L.* There are a number of symbols for this line integral such as

$$\int_C f(x, y)\, dx \qquad \text{and} \qquad (C)\!\int_A^B f(x, y)\, dx. \qquad (2)$$

Note that the value of the integral will depend, in general, not only on f and the points A and B but also on the particular arc C selected.

The expression (1) is one of two types of sums which are commonly formed in line integrations. We also introduce the sum

$$\sum_{i=1}^{n} f(\xi_i, \eta_i)(y_i - y_{i-1})$$

in which the points (ξ_i, η_i) are selected as before. The limit, if it exists, (as $\|\Delta\| \to 0$) is the line integral

$$(C)\!\int_A^B f(x, y)\, dy, \qquad (3)$$

and will generally have a value different from (2).

In Section 16, we shall give an application of line integration to a physical problem.

If the arc C happens to be a segment of the x-axis, then the line integral $\int_C f(x, y)\, dx$ reduces to an ordinary integral. To see this we note that in the approximating sums all the $\eta_i = 0$. Therefore we have

$$(C)\!\int_A^B f(x, y)\, dx = \int_a^c f(x, 0)\, dx.$$

On the other hand, when C is a segment of the x-axis, the integral $\int_C f(x, y)\, dy$ always vanishes, since in each approximating sum $y_i - y_{i-1} = 0$ for every i.

Simple properties of line integrals, analogous to those for ordinary integrals, may be derived directly from the definition. For example, if the arc C is traversed in the opposite direction, the line integral changes sign. That is,

$$(C)\!\int_A^B f(x, y)\, dx = -(C)\!\int_B^A f(x, y)\, dx.$$

If C_1 is an arc extending from A_1 to A_2 and C_2 is an arc extending from A_2 to A_3, then

$$(C_1)\!\int_{A_1}^{A_2} f(x, y)\, dx + (C_2)\!\int_{A_2}^{A_3} f(x, y)\, dx = (C_1 + C_2)\!\int_{A_1}^{A_3} f(x, y)\, dx, \qquad (4)$$

where the symbol $C_1 + C_2$ has the obvious meaning. As in the case of ordinary integrals, line integrals satisfy the additive property:

$$\int_C [f(x, y) + g(x, y)]\, dx = \int_C f(x, y)\, dx + \int_C g(x, y)\, dx.$$

Statements similar to those above hold for integrals of the type $\int_C f(x, y)\, dy$.

There is one more type of line integral which we can define. If the arc C and the function f are as before and if s denotes arc length along C measured from the point A to the point B, we can define the *line integral with respect to the arc length s.* We use the symbol

$$(C) \int_A^B f(x, y)\, ds$$

for this line integral. If C is given in the form $y = g(x)$, we use the relation $ds = [1 + (g'(x))^2]^{1/2}\, dx$ to define:

$$(C) \int_A^B f(x, y)\, ds = (C) \int_A^B f(x, y)\sqrt{1 + (g'(x))^2}\, dx,$$

in which the right-hand side has already been defined. If the curve C is in the form $x = h(y)$, we may write

$$(C) \int_A^B f(x, y)\, ds = (C) \int_A^B f(x, y)\sqrt{1 + (h'(y))^2}\, dy.$$

If C is in neither the form $y = g(x)$ nor the form $x = h(y)$, it may be broken up into a sum of arcs, each one of which does have the appropriate functional behavior. Then the integrals over each piece may be calculated and the results added.

FIGURE 20–23

For ordinary integrals we stated a simple theorem to the effect that if a function f is continuous on an interval $[a, b]$, then it is integrable there. (See page 218.) It can be shown that if $f(x, y)$ is continuous and if the arc C is rectifiable (has finite length), then the line integrals exist. We shall consider throughout only functions and arcs which are sufficiently smooth so that the line integrals always exist. It is worth remarking that if C consists of a collection of smooth arcs joined together (Fig. 20–23), then because of (4) the line integral along C exists as the sum of the line integrals taken along each of the pieces.

Line integrals in three dimensions may be defined similarly to the way they were defined in the plane. An arc C joining the points A and B in three space may be given either parametrically by three equations,

$$x = x(t), \qquad y = y(t), \qquad z = z(t), \qquad t_0 \leq t \leq t_1,$$

or nonparametrically by two equations,

$$y = g_1(x), \qquad z = g_2(x).$$

If $f(x, y, z)$ is a function defined along C, then a subdivision of the arc C leads to a sum of the form

$$\sum_{i=1}^{n} f(\xi_i, \eta_i, \zeta_i) (x_i - x_{i-1})$$

which, in turn, is an approximation to the line integral

$$\int_C f(x, y, z) \, dx.$$

Line integrals such as $\int_C f(x, y, z) \, dy$, $\int_C f(x, y, z) \, dz$ are defined similarly.

15. CALCULATION OF LINE INTEGRALS

In the study of integration of functions of one variable, we saw that the definition of integral (page 213) turned out to be fairly worthless as a tool for computing the value of any specific integral. While we did have a certain amount of practice in calculating areas by sums (page 203), the methods we employed for performing integration most often used certain properties of integrals, special formulas for antiderivatives, and so forth (page 223).

The situation with line integrals is similar. In the last section we defined various types of line integrals, and now we shall exhibit methods for calculating the value of these integrals when the curve C and the function f are specifically given. It is an interesting fact that *all such integrals may be reduced to ordinary integrations of the type we have already studied.* Once the reduction is made, the problem becomes routine and all the formulas we learned for evaluation of integrals may be used.

The next theorem establishes the rule for reducing a line integration to an ordinary integration of a function of a single variable.

Theorem 14. *Let C be a rectifiable arc given in the form*

$$x = x(t), \qquad y = y(t), \qquad t_0 \le t \le t_1, \tag{1}$$

so that the point $A(a, b)$ corresponds to t_0, and $B(c, d)$ corresponds to t_1. Suppose $f(x, y)$ is a continuous function along C, and $x'(t)$, $y'(t)$ are continuous. Then

$$(C)\int_A^B f(x, y) \, dx = \int_{t_0}^{t_1} f[x(t), y(t)]x'(t) \, dt,$$

$$(C)\int_A^B f(x, y) \, dy = \int_{t_0}^{t_1} f[x(t), y(t)]y'(t) \, dt,$$

$$(C)\int_A^B f(x, y) \, ds = \int_{t_0}^{t_1} f[x(t), y(t)]\sqrt{(x'(t))^2 + (y'(t))^2} \, dt.$$

For a proof of this theorem, see Morrey, *University Calculus*, page 590. A similar theorem is valid for line integrals in three-space.

Corollary. *If the arc C is in the form* $y = g(x)$, *then*

$$(C)\int_A^B f(x, y)\, dx = \int_a^c f[x, g(x)]\, dx.$$

For, if $y = g(x)$, then x may be used as a parameter in place of t in (1) and the corollary is a restatement of the theorem. Similar statements may be made if C is given by an equation of the type $x = h(y)$.

——————

EXAMPLE 1. Evaluate the integrals

$$\int_C (x^2 - y^2)\, dx - \int_C 2xy\, dy$$

where C is the arc (Fig. 20–24):

$$x = t^2 - 1, \qquad y = t^2 + t + 2, \qquad 0 \le t \le 1.$$

Solution. According to Theorem 14, we compute

$$x'(t) = 2t, \qquad y'(t) = 2t + 1$$

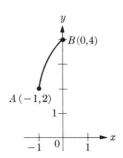

FIGURE 20–24

and make the appropriate substitutions. We get

$$\int_C (x^2 - y^2)\, dx = \int_0^1 \left[(t^2 - 1)^2 - (t^2 + t + 2)^2\right] \cdot 2t\, dt,$$

$$-\int_C 2xy\, dy = -2\int_0^1 (t^2 - 1)(t^2 + t + 2)(2t + 1)\, dt.$$

Multiplying out the integrands, we find

$$\int_C (x^2 - y^2)\, dx = 2\int_0^1 (-2t^3 - 7t^2 - 4t - 3)t\, dt,$$

$$-2\int_C xy\, dy = -2\int_0^1 (t^4 + t^3 + t^2 - t - 2)(2t + 1)\, dt.$$

The integration is now routine, and the final result is

$$\int_C [(x^2 - y^2)\, dx - 2xy\, dy] = -2\int_0^1 (2t^5 + 5t^4 + 10t^3 + 3t^2 - 2t - 2)\, dt$$

$$= -\frac{11}{3}.$$

EXAMPLE 2. Evaluate the integral

$$\int_C (x^2 - 3xy + y^3)\, dx$$

where C is the arc

$$y = 2x^2, \qquad 0 \le x \le 2.$$

Solution. We have

$$\int_C (x^2 - 3xy + y^3)\, dx = \int_0^2 [x^2 - 3x(2x^2) + (2x^2)^3]\, dx$$

$$= \left[\frac{x^3}{3} - \frac{3}{2}x^4 + \frac{8}{7}x^7 \right]_0^2 = \frac{2624}{21}.$$

EXAMPLE 3. Evaluate

$$\int_C y\, ds$$

where C is the arc

$$y = \sqrt{x}, \qquad 0 \le x \le 6.$$

Solution. We have

$$ds = \sqrt{1 + \left(\frac{dy}{dx}\right)^2}\, dx = \frac{1}{2}\sqrt{\frac{1 + 4x}{x}}\, dx,$$

and therefore

$$\int_C y\, ds = \frac{1}{2}\int_0^6 \sqrt{x}\,\sqrt{\frac{1 + 4x}{x}}\, dx = \frac{1}{8}\int_0^6 \sqrt{1 + 4x}\; d(1 + 4x)$$

$$= \left[\frac{1}{8} \cdot \frac{2}{3}(1 + 4x)^{3/2} \right]_0^6 = \frac{31}{3}.$$

The next example shows how we evaluate integrals when the arc C consists of several pieces.

EXAMPLE 4. Evaluate

$$\int_C [(x + 2y)\, dx + (x^2 - y^2)\, dy],$$

where C is the line segment C_1 from $(0, 0)$ to $(1, 0)$ followed by the line segment C_2 from $(1, 0)$ to $(1, 1)$ (Fig. 20–25).

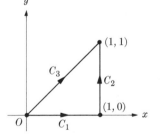

FIGURE 20–25

Solution. Along C_1 we have $x = x$, $y = 0$, $0 \le x \le 1$, so $dx = dx$, $dy = 0$, and

$$\int_{C_1} [(x + 2y)\, dx + (x^2 - y^2)\, dy] = \int_0^1 x\, dx = \frac{1}{2}.$$

Along C_2 we have $x = 1$, $y = y$, and so $dx = 0$, $dy = dy$. We obtain

$$\int_{C_2} [(x + 2y)\, dx + (x^2 - y^2)\, dy] = \int_0^1 (1 - y^2)\, dy = \frac{2}{3}.$$

Therefore

$$\int_C [(x + 2y)\, dx + (x^2 - y^2)\, dy] = \frac{1}{2} + \frac{2}{3} = \frac{7}{6}.$$

EXAMPLE 5. Evaluate the integral of Example 4 where the arc C is now the line segment C_3 from $(0, 0)$ to $(1, 1)$. (See Fig. 20–25.)

Solution. Along C_3 we have $y = x$, and so $dy = dx$. Therefore

$$\int_{C_3} [(x + 2y)\, dx + (x^2 - y^2)\, dy] = \int_0^1 3x\, dx = \frac{3}{2}.$$

The next example illustrates the method for evaluation of line integrals in three space.

EXAMPLE 6. Evaluate the integral

$$\int_C [(x^2 + y^2 - z^2)\, dx + yz\, dy + (x - y)\, dz]$$

where C is the arc

$$x = t^2 + 2, \qquad y = 2t - 1, \qquad z = 2t^2 - t, \qquad 0 \le t \le 1. \qquad (2)$$

Solution. We substitute for x, y, z from (2) and insert the values $dx = 2t\, dt$, $dy = 2\, dt$, $dz = (4t - 1)\, dt$, to obtain

$$\int_0^1 \{[(t^2 + 2)^2 + (2t - 1)^2 - (2t^2 - t)^2]2t\, dt + (2t - 1)(2t^2 - t)2\, dt$$
$$+ (t^2 - 2t + 3)(4t - 1)\, dt\}.$$

Upon multiplying out all the terms and performing the resulting routine integration we get the value $263/30$.

EXERCISES

In each of problems 1 through 10, evaluate $\int_C (P\, dx + Q\, dy)$ and draw a sketch of the arc C.

1. $\int_C [(x + y)\, dx + (x - y)\, dy]$ where C is the segment from $(0, 0)$ to $(2, 1)$.
2. $\int_C [(x + y)\, dx + (x - y)\, dy]$ where C consists of the segment from $(0, 0)$ to $(2, 0)$ followed by that from $(2, 0)$ to $(2, 1)$.
3. $\int_C [(x^2 - 2y)\, dx + (2x + y^2)\, dy]$ where C is the arc of $y^2 = 4x - 1$ going from $(\frac{1}{2}, -1)$ to $(\frac{5}{4}, 2)$.
4. $\int_C [(x^2 - 2y)\, dx + (2x + y^2)\, dy]$ where C is the segment going from $(\frac{1}{2}, -1)$ to $(\frac{5}{4}, 2)$.
5. $\int_C [y\, dx + (x^2 + y^2)\, dy]$ where C is the arc of the circle $y = +\sqrt{4 - x^2}$ from $(-2, 0)$ to $(0, 2)$.
6. $\int_C [y\, dx + (x^2 + y^2)\, dy]$ where C consists of the line segment from $(-2, 0)$ to $(0, 0)$ followed by that from $(0, 0)$ to $(0, 2)$.

7. $\displaystyle \int_C \left(\frac{x^2}{\sqrt{x^2 - y^2}}\, dx + \frac{2y}{4x^2 + y^2}\, dy \right)$

where C is the arc $y = \frac{1}{2}x^2$ from $(0, 0)$ to $(2, 2)$.

8. $\int_C \left(\dfrac{x^2}{\sqrt{x^2 - y^2}} \, dx + \dfrac{2y}{4x^2 + y^2} \, dy \right)$

where C consists of the line segment from $(0, 0)$ to $(2, 0)$, followed by the line segment from $(2, 0)$ to $(2, 2)$.

9. $\int_C \left(\dfrac{-y}{x\sqrt{x^2 - y^2}} \, dx + \dfrac{1}{\sqrt{x^2 - y^2}} \, dy \right)$

where C is the arc of $x^2 - y^2 = 9$ from $(3, 0)$ to $(5, 4)$.

10. Same integral as in problem 9, where C consists of the line segment from $(3, 0)$ to $(5, 0)$, followed by the line segment from $(5, 0)$ to $(5, 4)$.

11. Calculate $\int_C \sqrt{x + (3y)^{5/3}} \, ds$ where C is the arc $y = \frac{1}{3}x^3$ going from $(0, 0)$ to $(3, 9)$.

12. Calculate $\int_C \sqrt{x + 3y} \, ds$ where C is the straight line segment going from $(0, 0)$ to $(3, 9)$.

13. Calculate $\int_C y^2 \sin^3 x \sqrt{1 + \cos^2 x} \, ds$ where C is the arc $y = \sin x$ going from $(0, 0)$ to $(\pi/2, 1)$.

14. Calculate $\int_C (2x^2 + 3y^2 - xy) \, ds$ where C is the arc

$$\left. \begin{array}{l} x = 3 \cos t \\ y = 3 \sin t \end{array} \right\} \quad 0 \leq t \leq \dfrac{\pi}{4}.$$

15. Calculate $\int_C x^2 \, ds$ where C is the arc $x = 2y^{3/2}$ going from $(2, 1)$ to $(16, 4)$.

16. Calculate $\int_C [(x^2 + y^2) \, dx + (x^2 - y^2) \, dy]$ where C is the arc

$$\left. \begin{array}{l} x = t^2 + 3 \\ y = t - 1 \end{array} \right\} \quad 1 \leq t \leq 2.$$

17. Calculate $\int_C [\sin x \, dy + \cos y \, dx]$ where C is the arc

$$\left. \begin{array}{l} x = t^2 + 3 \\ y = 2t^2 - 1 \end{array} \right\} \quad 0 \leq t \leq 2.$$

18. Calculate $\int_C [(x - y) \, dx + (y - z) \, dy + (z - x) \, dz]$ where C is the line segment extending from $(1, -1, 2)$ to $(2, 3, 1)$.

19. Calculate $\int_C [(x^2 - y^2) \, dx + 2xz \, dy + (xy - yz) \, dz]$ where C is the line segment

$$\left. \begin{array}{l} x = 2t - 1 \\ y = t + 1 \\ z = t - 2 \end{array} \right\} \quad 0 \leq t \leq 3.$$

20. Calculate $\int_C [(x - y + z) \, dx + (y + z - x) \, dy + (z + x - y) \, dz]$ where C consists of straight line segments connecting the points $(1, -1, 2)$, $(2, -1, 2)$, $(2, 3, 2)$, and $(2, 3, 1)$, in that order.

21. Calculate

$$\int_C \frac{x\,dx + y\,dy + z\,dz}{x^2 + y^2 + z^2}$$

where C is the arc

$$x = 2t, \qquad y = 2t + 1, \qquad z = t^2 + t,$$

joining the points $(0, 1, 0)$ and $(2, 3, 2)$.

22. Same as problem 21, where C is the straight line segment joining $(0, 1, 0)$ and $(2, 3, 2)$.

23. Evaluate

$$\int_C \frac{y\,dx + x\,dy}{\sqrt{x^2 + y^2}}$$

where C is the *closed curve*

$$\left. \begin{array}{l} x = \cos t \\[1mm] y = \sin t \end{array} \right\} -\pi \le t \le \pi.$$

24. Evaluate

$$\int_C \frac{-y\,dx + x\,dy}{\sqrt{x^2 + y^2}}$$

where C is the same curve as in problem 23.

16. PATH–INDEPENDENT LINE INTEGRALS. WORK

In general, the value of a line integral depends on the integrand, on the two endpoints, and on the arc connecting these endpoints. However, there are special circumstances when the value of a line integral depends solely on the integrand and endpoints but *not* on the arc on which the integration is performed. When such conditions prevail, we say that the integral is *independent of the path*. The next theorem establishes the connection between path-independent integrals and exact differentials. (See Section 13.)

Theorem 15. *Suppose that $P(x, y)\,dx + Q(x, y)\,dy$ is an exact differential. That is, there is a function $f(x, y)$ with*

$$df = P\,dx + Q\,dy.$$

Let C be an arc given parametrically by

$$x = x(t), \qquad y = y(t), \qquad t_0 \le t \le t_1$$

where $x'(t)$, $y'(t)$ are continuous. Then

$$\int_C (P\,dx + Q\,dy) = f[x(t_1), y(t_1)] - f[x(t_0), y(t_0)].$$

Thus the integral depends only on the endpoints and not on the arc C joining them.

Proof. We define the function $F(t)$ by

$$F(t) = f[x(t), y(t)], \qquad t_0 \leq t \leq t_1.$$

We use the Chain Rule to calculate the derivative:

$$F'(t) = f_{,1}x'(t) + f_{,2}y'(t)$$

and

$$F'(t) = P[x(t), y(t)]x'(t) + Q[x(t), y(t)]y'(t). \tag{1}$$

Integrating both sides of (1) with respect to t and employing Theorem 14, we conclude that

$$F(t_1) - F(t_0) = \int_C (P\, dx + Q\, dy).$$

The result follows when we note that

$$F(t_1) = f[x(t_1), y(t_1)] \qquad \text{and} \qquad F(t_0) = f[x(t_0), y(t_0)].$$

Corollary. *If $P\, dx + Q\, dy + R\, dz$ is an exact differential, then*

$$\int_C (P\, dx + Q\, dy + R\, dz) = f[x(t_1), y(t_1), z(t_1)] - f[x(t_0), y(t_0), z(t_0)]$$

where $df = P\, dx + Q\, dy + R\, dz$ and the parametric equations of C are:

$$\{x(t), y(t), z(t)\}, \qquad t_0 \leq t \leq t_1.$$

EXAMPLE 1. Show that the integrand of

$$\int_C [(2x + 3y)\, dx + (3x - 2y)\, dy]$$

is an exact differential and find the value of the integral over any arc C going from the point $(1, 3)$ to the point $(-2, 5)$.

Solution. Setting $P = 2x + 3y$, $Q = 3x - 2y$, we have

$$\frac{\partial P}{\partial y} = 3 = \frac{\partial Q}{\partial x}.$$

By Theorem 12, the integrand is an exact differential. Using the methods of Section 13 for integrating exact differentials, we find that

$$f(x, y) = x^2 + 3xy - y^2 + C_1.$$

Therefore

$$\int_C [(2x + 3y)\, dx + (3x - 2y)\, dy] = f(-2, 5) - f(1, 3) = -52.$$

Notice that in the evaluation process the constant C_1 disappears.

EXAMPLE 2. Show that the integrand of

$$\int_C (3x^2 + 6xy)\, dx + (3x^2 - 3y^2)\, dy$$

is an exact differential, and find the value of the integral over any arc C going from the point $(1, 1)$ to the point $(2, 3)$.

Solution. Setting $P = 3x^2 + 6xy$, $Q = 3x^2 - 3y^2$, we have

$$\frac{\partial P}{\partial y} = 6x = \frac{\partial Q}{\partial x}.$$

Instead of finding the function f with the property that $df = P\, dx + Q\, dy$, we may pick *any* simple path joining $(1, 1)$ and $(2, 3)$ and evaluate the integral along that path. We select the horizontal path C_1 from $(1, 1)$ to $(2, 1)$, followed by the vertical path from $(2, 1)$ to $(2, 3)$, as shown in Fig. 20–26. The result is

$$\int_{C_1} (3x^2 + 6x)\, dx + \int_{C_2} (12 - 3y^2)\, dy = \left[x^3 + 3x^2\right]_1^2 + \left[12y - y^3\right]_1^3 = 14.$$

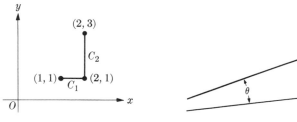

FIGURE 20–26   FIGURE 20–27

An application of line integrals occurs in the determination of the work done by a force acting on a particle in motion along a path. We recall that we considered the work done in the case of the motion of objects along a straight line. (See page 244.) The basic formula depends on the elementary idea that if the force F is constant and if the distance the particle moves (along a straight line) is d, then the work W is given by the relation

$$W = Fd.$$

For motion in the plane, *force* is a vector quantity, since it has both *magnitude* and, at the point of application, a *direction* along which it acts. We employ the representation

$$\mathbf{F} = P\mathbf{i} + Q\mathbf{j}$$

for a force vector in the plane. Suppose a particle is constrained to move in the direction of a straight line l. If the motion is caused by a force $\mathbf{F}$, then the only portion of $\mathbf{F}$ which has any effect on the motion is the component of $\mathbf{F}$ in the direction of l. We recall that this quantity is called the *projection* of $\mathbf{F}$ on l (Fig. 20–27), and is given by

$$|\mathbf{F}| \cos \theta,$$

where θ is the angle between the direction of $\mathbf{F}$ and the direction of l.

If the particle moves along l a distance d and if the force $\mathbf{F}$ is constant then, according to the elementary principle, the work done is

$$W = |\mathbf{F}| \cos \theta \cdot d.$$

We may represent the quantity above in another way. Let $\mathbf{r}$ be a vector of length d in the direction of l. Then we may write $|\mathbf{r}| = d$ and

$$W = |\mathbf{F}| \cdot |\mathbf{r}| \cos \theta.$$

We recognize this quantity as the inner, or scalar, product of the vectors $\mathbf{F}$ and $\mathbf{r}$. That is,

$$W = \mathbf{F} \cdot \mathbf{r}, \tag{2}$$

where $\mathbf{r}$ is a vector of the appropriate length in the direction of motion. Note that work is a scalar quantity.

Using (2) as the basic formula for motion in the plane, we proceed to define work when the force is variable and the motion is along a curved path. We write

$$\mathbf{F} = P(x, y)\mathbf{i} + Q(x, y)\mathbf{j}$$

for a force which may vary from point to point. We let C be an arc and suppose that a particle is constrained so that it must move along C (as a bead on a wire); we suppose the motion is caused by a force $\mathbf{F}$. We let the arc C be given by the equations

$$x = x(t), \qquad y = y(t), \qquad a \le t \le b,$$

and make a subdivision $a = t_0 < t_1 < \cdots < t_{n-1} < t_n = b$ of the interval $a \le t \le b$. We thus get a subdivision $P_0, P_1, \ldots, P_{n-1}, P_n$ of the arc C. We now replace each subarc by a straight line segment and *assume* that the force is approximately constant along each such subarc. Denoting the ith subarc by $P_{i-1}P_i$ and the force along this subarc by $\mathbf{F}_i$, we obtain, for the work done along this arc, the approximate quantity (Fig. 20–28),

$$W_i = |\mathbf{F}_i| \cos \theta_i \sqrt{[x(t_i) - x(t_{i-1})]^2 + [y(t_i) - y(t_{i-1})]^2}.$$

If we introduce the vector

$$\Delta_i x \mathbf{i} + \Delta_i y \mathbf{j}$$

and write $\mathbf{F}_i = P_i \mathbf{i} + Q_i \mathbf{j}$ then, taking (2) into account, the work is

$$W_i = P_i \Delta_i x + Q_i \Delta_i y.$$

FIGURE 20–28

The total work done is the sum of the amounts of work done on the individual subarcs. (See page 244, PRINCIPLE 1.) We have, approximately,

$$W = \sum_{i=1}^{n} P[x(\tau_i), y(\tau_i)] \Delta_i x + Q[x(\tau_i), y(\tau_i)] \Delta_i y.$$

Proceeding to the limit, we *define* the *total work* by the formula

$$W = \int_C (P \, dx + Q \, dy).$$

For motion in three dimensions with the force given by a vector

$$\mathbf{F} = P(x, y, z)\mathbf{i} + Q(x, y, z)\mathbf{j} + R(x, y, z)\mathbf{k},$$

work is defined by the formula

$$W = \int_C (P \, dx + Q \, dy + R \, dz).$$

EXAMPLE 3.   A particle moves along the curve $y = x^2$ from the point $(1, 1)$ to the point $(3, 9)$. If the motion is caused by the force $\mathbf{F} = (x^2 - y^2)\mathbf{i} + x^2 y\mathbf{j}$ applied to the particle, find the total work done.

Solution. Using the formula for work, we have

$$W = \int_C [(x^2 - y^2) \, dx + x^2 y \, dy].$$

Employing the normal methods for calculating such integrals, we find

$$W = \int_1^3 [(x^2 - x^4) \, dx + x^2 (x^2)(2x) \, dx]$$

$$= \left[\frac{1}{3} x^6 - \frac{1}{5} x^5 + \frac{1}{3} x^3 \right]_1^3 = \frac{3044}{15}.$$

If the arc is measured in inches and the force in pounds, the total work is $\frac{3044}{15}$ in.-lb.

EXERCISES

In each of problems 1 through 11, show that the integrand is an exact differential and evaluate the integral.

1. $\int_C [(x^2 + 2y) \, dx + (2y + 2x) \, dy]$ where C is any arc from $(2, 1)$ to $(4, 2)$.

2. $\int_C [(3x^2 + 4xy - 2y^2) \, dx + (2x^2 - 4xy - 3y^2) \, dy]$ where C is any arc from $(1, 1)$ to $(3, 2)$.

3. $\int_C (e^x \cos y \, dx - e^x \sin y \, dy)$ where C is any arc from $(1, 0)$ to $(0, 1)$.

4. $\int_C \left[\left(\frac{2xy^2}{1 + x^2} + 3 \right) dx + (2y \ln (1 + x^2) - 2) \, dy \right]$

    where C is any arc from $(0, 2)$ to $(5, 1)$.

5. $\int_C \left[\frac{y^2}{(x^2 + y^2)^{3/2}} \, dx - \frac{xy}{(x^2 + y^2)^{3/2}} \, dy \right]$

    where C is any arc from $(4, 3)$ to $(-3, 4)$ which does not pass through the origin.

6. $\displaystyle\int_C \left[\frac{x}{\sqrt{1 + x^2 + y^2}}\, dx + \frac{y}{\sqrt{1 + x^2 + y^2}}\, dy\right]$

where C is any arc from $(-2, -2)$ to $(4, 1)$.

7. $\int_C \{[ye^{xy}(\cos xy - \sin xy) + \cos x]\, dx + [xe^{xy}(\cos xy - \sin xy) + \sin y]\, dy\}$
where C is any arc from $(0, 0)$ to $(3, -2)$.

8. $\int_C [(2x - 2y + z + 2)\, dx + (2y - 2x - 1)\, dy + (-2z + x)\, dz]$ where C is any arc from $(1, 0, 2)$ to $(3, -1, 4)$.

9. $\int_C [(2x + y - z)\, dx + (-2y + x + 2z + 3)\, dy + (4z - x + 2y - 2)\, dz]$ where C is any arc from $(0, 2, -1)$ to $(1, -2, 4)$.

10. $\int_C [(3x^2 - 3yz + 2xz)\, dx + (3y^2 - 3xz + z^2)\, dy + (3z^2 - 3xy + x^2 + 2yz)\, dz]$ where C is any arc from $(-1, 2, 3)$ to $(3, 2, -1)$.

11. $\int_C [(yze^{xyz} \cos x - e^{xyz} \sin x + y \cos xy + z \sin xz)\, dx$

$\qquad\qquad + (xze^{xyz} \cos x + x \cos xy)\, dy + (xye^{xyz} \cos x + x \sin xz)\, dz]$

where C is any arc from $(0, 0, 0)$ to $(-1, -2, -3)$.

12. A particle is moving along the path

$$x = t + 1, \qquad y = 2t^2 + t + 2$$

from the point $(1, 2)$ to the point $(2, 5)$, subject to the force $\mathbf{F} = (x^2 + y)\mathbf{i} + 2xy\mathbf{j}$. Find the total work done.

13. A particle is moving in the xy-plane along a straight line from the point $A(a, b)$ to the point $B(c, d)$, subject to the force

$$\mathbf{F} = \frac{-x}{x^2 + y^2}\,\mathbf{i} - \frac{y}{x^2 + y^2}\,\mathbf{j}.$$

Find the work done. Show that the work done is the same if a different path between A and B is selected. (The path does not go through the origin.)

14. A particle moves in the xy-plane along the straight line connecting $A(a, b)$ and $B(c, d)$, subject to the force

$$\mathbf{F} = \frac{-x}{(x^2 + y^2)^{3/2}}\,\mathbf{i} + \frac{-y}{(x^2 + y^2)^{3/2}}\,\mathbf{j}.$$

Find the work done. Show that the work done is the same if a different path is selected joining the points A and B but not going through the origin.

15. A particle moves along the straight line (in three space) joining the points $A(a, b, c)$ and $B(d, e, f)$, subject to the force

$$\mathbf{F} = \frac{-x}{(x^2 + y^2 + z^2)^{3/2}}\,\mathbf{i} - \frac{y}{(x^2 + y^2 + z^2)^{3/2}}\,\mathbf{j} - \frac{z}{(x^2 + y^2 + z^2)^{3/2}}\,\mathbf{k}.$$

Find the work done. Show that the work done is the same if a different path is selected joining the points A and B but not going through the origin.

16. Same as problem 15, with

$$\mathbf{F} = \frac{x}{(x^2 + y^2 + z^2)^2}\,\mathbf{i} + \frac{y}{(x^2 + y^2 + z^2)^2}\,\mathbf{j} + \frac{z}{(x^2 + y^2 + z^2)^2}\,\mathbf{k}.$$

CHAPTER 21

Multiple Integration

---

1. DEFINITION OF THE DOUBLE INTEGRAL

Let F be a region of area A situated in the xy-plane. We shall always assume that a region includes its boundary curve. Such regions are sometimes called *closed regions* in analogy with closed intervals on the real line—that is, ones which include their endpoints. We subdivide the xy-plane into rectangles by drawing lines parallel to the coordinate axes. These lines may or may not be equally spaced (Fig. 21–1). Starting in some convenient place (such as the upper left-hand corner of F), we systematically number all the rectangles *lying entirely within* F. Suppose there are n such and we label them $r_1, r_2, \ldots, r_n$. We use the symbols $A(r_1), A(r_2), \ldots, A(r_n)$ for the areas of these rectangles. The collection of n rectangles $\{r_1, r_2, \ldots, r_n\}$ is called a *subdivision* Δ of F. The *norm of the subdivision*, denoted as usual by $\|\Delta\|$, is the length of the diagonal of the largest rectangle in the subdivision Δ.

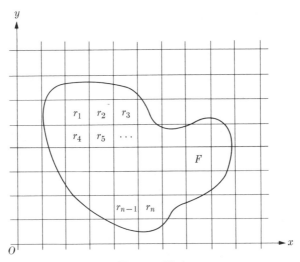

FIGURE 21–1

Suppose that $f(x, y)$ is a function defined for all (x, y) in the region F. The definition of the *double integral of f over the region F* is similar to the definition of the integral for functions of one variable. (See page 213.) Select arbitrarily a point in each of the rectangles of the subdivision Δ, denoting the coordinates of the point in the rectangle r_i by (ξ_i, η_i). (See Fig. 21–2.) Now form the sum

$$f(\xi_1, \eta_1)A(r_1) + f(\xi_2, \eta_2)A(r_2) + \cdots + f(\xi_n, \eta_n)A(r_n)$$

or, more compactly,

$$\sum_{i=1}^{n} f(\xi_i, \eta_i)A(r_i). \qquad (1)$$

This sum is an approximation to the double integral we shall define. Sums such as (1) may be formed for subdivisions with any positive norm and with the ith point (ξ_i, η_i) chosen in any way whatsoever in the rectangle r_i.

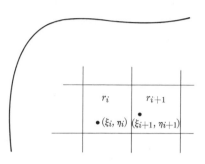

FIGURE 21–2

DEFINITION. We say that *a number L is the limit of sums of type* (1) and write

$$\lim_{||\Delta|| \to 0} \sum_{i=1}^{n} f(\xi_i, \eta_i)A(r_i) = L$$

if the number L has the property: for each $\epsilon > 0$ there is a $\delta > 0$ such that

$$\left| \sum_{i=1}^{n} f(\xi_i, \eta_i)A(r_i) - L \right| < \epsilon$$

for every subdivision Δ with $||\Delta|| < \delta$ and for all possible choices of the points (ξ_i, η_i) in the rectangles r_i.

It can be shown that if the number L exists, then it must be unique.

DEFINITION. If f is defined in a region F and the number L defined above exists, we say that *f is integrable over F* and write

$$\iint_{F} f(x, y)\, dA.$$

We also call the expression above the *double integral of f over F.*

The double integral has a geometric interpretation in terms of the volume of a solid. We recall the methods of finding volumes of solids of revolution developed on page 482. Now we shall discuss the notion of volume in somewhat more detail. The definition of volume depends on (i), the definition of the volume of a cube—namely, length times width times height, and (ii), a limiting process.

Let S be a solid in three-space. We divide all of space into cubes by constructing planes parallel to the coordinate planes at a distance apart of $1/2^n$ units, with n some positive integer. In such a network, the cubes are of three kinds: type (1), those cubes entirely within S; type (2), those cubes partly in S and partly outside S; and type (3), those cubes entirely outside S (Fig. 21–3). We define

$$V_n^-(S) = \frac{1}{8^n} \text{ times the number of cubes of type (1),}$$

$$V_n^+(S) = V_n^-(S) + \frac{1}{8^n} \text{ times the number of cubes of type (2).}$$

FIGURE 21–3

(Compare this discussion with that for area, page 200 ff.) Intuitively we expect that, however the volume of S is defined, the number $V_n^-(S)$ would be smaller than the volume, while the number $V_n^+(S)$ would be larger. It can be shown that, as n increases, $V_n^-(S)$ gets larger or at least does not decrease, while $V_n^+(S)$ gets smaller or is at least nonincreasing. Obviously,

$$V_n^-(S) \leq V_n^+(S),$$

always. Since bounded increasing sequences and bounded decreasing sequences tend to limits, the following definitions are appropriate.

DEFINITIONS. The *inner volume* of a solid S, denoted $V^-(S)$, is $\lim_{n\to\infty} V_n^-(S)$. The *outer volume*, denoted $V^+(S)$, is $\lim_{n\to\infty} V_n^+(S)$. A set of points S in three-space has a *volume* whenever $V^-(S) = V^+(S)$. This common value is denoted by $V(S)$ and is called the volume of S.

Remark. It is not difficult to construct point sets for which $V^-(S) \neq V^+(S)$. For example, take S to be all points (x, y, z) such that x, y, and z are rational and $0 \leq x \leq 1, 0 \leq y \leq 1, 0 \leq z \leq 1$. The student can verify that $V_n^-(S) = 0$ for every n, while $V_n^+(S) = 1$ for every n.

If S_1 and S_2 are two solids with no points in common, it can be shown, as expected, that $V(S_1 + S_2) = V(S_1) + V(S_2)$. Also, the subdivision of all of space into cubes is not vital. Rectangular parallelepipeds would do equally well, with the formula for the volume of a rectangular parallelepiped taken as length times width times height.

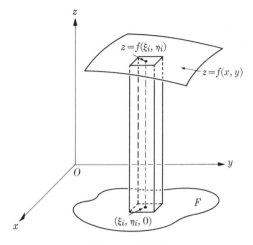

FIGURE 21–4

The volume of a solid is intimately connected with the double integral in the same way that the area of a region is connected with the single integral. (See page 213.) We now exhibit this connection.

Suppose that $f(x, y)$ is a positive function defined for (x, y) in some region F (Fig. 21–4). An item in the sum (1) approximating the double integral is

$$f(\xi_i, \eta_i)A(r_i),$$

which we recognize as the volume of the rectangular column of height $f(\xi_i, \eta_i)$ and area of base $A(r_i)$ (Fig. 21–4). The sum of such columns is an approximation to the volume of the cylindrical solid bounded by the surface $z = f(x, y)$, the plane figure F, and lines parallel to the z-axis through the boundary of F (Fig. 21–5). It can be shown that, with appropriate hypotheses on the function f, the double integral

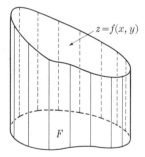

$$\iint_F f(x, y) \, dA$$

measures the "volume under the surface" in the same way that a single integral

$$\int_a^b f(x) \, dx$$

FIGURE 21–5

measures the area under the curve. An outline of a proof of the following theorem is given in Morrey, *University Calculus*, page 596.*

---

* Actually it is shown there that the rectangles r_i may be replaced by any figures F_i (i.e., any regions which have area) in the sums $\sum f(\xi_i, \eta_i)A(F_i)$ approximating the integral.

Theorem 1. *If $f(x, y)$ is continuous for (x, y) in a closed region F, then f is integrable over F. Furthermore, if $f(x, y) > 0$ for (x, y) in F, then*

$$V(S) = \iint_F f(x, y) \, dA,$$

where $V(S)$ is the volume of the solid defined by

$$(x, y) \text{ in } F \text{ and } 0 \le z \le f(x, y).$$

Methods for the evaluation of double integrals are discussed in Section 3.

EXAMPLE. Given $f(x, y) = 1 + xy$ and the region F bounded by the lines $y = 0$, $y = x$, and $x = 1$ (Fig. 21–6), let Δ be the subdivision formed by the lines $x = 0, 0.2$, $0.5, 0.8, 1$ and $y = 0, 0.2, 0.5, 0.7, 1$. Find the value of the approximating sum

$$\sum_{i=1}^{n} f(\xi_i, \eta_i) A(r_i)$$

to the double integral

$$\iint_F f(x, y) \, dA$$

if the points (ξ_i, η_i) are selected at the centers of the rectangles.

Solution. Referring to Fig. 21–6, we see that there are 6 rectangles in the subdivision which we label $r_1, r_2, \ldots, r_6$, as shown, We compute:

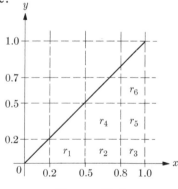

$$A(r_1) = 0.06, \quad f(0.35, \ 0.1) = 1.035$$
$$A(r_2) = 0.06, \quad f(0.65, \ 0.1) = 1.065$$
$$A(r_3) = 0.04, \quad f(0.9, \quad 0.1) = 1.090$$
$$A(r_4) = 0.09, \quad f(0.65, 0.35) = 1.2275$$
$$A(r_5) = 0.06, \quad f(0.9, \quad 0.35) = 1.315$$
$$A(r_6) = 0.04, \quad f(0.9, \quad 0.6) = 1.540$$

Multiplying and adding, we find that

$$\sum_{i=1}^{6} f(\xi_i, \eta_i) A(r_i) = 0.420575 \quad \text{(Answer)}.$$

FIGURE 21–6

EXERCISES

In each of problems 1 though 10, calculate the sum $\sum_{i=1}^{n} f(\xi_i, \eta_i) A(r_i)$ for the subdivision Δ of the region F formed by the given lines and with the points (ξ_i, η_i) selected as directed in each case.

1. $f(x, y) = x^2 + 2y^2$; F is the rectangle $0 \le x \le 1, 0 \le y \le 1$. The subdivision Δ is: $x = 0, 0.4, 0.8, 1$; $y = 0, 0.3, 0.7, 1$. For each i the point (ξ_i, η_i) is taken at the center of the rectangle r_i.

2. Same as problem 1, with (ξ_i, η_i) taken at the point of r_i which is closest to the origin.

3. $f(x, y) = 1 + x^2 - y^2$; F is the triangular region formed by the lines $y = 0$, $y = x$, $x = 2$. The subdivision Δ is: $x = 0, 0.5, 1, 1.6, 2$; $y = 0, 0.6, 1, 1.5, 2$. For each i, the point (ξ_i, η_i) is taken at the center of the rectangle r_i.

4. Same as problem 3, with (ξ_i, η_i) taken at the point of r_i which is closest to the origin.

5. Same as problem 3, with (ξ_i, η_i) selected on the lower edge of r_i, midway between the vertical subdivision lines.

6. $f(x, y) = x^2 - 2xy + 3x - 2y$; F is the trapezoid bounded by the lines $x = 0$, $x = 2$, $y = 0$, $y = x + 1$. The subdivision Δ is: $x = 0, 0.4, 1, 1.5, 2$; $y = 0$, $0.6, 1, 1.4, 1.8, 2, 3$. For each i the point (ξ_i, η_i) is taken at the center of the rectangle r_i.

7. Same as problem 6, with (ξ_i, η_i) taken at the point of r_i farthest from the origin.

8. Same as problem 6, with (ξ_i, η_i) taken at the point of r_i closest to the origin.

9. Same as problem 6, with the subdivision Δ: $x = 0, 0.4, 0.8, 1, 1.5, 1.8, 2$; $y = 0$, $0.3, 0.6, 1, 1.4, 1.6, 1.8, 2, 3$. Can any statement be made comparing the results of problems 6 and 9 with $\iint_F f(x, y)\, dA$?

10. We have

$$f(x, y) = \frac{x - y}{1 + x + y};$$

F is the region bounded by the line $y = 0$ and the curve $y = 2x - x^2$. The subdivision Δ is: $x = 0, 0.5, 1.0, 1.5, 2$; $y = 0, 0.2, 0.4, 0.6, 0.8, 1$. For each i, the point (ξ_i, η_i) is taken at the center of the rectangle r_i.

2. PROPERTIES OF THE DOUBLE INTEGRAL

In analogy with the properties of the definite integral of functions of one variable (page 219), we state several basic properties of the double integral. The simplest properties are given in the two following theorems.

Theorem 2. *If c is any number and f is integrable over a closed region F, then cf is integrable and*

$$\iint_F cf(x, y)\, dA = c \iint_F f(x, y)\, dA.$$

Theorem 3. *If f and g are integrable over a closed region F, then*

$$\iint_F [f(x, y) + g(x, y)]\, dA = \iint_F f(x, y)\, dA + \iint_F g(x, y)\, dA.$$

The result holds for the sum of any finite number of integrable functions. The proofs of Theorems 2 and 3 are obtained directly from the definition.

Theorem 4. *Suppose that f is integrable over a closed region F and*

$$m \leq f(x, y) \leq M \text{ for all } (x, y) \text{ in } F.$$

Then, if A(F) denotes the area of F, we have

$$mA(F) \leq \iint\limits_{F} f(x, y) \, dA \leq MA(F).$$

The proof of Theorem 4 follows exactly the same pattern as does the proof in the one-variable case. (See page 220, Theorem 6.)

Theorem 5. *If f and g are integrable over F and $f(x, y) \leq g(x, y)$ for all (x, y) in F, then*

$$\iint\limits_{F} f(x, y) \, dA \leq \iint\limits_{F} g(x, y) \, dA.$$

The proof is established by the same argument used in the one-variable case (page 221, Theorem 7).

Theorem 6. *If the closed region F is decomposed into regions F_1 and F_2 and if f is continuous over F, then*

$$\iint\limits_{F} f(x, y) \, dA = \iint\limits_{F_1} f(x, y) \, dA + \iint\limits_{F_2} f(x, y) \, dA.$$

The proof depends on the definition of double integral and on the basic theorems on limits.

EXERCISES

In problems 1 through 7, use Theorem 4 to find in each case the largest and smallest values the given double integrals can possibly have.

1. $\iint\limits_{F} xy \, dA$ where F is the region bounded by the lines $x = 0$, $y = 0$, $x = 2$, $y = x + 3$.

2. $\iint\limits_{F} (x^2 + y^2) \, dA$ where F is the region bounded by the lines $x = -2$, $x = 3$, $y = x + 2$, $y = -2$.

3. $\iint\limits_{F} (1 + 2x^2 + y^2) \, dA$ where F is the region bounded by the lines $x = -3$, $x = 3$, $y = 4$, $y = -4$.

4. $\iint\limits_{F} y^4 \, dA$ where F is the region bounded by the line $y = 0$ and the curve $y = 2x - x^2$.

5. $\iint\limits_{F} (x - y) \, dA$ where F is the region enclosed in the circle $x^2 + y^2 = 9$.

6. $\iint\limits_{F} [1/(1 + x^2 + y^2)] \, dA$ where F is the region enclosed in the ellipse $4x^2 + 9y^2 = 36$.

7. $\iint\limits_{F} \sqrt{1 + x^2 + y^2} \, dA$ where F is the region bounded by the curves $y = 3x - x^2$ and $y = x^2 - 3x$.

8. Write out a proof of Theorem 3.   9. Write out a proof of Theorem 4.

10. Write out a proof of Theorem 5.   11. Write out a proof of Theorem 6.

3.   EVALUATION OF DOUBLE INTEGRALS.   ITERATED INTEGRALS

The definition of the double integral is useless as a tool for evaluation in any particular case. Of course, it may happen that the function $f(x, y)$ and the region F are particularly simple, so that the limit of the sum $\sum_{i=1}^{n} f(\xi_i, \eta_i) A(r_i)$ can be found directly. However, such limits cannot generally be found. As in the case of ordinary integrals and line integrals, it is important to develop simple and routine methods for determining the value of a given double integral. In this section we show how the evaluation of a double integral may be performed by successive evaluations of single integrals. In other words, we reduce the problem to one we have already studied extensively. The student will recall that the evaluation of line integrals was reduced to known techniques for single integrals in a similar way.

Let F be the rectangle with sides $x = a$, $x = b$, $y = c$, $y = d$, as shown in Fig. 21–7. Suppose that $f(x, y)$ is continuous for (x, y) in F. We form the ordinary integral with respect to x,

$$\int_a^b f(x, y)\, dx,$$

in which we keep y fixed when performing the integration. Of course, the value of the above integral will depend on the value of y used, and so we may write

$$A(y) = \int_a^b f(x, y)\, dx.$$

The function $A(y)$ is defined for $c \leq y \leq d$ and, in fact, it can be shown that if $f(x, y)$ is continuous on F, then $A(y)$ is continuous on $[c, d]$. The integral of $A(y)$ may be computed, and we write

$$\int_c^d A(y)\, dy = \int_c^d \left[\int_a^b f(x, y)\, dx \right] dy. \tag{1}$$

We could start the other way around by fixing x and forming the integral

$$B(x) = \int_c^d f(x, y)\, dy.$$

Then

$$\int_a^b B(x)\, dx = \int_a^b \left[\int_c^d f(x, y)\, dy \right] dx. \tag{2}$$

FIGURE 21–7

Note that the integrals are computed *successively*; in (1) we first integrate with respect to x (keeping y constant) and then with respect to y; in (2) we first integrate with respect to y (keeping x constant) and then with respect to x.

DEFINITION. The integrals

$$\int_c^d \left[\int_a^b f(x, y)\, dx \right] dy, \qquad \int_a^b \left[\int_c^d f(x, y)\, dy \right] dx$$

are called the *iterated integrals* of f. The terms *repeated* integrals and *successive* integrals are also used.

NOTATION. The brackets in iterated integrals are unwieldy, and we will write

$$\int_c^d \int_a^b f(x, y)\, dx\, dy \qquad \text{to mean} \qquad \int_c^d \left[\int_a^b f(x, y)\, dx \right] dy,$$

$$\int_a^b \int_c^d f(x, y)\, dy\, dx \qquad \text{to mean} \qquad \int_a^b \left[\int_c^d f(x, y)\, dy \right] dx.$$

Iterated integrals are computed in the usual way, as the next example shows.

EXAMPLE 1. Evaluate

$$\int_1^4 \int_{-2}^3 (x^2 - 2xy^2 + y^3)\, dx\, dy.$$

Solution. Keeping y fixed, we have

$$\int_{-2}^3 (x^2 - 2xy^2 + y^3)\, dx = \left[\frac{1}{3} x^3 - x^2 y^2 + y^3 x \right]_{-2}^3$$

$$= 9 - 9y^2 + 3y^3 - \left(-\frac{8}{3} - 4y^2 - 2y^3 \right)$$

$$= \frac{35}{3} - 5y^2 + 5y^3.$$

Therefore

$$\int_1^4 \int_{-2}^3 (x^2 - 2xy^2 + y^3)\, dx\, dy = \int_1^4 \left(\frac{35}{3} - 5y^2 + 5y^3 \right) dy$$

$$= \left[\frac{35}{3} y - \frac{5}{3} y^3 + \frac{5}{4} y^4 \right]_1^4 = \frac{995}{4}.$$

Iterated integrals may be defined over regions F which have curved boundaries. This situation is more complicated than the one just discussed. Consider a region F such as that shown in Fig. 21–8, in which the boundary consists of the lines $x = a$, $x = b$, and the graphs of the functions $p(x)$ and $q(x)$ with $p(x) \le q(x)$ for $a \le x \le b$. We may define

$$\int_a^b \int_{p(x)}^{q(x)} f(x, y)\, dy\, dx,$$

FIGURE 21–8

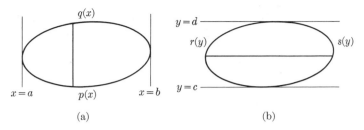

FIGURE 21–9

in which we first integrate (for fixed x) from the lower curve to the upper curve, i.e., along a typical line as shown in Fig. 21–8; then we integrate with respect to x over all such typical segments from a to b.

More generally, iterated integrals may be defined over a region F such as the one shown in Fig. 21–9(a). Integrating first with respect to y, we have

$$\int_a^b \int_{p(x)}^{q(x)} f(x, y)\, dy\, dx.$$

On the other hand, the integral taken first with respect to x requires that we represent F as shown in Fig. 21–9(b). Then we have

$$\int_c^d \int_{r(y)}^{s(y)} f(x, y)\, dx\, dy.$$

 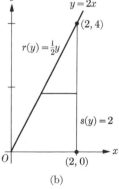

FIGURE 21–10

EXAMPLE 2. Given the function $f(x, y) = xy$ and the triangular region F bounded by the lines $y = 0$, $y = 2x$, $x = 2$ [Fig. 21–10(a)], find the value of both iterated integrals.

Solution. Referring to Fig. 21–10(a), we see that for

$$\int_a^b \int_{p(x)}^{q(x)} xy\, dy\, dx,$$

we have $p(x) = 0$, $q(x) = 2x$, $a = 0$, $b = 2$. Therefore

$$\int_0^2 \int_0^{2x} xy\ dy\ dx = \int_0^2 \left[\frac{1}{2}xy^2\right]_0^{2x} dx$$

$$= \int_0^2 2x^3\ dx = \left[\frac{1}{2}x^4\right]_0^2 = 8.$$

Integrating with respect to x first [Fig. 5–10(b)], we have

$$\int_c^d \int_{r(y)}^{s(y)} xy\ dx\ dy$$

with

$$r(y) = \frac{1}{2}y, \quad s(y) = 2, \quad c = 0, \quad d = 4.$$

Therefore

$$\int_0^4 \int_{y/2}^2 xy\ dx\ dy = \int_0^4 \left[\frac{1}{2}x^2 y\right]_{y/2}^2 dy$$

$$= \int_0^4 \left(2y - \frac{1}{8}y^3\right) dy = \left[y^2 - \frac{1}{32}y^4\right]_0^4 = 8.$$

It is not accidental that the two integrals in Example 2 have the same value. The next theorem describes the general situation.

Theorem 7. *Suppose F is a closed region consisting of all (x, y) such that*

$$a \le x \le b, \qquad p(x) \le y \le q(x),$$

where p and q are continuous and $p(x) \le q(x)$ for $a \le x \le b$. Suppose that $f(x, y)$ is continuous for (x, y) in F. Then

$$\iint_F f(x, y)\ dA = \int_a^b \int_{p(x)}^{q(x)} f(x, y)\ dy\ dx.$$

The corresponding result holds if the closed region F has the representation

$$c \le y \le d, \qquad r(y) \le x \le s(y)$$

where $r(y) \le s(y)$ for $c \le y \le d$. In such a case,

$$\iint_F f(x, y)\ dA = \int_c^d \int_{r(y)}^{s(y)} f(x, y)\ dx\ dy.$$

In other words, both iterated integrals, when computable, are equal to the double integral and therefore equal to each other.

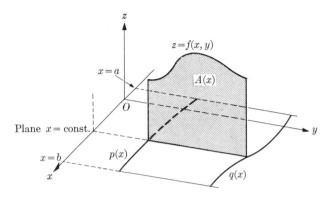

FIGURE 21–11

Partial proof. We shall discuss the first result, the second being similar. Suppose first that $f(x, y)$ is positive. A plane $x = $ const intersects the surface $f(x, y)$ in a curve (Fig. 21–11). The area under this curve in the $x = $ const plane is shown as a shaded region. Denoting the area of this region by $A(x)$, we have the formula

$$A(x) = \int_{p(x)}^{q(x)} f(x, y) \, dy.$$

It can be shown that $A(x)$ is continuous. Furthermore, it can also be shown (Morrey, *University Calculus*, pp. 599–601) that if $A(x)$ is integrated between $x = a$ and $x = b$, the volume V under the surface $f(x, y)$ is swept out. We recall that a similar argument was used in obtaining volumes of revolution by the disc method. (See page 482.) The double integral yields the volume under the surface, and so we write

$$V = \iint_F f(x, y) \, dA.$$

On the other hand, we obtain the volume by integrating $A(x)$; that is,

$$V = \int_a^b A(x) \, dx = \int_a^b \int_{p(x)}^{q(x)} f(x, y) \, dy \, dx.$$

If $f(x, y)$ is not positive but is bounded from below by the plane $z = c$, then subtraction of the volume of the cylinder of height c and cross-section F leads to the same result.

Remarks. We have considered two ways of expressing a region F in the xy-plane. They are

$$a \le x \le b, \qquad p(x) \le y \le q(x) \tag{3}$$

and

$$c \le y \le d, \qquad r(y) \le x \le s(y). \tag{4}$$

It frequently happens that a region F is expressible more simply in one of the

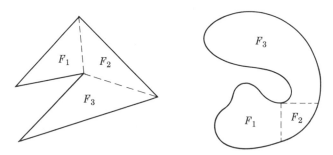

FIGURE 21–12

above forms than in the other. In doubtful cases, a sketch of F may show which is simpler and, therefore, which of the iterated integrals is evaluated more easily.

A region F may not be expressible in either the form (3) or the form (4). In such cases, F may sometimes be subdivided into a number of regions, each having one of the two forms. The integrations are then performed for each subregion and the results added. Figure 21–12 gives examples of how the subdivision process might take place.

EXAMPLE 3. Evaluate $\iint_F x^2 y^2 \, dA$ where F is the figure bounded by the lines $y = 1$, $y = 2$, $x = 0$, and $x = y$ (Fig. 21–13).

Solution. The closed region F is the set of (x, y) such that

$$1 \le y \le 2, \qquad 0 \le x \le y.$$

We use Theorem 7 and evaluate the iterated integral, to find

$$\iint_F x^2 y^2 \, dA = \int_1^2 \int_0^y x^2 y^2 \, dx \, dy = \int_1^2 \left[\frac{1}{3} x^3 y^2 \right]_0^y dy$$

$$= \frac{1}{3} \int_1^2 y^5 \, dy = \frac{7}{2}.$$

Note that in the above example the iterated integral in the other order is a little more difficult, since the curves $p(x)$, $q(x)$ are

$$p(x) = \begin{cases} 1 \text{ for } 0 \le x \le 1 \\ x \text{ for } 1 \le x \le 2 \end{cases}, \qquad q(x) = 2, \;\; 0 \le x \le 2.$$

The evaluation would have to take place in two parts, so that

$$\iint_F x^2 y^2 \, dA = \int_0^1 \int_1^2 x^2 y^2 \, dy \, dx + \int_1^2 \int_x^2 x^2 y^2 \, dy \, dx.$$

FIGURE 21–13   FIGURE 21–14

EXAMPLE 4. Evaluate

$$\int_0^2 \int_0^{x^2/2} \frac{x}{\sqrt{1 + x^2 + y^2}} \, dy \, dx.$$

Solution. Carrying out the integration first with respect to y is possible but difficult and leads to a complicated integral for x. Therefore we shall try to express the integral as an iterated integral in the opposite order and use Theorem 7. We construct the region F as shown in Fig. 21–14. The region is expressed by the inequalities

$$0 \le x \le 2 \quad \text{and} \quad 0 \le y \le \tfrac{1}{2}x^2.$$

However, it is also expressed by the inequalities

$$0 \le y \le 2 \quad \text{and} \quad \sqrt{2y} \le x \le 2.$$

Therefore, integrating with respect to x first, we have

$$\int_0^2 \int_0^{x^2/2} \frac{x}{\sqrt{1 + x^2 + y^2}} \, dy \, dx$$

$$= \iint_F \frac{x}{\sqrt{1 + x^2 + y^2}} \, dA = \int_0^2 \int_{\sqrt{2y}}^2 \frac{x}{\sqrt{1 + x^2 + y^2}} \, dx \, dy$$

$$= \int_0^2 \left[\sqrt{1 + x^2 + y^2} \right]_{\sqrt{2y}}^2 dy = \int_0^2 \left[\sqrt{5 + y^2} - (1 + y) \right] dy$$

$$= \left[\tfrac{5}{2} \ln (y + \sqrt{y^2 + 5}) + \tfrac{1}{2}y\sqrt{y^2 + 5} - y - \tfrac{1}{2}y^2 \right]_0^2$$

$$= \tfrac{5}{2} \ln 5 + 3 - 4 - \tfrac{5}{2} \ln \sqrt{5} = -1 + \tfrac{5}{4} \ln 5.$$

The next example shows how the volume of a solid may be found by iterated integration.

EXAMPLE 5. Let S be the solid bounded by the surface $z = xy$, the cylinders $y = x^2$ and $y^2 = x$, and the plane $z = 0$. Find the volume $V(S)$.

FIGURE 21–15

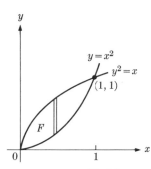

FIGURE 21–16

Solution. The solid S is shown in Fig. 21–15. It consists of all points "under" the surface $z = xy$, bounded by the cylinders, and "above" the xy-plane. The region F in the xy-plane is bounded by the curves $y = x^2, y^2 = x$ and is shown in Fig. 21–16. Therefore

$$V(S) = \iint_F xy \, dA = \int_0^1 \int_{x^2}^{\sqrt{x}} xy \, dy \, dx = \int_0^1 \left[\frac{xy^2}{2} \right]_{x^2}^{\sqrt{x}} dx$$

$$= \frac{1}{2} \int_0^1 (x^2 - x^5) \, dx = \frac{1}{12}.$$

If a solid S is bounded by two surfaces of the form $z = f(x, y)$ and $z = g(x, y)$ with $f(x, y) \le g(x, y)$, then the volume between the surfaces may be found as a double integral, and that integral in turn may be evaluated by iterated integrals. The closed region F over which the integration is performed is found by the projection onto the xy-plane of the curve of intersection of the two surfaces. To find this projection we merely set

$$f(x, y) = g(x, y)$$

and trace this curve in the xy-plane. The next example shows the method.

EXAMPLE 6. Find the volume bounded by the surfaces

$$z = x^2 \quad \text{and} \quad z = 4 - x^2 - y^2.$$

Solution. A portion of the solid S (the part corresponding to $y \le 0$) is shown in Fig. 21–17. We set $x^2 = 4 - x^2 - y^2$ and find that the closed region F in the xy-plane is the ellipse (Fig. 21–18)

$$\frac{x^2}{2} + \frac{y^2}{4} = 1.$$

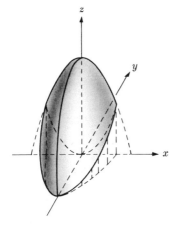

FIGURE 21-17   FIGURE 21-18

Note that the surface $z = 4 - x^2 - y^2 \equiv g(x, y)$ is above the surface $z = x^2 \equiv f(x, y)$ for (x, y) inside the above ellipse. Therefore

$$V(S) = \iint_F (4 - y^2 - x^2 - x^2) \, dA$$

$$= \int_{-2}^{2} \int_{-\sqrt{4-y^2}/\sqrt{2}}^{+\sqrt{4-y^2}/\sqrt{2}} (4 - y^2 - 2x^2) \, dx \, dy$$

$$= \int_{-2}^{2} \frac{2\sqrt{2}}{3} (4 - y^2)^{3/2} \, dy = \frac{4\sqrt{2}}{3} \int_{0}^{2} (4 - y^2)^{3/2} \, dy$$

$$= \frac{64\sqrt{2}}{3} \int_{0}^{\pi/2} \cos^4 \theta \, d\theta = \frac{16\sqrt{2}}{3} \int_{0}^{\pi/2} (1 + 2\cos 2\theta + \cos^2 2\theta) \, d\theta$$

$$= \frac{8\pi\sqrt{2}}{3} + \left[\frac{16\sqrt{2}}{3} \sin 2\theta \right]_{0}^{\pi/2} + \frac{8\sqrt{2}}{3} \int_{0}^{\pi/2} (1 + \cos 4\theta) \, d\theta = 4\pi\sqrt{2}.$$

EXERCISES

In problems 1 through 10, evaluate the iterated integrals as indicated. Sketch the region F in the xy-plane over which the integration is taken.

1. $\displaystyle\int_{1}^{4} \int_{2}^{5} (x^2 - y^2 + xy - 3) \, dx \, dy$ 2. $\displaystyle\int_{0}^{2} \int_{-3}^{2} (x^3 + 2x^2y - y^3 + xy) \, dy \, dx$

3. $\displaystyle\int_{1}^{4} \int_{\sqrt{x}}^{x^2} (x^2 + 2xy - 3y^2) \, dy \, dx$ 4. $\displaystyle\int_{0}^{1} \int_{x^3}^{x^2} (x^2 - xy) \, dy \, dx$

5. $\displaystyle\int_{2}^{3} \int_{1+y}^{\sqrt{y}} (x^2y + xy^2) \, dx \, dy$ 6. $\displaystyle\int_{-2}^{2} \int_{-\sqrt{4-x^2}}^{+\sqrt{4-x^2}} y \, dy \, dx$

7. $\int_{-3}^{3} \int_{-\sqrt{18-2y^2}}^{+\sqrt{18-2y^2}} x \, dx \, dy$

8. $\int_{-3}^{3} \int_{x^2}^{18-x^2} xy^3 \, dy \, dx$

9. $\int_{0}^{2} \int_{x^2}^{2x^2} x \cos y \, dy \, dx$

10. $\int_{1}^{2} \int_{x^3}^{4x^3} \frac{1}{y} \, dy \, dx$

In problems 11 through 17, evaluate the double integrals as indicated. Sketch the region F.

11. $\iint_F (x^2 + y^2) \, dA, \ F: 0 \le y \le 2, \ y^2 \le x \le 4$

12. $\iint_F x \cos y \, dA, \ F$ bounded by the curve $y = x^2$ and the lines $y = 0, \ x = \sqrt{\pi/2}$

13. $\iint_F \frac{x}{x^2 + y^2} \, dA, \ F$ bounded by $y = 0, \ y = x, \ x = 1,$ and $x = \sqrt{3}$

14. $\iint_F \ln y \, dA, \ F$ bounded by $y = 1, \ y = x - 1,$ and $x = 3$

15. $\iint_F \frac{x}{\sqrt{1 - y^2}} \, dA, \ F$ bounded by $x = 0, \ y = 0, \ y = \frac{1}{2},$ and $y = x.$

16. $\iint_F \frac{x}{\sqrt{x^2 + y^2}} \, dA, \ F$ bounded by $y = x, \ y = 1,$ and $x = 2$

17. $\iint_F \frac{1}{y^2} e^{x/\sqrt{y}} \, dA, \ F$ bounded by $x = 1, \ y = 2,$ and $y = x^2 (x \ge 1)$

In each of problems 18 through 22, (a) sketch the domain over which the integration is performed; (b) write the equivalent iterated integral in the reverse order; (c) evaluate the integral obtained in (b).

18. $\int_{1}^{2} \int_{1}^{x} \frac{x^2}{y^2} \, dy \, dx$

19. $\int_{-2}^{2} \int_{-\sqrt{4-x^2}}^{+\sqrt{4-x^2}} xy \, dy \, dx$

20. $\int_{0}^{a} \int_{0}^{\sqrt{a^2-x^2}} (a^2 - y^2)^{3/2} \, dy \, dx$

21. $\int_{0}^{1} \int_{y}^{1} \sqrt{1 + x^2} \, dx \, dy$

22. $\int_{0}^{1} \int_{\sqrt{x}}^{1} \sqrt{1 + y^3} \, dy \, dx$

In each of problems 23 through 32, find the volume $V(S)$ of the solid described.

23. S is bounded by the surfaces $z = 0, \ z = x,$ and $y^2 = 2 - x.$

24. S is bounded by the planes $z = 0, \ y = 0, \ y = x, \ x + y = 2,$ and $x + y + z = 3.$

25. S is bounded by the surfaces $x = 0, \ z = 0, \ y^2 = 4 - x,$ and $z = y + 2.$

26. S is bounded by the surfaces $x^2 + z^2 = 4, \ y = 0,$ and $x + y + z = 3.$

27. S is bounded by the surfaces $y^2 = z, \ y = z^3, \ z = x,$ and $y^2 = 2 - x.$

28. S is bounded by the coordinate planes and the surface $x^{1/2} + y^{1/2} + z^{1/2} = a^{1/2}.$

29. S is bounded by the surfaces $y = x^2$ and $z^2 = 4 - y$.
30. S is bounded by the surfaces $y^2 = x$, $x + y = 2$, $x + z = 0$, and $z = x + 1$.
31. S is bounded by the surfaces $x^2 = y + z$, $y = 0$, $z = 0$, and $x = 2$.
32. S is bounded by the surfaces $y^2 + z^2 = 2x$ and $y = x - \frac{3}{2}$.

4. AREA, DENSITY, AND MASS

The double integral of a nonnegative function $z = f(x, y)$ taken over a region F may be interpreted as a volume. The value of such an integral is the volume of the cylinder having generators parallel to the z-axis and situated between the surface $z = f(x, y)$ and the region F in the xy-plane.

If we select for the surface f the particularly simple function $z = 1$, then the volume V is given by the formula

$$V = \iint_F 1 \, dA.$$

On the other hand, the volume of a right cylinder of cross-section F and height 1 is

$$V = A(F) \cdot 1.$$

(See Fig. 21–19.) Therefore

$$A(F) = \iint_F dA.$$

FIGURE 21–19

We see that *the double integral of the function* 1 *taken over F is precisely the area of F.* By Theorem 7, we conclude that the iterated integral of the function 1 also yields the area of F.

EXAMPLE 1. Use iterated integration to find the area of the region F bounded by the curves $y = x^4$ and $y = 4 - 3x^2$.

Solution. The region F is shown in Fig. 21–20. One of the iterated integrals for the area is

$$A(F) = \int_{-1}^{1} \int_{x^4}^{4-3x^2} dy \, dx,$$

and its evaluation gives

$$A(F) = \int_{-1}^{1} [y]_{x^4}^{4-3x^2} \, dx = \int_{-1}^{1} (4 - 3x^2 - x^4) \, dx$$

$$= \left[4x - x^3 - \frac{1}{5}x^5 \right]_{-1}^{1} = \frac{28}{5}.$$

Note that the iterated integral in the other direction is more difficult to evaluate.

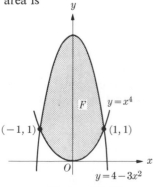

FIGURE 21–20

If a flat object is made of an extremely thin uniform material, then the mass of the object is just a multiple of the area of the plane region on which the object rests. (The multiple depends on the units used.) If a thin object (resting on the xy-plane) is made of a nonuniform material, then the mass* of the object may be expressed in terms of the density $\rho(x, y)$ of the material at any point. It is assumed that the material is uniform in the z-direction. Letting F denote the region occupied by the object, we decompose F into rectangles $r_1, r_2, \ldots, r_n$ in the usual way. Then an approximation to the mass of the ith rectangle is given by

$$\rho(\xi_i, \eta_i)A(r_i),$$

where $A(r_i)$ is the area of r_i and (ξ_i, η_i) is a point in r_i. The total mass of F is approximated by

$$\sum_{i=1}^{n} \rho(\xi_i, \eta_i)A(r_i),$$

and when we proceed to the limit in the customary manner, the mass $M(F)$ is

$$M(F) = \iint_{F} \rho(x, y)\, dA.$$

In other words, the double integral is a useful device for finding the mass of a thin object with variable density.

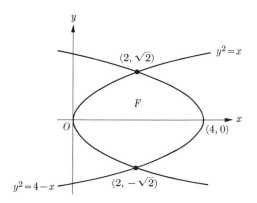

FIGURE 21–21

EXAMPLE 2. A thin object occupies the region F bounded by the curves $y^2 = x$ and $y^2 = 4 - x$. The density is given by $\rho(x, y) = 1 + 2x + y$. Find the total mass.

Solution. We have

$$M(F) = \iint_{F} (1 + 2x + y)\, dA.$$

_____

* For a precise definition of mass in terms of set functions, see Morrey, *University Calculus*, page 610.

Sketching the region F (Fig. 21–21), we obtain for $M(F)$ the iterated integral

$$M(F) = \int_{-\sqrt{2}}^{\sqrt{2}} \int_{y^2}^{4-y^2} (1 + 2x + y)\, dx\, dy$$

$$= \int_{-\sqrt{2}}^{\sqrt{2}} [x + x^2 + xy]_{y^2}^{4-y^2}\, dy$$

$$= \int_{-\sqrt{2}}^{\sqrt{2}} (20 + 4y - 10y^2 - 2y^3)\, dy$$

$$= \left[20y + 2y^2 - \frac{10}{3}y^3 - \frac{1}{2}y^4 \right]_{-\sqrt{2}}^{\sqrt{2}} = \frac{80}{3}\sqrt{2}.$$

EXERCISES

In each of problems 1 through 5 use iterated integration to find the area of the given region F. Subdivide F and do each part separately whenever necessary.

1. F is bounded by $y = x^3$ and $y = \sqrt{x}$.
2. F is determined by the inequalities

$$y \geq 1, \qquad y \geq x, \qquad y^2 \leq 4x.$$

3. F is determined by the inequalities

$$xy \leq 4, \qquad y \leq x, \qquad 27y \geq 4x^2.$$

4. F is determined by the inequalities

$$y^2 \leq x, \qquad y^2 \leq 6 - x, \qquad y \leq x - 2.$$

5. F is determined by the inequalities

$$x^2 + y^2 \leq 9, \qquad y \leq x + 3, \qquad y \leq -x.$$

In each of problems 6 through 14, find the mass of the given region F.

6. F is the interior of the circle $x^2 + y^2 = 64$; $\rho = x^2 + y^2$.
7. F is bounded by the curves $y = x^2$ and $y^2 = x$; $\rho = 3y$.
8. F is bounded by $y = x^2$ and $y = x + 2$; $\rho = x^2 y$.
9. F is bounded by $y = x^3$ and $y = \sqrt{x}$; $\rho = 2x$.
10. F is bounded by $x + y = 5$ and $xy = 4$; $\rho = 4y$.
11. F is bounded by $y^2 = x$ and $x = y + 2$; $\rho = x^2 y^2$.
12. F is the triangle with vertices at $(0, 0)$, $(a, 0)$, (b, c), $a > b > 0$, $c > 0$; $\rho = 2x$.
13. F is bounded by $y = 0$ and $y = \sqrt{a^2 - x^2}$; $\rho = 3y$.
14. F is a rectangle with vertices at $(0, 0)$, $(a, 0)$, (a, b), $(0, b)$; $\rho = 3x/(1 + x^2y^2)$.

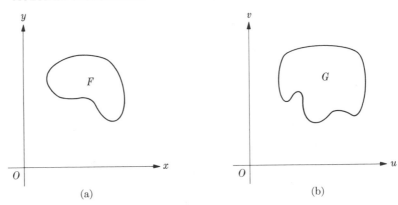

FIGURE 21–22

5.   TRANSFORMATIONS AND MAPPINGS IN THE PLANE

Consider a pair of equations

$$u = f(x, y), \qquad v = g(x, y) \tag{1}$$

defined for (x, y) in some region F in the xy-plane. Letting (u, v) denote rectangular coordinates in another plane (Fig. 21–22), we see that the above pair of equations assigns to each point of F a point in the uv-plane. The totality of points so determined in the uv-plane (denoted by G) is called the *image* of F under the *transformation* or *mapping* defined by (1).

It sometimes happens that the system (1) can be solved for x and y in terms of u and v. In such a case we write

$$x = p(u, v), \qquad y = q(u, v),$$

although the domain and image of this *inverse* transformation may not correspond precisely to the regions G and F of the original transformation.

One of the simplest types of transformations is determined by the equations

$$u = x + h, \qquad v = y + k$$

and is called a *translation* mapping. The inverse transformation is

$$x = u - h, \qquad y = v - k.$$

Another simple mapping is a *rotation* mapping (see page 322), given by the equations

$$u = x \cos \theta + y \sin \theta, \qquad v = -x \sin \theta + y \cos \theta, \tag{2}$$

with the inverse transformation given by

$$x = u \cos \theta - v \sin \theta, \qquad y = u \sin \theta + v \cos \theta. \tag{3}$$

The transformation

$$u = ax + by, \qquad v = cx + dy, \tag{4}$$

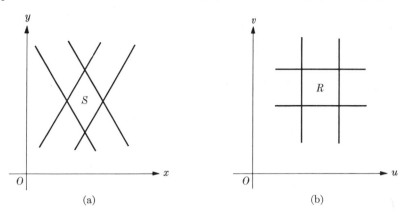

FIGURE 21–23

with a, b, c, d constants is called a *linear transformation*. If $ad - bc \neq 0$, then we may solve for x, y in terms of u, v uniquely. We note that a rectangle R formed by lines parallel to the axes in the uv-plane corresponds to a parallelogram S in the xy-plane (Fig. 21–23). In general, the areas of R and S will be different.

The transformation

$$u = \sqrt{x^2 + y^2}, \qquad v = \arctan \frac{y}{x}, \qquad x > 0 \tag{5}$$

has the inverse mapping

$$x = u \cos v, \quad y = u \sin v; \qquad u > 0, \quad -\frac{\pi}{2} < v < \frac{\pi}{2}. \tag{6}$$

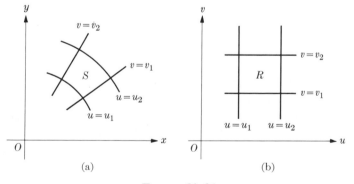

FIGURE 21–24

Figure 21–24 shows how a rectangle R in the uv-plane corresponds to a region S in the xy-plane bounded by two circular arcs and two rays through the origin.

––––––––––––

EXAMPLE. Given the transformation (5). Find the area S in the xy-plane corresponding to the rectangle R in the uv-plane determined by the lines $u = u_1$, $u = u_2$, $v = v_1$, $v = v_2$ with $u_2 > u_1$, $v_2 > v_1$.

Solution. The area of a sector of a circle with angle opening θ (measured in radians) and radius r is given by the elementary formula $\frac{1}{2}\theta r^2$. The lines $v = v_1$ and $v = v_2$ determine an angle of $v_2 - v_1$ radians in the xy-plane. Therefore the area $A(S)$ is given by

$$A(S) = \tfrac{1}{2}(v_2 - v_1)u_2^2 - \tfrac{1}{2}(v_2 - v_1)u_1^2 = \tfrac{1}{2}(v_2 - v_1)(u_2^2 - u_1^2)$$

$$= \tfrac{1}{2}(v_2 - v_1)(u_2 - u_1)(u_2 + u_1) = \tfrac{1}{2}(u_2 + u_1)A(R).$$

In order to identify the plane in which the areas are computed, we write

$$A_{x,y}(S)$$

for the area of a region S in the xy-plane. The above relation then becomes

$$A_{x,y}(S) = \tfrac{1}{2}(u_1 + u_2)A_{u,v}(R).$$

Some mappings, such as translations and rotations, transform a region with a given area into a region with the same area. Such mappings are called *area-preserving*. A mapping which leaves the distance between any two points unchanged is called *isometric*.

EXERCISES

1. Show that translation and rotation mappings are both area-preserving and isometric.

2. Show that the transformation

   $$u = x \cos \theta + y \sin \theta + h, \qquad v = -x \sin \theta + y \cos \theta + k$$

   is both area-preserving and isometric.

3. The mapping
   $$u = \alpha x, \qquad v = \beta y,$$

   with $\alpha > 0, \beta > 0$ is called a *stretching*. If S is a region in the xy-plane and R its image under the stretching, find the relation between $A_{x,y}(S)$ and $A_{u,v}(R)$.

4. If $ad - bc \neq 0$ in (4) and R is a rectangle in the uv-plane, S its image under the mapping inverse to (4), find the formula relating $A_{x,y}(S)$ and $A_{u,v}(R)$.

*5. Show that a linear transformation (4) with $ad - bc = 1$ is area-preserving.

6. EVALUATION OF DOUBLE INTEGRALS BY POLAR COORDINATES

The polar coordinates (r, θ) of a point in the plane are related to the rectangular coordinates (x, y) of the same point by the equations

$$x = r \cos \theta, \qquad y = r \sin \theta, \qquad r > 0. \tag{1}$$

We recall that certain problems concerned with finding areas by integration are solved more easily in polar coordinates than in rectangular coordinates. (See page 416.) The same situation prevails in problems involving double integration.

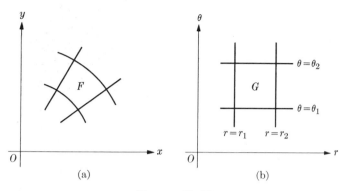

FIGURE 21–25

Instead of considering (1) as a means of representing a point in two different coordinate systems, we interpret the equations as a mapping between the xy-plane and the $r\theta$-plane. In the context of mappings as discussed in Section 5, we draw the $r\theta$-plane as shown in Fig. 21–25, treating $r = 0$ and $\theta = 0$ as perpendicular straight lines. A rectangle G in the $r\theta$-plane bounded by the lines $r = r_1$, $r = r_2$, and $\theta = \theta_1$, $\theta = \theta_2$ (θ in radians) with $2\pi > \theta_2 > \theta_1 \geq 0$, $r_2 > r_1 > 0$ has an image F in the xy-plane bounded by two circular arcs and two rays. (See the example in Section 5.) For the area of F we have

$$A_{x,y}(F) = \tfrac{1}{2}(r_2^2 - r_1^2)(\theta_2 - \theta_1).$$

This area may be written as an iterated integral. A simple calculation shows that

$$A_{x,y}(F) = \int_{\theta_1}^{\theta_2}\left[\int_{r_1}^{r_2} r\,dr\right] d\theta.$$

Because double integrals and iterated integrals are equivalent for evaluation purposes, we can also write

$$A_{x,y}(F) = \iint_G r\,dA_{r,\theta}, \tag{2}$$

where $dA_{r,\theta}$ is an element of area in the $r\theta$-plane, r and θ being treated as rectangular coordinates.

More generally, it can be shown (Morrey, *University Calculus*, page 672) that if G is *any region* in the $r\theta$-plane and F is its image under the transformation (1), then the area of F may be found by formula (2). Thus, areas of regions may be determined by expressing the double integral in polar coordinates as in (2) and then evaluating the double integral by iterated integrals in the usual way.

EXAMPLE 1. A region F above the x-axis is bounded on the left by the line $y = -x$, and on the right by the curve $C: x^2 + y^2 = 3\sqrt{x^2 + y^2} - 3x$, as shown in Fig. 21–26. Find its area.

FIGURE 21–26

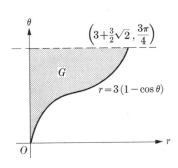

FIGURE 21–27

Solution. We employ polar coordinates to describe the region. The curve C is the cardioid $r = 3(1 - \cos \theta)$, and the line $y = -x$ is the ray $\theta = 3\pi/4$. The region F is described by the inequalities

$$0 \leq \theta \leq \frac{3\pi}{4}$$

and

$$0 \leq r \leq 3(1 - \cos \theta).$$

Employing the $r\theta$-plane, we see that F is the image, under the mapping (1), of the region G shown in Fig. 21–27. Therefore, for the area $A(F)$ we obtain

$$A(F) = \iint_F dA_{x,y} = \iint_G r \, dA_{r,\theta} = \int_0^{3\pi/4} \int_0^{3(1-\cos \theta)} r \, dr \, d\theta$$

$$= \int_0^{3\pi/4} \frac{1}{2} [r^2]_0^{3(1-\cos \theta)} \, d\theta = \frac{9}{2} \int_0^{3\pi/4} (1 - \cos \theta)^2 \, d\theta.$$

To perform the integration we multiply out and find that

$$A(F) = \frac{9}{2} \int_0^{3\pi/4} (1 - 2 \cos \theta + \cos^2 \theta) \, d\theta$$

$$= \frac{9}{2} \left[\theta - 2 \sin \theta + \frac{1}{2} \theta + \frac{1}{4} \sin 2\theta \right]_0^{3\pi/4}$$

$$= \frac{9}{8} \left(\frac{9}{2} \pi - 4\sqrt{2} - 1 \right).$$

The transformation of regions from the xy-plane to the $r\theta$-plane is useful because general double integrals as well as areas may be evaluated by means of polar coordinates. The theoretical basis for the method is the Fundamental Lemma on Integration, a proof of which may be found in Morrey, *University Calculus*, page 611.

Theorem 8. (Fundamental Lemma on Integration.) *Assume that f and g are continuous on some region F. Then for each $\epsilon > 0$ there is a $\delta > 0$ such that*

$$\left| \sum_{i=1}^{n} f_i g_i A(F_i) - \iint_F f(x, y) g(x, y) \, dA \right| < \epsilon$$

for every subdivision $F_1, F_2, \ldots, F_n$ of F with norm less than δ and any numbers $f_1, f_2, \ldots, f_n, g_1, g_2, \ldots, g_n$ where each f_i and each g_i is between the minimum and maximum values of f and g, respectively, on F_i.

The fundamental lemma is the basis for the next theorem, the proof of which we sketch. (See Morrey, *University Calculus*, page 613.)

Theorem 9. *Suppose F and G are regions related according to the mapping $x = r \cos \theta$, $y = r \sin \theta$ and $f(x, y)$ is continuous on F. Then the function $g(r, \theta) = f(r \cos \theta, r \sin \theta)$ is defined and continuous on G and*

$$\iint_F f(x, y) \, dA_{x,y} = \iint_G g(r, \theta) r \, dA_{r,\theta}.$$

Sketch of proof. Consider a subdivision of G into "figures" $G_1, \ldots, G_n$. (See the discussion of volume in Section 1 and, in particular, the footnote on page 739.) Let (r_i, θ_i) be in G_i for each i, and let (ξ_i, η_i) and F_i be the respective images of (r_i, θ_i) and G_i. Then $(F_1, \ldots, F_n)$ is a subdivision of F. From the expression for area in the xy-plane as an integral, we obtain

$$A_{x,y}(F_i) = \iint_{G_i} r \, dA_{r,\theta}.$$

Using Theorem 4 concerning bounds for integrals, we obtain

$$\iint_{G_i} r \, dA_{r,\theta} = \bar{r}_i \, A_{r,\theta}(G_i),$$

where $\bar{r}_i$ is between the minimum and maximum of r on G_i. Thus

$$\sum_{i=1}^{n} f(\xi_i, \eta_i) A_{x,y}(F_i) = \sum_{i=1}^{n} g(r_i, \theta_i) \cdot \bar{r}_i \cdot A_{r,\theta}(G_i).$$

The theorem follows by letting the norms of the subdivisions $\to 0$, using the fundamental lemma to evaluate the limit of the sum on the right.

EXAMPLE 2. Use polar coordinates to evaluate

$$\iint_F \sqrt{x^2 + y^2} \, dA_{x,y},$$

where F is the circular area bounded by $x^2 + y^2 = 2x$.

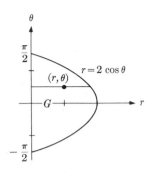

FIGURE 21–28   FIGURE 21–29

Solution. *F* may be described in polar coordinates by the inequalities

$$-\frac{\pi}{2} \le \theta \le \frac{\pi}{2}, \qquad 0 \le r \le 2 \cos \theta.$$

(See Fig. 21–28.) Figure 21–29 shows *G*, the image of *F* in the *r*θ-plane. Therefore

$$\iint_F \sqrt{x^2 + y^2}\, dA_{x,y} = \iint_G r \cdot r\, dA_{r,\theta} = \int_{-\pi/2}^{\pi/2} \int_0^{2\cos\theta} r^2\, dr\, d\theta$$

$$= \int_{-\pi/2}^{\pi/2} \frac{8}{3} \cos^3 \theta\, d\theta = \frac{16}{3} \int_0^{\pi/2} (1 - \sin^2 \theta) \cos \theta\, d\theta = \frac{32}{9}.$$

Although the construction of the region *G* in the *r*θ-plane is helpful in understanding the transformation (1), it is not necessary for determining the limits in the iterated integrals. The limits of integration in polar coordinates may be found by using rectangular and polar coordinates in the same plane and using a sketch of the region *F* to read off the limits for *r* and *θ*.

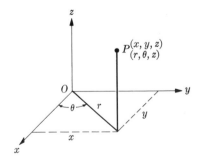

FIGURE 21–30

Double integrals are useful for finding volumes bounded by surfaces. Cylindrical coordinates (r, θ, z) are a natural extension to three-space of polar coordinates in the plane. The *z*-direction is selected as in rectangular coordinates, as shown in Fig. 21–30. If a closed surface in space is expressed in cylindrical coordinates, we may find the volume enclosed by this surface by evaluating a double integral in polar coordinates. An example illustrates the method.

EXAMPLE 3. A region S is bounded by the surfaces $x^2 + y^2 - 2x = 0, 4z = x^2 + y^2$, $z^2 = x^2 + y^2$. Use cylindrical coordinates to find the volume $V(S)$.

Solution.   In cylindrical coordinates, the paraboloid $4z = x^2 + y^2$ has equation $4z = r^2$; the cylinder $x^2 + y^2 - 2x = 0$ has equation $r = 2\cos\theta$; and the cone $z^2 = x^2 + y^2$ has equation $z^2 = r^2$. The region is shown in Fig. 21–31, and we note that the projection of S on the xy-plane is precisely the plane region F of Example 2. We obtain

$$V(S) = \iint_F \left[\sqrt{x^2 + y^2} - \frac{x^2 + y^2}{4} \right] dA_{x,y}$$

$$= \iint_G \left(r - \frac{1}{4} r^2 \right) r\, dA_{r,\theta}$$

$$= \int_{-\pi/2}^{\pi/2} \int_0^{2\cos\theta} \left(r^2 - \frac{1}{4} r^3 \right) dr\, d\theta$$

$$= \int_{-\pi/2}^{\pi/2} \left(\frac{8}{3} \cos^3\theta - \cos^4\theta \right) d\theta$$

$$= \frac{32}{9} - \frac{1}{2} \int_0^{\pi/2} \left(1 + 2\cos 2\theta + \frac{1 + \cos 4\theta}{2} \right) d\theta = \frac{32}{9} - \frac{3\pi}{8}.$$

FIGURE 21–31

EXERCISES

In each of problems 1 through 7, evaluate the given integral by first expressing it as a double integral and then changing to polar coordinates.

1. $\displaystyle\int_0^2 \int_0^{\sqrt{4-y^2}} \sqrt{x^2 + y^2}\, dx\, dy$

2. $\displaystyle\int_{-2}^2 \int_{-\sqrt{4-x^2}}^{\sqrt{4-x^2}} e^{-(x^2+y^2)}\, dy\, dx$

3. $\displaystyle\int_{-\sqrt{\pi}}^{\sqrt{\pi}} \int_{-\sqrt{\pi-y^2}}^{\sqrt{\pi-y^2}} \sin(x^2 + y^2)\, dx\, dy$

4. $\displaystyle\int_0^4 \int_{-\sqrt{4x-x^2}}^{\sqrt{4x-x^2}} \sqrt{x^2 + y^2}\, dy\, dx$

5. $\displaystyle\int_{-2}^2 \int_{2-\sqrt{4-x^2}}^{2+\sqrt{4-x^2}} \sqrt{16 - x^2 - y^2}\, dy\, dx$

6. $\displaystyle\int_0^2 \int_0^x (x^2 + y^2)\, dy\, dx$

7. $\displaystyle\int_0^1 \int_y^{\sqrt{y}} (x^2 + y^2)^{-1/2}\, dx\, dy$

In each of problems 8 through 10, use polar coordinates to find the area of the region given.

8. The region inside the circle $x^2 + y^2 - 8y = 0$ and outside the circle $x^2 + y^2 = 9$.

9. The region bounded by $y^2 = 4x$ and $y = \frac{1}{2}x$.

10. The region interior to the curve $(x^2 + y^2)^3 = 16x^2$.

In each of problems 11 through 26, find the volume of S.

11. S is the set bounded by the surfaces $z = 0$, $2z = x^2 + y^2$, and $x^2 + y^2 = 4$.

12. S is the set bounded by the cone $z^2 = x^2 + y^2$ and the cylinder $x^2 + y^2 = 4$.

13. S is the set cut from a sphere of radius 4 by a cylinder of radius 2 whose axis is a diameter of the sphere.

14. S is the set above the cone $z^2 = x^2 + y^2$ and inside the sphere

$$x^2 + y^2 + z^2 = a^2.$$

15. S is the set bounded by the cone $z^2 = x^2 + y^2$ and the cylinder

$$x^2 + y^2 - 2y = 0.$$

16. S is the set bounded by the sphere $x^2 + y^2 + z^2 = 4$ and the cylinder

$$x^2 + y^2 = 2x.$$

17. S is the set bounded by the cone $z^2 = x^2 + y^2$ and the paraboloid

$$3z = x^2 + y^2.$$

18. S is bounded by the surfaces $z = 0$, $2z = x^2 + y^2$, and $2y = x^2 + y^2$.

19. S is bounded by the cylinder $x^2 + y^2 = 4$ and the hyperboloid

$$x^2 + y^2 - z^2 = 1.$$

20. S is bounded by the cone $z^2 = x^2 + y^2$ and the cylinder $r = 1 + \cos \theta$.

21. S is bounded by the surfaces $z = x$ and $2z = x^2 + y^2$.

22. S is bounded by the surfaces $z = 0$, $z = x^2 + y^2$, and $r = 2(1 + \cos \theta)$.

23. S is inside the sphere $x^2 + y^2 + z^2 = a^2$ and inside the cylinder erected on one loop of the curve $z = 0$, $r = a \cos 2\theta$.

24. S is inside the sphere $x^2 + y^2 + z^2 = 4$ and inside the cylinder erected on one loop of the curve $z = 0$, $r^2 = 4 \cos 2\theta$.

25. S is bounded by the surfaces $z^2 = x^2 + y^2$, $y = 0$, $y = x$, and $x = a$.

*26. S is bounded by the surfaces $z^2 = x^2 + y^2$ and $x - 2z + 2 = 0$.

7. MOMENT OF INERTIA AND CENTER OF MASS

Consider the idealized situation in which an object of mass m occupies a single point. Let L be a line which we designate as an axis.

DEFINITION. The *moment of inertia of a particle of mass m about the axis L is* mr^2, where r is the perpendicular distance of the object from the axis (Fig. 21–32). If we have a system of particles m_1, m_2, $\ldots$, m_n at perpendicular distances,

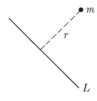

FIGURE 21–32

respectively, of $r_1, r_2, \ldots, r_n$ from the axis L, then the *moment of inertia of the system, I,* is given by

$$I = m_1 r_1^2 + m_2 r_2^2 + \cdots + m_n r_n^2$$

$$= \sum_{i=1}^{n} m_i r_i^2.$$

Let F be an object made of thin material occupying a region in the xy-plane (Fig. 21–33). We wish to define the moment of inertia of F about an axis L. The axis L may be any line in three-dimensional space. We proceed as in the definition of integration. First we make a subdivision of the plane into rectangles or squares. We designate the rectangles either wholly or partly in F by $F_1, F_2, \ldots, F_n$. Since the object F may be of irregular shape and of variable density, the mass of the subregions may not be calculable exactly. We select a point in each subregion F_i and denote its coordinates (ξ_i, η_i). We assume that the entire mass of F_i, denoted $m(F_i)$, is concentrated at the point (ξ_i, η_i). Letting r_i be the perpendicular distance of (ξ_i, η_i) from the line L, we form the sum

$$\sum_{i=1}^{n} m(F_i) r_i^2.$$

DEFINITION. If the above sums tend to a limit (called I) as the norms of the subdivisions tend to zero, and if this limit is independent of the manner in which the (ξ_i, η_i) are selected within the F_i, then we say that I is the *moment of inertia of the mass distribution about the axis L.*

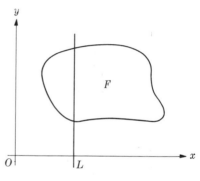

FIGURE 21–33

The above definition of moment of inertia leads in a natural way to the next theorem.

Theorem 10. *Given a mass distribution occupying a region F in the xy-plane and having a continuous density $\rho(x, y)$. Then the moment of inertia about the y-axis, I_1, is given by*

$$I_1 = \iint_F x^2 \rho(x, y) \, dA.$$

Similarly, the moments of inertia about the x-axis and the z-axis are, respectively,

$$I_2 = \iint_F y^2 \rho(x, y) \, dA, \qquad I_3 = \iint_F (x^2 + y^2) \rho(x, y) \, dA.$$

The proof depends on the Fundamental Lemma of Integration. (See Exercise 29 at the end of this section.)

Corollary. *The moments of inertia of F about the lines* L_1: $x = a$, $z = 0$; L_2: $y = b$, $z = 0$; L_3: $x = a$, $y = b$ *are, respectively,*

$$I_1^a = \iint_F (x - a)^2 \rho(x, y)\, dA, \qquad I_2^b = \iint_F (y - b)^2 \rho(x, y)\, dA,$$

$$I_3^{a,b} = \iint_F [(x - a)^2 + (y - b)^2]\rho(x, y)\, dA.$$

EXAMPLE 1. Find the moment of inertia about the *x*-axis of the homogeneous plate bounded by the line $y = 0$ and $y = 4 - x^2$ (Fig. 21–34).

Solution. According to Theorem 10, we have

$$I_2 = \iint_F y^2 \rho\, dA = \rho \iint_F y^2\, dy\, dx = \rho \int_{-2}^{2} \int_{0}^{4-x^2} y^2\, dy\, dx = \frac{\rho}{3} \int_{-2}^{2} (4 - x^2)^3\, dx$$

$$= \frac{\rho}{3} \int_{-2}^{2} (64 - 48x^2 + 12x^4 - x^6)\, dx = \frac{4096\rho}{105}.$$

FIGURE 21–34

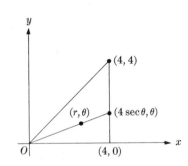

FIGURE 21–35

EXAMPLE 2. Find the moment of inertia about the *z*-axis of the homogeneous triangular plate bounded by the lines $y = 0$, $y = x$, and $x = 4$.

Solution 1. We have

$$I_3 = \iint_F (x^2 + y^2)\rho\, dA = \rho \int_{0}^{4} \int_{0}^{x} (x^2 + y^2)\, dy\, dx$$

$$= \rho \int_{0}^{4} \left[x^2 y + \frac{1}{3} y^3\right]_0^x dx = \frac{4\rho}{3} \int_{0}^{4} x^3\, dx = \frac{256\rho}{3}.$$

Solution 2. We may introduce polar coordinates as shown in Fig. 21–35. Then

$$I_3 = \iint_F (x^2 + y^2)\rho\, dA_{x,y} = \rho \iint_G r^2 \cdot r\, dr\, d\theta = \rho \int_{0}^{\pi/4} \int_{0}^{4\sec\theta} r^3\, dr\, d\theta$$

$$= 64\rho \int_{0}^{\pi/4} \sec^4 \theta\, d\theta = 64\rho \left[\tan\theta + \frac{1}{3} \tan^3 \theta\right]_0^{\pi/4} = \frac{256\rho}{3}.$$

The moment of inertia about the z-axis of two-dimensional objects in the xy-plane is called the *polar moment of inertia*. Since the combination $x^2 + y^2 = r^2$ is always present in calculating polar moments, a change to polar coordinates is frequently indicated.

A quantity known as the radius of gyration is intimately connected with the notion of moment of inertia. It is defined in terms of the total mass m of an object and the moment of inertia I about a specific axis.

DEFINITION. The *radius of gyration of an object about an axis L* is that number R such that

$$R^2 = \frac{I}{m},$$

where I is the moment of inertia about L, and m is the total mass of the object.

If we imagine the total mass of a body as concentrated at one point which is at distance R from the axis L, then the moment of inertia of this idealized "point mass" will be the same as the moment of inertia of the original body.

———————

EXAMPLE 3. Find the radius of gyration for the problem in Example 1. Do the same for Example 2.

Solution. The mass m of the homogeneous plate in Example 1 is its area multiplied by ρ. We have

$$m = \rho \int_{-2}^{2} \int_{0}^{4-x^2} dy \, dx = \rho \int_{-2}^{2} (4 - x^2) \, dx = \rho \left[4x - \frac{x^3}{3} \right]_{-2}^{2} = \frac{32\rho}{3}.$$

Therefore

$$R = \sqrt{\frac{I}{m}} = \left(\frac{4096\rho}{105} \cdot \frac{3}{32\rho} \right)^{1/2} = 8 \sqrt{\frac{2}{35}}.$$

The mass of the triangular plate in Example 2 is 8ρ, and so

$$R = \sqrt{\frac{I}{m}} = \left(\frac{256\rho}{3} \cdot \frac{1}{8\rho} \right)^{1/2} = 4 \sqrt{\frac{2}{3}}.$$

———————

The center of mass of an object was defined on page 508 ff. To calculate the center of mass we make use of the *moment of a mass m* with respect to one of the coordinate axes. We recall that if particles of masses $m_1, m_2, \ldots, m_n$ are situated at the points $(x_1, y_1), (x_2, y_2), \ldots, (x_n, y_n)$, respectively, then the *algebraic moment* (sometimes called *first moment* or simply *moment*) of this system about the y-axis is

$$m_1 x_1 + m_2 x_2 + \cdots + m_n x_n = \sum_{i=1}^{n} m_i x_i.$$

Its algebraic moment about the x-axis is

$$\sum_{i=1}^{n} m_i y_i.$$

More generally, the algebraic moments about the line $x = a$ and about the line $y = b$ are, respectively,

$$\sum_{i=1}^{n} m_i(x_i - a) \quad \text{and} \quad \sum_{i=1}^{n} m_i(y_i - b).$$

We now define the moment of a thin object occupying a region F in the xy-plane.

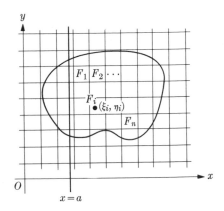

FIGURE 21–36

DEFINITION. Assume that a thin mass occupies a region F in the xy-plane. Let $F_1, F_2, \ldots, F_n$ be a subdivision of F as shown in Fig. 21–36. Choose a point (ξ_i, η_i) in each F_i and replace the mass in F_i by a particle of mass $m(F_i)$ located at (ξ_i, η_i). The n idealized masses have moment

$$\sum_{i=1}^{n} (\xi_i - a)m(F_i)$$

about the line $x = a$. If the above sum tends to a limit M_1 as the norms of the subdivision tend to zero and for any choices of the points (ξ_i, η_i) in F_i, then we define the limit M_1 as the *moment of the mass distribution about the line* $x = a$. An analogous definition for the limit M_2 of sums of the form

$$\sum_{i=1}^{n} (\eta_i - b)m(F_i)$$

yields the first moment about the line $y = b$.

The definition of first moment and the Fundamental Lemma on Integration yield the next theorem.

Theorem 11. *If a distribution of mass over a region F in the xy-plane has a continuous density $\rho(x, y)$, then the moments M_1 and M_2 of F about the lines $x = a$ and $y = b$ are given by the formulas*

$$M_1 = \iint\limits_{F} (x - a)\rho(x, y)\, dA, \qquad M_2 = \iint\limits_{F} (y - b)\rho(x, y)\, dA.$$

Corollary. *Given a distribution of mass over a region F in the xy-plane as in Theorem 11, then there are unique values of a and b (denoted $\bar{x}$ and $\bar{y}$, respectively)* *such that* $M_1 = M_2 = 0$. *In fact, the values of* $\bar{x}$ *and* $\bar{y}$ *are given by*

$$\bar{x} = \frac{\displaystyle\iint_F x\rho(x, y)\, dA}{m(F)}\,, \qquad \bar{y} = \frac{\displaystyle\iint_F y\rho(x, y)\, dA}{m(F)}\,, \qquad where \quad m(F) = \iint_F \rho(x, y)\, dA.$$

Proof. If we set $M_1 = 0$, we get

$$0 = \iint_F (x - a)\rho(x, y)\, dA = \iint_F x\rho(x, y)\, dA - a\iint_F \rho(x, y)\, dA.$$

Since $m(F) = \int\int_F \rho(x, y)\, dA$, we find for the value of a:

$$a = \frac{\displaystyle\iint_F x\rho(x, y)\, dA}{m(F)} = \bar{x}.$$

The value $\bar{y}$ is found similarly.

DEFINITION. The point $(\bar{x}, \bar{y})$ is called the *center of mass* of the distribution over F.

EXAMPLE 4. Find the center of mass of the region F bounded by $y = x^3$ and $y = \sqrt{x}$ if the density of F is given by $\rho = 3x$.

Solution. (See Fig. 21–37.) For the first moments, we have

$$M_1 = \iint_F x\rho\, dA = 3\int_0^1 \int_{x^3}^{\sqrt{x}} x^2\, dy\, dx$$

$$= 3\int_0^1 x^2[y]_{x^3}^{\sqrt{x}}\, dx$$

$$= 3\int_0^1 (x^{5/2} - x^5)\, dx = \frac{5}{14}\,,$$

$$M_2 = \iint_F y\rho\, dA = 3\int_0^1 \int_{x^3}^{\sqrt{x}} yx\, dy\, dx = \frac{3}{2}\int_0^1 x[y^2]_{x^3}^{\sqrt{x}}\, dx$$

$$= \frac{3}{2}\int_0^1 (x^2 - x^7)\, dx = \frac{5}{16}\,,$$

$$m(F) = \iint_F \rho\, dA = 3\int_0^1 \int_{x^3}^{\sqrt{x}} x\, dy\, dx = 3\int_0^1 x[y]_{x^3}^{\sqrt{x}}\, dx$$

$$= 3\int_0^1 (x^{3/2} - x^4)\, dx = \frac{3}{5}\,.$$

FIGURE 21–37

Therefore

$$\bar{x} = \frac{M_1}{m(F)} = \frac{5}{14} \cdot \frac{5}{3} = \frac{25}{42}; \qquad \bar{y} = \frac{M_2}{m(F)} = \frac{5}{16} \cdot \frac{5}{3} = \frac{25}{48}.$$

EXAMPLE 5. Find the center of mass of a plate in the form of a circular sector of radius a and central angle 2α if its thickness is proportional to its distance from the center of the circle from which the sector is taken.

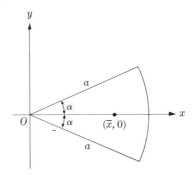

FIGURE 21–38

Solution. Select the sector so that the vertex is at the origin and the x-axis bisects the region (Fig. 21–38). Then the density is given by $\rho = kr$, where k is a proportionality constant. By symmetry we have $\bar{y} = 0$. Using polar coordinates, we obtain

$$M_1 = \iint_F xkr \, dA_{x,y} = k \int_{-\alpha}^{\alpha} \int_0^a r^2 \cos\theta \, r \, dr \, d\theta$$

$$= \frac{ka^4}{4} \int_{-\alpha}^{\alpha} \cos\theta \, d\theta = \frac{1}{2} ka^4 \sin\alpha,$$

$$m(F) = k \iint_F r \, dA_{x,y} = k \int_{-\alpha}^{\alpha} \int_0^a r^2 \, dr \, d\theta = \frac{2}{3} ka^3 \alpha.$$

Therefore

$$\bar{x} = \frac{M_1}{m(F)} = \frac{3a \sin\alpha}{4\alpha}.$$

EXERCISES

In each of problems 1 through 7, find the moment of inertia and the radius of gyration about the given axis of the plate whose density and bounding curves are given.

1. F is the square with vertices $(0, 0)$, $(a, 0)$, (a, a), $(0, a)$, $\rho = $ constant; y-axis.

2. F is the triangle with vertices $(0, 0)$, $(a, 0)$, (b, c), with $a > 0$, $c > 0$, $\rho = $ constant; x-axis.

3. F is bounded by $y = \sqrt{x}$ and $y = x^2$, $\rho = $ constant; y-axis.

4. F is bounded by $x + y = 5$, $xy = 4$, $\rho = ky$; x-axis.

5. F is bounded by $y = 0$ and $y = \sqrt{a^2 - x^2}$; $\rho = ky$; x-axis.

6. F is bounded by $x + y = 5$, $xy = 4$, ρ = constant; x-axis.

7. F is bounded by $y = 0$ and the arch of $y = \sin x$ for $0 \le x \le \pi$, ρ = constant; y-axis.

In each of problems 8 through 17, find the moment of inertia about the given axis of the plate whose density and bounding curves are given.

8. F is bounded by $x^2 + y^2 = a^2$, $\rho = k\sqrt{x^2 + y^2}$; z-axis.

9. F is bounded by $y = x^2$ and $y = x + 2$, ρ = constant; x-axis.

10. F is the square with vertices $(0, 0)$, $(a, 0)$, (a, a), $(0, a)$, ρ = constant; z-axis.

11. F is bounded by $y = x^2$ and $y^2 = x$, $\rho = ky$; y-axis.

12. F is bounded by $y = x^2$ and $y = x + 2$, ρ = constant; axis is line $y = 4$.

13. F is bounded by $x^2 + y^2 = a^2$, $\rho = k\sqrt{x^2 + y^2}$; x-axis.

14. F is bounded by $r = 2a \cos \theta$, $\rho = kr$; z-axis.

15. F is bounded by one loop of $r^2 = a^2 \cos 2\theta$, ρ = constant; z-axis.

16. F is bounded by one loop of $r^2 = a^2 \cos 2\theta$, ρ = constant; x-axis.

17. F is in the first quadrant, inside $r = 1$, and bounded by $r = 1$, $\theta = r$ and $\theta = \pi/2$, ρ = constant; z-axis.

In each of problems 18 through 28, find the center of mass of the plate described.

18. F is bounded by $x + y = 5$ and $xy = 4$, $\rho = ky$.

19. F is bounded by $y^2 = x$ and $x = y + 2$, $\rho = kx$.

20. F is the triangle with vertices at $(0, 0)$, $(a, 0)$, (b, c) with $0 < b < a$, $0 < c$, $\rho = kx$.

21. F is bounded by $y = x^2$ and $y^2 = x$, $\rho = ky$.

22. F is bounded by $y = x^2$ and $y = x + 2$, ρ = constant.

23. F is the square with vertices at $(0, 0)$, $(a, 0)$, (a, a), $(0, a)$, $\rho = k(x^2 + y^2)$.

24. F is the triangle with vertices at $(0, 0)$, $(1, 0)$, $(1, 1)$, $\rho = kr^2$.

25. F is bounded by the cardioid $r = 2(1 + \cos \theta)$, ρ = constant.

26. F is bounded by one loop of the curve $r = 2 \cos 2\theta$, ρ = constant.

27. F is bounded by $3x^2 + 4y^2 = 48$ and $(x - 2)^2 + y^2 = 1$, ρ = constant.

28. F is bounded by one loop of the curve $r^2 = a^2 \cos 2\theta$, ρ = constant.

29. The *Theorem of the Mean* for double integrals states that *if f is integrable over a region F of area $A(F)$ and if $m \le f(x, y) \le M$ for all (x, y) on F, then there is a number $\bar{f}$ between m and M such that*

$$\iint_F f(x, y) \, dA = \bar{f} A(F).$$

Use the Fundamental Lemma of Integration and the Theorem of the Mean to establish Theorem 10. Use the idea of the proof of Theorem 9.

30. Show that if a mass distribution F lies between the lines $x = a$ and $x = b$, then $a \le \bar{x} \le b$. Similarly, if F lies between the lines $y = c$ and $y = d$, then $c \le \bar{y} \le d$.

31. Let $F_1, F_2, \ldots, F_n$ be regions no two of which have any points in common, and let $(\bar{x}_1, \bar{y}_1), (\bar{x}_2, \bar{y}_2), \ldots, (\bar{x}_n, \bar{y}_n)$ be their respective centers of mass. Denote the mass of F_i by m_i. If F is the region containing all the points in every F_i, show that the center of mass $(\bar{x}, \bar{y})$ of F is given by

$$\bar{x} = \frac{m_1\bar{x}_1 + m_2\bar{x}_2 + \cdots + m_n\bar{x}_n}{m_1 + m_2 + \cdots + m_n}, \qquad \bar{y} = \frac{m_1\bar{y}_1 + m_2\bar{y}_2 + \cdots + m_n\bar{y}_n}{m_1 + m_2 + \cdots + m_n}.$$

32. Show that if F is symmetric with respect to the x-axis and $\rho(x, -y) = \rho(x, y)$ for all (x, y) on F, then $\bar{y} = 0$. A similar result holds for symmetry with respect to the y-axis.

8. SURFACE AREA

To define surface area we employ a procedure similar to that used for defining area in the plane. First, we define surface area in the simplest case and, second, we employ a limiting process for the definition of surface area of a general curved surface.

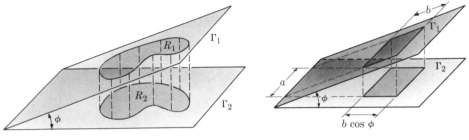

FIGURE 21–39   FIGURE 21–40

Suppose two planes Γ_1 and Γ_2 intersect at an angle ϕ (Fig. 21–39). From each point of R_1, a region in the plane Γ_1, we drop a perpendicular to the plane Γ_2. The set of points of intersection of these perpendiculars with Γ_2 forms a region which we denote R_2. The set R_2 is called the *projection* of R_1 on Γ_2. We shall now determine the relationship between the area $A(R_1)$ of R_1 and the area $A(R_2)$ of R_2. If R_1 is a rectangle—the simplest possible case—the problem may be solved by elementary geometry. For convenience, we select the rectangle in Γ_1 so that one side is parallel to the line of intersection of the two planes (Fig. 21–40). Let the lengths of the sides of the rectangle be a and b, as shown. The projection of the rectangle in Γ_1 onto Γ_2 is a rectangle, as the student may easily verify. The lengths of the sides of the rectangle in Γ_2 are a and $b \cos \phi$. The area $A_1 = ab$ of the rectangle in Γ_1 and the area $A_2 = ab \cos \phi$ of the rectangle in Γ_2 satisfy the relation

$$A_2 = A_1 \cos \phi. \tag{1}$$

Equation (1) is the basis of the next useful result.

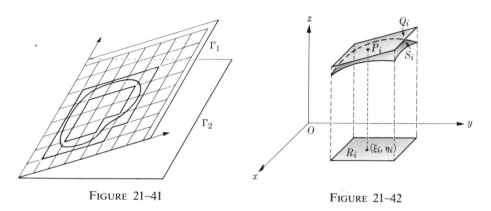

FIGURE 21–41   FIGURE 21–42

Lemma. Let R_1 be a region in a plane Γ_1 and let R_2 be the projection of R_1 onto a plane Γ_2. Then

$$A(R_2) = A(R_1) \cos \phi, \tag{2}$$

where ϕ is the angle between the planes Γ_1 and Γ_2.

This lemma is proved by subdividing the plane Γ_1 into a network of rectangles and observing that these rectangles project onto rectangles in Γ_2 with areas related by equation (1). Since the areas of R_1 and R_2 are obtained as limits of sums of the areas of rectangles, formula (2) holds in the limit (Fig. 21–41). (The details of this argument are given in Morrey, *University Calculus*, page 623.) We observe that if the planes are parallel, then ϕ is zero, the region and its projection are congruent, and the areas are equal. If the planes are perpendicular, then $\phi = \pi/2$, the projection of R_1 degenerates into a line segment, and $A(R_2)$ vanishes. Thus formula (2) is valid for all angles ϕ such that $0 \leq \phi \leq \pi/2$.

Suppose we have a surface S represented by an equation

$$z = f(x, y)$$

for (x, y) on some region F in the xy-plane. We shall consider only functions f which have continuous first partial derivatives for all (x, y) on F.

To define the area of the surface S we begin by subdividing the xy-plane into a rectangular mesh. Suppose R_i, a rectangle of the subdivision, is completely contained in F. Select a point (ξ_i, η_i) in R_i. This selection may be made in any manner whatsoever. The point $P_i(\xi_i, \eta_i, \zeta_i)$, with $\zeta_i = f(\xi_i, \eta_i)$, is on the surface S. Construct the plane tangent to the surface S at P_i (Fig. 21–42). Planes parallel to the z-axis and through the edges of R_i cut out a portion (denoted S_i) of the surface, and they cut out a quadrilateral, denoted Q_i, from the tangent plane. The projection of Q_i on the xy-plane is R_i. If the definition of surface area is to satisfy our intuition, then the area of S_i must be close to the area of Q_i whenever the subdivision in the xy-plane is sufficiently fine. However, Q_i is a plane region, and its area can be found exactly. We recall from Chapter 20 (page 675) that we can determine the equation of a plane tangent to a surface $z = f(x, y)$

at a given point on the surface. Such a determination is possible because the quantities

$$f_{,1}(\xi_i, \eta_i), \qquad f_{,2}(\xi_i, \eta_i), \qquad -1$$

form a set of attitude numbers for the tangent plane at the point (ξ_i, η_i, ζ_i) where $\zeta_i = f(\xi_i, \eta_i)$.

On page 549 we showed that the formula for the angle between two planes is

$$\cos \phi = \frac{|a_1 b_1 + a_2 b_2 + a_3 b_3|}{\sqrt{a_1^2 + a_2^2 + a_3^2} \sqrt{b_1^2 + b_2^2 + b_3^2}},$$

where a_1, a_2, a_3 and b_1, b_2, b_3 are sets of attitude numbers of the two planes. We now find the cosine of the angle between the plane tangent to the surface and the xy-plane. Letting ϕ denote the angle between the tangent plane and the xy-plane and recalling that the xy-plane has attitude numbers $0, 0, -1$, we get

$$\cos \phi = \frac{0 \cdot f_{,1} + 0 \cdot f_{,2} + 1 \cdot 1}{\sqrt{1 + f_{,1}^2 + f_{,2}^2}} = (1 + f_{,1}^2 + f_{,2}^2)^{-1/2}.$$

According to the above lemma, we have

$$A(R_i) = A(Q_i) \cos \phi$$

or

$$A(Q_i) = A(R_i)\sqrt{1 + f_{,1}^2(\xi_i, \eta_i) + f_{,2}^2(\xi_i, \eta_i)}.$$

We add all expressions of the above type for rectangles R_i which are in F. We obtain the sum

$$\sum_{i=1}^{n} A(Q_i) = \sum_{i=1}^{n} A(R_i)\sqrt{1 + f_{,1}^2(\xi_i, \eta_i) + f_{,2}^2(\xi_i, \eta_i)}, \qquad (3)$$

and we expect that this sum is a good approximation to the (as yet undefined) surface area if the norm of the rectangular subdivision in the xy-plane is sufficiently small.

DEFINITION. If the limit of the sums (3) exists as the norms of the subdivisions tend to zero and for arbitrary selections of the values (ξ_i, η_i) in R_i, then we say that the surface $z = f(x, y)$ has *surface area*. The *value of the surface area* $A(S)$ of S is the limit of the sum (3).

Theorem 12. *The sums in* (3) *tend to*

$$\iint_F \sqrt{1 + [f_{,1}(x, y)]^2 + [f_{,2}(x, y)]^2} \, dA$$

whenever the first derivatives $f_{,1}$ and $f_{,2}$ are continuous on F.

This theorem is an immediate consequence of Theorem 1 and the fact that $\sqrt{1 + f_{,1}^2 + f_{,2}^2}$ is continuous if $f_{,1}$ and $f_{,2}$ are. The integration formula of the theorem may be used to calculate surface area, as the next examples show.

EXAMPLE 1. Find the area of the surface $z = \frac{2}{3}(x^{3/2} + y^{3/2})$ situated above the square $F: 0 \leq x \leq 1, 0 \leq y \leq 1$ (Fig. 21–43).

Solution. Setting $z = f(x, y)$, we have $f_{,1} = x^{1/2}, f_{,2} = y^{1/2}$, and

$$A(S) = \iint_F (1 + x + y)^{1/2} \, dA = \int_0^1 \int_0^1 (1 + x + y)^{1/2} \, dy \, dx.$$

Therefore

$$A(S) = \int_0^1 \frac{2}{3}[(1 + x + y)^{3/2}]_0^1 \, dx = \frac{2}{3}\int_0^1 [(2 + x)^{3/2} - (1 + x)^{3/2}] \, dx$$

$$= \frac{4}{15}[(2 + x)^{5/2} - (1 + x)^{5/2}]_0^1 = \frac{4}{15}(1 + 9\sqrt{3} - 8\sqrt{2}).$$

FIGURE 21–43

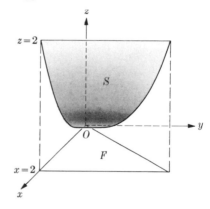

FIGURE 21–44

EXAMPLE 2. Find the area of the part of the cylinder $z = \frac{1}{2}x^2$ cut out by the planes $y = 0, y = x,$ and $x = 2$.

Solution. See Figs. 21–44 and 21–45, which show the surface S and the projection F. We have $\partial z/\partial x = x, \partial z/\partial y = 0$. Therefore

$$A(S) = \iint_F \sqrt{1 + x^2} \, dA = \int_0^2 \int_0^x \sqrt{1 + x^2} \, dy \, dx$$

$$= \int_0^2 x\sqrt{1 + x^2} \, dx = \frac{1}{3}[(1 + x^2)^{3/2}]_0^2$$

$$= \frac{1}{3}(5\sqrt{5} - 1).$$

FIGURE 21–45

The next example shows that it is sometimes useful to use polar coordinates for the evaluation of the double integral.

———————

EXAMPLE 3.   Find the surface area of the part of the sphere $x^2 + y^2 + z^2 = a^2$ cut out by the vertical cylinder erected on one loop of the curve whose equation in polar coordinates is $r = a \cos 2\theta$.

Solution. (See Fig. 21–46.) The surface consists of two parts, one above and one below the xy-plane, symmetrically placed. The area of the upper half will be found. We have

$$z = \sqrt{a^2 - x^2 - y^2},$$

$$\frac{\partial z}{\partial x} = \frac{-x}{\sqrt{a^2 - x^2 - y^2}},$$

$$\frac{\partial z}{\partial y} = \frac{-y}{\sqrt{a^2 - x^2 - y^2}}.$$

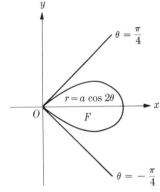

Therefore (Fig. 21–46), we obtain

$$A(S) = \iint_F \frac{a}{\sqrt{a^2 - x^2 - y^2}} \, dA_{x,y}$$

$$= \int_{-\pi/4}^{\pi/4} \int_0^{a \cos 2\theta} \frac{ar}{\sqrt{a^2 - r^2}} \, dr \, d\theta.$$

FIGURE 21–46

This integral is an improper integral, but it can be shown to be convergent. Taking this fact for granted, we get

$$A(S) = 2a \int_0^{\pi/4} \left[-\sqrt{a^2 - r^2} \right]_0^{a \cos 2\theta} d\theta$$

$$= 2a^2 \int_0^{\pi/4} (1 - \sin 2\theta) \, d\theta = \frac{1}{2} a^2 (\pi - 2).$$

The total surface area is $a^2(\pi - 2)$.

———————

If the given surface is of the form $y = f(x, z)$ or $x = f(y, z)$, we get similar formulas for the surface area. These are

$$A(S) = \iint_F \sqrt{1 + \left(\frac{\partial z}{\partial x}\right)^2 + \left(\frac{\partial z}{\partial y}\right)^2} \, dA_{x,y} \qquad \text{if} \quad z = f(x, y),$$

$$A(S) = \iint_F \sqrt{1 + \left(\frac{\partial y}{\partial x}\right)^2 + \left(\frac{\partial y}{\partial z}\right)^2} \, dA_{x,z} \qquad \text{if} \quad y = f(x, z),$$

$$A(S) = \iint_F \sqrt{1 + \left(\frac{\partial x}{\partial y}\right)^2 + \left(\frac{\partial x}{\partial z}\right)^2} \, dA_{y,z} \qquad \text{if} \quad x = f(y, z).$$

EXERCISES

In each of the problems 1 through 18, find the area of the surface described.

1. The portion of the surface $z = \frac{2}{3}(x^{3/2} + y^{3/2})$ situated above the triangle

$$F: \{0 \le x \le y, 0 \le y \le 1\}.$$

2. The portion of the plane $x/a + y/b + z/c = 1$ in the first octant ($a > 0$, $b > 0$, $c > 0$).

3. The part of the cylinder $x^2 + z^2 = a^2$ inside the cylinder $x^2 + y^2 = a^2$.

4. The part of the cylinder $x^2 + z^2 = a^2$ above the square $|x| \le \frac{1}{2}a$, $|y| \le \frac{1}{2}a$.

5. The part of the cone $z^2 = x^2 + y^2$ inside the cylinder $x^2 + y^2 = 2x$.

6. The part of the cone $z^2 = x^2 + y^2$ above the figure bounded by one loop of the curve $r^2 = 4 \cos 2\theta$.

7. The part of the cone $x^2 = y^2 + z^2$ between the cylinder $y^2 = z$ and the plane $y = z - 2$.

8. The part of the cone $y^2 = x^2 + z^2$ cut off by the plane $2y = (x + 2)\sqrt{2}$.

9. The part of the cone $x^2 = y^2 + z^2$ inside the sphere $x^2 + y^2 + z^2 = 2z$.

10. The part of the surface $z = xy$ inside the cylinder $x^2 + y^2 = a^2$.

11. The part of the surface $4z = x^2 - y^2$ above the region bounded by the curve $r^2 = 4 \cos \theta$.

12. The part of the surface of a sphere of radius $2a$ inside a cylinder of radius a if the center of the sphere is on the surface of the cylinder.

13. The part of the surface of a sphere of radius a, center at the origin, inside the cylinder erected on one loop of the curve $r = a \cos 3\theta$.

14. The part of the sphere $x^2 + y^2 + z^2 = 4z$ inside the paraboloid $x^2 + y^2 = z$.

15. The part of the cylinder $y^2 + z^2 = 2z$ cut off by the cone $x^2 = y^2 + z^2$.

16. The part of the cylinder $x^2 + y^2 = 2ax$ inside the sphere $x^2 + y^2 + z^2 = 4a^2$.

17. The part of the cylinder $y^2 + z^2 = 4a^2$ above the xy-plane and bounded by the planes $y = 0$, $x = a$, and $y = x$.

18. The part of the paraboloid $y^2 + z^2 = 4ax$ cut off by the cylinder $y^2 = ax$ and the plane $x = 3a$.

19. (a) Use elementary geometry (and trigonometry) to establish equation (2) for an arbitrary triangle. (b) Use the result of (a) to establish equation (2) for an arbitrary polygon.

9. VOLUMES OF SOLIDS OF REVOLUTION

We previously developed methods for finding the volume of certain solids of revolution. These techniques were applicable whenever the resulting process reduced to a single integration. (See page 482 ff.) Now that areas may be determined in a more general way by double integrations, we can calculate the volume of a greater variety of solids of revolution. The basic tool is the Theorem of Pappus which we now state. (See also page 523.)

Theorem 13. (*Theorem of Pappus.*) *If a plane figure F lies on one side of a line L in its plane, the volume of the set S generated by revolving F around L is equal to the product of A(F), the area of F, and the length of the path described by the centroid of F; in other words, if F is in the xy-plane and L is the x-axis (see Fig. 21–47), then*

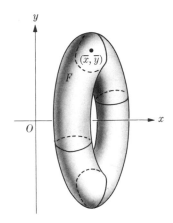

$$V(S) = 2\pi\bar{y}A(F) = \iint\limits_{F} 2\pi y \, dA. \qquad (1)$$

The second equality in (1) above follows from the definition of $\bar{y}$. In case F is a rectangle of the form $a \le x \le b$, $c \le y \le d$, where $c \ge 0$, then S is just a circular ring of altitude $b - a$, inner radius of base c (if $c > 0$) and outer radius d. Thus

FIGURE 21–47

$$V(S) = \pi(d^2 - c^2)(b - a) = 2\pi\left(\frac{c+d}{2}\right)A(F) = 2\pi\bar{y}A(F)$$
$$= \iint\limits_{F} 2\pi y \, dA.$$

The theorem is proved in general by subdividing F and noting that

$$\sum_{i=1}^{n} V(S_i) = \sum_{i=1}^{n} \iint\limits_{F_i} 2\pi y \, dA = \iint\limits_{F_n^*} 2\pi y \, dA,$$

where F_n^* is the union of the F_i; we then pass to the limit. Additional details may be found in Morrey, *University Calculus*, page 627.

EXAMPLE 1.   The region F bounded by the curves $y = x^3$ and $y = \sqrt{x}$ is revolved about the x-axis. Find the volume generated.

Solution. See Fig. 21–48. We have

$$V(S) = 2\pi \iint\limits_{F} y \, dA = 2\pi \int_0^1 \int_{x^3}^{\sqrt{x}} y \, dy \, dx$$

$$= \pi \int_0^1 (x - x^6) \, dx = \frac{5}{14}\pi.$$

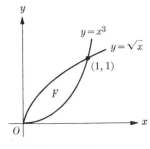

FIGURE 21–48

The Theorem of Pappus in this more general form is especially useful whenever the transformation to polar coordinates is appropriate. The next example illustrates this point.

EXAMPLE 2. Find the volume of the set S generated by revolving around the x-axis the upper half F of the area bounded by the cardioid $r = a(1 + \cos \theta)$. (See Fig. 21–49.)

Solution. We have

$$V(S) = \iint_F 2\pi y \, dA = \iint_F 2\pi r \sin \theta \, dA_{x,y}$$

$$= 2\pi \int_0^\pi \int_0^{a(1+\cos \theta)} r^2 \sin \theta \, dr \, d\theta$$

$$= \frac{2}{3} \pi a^3 \int_0^\pi (1 + \cos \theta)^3 \sin \theta \, d\theta$$

$$= \frac{\pi a^3}{6} \left[-(1 + \cos \theta)^4 \right]_0^\pi = \frac{8\pi a^3}{3}.$$

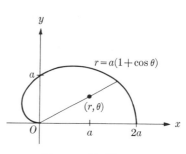

FIGURE 21–49

The formula analogous to (1) for revolving a region F in the xy-plane about the y-axis is

$$V(S) = 2\pi \bar{x} A(F) = 2\pi \iint_F x \, dA.$$

EXERCISES

In each of problems 1 through 12, find the volume of the set obtained by revolving the region described about the axis indicated. Sketch the region.

1. The upper half of the ellipse $x^2/a^2 + y^2/b^2 = 1$; the x-axis.

2. The region in the first quadrant inside $3x^2 + 4y^2 = 48$ and outside $(x - 2)^2 + y^2 = 1$; the x-axis.

3. The region satisfying the inequalities $xy \le 4$, $y \le x$, $27y \ge 4x^2$; the x-axis.

4. The upper half of the figure bounded by the right-hand loop of the curve $r^2 = a^2 \cos \theta$; the x-axis.

5. The upper half of the right-hand loop of the curve $r = a \cos^2 \theta$; the x-axis.

6. The region inside $x^2 + y^2 = 64$ and outside $x^2 + y^2 = 8x$; the line $x = 8$.

7. The loop of $r^3 = \sin 2\theta$ in the first quadrant; the y-axis.

8. The upper half of the area outside the circle $r = 4$ and inside the limaçon $r = 3 + 2 \cos \theta$; the x-axis.

9. The upper half of the area to the right of the line $x = \frac{3}{2}$ and inside the cardioid $r = 2(1 + \cos \theta)$; the x-axis.

10. The upper half of the area to the right of the parabola $r = 9/(1 + \cos \theta)$ and inside the cardioid $r = 4(1 + \cos \theta)$; the x-axis.

11. The right-hand horizontal loop of the curve $r = 2 \cos 2\theta$; the y-axis. Find the centroid of that loop.

12. The upper half of the right-hand loop of the curve $r^2 = a^2 \cos 2\theta$; the x-axis.

10. THE TRIPLE INTEGRAL

The definition of the triple integral parallels that of the double integral. In the simplest case, we consider a rectangular box R bounded by the six planes $x = a_0$, $x = a_1$, $y = b_0$, $y = b_1$, $z = c_0$, $z = c_1$ (Fig. 21–50). Let $f(x, y, z)$ be a function of three variables defined for (x, y, z) in R. We subdivide the entire three-dimensional space into rectangular boxes by constructing planes parallel to the coordinate planes. Let $B_1, B_2, \ldots, B_n$ be those boxes of the subdivision which contain points of R. Denote by $V(B_i)$ the volume of the ith box, B_i. We select a point $P_i(\xi_i, \eta_i, \zeta_i)$ in B_i; this selection may be made in any manner whatsoever. The sum

$$\sum_{i=1}^{n} f(\xi_i, \eta_i, \zeta_i) V(B_i)$$

is an approximation to the triple integral. The *norm of the subdivision* is the length of the longest diagonal of the boxes $B_1, B_2, \ldots, B_n$. If the above sums tend to a limit as the norms of the subdivisions tend to zero and for any choices of the points P_i, we call this limit the *triple integral of f over R*. The expression

$$\iiint\limits_{R} f(x, y, z) \, dV$$

is used to represent this limit.

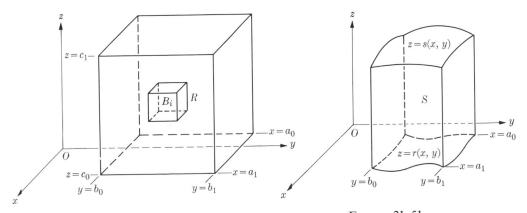

FIGURE 21–50   FIGURE 21–51

Just as the double integral is equal to a twice-iterated integral, so the triple integral has the same value as a threefold iterated integral. In the case of the rectangular box R, we obtain

$$\iiint\limits_{R} f(x, y, z) \, dV = \int_{a_0}^{a_1} \left\{ \int_{b_0}^{b_1} \left[\int_{c_0}^{c_1} f(x, y, z) \, dz \right] dy \right\} dx.$$

Suppose a region S is bounded by the planes $x = a_0$, $x = a_1$, $y = b_0$, $y = b_1$, and by the surfaces $z = r(x, y)$, $z = s(x, y)$, as shown in Fig. 21–51. The triple integral may be defined in the same way as for a rectangular box R, and once again it is equal to the iterated integral. We have

$$\iiint_S f(x, y, z)\, dV = \int_{a_0}^{a_1} \left\{ \int_{b_0}^{b_1} \left[\int_{r(x,y)}^{s(x,y)} f(x, y, z)\, dz \right] dy \right\} dx.$$

We state without proof the following theorem, which applies in the general case.

Theorem 14. *Suppose that S is a region defined by the inequalities*

$$S: a \le x \le b, \qquad p(x) \le y \le q(x), \qquad r(x, y) \le z \le s(x, y),$$

where the functions p, q, r, and s are continuous. If f is a continuous function on S, then

$$\iiint_S f(x, y, z)\, dV = \int_{a}^{b} \left\{ \int_{p(x)}^{q(x)} \left[\int_{r(x,y)}^{s(x,y)} f(x, y, z)\, dz \right] dy \right\} dx.$$

The iterated integrations are performed in turn by holding all variables constant except the one being integrated. Brackets and braces in multiple integrals will be omitted unless there is danger of confusion.

EXAMPLE 1. Evaluate the iterated integral

$$\int_0^3 \int_0^{6-2z} \int_0^{4-(2/3)y-(4/3)z} yz\, dx\, dy\, dz.$$

Solution. We have

$$\int_0^3 \int_0^{6-2z} \int_0^{4-(2/3)y-(4/3)z} yz\, dx\, dy\, dz$$

$$= \int_0^3 \int_0^{6-2z} \left[xyz \right]_0^{4-(2/3)y-(4/3)z} dy\, dz$$

$$= \int_0^3 \int_0^{6-2z} yz \left(4 - \frac{2}{3}y - \frac{4}{3}z \right) dy\, dz$$

$$= \int_0^3 \left[2zy^2 - \frac{2}{9}zy^3 - \frac{2}{3}y^2z^2 \right]_0^{6-2z} dz$$

$$= \int_0^3 \left[\left(2z - \frac{2}{3}z^2 \right)(6 - 2z)^2 - \frac{2}{9}z(6 - 2z)^3 \right] dz$$

$$= \frac{1}{9} \int_0^3 z(6 - 2z)^3 \, dz.$$

The integration may be performed by the substitution $u = 6 - 2z$. The result is $54/5$.

The determination of the limits of integration is the principal difficulty in reducing a triple integral to an iterated integral. The student who works a large number of problems will develop good powers of visualization of three-dimensional figures. There is no simple mechanical technique for determining the limits of integration in the wide variety of problems we encounter. The next examples illustrate the process.

EXAMPLE 2. Evaluate

$$\iiint_S x \, dV,$$

where S is the region bounded by the surfaces $y = x^2$, $y = x + 2$, $4z = x^2 + y^2$, and $z = x + 3$.

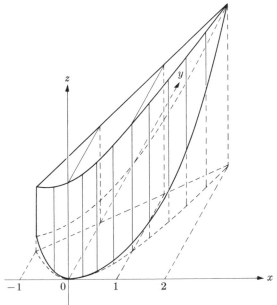

FIGURE 21–52

Solution. To transform the triple integral into an iterated integral, we must determine the limits of integration. The region S is sketched in Fig. 21–52. The projection of S on the xy-plane is the region F bounded by the curves $y = x^2$ and $y = x + 2$, as shown in Fig. 21–53. From this projection, the region rises with vertical walls, bounded from below by the paraboloid $z = \frac{1}{4}(x^2 + y^2)$ and above by the plane $z = x + 3$. Since F is described by the inequalities

$$-1 \leq x \leq 2, \qquad x^2 \leq y \leq x + 2,$$

we have

$$S: \begin{cases} -1 \leq x \leq 2, \\ x^2 \leq y \leq x + 2, \\ \frac{1}{4}(x^2 + y^2) \leq z \leq x + 3. \end{cases}$$

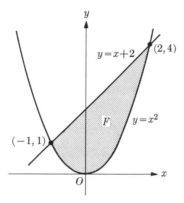

FIGURE 21–53

Therefore

$$\iiint\limits_{S} x \, dV = \int_{-1}^{2} \int_{x^2}^{x+2} \int_{(x^2+y^2)/4}^{x+3} x \, dz \, dy \, dx$$

$$= \int_{-1}^{2} \int_{x^2}^{x+2} \left[x^2 + 3x - \frac{1}{4}(x^3 + xy^2) \right] dy \, dx$$

$$= \int_{-1}^{2} \left\{ \left(3x + x^2 - \frac{1}{4}x^3 \right)(2 + x - x^2) - \frac{x}{12}[(2 + x)^3 - x^6] \right\} dx$$

$$= \frac{837}{160}.$$

In the case of double integrals there are two possible orders of integration, one of them often being easier to calculate than the other. In the case of triple integrals there are six possible orders of integration. It becomes a matter of practice and trial and error to find which order is the most convenient.

The limits of integration may sometimes be found by projecting the region on one of the coordinate planes and then finding the equations of the "bottom" and "top" surfaces. This method was used in Example 2. If part of the boundary is a cylinder perpendicular to one of the coordinate planes, that fact can be used to determine the limits of integration.

EXAMPLE 3. Express the integral

$$I = \iiint\limits_{S} f(x, y, z) \, dV$$

as an iterated integral in six different ways if S is the region bounded by the surfaces

$$z = 0, \qquad z = x, \qquad \text{and} \qquad y^2 = 4 - 2x.$$

FIGURE 21–54

FIGURE 21–55

FIGURE 21–56

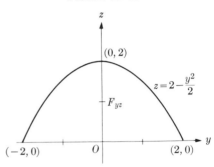

FIGURE 21–57

Solution. The region S is shown in Fig. 21–54. The projection of S on the xy-plane is the two-dimensional region F_{xy} bounded by $x = 0$ and $y^2 = 4 - 2x$, as shown in Fig. 21–55. Therefore the integral may be written

$$I = \int_0^2 \int_{-\sqrt{4-2x}}^{+\sqrt{4-2x}} \int_0^x f(x, y, z)\, dz\, dy\, dx$$

$$= \int_{-2}^2 \int_0^{2-(1/2)y^2} \int_0^x f(x, y, z)\, dz\, dx\, dy.$$

The projection of S on the xz-plane is the triangular region bounded by the curves $z = 0$, $z = x$, and $x = 2$, as shown in Fig. 21–56. The iterated integral in this case becomes

$$I = \int_0^2 \int_0^x \int_{-\sqrt{4-2x}}^{+\sqrt{4-2x}} f(x, y, z)\, dy\, dz\, dx$$

$$= \int_0^2 \int_z^2 \int_{-\sqrt{4-2x}}^{+\sqrt{4-2x}} f(x, y, z)\, dy\, dx\, dz.$$

The projection of S on the yz-plane is the plane region bounded by $z = 0$ and $z = 2 - \frac{1}{2}y^2$ (Fig. 21–57). Then I takes the form

$$I = \int_{-2}^{2} \int_{0}^{2-(1/2)y^2} \int_{z}^{2-(1/2)y^2} f(x, y, z)\, dx\, dz\, dy$$

$$= \int_{0}^{2} \int_{-\sqrt{4-2z}}^{+\sqrt{4-2z}} \int_{z}^{2-(1/2)y^2} f(x, y, z)\, dx\, dy\, dz.$$

EXERCISES

In each of problems 1 through 6, find the value of the iterated integral.

1. $\displaystyle\int_{0}^{1} \int_{0}^{x} \int_{0}^{x-y} x\, dz\, dy\, dx$

2. $\displaystyle\int_{-1}^{1} \int_{0}^{1-y^2} \int_{-\sqrt{x}}^{\sqrt{x}} 2y^2\sqrt{x}\, dz\, dx\, dy$

3. $\displaystyle\int_{0}^{1} \int_{y^2}^{\sqrt{y}} \int_{0}^{y+z} xy\, dx\, dz\, dy$

4. $\displaystyle\int_{0}^{4} \int_{0}^{\sqrt{16-x^2}} \int_{0}^{\sqrt{16-x^2-y^2}} (x + y + z)\, dz\, dy\, dx$

5. $\displaystyle\int_{0}^{2} \int_{0}^{\sqrt{4-z^2}} \int_{0}^{2-z} z\, dx\, dy\, dz$

6. $\displaystyle\int_{0}^{1} \int_{0}^{x} \int_{0}^{y} \frac{1 + \sqrt[3]{z}}{\sqrt{z}}\, dz\, dy\, dx$

In problems 7 through 17, evaluate

$$\iiint_{S} f(x, y, z)\, dV$$

where S is bounded by the given surfaces and f is the given function.

7. $z = 0,\ y = 0,\ y = x,\ x + y = 2,\ x + y + z = 3;\ f(x, y, z) = x$

8. $x = 0,\ x = \sqrt{a^2 - y^2 - z^2};\ f(x, y, z) = x$

9. $z = 0,\ x^2 + z = 1,\ y^2 + z = 1,\ f(x, y, z) = z^2$

10. $x^2 + z^2 = a^2,\ y^2 + z^2 = a^2,\ f(x, y, z) = x^2 + y^2$

11. $x = 0,\ y = 0,\ z = 0,\ (x/a) + (y/b) + (z/c) = 1,\ (a, b, c > 0);\ f(x, y, z) = z$

12. $y = z^2,\ y^2 = z,\ x = 0,\ x = y - z^2;\ f(x, y, z) = y + z^2$

13. $x = 0,\ y = 0,\ z = 0,\ x^{1/2} + y^{1/2} + z^{1/2} = a^{1/2};\ f(x, y, z) = z$

14. $x = 0,\ y = 0,\ z = 0,\ y^2 = 4 - z,\ x = y + 2;\ f(x, y, z) = x^2$

15. $z = x^2 + y^2,\ z = 27 - 2x^2 - 2y^2;\ f(x, y, z) = 1$

16. $z^2 = 4ax,\ x^2 + y^2 = 2ax;\ f(x, y, z) = 1$

*17. $y^2 + z^2 = 4ax,\ y^2 = ax,\ x = 3a;\ f(x, y, z) = x^2$

In problems 18 through 22, express each iterated integral as a triple integral by describing the set S over which the integration is performed. Sketch the set S and then express the iterated integral in two orders differing from the original. Do not evaluate the integrals.

18. $\displaystyle\int_{0}^{1} \int_{0}^{x} \int_{0}^{x-y} x\, dz\, dy\, dx$

19. $\displaystyle\int_{-1}^{1} \int_{0}^{1-y^2} \int_{-\sqrt{x}}^{\sqrt{x}} 2y^2\sqrt{x}\, dz\, dx\, dy$

20. $\displaystyle\int_0^1\int_{y^2}^{\sqrt{y}}\int_0^{y+z} xy \, dx \, dz \, dy$ 21. $\displaystyle\int_{-2}^2\int_0^{4-y^2}\int_0^{y+2} (y^2 + z^2) \, dz \, dx \, dy$

22. $\displaystyle\int_0^1\int_{x^2}^{\sqrt{x}}\int_0^{y-x^2} f(x, y, z) \, dz \, dy \, dx$

23. Express the integral of $f(x, y, z)$ over the region S bounded by the surface $z = \sqrt{16 - x^2 - y^2}$ and the plane $z = 2$ in 6 ways.

24. Express the integral

$$\int_0^2\int_0^z\int_0^x (x^2 + y^2 + z^2) \, dy \, dx \, dz$$

in 5 additional ways.

11. MASS OF A SOLID. TRIPLE INTEGRALS IN CYLINDRICAL AND SPHERICAL COORDINATES

From the definition of triple integral we see that if $f(x, y, z) \equiv 1$, then the triple integral taken over a region S is precisely the volume $V(S)$. More generally, if a solid object occupies a region S, and if the density at any point is given by $\delta(x, y, z)$, then the total mass, $m(S)$, is given by the triple integral

$$m(S) = \iiint\limits_S \delta(x, y, z) \, dV.$$

Notation. For the remainder of this chapter the symbol δ will be used for density. The quantity ρ, which we previously used for density, will denote one of the variables in spherical coordinates.

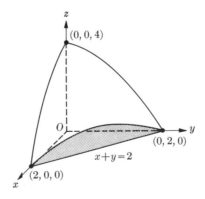

FIGURE 21-58

EXAMPLE 1. The solid S in the first octant is bounded by the surfaces $z = 4 - x^2 - y^2$, $z = 0$, $x + y = 2$, $x = 0$, $y = 0$. The density is given by $\delta(x, y, z) = 2z$. Find the total mass.

Solution. We have (Fig. 21–58)

$$m(S) = \iiint_S 2z \, dV = 2 \int_0^2 \int_0^{2-x} \int_0^{4-x^2-y^2} z \, dz \, dy \, dx$$

$$= \int_0^2 \int_0^{2-x} (4 - x^2 - y^2)^2 \, dy \, dz$$

$$= \int_0^2 \int_0^{2-x} (16 + x^4 + y^4 - 8x^2 - 8y^2 + 2x^2 y^2) \, dy \, dz$$

$$= \int_0^2 \left[(4 - x^2)^2 y - \frac{2}{3} (4 - x^2) y^3 + \frac{1}{5} y^5 \right]_0^{2-x} \, dx$$

$$= \int_0^2 \left[2(4 - x^2)^2 - x(4 - x^2)^2 - \frac{2}{3} (4 - x^2)(2 - x)^3 + \frac{1}{5} (2 - x)^5 \right] dx.$$

The above integral, a polynomial in x, can be evaluated. The answer is 704/45.

We found that certain double integrals are easy to evaluate if a polar coordinate system is used. Similarly, there are triple integrals which, although difficult to evaluate in rectangular coordinates, are simple integrations when transformed into other systems. The most useful transformations are those to cylindrical and spherical coordinates. (See Chapter 17, page 567.)

Cylindrical coordinates consist of polar coordinates in the plane and a z-coordinate as in a rectangular system. The transformation from rectangular to cylindrical coordinates is

$$x = r \cos \theta, \qquad y = r \sin \theta, \qquad z = z. \tag{1}$$

A region S in (x, y, z) space corresponds to a region U in (r, θ, z) space. The volume of S, $V(S)$, may be found in terms of a triple integral in (r, θ, z) space by the formula (Fig. 21–59)

$$V(S) = \iiint_U r \, dV_{r\theta z}.$$

This formula is a natural extension of the formula relating area in rectangular and in polar coordinates. (See page 759.)

More generally, if $f(x, y, z)$ is a continuous function, and if we define

$$g(r, \theta, z) = f(r \cos \theta, r \sin \theta, z),$$

then we have the following relationship between triple integrals:

$$\iiint_S f(x, y, z) \, dV_{xyz} = \iiint_U g(r, \theta, z) r \, dV_{r\theta z}.$$

A triple integral in cylindrical coordinates may be evaluated by iterated integrals. We write

$$\iiint g(r, \theta, z)r\, dV_{r\theta z} = \iiint g(r, \theta, z)r\, dr\, d\theta\, dz$$

and, as before, there are five other orders of integration possible. Once again the major problem is the determination of the limits of integration. For this purpose it is helpful to superimpose cylindrical coordinates on a rectangular system, sketch the surface, and read off the limits of integration. The next example shows the method.

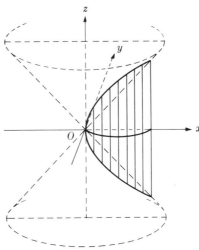

FIGURE 21–59   FIGURE 21–60

EXAMPLE 2. Find the mass of the solid bounded by the cylinder $x^2 + y^2 = ax$ and the cone $z^2 = x^2 + y^2$ if the density $\delta = k\sqrt{x^2 + y^2}$ (Fig. 21–60).

Solution. We change to cylindrical coordinates. The cylinder is $r = a\cos\theta$ and the cone is $z^2 = r^2$. The density is kr. The region S corresponds to the region U given by

$$U: \quad -\frac{\pi}{2} \le \theta \le \frac{\pi}{2}, \qquad 0 \le r \le a\cos\theta, \qquad -r \le z \le r.$$

Therefore

$$m(S) = \iiint_S k\sqrt{x^2 + y^2}\, dV_{xyz} = k\iiint_U r \cdot r \cdot dV_{r\theta z}$$

$$= k\int_{-\pi/2}^{\pi/2}\int_0^{a\cos\theta}\int_{-r}^{r} r^2\, dz\, dr\, d\theta$$

$$= 2k\int_{-\pi/2}^{\pi/2}\int_0^{a\cos\theta} r^3\, dr\, d\theta = \frac{1}{2}ka^4\int_{-\pi/2}^{\pi/2}\cos^4\theta\, d\theta$$

$$= \frac{1}{8}ka^4\int_{-\pi/2}^{\pi/2}\left(1 + 2\cos 2\theta + \frac{1 + \cos 4\theta}{2}\right)d\theta = \frac{3k\pi a^4}{16}.$$

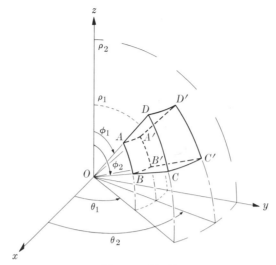

FIGURE 21–61

The transformation from rectangular to spherical coordinates is given by the equations (see page 568)

$$x = \rho \cos \theta \sin \phi, \qquad y = \rho \sin \theta \sin \phi, \qquad z = \rho \cos \phi. \qquad (2)$$

The region U determined by the inequalities

$$\rho_1 \leq \rho \leq \rho_2, \qquad \theta_1 \leq \theta \leq \theta_2, \qquad \phi_1 \leq \phi \leq \phi_2$$

corresponds to a rectangular box in (ρ, θ, ϕ) space. We wish to find the volume of the solid S in (x, y, z) space which corresponds to U under the transformation (2). Referring to Fig. 21–61, we see that S is a region such as $ABCDA'B'C'D'$ between the spheres $\rho = \rho_1$ and $\rho = \rho_2$, between the planes $\theta = \theta_1$ and $\theta = \theta_2$, and between the cones $\phi = \phi_1(OADD'A')$ and $\phi = \phi_2(OBCC'B')$. The region S is obtained by sweeping the plane region $F(ABCD$ shown in Fig. 21–62) through an angle $\Delta\theta = \theta_2 - \theta_1$. The Theorem of Pappus (page 523) for determining volumes of solids of revolution applies also for areas swept through any angle about an axis. We obtain

$$V(S) = \Delta\theta \iint_F x \, dA_{zx}.$$

Since ρ, ϕ are polar coordinates in the zx-plane (Fig. 21–62), we have $x = \rho \sin \phi$ and $dA_{zx} = \rho \, dA_{\rho\phi} = \rho \, d\rho \, d\phi$. Therefore

$$V(S) = \Delta\theta \int_{\phi_1}^{\phi_2} \int_{\rho_1}^{\rho_2} \rho^2 \sin \phi \, d\rho \, d\phi$$

$$= \int_{\theta_1}^{\theta_2} \int_{\phi_1}^{\phi_2} \int_{\rho_1}^{\rho_2} \rho^2 \sin \phi \, d\rho \, d\phi \, d\theta$$

$$= \iiint_U \rho^2 \sin \phi \, dV_{\rho\theta\phi}.$$

FIGURE 21–62

More generally, if $f(x, y, z)$ is continuous on a region S and if

$$g(\rho, \theta, \phi) = f(\rho \cos \theta \sin \phi, \rho \sin \theta \sin \phi, \rho \cos \phi),$$

then the triple integral of f may be transformed according to the formula

$$\iiint_S f(x, y, z)\, dV_{xyz} = \iiint_U g(\rho, \theta, \phi)\rho^2 \sin \phi\, dV_{\rho\theta\phi}.$$

Once again, the triple integral is evaluated by iterated integrations. The next example illustrates the process.

EXAMPLE 3. Find the volume above the cone $z^2 = x^2 + y^2$ and inside the sphere $x^2 + y^2 + z^2 = 2az$ (Fig. 21–63).

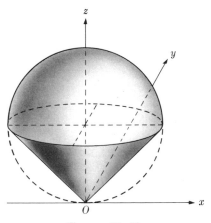

FIGURE 21–63

Solution. In spherical coordinates the cone and sphere have the equations

$$\phi = \frac{\pi}{4} \qquad \text{and} \qquad \rho = 2a \cos \phi,$$

respectively. Therefore

$$V(S) = \iiint_S dV_{xyz} = \iiint_U \rho^2 \sin \phi\, dV_{\rho\theta\phi}$$

$$= \int_0^{\pi/4} \int_0^{2a \cos \phi} \int_0^{2\pi} \rho^2 \sin \phi\, d\theta\, d\rho\, d\phi$$

$$= 2\pi \int_0^{\pi/4} \int_0^{2a \cos \phi} \rho^2 \sin \phi\, d\rho\, d\phi = \frac{16a^3\pi}{3} \int_0^{\pi/4} \cos^3 \phi \sin \phi\, d\phi$$

$$= \frac{4a^3\pi}{3} \left[-\cos^4 \phi\right]_0^{\pi/4} = \pi a^3.$$

EXERCISES

In each of problems 1 through 16, find the mass of the solid having the given density δ and bounded by the surfaces whose equations are given.

1. $z^2 = x^2 + y^2$, $x^2 + y^2 + z^2 = a^2$, above the cone, δ = const.

2. The rectangular parallelepiped bounded by $x = -a$, $x = a$, $y = -b$, $y = b$, $z = -c$, $z = c$, $\delta = k(x^2 + y^2 + z^2)$.

3. $x^2 + y^2 + z^2 = a^2$, $x^2 + y^2 + z^2 = b^2$, $a < b$, $\delta = k\sqrt{x^2 + y^2 + z^2}$.

4. The rectangular parallelepiped bounded by $x = 0$, $x = 2a$, $y = 0$, $y = 2b$, $z = 0$, $z = 2c$, $\delta = k(x^2 + y^2 + z^2)$.

5. $x^2 + y^2 = a^2$, $x^2 + y^2 + z^2 = 4a^2$; $\delta = kz^2$; outside the cylinder.

6. The tetrahedron bounded by the coordinate planes and $x + y + z = 1$; $\delta = kxyz$.

7. $x^2 + y^2 = 2ax$, $x^2 + y^2 + z^2 = 4a^2$; $\delta = k(x^2 + y^2)$.

8. $z^2 = 25(x^2 + y^2)$, $z = x^2 + y^2 + 4$; δ = const; above the paraboloid.

9. $z^2 = x^2 + y^2$, $x^2 + y^2 + z^2 = 2az$; above the cone; $\delta = kz$.

10. Interior of $x^2 + y^2 + z^2 = a^2$; $\delta = k(x^2 + y^2 + z^2)^n$, n a positive number.

11. $x^2 + y^2 = az$, $x^2 + y^2 + z^2 = 2az$; above the paraboloid; δ = const.

12. $2z = x^2 + y^2$, $z = 2x$; $\delta = k\sqrt{x^2 + y^2}$.

13. $x^2 + y^2 + z^2 = a^2$, $r^2 = a^2 \cos 2\theta$ (cylindrical coordinates); δ = const.

14. $x^2 + y^2 + z^2 = 4az$, $z = 3a$, above the plane; $\delta = k\sqrt{x^2 + y^2 + z^2}$.

15. $z^2 = x^2 + y^2$, $(x^2 + y^2)^2 = a^2(x^2 - y^2)$; $\delta = k\sqrt{x^2 + y^2}$.

*16. $z^2 = x^2 + y^2$, $x^2 + y^2 + z^2 = 2ax$; δ = const; above the cone.

12. MOMENT OF INERTIA. CENTER OF MASS

The definition of moment of inertia of a solid body is similar to the definition of moment of inertia of a plane region (page 764). The following definition is basic for the material of this section.

DEFINITION. Suppose that a solid body occupies a region S and let L be any line in three-space. We make a subdivision of space into rectangular boxes and let $S_1, S_2, \ldots, S_n$ be those boxes which contain points of S. For each i, select any point $P_i(\xi_i, \eta_i, \zeta_i)$ in S_i. If the sums

$$\sum_{i=1}^{n} r_i^2 m(S_i) \qquad (r_i = \text{distance of } P_i \text{ from } L)$$

tend to a limit I as the norms of the subdivisions tend to zero, and for any choices of the P_i, then I is called the *moment of inertia of the solid S about L.*

It can be shown that if a solid S has continuous density $\delta(x, y, z)$, then the moments of inertia I_x, I_y, and I_z about the x, y, and z axes, respectively, are given by the triple integrals

$$I_x = \iiint_S (y^2 + z^2)\, \delta(x, y, z)\, dV,$$

$$I_y = \iiint_S (x^2 + z^2)\, \delta(x, y, z)\, dV,$$

$$I_z = \iiint_S (x^2 + y^2)\, \delta(x, y, z)\, dV.$$

If a solid S has a density $\delta(x, y, z)$ and a mass $m(S)$, the point $(\bar{x}, \bar{y}, \bar{z})$, defined by the formulas

$$\bar{x} = \frac{\iiint_S x\, \delta(x, y, z)\, dV}{m(S)}, \qquad \bar{y} = \frac{\iiint_S y\, \delta(x, y, z)\, dV}{m(S)}, \qquad \bar{z} = \frac{\iiint_S z\, \delta(x, y, z)\, dV}{m(S)},$$

is called the *center of mass of S.*

In determining the center of mass, it is helpful to take into account all available symmetries. The following rules are noted:

   (a) *If S is symmetric in the xy-plane and* $\delta(x, y, -z) = \delta(x, y, z)$, *then* $\bar{z} = 0$. *A similar result holds for other coordinate planes.*

   (b) *If S is symmetric in the x-axis and* $\delta(x, -y, -z) = \delta(x, y, z)$, *then* $\bar{y} = \bar{z} = 0$. *A similar result holds for the other axes.*

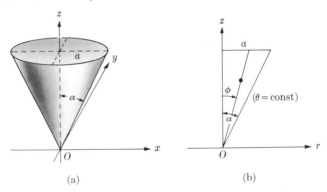

(a)   (b)

FIGURE 21–64

EXAMPLE 1. Find the moment of inertia of a homogeneous solid cone of base radius a and altitude h about a line through the vertex and perpendicular to the axis.

Solution. We take the vertex at the origin, the z-axis as the axis of the cone, and the x-axis as the line L about which the moment of inertia is to be computed (Fig. 21–64).

Let $\alpha = \arctan(a/h)$ be half the angle opening of the cone. In spherical coordinates we get

$$I = \iiint_S (y^2 + z^2)\, dV_{xyz} = \int_0^\alpha \int_0^{h \sec \phi} \int_0^{2\pi} \rho^2 (\sin^2 \phi \sin^2 \theta + \cos^2 \phi)\rho^2 \sin \phi\, d\theta\, d\rho\, d\phi.$$

Since

$$\int_0^{2\pi} \sin^2 \theta \, d\theta = \pi,$$

we obtain

$$I = \pi \int_0^\alpha \int_0^{h \sec \phi} \rho^4 (1 + \cos^2 \phi) \sin \phi \, d\rho \, d\phi$$

$$= \frac{\pi h^5}{5} \int_0^\alpha \left[(\cos \phi)^{-5} + (\cos \phi)^{-3} \right] \sin \phi \, d\phi$$

$$= \frac{\pi h^5}{5} \left[\frac{\sec^4 \alpha - 1}{4} + \frac{\sec^2 \alpha - 1}{2} \right] = \frac{\pi h a^2}{20} (4h^2 + a^2),$$

since $\tan \alpha = a/h$.

EXAMPLE 2. Find the center of gravity of a solid hemisphere of radius a which has density proportional to the distance from the center.

Solution. We select the hemisphere so that the plane section is in the xy-plane and the z-axis is an axis of symmetry (Fig. 21–65). Then $\bar{x} = \bar{y} = 0$. Changing to spherical coordinates, we have

$$m(S) = \int_0^{2\pi} \int_0^{\pi/2} \int_0^a k\rho \cdot \rho^2 \sin \phi \, d\rho \, d\phi \, d\theta = \frac{1}{2} \pi k a^4$$

and

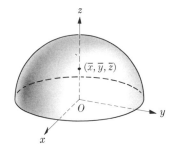

$$\bar{z} = \frac{\int_0^{2\pi} \int_0^{\pi/2} \int_0^a \rho \cos \phi \cdot k\rho \cdot \rho^2 \sin \phi \, d\rho \, d\phi \, d\theta}{\frac{1}{2}\pi k a^4}$$

$$= \frac{2}{\pi a^4} \cdot \frac{1}{5} a^5 \cdot 2\pi \int_0^{\pi/2} \cos \phi \sin \phi \, d\phi$$

$$= \frac{4}{5} a \left[\frac{\sin^2 \phi}{2} \right]_0^{\pi/2} = \frac{2a}{5}.$$

The center of gravity is at $(0, 0, 2a/5)$.   FIGURE 21–65

EXERCISES

In each of problems 1 through 15, find the moment of inertia about the given axis of the solid having the specified density δ and bounded by the surfaces as described.

1. A cube of side a; $\delta = $ const; about an edge.

2. A cube of side a; $\delta = $ const; about a line parallel to an edge, at distance 2 from it, and in a plane of one of the faces.

3. Bounded by $x = 0$, $y = 0$, $z = 0$, $x + z = a$, $y = z$; $\delta = kx$; about the x-axis.

4. $x^2 + y^2 = a^2$; $x^2 + z^2 = a^2$; $\delta = $ const; about the z-axis.

5. $z = x$, $y^2 = 4 - 2z$, $x = 0$; $\delta = $ const; about the z-axis.

6. $x = 0$, $y = 0$, $z^2 = 1 - x - y$; $\delta = $ const; about the z-axis.

7. $z^2 = y^2(1 - x^2)$, $y = 1$; $\delta = $ const; about the x-axis.

8. $x^2 + y^2 = a^2$, $x^2 + y^2 = b^2$, $z = 0$, $z = h$; $\delta = k\sqrt{x^2 + y^2}$; about the x-axis $(a < b)$.

9. $x^2 + y^2 + z^2 = a^2$, $x^2 + y^2 + z^2 = b^2$; $\delta = k\sqrt{x^2 + y^2 + z^2}$; about the z-axis $(a < b)$.

10. $\rho = 4$, $\rho = 5$, $z = 1$, $z = 3$ $(1 \leq z \leq 3)$; $\delta = $ const; about the z-axis.

11. $z^2 = x^2 + y^2$, $(x^2 + y^2)^2 = a^2(x^2 - y^2)$; $\delta = k\sqrt{x^2 + y^2}$; about the z-axis.

12. $z = 0$, $z = \sqrt{a^2 - x^2 - y^2}$; $\delta = kz$; about the x-axis.

13. $x^2/a^2 + y^2/b^2 + z^2/c^2 = 1$; $\delta = $ const; about the z-axis. (Divide the integral into two parts.)

14. $(r - b)^2 + z^2 = a^2$ $(0 < a < b)$; $\delta = kz$; about the z-axis. Assume $z \geq 0$.

15. $\rho = b$, $\rho = c$, $r = a$ $(a < b < c)$; outside $r = a$, between $\rho = b$ and $\rho = c$; $\delta = $ const; about the z-axis.

In each of problems 16 through 32, find the center of mass of the solid having the given density and bounded by the surfaces as described.

16. $x = 0$, $y = 0$, $z = 0$, $x/a + y/b + z/c = 1$; $\delta = $ const.

17. $x = 0$, $y = 0$, $z = 0$, $x + z = a$, $y = z$; $\delta = kx$.

18. $x^2 + y^2 = a^2$, $x^2 + z^2 = a^2$, $\delta = $ const; the portion where $x \geq 0$.

19. $z = x$, $z = -x$, $y^2 = 4 - 2x$; $\delta = $ const.

20. $z^2 = y^2(1 - x^2)$, $y = 1$; $\delta = $ const.

21. $z = 0$, $x^2 + z = 1$, $y^2 + z = 1$; $\delta = $ const.

22. $x = 0$, $y = 0$, $z = 0$, $x^{1/2} + y^{1/2} + z^{1/2} = a^{1/2}$; $\delta = $ const.

23. $y^2 + z^2 = 4ax$, $y^2 = ax$, $x = 3a$; $\delta = $ const. (Inside $y^2 = ax$.)

24. $z^2 = 4ax$, $x^2 + y^2 = 2ax$; $\delta = $ const.

25. $z^2 = x^2 + y^2$, $x^2 + y^2 + z^2 = a^2$, above the cone; $\delta = $ const.

26. $z^2 = x^2 + y^2$, $x^2 + y^2 = 2ax$; $\delta = k(x^2 + y^2)$.

27. $z^2 = x^2 + y^2$, $x^2 + y^2 + z^2 = 2az$, above the cone; $\delta = kz$.

28. $x^2 + y^2 = az$, $x^2 + y^2 + z^2 = 2az$, above the paraboloid; $\delta = $ const.

29. $x^2 + y^2 + z^2 = 4az$, $z = 3a$, above the plane; $\delta = k\sqrt{x^2 + y^2 + z^2}$.

30. $\rho = 4$, $\rho = 5$, $z = 1$, $z = 3$ $(1 \leq z \leq 3)$; $\delta = $ const.

*31. $z^2 = x^2 + y^2$, $(x^2 + y^2)^2 = a^2(x^2 - y^2)$; $\delta = k\sqrt{x^2 + y^2}$; the part for which $x \geq 0$.

*32. $z^2 = x^2 + y^2$, $x^2 + y^2 + z^2 = 2ax$, above the cone; $\delta = $ const.

CHAPTER 22

Linear Algebra

1. SOLUTION OF SYSTEMS OF EQUATIONS IN n VARIABLES BY ELIMINATION

The algebraic problem of solving two simultaneous linear equations in two unknowns is equivalent to the geometric problem of finding the point of intersection of two lines in a plane. We know that a solution can always be found except when the lines are parallel. The algebraic problem of solving three simultaneous linear equations in three unknowns is equivalent to the problem of finding the point of intersection of three planes in space. A solution can be obtained under most circumstances. There are, however, a number of exceptional cases which occur when two or three of the planes are parallel, when the planes intersect in three parallel lines, and so forth. One of the simplest techniques for solving systems of two or three simultaneous linear equations is the method of elimination which the student learned in high school and which was discussed on pages 57 and 58. The process, which works whenever there is a solution, is easily extended to equations in n unknowns with $n > 3$. We illustrate with an example.

EXAMPLE 1. Solve the following system of simultaneous equations:

$$
\begin{aligned}
2x - y + 3z - 2w &= 4, \\
x + 7y + z - w &= 2, \\
3x + 5y - 5z + 3w &= 0, \\
4x - 3y + 2z - w &= 5.
\end{aligned}
$$

Solution. We multiply the second equation by 2 and subtract it from the first, getting

$$-15y + z = 0.$$

Next we multiply the second equation by 3 and subtract it from the third equation; then we multiply the second equation by 4 and subtract it from the fourth equation. In this way we obtain the system

$$
\begin{aligned}
-15y + z &= 0, \\
-16y - 8z + 6w &= -6, \\
-31y - 2z + 3w &= -3,
\end{aligned}
$$

in which only the variables y, z, and w are present. This reduced system may be solved simultaneously by elimination. The quantity w may be eliminated from the second and third equations to give the system

$$-15y + z = 0,$$
$$46y - 4z = 0,$$

which has the solution $y = z = 0$. The value of w may be found from the second or third equation of the preceding set by setting $y = z = 0$. We get $w = -1$. Finally, inserting $y = z = 0$ and $w = -1$ in any of the four original equations, we obtain $x = 1$. We may verify the result in two ways: (1) by substituting $x = 1$, $y = 0$, $z = 0$, $w = -1$ in all four of the original equations and checking the equality, or (2) by noticing that in the elimination process each step is reversible. Therefore, we can begin with the equations $x = 1$, $y = 0$, $z = 0$, $w = -1$ and derive the system we set out to solve.

EXAMPLE 2. Solve the simultaneous system:

$$x - 2y + z - 4w + t = 14,$$
$$2x + 2y - z + w + 3t = 0,$$
$$-x + y + 2z - w + 2t = 8,$$
$$3x - y + 2z + 2w - 2t = 5,$$
$$x + 3y + 2z + 2w - 3t = -7.$$

Solution. We solve the first equation for x in terms of the other unknowns, getting

$$x = 14 + 2y - z + 4w - t.$$

Next we substitute this value of x in each of the remaining four equations to obtain the system of four equations in four unknowns:

$$6y - 3z + 9w + t = -28,$$
$$-y + 3z - 5w + 3t = 22,$$
$$5y - z + 14w - 5t = -37,$$
$$5y + z + 6w - 4t = -21.$$

Solving the second of these equations for y in terms of the remaining quantities, we get

$$y = -22 + 3z - 5w + 3t.$$

Substitution of this value of y in the remaining three equations yields

$$15z - 21w + 19t = 104,$$
$$14z - 11w + 10t = 73,$$
$$16z - 19w + 11t = 89.$$

These three equations in the unknowns z, w, t may be reduced by solving the second equation for t in terms of z and w and then substituting in the first and third equations. The result is

$$116z + w = 347,$$
$$2z - 23w = 29.$$

Finally, we solve the first equation above for w in terms of z and substitute in the second equation to get $z = 3$. Now we can select the following equations from the various systems above:

$$x - 2y + t - 4w + z = 14,$$
$$-y + 3t - 5w + 3z = 22,$$
$$10t - 11w + 14z = 73,$$
$$w + 116z = 347,$$
$$z = 3.$$

A system of this type is called a *triangular form* and may be solved almost by inspection by starting with the last equation and substituting successively in each of the preceding equations. The solution is $x = 1$, $y = -2$, $z = 3$, $w = -1$, $t = 2$. The triangular system is completely equivalent to the original system in that each may be derived from the other.

———————

In both examples it turned out that there is exactly one solution to the system of equations. The question of determining *when* a system of n equations has any solution at all or when it may have many solutions is discussed in Section 6. The more complicated problem of solutions of systems in which the number of equations differs from the number of unknowns is treated in Section 8.

EXERCISES

In the following problems, solve the systems of simultaneous equations, and check the answers.

1. $x - y - 2z = -2$
$3x - 2y - 4z = -5$
$2y + 3z = 2$

2. $2x + y + 3z = 6$
$2x + z = 5$
$-7x + 2y + z = -15$

3. $2x + y - z = -1$
$3x - 2y + z = 7$
$x + 2y + 2z = 3$

4. $2x - 3y - 2z = -10$
$3x + 2y - 4z = -3$
$4x - 2y + 3z = -5$

5. $x - y + 2z + w = -3$
$2x + y - z - w = 8$
$2x + 2y + 3z + w = 1$
$-x + y - 2z + 3w = -5$

6. $2x - 3y + z - w = 7$
$x + 2y - z + 2w = 1$
$-x + y + 2z + w = 4$
$3x - 2y + z - 2w = 3$

7. $3x + y - 2z + w = 5$
$2x - y + z - 2w = 2$
$-2x + 2y - z + 2w = -1$
$-3x - 2y - 3z + w = -3$

8. $2x - y + 3z + w = 6$
$x + 2y - z + 2w = -9$
$-x + 3y - 2z - 3w = -1$
$2x + y + z - 2w = 9$

9. $2x + 3y - 2z + 2w = 14$
$3x - 2y + 3z + 4w = 4$
$-2x + 2y + 2z - 3w = -6$
$3x + 2y - 2z - 2w = 5$

10. $3x - 2y + 2z + 3w = 15$
$-2x + 2y + 3z - 2w = -2$
$2x + 3y - 2z + 2w = -1$
$4x - 2y - 3z + 3w = 7$

11.
$$
\begin{aligned}
2x - y + 3z - w + t &= 0 \\
x + y + 2z + 2w - 3t &= 13 \\
2x + 3y - 2z + 4w - t &= 15 \\
-x - 3y + 4z - 2w + t &= -7 \\
4x + y - 5z + 2w - 3t &= 19
\end{aligned}
$$

12.
$$
\begin{aligned}
x + 2y - 3z + 4w - 2t &= -1 \\
-x - y - z + 4w - 4t &= -19 \\
2x + 4y - 3z + w &= 14 \\
x + 3z + 5w - t &= -9 \\
2x + 3y + 4z - 2w + 3t &= 17
\end{aligned}
$$

2. MATRICES

A *matrix* is a rectangular array of numbers enclosed in parentheses. For example, the array

$$
\begin{pmatrix}
3 & 2 & 0 & -1 \\
1 & 4 & 6 & 2 \\
-3 & 1 & 3 & 0
\end{pmatrix}
$$

is a matrix with three rows and four columns. A matrix with m rows and n columns is written

$$
\begin{pmatrix}
a_{11} & a_{12} & a_{13} & \cdots & a_{1n} \\
a_{21} & a_{22} & a_{23} & \cdots & a_{2n} \\
\vdots & & & & \vdots \\
a_{m1} & a_{m2} & a_{m3} & \cdots & a_{mn}
\end{pmatrix}
$$

The individual entries in the matrix are called its *elements*; the quantity a_{ij} in the above matrix is the element in the ith row and jth column. The subscripts used to indicate the elements will always denote the row first and the column second. If the number of rows of a matrix is the same as the number of columns, it is said to be *square*. We shall use capital letters such as A, B, C, ... to denote matrices. The corresponding lower-case letters with subscripts, such as a_{ij}, b_{ij}, c_{ij}, etc., will be used to denote the elements. We use the expression "m by n matrix" and write "$m \times n$ matrix" for a matrix with m rows and n columns.

A matrix with one row and n columns is called a *row vector*. For example, the matrix

$$(3, \quad -1, \quad 2, \quad 0, \quad 5, \quad 4)$$

is a row vector with 6 columns. A matrix with m rows and one column is called a *column vector*. The array

$$
\begin{pmatrix}
-3 \\
0 \\
2 \\
4 \\
5
\end{pmatrix}
$$

is a column vector with 5 rows. We say that two matrices are of the *same size* if and only if they have the same number of rows and the same number of columns.

The most important properties of matrices are contained in the rules of operation which we now define.

RULE I. (Multiplication by a constant.) *If A is a matrix and c is a number, then cA is the matrix obtained by multiplying each element of A by the number c. For example, if c* = 3 *and*

$$A = \begin{pmatrix} 3 & -2 & 0 \\ 1 & 4 & 2 \\ -1 & -3 & 1 \end{pmatrix}, \quad then \quad 3A = \begin{pmatrix} 9 & -6 & 0 \\ 3 & 12 & 6 \\ -3 & -9 & 3 \end{pmatrix}$$

We use the symbol $-A$ for the matrix $(-1)A$.

RULE II. (Addition of matrices.) *If A and B are of the same size and have elements a_{ij} and b_{ij}, respectively, we define their sum A + B as the matrix C with elements c_{ij} such that*

$$c_{ij} = a_{ij} + b_{ij}$$

for each i and j.

For example, if

$$A = \begin{pmatrix} 3 & 2 & -1 \\ 4 & 6 & 0 \end{pmatrix}, \quad B = \begin{pmatrix} -2 & 1 & 5 \\ 0 & 4 & -2 \end{pmatrix},$$

then

$$C = A + B = \begin{pmatrix} 1 & 3 & 4 \\ 4 & 10 & -2 \end{pmatrix}$$

It is important to remember that addition of matrices can be defined only for matrices of the *same size*. Subtraction of two matrices is defined in terms of addition. We have $A - B = A + (-1)B$.

RULE III. (Equality of matrices.) *Two matrices are equal if and only if all their corresponding elements are equal. That is, in order that A = B we must have A and B the same size and $a_{ij} = b_{ij}$ for each i and j; in other words A and B denote the same matrix.*

———————

EXAMPLE 1. Solve the following matrix equation for A:

$$2A - 3\begin{pmatrix} 2 & -1 & 3 \\ -3 & 2 & 1 \end{pmatrix} = \begin{pmatrix} -2 & 3 & -3 \\ 1 & 4 & 3 \end{pmatrix}$$

Solution. In order to make sense, A must be a 2 × 3 matrix. We may use the rules for adding matrices to write

$$2A = \begin{pmatrix} -2 & 3 & -3 \\ 1 & 4 & 3 \end{pmatrix} + 3\begin{pmatrix} 2 & -1 & 3 \\ -3 & 2 & 1 \end{pmatrix}$$

$$= \begin{pmatrix} -2 & 3 & -3 \\ 1 & 4 & 3 \end{pmatrix} + \begin{pmatrix} 6 & -3 & 9 \\ -9 & 6 & 3 \end{pmatrix} = \begin{pmatrix} 4 & 0 & 6 \\ -8 & 10 & 6 \end{pmatrix}$$

Therefore

$$A = \begin{pmatrix} 2 & 0 & 3 \\ -4 & 5 & 3 \end{pmatrix}$$

We define the *zero matrix* as the matrix with all elements zeros.

RULE IV. (Multiplication of matrices.) *Let A be an m × n matrix and B an n × p matrix. The product AB is that m × p matrix C with elements c_{ij} given by*

$$c_{ij} = \sum_{k=1}^{n} a_{ik}b_{kj}, \qquad i = 1, 2, \ldots, m; \qquad j = 1, 2, \ldots, p.$$

It is extremely important to note that the product of two matrices is defined *only* when the number of columns in the first matrix is equal to the number of rows in the second matrix.

EXAMPLE 2. Compute AB, given that

$$A = \begin{pmatrix} 2 & -1 & 3 \\ 1 & -2 & -1 \end{pmatrix}, \qquad B = \begin{pmatrix} 3 & -1 \\ 1 & 2 \\ -1 & 1 \end{pmatrix}.$$

Solution.

$$AB = \begin{pmatrix} 2\cdot 3 + (-1)\cdot 1 + 3\cdot(-1) & 2\cdot(-1) + (-1)\cdot 2 + 3\cdot 1 \\ 1\cdot 3 + (-2)\cdot 1 + (-1)(-1) & 1\cdot(-1) + (-2)\cdot 2 + (-1)\cdot 1 \end{pmatrix}$$

$$= \begin{pmatrix} 2 & -1 \\ 2 & -6 \end{pmatrix}$$

Remarks. Note that A is a 2 × 3 matrix and B is a 3 × 2 matrix. Therefore the product can be formed, and the result is a 2 × 2 matrix. The product BA can also be formed, the result being a 3 × 3 matrix. It is clear that $AB \neq BA$, since AB is a 2 × 2 matrix and BA is a 3 × 3 matrix. In general, *multiplication of matrices is not commutative.* This is true even for square matrices. We observe that if

$$A = \begin{pmatrix} 1 & 2 \\ -1 & 1 \end{pmatrix} \quad \text{and} \quad B = \begin{pmatrix} 2 & 0 \\ 1 & -1 \end{pmatrix},$$

then

$$AB = \begin{pmatrix} 4 & -2 \\ -1 & -1 \end{pmatrix}, \qquad BA = \begin{pmatrix} 2 & 4 \\ 2 & 1 \end{pmatrix}$$

The student can easily establish the following result, which is stated in the form of a theorem.

Theorem 1. (a) *If A is an m × n matrix and B and C are n × p matrices, then*

$$A(B + C) = AB + AC.$$

(b) *If A and B are m × n matrices and C is an n × p matrix, then*

$$(A + B)C = AC + BC.$$

(c) *If A is an m × n matrix, B is an n × p matrix, and c is a number, then*

$$(cA)B = A(cB) = c(AB).$$

If the matrix C is the product of the matrices A and B, the elements of C may be expressed in terms of the inner or scalar product of two vectors. The element in the ith row and jth column of C is the inner product of the ith row vector of A with the jth column vector of B. The formula

$$c_{ij} = a_{i1}b_{1j} + a_{i2}b_{2j} + \cdots + a_{in}b_{nj}$$

verifies this fact.

A system of linear equations is easily written in matrix form. For example, the system

$$
\begin{aligned}
a_{11}x_1 + a_{12}x_2 + \cdots + a_{1n}x_n &= b_1 \\
a_{21}x_1 + a_{22}x_2 + \cdots + a_{2n}x_n &= b_2 \\
&\vdots \\
a_{m1}x_1 + a_{m2}x_2 + \cdots + a_{mn}x_n &= b_m
\end{aligned}
$$

has m equations and the n unknowns $x_1, x_2, \ldots, x_n$; it may be written in the form

$$AX = B,$$

where A is the $m \times n$ matrix with elements a_{ij} and where X and B are the column vectors with n rows and m rows, respectively:

$$
X = \begin{pmatrix} x_1 \\ x_2 \\ \vdots \\ x_n \end{pmatrix}, \qquad
B = \begin{pmatrix} b_1 \\ b_2 \\ \vdots \\ b_m \end{pmatrix}
$$

A precise definition of an $m \times n$ matrix may be given in terms of functions. The domain of a matrix function consists of all ordered pairs (i, j) of integers with $1 \le i \le m$ and $1 \le j \le n$. The range of the function is the real number system. The particular nature of the function is determined by the rules of operation which we described in terms of rectangular arrays.

EXERCISES

In problems 1 through 7, solve for A.

1. $A = 2\begin{pmatrix} 1 & -2 \\ 2 & 3 \end{pmatrix} - 3\begin{pmatrix} 2 & 1 \\ -1 & 4 \end{pmatrix}$

2. $A = 3\begin{pmatrix} 2 & -3 & 1 \\ 0 & 1 & -1 \end{pmatrix} - 2\begin{pmatrix} 1 & -1 & 2 \\ 2 & 3 & -1 \end{pmatrix}$

3. $2A - \begin{pmatrix} 1 & 2 & 3 \\ 2 & -1 & 2 \end{pmatrix} = 3\begin{pmatrix} 3 & 0 & 5 \\ 2 & 1 & 4 \end{pmatrix}$

4. $3A + \begin{pmatrix} 1 & -1 \\ 2 & 3 \\ -1 & 2 \end{pmatrix} = 2\begin{pmatrix} 2 & 1 \\ 1 & -3 \\ 1 & 4 \end{pmatrix}$

5. $\begin{pmatrix} 2 & -1 & 3 \\ -1 & 3 & 2 \\ 1 & 2 & -1 \end{pmatrix} - 2A = \begin{pmatrix} 2 & 3 & 1 \\ 3 & -1 & 2 \\ 1 & -2 & 1 \end{pmatrix}$

6. $\begin{pmatrix} 2 & 1 \\ 0 & 3 \end{pmatrix} A = \begin{pmatrix} 3 & 0 \\ -3 & -6 \end{pmatrix}$

7. $A\begin{pmatrix} 3 & 1 \\ -2 & 2 \end{pmatrix} = \begin{pmatrix} 5 & 7 \\ -5 & 9 \end{pmatrix}$

8. If A is a matrix and c and d are numbers, show that $c(dA) = (cd)A$.

9. If A and B are matrices of the same size and c and d are numbers, show that

$$(c + d)A = cA + dA \quad \text{and} \quad c(A + B) = cA + cB.$$

In problems 10 through 13, solve simultaneously for A and B.

10. $A - 2B = \begin{pmatrix} 1 & 2 \\ -1 & 1 \end{pmatrix}, \quad A - B = \begin{pmatrix} 2 & 1 \\ 1 & -1 \end{pmatrix}$

11. $A + 2B = \begin{pmatrix} 2 & 1 & 0 \\ 1 & -1 & 2 \end{pmatrix}, \quad 2A + 3B = \begin{pmatrix} 1 & 2 & -1 \\ 2 & 0 & 1 \end{pmatrix}$

12. $A - B = \begin{pmatrix} 1 & -2 \\ -1 & 3 \end{pmatrix}, \quad A + B = \begin{pmatrix} 3 & 0 \\ 3 & 1 \end{pmatrix}$

13. $2A - B = \begin{pmatrix} 3 & -3 & 0 \\ 3 & 3 & 2 \end{pmatrix}, \quad -A + 2B = \begin{pmatrix} 0 & 3 & 3 \\ -3 & 0 & -4 \end{pmatrix}$

In problems 14 through 21, compute AB when possible and compute BA when possible.

14. $A = \begin{pmatrix} 2 & -1 \\ 1 & 2 \end{pmatrix}, \quad B = \begin{pmatrix} 1 & 0 \\ 2 & 1 \end{pmatrix}$ 15. $A = \begin{pmatrix} 1 & -1 \\ 2 & 3 \end{pmatrix}, \quad B = \begin{pmatrix} 2 & -1 \\ 1 & 3 \end{pmatrix}$

16. $A = \begin{pmatrix} 1 & 0 \\ 0 & 0 \end{pmatrix}, \quad B = \begin{pmatrix} 0 & 0 \\ 1 & 1 \end{pmatrix}$ 17. $A = \begin{pmatrix} 1 & 0 \\ 0 & 1 \end{pmatrix}, \quad B = \begin{pmatrix} 0 & 1 \\ 0 & 1 \end{pmatrix}$

18. $A = \begin{pmatrix} 1 & 0 & 2 \\ -2 & 1 & 3 \end{pmatrix}, \quad B = \begin{pmatrix} 2 & 1 \\ -1 & 1 \\ 1 & 2 \end{pmatrix}$

19. $A = \begin{pmatrix} 1 & 2 & -1 \\ -2 & 1 & 3 \end{pmatrix}, \quad B = \begin{pmatrix} 2 & -1 & 1 \\ 1 & 3 & -2 \\ -1 & 2 & 1 \end{pmatrix}$

20. $A = \begin{pmatrix} 2 & 1 \\ -1 & 2 \\ -2 & 3 \end{pmatrix}, \quad B = \begin{pmatrix} 1 & 2 & -1 & -2 \\ -1 & 3 & 1 & -1 \end{pmatrix}$

21. $A = \begin{pmatrix} 1 & 1 & 0 \\ 0 & 0 & 0 \\ 0 & 1 & 0 \end{pmatrix}$, $B = \begin{pmatrix} 0 & 0 & 0 \\ 0 & 0 & 0 \\ 1 & 0 & 0 \end{pmatrix}$

22. Prove Theorem 1.

23. Let

$$A = \begin{pmatrix} 0 & 0 \\ 0 & 0 \end{pmatrix} \quad \text{and} \quad B = \begin{pmatrix} 1 & 0 \\ 0 & 1 \end{pmatrix}$$

Show that A and B commute with all 2×2 matrices. Are there any other matrices which commute with all 2×2 matrices?

24. Find two 3×3 matrices A and B with the property that $AB = 0$, and $BA = 0$ and $A \neq 0$, $B \neq 0$.

3. MATRICES, CONTINUED. DOUBLE SUMS AND DOUBLE SEQUENCES

If A is an $m \times n$ matrix, the *transpose of A* is that $n \times m$ matrix obtained from A by interchanging its rows and columns. We use the symbol A^t for the transpose of A. The element in the ith row and jth column of A^t, denoted a^t_{ij}, is given by

$$a^t_{ij} = a_{ji}, \quad i = 1, 2, \ldots, n; \quad j = 1, 2, \ldots, m.$$

For example, if

$$A = \begin{pmatrix} 2 & -1 & 3 \\ 1 & -2 & -1 \end{pmatrix}, \quad \text{then} \quad A^t = \begin{pmatrix} 2 & 1 \\ -1 & -2 \\ 3 & -1 \end{pmatrix}$$

The following theorem follows from the definition of transpose.

Theorem 2. (a) *If A and B are $m \times n$ matrices and c is a constant, then*

$$(A + B)^t = A^t + B^t, \quad (cA)^t = cA^t.$$

(b) *If A is an $m \times n$ matrix and B is an $n \times p$ matrix, then*

$$(AB)^t = B^t A^t.$$

Proof. Part (a) can be performed by the student. (See problem 8 at the end of this section.) To prove (b), we let $C = AB$. Then C is an $m \times p$ matrix, and C^t is a $p \times m$ matrix. Using a_{ij}, b_{ij}, and c_{ij} for elements of A, B, and C, respectively, we have

$$c_{ij} = \sum_{k=1}^{n} a_{ik}b_{kj}, \quad i = 1, 2, \ldots, m; \quad j = 1, 2, \ldots, p.$$

Also

$$c^t_{ij} = c_{ji} = \sum_{k=1}^{n} a_{jk}b_{ki}, \quad i = 1, 2, \ldots, p; \quad j = 1, 2, \ldots, m.$$

We must show that the elements of $B^t A^t$ are precisely c_{ij}^t. We let $D = B^t A^t$. Since B^t is a $p \times n$ matrix and since A^t is an $n \times m$ matrix, the matrix D is $p \times m$, and we have

$$b_{ij}^t = b_{ji}, \qquad i = 1, 2, \ldots, p, \qquad j = 1, 2, \ldots, n,$$
$$a_{ij}^t = a_{ji}, \qquad i = 1, 2, \ldots, n, \qquad j = 1, 2, \ldots, m,$$
$$d_{ij} = \sum_{k=1}^{n} b_{ik}^t a_{kj}^t = \sum_{k=1}^{n} b_{ki} a_{jk} = \sum_{k=1}^{n} a_{jk} b_{ki} = c_{ji} = c_{ij}^t.$$

DEFINITIONS. If A is a *square matrix*, we call those elements of the form a_{ii} *diagonal elements*, and we call the totality of diagonal elements the *diagonal* of the matrix. A *diagonal matrix* is one in which all elements are zero, except possibly those on the diagonal. That is,

$$a_{ij} = 0 \quad \text{if} \quad i \neq j.$$

If, in a diagonal matrix A, we have $a_{ii} = 1$ for all i, the matrix is called the *identity matrix* and is denoted by I. A square matrix is said to be *triangular* if and only if all the elements on one side of the diagonal are zero, i.e.,

$$a_{ij} = 0 \quad \text{for} \quad i > j \qquad \text{or} \qquad a_{ij} = 0 \quad \text{for} \quad i < j.$$

Examples of 4×4 diagonal, identity, and triangular matrices are shown below.

$$D = \begin{pmatrix} 3 & 0 & 0 & 0 \\ 0 & 2 & 0 & 0 \\ 0 & 0 & 1 & 0 \\ 0 & 0 & 0 & 4 \end{pmatrix} \qquad I = \begin{pmatrix} 1 & 0 & 0 & 0 \\ 0 & 1 & 0 & 0 \\ 0 & 0 & 1 & 0 \\ 0 & 0 & 0 & 1 \end{pmatrix}$$

$$\qquad\qquad\text{Diagonal} \qquad\qquad\qquad\qquad\qquad \text{Identity}$$

$$T_1 = \begin{pmatrix} 3 & -1 & 0 & 4 \\ 0 & 2 & 1 & 5 \\ 0 & 0 & 3 & 4 \\ 0 & 0 & 0 & 5 \end{pmatrix} \qquad T_2 = \begin{pmatrix} 2 & 0 & 0 & 0 \\ 1 & 3 & 0 & 0 \\ 2 & 5 & 1 & 0 \\ 0 & 4 & 6 & 2 \end{pmatrix}$$

$$\quad a_{ij} = 0 \quad \text{if} \quad i > j \qquad\qquad a_{ij} = 0 \quad \text{if} \quad i < j$$

It is useful to introduce the *Kronecker delta* symbol δ_{ij}, which is defined by the relation

$$\delta_{ij} = \begin{cases} 1 & \text{if} \quad i = j, \\ 0 & \text{if} \quad i \neq j. \end{cases}$$

If B is a square matrix with elements b_{ij}, then the relation $b_{ij} = \delta_{ij}$ implies that the matrix B is the identity matrix I. We also notice that the Kronecker delta allows simplifications of the type

$$\sum_{j=1}^{n} \delta_{ij} x_j = x_i, \qquad \sum_{i=1}^{n} \delta_{ij} y_i = y_j.$$

Theorem 3. (a) *If A and B are each n × n diagonal matrices, then AB = BA and this is a diagonal matrix.* (b) *If A is any n × n matrix and I is the n × n identity matrix, then IA = AI = A.*

The proofs are left to the reader. (See problems 9 and 10 at the end of this section.)

We recall that a sequence is a succession of numbers such as

$$a_1, \quad a_2, \quad a_3, \quad \ldots, \quad a_{14}.$$

If there is a first and last element, the sequence is called *finite*; otherwise it is *infinite*. We may consider a sequence as a function with domain consisting of a portion of the integers (i.e., the subscripts) and with the range (the numbers a_i) consisting of a portion of the real number system.

A *double sequence* is a function the domain of which is some set S of ordered pairs (i, j) of integers and with range consisting of a portion of the real number system. A matrix is a special type of double sequence in which the domain S consists of pairs (i, j) in which $1 \leq i \leq m$ and $1 \leq j \leq n$. In general, the domain S of a double sequence is not restricted in this way; in fact, S may be infinite, in which case we say that the double sequence is *infinite*.

A finite *double sum* is an expression of the form

$$\sum_{(i,j)\in S} a_{ij},$$

in which the a_{ij} form a finite double sequence with domain S and with the sum extending over all elements of S. The symbol $(i, j) \in S$, which we read "(i, j) belongs to S," indicates this fact. The general commutative property for addition of ordinary numbers shows that the order in which we add the terms of a finite double sum is irrelevant.

Suppose the domain of a double sequence consists of all pairs (i, j) for which $1 \leq i \leq m$ and $1 \leq j \leq n$. Then we can easily conclude that

$$\sum_{(i,j)\in S} a_{ij} = \sum_{i=1}^{m}\left[\sum_{j=1}^{n} a_{ij}\right] = \sum_{j=1}^{n}\left[\sum_{i=1}^{m} a_{ij}\right]. \tag{1}$$

The latter two sums are called *iterated sums*, since we sum first with respect to one index and then with respect to the other. The fact that double sums and iterated sums are identical leads to many conveniences, and we shall use this fact on a number of occasions. For example, it follows that

$$\left(\sum_{i=1}^{m} a_i\right)\left(\sum_{j=1}^{n} b_j\right) = \sum_{(i,j)\in S} a_i b_j, \qquad S:\{1 \leq i \leq m, \quad 1 \leq j \leq n\}.$$

A convenient notation consists of the symbol $1 \leq i < j \leq n$ used to represent the set S, which consists of all (i, j) for which $1 \leq i \leq n$, $1 \leq j \leq n$ and $i < j$.

Note that i cannot have the value n, since i must be strictly less than j and j can be at most n. Similarly, j cannot have the value 1. We write

$$\sum_{1 \le i < j \le n} a_{ij} \qquad \text{to mean} \qquad \sum_{(i,j) \in S} a_{ij},$$

in which S is the set described above. We may also conclude on the basis of the equivalence of double sums and iterated sums that

$$\sum_{1 \le i < j \le n} a_{ij} = \sum_{i=1}^{n-1} \sum_{j=i+1}^{n} a_{ij}. \tag{2}$$

It can also be shown that

$$\sum_{1 \le i < j \le n} a_{ij} = \sum_{j=2}^{n} \sum_{i=1}^{j-1} a_{ij}. \tag{3}$$

The set S for $n = 6$ is shown schematically below.

```
j
6 | x   x   x   x   x
5 | x   x   x   x
4 | x   x   x
3 | x   x
2 | x
1 |            1 ≤ i < j ≤ 6
  |_____
      1   2   3   4   5   6          i
```

EXAMPLE 1. Write out the iterated sum

$$\sum_{i=1}^{4} \sum_{j=1}^{i} a_{ij}.$$

Solution. We have

$$\sum_{i=1}^{4} \sum_{j=1}^{i} a_{ij} = \left[\sum_{j=1}^{1} a_{1j} \right] + \left[\sum_{j=1}^{2} a_{2j} \right] + \left[\sum_{j=1}^{3} a_{3j} \right] + \left[\sum_{j=1}^{4} a_{4j} \right]$$

$$= a_{11} + (a_{21} + a_{22}) + (a_{31} + a_{32} + a_{33})$$

$$+ (a_{41} + a_{42} + a_{43} + a_{44}).$$

EXAMPLE 2. Verify formulas (2) and (3) for $n = 3$.

Solution. The symbol

$$\sum_{1 \le i < j \le 3} a_{ij} \qquad \text{means} \qquad \sum_{(i,j) \in S} a_{ij},$$

where S consists of all (i, j) for which $1 \leq i \leq 3, 1 \leq j \leq 3$ and $i < j$. Therefore

$$\sum_{1 \leq i < j \leq 3} a_{ij} = a_{12} + a_{13} + a_{23}.$$

From formulas (2) and (3) we have

$$\sum_{i=1}^{2} \sum_{j=i+1}^{3} a_{ij} = \sum_{j=2}^{3} a_{1j} + \sum_{j=3}^{3} a_{2j} = (a_{12} + a_{13}) + a_{23},$$

$$\sum_{j=2}^{3} \sum_{i=1}^{j-1} a_{ij} = \sum_{i=1}^{1} a_{i2} + \sum_{i=1}^{2} a_{i3} = a_{12} + (a_{13} + a_{23}).$$

Theorem 4. (Associative Law for Multiplication of Matrices.) *Suppose that A, B, and C are $m \times n$, $n \times p$, and $p \times q$ matrices, respectively. Then*

$$(AB)C = A(BC).$$

Proof. We define $D = AB$ and $F = DC = (AB)C$. Also, we define $E = BC$ and $G = AE = A(BC)$. We must show that $F = G$. Using lower-case letters for the elements of the matrix with the corresponding capital letters, we have

$$d_{ij} = \sum_{k=1}^{n} a_{ik}b_{kj}, \qquad f_{ij} = \sum_{l=1}^{p} d_{il}c_{lj}.$$

We substitute the expression for d_{ij} on the left into that for f_{ij} (changing subscripts in the process), and we find

$$f_{ij} = \sum_{l=1}^{p} \sum_{k=1}^{n} a_{ik}b_{kl}c_{lj}.$$

Similarly, we may write

$$e_{ij} = \sum_{l=1}^{p} b_{il}c_{lj}, \qquad g_{ij} = \sum_{k=1}^{n} a_{ik}e_{kj}.$$

A straight substitution shows that the expressions for f_{ij} and g_{ij} are identical.

EXERCISES

In each of problems 1 through 6, compute the quantities $(AB)^t$ and $B^t A^t$ for the given matrices A and B. Verify that the expressions are equal.

1. $A = \begin{pmatrix} 2 & 3 & 1 \\ -1 & 0 & 2 \end{pmatrix}$, $B = \begin{pmatrix} 1 & 1 \\ 0 & 1 \\ 1 & 1 \end{pmatrix}$

2. $A = \begin{pmatrix} 3 & 1 \\ 2 & -1 \end{pmatrix}$, $B = \begin{pmatrix} 3 & 2 \\ -1 & -2 \end{pmatrix}$

3. $A = \begin{pmatrix} 1 & 2 & -1 \\ 3 & -2 & 1 \end{pmatrix}$, $B = \begin{pmatrix} 2 & 1 & 0 \\ -1 & 1 & 2 \\ 0 & 1 & 0 \end{pmatrix}$

4. $A = \begin{pmatrix} 4 \\ 1 \\ 2 \\ 3 \end{pmatrix}$, $B = (2 \quad 5 \quad -1 \quad 4)$

5. $A = \begin{pmatrix} 3 & -1 & 2 & 5 \\ 4 & 1 & 2 & 4 \\ -1 & 0 & 2 & 0 \\ 6 & 1 & 5 & 4 \end{pmatrix}$, $B = \begin{pmatrix} 3 & -2 & 1 & 4 \\ -2 & 0 & 5 & -2 \\ 1 & 5 & 1 & 3 \\ 4 & -2 & 3 & 2 \end{pmatrix}$

6. $A = \begin{pmatrix} 3 & 2 & -1 & 4 \\ 1 & 6 & 8 & 5 \end{pmatrix}$, $B = \begin{pmatrix} 4 & 2 \\ 1 & 6 \\ 8 & 5 \\ -1 & 0 \end{pmatrix}$

7. Show that $IA = A$ if I is the $m \times m$ identity and A is any $m \times n$ matrix.

8. Prove part (a) of Theorem 2.

9. Prove part (a) of Theorem 3.

10. Prove part (b) of Theorem 3.

11. Verify formula (1) of this section for $m = 2$ and $n = 3$.

12. Verify formula (1) of this section for $m = 4$ and $n = 3$.

13. Verify the formula

$$\left(\sum_{i=1}^{m} a_i \right) \left(\sum_{j=1}^{n} b_j \right) = \sum_{(i,j) \in S} a_i b_j, \qquad S: 1 \le i \le m; \quad 1 \le j \le n$$

for $m = 3$ and $n = 4$.

14. Verify the formula

$$\sum_{1 \le i < j \le n} a_{ij} = \sum_{i=1}^{n-1} \sum_{j=i+1}^{n} a_{ij}$$

for $n = 4$.

15. Verify the formula

$$\sum_{1 \le i < j \le n} a_{ij} = \sum_{j=2}^{n} \sum_{i=1}^{j-1} a_{ij}$$

for $n = 5$.

In each of problems 16 through 18, write out and evaluate the following double sums.

16. $\displaystyle\sum_{(i,j) \in S} (i + j)$, $S: 1 \le i \le 3, \quad 1 \le j \le 4$.

17. $\displaystyle\sum_{(i,j) \in S} ij$, $S = $ all (i, j) with $1 \le i \le 4, 1 \le j \le 4, j \le i$.

18. $\displaystyle\sum_{(i,j) \in S} (3i + 2j)$, $S = $ all (i, j) with $0 \le i \le 4, 0 \le j \le 4, 0 \le i + j \le 4$.

In each of problems 19 through 23, write out and evaluate the given iterated sums.

19. $\displaystyle\sum_{i=1}^{4}\sum_{j=1}^{3}(i-j)$

20. $\displaystyle\sum_{i=1}^{4}\sum_{j=1}^{5-i}(i^2 j)$

21. $\displaystyle\sum_{i=0}^{3}\sum_{j=i+1}^{i+3}(i+j+1)$

22. $\displaystyle\sum_{i=-1}^{4}\sum_{j=0}^{5}\frac{i}{j+2}$

23. $\displaystyle\sum_{i=0}^{3}\sum_{j=0}^{i+1} ij$

24. Write the iterated sum in Example 1 as an iterated sum in the other order (i.e., with j in the "outside" summation).

25. Write the double sum in problem 18 as an iterated sum with j in the outside summation.

26. In the sum in problem 18, let $p = i + j$ be the index in the outer sum and verify that

$$\sum_{(i,j)\in S}(3i+2j) = \sum_{p=0}^{4}\sum_{j=0}^{p}[3(p-j)+2j] = \sum_{p=0}^{4}\sum_{j=0}^{p}(3p-j).$$

4. DETERMINANTS

With each $n \times n$ square matrix we associate a number called its *determinant*. If the matrix is A, we denote its determinant by *det A*. If the matrix A is written out as a square array, its determinant is denoted by the same array between vertical bars. For example, if

$$A = \begin{pmatrix} 2 & -1 & 3 \\ 3 & 1 & 2 \\ -1 & 2 & -3 \end{pmatrix}, \quad \text{then} \quad \det A = \begin{vmatrix} 2 & -1 & 3 \\ 3 & 1 & 2 \\ -1 & 2 & -3 \end{vmatrix}.$$

DEFINITIONS. The *order* of an $n \times n$ square matrix is the integer n. A *submatrix* of a given matrix is any matrix obtained by deleting certain rows and columns from the original matrix and consolidating the remaining elements.

For example, the matrix

$$\begin{pmatrix} 2 & 0 & 1 & 4 \\ -3 & \frac{1}{2} & 2 & 5 \\ \sqrt{6} & 7 & 8 & 1 \\ 0 & 5 & 4 & -6 \end{pmatrix}$$

has the submatrix

$$\begin{pmatrix} 2 & 0 & 4 \\ \sqrt{6} & 7 & 1 \\ 0 & 5 & -6 \end{pmatrix},$$

obtained by deleting the second row and third column. Another submatrix, obtained by striking out the third and fourth rows and the fourth column, is

$$\begin{pmatrix} 2 & 0 & 1 \\ -3 & \frac{1}{2} & 2 \end{pmatrix}$$

A *determinant* is a function the domain of which is the collection of square matrices; its range is the real number system. To define the determinant of a matrix, we proceed inductively with respect to its order n. For $n = 1$, we define

$$\det(a_{11}) = a_{11}.$$

Assuming, for $n > 1$, that we have defined determinants of order $\leq n - 1$, we define those of order n by the formula

$$\det A \equiv \begin{vmatrix} a_{11} & a_{12} & \cdots & a_{1n} \\ a_{21} & a_{22} & \cdots & a_{2n} \\ \vdots & & & \vdots \\ a_{n1} & a_{n2} & \cdots & a_{nn} \end{vmatrix} = \sum_{i=1}^{n} (-1)^{i+n} a_{in} M_{in}. \tag{1}$$

In this formula M_{in} is the determinant of the $(n - 1) \times (n - 1)$ submatrix of A, obtained by deleting its ith row and nth column. The determinant M_{in} is called the *minor* of the element a_{in}.

To illustrate formula (1), we obtain for $n = 2$

$$\begin{vmatrix} a_{11} & a_{12} \\ a_{21} & a_{22} \end{vmatrix} = (-1)^{1+2} a_{12} a_{21} + (-1)^{2+2} a_{22} a_{11} = a_{11} a_{22} - a_{12} a_{21};$$

for $n = 3$,

$$\begin{vmatrix} a_{11} & a_{12} & a_{13} \\ a_{21} & a_{22} & a_{23} \\ a_{31} & a_{32} & a_{33} \end{vmatrix} = (-1)^{1+3} a_{13} \begin{vmatrix} a_{21} & a_{22} \\ a_{31} & a_{32} \end{vmatrix} + (-1)^{2+3} a_{23} \begin{vmatrix} a_{11} & a_{12} \\ a_{31} & a_{32} \end{vmatrix}$$

$$+ (-1)^{3+3} a_{33} \begin{vmatrix} a_{11} & a_{12} \\ a_{21} & a_{22} \end{vmatrix}$$

$$= a_{13}(a_{21}a_{32} - a_{31}a_{22}) - a_{23}(a_{11}a_{32} - a_{31}a_{12})$$

$$+ a_{33}(a_{11}a_{22} - a_{21}a_{12}).$$

In formula (1) it is convenient to consolidate the quantity $(-1)^{i+n}$ and the minor M_{in}. We define the *cofactor* A_{ij} of the element a_{ij} in $\det A$ of (1) by the relation

$$A_{ij} = (-1)^{i+j} M_{ij}. \tag{2}$$

In terms of cofactors we obtain the basic expansion theorem for determinants:

Theorem 5. *If A is an $n \times n$ matrix with $n \geq 2$, then*

$$\text{(a)} \quad \det A = \sum_{i=1}^{n} a_{ij} A_{ij} \text{ for each fixed } j, \quad 1 \leq j \leq n;$$

$$(b) \ \det A = \sum_{j=1}^{n} a_{ij}A_{ij} \ \text{ for each fixed } i, \quad 1 \le i \le n.$$

We postpone the proof until the next section.

The formula in (a) is called the *expansion of det A according to its jth column*; that in (b) is called the *expansion of det A according to its ith row. From* (2) *it follows that the signs preceding M_{ij} alternate as one proceeds along a row or column, so that* (2) *is needed only to get the first sign correct.*

——————

EXAMPLE 1.   Evaluate the following determinant by expanding it according to its second column and then evaluating the 2 × 2 determinants

$$\det A = \begin{vmatrix} 1 & -2 & 3 \\ 2 & 1 & -1 \\ -2 & -1 & 2 \end{vmatrix}$$

Solution. Expanding according to the second column, we have

$$\det A = -(-2) \begin{vmatrix} 2 & -1 \\ -2 & 2 \end{vmatrix} + 1 \begin{vmatrix} 1 & 3 \\ -2 & 2 \end{vmatrix} - (-1) \begin{vmatrix} 1 & 3 \\ 2 & -1 \end{vmatrix}$$

$$= 2(4 - 2) + 1(2 + 6) + 1(-1 - 6) = 5.$$

EXAMPLE 2.   Write out the expansion of the determinant

$$\det A = \begin{vmatrix} -1 & 2 & 3 & -4 \\ 4 & 2 & 0 & 1 \\ -1 & 1 & 2 & 3 \\ -5 & 1 & 6 & 2 \end{vmatrix}$$

according to the fourth column.   Do not evaluate.

Solution.

$$\det A = -(-4) \begin{vmatrix} 4 & 2 & 0 \\ -1 & 1 & 2 \\ -5 & 1 & 6 \end{vmatrix} + 1 \begin{vmatrix} -1 & 2 & 3 \\ -1 & 1 & 2 \\ -5 & 1 & 6 \end{vmatrix} - 3 \begin{vmatrix} -1 & 2 & 3 \\ 4 & 2 & 0 \\ -5 & 1 & 6 \end{vmatrix}$$

$$+ 2 \begin{vmatrix} -1 & 2 & 3 \\ 4 & 2 & 0 \\ -1 & 1 & 2 \end{vmatrix}$$

EXERCISES

In each of problems 1 through 4, evaluate the given determinant by expanding it according to (a) the second row, and (b) the third column.

1. $\begin{vmatrix} 3 & 2 & -1 \\ -1 & 0 & 1 \\ 2 & 1 & -2 \end{vmatrix}$

2. $\begin{vmatrix} 1 & 0 & 3 \\ 2 & -1 & -2 \\ 1 & 3 & 2 \end{vmatrix}$

3. $\begin{vmatrix} 2 & 3 & 1 \\ 1 & 2 & -2 \\ -2 & 1 & 3 \end{vmatrix}$ 4. $\begin{vmatrix} 1 & \frac{1}{2} & 5 \\ 2 & 1 & 0 \\ 3 & -6 & \frac{1}{3} \end{vmatrix}$

In problems 5 through 7, expand in each case according to the second row. Do not evaluate.

5. $\begin{vmatrix} 2 & 0 & 2 & 3 \\ -1 & 3 & 6 & -1 \\ 1 & -1 & -2 & 4 \\ 0 & 4 & 8 & 2 \end{vmatrix}$ 6. $\begin{vmatrix} 0 & 1 & -1 & 2 \\ 4 & 4 & -4 & 2 \\ 3 & -1 & 2 & 3 \\ 1 & -2 & 3 & 4 \end{vmatrix}$

7. $\begin{vmatrix} 8 & 0 & 2 & 5 \\ 6 & -1 & -1 & 4 \\ 0 & 2 & 5 & 1 \\ 4 & 4 & 0 & 0 \end{vmatrix}$

In each of problems 8 through 10, expand according to the fourth column. Do not evaluate.

8. $\begin{vmatrix} 6 & 1 & 2 & 0 \\ 0 & 1 & -1 & -1 \\ -1 & -1 & 3 & 2 \\ 0 & 2 & 5 & 1 \end{vmatrix}$ 9. $\begin{vmatrix} -1 & 1 & 6 & -3 & -5 \\ -2 & 2 & 0 & -1 & 6 \\ 1 & 0 & 6 & 2 & 1 \\ -3 & 3 & 2 & 4 & 1 \\ 3 & 1 & 4 & 1 & 2 \end{vmatrix}$

10. $\begin{vmatrix} 3 & -1 & 2 & 4 & 6 \\ 7 & 8 & 2 & 0 & 5 \\ 4 & -1 & -2 & 0 & \frac{1}{2} \\ 6 & 2 & 8 & 5 & 1 \\ 7 & 4 & 3 & 0 & 5 \end{vmatrix}$

11. Prove the identity

$$\begin{vmatrix} 1 & a & a^2 \\ 1 & b & b^2 \\ 1 & c & c^2 \end{vmatrix} = (b - a)(c - a)(c - b).$$

12. Show that in the plane the equation of a line through the points (x_0, y_0) and (x_1, y_1) is given by

$$\begin{vmatrix} x & y & 1 \\ x_0 & y_0 & 1 \\ x_1 & y_1 & 1 \end{vmatrix} = 0.$$

13. Expand a general 4×4 determinant (a) according to the third column, and (b) according to the second row. Do not evaluate.

14. Show that if $\mathbf{u} = a_1\mathbf{i} + a_2\mathbf{j} + a_3\mathbf{k}$ and $\mathbf{v} = b_1\mathbf{i} + b_2\mathbf{j} + b_3\mathbf{k}$ then (formally)

$$\mathbf{u} \times \mathbf{v} = \begin{vmatrix} \mathbf{i} & \mathbf{j} & \mathbf{k} \\ a_1 & a_2 & a_3 \\ b_1 & b_2 & b_3 \end{vmatrix}$$

5. PROPERTIES OF DETERMINANTS

The evaluation of determinants of high order by expansion in rows or columns is a tedious and lengthy process. We now establish a number of important theorems which lead to rapid methods of evaluating determinants.

Theorem 6. *If A is an n × n matrix, then*

$$\det A^t = \det A.$$

Proof. We proceed by induction on the order n. For $n = 1$ the result is obvious. Now let $n > 1$ and denote $B = A^t$. Assume that the result holds for all matrices of order $\leq n - 1$. We wish to show that it holds for a matrix of order n. Using lower-case letters in the usual way, we write

$$b_{ij} - a^t_{ij} = a_{ji}.$$

The cofactor of b_{ij} is denoted B_{ij} and the cofactor of a_{ji} is the determinant A_{ji}. The determinants A_{ji} and B_{ij} come from two $(n - 1) \times (n - 1)$ matrices, each of which is the transpose of the other. According to the induction hypothesis,

$$B_{ij} = A_{ji}.$$

Expanding $\det B$ according to its ith row, we obtain

$$\det B = \sum_{j=1}^{n} b_{ij}B_{ij} = \sum_{j=1}^{n} a_{ji}A_{ji} = \det A.$$

Theorem 7. (a) *If all the elements in the kth row or kth column $(1 \leq k \leq n)$ of a matrix A are zero, then $\det A = 0$.*
(b) *If a matrix A′ is obtained from A by multiplying the elements of the kth row or column by a constant c, then*

$$\det A' = c \det A.$$

(c) *If each element a_{kj} of the kth row of a matrix A equals $a'_{kj} + a''_{kj}$, then*

$$\det A = \det A' + \det A'',$$

where A′ and A″ are obtained from A by replacing a_{kj} by a'_{kj} and by a''_{kj}, respectively. The analogous result holds for the kth column.

Proof. (a) Expanding according to the kth row (or kth column), we introduce the factor zero in each term.
(b) Expanding according to the kth row (or kth column), we introduce the factor c in each term of the expansion.
(c) Expanding according to the kth row and setting $a_{kj} = a'_{kj} + a''_{kj}$, we get expansions of A' and A'' in terms of the kth row.

As an example of part (c) of the theorem, we have

$$
\begin{vmatrix} a_{11} & a_{12} & a_{13} \\ a_{21} & a_{22} & a_{23} \\ a'_{31}+a''_{31} & a'_{32}+a''_{32} & a'_{33}+a''_{33} \end{vmatrix} = \begin{vmatrix} a_{11} & a_{12} & a_{13} \\ a_{21} & a_{22} & a_{23} \\ a'_{31} & a'_{32} & a'_{33} \end{vmatrix} + \begin{vmatrix} a_{11} & a_{12} & a_{13} \\ a_{21} & a_{22} & a_{23} \\ a''_{31} & a''_{32} & a''_{33} \end{vmatrix}
$$

Theorem 8.   (a) *If A' is obtained from A by interchanging two rows or two columns, then*

$$\det A' = -\det A.$$

(b) *If two rows or two columns of A are proportional, then* $\det A = 0$.

Proof. (a) We proceed by induction on n. If $n = 1$, there is nothing to prove. For $n = 2$, the result follows at once by inspection of the formula

$$\begin{vmatrix} a_{11} & a_{12} \\ a_{21} & a_{22} \end{vmatrix} = a_{11}a_{22} - a_{21}a_{12}.$$

We let $n > 2$, suppose that two rows are interchanged, and assume that the result holds for $n - 1$. Now we expand A according to the ith row, where the ith row is *not* one of those being interchanged. Then $a'_{ij} = a_{ij}$, and each cofactor A'_{ij} is obtained from A_{ij} by interchanging two rows. Invoking the induction hypothesis, we have

$$A'_{ij} = -A_{ij}.$$

Therefore

$$\det A' = \sum_{j=1}^{n} a'_{ij}A'_{ij} = -\sum_{j=1}^{n} a_{ij}A_{ij} = -\det A.$$

The proof is identical for the case when two columns are interchanged.

(b) If two rows (or columns) are proportional, then either one row consists of zeros so that the determinant is zero, or else one row (or column) is a constant c times the other row (or column). Using part (b) of Theorem 7, we see that the determinant $D = cD'$ where D' has two identical rows (or columns). Interchanging the two identical rows and employing part (a) (which was just established), we find $D' = -D'$, so that D' is zero; therefore $D = 0$.

By combining part (c) of Theorem 7 and part (b) of Theorem 8, we obtain the next extremely useful result.

Theorem 9. *If A' is obtained from A by multiplying the kth row by the constant c and adding the result to the ith row where $i \neq k$, then*

$$\det A' = \det A.$$

The same result holds for two columns.

Proof. The element a'_{ij} of A' is of the form $a_{ij} + ca_{kj}$, so that [by Theorem 7(c)]

$$\det A' = \det A + c \det A'',$$

where A'' is obtained from A by replacing the ith row by the kth row. But then the ith and kth rows of A'' are identical, so that $\det A'' = 0$. The same proof holds for columns.

Corollary. *If A' is obtained from A by multiplying the kth row by c_i and adding the result to the ith row for $i = 1, 2, \ldots, k - 1, k + 1, \ldots, n$ in turn, then $\det A' = \det A$. The same is true for columns.*

Proof. Each step of the process is one for which Theorem 9 applies and which leaves $\det A$ unchanged. Therefore a succession of such steps will not alter the determinant.

The next example shows how to use the results of this section to simplify and evaluate a determinant.

EXAMPLE 1. Simplify by using the corollary, and use the expansion theorem to evaluate the determinant

$$D = \begin{vmatrix} 2 & -1 & 1 & 0 \\ -3 & 0 & 1 & -2 \\ 1 & 1 & -1 & 1 \\ 2 & -1 & 5 & -1 \end{vmatrix}$$

Solution. By adding the third row to the first and fourth rows in turn, we find that

$$D = \begin{vmatrix} 3 & 0 & 0 & 1 \\ -3 & 0 & 1 & -2 \\ 1 & 1 & -1 & 1 \\ 3 & 0 & 4 & 0 \end{vmatrix}$$

Expanding according to the second column, we obtain

$$D = (-1) \begin{vmatrix} 3 & 0 & 1 \\ -3 & 1 & -2 \\ 3 & 4 & 0 \end{vmatrix}$$

Multiplying the first row by 2 and adding the result to the second row, we get

$$D = - \begin{vmatrix} 3 & 0 & 1 \\ 3 & 1 & 0 \\ 3 & 4 & 0 \end{vmatrix} = - \begin{vmatrix} 3 & 1 \\ 3 & 4 \end{vmatrix} = -9.$$

The 2×2 determinant was obtained by expansion according to the third column.

EXAMPLE 2. Show that

$$D = \begin{vmatrix} x & x^2 & x^3 \\ y & y^2 & y^3 \\ z & z^2 & z^3 \end{vmatrix} = xyz(y - x)(z - y)(z - x).$$

Solution. We may factor out an x from the first row, a y from the second row, and a z from the third row, to obtain

$$D = xyz \begin{vmatrix} 1 & x & x^2 \\ 1 & y & y^2 \\ 1 & z & z^2 \end{vmatrix}$$

Subtracting the third row from the first and second in turn, and then expanding in terms of the first column, we get

$$D = xyz \begin{vmatrix} 0 & x - z & x^2 - z^2 \\ 0 & y - z & y^2 - z^2 \\ 1 & z & z^2 \end{vmatrix} = xyz \begin{vmatrix} x - z & x^2 - z^2 \\ y - z & y^2 - z^2 \end{vmatrix}$$

$$= xyz(x - z)(y - z) \begin{vmatrix} 1 & x + z \\ 1 & y + z \end{vmatrix} = xyz(y - x)(z - x)(z - y).$$

The next theorem is employed in Section 6.

Theorem 10. *For any square matrix A, we have*

$$\text{(a)} \quad \sum_{i=1}^{n} a_{ij} A_{ik} = \delta_{ik} (\det A),$$

$$\text{(b)} \quad \sum_{k=1}^{n} a_{ik} A_{jk} = \delta_{ij} (\det A).$$

Proof. (a) If $j = k$, then $\delta_{jk} = 1$ and the formula (a) is the statement of the expansion theorem (Theorem 5) according to the kth column. If $j \ne k$, then $\delta_{jk} = 0$ and the right side of (a) is zero. As for the left side of (a), we introduce the matrix A' obtained from A by replacing the kth column with the jth column. Then the left side of (a) is the expansion of A' according to the jth column. But since A' has two columns alike (jth and kth), we have $\det A' = 0$, and so the left side of (a) vanishes. The proof of (b) is the same.

We conclude this section with a proof of Theorem 5, stated in Section 4.

Proof of Theorem 5. Our first aim is to establish the formula

$$\det A = \sum_{i=1}^{n} a_{ij} A_{ij} \text{ for each fixed } j, \quad 1 \le j \le n. \tag{1}$$

If $j = n$, the above formula is just the definition of $\det A$. It must be shown that all other expansions, $1 \le j \le n - 1$, yield the same result.

We proceed by induction on n. If $n = 1$, there is nothing to prove. If $n = 2$, the result is easily verified by inspection of the expansion of a 2×2 matrix. So we let $n > 2$ and assume the result is true for all determinants of order $\le n - 1$.

Choose j, $1 \le j \le n - 1$, and let $M_{ik,jn}$ denote the determinant formed from A by deleting its ith and kth rows and its jth and nth columns. $M_{ik,jn}$ is the determinant of an $(n - 2) \times (n - 2)$ matrix. Recalling that M_{in} is the minor of the element a_{in}, we obtain from the definition of determinant

$$D \equiv \det A = \sum_{i=1}^{n} (-1)^{i+n} a_{in} M_{in}. \tag{2}$$

Now, using our induction hypothesis, we may expand each M_{in} according to its jth column. The determinant of A is shown below with lines through the ith row and nth column so that the remaining terms form M_{in}.

$$
\begin{vmatrix}
a_{11} & a_{12} & \cdots & a_{1j} & \cdots & a_{1n} \\
\vdots & & & & & \\
a_{k1} & a_{k2} & \cdots & a_{kj} & \cdots & a_{kn} \\
\vdots & & & & & \\
a_{i1} & a_{i2} & & a_{ij} & & a_{in} \\
\vdots & & & & & \\
a_{n1} & a_{n2} & \cdots & a_{nj} & \cdots & a_{nn}
\end{vmatrix}
$$

If $k < i$ (as shown above), then a_{kp} is in the kth row of M_{in} but, if $k > i$, then each a_{kp} is in the $(k - 1)$st row of M_{in}. Therefore, if $1 < i < n$, we have the expansion

$$M_{in} = \sum_{k=1}^{i-1} (-1)^{k+j} a_{kj} M_{ik,jn} + \sum_{k=i+1}^{n} (-1)^{k-1+j} a_{kj} M_{ik,jn}. \tag{3}$$

If $i = 1$, the first sum in (3) is missing while, if $i = n$, the second sum is absent. Substituting M_{in} from (3) into (2), we see that

$$D = \sum_{i=2}^{n} \sum_{k=1}^{i-1} (-1)^{i+k+j+n} a_{in} a_{kj} M_{ik,jn} - \sum_{i=1}^{n-1} \sum_{k=i+1}^{n} (-1)^{i+k+j+n} a_{in} a_{kj} M_{ik,jn}. \tag{4}$$

If we interchange the indices i and k in the first sum and make use of the double-sum notation of Section 3, we can combine the two iterated sums in (4) into the single double sum

$$D = \sum_{1 \le i < k \le n} (-1)^{i+k+j+n} (a_{kn} a_{ij} - a_{in} a_{kj}) M_{ik,jn}. \tag{5}$$

The relation $M_{ik,jn} = M_{ki,jn}$, which follows directly from the definition of these four-subscript determinants, was used to obtain (5).

To establish (1), it is sufficient to show that the expansion

$$\sum_{k=1}^{n} (-1)^{k+j} a_{kj} M_{kj} \tag{6}$$

is equal to (5). To do so, we expand M_{kj} according to its $(n - 1)$st column, noting that the $(n - 1)$st column of M_{kj} is the nth column of D with a_{kn} removed. If $i < k$, then the elements a_{ip} are in the ith row of M_{kj} but, if $i > k$, then the a_{ip} are in the $(i - 1)$st row of M_{kj}. If we then write out the expansion of M_{kj}, collect terms, and substitute in (6), we find an expression which is identical with (5).

The proof of the formula

$$\det A = \sum_{k=1}^{n} a_{ik} A_{ik} \quad \text{for each fixed } i, \qquad 1 \leq i \leq n,$$

is obtained by first showing that an expansion according to the nth row is equal to the expansion according to the nth column. This proof is omitted. Then the proof that the expansion according to two different rows yields the same result is analogous to the proof for columns.

EXERCISES

In each of problems 1 through 12, simplify and evaluate the determinant.

1. $\begin{vmatrix} 2 & -1 & 3 \\ 2 & -1 & 1 \\ 1 & 3 & -2 \end{vmatrix}$

2. $\begin{vmatrix} 3 & 1 & -1 \\ 1 & 3 & -2 \\ -2 & 1 & 3 \end{vmatrix}$

3. $\begin{vmatrix} 1 & 2 & 3 \\ 1 & -1 & 1 \\ 2 & 4 & -1 \end{vmatrix}$

4. $\begin{vmatrix} 5 & 0 & -1 & 1 \\ 1 & -1 & 1 & -2 \\ 4 & -4 & 2 & 1 \\ -2 & 1 & 1 & 0 \end{vmatrix}$

5. $\begin{vmatrix} 2 & 3 & 6 & 3 \\ 0 & 1 & 3 & 1 \\ -1 & -2 & 0 & 4 \\ 1 & 2 & 4 & -1 \end{vmatrix}$

6. $\begin{vmatrix} 2 & -1 & 3 & 2 \\ 1 & -2 & -2 & 3 \\ -1 & 3 & 2 & 0 \\ 3 & 2 & -2 & 1 \end{vmatrix}$

7. $\begin{vmatrix} -2 & 3 & 2 & 4 \\ -3 & 1 & -2 & 3 \\ 2 & 2 & 3 & -2 \\ 4 & -3 & 2 & 1 \end{vmatrix}$

8. $\begin{vmatrix} 1 & 2 & -3 & 4 \\ 3 & -4 & 2 & -1 \\ 2 & -2 & 3 & 4 \\ 1 & 2 & -2 & 3 \end{vmatrix}$

9. $\begin{vmatrix} 3 & 2 & -1 & 4 \\ 2 & -3 & 4 & 1 \\ -4 & 2 & 0 & 3 \\ 2 & 4 & -1 & 2 \end{vmatrix}$

10. $\begin{vmatrix} 2 & -1 & 3 & 4 & 0 \\ -1 & 2 & 1 & 0 & -1 \\ -3 & 0 & 0 & 1 & 0 \\ 0 & 1 & 0 & -1 & 2 \\ 0 & -2 & 0 & 2 & -1 \end{vmatrix}$

11. $\begin{vmatrix} 1 & 2 & 0 & -1 & 2 \\ 2 & 3 & -1 & 0 & 1 \\ 0 & -1 & 2 & 4 & -2 \\ -1 & 0 & 4 & -1 & 0 \\ 1 & 2 & -1 & 0 & 1 \end{vmatrix}$

12. $\begin{vmatrix} 2 & -1 & 0 & 4 & 1 & -3 \\ 2 & 1 & 2 & 1 & 3 & 2 \\ 4 & -1 & 0 & 2 & -2 & 3 \\ 1 & 5 & 4 & 0 & 2 & 0 \\ 6 & 2 & 1 & 4 & -3 & 0 \\ -1 & 2 & 5 & -3 & 4 & 2 \end{vmatrix}$

13. Show that

$$\begin{vmatrix} 1 & x & x^2 & x^3 \\ 1 & y & y^2 & y^3 \\ 1 & z & z^2 & z^3 \\ 1 & w & w^2 & w^3 \end{vmatrix} = (x - y)(y - z)(z - w)(x - z)(x - w)(y - w).$$

[*Hint:* Use the relation $a^3 - b^3 = (a - b)(a^2 + ab + b^2)$.]

14. Show that the equation of a plane through the three points $P_0(x_0, y_0, z_0)$, $P_1(x_1, y_1, z_1)$, and $P_2(x_2, y_2, z_2)$ is given by

$$\begin{vmatrix} 1 & x & y & z \\ 1 & x_0 & y_0 & z_0 \\ 1 & x_1 & y_1 & z_1 \\ 1 & x_2 & y_2 & z_2 \end{vmatrix} = 0.$$

15. Given the matrix

$$A = \begin{pmatrix} 3 & -1 & 2 \\ 1 & 4 & -1 \\ 2 & 0 & 5 \end{pmatrix},$$

verify Theorem 10 by computing

$$a_{11}A_{13} + a_{21}A_{23} + a_{31}A_{33},$$

and showing that the result vanishes.

16. Given the matrices

$$A = \begin{pmatrix} 1 & 2 & -1 \\ 3 & 1 & 1 \\ -2 & 0 & 5 \end{pmatrix}, \quad B = \begin{pmatrix} 3 & -1 & 2 \\ 4 & 0 & 1 \\ -2 & 1 & 5 \end{pmatrix}$$

Show that det $(AB) = $ (det A) (det B).

6. CRAMER'S RULE

With the aid of determinants, we are able to give a formula for the solution of n simultaneous linear equations in n unknowns. The resulting theorem is known as *Cramer's Rule*.

Theorem 11. *If* det $A \neq 0$. *the system of equations*

$$\begin{aligned} a_{11}x_1 + a_{12}x_2 + \cdots + a_{1n}x_n &= b_1 \\ a_{21}x_1 + a_{22}x_2 + \cdots + a_{2n}x_n &= b_2 \\ &\vdots \\ a_{n1}x_1 + a_{n2}x_2 + \cdots + a_{nn}x_n &= b_n \end{aligned} \tag{1}$$

has a unique solution given by

$$x_k = \frac{1}{D} \begin{vmatrix} a_{11} & \cdots & a_{1,k-1} & b_1 & a_{1,k+1} & \cdots & a_{1n} \\ \vdots & & & & & & \vdots \\ a_{n1} & \cdots & a_{n,k-1} & b_n & a_{n,k+1} & \cdots & a_{nn} \end{vmatrix}, \quad \begin{array}{l} D = \det A, \\ \\ k = 1, 2, \ldots, n, \end{array} \tag{2}$$

where, if $k = 1$ or n, the column of b's is in the first or nth column, respectively.

Proof. We must show that (1) implies (2) and that (2) implies (1). Suppose first that $x_1, x_2, \ldots, x_n$ are numbers which satisfy (1). Multiply the ith equation of (1) by A_{ik}, the cofactor of a_{ik}, where k is a fixed number between 1 and n. We get

$$\sum_{j=1}^{n} a_{ij} A_{ik} x_j = b_i A_{ik}.$$

Now we add all such equations; that is, we sum on the index i. After interchanging the order of the iterated sum, we obtain

$$\sum_{j=1}^{n} \left[\sum_{i=1}^{n} a_{ij} A_{ik} \right] x_j = \sum_{i=1}^{n} b_i A_{ik}. \tag{3}$$

The sum on the right in (3) is the expansion according to the kth column of the determinant displayed in (2). As for the left side of (3), the quantity in brackets is precisely the expression which appears in Theorem 10 of the last section and is equal to $\delta_{jk} (\det A)$. Therefore, using the property of the Kronecker δ, we find that

$$\sum_{j=1}^{n} \delta_{jk} (\det A) x_j = D x_k = \sum_{i=1}^{n} b_i A_{ik},$$

and the formula (2) follows.

If we assume formula (2) holds, we see that

$$D x_k = \sum_{i=1}^{n} b_i A_{ik}.$$

We multiply this expression by a_{jk} and sum with respect to k to get (after interchanging the order of summation)

$$D \sum_{k=1}^{n} a_{jk} x_k = \sum_{i=1}^{n} \left[\sum_{k=1}^{n} a_{jk} A_{ik} \right] b_i.$$

Using Theorem 10 of Section 5 again, we obtain

$$D \sum_{k=1}^{n} a_{jk} x_k = \sum_{i=1}^{n} \delta_{ij} (\det A) b_i = D b_j,$$

from which (1) follows.

_____

EXAMPLE. Solve, using Cramer's Rule,

$$3x_1 - 2x_2 + 4x_3 = 5,$$
$$x_1 + x_2 + 3x_3 = 2,$$
$$-x_1 + 2x_2 - x_3 = 1.$$

Solution. We have

$$D = \begin{vmatrix} 3 & -2 & 4 \\ 1 & 1 & 3 \\ -1 & 2 & -1 \end{vmatrix} = \begin{vmatrix} 5 & -2 & 10 \\ 0 & 1 & 0 \\ -3 & 2 & -7 \end{vmatrix} = \begin{vmatrix} 5 & 10 \\ -3 & -7 \end{vmatrix} = -5,$$

$$x_1 = -\tfrac{1}{5}\begin{vmatrix} 5 & -2 & 4 \\ 2 & 1 & 3 \\ 1 & 2 & -1 \end{vmatrix} = -\tfrac{1}{5}\begin{vmatrix} 9 & 0 & 10 \\ 2 & 1 & 3 \\ -3 & 0 & -7 \end{vmatrix} = -\tfrac{1}{5}\begin{vmatrix} 9 & 10 \\ -3 & -7 \end{vmatrix} = \tfrac{33}{5}.$$

In a similar way, we find that

$$x_2 = -\tfrac{1}{5}\begin{vmatrix} 3 & 5 & 4 \\ 1 & 2 & 3 \\ -1 & 1 & -1 \end{vmatrix} = \tfrac{13}{5}, \qquad x_3 = -\tfrac{1}{5}\begin{vmatrix} 3 & -2 & 5 \\ 1 & 1 & 2 \\ -1 & 2 & 1 \end{vmatrix} = -\tfrac{12}{5}.$$

Cramer's Rule is useful in many theoretical investigations, since it gives an explicit formula for the solution. However, because of the enormous work of evaluating $n + 1$ determinants when n is large, Cramer's Rule is rather poor for numerical computations. Furthermore, there are many chances for error in the large number of multiplications and additions which must be performed. Techniques for solving linear systems which proceed by iteration and elimination are computationally superior not only because there are fewer arithmetical operations, but also because numerical errors are frequently self-correcting.

EXERCISES

Solve the following systems, using Cramer's Rule.

1. $2x_1 - x_2 + 3x_3 = 1$
   $3x_1 + x_2 - x_3 = 2$
   $x_1 + 2x_2 + 3x_3 = -6$

2. $2x_1 - x_2 + x_3 = -3$
   $x_1 + 3x_2 - 2x_3 = 0$
   $x_1 - x_2 + x_3 = -2$

3. $x_1 + 3x_2 - 2x_3 = 4$
   $-2x_1 + x_2 + 3x_3 = 2$
   $2x_1 + 4x_2 - x_3 = -1$

4. $2x_1 + x_2 - x_3 = 1$
   $x_1 - 2x_2 + 3x_3 = 0$
   $2x_1 - 3x_2 + 4x_3 = 0$

5. $2x_1 - x_2 + 2x_3 = 11$
   $x_1 + 2x_2 - x_3 = -3$
   $3x_1 - 2x_2 - 3x_3 = -1$

6. $2x_1 - x_2 - 2x_3 = 0$
   $-x_1 + 2x_2 - 3x_3 = 11$
   $3x_1 - 2x_2 + 4x_3 = -15$

7. $x_1 - 2x_2 + 2x_3 = -1$
   $2x_1 - 3x_2 - 3x_3 = 1$
   $3x_1 + x_2 + 2x_3 = 3$

8. $x_1 \qquad + x_3 - 2x_4 = 3$
   $x_2 + 2x_3 - x_4 = 2$
   $2x_1 + 3x_2 - 2x_3 \qquad = -1$
   $x_1 - x_2 \qquad - 4x_4 = 0$

9. $3x_1 + 2x_2 \qquad\qquad - 4x_4 = 0$
   $x_2 - 2x_3 + x_4 = -1$
   $2x_1 + 3x_2 \qquad\qquad = 1$
   $x_1 \qquad\qquad + 4x_3 - 2x_4 = 2$

10. $2x_1 + x_2 - 2x_3 + 3x_4 - 4x_5 = 0$
    $4x_1 - x_2 + x_3 - 3x_4 + 2x_5 = 1$
    $-2x_1 + x_2 + 2x_3 + 6x_4 - 2x_5 = -2$
    $-4x_1 + 3x_2 - 5x_3 - 6x_4 + 4x_5 = 13$
    $6x_1 - 3x_2 + 4x_3 + 9x_4 - 6x_5 = -13$

7. THE RANK OF A MATRIX. ELEMENTARY TRANSFORMATIONS

Cramer's Rule applies when the number of equations is the same as the number of unknowns and when the determinant of the coefficients is not zero. In order to treat systems in which the number of equations is different from the number of unknowns, it is necessary to introduce a quantity called the *rank* of a matrix.

DEFINITIONS. A square matrix is said to be *nonsingular* if its determinant is not zero. The *rank* of an $m \times n$ matrix is the largest integer r for which a nonsingular $r \times r$ submatrix exists. The rank of any *matrix of zeros* is zero.

For example, the matrix
$$\begin{pmatrix} 4 & 0 & 0 & 0 \\ 1 & 0 & 3 & 0 \\ 2 & 0 & 0 & 0 \end{pmatrix}$$

is of rank 2, since the 2×2 submatrix

$$\begin{pmatrix} 4 & 0 \\ 1 & 3 \end{pmatrix},$$

obtained by deleting the third row and the second and fourth columns, is nonsingular, and since every 3×3 submatrix has zero determinant.

We note that the rank of an $m \times n$ matrix can never exceed the smaller of the numbers m and n.

DEFINITION. An *elementary transformation* of a matrix is a process of obtaining a second matrix from the given matrix in one of the following ways:
   (a) interchanging two rows or two columns,
   (b) multiplying a row or column by a nonzero constant,
   (c) multiplying one row (or column) by a constant and adding it to another row (or column).

We observe that transformations of type (c) are just those which we used for simplifying and evaluating determinants.

Theorem 12. *If A′ is obtained from A by an elementary transformation, the rank of A′ equals the rank of A.*

Proof. For transformations of type (a) and (b), the result is immediate from the definition. To prove the result for type (c), let r be the rank of A. If A is an $m \times n$ matrix and r is the smaller of m and n (i.e., the rank of A is as large as possible), then
$$\text{rank } A' \leq \text{rank } A. \tag{1}$$

We show first that (1) holds regardless of the rank of A. Suppose that r is smaller than m and n; let D' be a $k \times k$ submatrix of A' with $k > r$. To be specific,

suppose that A' is obtained from A by multiplying the first row of A by c and adding the result to the second row. If D' contains both the first and second rows of
A', then det $D' = \det D$, where D is the corresponding matrix in A. But det $D = 0$,
since $k > r$ and since A is of rank r. The same result holds if D' contains neither
the first nor the second row. If D' contains only the first row, we again have
det $D' = \det D$. The only remaining case occurs when D' contains the second row
but not the first. But then det D' is a linear combination of two determinants
of A of order k. Since all determinants of A of order k are zero, we conclude that
det $D' = 0$. Thus the determinant of every $k \times k$ submatrix of A' with $k > r$
is zero, and therefore (1) is established for every rank r. The argument just given
works for any two matrices which are related to each other by a transformation
of type (c). But since A can be obtained from A' in this manner, we conclude that

$$\text{rank } A \leq \text{rank } A'. \qquad (2)$$

Combining (1) and (2), we get rank $A = $ rank A'.

We say that two matrices are *equivalent* if and only if it is possible to pass
from one to the other by applying a finite number of elementary transformations.
We write $A \cong B$ if A and B are equivalent. From Theorem 12 we conclude that
equivalent matrices have the same rank.

To compute the rank of an $m \times n$ matrix A directly from the definition, we
must evaluate the determinant of every square submatrix of A. If m and n are
large, this task is laborious, unless A has many zero entries. However, with the
aid of elementary transformations and without an undue amount of computation,
we can find a matrix equivalent to A whose rank can be determined by inspection. We first illustrate the technique with an example and then establish the
appropriate theorem.

EXAMPLE 1. Determine the rank of the 4×5 matrix

$$A = \begin{pmatrix} -2 & -3 & -1 & 1 & 0 \\ 0 & 1 & 7 & 1 & -4 \\ 1 & 2 & 4 & 0 & -2 \\ -2 & -2 & 6 & 2 & -4 \end{pmatrix}$$

Solution. Interchanging the first and third rows, we find that

$$A \cong \begin{pmatrix} 1 & 2 & 4 & 0 & -2 \\ 0 & 1 & 7 & 1 & -4 \\ -2 & -3 & -1 & 1 & 0 \\ -2 & -2 & 6 & 2 & -4 \end{pmatrix}$$

Multiplying the first row of this new matrix by 2 and adding the result to the third and
fourth rows, we obtain

$$A \cong \begin{pmatrix} 1 & 2 & 4 & 0 & -2 \\ 0 & 1 & 7 & 1 & -4 \\ 0 & 1 & 7 & 1 & -4 \\ 0 & 2 & 14 & 2 & -8 \end{pmatrix}$$

Multiplying the second row by 1 and 2 and subtracting the results from the third and fourth rows, respectively, we get

$$A \cong \begin{pmatrix} 1 & 2 & 4 & 0 & -2 \\ 0 & 1 & 7 & 1 & 4 \\ 0 & 0 & 0 & 0 & 0 \\ 0 & 0 & 0 & 0 & 0 \end{pmatrix} = A'.$$

By inspection, A' is seen to have rank 2. Therefore A has rank 2.

We now state a theorem which describes the process developed in the above example.

Theorem 13. *By a succession of elementary transformations of type* (a) *and* (c) *operating on rows only, any $m \times n$ matrix A can be reduced to an equivalent matrix A' in which*

$$a'_{ij} = 0 \quad \text{for} \quad j < j_i, \quad i = 1, 2, \ldots, m,$$

where

$$1 \leq j_1 < j_2 < \cdots < j_r \leq n,$$
$$j_i = n + 1 \quad \text{for} \quad i = r + 1, \ r + 2, \ldots, m. \tag{3}$$

The rank r is the integer equal to the number of rows which do not consist entirely of zeros. A corresponding result holds for columns.

Before proceeding with the proof, we give an example of the content of (3).

$$\begin{array}{l} j_1 = 1 \\ j_2 = 2 \\ j_3 = 4 \\ j_4 = 5 \\ \vdots \\ j_m = n + 1 \end{array} \begin{pmatrix} 3 & 2 & 3 & \cdots & & & & \\ 0 & 1 & 2 & 5 & \cdots & & & \\ 0 & 0 & 0 & 2 & -1 & 4 & \cdots & \\ 0 & 0 & 0 & 0 & 1 & 3 & \cdots & \\ \vdots & \vdots & \vdots & \vdots & & & & \\ 0 & 0 & 0 & 0 & 0 & \cdots & 0 & 0 \end{pmatrix}$$

In other words, by means of elementary transformations we introduce as many zeros as possible in the bottom row, the second largest number of zeros in the second from bottom row, and so on until, in the first row, we introduce the fewest zeros (or perhaps none).

Proof. If A is the zero matrix, then $j_1 = j_2 = \cdots j_m = n + 1$, and A is already in the desired form. The rank is zero. Otherwise we let the j_1st column be the first column which does not consist entirely of zeros. If a nonzero element occurs in the first column, then $j_1 = 1$. We interchange rows, if necessary, so that the element $a_{1,j_1} \neq 0$. Then, by elementary transformations of type (c), we make the remainder of that column all zeros; of course, all the numbers (if any) to the left of the j_1st column are still 0. If all the numbers below the first row are zero, then $j_2 = j_3 = \cdots = j_m = n + 1$, and the matrix is in the desired form; then $r = 1$. Otherwise, we let the j_2nd column (of course $j_2 > j_1$) be the first one which contains a nonzero element below the first row. By interchanging rows and performing elementary transformations of type (c), we arrange that $a_{2,j_2} \neq 0$ but that all the numbers $a_{i,j_2} = 0$ if $i > 2$; of course, all $a_{ij} = 0$ if $i \geq 2$ and $j < j_2$. If all the a_{ij} with $i > 2$ are zero, then $j_3 = \cdots j_m = n + 1$, and the matrix has been reduced to the desired form with $r = 2$. In any case, the process will stop after some step, say the rth, where $r \leq m$; if $r < m$, all the rows below the rth will consist of zeros. If, now, we select the submatrix of A' consisting of the first r rows and the $j_1, \ldots, j_r$ columns, this $r \times r$ submatrix has the form

$$
\begin{pmatrix}
a_{1j_1} & * & * & * & \cdots & * \\
0 & a_{2j_2} & * & * & \cdots & * \\
0 & 0 & . & & & . \\
0 & 0 & & . & & . \\
\vdots & \vdots & & & . & . \\
0 & 0 & \cdots & 0 & & a_{rj_r}
\end{pmatrix}
$$

The diagonal elements are all nonzero and the asterisks stand for numbers which may or may not be zero. The matrix is triangular and nonsingular. The rank of A is r.

The proof for columns is the same.

Corollary 1. *If A is an $n \times n$ matrix, the process described in the proof of Theorem 13 transforms A to a triangular matrix with all zeros below the diagonal.*

Corollary 2. *If A is a nonsingular $n \times n$ matrix, it can be reduced by means of elementary transformations, as in Theorem 13, to a matrix having nonzero elements along the diagonal and zeros elsewhere.*

Proof. By Corollary 1, we make A into the triangular matrix A'. The value of the determinant is then the product of the diagonal elements; hence all diagonal elements are nonzero. Now, starting with the last column and the element in the lower right-hand corner, we use elementary transformation of type (c) to transform to zero all the elements above the bottom one in the last column. Proceeding to the second-from-last column, we transform to zero all the elements above the diagonal element. Continuing, we get a diagonal matrix which is equivalent to A.

Corollary 3. *The basic process as described in the proof of Theorem 13 leads to the simultaneous reduction to a similar form of each of the submatrices A_l, which are obtained by deleting all but the first l columns of A. The rank of A_l is the integer equal to the number of rows in A_l' which have nonzero elements.*

The proof of the theorem shows that, in principle, elementary transformations of type (b) are not needed to carry out the reduction from A to A'. However, if we have matrices with integers or if, in carrying out the reduction, we wish to avoid arithmetical difficulties, transformations of type (b) are helpful. The next example illustrates the use of type (b) transformations in performing the reduction.

———————

EXAMPLE 2. Given the matrix

$$A = \begin{pmatrix} 3 & 2 & -2 & 3 \\ 2 & 3 & -3 & 4 \\ -2 & 4 & 2 & 3 \\ 5 & -2 & 4 & 2 \\ 3 & 4 & 2 & 3 \end{pmatrix}$$

determine the rank of A, as in Example 1. Use transformations of type (b) when convenient.

Solution. We begin by interchanging the first two rows and then multiplying the second, fourth, and fifth rows by 2. In this way we avoid fractions. The reduction then proceeds as follows:

$$A \cong \begin{pmatrix} 2 & 3 & -3 & 4 \\ 6 & 4 & -4 & 6 \\ -2 & 4 & 2 & 3 \\ 10 & -4 & 8 & 4 \\ 6 & 8 & 4 & 6 \end{pmatrix} \cong \begin{pmatrix} 2 & 3 & -3 & 4 \\ 0 & -5 & 5 & -6 \\ 0 & 7 & -1 & 7 \\ 0 & -19 & 23 & -16 \\ 0 & -1 & 13 & -6 \end{pmatrix} \cong \begin{pmatrix} 2 & 3 & -3 & 4 \\ 0 & -1 & 13 & -6 \\ 0 & -5 & 5 & -6 \\ 0 & 7 & -1 & 7 \\ 0 & -19 & 23 & -16 \end{pmatrix}$$

$$\cong \begin{pmatrix} 2 & 3 & -3 & 4 \\ 0 & -1 & 13 & -6 \\ 0 & 0 & -60 & 24 \\ 0 & 0 & 90 & -35 \\ 0 & 0 & -224 & 98 \end{pmatrix} \cong \begin{pmatrix} 2 & 3 & -3 & 4 \\ 0 & -1 & 13 & -6 \\ 0 & 0 & -5 & 2 \\ 0 & 0 & 18 & -7 \\ 0 & 0 & -16 & 7 \end{pmatrix}$$

Multiplying the third row of the last matrix by 3 and combining with the fourth and fifth rows, we get

$$A \cong \begin{pmatrix} 2 & 3 & -3 & 4 \\ 0 & -1 & 13 & -6 \\ 0 & 0 & -5 & 2 \\ 0 & 0 & 3 & -1 \\ 0 & 0 & -1 & 1 \end{pmatrix} \cong \begin{pmatrix} 2 & 3 & -3 & 4 \\ 0 & -1 & 13 & -6 \\ 0 & 0 & -1 & 1 \\ 0 & 0 & 3 & -1 \\ 0 & 0 & -5 & 2 \end{pmatrix} \cong \begin{pmatrix} 2 & 3 & -3 & 4 \\ 0 & -1 & 13 & -6 \\ 0 & 0 & -1 & 1 \\ 0 & 0 & 0 & 2 \\ 0 & 0 & 0 & -3 \end{pmatrix}$$

Finally, we obtain

$$A \cong \begin{pmatrix} 2 & 3 & -3 & 4 \\ 0 & -1 & 13 & -6 \\ 0 & 0 & -1 & 1 \\ 0 & 0 & 0 & 2 \\ 0 & 0 & 0 & 0 \end{pmatrix} = A',$$

and A is of rank 4.

The next example shows how the reduction proceeds when only elementary transformations involving columns are used.

———————

EXAMPLE 3. Given the matrix

$$A = \begin{pmatrix} 2 & 1 & -1 & -2 \\ 4 & 2 & -2 & -4 \\ -5 & -2 & 3 & 2 \\ 1 & -1 & -2 & 8 \\ 8 & 3 & -2 & 1 \end{pmatrix}$$

reduce A to the form described in Theorem 13, using only elementary transformations involving columns. Find the rank of A.

Solution. We begin by interchanging the first two columns; we then introduce zeros in the first row.

$$A \cong \begin{pmatrix} 1 & 2 & -1 & -2 \\ 2 & 4 & -2 & -4 \\ -2 & -5 & 3 & 2 \\ -1 & 1 & -2 & 8 \\ 3 & 8 & -2 & 1 \end{pmatrix} \cong \begin{pmatrix} 1 & 0 & 0 & 0 \\ 2 & 0 & 0 & 0 \\ -2 & -1 & 1 & -2 \\ -1 & 3 & -3 & 6 \\ 3 & 2 & 1 & 7 \end{pmatrix}$$

$$\cong \begin{pmatrix} 1 & 0 & 0 & 0 \\ 2 & 0 & 0 & 0 \\ -2 & -1 & 0 & 0 \\ -1 & 3 & 0 & 0 \\ 3 & 2 & 3 & 3 \end{pmatrix} \cong \begin{pmatrix} 1 & 0 & 0 & 0 \\ 2 & 0 & 0 & 0 \\ -2 & -1 & 0 & 0 \\ -1 & 3 & 0 & 0 \\ 3 & 2 & 3 & 0 \end{pmatrix}$$

The rank is 3.

EXERCISES

In each of problems 1 through 9, reduce A to a matrix A', using elementary transformations involving rows, in accordance with the procedure of Theorem 13. Determine the rank of A.

1. $\begin{pmatrix} 1 & 4 & 6 & 1 \\ 1 & -1 & 2 & 3 \\ 1 & -11 & -6 & 7 \end{pmatrix}$

2. $\begin{pmatrix} 1 & 4 & -2 & 3 \\ 1 & 5 & 0 & 1 \\ -1 & -1 & 8 & -6 \\ 2 & 10 & 0 & 7 \end{pmatrix}$

3. $\begin{pmatrix} 1 & -1 & 0 & 3 \\ 2 & 1 & 0 & 1 \\ 2 & -2 & 0 & 6 \\ 1 & -2 & 1 & 2 \end{pmatrix}$

4. $\begin{pmatrix} 1 & 0 & -2 & -5 & -1 \\ 0 & -1 & 3 & 1 & 2 \\ 0 & 1 & 0 & 0 & 3 \\ 1 & 1 & -1 & 0 & 4 \end{pmatrix}$

5. $\begin{pmatrix} 1 & 1 & -2 & 0 \\ 2 & 1 & -3 & 0 \\ -4 & 2 & 2 & 0 \\ 6 & -1 & -5 & 0 \\ 7 & -3 & -4 & 1 \end{pmatrix}$

6. $\begin{pmatrix} 1 & 2 & -1 & 3 & 1 \\ -3 & -5 & -1 & 0 & -2 \\ 1 & 1 & 3 & -6 & 0 \\ 4 & 7 & 0 & 3 & 3 \\ 1 & 0 & 7 & -15 & -1 \end{pmatrix}$

7. $\begin{pmatrix} 3 & -3 & 2 & -2 \\ 2 & -1 & 3 & -2 \\ -2 & 3 & -2 & 1 \\ 4 & -2 & 1 & 3 \end{pmatrix}$ 8. $\begin{pmatrix} 2 & 3 & -3 & -2 \\ -3 & 2 & 2 & 3 \\ 4 & -2 & 3 & 2 \\ 5 & 4 & -2 & 2 \end{pmatrix}$

9. $\begin{pmatrix} 3 & \frac{2}{3} & 1 & \frac{1}{2} & 6 \\ 2 & -\frac{1}{4} & 3 & -2 & 1 \\ 6 & -\frac{2}{5} & 3 & -\frac{1}{3} & 5 \end{pmatrix}$

In each of problems 10 through 14, reduce A to a matrix A' as above, but use elementary transformations involving columns only. Determine the rank of A in each case.

10. A is the matrix in problem 3.   11. A is the matrix in problem 4.

12. A is the matrix in problem 7.   13. A is the matrix in problem 8.

14. A is the matrix in problem 9.

In problems 15 through 17, in each case reduce the given matrix to diagonal form as in Corollary 2.

15. $\begin{pmatrix} 1 & -2 & -4 & 2 \\ 1 & -3 & -2 & 1 \\ 2 & -2 & -11 & 4 \\ -1 & 3 & 3 & 0 \end{pmatrix}$ 16. $\begin{pmatrix} 2 & -1 & -2 & 3 \\ 1 & -2 & -1 & 2 \\ 3 & -1 & 2 & 1 \\ -1 & 2 & -3 & 2 \end{pmatrix}$

17. $\begin{pmatrix} 1 & 3 & -1 & 2 & 1 \\ 4 & 1 & 5 & -1 & 2 \\ 3 & 2 & 1 & 6 & 5 \\ 2 & -1 & 4 & -2 & 1 \\ 3 & 1 & -5 & 6 & 3 \end{pmatrix}$

18. Show that every $n \times n$ matrix may be reduced by elementary row transformations to triangular form, with all elements above the diagonal consisting of zeros.

19. Let A be an $m \times n$ matrix with $m \le n$. If A is of rank r with $r < m$, describe a process using elementary row transformations which reduces A to a form having the first $m - r$ rows consisting entirely of zeros.

20. Show that every $n \times n$ nonsingular matrix A may be reduced by row transformations to a form in which the only nonzero elements are a_{n1}, $a_{n-1,2}$, $a_{n-2,3}$, $\cdots$, $a_{2,n-1}$, a_{1n}.

8. GENERAL LINEAR SYSTEMS

We consider a system of m linear equations in n unknowns in which m may be different from n. In a system such as

$$\left. \begin{aligned} a_{11}x_1 + a_{12}x_2 + \cdots + a_{1n}x_n &= b_1 \\ a_{21}x_1 + a_{22}x_2 + \cdots + a_{2n}x_n &= b_2 \\ \vdots \qquad\qquad \vdots \qquad\qquad \vdots \\ a_{m1}x_1 + a_{m2}x_2 + \cdots + a_{mn}x_n &= b_m \end{aligned} \right\} , \qquad (1)$$

we call the $m \times n$ matrix

$$A = \begin{pmatrix} a_{11} & a_{12} & \cdots & a_{1n} \\ a_{21} & a_{22} & \cdots & a_{2n} \\ \vdots & \vdots & & \vdots \\ a_{m1} & a_{m2} & \cdots & a_{mn} \end{pmatrix}$$

the *coefficient matrix* of the system (1). The $m \times (n + 1)$ matrix

$$B = \begin{pmatrix} a_{11} & a_{12} & \cdots & a_{1n} & b_1 \\ a_{21} & a_{22} & \cdots & a_{2n} & b_2 \\ \vdots & \vdots & & \vdots & \vdots \\ a_{m1} & a_{m2} & \cdots & a_{mn} & b_m \end{pmatrix}$$

is called the *augmented matrix* of (1).

As an illustration, suppose we wish to solve the system of equations

$$\begin{aligned} 3x + 2y - 2z &= 3, \\ 2x + 3y - 3z &= 4, \\ -2x + 4y + 2z &= 3, \\ 5x - 2y + 4z &= 2, \\ 3x + 4y + 2z &= 3. \end{aligned} \tag{2}$$

The reader, noticing that there are more equations than there are unknowns, would not expect a solution. However, sometimes such systems do have solutions. Geometrically, the above system represents five planes in three-dimensional space. If it should accidentally happen that the five planes have a point in common, then (2) has a solution. We shall show that the existence of a solution of (2) depends on the behavior of both the coefficient matrix and the augmented matrix.

Suppose now that we proceed to reduce an augmented matrix of a given system such as (1), using the methods of elementary transformations as described in the preceding section. First we note that the coefficient matrix is reduced simultaneously. Second, the interchange of two rows of a matrix corresponds to an interchange of two rows of the system of equations and does not affect the solution. Multiplication of a row by a constant is the same as multiplication of an equation by a constant and also has no effect on the solution. A transformation of type (c) is the same as multiplication of one equation by a constant and addition of the resulting equation to another equation. Again, the solution is unaffected. Thus to each elementary transformation of the augmented matrix involving only rows, there corresponds an operation which we call the *corresponding elementary transformation of the given system of equations*. By now, the following important theorem is evident.

Theorem 14. *Suppose B is the augmented matrix of a certain system of equations and B' is obtained from B by applying a finite number of elementary*

*transformations involving only rows.   Then B' is the augmented matrix of that
system of equations which is obtained from the original system by performing
the corresponding elementary transformations.   The coefficient matrix of the
transformed system is obtained from B' by omitting the last column.   The systems
corresponding to B and B' have the same solutions.   We say the systems are
equivalent.*

The augmented matrix of (2) is

$$\begin{pmatrix} 3 & 2 & -2 & 3 \\ 2 & 3 & -3 & 4 \\ -2 & 4 & 2 & 3 \\ 5 & -2 & 4 & 2 \\ 3 & 4 & 2 & 3 \end{pmatrix}$$

We recognize this matrix as the one in Example 2 of the preceding section.
The result of reduction shows that

$$\begin{pmatrix} 3 & 2 & -2 & 3 \\ 2 & 3 & -3 & 4 \\ -2 & 4 & 2 & 3 \\ 5 & -2 & 4 & 2 \\ 3 & 4 & 2 & 3 \end{pmatrix} \cong \begin{pmatrix} 2 & 3 & -3 & 4 \\ 0 & -1 & 13 & -6 \\ 0 & 0 & -1 & 1 \\ 0 & 0 & 0 & 2 \\ 0 & 0 & 0 & 0 \end{pmatrix}$$

We now may use Theorem 14 to conclude that the system (2) is equivalent to the
system

$$\begin{aligned} 2x + 3y - 3z &= 4 \\ - y + 13z &= -6 \\ -z &= 1 \\ 0 &= 2 \\ 0 &= 0, \end{aligned}$$

which has no solution.   However, if the column of numbers on the right in (2)
is replaced by the column

$$\begin{matrix} -3 \\ -7 \\ -2 \\ 15 \\ 3, \end{matrix}$$

so that the system becomes

$$\begin{aligned} 3x + 2y - 2z &= -3 \\ 2x + 3y - 3z &= -7 \\ -2x + 4y + 2z &= -2 \\ 5x - 2y + 4z &= 15 \\ 3x + 4y + 2z &= 3, \end{aligned} \tag{3}$$

we see that exactly the same elementary transformations as before bring about an equivalent system. We obtain

$$
\begin{aligned}
2x + 3y - 3z &= -7 \\
-y + 13z &= 27 \\
-z &= -2 \\
0 &= 0 \\
0 &= 0,
\end{aligned}
$$

which has the solution $x = 1$, $y = -1$, $z = 2$. The student can easily verify that this set of numbers satisfies all equations in (3).

EXAMPLE. Solve, if possible, the following system of equations by using elementary row transformations on the augmented matrix to reduce the system to a simpler equivalent form:

$$
\begin{aligned}
x_1 + 2x_2 - 2x_3 + 3x_4 - 4x_5 &= -3, \\
2x_1 + 4x_2 - 5x_3 + 6x_4 - 5x_5 &= -1, \\
-x_1 - 2x_2 - 3x_4 + 11x_5 &= 15.
\end{aligned}
$$

Solution. The augmented matrix is

$$
B = \begin{pmatrix}
1 & 2 & -2 & 3 & -4 & -3 \\
2 & 4 & -5 & 6 & -5 & -1 \\
-1 & -2 & 0 & -3 & 11 & 15
\end{pmatrix},
$$

and the part of B to the left of the dotted vertical line is the coefficient matrix. We multiply the first row by 2 and subtract from the second row. Then, adding the first row to the third row, we obtain

$$
B \cong \begin{pmatrix}
1 & 2 & -2 & 3 & -4 & -3 \\
0 & 0 & -1 & 0 & 3 & 5 \\
0 & 0 & -2 & 0 & 7 & 12
\end{pmatrix} \cong \begin{pmatrix}
1 & 2 & -2 & 3 & -4 & -3 \\
0 & 0 & -1 & 0 & 3 & 5 \\
0 & 0 & 0 & 0 & 1 & 2
\end{pmatrix}.
$$

Therefore, the given system is equivalent to the system

$$
\begin{aligned}
x_1 + 2x_2 - 2x_3 + 3x_4 - 4x_5 &= -3, \\
- x_3 + 3x_5 &= 5, \\
x_5 &= 2.
\end{aligned}
$$

From the last two equations we get at once $x_5 = 2$ and $x_3 = 1$. Solving the first equation for x_1, we find that

$$
x_1 = 7 - 2x_2 - 3x_4.
$$

In other words, regardless of the values we assign to x_2 and x_4, the remaining values of x_1, x_3, and x_5 will satisfy the given system. There is an infinite number of solutions.

We now give a criterion (in terms of the ranks of both the coefficient matrix and the augmented matrix) which determines when a general linear system has a solution. However, the actual solution of a problem is best performed as in the example above.

Theorem 15. (a) *A system of m linear equations in n unknowns has a solution if and only if the rank r of the augmented matrix equals that of the coefficient matrix.*
(b) *If the two matrices have the same rank r and r = n, the solution is unique.*
(c) *If the two matrices have the same rank r and r < n, then at least one set of r of the unknowns can be solved in terms of the remaining n − r unknowns.*

Proof. Let A be the $m \times n$ coefficient matrix and B be the $m \times (n + 1)$ augmented matrix of the given system. Suppose that B is reduced to the matrix B' as in Theorem 13 (using rows only). The coefficient matrix of the equivalent system corresponding to A is the submatrix A' of B' obtained by deleting the last column. If A and B are not of the same rank, neither are A' and B'. Then the last column of B' has at least one nonzero element b' in which all remaining elements of that row are zeros. The corresponding equation of the equivalent system is

$$0 = b',$$

which is clearly impossible.

If A' and B' are of the same rank r and $r = n$, then there are as many equations as unknowns and Cramer's Rule applies. There is a unique solution.

If $r < n$, we select an $r \times r$ submatrix of A' which is nonsingular, and we apply Cramer's Rule to solve for r of the unknowns in terms of the remaining $n - r$ unknowns. Thus part (c) of the theorem is established.

A system of linear equations is said to be *homogeneous* if and only if the numbers on the right [i.e., $b_1, b_2, \ldots, b_m$ in (1)] are all zero. In this case, it is clear that the rank of the augmented matrix equals that of the coefficient matrix. Every homogeneous system has the solution $x_1 = x_2 = \cdots = x_n = 0$. Moreover, if $x_1, x_2, \ldots, x_n$ and $y_1, y_2, \ldots, y_n$ are solutions of a homogeneous system and c is a constant, then

$$x_1 + y_1, x_2 + y_2, \ldots, x_n + y_n \quad \text{and} \quad cx_1, cx_2, \ldots, cx_n$$

are solutions. If the rank of a homogeneous system is n, then the solution is unique and $x_1 = x_2 = \cdots = x_n = 0$ is the only solution. We have just derived the following corollary.

Corollary. *A homogeneous system of m equations in n unknowns has a solution $x_1, x_2, \ldots, x_n$ in which not all the x_j are zero if and only if the rank r of the coefficient matrix is less than n. When $r < n$, some group of r of the x_j can be expressed in terms of the remaining x_j.*

EXERCISES

Find all the solutions, if any, of the following systems of equations. Begin by reducing the augmented matrix (and thus the coefficient matrix) to the simplified form, using only row transformations. Find the rank r of the coefficient matrix and the rank r^* of the augmented matrix.

1. $\begin{aligned} x_1 - x_2 + 2x_3 &= -2 \\ 3x_1 - 2x_2 + 4x_3 &= -5 \\ 2x_2 - 3x_3 &= 2 \end{aligned}$

2. $\begin{aligned} x_1 + x_2 - 5x_3 &= 26 \\ x_1 + 2x_2 + x_3 &= -4 \\ x_1 + 3x_2 + 7x_3 &= -34 \end{aligned}$

3. $\begin{aligned} 2x_1 + 3x_2 - x_3 &= -15 \\ 3x_1 + 5x_2 + 2x_3 &= 0 \\ x_1 + 3x_2 + 3x_3 &= 11 \\ 7x_1 + 11x_2 &= -30 \end{aligned}$

4. $\begin{aligned} x_1 - x_3 + x_4 &= -2 \\ -x_2 + 2x_3 + x_4 &= 5 \\ x_1 - x_3 + 2x_4 &= 3 \\ 2x_1 + x_2 - x_3 &= -6 \end{aligned}$

5. $\begin{aligned} 3x_1 - x_2 + 2x_3 &= 3 \\ 2x_1 + 2x_2 + x_3 &= 2 \\ x_1 - 3x_2 + x_3 &= 4 \end{aligned}$

6. $\begin{aligned} 4x_1 - 6x_2 + 7x_3 &= 8 \\ x_1 - 2x_2 + 6x_3 &= 4 \\ 8x_1 - 10x_2 - 3x_3 &= 8 \end{aligned}$

7. $\begin{aligned} 2x_1 - x_2 + x_4 &= 2 \\ -3x_1 + x_3 - 2x_4 &= -4 \\ x_1 + x_2 - x_3 + x_4 &= 2 \\ 2x_1 - x_2 + 5x_3 &= 6 \end{aligned}$

8. $\begin{aligned} x_1 + x_2 + 2x_3 - x_4 &= 3 \\ 2x_1 - x_2 + x_3 + x_4 &= 1 \\ x_1 - 5x_2 - 4x_3 + 5x_4 &= -7 \\ 4x_1 - 5x_2 - x_3 + 5x_4 &= -3 \end{aligned}$

9. $\begin{aligned} 2x_1 - 7x_2 - 6x_3 &= 0 \\ 3x_1 + 5x_2 - 2x_3 &= 0 \\ 4x_1 - 2x_2 - 7x_3 &= 0 \end{aligned}$

10. $\begin{aligned} x_1 - x_2 - 5x_3 &= 0 \\ 2x_1 + 3x_2 &= 0 \\ 4x_1 - 5x_2 - 22x_3 &= 0 \end{aligned}$

11. $\begin{aligned} 2x_1 + 3x_2 - x_3 - x_4 &= 0 \\ x_1 - x_2 - 2x_3 - 4x_4 &= 0 \\ 3x_1 + x_2 + 3x_3 - 2x_4 &= 0 \\ 6x_1 + 3x_2 - 7x_4 &= 0 \end{aligned}$

12. $\begin{aligned} x_1 - 2x_2 + 10x_3 - 4x_4 &= 0 \\ 3x_1 - x_2 &= 0 \\ -2x_1 + x_2 + 5x_3 - 2x_4 &= 0 \\ 2x_1 - 3x_2 - 5x_3 + 2x_4 &= 0 \end{aligned}$

13. $\begin{aligned} x_1 + x_2 - 3x_3 + x_4 &= 1 \\ 2x_1 - 4x_2 + 2x_4 &= 2 \\ 3x_1 - 4x_2 - 2x_3 &= 0 \\ x_1 - 2x_3 + 3x_4 &= 3 \end{aligned}$

14. $\begin{aligned} x_1 - 2x_2 + 2x_3 + 3x_4 &= 1 \\ -x_1 + 4x_2 - x_3 - 5x_4 &= 2 \\ 2x_1 - 2x_2 + 5x_3 + 4x_4 &= 5 \\ -x_1 + 6x_2 - x_4 &= 12 \end{aligned}$

15. $\begin{aligned} x_1 + 3x_2 - 2x_3 - 3x_4 + 2x_5 &= 4 \\ -x_1 - 3x_2 + 4x_3 + 4x_4 + 4x_5 &= -1 \\ -x_1 - 3x_2 + 4x_3 + 4x_4 - x_5 &= -2 \\ -2x_1 - 6x_2 + 10x_3 + 9x_4 - 4x_5 &= 1 \end{aligned}$

16. $\begin{aligned} 2x_1 + x_2 - 3x_3 + x_4 + x_5 &= 0 \\ x_1 + 2x_2 - x_3 + 4x_4 + 2x_5 &= 1 \\ 2x_1 - 3x_2 + 2x_3 - x_4 + 3x_5 &= -6 \\ -x_1 + 2x_3 + 3x_4 - x_5 &= 8 \\ 2x_2 + x_3 + 2x_4 + 3x_5 &= -7 \\ 3x_1 - 4x_2 + 5x_3 - 2x_4 + x_5 &= 0 \end{aligned}$

9. NUMERICAL SOLUTIONS BY ITERATIVE METHODS

Suppose we have a system of n linear equations in n unknowns which may be written in the matrix form

$$AX = B, \tag{1}$$

where A is an $n \times n$ matrix and X and B are $n \times 1$ matrices. If A is nonsingular, so that A^{-1} exists, the matrix equation (1) has the unique solution

$$X = A^{-1}B. \tag{2}$$

The individual components of X may be read off from (2), once the inverse of A is found and the product $A^{-1}B$ is computed.

From the numerical point of view, it is difficult to find the inverse of a non-singular $n \times n$ matrix when n is large. For $n = 2, 3$, or 4, the inverse of a matrix is computable by hand directly from the definition. If n is below 10, it is still possible to find the inverse by using an electric desk calculator. However, if n is 100 or 1000, the situation is clearly hopeless. In recent times, many problems have arisen in engineering, economics, biology, etc., which lead to systems of linear equations with an enormous number of unknowns.

In Section 1 we discussed the solution of a linear system by the method of elimination. If the number of equations is relatively small, such techniques are quite adequate. We shall now take up a method of solving the system (1) which has many computational advantages, especially when the number of equations and unknowns is large and computing machines are available. We shall illustrate the method with an example and then state a theorem which justifies the process.

EXAMPLE 1. Find a solution of the system

$$\begin{aligned} 6x + 2y - 3z &= 5, \\ -x + 8y + 3z &= -10, \\ x + 4y + 12z &= 12. \end{aligned} \tag{3}$$

Solution. We rewrite the system in the form

$$\begin{aligned} x &= \frac{5 - 2y + 3z}{6}, \\ y &= \frac{-10 + x - 3z}{8}, \\ z &= \frac{12 - x - 4y}{12}, \end{aligned} \tag{4}$$

in which we solve the first equation in (3) for x in terms of the remaining variables, the second equation for y in terms of x and z, and the third equation for z in terms of x and y. Now we *guess* at the solution. The guess may be good or bad, a fact which we shall discuss later. Suppose the guess is $x = 1$, $y = 1$, $z = 1$. We call this guess $x^{(0)} = 1$, $y^{(0)} = 1$, $z^{(0)} = 1$ and insert these values in the *right side* of (4). We find, for the left side, the values

$$x = 1, \qquad y = -\tfrac{3}{2}, \qquad z = \tfrac{7}{12}.$$

These values are denoted $x^{(1)} = 1$, $y^{(1)} = -\tfrac{3}{2}$, $z^{(1)} = \tfrac{7}{12}$, and we insert these in the right side of (4). The corresponding values on the left, which we call $x^{(2)}$, $y^{(2)}$, $z^{(2)}$, are

$$x^{(2)} = \tfrac{13}{8}, \qquad y^{(2)} = -\tfrac{43}{32}, \qquad z^{(2)} = \tfrac{17}{12}.$$

Continuing the process by substituting these values in the right side of (4), we obtain

$$x^{(3)} = \tfrac{191}{96}, \qquad y^{(3)} = -\tfrac{101}{64}, \qquad z^{(3)} = \tfrac{21}{16}.$$

Repeating the iteration once again, we get

$$x^{(4)} = \tfrac{387}{192}, \qquad y^{(4)} = -\tfrac{1147}{768}, \qquad z^{(4)} = \tfrac{1567}{1152}.$$

Of course, a simple calculation shows that the true answer is $x = 2$, $y = -\tfrac{3}{2}$, $z = \tfrac{4}{3}$, while the fourth iteration above, in decimal form, is $x^{(4)} = 2.015^+$, $y^{(4)} = -1.493^+$, $z^{(4)} = 1.360^+$.

_____

If the system (1) is written out in coordinates

$$
\begin{aligned}
a_{11}x_1 + a_{12}x_2 + \cdots + a_{1n}x_n &= b_1 \\
a_{21}x_1 + a_{22}x_2 + \cdots + a_{2n}x_n &= b_2 \\
&\vdots \\
a_{n1}x_1 + a_{n2}x_2 + \cdots + a_{nn}x_n &= b_n
\end{aligned}
$$

then the iteration method described in Example 1 has the appearance

$$x_1 = \frac{b_1 - (a_{12}x_2 + \cdots + a_{1n}x_n)}{a_{11}}$$

$$x_2 = \frac{b_2 - (a_{21}x_1 + a_{23}x_3 + \cdots + a_{2n}x_n)}{a_{22}}$$

$$\vdots$$

$$x_n = \frac{b_n - (a_{n1}x_1 + a_{n2}x_2 + \cdots + a_{n,n-1}x_{n-1})}{a_{nn}}.$$

We may write this more compactly as

$$x_i = \frac{1}{a_{ii}}\left[b_i - \sum_{\substack{j=1 \\ j \neq i}}^{n} a_{ij}x_j \right], \qquad i = 1, 2, \ldots, n. \tag{5}$$

The general iteration method begins with the guess

$$x_1^{(0)}, \quad x_2^{(0)}, \quad \ldots, \quad x_n^{(0)},$$

which is inserted in the right side of (5). The values obtained on the left are labeled $x_1^{(1)}$, $x_2^{(1)}$, $\ldots$, $x_n^{(1)}$, and the process is repeated with the new values put into (5) on the right. The general process after k steps is described by the system

$$x_i^{(k+1)} = \frac{1}{a_{ii}}\left[b_i - \sum_{\substack{j=1 \\ j \neq i}}^{n} a_{ij}x_j^{(k)} \right], \qquad i = 1, 2, \ldots, n. \tag{6}$$

It *may* happen that

$$\lim_{k \to \infty} x_i^{(k)} \quad \text{exists for} \quad i = 1, 2, \ldots, n. \tag{7}$$

Calling the limiting values $\bar{x}_1, \bar{x}_2, \ldots, \bar{x}_n$, it is clear that this set of values will satisfy (5) and therefore (1). It is the desired solution.

It is natural to ask when the limit in (7) will exist. At first, we may think it will depend on the initial guess. After all, if by accident we take for

$$x_1^{(0)}, \quad x_2^{(0)}, \quad \ldots, \quad x_n^{(0)}$$

the true solution, the iteration stops after one step. The next theorem shows that under certain circumstances, the initial guess plays no part in the existence of the limit in (7).

The iteration method (5) is actually most useful when the coefficients of the diagonal terms a_{ii} are *much larger* than any of the other coefficients. A sufficient condition for convergence is stated (without proof) in the following theorem.

Theorem 16. *Suppose that the matrix $A = (a_{ij})$ has the property that*

$$|a_{ii}| > \sum_{\substack{j=1 \\ j \neq i}}^{n} |a_{ij}| \quad \text{for} \quad i = 1, 2, \ldots, n. \tag{8}$$

Then the matrix A is nonsingular, and the iteration method (6) converges to the unique solution of (1) no matter what values are selected for the initial guess

$$x_1^{(0)}, \quad x_2^{(0)}, \quad \ldots, \quad x_n^{(0)}.$$

Remarks. Note that in Example 1 the conditions of the Theorem are satisfied. There are many conditions weaker than (8) which are sufficient for the convergence of the iteration method. It is of the utmost importance to observe that a solution is obtained regardless of the initial guess. Suppose that after a certain number of steps, an error is made. Instead of destroying the convergence, this merely means that a new initial guess is at hand and, unless further errors occur, convergence will take place. Of course, the "rate of convergence" is slowed by errors but, unless computing mistakes occur repeatedly, the method must lead to a solution. A good initial guess is helpful in that the number of steps required to obtain a given degree of accuracy is smaller for a good first guess than for a poor one.

The subject of the numerical solution of linear equations is replete with theorems similar to Theorem 16 which guarantee convergence under a variety of hypotheses on A. In order to save as much computation as possible, it is essential to find methods which converge rapidly. The following scheme, called the Gauss-Seidel method, is a refinement of the method (6) above and leads to more rapid convergence than does (6). The Gauss-Seidel iteration method is described by the system

$$x_i^{(k+1)} = \frac{1}{a_{ii}}\left[b_i - \sum_{j=1}^{i-1} a_{ij}x_j^{(k+1)} - \sum_{j=i+1}^{n} a_{ij}x_j^{(k)}\right], \qquad i = 1, 2, \ldots, n, \quad (9)$$

where, if $i = 1$, the first sum on the right is absent while, if $i = n$, the second sum is absent. In essence, the iteration (9) states that at each step we use the latest information available. To illustrate the point, we shall work Example 1, using the iteration scheme (9).

EXAMPLE 2. Find a solution of the system

$$6x + 2y - 3z = 5,$$
$$-x + 8y + 3z = -10,$$
$$x + 4y + 12z = 12,$$

by the Gauss-Seidel method.

Solution. As before, we take $x^{(0)} = y^{(0)} = z^{(0)} = 1$ as the initial guess and find that

$$x^{(1)} = \frac{5 - 2 + 3}{6} = 1,$$

$$y^{(1)} = \frac{-10 + x^{(1)} - 3z^{(0)}}{8} = -\frac{3}{2},$$

$$z^{(1)} = \frac{12 - x^{(1)} - 4y^{(1)}}{12} = \frac{12 - 1 + 6}{12} = \frac{17}{12}.$$

The second iteration is

$$x^{(2)} = \frac{5 - 2y^{(1)} + 3z^{(1)}}{6} = \frac{49}{24},$$

$$y^{(2)} = \frac{-10 + x^{(2)} - 3z^{(1)}}{8} = -\frac{293}{192},$$

$$z^{(2)} = \frac{12 - x^{(2)} - 4y^{(2)}}{12} = \frac{257}{192}.$$

A third iteration yields $x^{(3)} = 2317/1152$, $y^{(3)} = -13,829/9216$, $z^{(3)} = 12,281/9216$ which, in decimal form, is

$$x^{(3)} = 2.012^+, \qquad y^{(3)} = -1.500^+, \qquad z^{(3)} = 1.332^+.$$

We note that the Gauss-Seidel method after three iterations yields values which are closer to the true result than the iteration process (5) does after four iterations.

Remarks. It sometimes happens that a matrix will have a dominant term in each row but that this dominant term is not always the diagonal term. A relabeling of the unknowns or an interchange in the ordering of the equations may bring the matrix A into the appropriate form. It can be shown that convergence of the iteration process takes place if (8) is replaced by

$$|a_{ii}| \geq \sum_{\substack{j=1 \\ j \neq i}}^{n} |a_{ij}| \quad \text{for} \quad i = 1, 2, \ldots, n,$$

and if there is *at least one i* for which the strict inequality holds.

EXERCISES

Solve each of the following systems by the iteration process (5) and by the Gauss-Seidel method (9), repeating the iterations the number of times indicated by the value of n. Use the initial guess as shown. Compare the result with that obtained by elimination.

1. $5x_1 + 2x_2 - x_3 = -2,$
   $2x_1 + 4x_2 + x_3 = -3,$
   $x_1 + 2x_2 + 6x_3 = 15,$ $n = 4.$
   Select $x_1^{(0)} = x_2^{(0)} = x_3^{(0)} = 0.$

2. $4x_1 - x_2 + x_3 = 10,$
   $2x_1 + 5x_2 - 2x_3 = -3,$
   $2x_1 + x_2 + 6x_3 = 9,$ $n = 4.$
   Select $x_1^{(0)} = x_2^{(0)} = x_3^{(0)} = 0.$

3. $7x_1 - 2x_2 + 3x_3 = 19,$
   $x_1 + 8x_2 - 6x_3 = 9,$
   $2x_1 + 4x_2 + 9x_3 = 5,$ $n = 3.$
   Select $x_1^{(0)} = x_2^{(0)} = x_3^{(0)} = 1.$

4. $12x_1 - 2x_2 + 4x_3 = -14,$
   $3x_1 + 8x_2 + 2x_3 = 23,$
   $6x_1 - 3x_2 + 16x_3 = 10,$ $n = 4.$
   Select $x_1^{(0)} = x_2^{(0)} = x_3^{(0)} = 1.$

5. $6x_1 + 2x_2 + 2x_3 \qquad = 20,$
   $x_1 + 5x_2 \qquad + x_4 = -5,$
   $x_1 + 3x_2 + 7x_3 \qquad = -2,$
   $x_2 + 2x_3 - 8x_4 = -10,$ $n = 3.$
   Select $x_1^{(0)} = x_2^{(0)} = x_3^{(0)} = x_4^{(0)} = 1.$

6. $6x_1 + 3x_2 - 2x_3 = 5,$
   $3x_1 + 9x_2 + 2x_3 = 17,$
   $-3x_1 + 3x_2 + 6x_3 = 11,$ $n = 4.$
   Select $x_1^{(0)} = x_2^{(0)} = x_3^{(0)} = 1.$

7. $5x_1 - 2x_2 + 3x_3 = -5,$
   $2x_1 + 3x_2 - 7x_3 = 3,$
   $4x_1 + 5x_2 - x_3 = -17,$ $n = 4.$
   Select $x_1^{(0)} = x_2^{(0)} = x_3^{(0)} = 0.$

Answers to
Odd-Numbered Exercises

Answers to
Odd-Numbered Exercises

CHAPTER 1

SECTION 1

1. $x < \frac{7}{3}$

3. $x < -\frac{27}{13}$

5. $x < 2$

7. all x not in interval $[0, \frac{20}{3}]$

9. all x not in interval $[2, \frac{13}{4}]$

11. x in interval $(\frac{5}{3}, 4)$

13. all x not in interval $[2, 3]$

15. all x in interval $(\frac{1}{3}, 4)$

17. all x in $(\frac{11}{5}, \frac{36}{5})$

19. all x in $(-\infty, 1)$, $(\frac{3}{2}, 2)$, $(\frac{17}{7}, \infty)$ satisfy both inequalities

21. all x in $(-\infty, 0)$ and $(\frac{3}{5}, \frac{5}{4})$ satisfy both inequalities

SECTION 2

1. $1, -4$

3. $x = 1, \frac{11}{5}$

5. $x = \frac{7}{3}, -\frac{5}{3}$

7. $x = \frac{7}{10}, -\frac{3}{4}$

9. $x = 3, -3$

11. $x = -\frac{13}{2}, -\frac{17}{4}$

13. all x in $(-4, -1)$

15. all x in $[-\frac{13}{5}, -\frac{11}{5}]$

17. all x not in $[-\frac{11}{2}, -\frac{5}{6}]$

19. all x in $[-\frac{1}{3}, 7]$

SECTION 3

1. $M = 20$

3. $M = 1044$

5. $M = 98.5$

7. $M = 10$

9. none

CHAPTER 2

SECTION 2

1. $f(-3) = 6$; $f(-1) = 2$; $f(-2) = 3$; $f(0) = 3$; $f(1) = 6$; $f(2) = 11$, $f(3) = 18$; $f(a - 1) = a^2 + 2$

3. $f(-4) = \frac{2}{5}$; $f(-3) = \frac{1}{3}$; $f(-2) = 0$; $f(-1) = 1$; $f(0) = \frac{2}{3}$; $f(1) = \frac{3}{5}$; $f(-1000) = \frac{998}{1997}$; $f(1000) = \frac{1002}{2003}$; $f[f(x)] = \dfrac{5x + 8}{8x + 13}$; all x except $x = -\frac{3}{2}$

5. $f(-1000) = \dfrac{-1000}{1,000,001}$; $f(-3) = -\frac{3}{10}$; $f(-2) = -\frac{2}{5}$; $f(-1) = -\frac{1}{2}$; $f(0) = 0$; $f(1) = \frac{1}{2}$; $f(2) = \frac{2}{5}$; $f(3) = \frac{3}{10}$; $f(1000) = \dfrac{1000}{1,000,001}$

7. Domain: $-1 - \sqrt{3} \le x \le -1 + \sqrt{3}$

9. Domain: all x except $-6, -2, 2$

11. $2x + h$

13. $3x^2 + 3xh + h^2$

15. $-\dfrac{2x + h}{x^2(x + h)^2}$

17. $\dfrac{2x + h}{\sqrt{(x + h)^2 + 3} + \sqrt{x^2 + 3}}$

	Intercepts	Symmetry	Asymptotes		Intercepts	Symmetry	Asymptotes
1.	x: 0 y: 0	y-axis	none	3.	x: 0 y: 0	x-axis	none
5.	x: $\pm\sqrt{2}$ y: 2	y-axis	none	7.	none	y-axis	$x = 0$ $y = 0$
9.	x: none y: ± 2	x, y-axes origin	no vert. or horiz.	11.	x: ± 2 y: $\pm\sqrt{6}$	x, y-axes origin	none
13.	x: none y: ± 3	x, y-axes origin	no vert. or horiz.	15.	x: none y: $\pm\sqrt{2}$	origin	$y = 0$
17.	none	x, y-axes origin	$x = \pm 2$ $y = 0$	19.	x: none y: ± 1	x-axis	$x = 2$ $y = 0$
21.	x: none y: $\pm 2\sqrt{3}/3$	x-axis	$x = 1, 3$ $y = 0$	23.	x: 0 y: 0	y-axis	$x = 0$ $y = \pm 2$
25.	x: 0 y: 0, ± 1	x, y-axes origin	none	27.	x: $\frac{5}{2}, \frac{3}{2}$ y: 3, 5	none	$x = 2$ $y = 4$
29.	x: -2 y: none	x-axis	$x = 2$ $y = 0$				

CHAPTER 3

1. $\overline{AB} = 5$, $\overline{AC} = \sqrt{58}$, $\overline{BC} = \sqrt{157}$ 3. $\overline{AB} = \sqrt{26}$, $\overline{AC} = \sqrt{13}$, $\overline{BC} = 5$

5. $(5, 5\frac{1}{2})$ 7. $(10, -\frac{3}{2})$ 9. $(-16, -1)$

11. $\frac{1}{2}\sqrt{149}$, $\frac{1}{2}\sqrt{389}$, $\frac{1}{2}\sqrt{338}$ 13. $\overline{AB} = \overline{BC} = \sqrt{41}$

15. $\overline{AB} = \sqrt{13}$, $\overline{BC} = \sqrt{65}$, $\overline{AC} = 2\sqrt{13}$, $\overline{AB}^2 + \overline{AC}^2 = \overline{BC}^2$

17. $\overline{AB} = \overline{BC} = \overline{CD} = \overline{DA} = 3\sqrt{2}$; $\overline{AB}^2 + \overline{BC}^2 = \overline{AC}^2$

19. intersect at $(\frac{3}{2}, 2)$

1. parallel   3. perpendicular   5. parallel
7. yes   9. no   11. $3x - 4y - 23 = 0$
13. parallelogram   15. trapezoid   17. none
19. none of these   21. rhombus   23. none of these

1. $3x - y + 13 = 0$ 3. $4x + 3y - 17 = 0$ 5. $11x + 5y - 8 = 0$
7. $y - 8 = 0$ 9. $y + 2 = 0$ 11. $y + 5 = 0$
13. $x - 3y - 3 = 0$ 15. $3x + y = 0$ 17. $3x + 4y + 12 = 0$
19. $13x - 3y - 21 = 0$ 21. slope: $-\frac{2}{7}$; y-intercept: $-\frac{1}{7}$
23. x-intercept: -4; y-intercept: $-\frac{8}{5}$ 25. $x + 5y + 19 = 0$
27. $3x - 2y - 13 = 0$ 29. $5x + 8y + 29 = 0$ 31. $15x - y + 78 = 0$
33. $14x - 2y - 30 = 0$

1. $x = -1$, $y = 1$ 3. $x = -\frac{51}{32}$, $y = \frac{7}{16}$ 5. yes, $(x = -1, y = 5)$
7. no   9. no   11. concurrent at $(7, \frac{8}{5})$

SECTION 6

1. Polygon with vertices at $(2, 2)$, $(2, 1)$, $(5, -2)$, $(6, -\frac{5}{2})$, $(6, 2)$
3. Triangle with vertices at $(-1, 1)$, $(0, 1)$, $(0, \frac{4}{3})$
5. yes   7. $(0, 1)$

CHAPTER 4

SECTION 1

1. 6   3. 18   5. $-\frac{1}{2}$ 7. $\frac{1}{4}$
9. $-\frac{2}{3}$ 11. 6   13. 7   15. 6
17. $\sqrt{5}/20$ 19. $\frac{4}{3}$ 21. $1/\sqrt{b}$ 23. -6144

SECTION 2

1. 20   3. 48   5. $6a$ 7. -4 9. $-\frac{1}{9}$
11. $-2x$ 13. 29   15. 0   17. $\frac{3}{2}\sqrt{x}$ 19. $2c + 3$

SECTION 3

1. $4x$ 3. $6x + 2$ 5. $4x^3$ 7. $-\dfrac{1}{(x - 1)^2}$

9. $-\dfrac{3}{x^4}$ 11. $\dfrac{1}{(1 - x)^2}$ 13. $\dfrac{4x}{(x^2 + 1)^2}$ 15. $-\dfrac{1}{2x^{3/2}}$

17. $\frac{3}{2}\sqrt{x}$ 19. $\dfrac{x - 2}{2(x - 1)^{3/2}}$ 21. $-x/\sqrt{4 - x^2}$

SECTION 4

1. tangent: $3x + y = 0$; normal: $x - 3y + 10 = 0$
3. tangent: $2x - y - 4 = 0$; normal: $x + 2y - 2 = 0$
5. tangent: $9x + y - 17 = 0$; normal: $x - 9y - 11 = 0$
7. tangent: $x - 2y + 2 = 0$; normal: $2x + y - 6 = 0$
9. tangent: $x + 16y - 14 = 0$; normal: $32x - 2y - 191 = 0$
11. decreasing if $x \le 2$; increasing if $x \ge 2$, $x = 2$ a rel. min.
13. increasing if $x \le -1$, decreasing if $-1 \le x \le 2$, increasing if $x \ge 2$, $x = -1$ a rel. max., $x = 2$ a rel. min.
15. decreasing if $x \le 0$; increasing if $0 \le x \le 2$; decreasing if $x \ge 2$; $x = 0$ a rel. min.; $x = 2$ a rel. max.
17. decreasing if $x \le -1$, increasing if $-1 \le x \le 1$, decreasing if $1 \le x \le 2$, increasing if $x \ge 2$; $x = -1, 2$ are rel. min.; $x = 1$ a rel. max.

SECTION 5

1. $v = 1$, moving right   3. $v = -10$, moving left
5. $v = 0$ 7. $v = 2t - 4$, $a = 2$
9. $v = t^2 - 4t + 3$, $a = 2t - 4$ 11. $v = 2bt + c$, $a = 2b$
13. $v = 2t - 4$, $a = 2$, moving left if $t < 2$, moving right if $t > 2$
15. $v = 6(t - 2)(t + 1)$; moving left if $-1 < t < 2$, moving right if $t < -1$ or $t > 2$; $a = 6(2t - 1)$
17. $v = \dfrac{(1 - t)(1 + t)}{(1 + t^2)^2}$; moving left if $t < -1$ or $t > 1$; moving right if $-1 < t < 1$;
    $a = -2t(3 - t^2)(1 + t^2)^{-3}$

SECTION 6

1. $s = t^2 + 3t - 1$
5. $s = 6t - t^2 - t^3$
9. Sum $= 2.000$, exact area $= 2$.
13. $\frac{1}{3}$ 15. $\frac{4}{3}$
21. 2.330   23. 0.786

3. $s = \frac{1}{3}t^3 + \frac{1}{2}t^2 - 2t - \frac{1}{6}$
7. Rises for 2 sec; stays in air for 4 sec.
11. Sum $= 2.700$, exact area $= \frac{8}{3}$.
17. $\frac{13}{6}$ 19. $\frac{13}{6}$

CHAPTER 5

SECTION 1

1. $\delta = 0.0005$
7. $\delta = 0.0398$

3. $\delta = 0.005$
9. $\delta = \frac{84}{121}$

5. 0.029701
11. $\delta = \frac{1}{101}$

13. $\delta = \frac{200}{2601}$ 15. $\delta = \dfrac{\sqrt{101} - 10}{10}$

17. $\delta = 0.05$, although it is not the largest possible δ.

19. $\delta = \epsilon_1(2\sqrt{2} - \epsilon_1)$ where ϵ_1 is the smaller of ϵ and $\sqrt{2}$.   21. $\delta = \dfrac{9\epsilon}{1 + 3\epsilon}$

SECTION 2

1. 5   3. 4   5. 3   7. $\frac{3}{4}$ 9. $\frac{3}{2}$
11. 2   13. $\sqrt{3}$ 15. $1/2\sqrt{x}$ 17. $-\frac{1}{2}$

SECTION 3

1. continuous   3. continuous   5. continuous
7. continuous   9. continuous   11. discontinuous at $x = 2$
13. discontinuous at $x = 2$ 15. continuous   17. discontinuous at $x = 4$
19. continuous

SECTION 4

1. $\frac{3}{2}$ 3. 0   5. -1 7. 0   9. 1
11. ∞ 13. ∞ 15. $+\infty$ 17. $+\infty$ 19. $+\infty$

SECTION 5

1. 0   3. $-\frac{2}{3}$ 5. ∞ 7. 0   9. 2   11. 0   13. 0

17. $n = 1 \cdot 2 \cdot \dfrac{3}{2} \cdot \dfrac{4}{3} \cdot \dfrac{5}{4} \cdot \cdots \cdot \dfrac{n-1}{n-2} \cdot \dfrac{n}{n-1}$ and $\dfrac{n}{3^n} = \dfrac{1}{3} \cdot \dfrac{2}{3} \cdot \dfrac{\frac{3}{2}}{3} \cdot \dfrac{\frac{4}{3}}{3} \cdot \cdots \cdot \dfrac{n/(n-1)}{3}$

19. yes

CHAPTER 6

SECTION 1

1. $2x - 3$
5. $-3x^{-4} - 20x^{-6} + 24x^{-9}$
9. $2x + 2 + 2x^{-3}$
13. $9x^2 + 14x + 2$
15. $(3x^2 + 12x - 2)(x^2 + 3x - 5) + (x^3 + 6x^2 - 2x + 1)(2x + 3)$
17. $2(x^2 - 2)/x^2$

3. $15x^{14} + 24x - 8$
7. $3x^2 + 4x - 3 + 2x^{-2} - 8x^{-3}$
11. $-\frac{21}{4}x^{-8}$

19. $3x^{-2} - 8x^{-3} + 6x^{-4}$

21. $2/(x + 1)^2$

23. $13/(2x + 3)^2$

25. $(1 - x^2)/(1 + x^2)^2$

27. $-\dfrac{x^2 + 2x}{(x^2 + 2x + 2)^2}$

29. $\dfrac{4x^2 + 12x + 1}{(2x + 3)^2}$

31. (a) $4(x^2 + 2x - 1)(x + 1)$

    (b) $2(x^3 + 7x^2 - 8x - 6)(3x^2 + 14x - 8)$

    (c) $2(x^7 - 2x + 3x^{-2})(7x^6 - 2 - 6x^{-3})$

33. $f'(x) = \dfrac{uvw' + u'vw - uv'w}{v^2}$

SECTION 2

1. $30(3x + 5)^9$

3. $-21(6 - 3x)^6$

5. $-3(x + 5)^{-4}$

7. $4(x^3 + 2x - 3 + x^{-2})^3(3x^2 + 2 - 2x^{-3})$

9. $-2x(x^2 + 2 - x^{-2})^{-2}(1 + x^{-4})$

11. $2x(x^2 + 1)(x^2 - 2)(5x^4 - 3x^2 - 2)$

13. $\dfrac{(x^3 + 2x - 6)^6}{x^2}(23x^6 + 39x^4 - 32x^3 + 14x^2 - 12x - 6)$

15. $\dfrac{2x(x^2 + 1)^2(x^2 + 4)}{(x^2 + 2)^3}$

17. $-\dfrac{(x^2 + 2)(2x^5 + 12x^3 - 7x^2 - 6)}{x^2(x^2 + x^{-1})^4}$

19. $\dfrac{x^3 - 2x^{-2}}{(x^2 + x^{-1})^2}(4x^4 + 7x + 12x^{-1} + 6x^{-4})$

21. $(x + 5)(3x - 6)^2(7x^2 + 1)^3(273x^3 + 735x^2 - 1665x + 33)$

23. $2(x^2 + 1)^4(3x - 7)^7(x^2 + 5x - 4)^{-7}(9x^4 + 97x^3 - 184x^2 + 197x + 57)$

25. $(x^2 + x^{-2})^3(x^{-1} + x^{-2})^2(x^{-2} + 3x^{-4} + 7x^{-5})^{-9}$

    $\times\ [8(x^{-1} + x^{-2})(x - x^{-3})(x^{-2} + 3x^{-4} + 7x^{-5})$

    $-\ 3(x^2 + x^{-2})(x^{-2} + 2x^{-3})(x^{-2} + 3x^{-4} + 7x^{-5})$

    $+\ 8(x^2 + x^{-2})(x^{-1} + x^{-2})(2x^{-3} + 12x^{-5} + 35x^{-6})]$

SECTION 3

1. $\frac{5}{3}x^{2/3} - 2x^{-1/3} - \frac{4}{3}x^{-4/3}$

3. $-\frac{2}{3}x^{-5/3} + \frac{3}{4}x^{-7/4} + \frac{8}{7}x^{-3/7}$

5. $x^{-1/3} + x^{-1/2} + x^{-2}$

7. $\frac{3}{10}x^{1/2} - \frac{1}{5}x^{-1/2} - \frac{2}{5}x^{-3/2}$

9. $3x^{1/2} + 2x^{-1/3} - 7x^{2/5}$

11. $\frac{3}{4}x^{1/2} - \frac{3}{4}x^{-1/2} - \frac{1}{2}x^{-3/2}$

13. $\frac{20}{3}(2x + 3)^{7/3}$

15. $3(x + 1)(x^2 + 2x + 3)^{1/2}$

17. $-(2x^2 - 2x + 1)(2x^3 - 3x^2 + 3x - 1)^{-4/3}$

19. $2(x^2 + 1)(x^3 + 3x + 2)^{-1/3}$

21. $\frac{3}{10}(2x + 1)(x^2 + x - 3)^{1/2}$

23. $(2x + 3)^3(3x - 2)^{4/3}(38x + 5)$

25. $(2x - 1)^{3/2}(7x - 3)^{-4/7}(41x - 18)$

27. $\frac{1}{6}(x + 1)^{-1/3}(x - 1)^{-1/2}(7x - 1)$

29. $-2t^{-2}(2 + 6t)^{-2/3}(1 + 2t)$

31. $\frac{7}{2}(y^2 + 3y + 4)^{-3/2}$

33. $(s - 1)/\sqrt{2}s^{3/2}$

35. $\dfrac{x + 10}{6(x - 2)^{1/2}(x + 2)^{4/3}}$

37. $\dfrac{1}{(\tau + 1)\sqrt{\tau^2 - 1}}$

39. $-6(3t + 4)^{-2/3}(3t - 2)^{-4/3}$

41. 0

43. $\frac{3725}{6}$

45. tan: $5x - y - 9 = 0$; norm: $x + 5y - 7 = 0$

47. tan: $7x + 3y - 64 = 0$; norm: $3x - 7y + 72 = 0$

49. tan: $7x + 12y - 32 = 0$; norm; $24x - 14y - 27 = 0$

51. $f'(x) = u^{m-1} v^{n-1}[mu'v + nuv']$

SECTION 4

1. $y' = x/3y$

3. $y' = -\dfrac{x^3}{4y^3}$

5. $y' = \dfrac{x - y}{x - 2y}$

7. $y' = -\dfrac{x^2 + 2y}{2x + 5y^2}$

9. $y' = \dfrac{6x^2 - 6xy + 2y^2}{3x^2 - 4xy + 3y^2}$

11. $y' = \dfrac{6x^5 + 6x^2y - y^7}{-2x^3 + 7xy^6}$

13. $y = \dfrac{1}{2}x - \dfrac{3}{2}x^{-1}$; $y' = \dfrac{1}{2} + \dfrac{3}{2}x^{-2} = \dfrac{x - y}{x}$

15. $y = 4x^{-1}$; $y' = -4x^{-2} = -y/x$

17. $y = \pm(a^{2/3} - x^{2/3})^{3/2}$; $y' = \mp x^{-1/3}(a^{2/3} - x^{2/3})^{1/2} = -x^{-1/3}y^{1/3}$

19. $y = \pm(8 - 2x)^{1/2}$; $y' = \mp(8 - 2x)^{-1/2} = -1/y$

21. $y = \pm(2x^2 - 1)^{1/2}$; $y' = \pm\dfrac{2x}{\sqrt{2x^2 - 1}} = \dfrac{2x}{y}$

23. $y = \dfrac{-3x \pm \sqrt{41x^2 - 80}}{8}$; $y' = -\dfrac{3}{8} \pm \dfrac{41x}{8\sqrt{41x^2 - 80}} = \dfrac{4x - 3y}{3x + 8y}$

25. $y = -(2x)^{1/2}$; $y' = -\frac{1}{2}$

27. $y = -(10 - x^2)^{1/2}$; $y' = 3$

29. $y = \frac{3}{4}x - \frac{1}{4}(16 - 7x^2)^{1/2}$; $y' = \frac{1}{6}$

CHAPTER 7

SECTION 1

5. no

7. $(-1, -2)$

9. maximum at $(1, 2)$, minimum at $(3, -6)$

11. maximum $(2, 2)$; $f'(2) = 0$

SECTION 2

1. $x_0 = 1$

3. $x_0 = \frac{7}{3}$

5. $x_0 = 1$

7. $x_0 = \frac{1}{2}\sqrt{2}$

9. $x_0 = 0, \frac{1}{2}, 1$

11. $x_0 = 1$

13. The equation $-\dfrac{5}{(3x + 2)^2} = \dfrac{5}{2}$ has no solution.

15. $x_0 = -1$; Theorem of the Mean does not apply.

SECTION 3

1. decreasing for $x \leq -2$; increasing for $x \geq -2$; $x = -2$ a rel. min.

3. increasing for $x \leq \frac{3}{2}$; decreasing for $x \geq \frac{3}{2}$; $x = \frac{3}{2}$ rel. max.

5. increasing for $x \leq -1 - \sqrt{3}$; decreasing for $-1 - \sqrt{3} \leq x \leq -1 + \sqrt{3}$; increasing for $x \geq -1 + \sqrt{3}$; $x = -1 - \sqrt{3}$ rel. max.; $x = -1 + \sqrt{3}$ rel. min.

7. increasing for $x \leq \frac{1}{3}(-2 - \sqrt{13})$;
   decreasing for $\frac{1}{3}(-2 - \sqrt{13}) \leq x \leq \frac{1}{3}(-2 + \sqrt{13})$;
   increasing for $x \geq \frac{1}{3}(-2 + \sqrt{13})$;
   $x = \frac{1}{3}(-2 - \sqrt{13})$ rel. max.; $x = \frac{1}{3}(-2 + \sqrt{13})$ rel. min.
9. increasing for all x; $f'(x) = 0$ for $x = -2$
11. decreasing for $x \leq \frac{1}{3}$; increasing for $\frac{1}{3} \leq x \leq 1$; decreasing for $x \geq 1$; $x = \frac{1}{3}$ rel. min.; $x = 1$ rel. max.
13. decreasing for $x \leq -1$; increasing for $-1 \leq x \leq 0$; decreasing for $0 \leq x \leq 2$; increasing for $x \geq 2$; $x = -1, 2$ are rel. min.; $x = 0$ rel. max.
15. decreasing for $x \leq -\frac{3}{2}$; increasing for $x \geq -\frac{3}{2}$; $x = -\frac{3}{2}$ rel. min.
17. increasing for $x \leq -1$; decreasing for $-1 \leq x < 0$; decreasing for $0 < x \leq 1$; increasing for $x \geq 1$; $x = -1$ rel. max.; $x = 1$ rel. min.; $x = 0$ a vertical asymptote
19. increasing for $x < -1$; increasing for $x > -1$; $x = -1$ a vertical asymptote; $y = 1$ a horizontal asymptote
21. decreasing for $-1 < x \leq 0$; increasing for $x \geq 0$; $x = 0$ rel. min.; $x = -1$ a vertical asymptote
23. increasing for $x \leq -2$; decreasing for $-2 \leq x \leq 0$; increasing for $x \geq 0$; $x = -2$ rel. max.; $x = 0$ rel. min.; vertical tangent at $x = -3$
25. increasing for $x \leq 2$; decreasing for $2 \leq x \leq 3$; $x = 2$ rel. max.
27. decreasing for $-\sqrt{2} \leq x \leq -1$; increasing for $-1 \leq x \leq 1$; decreasing for $1 \leq x \leq \sqrt{2}$; $x = -1$ rel. min.; $x = 1$ rel. max.
29. increasing for all x; $x = 2$ a vertical asymptote

SECTION 4

1. Minimum at $x = \frac{3}{2}$; concave upward everywhere.
3. $x = 1$ a rel. min.; $x = -1$ a rel. max.; $x = 0$ a point of inflection; concave upward for $x \geq 0$; concave downward for $x \leq 0$.
5. $x = -\frac{3}{2}$ a rel. min.; concave upward for $x \leq -1$; concave downward for $-1 \leq x \leq 0$; concave upward for $x \geq 0$; $x = 0$ a point of inflection.
7. $x = -1, 1$ rel. minima; concave upward everywhere; $x = 0$ a vertical asymptote.
9. $x = -1$ rel. min.; $x = 1$ rel. max.; points of inflection at $x = 0, -\sqrt{3}, +\sqrt{3}$; concave downward for $x < -\sqrt{3}$ and for $0 < x < \sqrt{3}$; concave upward for $-\sqrt{3} < x < 0$ and for $x > \sqrt{3}$.
11. $x = -1$ rel. max.; $x = 2$ rel. min.; concave downward for $x \leq \frac{1}{2}$; concave upward for $x \geq \frac{1}{2}$; $x = \frac{1}{2}$ a point of inflection.
13. $x = \frac{2}{3}$ rel. max.; $x = 2$ rel. min.; concave downward for $x \leq \frac{4}{3}$; concave upward for $x \geq \frac{4}{3}$; $x = \frac{4}{3}$ a point of inflection.
15. No rel. max. or min.; concave downward for $x \leq \frac{1}{3}$; concave upward for $x \geq \frac{1}{3}$; $x = \frac{1}{3}$ a point of inflection.
17. $x = -1$ rel. min.; concave upward for $x \leq 0$; concave downward for $0 \leq x \leq 2$; concave upward for $x \geq 2$; $x = 0, 2$, points of inflection; horizontal tangent at $x = 2$.
19. $x = 0, (-15 - \sqrt{33})/8$ rel. minima; $x = (-15 + \sqrt{33})/8$ rel. max.; concave upward for $x \leq -2$; concave downward for $-2 \leq x \leq -\frac{1}{2}$; concave upward for $x \geq -\frac{1}{2}$; $x = -2, -\frac{1}{2}$ points of inflection.
21. $x = -2$ rel. min.; $x = 2$ rel. max.; concave downward for $x \leq -2\sqrt{3}$; concave upward for $-2\sqrt{3} \leq x \leq 0$; concave downward for $0 \leq x \leq 2\sqrt{3}$; concave upward for $x \geq 2\sqrt{3}$; $x = -2\sqrt{3}, 0, 2\sqrt{3}$ points of inflection.

23. $x = -2$ rel. min.; $x = 2$ rel. max.; concave upward for $-2\sqrt{2} \le x \le 0$; concave downward for $0 \le x \le 2\sqrt{2}$; $x = 0$ a point of inflection.

25. $x = -4$ rel. max.; $x = 0$ rel. min.; concave downward for $-5 \le x \le -4 + \frac{2}{3}\sqrt{6}$; concave upward for $x \ge -4 + \frac{2}{3}\sqrt{6}$; $x = -4 + \frac{2}{3}\sqrt{6}$ a point of inflection.

27. $x = 2$ rel. max.; concave downward for $x < -2$; concave downward for $-2 < x \le 2 - \sqrt{6}$; concave upward for $2 - \sqrt{6} \le x \le 0$; concave downward for $0 \le x \le 2 + \sqrt{6}$; concave upward for $x \ge 2 + \sqrt{6}$; $x = 2 - \sqrt{6}$, 0, $2 + \sqrt{6}$ points of inflection.

SECTION 5

1. minimum $(1, 4)$, maximum at $(-3, 20)$
3. minimum at $(-1, -7)$, maximum at $(2, 8)$
5. minimum at $(-1, 0)$, maximum at $(-3, 64)$
7. minimum at $(1, 0)$, maximum at $(5, 576)$
9. Minimum at $(-\frac{1}{2}, -1)$, maximum at $(1, \frac{1}{2})$.
13. No maximum or minimum. [For interval $-3 \le x \le 3$, minimum at $(-3, -49)$, maximum at $(3, 11)$.]
15. No maximum or minimum.

SECTION 6

1. length = width = 30; length = width = $\frac{1}{4}L$
3. height = $\frac{2}{3}\sqrt{3} R$; radius of base = $\frac{1}{3}\sqrt{6} R$
5. 7 and $17\frac{1}{2}$
7. $2'' \times 8'' \times 8''$
9. radius of semicircle = height of rectangle = $12/(4 + \pi)$
11. width = $2 + 2\sqrt{5}$; height = $3 + 3\sqrt{5}$
13. $(1, 2)$
15. $(-\frac{1}{2}, \pm\sqrt{2}/2)$
17. (a) base = $\frac{13}{2}$; height = $\frac{30}{13}$ (b) base = $\frac{1}{2}H$; height = $\dfrac{h}{2H}\sqrt{H^2 - h^2}$
19. Each number equals 10.
21. $\frac{9}{7}\sqrt{7}$ mi
23. $(2, 0)$

SECTION 7

1. (a) height = $\frac{10}{3}$; radius of base = 8
   (b) height = $\frac{1}{3}H$; radius of base = $2R/3$
3. altitude = $\sqrt{2} r$, r = radius of base
5. $2a^2/\sqrt{a^2 + b^2}$, $2b^2/\sqrt{a^2 + b^2}$
7. (a) $r = h = 2\sqrt[3]{2/\pi}$ (b) $r = h = \sqrt[3]{V/\pi}$
9. from $(5, 0)$ to $(0, 10)$
11. $2(\frac{16}{3})^{1/5}$; $8(\frac{16}{3})^{-1/5}$
13. (a) $\begin{cases} \text{radius of circle} = L/(2\pi + 8) \\ \text{side of square} = 2L/(2\pi + 8) \end{cases}$ (b) $\begin{cases} \text{radius of circle} = L/2\pi \\ \text{no square} \end{cases}$
15. height = $4R/3$; radius of base = $(2\sqrt{2}/3)R$
17. $\frac{13}{2}\sqrt{13}$ 19. $r = (3V/20\pi)^{1/3}$; $h = 6(3V/20\pi)^{1/3}$
21. $4(1 + 2^{2/3})^{3/2}$

SECTION 9

1. $dy = (3x^2 - 4x + 3)\,dx$

3. $dy = \dfrac{3x(x^2 + 6)}{\sqrt{x^2 + 8}}\,dx$

5. $dy = \dfrac{8x^2 - 15x + 2}{3(x^2 + 1)^{1/2}(2x - 5)^{2/3}}\,dx$

7. $df = 0.03; \Delta f = -0.0301$

9. $df = 0.180000; \Delta f = 0.180901$

11. $df = -0.01250; \Delta f = -0.01220$

13. $df = -0.05000; \Delta f = -0.04654$

15. 8.0625

17. 1.02000

19. 1.98750

21. 0.049

23. 1.67%, approximately

25. $6a^2t$ in^3 of paint

SECTION 10

1. $14(x^2 + 2x - 6)^6(x + 1)$

3. $6(3 - 2x)^{-4}$

5. $(3x - 1)(2x - 1)^{-1/2}$

7. $2(x + 1)(2x - 1)^2(5x + 2)$

9. $2(1 - x^2)(x^2 + 1)^{-2}$

11. $\frac{2}{3}x^{-1/3}(x + 1)^{-5/3}$

13. $-(x + 1)^{-1/2}(x - 1)^{-3/2}$

15. $\frac{2}{3}(1 - 2x^2)x^{-1/3}(x^2 + 1)^{-2}$

17. $(x - 7)(2x + 3)^{-1/2}(3x - 4)^{-4/3}$

19. $(4x + y + 2)/(-x + 2y + 3)$

21. $-y^{1/2}/x^{1/2}$

23. $(6x^2 - y^2 + 2)/(2xy + 3y^2 + 1)$

25. $-8\,\dfrac{(2u^2 + 2u + 1)r(r^2 + 5)^3}{u^2(u + 1)^2}$

27. $-\dfrac{(5x^3 + 6x^2 - 8x - 17)(3s^2 - 8)}{(y - 1)^2(x + 1)^{3/2}}$

SECTION 11

1. $5\sqrt{337}$ mi/hr

3. 1 in^2/min

5. $\frac{10}{3}$ ft/sec

7. $\dfrac{-150}{\sqrt{117}}$ ft/sec; $\dfrac{25}{\sqrt{10}}$ ft/sec

9. $\dfrac{6\sqrt{10}}{5}$

11. $\dfrac{dz}{dt} = \pm\frac{7}{6}$

13. 3.6 ft/sec

15. 0.12 ft/min

17. $\dfrac{1}{12\pi}$ ft/min

19. $\dfrac{5\sqrt{5}}{4}$ ft^2/min

21. $\dfrac{2}{\pi}$ ft/min

23. 2.4 ft/sec

25. $\frac{25}{3}$ ft/sec

CHAPTER 8

SECTION 2

1. 55   3. 20   5. $\frac{25}{12}$ 9. $\frac{3}{8}$ 11. 2

13. $\frac{7}{3}$ 15. $\frac{7}{3}$ 17. $\frac{1}{6}$ 21. $\frac{1}{5}$ 23. $\frac{2}{15}$

SECTION 3

1. $\underline{S}(\Delta) = 9.006; \overline{S}(\Delta) = 12.444$

3. $\underline{S}(\Delta) = 0.803; \overline{S}(\Delta) = 0.873$

5. $\underline{S}(\Delta) = 0.1588; \overline{S}(\Delta) = 0.2702$

7. $\underline{S}(\Delta) = 0.0321; \overline{S}(\Delta) = 2.171$

9. $\underline{S}(\Delta) = 1.000; \overline{S}(\Delta) = 7.000$

15. $\underline{S}(\Delta) \to \infty$ as $n \to \infty$

SECTION 4

3. Smallest value = 0; largest value = 12
5. Smallest value = $\frac{3}{5}$; largest value = $\frac{3}{2}$
7. Smallest value = 0; largest value = $\frac{64}{17}$
9. Smallest value = $3\sqrt{3}$; largest value = $3\sqrt{6}$
11. Smallest value = 0; largest value = 4
13. Smallest value = 0; largest value = $5\sqrt{5}$

SECTION 5

1. $\frac{2}{3}$ 3. 15 5. $\frac{20}{3}$ 7. $118\frac{2}{15}$
9. $\frac{100}{3}$ 11. $\frac{446}{135}$ 13. $x^3/3$
15. approx. = 2.330; exact = $2\frac{1}{3}$ 17. approx. = 0.497; exact = $\frac{1}{2}$
19. approx. = 10; exact = 10
21. approx. = exact = $(A/2)(b^2 - a^2) + B(b - a)$
25. approx. = 0.692⁻ 27. approx. = 0.793

SECTION 6

1. $f(-1 + \sqrt{7}) = 5$ 3. $f(3) = 6$
5. $f(0) = -6$, $f(2) = 8$, theorem does not apply.
7. $f(\frac{1}{4}) = \frac{1}{2}$, theorem applies as function is continuous.
9. $\xi = \frac{7}{2}$ 11. $\xi = (3 + \sqrt{129})/3$
13. $\xi = (3 - \sqrt{57})/12$ 15. $\xi = 0, \pm 1, \pm\sqrt{3}$
17. $\sqrt{14} - \sqrt{6}$ 19. $\frac{2}{3}$

21. $\int_{-b}^{b} f(x)\, dx = 2\int_{0}^{b} f(x)\, dx$

SECTION 7

1. $\frac{1}{14}(2x + 3)^7 + C$ 3. $\frac{3}{8}(2t + 1)^{4/3} + C$
5. $(3y + 1)^{1/3} + C$ 7. $\frac{3}{40}(2x^2 + 3)^{10/3} + C$

9. $-\frac{3}{4}(3 - 2x^2)^{1/3} + C$ 11. $\dfrac{-1}{6(3x^2 + 2)} + C$

13. $\frac{2}{9}(x^3 + 1)^{3/2} + C$ 15. $\frac{1}{2}(x^3 + 3x^2 + 1)^{2/3} + C$
17. $\frac{1}{40}(x^2 + 1)^4(4x^2 - 1) + C$ 19. $\frac{5}{612}(x^3 + 1)^{12/5}(12x^3 - 5) + C$
21. $\frac{33}{5}$ 23. $\frac{1}{4}$
25. $\frac{2}{3}(\sqrt{15} - 1)$ 27. $\frac{3}{5}[(\sqrt[3]{2} + 2)^5 - 243]$

SECTION 8

1. $12\frac{2}{3}$ 3. $\frac{46}{3}$ 5. 6 7. $\frac{3}{2}$
9. $\frac{4}{15}$ 11. $\frac{4}{3}(2\sqrt{2} - 1)$ 13. $3\frac{1}{3}$ 15. 72
17. $\frac{5}{12}$ 19. $10\frac{2}{3}$ 21. $7\frac{7}{48}$ 23. $\frac{3}{2}$
25. $\frac{5}{4} - (2^{-1/3} + \frac{1}{4} \cdot 4^{1/3})$ and $\frac{3}{2} - 2^{-1/3} - \frac{1}{4} \cdot 4^{1/3}$
27. $9\frac{1}{2}$ 29. $\frac{1}{3}$

SECTION 9

1. $\frac{197}{12}$ 3. $\frac{3}{20}$
5. 180 in.-lb 7. (a) 40 in.-lb; (b) 120 in.-lb
9. 2700 in.-lb; 8100 in.-lb 11. 400,000 ft-lb

13. $6562.5w$ ft-lb, $w = $ weight of one ft^3 of water

15. $\frac{40}{3}w$ ft-lb, $w = $ weight of one ft^3 of water

17. $4w$ ft-lb, $w = $ weight of one ft^3 of water   19. $\frac{7}{5}$ 21. $E/24$

SECTION 10

1. 625,000 lb   3. 125,000 lb   5. 2812.5 tons

7. 875,000 lb   9. $3,906.25\sqrt{2}$ lb   11. $266\frac{2}{3}$ lb

13. 6000 lb   15. $226.5w$ lb   17. $11,250ww\sqrt{3}$ lb

19. $169,600ww\sqrt{3}/3$ lb   23. (a) $10(4)^{5/7}$; (b) $216,000(1 - 4^{-2/7})$ ft-lb

CHAPTER 9

SECTION 1

1. 2   3. 1   5. 0   7. 2

9. 2   11. $\sqrt{61}/61$ 13. $\frac{9}{2}$ 15. 11

17. $(\frac{16}{3}, 0)$, $(-\frac{4}{3}, 0)$ 19. $(64, -44)$, $(4, -4)$

21. $x - 2y + 1 + 3\sqrt{5} = 0$; $x - 2y + 1 - 3\sqrt{5} = 0$

SECTION 2

1. $x - 3y + k = 0$ 3. $y = m(x - 2)$ 5. $y + 1 = m(x - 2)$

7. $x + y = a$ 9. $2x + y = 2a$ 11. $x/a + y/(10 - a) = 1$

13. $3x + 5y - 10 = 0$ 15. $28x - 7y + 35 = 0$ 17. $8x + y + 3 = 0$

19. $(17 \pm \sqrt{65})x + (25 \mp \sqrt{65})y - 6 \pm 12\sqrt{65} = 0$

SECTION 3

1. $x^2 + y^2 + 6x - 8y = 0$ 3. $x^2 + y^2 - 4x - 6y + 9 = 0$

5. $x^2 + y^2 - 12x - 8y + 44 = 0$ 7. $x^2 + y^2 - 6x - 8y + 9 = 0$

9. $x^2 + y^2 - 4x - 2y - 5 = 0$ 11. $x^2 + y^2 - 4x - 6y - 3 = 0$

13. $x^2 + y^2 + 12x - 12y + 36 = 0$ 15. circle; center at $(-3, 4)$, radius 5

17. point $(2, -1)$ 19. circle; center $(-\frac{3}{2}, \frac{5}{2})$, radius 3

21. circle; center $(-\frac{3}{4}, -\frac{5}{4})$, radius $\frac{3}{4}\sqrt{2}$

25. $x^2 + y^2 - 2x + 4y - 20 = 0$; $C(1, -2)$; $r = 5$

27. $x^2 + y^2 + 3x + 2y - 3 = 0$; $C(-\frac{3}{2}, -1)$; $r = \frac{5}{2}$

29. $7x^2 + 7y^2 - 19x + 15y - 58 = 0$ 31. $C(0, -1)$, $r = \sqrt{20}$

SECTION 4

1. $2x + y - 5 = 0$ 3. $9x - 8y - 26 = 0$ 5. $x + 2y + 4 = 0$

7. $5x + 8y - 38 = 0$ 9. $3x + 5y - 13 = 0$, $5x - 3y + 35 = 0$

11. No tangent lines as $P(3, 0)$ is inside circle.

13. There is no locus.   15. $x^2 + (y - k)^2 = 16$ 17. $x^2 + y^2 + kx = 0$

19. $x^2 + y^2 - 2hx - 6hy - 8h - \frac{8}{5} = 0$

23. $x = (1 \pm \sqrt{39})/10$; $y = (9 \pm \sqrt{39})/10$

25. $x = -1 \pm \frac{1}{12}\sqrt{251}$, $y = \frac{7}{12}$

27. $3x^2 + 3y^2 - 26x - 4y + 55 = 0$; circle

SECTION 6

1. amp. $= 2$; per. $= 4\pi$
5. amp. $= 3$, per. $= 3\pi$
9. amp. $= 2$, per. $= \pi$
13. amp. $= 3$, per. $= 4\pi$
17. per. $= \pi/2$
21. per. $= 4\pi$

3. amp. $= \quad 4$; per. $= 4$
7. amp. $= \quad 2$; per. $= \pi$
11. amp. $= \quad 4$, per. $= \pi$
15. amp. $= \quad 1$; per. $= \pi$
19. amp. $= \sqrt{2}$, per. $= 2\pi$
23. amp. $= \quad 4$, per. $= \pi$

SECTION 7

1. $\tan \phi = 3$
7. $\tan \phi = -\frac{3}{2}$
9. $\tan \phi = \frac{7}{4}$

3. $\tan \phi = -7$

5. $\tan \phi = -\frac{5}{12}$

11. $\tan \angle CAB = 8$; $\tan \angle ABC = \frac{2}{3}$; $\tan \angle ACB = 2$
13. $\tan \angle CAB = 1$; $\tan \angle ABC = 2$; $\tan \angle ACB = 3$
17. $3x + 4y - 5 = 0$, $x = -1$
19. $(\sqrt{3} - 1)x + (\sqrt{3} + 1)y + 3\sqrt{3} + 1 = 0$;
$\quad (\sqrt{3} + 1)x + (\sqrt{3} - 1)y + 3\sqrt{3} - 1 = 0$
21. -6; no
23. $\frac{8}{15}$
25. $4x - 7y = 0$; $7x + 4y = 0$;
27. $2x + y = 0$; $x - 2y = 0$
29. $x - 7y + 5 = 0$
31. $x - (3 + \sqrt{10})y + 10 + 3\sqrt{10} = 0$

SECTION 8

1. $x = \frac{2}{3}$; $y = \frac{2}{3}$
7. none
13. $x = (n - \frac{1}{6})\pi$, $n = 0, \pm 1, \pm 2, \ldots$
15. $x = (2n + 1)\pi/2$, $n = 0, \pm 1, \pm 2, \ldots$
19. $x = \pm 2y$

3. none
9. $y = 0$

21. $y = \pm x - 2$

5. $x = -1$, $y = 0$
11. $y = -1$

17. none
23. $y = x$

CHAPTER 10

SECTION 1

1. Focus $(2, 0)$, dir.: $x = -2$
5. Focus $(-\frac{7}{8}, 0)$, dir.: $x = \frac{7}{8}$
9. $x^2 = -8y$
13. $y^2 = \frac{9}{2}x$

3. Focus $(-3, 0)$, dir.: $x = 3$
7. $y^2 = -12x$
11. $x^2 = -6y$

15. Vertex: $(1, 2)$; focus: $(1, 2\frac{1}{4})$; directrix: $y = 1\frac{3}{4}$; axis: $x = 1$
17. Vertex: $(1, 7)$; focus $(1, 6\frac{7}{8})$; directrix: $y = 7\frac{1}{8}$; axis: $x = 1$
19. Vertex $(-6, 1)$; focus $(-6\frac{1}{4}, 1)$; directrix: $x = -5\frac{3}{4}$; axis: $y = 1$
21. Vertex $(-\frac{3}{2}, 2)$; focus $(-2, 2)$; directrix: $x = -1$; axis: $y = 2$
23. $y^2 = 12x - 36$
25. $x^2 = 32 - 8y$
27. $4x^2 + 4xy + y^2 + 4x + 32y + 16 = 0$
29. $32x - 8y - 17 = 0$
31. $y = -\frac{1}{4}x^2 + 4x - 3$

SECTION 2

1. $3x - 2y + 3 = 0$
5. $3x - 2y - 4 = 0$
9. $4x + 5y - 24 = 0$; $4x - 5y - 9 = 0$
11. $2x + (5 \pm \sqrt{29})y - 27 \mp 5\sqrt{29} = 0$

3. $x - 6y - 4 = 0$
7. $8x - y + 9 = 0$

13. $2x + (-5 \pm \sqrt{29})y - 27 \pm 5\sqrt{29} = 0$
15. $(1 \pm \sqrt{37})x + 6y + 19 \pm \sqrt{37} = 0$
17. $x - 3y - 4 = 0;\ x - 11y - 12 = 0$
19. No tangents
23. $\left(-\frac{36}{5}, -\frac{108}{25}\right)$

SECTION 3

	a	b	c	e	foci	vertices
1	5	4	3	$\frac{3}{5}$	$(\pm 3, 0)$	$(\pm 5, 0)$
3	4	3	$\sqrt{7}$	$\sqrt{7}/4$	$(\pm\sqrt{7}, 0)$	$(\pm 4, 0)$
5	$\sqrt{3}$	$\sqrt{2}$	1	$1/\sqrt{3}$	$(0, \pm 1)$	$(0, \pm\sqrt{3})$
7	$\sqrt{5}$	$\sqrt{2}$	$\sqrt{3}$	$\sqrt{\frac{3}{5}}$	$(0, \pm\sqrt{3})$	$(0, \pm\sqrt{5})$
9	$\sqrt{\frac{11}{2}}$	$\sqrt{\frac{11}{3}}$	$\sqrt{\frac{11}{6}}$	$1/\sqrt{3}$	$(\pm\sqrt{\frac{11}{6}}, 0)$	$(\pm\sqrt{\frac{11}{2}}, 0)$

11. $9x^2 + 25y^2 = 225$
15. $25x^2 + 9y^2 = 225$
19. $x^2 + 2y^2 = 18$
23. $3(x - 6)^2 + 4y^2 = 108$

13. $100x^2 + 36y^2 = 3600$
17. $7x^2 + 15y^2 = 247$
21. $16x^2 + 7y^2 = 688$

SECTION 4

1. $x^2 + 3y^2 = 24$
5. $144x^2 + 95y^2 = 4655$
9. $3x^2 + 4y^2 - 20x + 28 = 0$; major axis: $y = 0$; minor axis: $x = \frac{10}{3}$
11. $\sqrt{2}\,x - 6y - 9\sqrt{2} = 0$

3. $7x^2 + 3y^2 = 84$
7. $8x^2 + 9y^2 - 648 = 0$
13. $9\sqrt{5}\,x - 12y - 10\sqrt{5} = 0$

SECTION 5

	a	b	c	e	foci	vertices
1	3	4	5	$\frac{5}{3}$	$(\pm 5, 0)$	$(\pm 3, 0)$
3	5	12	13	$\frac{13}{5}$	$(0, \pm 13)$	$(0, \pm 5)$
5	$\sqrt{3}$	$\sqrt{2}$	$\sqrt{5}$	$\sqrt{\frac{5}{3}}$	$(\pm\sqrt{5}, 0)$	$(\pm\sqrt{3}, 0)$
7	$\sqrt{2}$	$\sqrt{5}$	$\sqrt{7}$	$\sqrt{\frac{7}{2}}$	$(\pm\sqrt{7}, 0)$	$(\pm\sqrt{2}, 0)$
9	$\sqrt{\frac{1}{3}}$	$\sqrt{\frac{1}{2}}$	$\sqrt{\frac{5}{6}}$	$\sqrt{\frac{5}{2}}$	$(\pm\sqrt{\frac{5}{6}}, 0)$	$(\pm\sqrt{\frac{1}{3}}, 0)$

11. $24x^2 - 25y^2 = 600$
15. $4x^2 - y^2 = 32$
19. $4y^2 - 5x^2 = 19$
23. $252(x - 6)^2 - 4y^2 = 63$

13. $9x^2 - 7y^2 + 343 = 0$
17. $y^2 - x^2 = 5$
21. $15x^2 - y^2 = 15$

SECTION 6

	a	b	c	e	foci	vertices	directrices	asymptotes
1	3	2	$\sqrt{13}$	$\sqrt{13}/3$	$(\pm\sqrt{13}, 0)$	$(\pm 3, 0)$	$x = \pm\dfrac{9}{\sqrt{13}}$	$y = \pm 2x/3$
3	2	1	$\sqrt{5}$	$\sqrt{5}/2$	$(\pm\sqrt{5}, 0)$	$(\pm 2, 0)$	$x = \pm\dfrac{4}{\sqrt{5}}$	$y = \pm x/2$
5	1	1	$\sqrt{2}$	$\sqrt{2}$	$(\pm\sqrt{2}, 0)$	$(\pm 1, 0)$	$x = \pm 1/\sqrt{2}$	$y = \pm x$
7	5	$\sqrt{8}$	$\sqrt{33}$	$\sqrt{33}/5$	$(0, \pm\sqrt{33})$	$(0, \pm 5)$	$y = \pm\dfrac{25}{\sqrt{33}}$	$y = \pm 5x/\sqrt{8}$

9. $4x^2 - y^2 = 144$
11. $63x^2 - 81y^2 = 448$
13. $400x^2 - 225y^2 = (72)^2$
15. $9x^2 - 4y^2 = 189$
17. $y^2 - x^2 = 2$
19. $x = -(45 + 9\sqrt{10})/(5 - 4\sqrt{10})$, $y = 90/(5 - 4\sqrt{10})$
23. $25x^2 - 16y^2 + 400 = 0$
27. $R: 11y \pm \sqrt{22}\, x \mp 4\sqrt{22} = 0$

SECTION 7

1. $(7, -1)$, $(1, 3)$, $(-3, -\frac{5}{2})$, $(-2, -6)$
3. $3x' - 7y' = 0$, $2x' - 5y' = 0$
5. Ellipse; center $(-1, 2)$; vertices $(-1, 7)$, $(-1, -3)$; foci $(-1, 5)$, $(-1, -1)$; $e = \frac{3}{5}$; directrices $y = \frac{31}{3}, -\frac{19}{3}$
7. Hyperbola; vertices $(-1, 5)$, $(-1, 1)$; foci $(-1, 2 \pm \sqrt{13})$; $e = \sqrt{13}/3$; directrices $y = 2 \pm 9\sqrt{13}/13$; asymptotes $y - 2 = \pm\frac{3}{2}(x + 1)$
9. Ellipse; vertices $(2, 2)$, $(-4, 2)$; foci $(-1 \pm \sqrt{5}, 2)$; $e = \sqrt{5}/3$; directrices $x = -1 \pm 9/\sqrt{5}$
11. Ellipse; vertices $(1, -\frac{5}{2})$, $(1, \frac{1}{2})$; foci $(1, -1 \pm \sqrt{5}/2)$; $e = \sqrt{5}/3$; directrices $y = -1 \pm 9/2\sqrt{5}$
13. Ellipse; vertices $(0, -1)$, $(4, -1)$; foci $(1, -1)$, $(3, -1)$; $e = \frac{1}{2}$; directrices $x = 6, -2$
15. Hyperbola; vertices $(-3, -2)$, $(1, -2)$; foci $(-1 \pm \sqrt{10}, -2)$; $e = \sqrt{10}/2$; directrices $x = -1 \pm \frac{2}{5}\sqrt{10}$; asymptotes: $y + 2 = \pm(\sqrt{6}/2)(x + 1)$
17. Two intersecting lines: $y - 2 = \pm\frac{2}{3}\sqrt{3}(x + 1)$
19. $16x^2 + 7y^2 - 64x - 14y - 41 = 0$
21. $x^2 - 5y^2 - 2x + 10y - 20 = 0$
23. $(y + 1)^2 = 6(x - \frac{7}{2})$
25. Ellipse; $4x^2 + 3y^2 - 16x - 12y + 16 = 0$
27. Circle; $x^2 + y^2 + 12x - 10y + 29 = 0$

SECTION 8

1. $5(x')^2 = 9$; locus consists of lines $x + 2y = \pm 3$
3. $x'^2 - y'^2 = 10$; hyperbola; vertices $(3, 1)$, $(-3, -1)$;

5. $x'^2 = 4\sqrt{2}\,y'$; parabola; focus $(1, -1)$; directrix $x - y + 2 = 0$

7. $17x'^2 + 4y'^2 = 884$; ellipse; vertices $(-3\sqrt{17}, 2\sqrt{17}), (3\sqrt{17}, -2\sqrt{17})$

9. $y'^2(1 + \sqrt{5}) - x'^2(-1 + \sqrt{5}) = 20$; hyperbola;

vertices $\left(\pm\sqrt{2\sqrt{5}}, \ \mp\sqrt{3\sqrt{5} - 5}\right)$

11. $x'^2(13 - 3\sqrt{13}) - y'^2(13 + 3\sqrt{13}) = 2\sqrt{13}$; hyperbola;

vertices $\left(\pm\left(\dfrac{\sqrt{13}+3}{\sqrt{13}-3}\right)\left(\dfrac{25}{13}\right)^{1/4}, \ \pm\left(\dfrac{25}{13}\right)^{1/4}\right)$

13. $4x''^2 - y''^2 = 0$; locus is the two lines $3x + y - 5 = 0$, $x + 3y + 1 = 0$

15. $x''^2 = -4\sqrt{5}\,y''$; parabola; vertex is at $(-1, 3)$; focus at $(0, 1)$; directrix $x - 2y + 12 = 0$

17. $28x''^2 + 3y''^2 = 0$; locus is the single point $(-\tfrac{3}{2}, 2)$

19. $9x''^2 + 4y''^2 = 36$; ellipse; center at $(2, -4)$

21. $3y''^2 - x''^2 = \tfrac{1}{3}(22 + 12\sqrt{3})$; hyperbola; center at $(-2\sqrt{3}/3, -\tfrac{4}{3} + \sqrt{3})$

CHAPTER 11

SECTION 2

1. 3

3. $\tfrac{4}{7}$

5. $\tfrac{1}{4}$

7. 1

9. 0

11. $\tfrac{1}{8}$

13. $f'(x) = 3 \sec^2 3x$

15. $f'(s) = 2s \sec(s^2) \tan(s^2)$

17. $f'(y) = -\csc^3 \tfrac{1}{3}y \cot \tfrac{1}{3}y$

19. $f'(x) = -2 \cot^2 2x$

21. $x'(s) = \sec^2 2s/\sqrt{\tan 2s}$

23. $f'(x) = x \tan \tfrac{1}{2}x(x \sec^2 \tfrac{1}{2}x + 2 \tan \tfrac{1}{2}x)$

25. $f'(x) = 2 \sec 2x \tan^3 2x$

27. $f'(x) = 2(x \cos 2x - \sin 2x)/x^3$

29. $f'(x) = -2 \cos 3x[x \cos 3x + 3(1 + x^2) \sin 3x]/(1 + x^2)^2$

31. $f'(x) = -6 \csc^3 2x \cos 3x \,(\cos 3x \cot 2x + \sin 3x)$

33. $f'(x) = -2 \cot ax[(1 + x^2)a \csc^2 ax + x \cot ax]/(1 + x^2)^2$

35. $f'(x) = \sin 4x(1 + \sin^2 2x)^{-1/2}$

37. $f'(x) = -\sin x \cos(\cos x)$

39. $f'(x) = -\dfrac{[x(1 + \cos^2 3x) + (1 + x^2) \sin 6x]}{(1 + x^2)^{3/2}(1 + \cos^2 3x)^{2/3}}$

SECTION 3

1. $-\tfrac{1}{7} \cos 7x$

3. $2 \tan [(x - 5)/2] + C$

5. $-\tfrac{1}{2} \csc 2x + C$

7. $-\tfrac{1}{2} \cot (2x - 6) - x + C$

9. $-\cos x(1 - \tfrac{2}{3} \cos^2 x + \tfrac{1}{5} \cos^4 x) + C$

11. $-\tfrac{1}{2} \cos (x^2) + C$

13. $\tfrac{1}{4} \sec^4 x + C$

15. $\tfrac{1}{6} \tan^6 x + C$

17. $-\tfrac{1}{6} \tan^3 (3 - 2x) + C$

19. $\tfrac{1}{2}x - \tfrac{1}{12} \sin 6x + C$

SECTION 4

1. There is inverse function; domain $-\infty < y < \infty$

3. There is inverse function; domain $-\infty < y < \infty$

5. No inverse function

7. There is inverse function; domain: $-\infty < y < 3$

9. There is inverse function; domain: $1 \le y < \infty$

11. Domain: $-2 \le x < \infty$ or $-\infty < x \le -2$.
Inverse functions are $g(y) = -2 \pm \sqrt{5 + y}$; Domain: $-5 \le y < \infty$
13. Domain: $-\frac{3}{4} \le x < \infty$ or $-\infty < x \le -\frac{3}{4}$.
Inverse functions are $g(y) = -\frac{3}{4} \pm \frac{1}{4}\sqrt{8y - 23}$; domain: $\frac{23}{8} \le y < \infty$
15. Domain: $-\infty < x < \infty$, $x \ne -1$.
Inverse function is $g(y) = y/(1 - y)$; domain: $-\infty < y < \infty$, $y \ne 1$
17. Domain: $-\infty < x < \infty$, $x \ne -2$.
Inverse function is $g(y) = (2y + 1)/(2 - y)$; domain: $-\infty < y < \infty$, $y \ne 2$
19. If domain is $1 \le x < \infty$, function has inverse with domain $2 \le y < \infty$. If domain is $-3 \le x \le 1$, function has inverse with domain $2 \le y \le 34$. If domain is $-\infty < x \le -3$, function has inverse with domain $-\infty < y \le 34$.
21. If domain is $-\infty < x < \infty$, function has an inverse with domain $-\infty < y < \infty$.

SECTION 5

1. (a) $\pi/3$; (b) $3\pi/4$; (c) $-\pi/4$ 3. (a) $\pi/6$; (b) $\pi/3$; (c) $-\pi/6$
5. $f'(x) = 2/(1 + 4x^2)$ 7. $\phi'(y) = -1/2\sqrt{y - y^2}$

9. $\dfrac{dy}{dx} = \arccos x - \dfrac{x}{\sqrt{1 - x^2}}$

11. $f'(x) = -\dfrac{3(1 + x^2) + 2x(1 + 9x^2)\operatorname{arccot} 3x}{(1 + 9x^2)(1 + x^2)^2}$

13. $f'(x) = 1/(1 + x^2)$ 15. $f'(x) = 1/(1 + x^2)$
17. $f'(x) = \arcsin 2x$ 19. $f'(x) = \sqrt{x^2 - 4}/x$
21. $f'(x) = 3/(5 + 4\cos x)$ 23. $f'(x) = 0$

SECTION 6

1. $\frac{1}{3}\arcsin 3x + C$ 3. $\operatorname{arcsec} 2x + C$ 5. $\dfrac{1}{\sqrt{7}}\arctan\sqrt{7}x + C$

7. $\frac{1}{2}\operatorname{arcsec}\frac{1}{2}x + C$ 9. $\dfrac{1}{\sqrt{10}}\operatorname{arcsec}\dfrac{x}{\sqrt{5}} + C$ 11. $\pi/2$

13. $\pi/6$ 15. $\pi/2$

SECTION 7

1. $\ln 4 = 1.38630$; $\ln 5 = 1.60944$; $\ln 6 = 1.79176$; $\ln 8 = 2.07945$; $\ln 9 = 2.19722$
3. $\ln 24 = 3.17806$; $\ln 25 = 3.21888$; $\ln 27 = 3.29583$; $\ln 30 = 3.40120$; $\ln 32 = 3.46575$
5. $\ln \sqrt{30} = 1.70060$; $\ln \sqrt[3]{270} = 1.86614$; $\ln \sqrt{\frac{2}{3}} = -0.20273$; $\ln \sqrt[4]{7.2} = 0.49352$
17. $f'(x) = 4/x$ 19. $f'(x) = 3(x^2 - 1)/(x^3 - 3x + 1)$
21. $h'(x) = 2\tan 2x$ 23. $F'(x) = 4(\ln x)^3/x$
25. $G'(x) = 1 + \ln x$ 27. $f'(x) = (x^2 + a^2)^{-1/2}$
29. $H'(x) = -4x/(x^4 - 1)$
31. $f'(x) = 2\ln x(1 + x^2 - x^2 \ln x)/x(1 + x^2)^2$
33. 0.91629   35. 0.47001   37. 1.09861   39. 0.47001

SECTION 8

15. (a) 4; (b) 2; (c) -5 17. (a) 0; (b) -2; (c) 1
23. $\ln 8/\ln 3$; $\ln 12/\ln 7$; $\ln 15/\ln 2$ 25. 2.522
27. -1.113 29. 1.613

SECTION 9

1. $f'(x) = 2e^{2x}$

3. $f'(x) = x^3 e^{-3x}(4 - 3x)$

5. $G'(x) = e^{2x}(1/x + 2 \ln x)$

7. $g'(x) = e^{\tan x} \sec^2 x$

9. $f'(x) = 3^{5x} 5 \ln 3$

11. $f'(x) = 2^{-7x}[3x^2 - 7(x^3 + 3) \ln 2]$

13. $F'(x) = x^{-1+\sin x}(\sin x + x \cos x \ln x)$

15. $G'(x) = x^{\sqrt{x}}(2 + \ln x)/2\sqrt{x}$

17. $H'(x) = (\ln x)^x[\ln (\ln x) + (1/\ln x)]$

19. $f'(x) = \left[\dfrac{2}{x} + \dfrac{1}{2x + 3} - \dfrac{8x}{x^2 + 1}\right] f(x)$

21. $g'(x) = \frac{1}{2}g(x)\left(\dfrac{1}{x + 2} + \dfrac{1}{x + 3} - \dfrac{1}{x + 1}\right)$

23. $g'(x) = g(x)\left[\dfrac{2}{x} + \dfrac{1}{(1 + x^2) \arctan x} - \dfrac{2x}{1 + x^2}\right]$

SECTION 11

1. tan: $x - 2y - 1 + \pi/2 = 0$; norm: $2x + y - 2 - \pi/4 = 0$

3. tan: $x + 2\sqrt{3}\,y + 2 + \frac{4}{3}\pi\sqrt{3} = 0$; norm: $2\sqrt{3}\,x - y + 4\sqrt{3} - \frac{2}{3}\pi = 0$

5. tan: $x - ey = 0$; norm: $ex + y - 1 - e^2 = 0$

7. tan: $2x - y - e = 0$; norm: $x + 2y - 3e = 0$

9. $(\frac{1}{2}\sqrt{2}, \pi/4)$; $\tan \theta = 2\sqrt{2}$

11. $(\ln 2, 4)$; $\tan \theta = \frac{4}{33}$

13. $(1, \pi/4)$; $\tan \theta = 2$

15. $(0, 0)$, $\tan \theta = 1$ and $(1, e^{-1})$, $\tan \theta = e^{-1}$

17. Rel. max. at $(1, e^{-1})$, point of inflection: $(2, 2e^{-2})$; f increasing for $-\infty < x \leq 1$; decreasing for $1 \leq x < \infty$; concave downward for $-\infty < x \leq 2$; concave upward for $2 \leq x < \infty$.

19. Rel. max. at $(0, 1)$; points of inflection: $(\frac{1}{2}\sqrt{2}, e^{-1/2})$, $(-\frac{1}{2}\sqrt{2}, e^{-1/2})$; concave downward for $-\frac{1}{2}\sqrt{2} \leq x \leq \frac{1}{2}\sqrt{2}$; concave upward for $-\infty < x \leq -\frac{1}{2}\sqrt{2}$; $\frac{1}{2}\sqrt{2} \leq x < \infty$. Increasing for $-\infty < x \leq 0$, decreasing for $0 \leq x < \infty$.

21. Rel. max. at $(1, e^{-1})$, $(-1, e^{-1})$; rel. min. at $(0, 0)$. Increasing for $-\infty < x \leq -1$ and $0 \leq x \leq 1$; decreasing for $-1 \leq x \leq 0$ and $1 \leq x < \infty$. Points of inflection at $x_1 = -\frac{1}{2}(5 + \sqrt{17})^{1/2}$, $x_2 = -\frac{1}{2}(5 - \sqrt{17})^{1/2}$, $x_3 = \frac{1}{2}(5 - \sqrt{17})^{1/2}$, $x_4 = \frac{1}{2}(5 + \sqrt{17})^{1/2}$; concave upward for $-\infty < x \leq x_1$, $x_2 \leq x \leq x_3$, $x_4 \leq x < \infty$; concave downward for $x_1 \leq x \leq x_2$, $x_3 \leq x \leq x_4$.

23. Rel. min. at $(e^{-1}, -e^{-1})$; decreasing for $0 < x \leq 1/e$, increasing for $1/e \leq x < \infty$, concave upward for all $x > 0$.

25. Rel. max. at $(e^{-2}, 8e^{-2})$; rel. min. at $(1, 0)$; increasing for $0 < x \leq e^{-2}$, $1 \leq x < \infty$, decreasing for $e^{-2} \leq x \leq 1$. Inflection point: $(e^{-1}, 2e^{-1})$; concave downward for $0 < x \leq e^{-1}$; concave upward for $e^{-1} \leq x < \infty$.

27. Rel. max. at $(-\pi/4, e^{\pi/4}\frac{1}{2}\sqrt{2})$; rel. min. at $(3\pi/4, -\frac{1}{2}\sqrt{2}\,e^{-3\pi/4})$, decreasing for $-\pi/4 \leq x \leq 3\pi/4$; increasing for $3\pi/4 \leq x \leq 7\pi/4$. Inflection points at $(0, 1)$ and $(\pi, -e^{-\pi})$, concave upward for $0 \leq x \leq \pi$; concave downward for $\pi \leq x \leq 2\pi$. Pattern repeats in each interval of length 2π, but the function f is not periodic.

29. $(52\pi/3)$ mi/min

31. 440 ft/sec

33. $(3/26)$ rad/sec

35. width $\geq 5\sqrt{5}$ ft

37. $\pi(6 - 2\sqrt{6})/3$ rad for any radius

39. $\dfrac{ds}{dt} = \dfrac{200}{\sqrt{34}}$ ft/sec if $t = 1$; $\lim\limits_{t \to 0} \dfrac{ds}{dt} = 20\sqrt{2}$

SECTION 12

19. $\cosh x = \frac{5}{3}$; $\sinh x = -\frac{4}{3}$; $\coth x = -\frac{5}{4}$; $\operatorname{sech} x = \frac{3}{5}$; $\operatorname{csch} x = -\frac{3}{4}$

21. $\sinh x = -\frac{1}{2}$; $\cosh x = \sqrt{5}/2$; $\tanh x = -1/\sqrt{5}$; $\coth x = -\sqrt{5}$; $\operatorname{sech} x = 2/\sqrt{5}$

23. $\sinh x = -\sqrt{3}$; $\tanh x = -\sqrt{3}/2$; $\coth x = -2/\sqrt{3}$; $\operatorname{sech} x = \frac{1}{2}$; $\operatorname{csch} x = -1/\sqrt{3}$

25. Minimum point at $(0, 1)$, concave upward for all x.

27. No max. or min.; concave downward for $x < 0$; concave upward for $x > 0$; $x = 0$ and $y = \pm 1$ are asymptotes.

29. No max. or min.; concave downward for $x > 1$; concave upward for $x < 1$.

SECTION 13

1. $\ln(\frac{1}{2} + \frac{1}{2}\sqrt{5})$ 3. $\ln(2 + \sqrt{3})$ 5. $\ln 3$

7. No max. or min.; $(0, 0)$ is a point of inflection; concave downward for $x \geq 0$; concave upward for $x \leq 0$.

9. No max. or min.; $(0, 0)$ is a point of inflection; concave upward for $0 \leq x < 2$; concave downward for $-2 < x \leq 0$.

11. No rel. max. or min.; point of inflection at $x = \sqrt{2}/8$; concave downward for $\sqrt{2}/8 \leq x < \frac{1}{4}$, concave upward for $0 < x \leq \sqrt{2}/8$.

13. $f'(x) = 2/\sqrt{1 + 4x^2}$

15. $g'(x) = -x^{-2} \operatorname{argtanh} x^2 + [2/(1 - x^4)]$

17. $G'(x) = \sec x$

19. $f'(x) = (4/\sqrt{4x^2 + 1}) \operatorname{argsinh}(2x)$ 21. $\ln(5 + 2\sqrt{6}) - \ln(2 + \sqrt{3})$

23. $\ln(\sqrt{2} - 1) - \ln(\sqrt{5} - 2)$ 25. $\ln(5 + \sqrt{21}) - \ln(3 + \sqrt{5})$

CHAPTER 12

SECTION 1

1. $5x + 2y = 0$ 3. $xy = 1$

5. $(x + 1)^2 + (y - 2)^2 = 4$ 7. $x^{2/3} + y^{2/3} = \sqrt[3]{4}$

9. $4(x - 2)^2 - 9(y + 1)^2 = 36$

11. $x^2 - 2xy + y^2 - 7x + 6y + 11 = 0$

13. $x^2 + y^2 = 25$ 15. $xy = 1$

17.

t	2	4	6	8	10
x	800	1600	2400	3200	4000
y	536	944	1224	1376	1400

19. $x = a\theta - b\sin\theta$, $y = a - b\cos\theta$

SECTION 2

1. $\dfrac{dy}{dx} = -\dfrac{5}{3}$; $\dfrac{d^2y}{dx^2} = 0$

3. $\dfrac{dy}{dx} = \dfrac{3t^2 + 2}{2t}$; $\dfrac{d^2y}{dx^2} = \dfrac{3t^2 - 2}{4t^3}$

5. $\dfrac{dy}{dx} = te^{-2t}$; $\dfrac{d^2y}{dx^2} = e^{-4t}\dfrac{1 - 2t}{2}$

7. $\dfrac{dy}{dx} = -\cos t$; $\dfrac{d^2y}{dx^2} = -\frac{1}{4}$

9. $\dfrac{dy}{dx} = -\tan\theta$; $\dfrac{d^2y}{dx^2} = \dfrac{1}{3a\sin\theta\cos^4\theta}$

11. $\dfrac{dy}{dx} = 2t;\ \dfrac{d^2y}{dx^2} = \dfrac{2}{3t^2 + 1};\ \dfrac{d^3y}{dx^3} = \dfrac{-12t}{(3t^2 + 1)^3};\ \dfrac{d^4y}{dx^4} = 12\,\dfrac{15t^2 - 1}{(3t^2 + 1)^5}$

13. tangent: $7x + 2y - 11 = 0$; normal: $2x - 7y - 94 = 0$

15. tangent: $x + 2y - 5 = 0$; normal: $4x - 2y - 5 = 0$

17. tangent: $x + ey - 2 = 0$; normal: $ex - y + 2/e = 0$

19. tangent: $x + y - \sqrt{2} = 0$; normal: $x - y = 0$

21. x increasing on $(-\pi/2, \pi/2)$ and on $(\pi/2, 3\pi/2)$, y decreasing on $-\pi/2 < \phi \le 0$, $\pi \le \phi < 3\pi/2$; y increasing on $0 \le \phi < \pi/2$ and on $\pi/2 < \phi \le \pi$; $4y^2 - x^2 = 4$.

23. x decreasing for $t \le -1$, x increasing for $t \ge -1$, y decreasing for $t \le -\tfrac{1}{2}$, y increasing for $t \ge -\tfrac{1}{2}$; $x^2 - 2xy + y^2 + x - 2y = 0$.

25. x increasing for all t; y increasing for all t; $(y - 1)^2 = 1/(x - 1)$.

SECTION 3

1. $\tfrac{1}{27}(31\sqrt{31} - 8)$

3. $\tfrac{14}{3}$

5. π

7. $\tfrac{9}{2}(4)^{1/3} - \tfrac{9}{2}$

9. $\sqrt{2}(1 - e^{-\pi/2})$

11. $\displaystyle\int_1^2 \sqrt{1 + 9x^4}\ dx$

13. $\dfrac{1}{2}\displaystyle\int_1^2 \dfrac{x + 1}{\sqrt{x}}\ dx$

15. $\displaystyle\int_1^5 \sqrt{9t^4 + 16t^2 - 4t + 5}\ dt$

17. $\dfrac{1}{5}\displaystyle\int_0^5 \sqrt{\dfrac{625 - 9x^2}{25 - x^2}}\ dx$

19. 8.51

21. 3.13

23. 1.52

25. 10.4

SECTION 4

1. $\kappa = -\tfrac{1}{2}(x + 1)^{-3/2};\ R = 2(x + 1)^{3/2}$

3. $\kappa = 2(1 + 4x^2)^{-3/2};\ R = \tfrac{1}{2}(1 + 4x^2)^{3/2}$

5. $\kappa = -\sin x(1 + \cos^2 x)^{-3/2};\ R = |\csc x|(1 + \cos^2 x)^{3/2}$

7. $\kappa = a^{-1}\operatorname{sech}^2(x/a);\ R = a\cosh^2(x/a)$

9. $\kappa = x(2 - x^2)^{-3/2};\ R = |x|^{-1}(2 - x^2)^{3/2}$

11. $\kappa = -a^4b(a^4 - c^2x^2)^{-3/2}$ with $c^2 = a^2 - b^2$
$R = a^{-4}b^{-1}(a^4 - c^2x^2)^{3/2}$

13. $\kappa = -2\csc^2 y \cot y(1 + \csc^4 y)^{-3/2}$
$R = \tfrac{1}{2}|\sin^2 y \tan y|(1 + \csc^4 y)^{3/2}$

15. $\kappa = -1/a;\ R = |a|$

17. $\kappa = |t|^{-1}(1 + t^2)^{-3/2}$

19. $\kappa = -2^{-1/2}e^{-t}$

21. $\kappa = -1/3|a \sin \theta \cos \theta|$

23. $\kappa = (1 + x^2)^{-3/2}$, max. at $x = 0$

25. $\kappa = 2x^3(1 + x^4)^{-3/2}$, max. at $x = \pm 1$

29. $\kappa = -\tfrac{4}{7} \cdot 7^{-1/2};\ x_c = (\pi/3) - 7\sqrt{3}/4,\ y_c = -3$

31. $\kappa = \dfrac{1}{2\sqrt{2}};\ x_c = -2,\ y_c = 3$

33. $x_c = a^{-1}c^2 \sec^3 t,\ y_c = -b^{-1}c^2 \tan^3 t$

CHAPTER 13

SECTION 1

1. $(2\sqrt{3}, 2)$, $(-\frac{3}{2}\sqrt{2}, \frac{3}{2}\sqrt{2})$, $(-2, 0)$, $(1, 0)$, $(2, 0)$
3. $(-1, 0)$, $(\sqrt{3}, -1)$, $(2, -2\sqrt{3})$, $(\frac{3}{2}\sqrt{2}, -\frac{3}{2}\sqrt{2})$, $(0, 0)$
5. $(3\sqrt{2}, \pi/4)$, $(4, \pi/2)$, $(2, 2\pi/3)$, $(1, -\pi/2)$, $(2, 0)$
7. $(2\sqrt{2}, 3\pi/4)$, $(3\sqrt{2}, -\pi/4)$, $(2, 5\pi/6)$, $(4, \pi/6)$, $(4, \pi/3)$
11. $\sqrt{13}$

SECTION 2

1. symmetric with respect to x-axis   3. symmetric with respect to y-axis
5. none   7. symmetric with respect to x-axis
9. symmetric with respect to y-axis   11. symmetric with respect to x-axis
13. symmetric with respect to y-axis
15. symmetric with respect to x-, y-axes and origin
17. symmetric with respect to x-, y-axes and origin
19. symmetric with respect to x-axis   21. symmetric with respect to x-axis
23. symmetric with respect to x-axis, y-axis and origin
25. symmetric with respect to x-axis, y-axis and origin
27. symmetric with respect to y-axis   29. symmetric with respect to x-axis
31. symmetric with respect to y-axis

SECTION 3

1. $r \cos \theta = 3$ 3. $\sin \theta + \cos \theta = 0$
5. $r(3 \cos \theta + \sqrt{3} \sin \theta) = 6$ 7. $r^2 \sin 2\theta = 8$
9. $r + 2 \cos \theta - 4 \sin \theta = 0$ 11. $r + 2 \cos \theta + 6 \sin \theta = 0$
13. $\sqrt{x^2 + y^2} = 7$ 15. $x^2 + y^2 = 3x$
17. $x = 5$ 19. $x + y = 2\sqrt{2}$
21. $x^2 - y^2 = 4$ 23. $(x^2 + y^2)^2 = 2xy$
25. $x^2 = 2y$ 27. $3x^2 - y^2 + 8x + 4 = 0$
29. $(x^2 + y^2)^2 = a(3x^2y - y^3)$
31. $x^4 + y^4 + 2x^2y^2 + 4x^2y + 4y^3 - x^2 + 3y^2 = 0$

SECTION 4

1. $r (\cos \theta + \sin \theta) = 3\sqrt{2}$ 3. $r (\sin \theta - \sqrt{3} \cos \theta) = 8$
5. $r \cos \theta = 3$ 7. $r \cos \theta = -\pi$
9. $r^2 - 6r \cos (\theta - \pi/6) + 5 = 0$ 11. $r = 8 \cos \theta$
13. $r^2 - 8r \cos (\theta - \pi/3) - 49 + 14(\sqrt{2} + \sqrt{6}) = 0$

15. $r = \dfrac{10\sqrt{3}}{3} \cos \left(\theta - \dfrac{\pi}{3}\right)$ 17. $r = \dfrac{10}{1 - 2 \cos \theta}$

19. $r = \dfrac{-1}{2 - \sin \theta}$ 21. $r = \dfrac{-6}{1 - \cos \theta + \sqrt{3} \sin \theta}$

23. $d = |r_1 \cos (\theta_1 - \alpha) - p|$ 25. $e = \frac{1}{2}$; $r \cos \theta = -9$
27. $e = 1$; $r \cos (\theta - \pi/2) = -2$ 29. $e = 2$; $r \cos (\theta - \pi/3) = -\frac{5}{2}$
31. $e = \frac{1}{6}$; $r \cos (\theta + \pi/2) = -4$

SECTION 5

1. $ds/d\theta = 2a$; $\cot \psi = -\tan \theta$
3. $ds/d\theta = |4 \cos (\theta/2)|$; $\cot \psi = -\tan (\theta/2)$

5. $ds/d\theta = 4\sqrt{1 + \theta^2}$; $\cot\psi = 1/\theta$

7. $ds/d\theta = \sqrt{13 + 12\cos\theta}$; $\cot\psi = -2\sin\theta/(3 + 2\cos\theta)$

9. $ds/d\theta = e^{5\theta}\sqrt{26}$; $\cot\psi = 5$

11. $ds/d\theta = 2\sqrt{5 - 4\sin\theta}/(2 - \sin\theta)^2$; $\cot\psi = \cos\theta/(2 - \sin\theta)$

13. $ds/d\theta = 2\sqrt{5 + 4\cos\theta}/(1 + 2\cos\theta)^2$; $\cot\psi = 2\sin\theta/(1 + 2\cos\theta)$

15. $16\sqrt{2} - 5\sqrt{5}$ 17. $3\pi/4$

21. $\kappa(\theta) = 1/a$ 23. $x = \frac{1}{4}$

SECTION 6

1. $4\pi^3/3$ 3. $\frac{1}{2}(e^{\pi/2} - 1)$ 5. $\pi^7/1792$

7. π 9. 2 11. 6π

13. $\pi/4$ if n is odd, $\pi/2$ if n is even   15. $2(2\pi + 3\sqrt{3})/3$

17. $4(3\sqrt{3} - \pi)/3$ 19. $(9\pi - 12\sqrt{3})/4$ 21. $(2\pi - 3\sqrt{3})/2$

CHAPTER 14

SECTION 2

1. $\mathbf{v} = -3\mathbf{i} - 2\mathbf{j}$ 3. $\mathbf{v} = 4\mathbf{i} + 5\mathbf{j}$

5. $\mathbf{v} = -5\mathbf{i} - 6\mathbf{j}$ 7. $\mathbf{v} = -5\mathbf{i}$

9. $\mathbf{u} = -\dfrac{5}{13}\mathbf{i} - \dfrac{12}{13}\mathbf{j}$ 11. $\mathbf{u} = -\dfrac{2}{\sqrt{29}}\mathbf{i} + \dfrac{5}{\sqrt{29}}\mathbf{j}$

13. $B(4, 6)$ 15. $A(4, 7)$

17. $A(-3, \frac{1}{2})$; $B(-5, \frac{7}{2})$ 19. $\pm 2\mathbf{i} + 2\mathbf{j}$

21. $-\mathbf{i} + \mathbf{j}$

SECTION 3

1. $|\mathbf{v}| = |\mathbf{w}| = 5$; $\cos\theta = 0$; proj. $= \mathbf{0}$

3. $|\mathbf{v}| = 13$; $|\mathbf{w}| = 25$; $\cos\theta = -\frac{36}{325}$; proj. $= -\frac{252}{625}\mathbf{i} - \frac{864}{625}\mathbf{j}$

5. $|\mathbf{v}| = |\mathbf{w}| = \sqrt{13}$; $\cos\theta = -\frac{5}{13}$; proj. $= -\frac{10}{13}\mathbf{i} + \frac{15}{13}\mathbf{j}$

7. $|\mathbf{v}| = \sqrt{13}$; $|\mathbf{w}| = \sqrt{29}$; $\cos\theta = -4/\sqrt{377}$; proj. $= -\frac{8}{29}\mathbf{i} - \frac{20}{29}\mathbf{j}$

9. proj. $= \frac{6}{17}\mathbf{i} + \frac{24}{17}\mathbf{j}$

11. proj. $= \mathbf{0}$

13. $\cos\theta = 1/\sqrt{5}$; $\cos\alpha = 1/\sqrt{5}$ 15. $\cos\theta = 2\sqrt{13}/13$; $\cos\alpha = 11/\sqrt{130}$

17. $\cos\theta = -1$; $\cos\alpha = 1$ 19. $a = \frac{3}{2}$

21. impossible

23. $a = (-240 + \sqrt{(240)^2 + (69)(407)})/407$

27. $|BC| = \sqrt{93}$; proj. of $\overrightarrow{AB}$ on $\overrightarrow{BC}$ is $-30/\sqrt{93}$

    proj. of $\overrightarrow{AC}$ on $\overrightarrow{BC}$ is $63/\sqrt{93}$

29. proj. of $\overrightarrow{AC}$ on $\overrightarrow{AB}$ is $\frac{33}{5}$; proj. of $\overrightarrow{BC}$ on $\overrightarrow{AB}$ is $-\frac{17}{5}$

31. $\mathbf{v}[\overrightarrow{DE}] = \frac{1}{2}\mathbf{v}[\overrightarrow{AC}] - \frac{2}{3}\mathbf{v}[\overrightarrow{AB}]$

33. $\mathbf{v}[\overrightarrow{EF}] = \frac{1}{3}\mathbf{v}[\overrightarrow{AC}] - \frac{1}{2}\mathbf{v}[\overrightarrow{AB}]$

SECTION 4

1. $\mathbf{f}'(t) = -2\mathbf{i} + 2\mathbf{j}$; $\mathbf{f}''(t) = \mathbf{0}$

3. $\mathbf{f}'(t) = 2(\cos 2t)\mathbf{i} + (\sec t\tan t)\mathbf{j}$;

    $\mathbf{f}''(t) = -4(\sin 2t)\mathbf{i} + \sec t(2\sec^2 t - 1)\mathbf{j}$

5. $\dfrac{2t(t^2 + 1)}{(t^2 + 2)^3} + 4t$

7. $\dfrac{2 \sin 4t - 3 \sin 6t}{2(\sin^2 2t + \cos^2 3t)^{1/2}}$

9. 0

11. $\dfrac{3t^2 + 40}{t^6}$

13. $\theta' = \dfrac{-3|2t^2 + t|}{(13t^2 + 4t + 1)(2t^2 + t)}$

SECTION 5

1. $\mathbf{v} = \mathbf{i} + t\mathbf{j}; \ \mathbf{a} = \mathbf{j}; \ s'(t) = \sqrt{1 + t^2}; \ s''(t) = t/\sqrt{1 + t^2}$

3. $\mathbf{v} = 12\mathbf{i} + (4 - 16t)\mathbf{j}; \ \mathbf{a} = -16\mathbf{j}; \ s'(t) = 4\sqrt{16t^2 - 8t + 10};$
   $s''(t) = (64t - 16)/\sqrt{16t^2 - 8t + 10}$

5. $\mathbf{v} = \mathbf{i} + (\tan t)\mathbf{j}; \ \mathbf{a} = (\sec^2 t)\mathbf{j}; \ s'(t) = |\sec t|; \ s''(t) = |\sec t| \tan t$

7. $\mathbf{v} = -3 (\sin t)\mathbf{i} + 2 (\cos t)\mathbf{j}; \ \mathbf{a} = -3 \cos t\,\mathbf{i} - 2 \sin t\,\mathbf{j};$
   $s'(t) = \sqrt{9 - 5 \cos^2 t}; \ s'' = 5 \sin t \cos t/s'(t)$

9. $\mathbf{v} = -e^{-t} (\cos t + \sin t)\mathbf{i} + e^{-t} (\cos t - \sin t)\mathbf{j}$
   $\mathbf{a} = 2e^{-t} (\sin t)\mathbf{i} - 2e^{-t} (\cos t)\mathbf{j}; \ s'(t) = \sqrt{2}\,e^{-t}; \ s''(t) = -\sqrt{2}\,e^{-t}$

11. $\mathbf{v} = \mathbf{i}; \ \mathbf{a} = 2\mathbf{i} + 2\mathbf{j}; \ s' = 1; \ s'' = 2$

13. $\mathbf{v} = 2\mathbf{i} + \tfrac{8}{3}\mathbf{j}; \ \mathbf{a} = \dfrac{10}{\sqrt{3}}\mathbf{i} + \dfrac{16}{3\sqrt{3}}\mathbf{j}; \ s' = \tfrac{10}{3}; \ s'' = \dfrac{154}{15\sqrt{3}}$

15. $\mathbf{v} = \tfrac{1}{3}\mathbf{i} - \tfrac{3}{4}\mathbf{j}; \ \mathbf{a} = -\tfrac{1}{9}\mathbf{i} + \tfrac{3}{4}\mathbf{j}; \ s' = \dfrac{\sqrt{97}}{12}; \ s'' = \dfrac{-259}{36\sqrt{97}}$

19. $\mathbf{T} = \dfrac{4e^{2t}\mathbf{i} - 3e^{-2t}\mathbf{j}}{(16e^{4t} + 9e^{-4t})^{1/2}}$

SECTION 6

1. $\mathbf{v} = (t^2 - 1)\mathbf{i} + 2t\mathbf{j}; \ s'(t) = t^2 + 1; \ a_T = s'' = 2t$
   $\mathbf{T} = \dfrac{(t^2 - 1)\mathbf{i} + 2t\mathbf{j}}{t^2 + 1}; \ a_N = 2; \ R = \dfrac{(t^2 + 1)^2}{2};$
   $\mathbf{N} = \dfrac{2t\mathbf{i} - (t^2 - 1)\mathbf{j}}{t^2 + 1}$

3. Let
$$\lambda = \frac{t}{|t|}.$$
   Then
$$s'(t) = \lambda t \sqrt{t^2 + 1}; \qquad \mathbf{v} = t\mathbf{i} + t^2\mathbf{j}$$
$$a_T = \frac{\lambda(2t^2 + 1)}{\sqrt{t^2 + 1}}; \qquad a_N = \frac{|t|}{\sqrt{t^2 + 1}}; \qquad R = |t|(1 + t^2)^{3/2}$$
$$\mathbf{N} = \frac{\lambda(-t\mathbf{i} + \mathbf{j})}{\sqrt{t^2 + 1}}; \qquad \mathbf{T} = \frac{\lambda(\mathbf{i} + t\mathbf{j})}{\sqrt{t^2 + 1}}$$

5. $\mathbf{v} = cp\mathbf{i} + cp (\sinh pt)\mathbf{j}; \ s'(t) = cp \cosh pt$
   $a_T = cp^2 \sinh pt, \ (c > 0); \ \mathbf{T}(t) = \operatorname{sech} pt\,\mathbf{i} + \tanh pt\,\mathbf{j};$
   $a_N = cp^2; \ R = c \cosh^2 pt; \ \mathbf{N} = -\tanh pt\,\mathbf{i} + \operatorname{sech} pt\,\mathbf{j}$

7. $\mathbf{v} = -w\,(\sin wt)\mathbf{i} + w\,(\cos wt)\mathbf{j}$; $s'(t) = |w|$;
   $a_T = 0$; $\mathbf{T}(t) = -\lambda\,(\sin wt\mathbf{i} - \cos wt\mathbf{j})$; $\lambda = w/|w|$
   $a_N = w^2$; $\mathbf{N} = -\lambda\,(\cos wt\mathbf{i} + \sin wt\mathbf{j})$; $R = 1$

9. $\cos\theta = t^2/(4 + t^4)^{1/2}$; $\cos\phi = t^2/(36 + t^4)^{1/2}$

11. $\cos\theta = \dfrac{t + \sinh 4t}{\sqrt{(1 + \cosh^2 2t)(1 + 4\sinh^2 2t)}}$

   $\cos\phi = \dfrac{t^2 + 2\sinh^2 2t}{\sqrt{(t^4 + \sinh^2 2t)(1 + 4\sinh^2 2t)}}$

13. $\mathbf{v} = v(\mathbf{i} + \mathbf{j})/\sqrt{2}$; $\mathbf{a} = v^2(\mathbf{i} - \mathbf{j})/4p$; $\mathbf{T}(t) = (\mathbf{i} + \mathbf{j})/\sqrt{2}$;
   $\mathbf{N} = (\mathbf{i} - \mathbf{j})/\sqrt{2}$; $s' = v$; $a_T = 0$; $a_N = v^2\sqrt{2}/4p$; $R = 2p\sqrt{2}$

CHAPTER 15

SECTION 1

1. $-\tfrac{3}{4}(1 - 2y)^{2/3} + C$

3. $-\tfrac{1}{2}\cos 2x + C$

5. $\tfrac{1}{2}\tan 2x + C$

7. $\tfrac{1}{3}\sinh 3x + C$

9. $2e^{x/2} + C$

11. $\tfrac{1}{12}\arctan (3x/4) + C$

13. $-2\cos\sqrt{x} + C$

15. $\tfrac{1}{2}e^{x^2+1} + C$

17. $\tfrac{1}{3}\sin^3 x + C$

19. $\tfrac{1}{8}\sinh^4 2x + C$

21. $\sin (\ln x) + C$

23. $\tfrac{2}{3}\operatorname{arcsec} (2x/3) + C$

25. $\ln |\sinh x| + C$

27. $\tfrac{1}{3}x^3 - 2x - (1/x) + C$

29. $\ln |\ln x| + C$

31. $\tfrac{1}{4}\tanh^2 2x + C$

33. $\tfrac{1}{14}\sec^7 2x + C$

35. $\ln (1 + e^x) + C$

37. $\tfrac{1}{3}\arctan (x\sqrt{x}/2) + C$

39. $\tfrac{1}{2}y - \ln (\cosh \tfrac{1}{2}y) + C$ or $y - \ln (1 + e^y) + C$

43. $2(\sqrt{7} - 1)$

45. $\tfrac{7}{3}$

47. $\pi/12$

49. $\tfrac{1}{4}$

51. $\tfrac{3}{2}$

53. $\tfrac{1}{3}(e^2 + 1)^{3/2} - \tfrac{2}{3}\sqrt{2}$

SECTION 2

1. $\tfrac{1}{2}\ln (x^2 + 2x + 2) + C$

3. $\ln |1 + \tan x| + C$

5. $\tfrac{1}{2}\ln |\sinh 2x| + C$

7. $\tfrac{1}{2}x^2 + 2x - 4\ln |x + 1| + C$

9. $\tfrac{1}{2}x + \tfrac{1}{4}\ln |2x - 1| + C$

11. $(\sqrt{3}/6)\arctan (x\sqrt{3}/2) + C$

13. $-\tfrac{1}{2}(x^2 + 1)^{-1} + C$

15. $[2^{x^2}/(2\ln 2)] + C$

17. $-\tfrac{1}{2}x^2 - 5x - 14\ln |x - 3| + C$

19. $x + \ln (x^2 + 1) + C$

21. $2x + \ln |x^2 + 2x - 2| + C$

23. $e^{\tan x} + C$

25. $\arcsin (e^x/\sqrt{3}) + C$

27. $2\sec\sqrt{x} + C$

29. $\tfrac{1}{2}\ln (2 + \cosh 2x) + C$

31. $-\sqrt{5 - x^2} - 2\arcsin (x/\sqrt{5}) + C$

33. $-\tfrac{1}{2}(2x + \cos x)^{-2} + C$

35. $(-\sqrt{3}/6)\arctan (\cos 2x/\sqrt{3}) + C$

SECTION 3

1. $(3\sqrt{3} + 1)/24$

3. $(32 - 19\sqrt{2})/20$

5. $\sqrt{3}/27$

7. $\pi/4$

9. $(\cosh^4 2 - 1)/4$

11. $3\pi/16$

13. $\tfrac{1}{32}\sinh 4 - \tfrac{1}{4}\sinh 2 + \tfrac{3}{8}$

15. $-2\cos (x/2) + \tfrac{4}{3}\cos^3 (x/2) - \tfrac{2}{5}\cos^5 (x/2) + C$

17. $\ln |\sin x| - \tfrac{1}{2}\sin^2 x + C$

19. $\tfrac{1}{4}\tan^2 2x + C$

21. $\frac{1}{2}\tanh 2x - \frac{1}{6}\tanh^3 2x + C$

23. $-\frac{1}{7}\csc^7 x + \frac{2}{5}\csc^5 x - \frac{1}{3}\csc^3 x + C$

25. $-x + \tan x + C$

27. $-\frac{1}{3}\cot^3 x + \cot x + x + C$

29. $-\frac{1}{2}\cos(x^2) + \frac{1}{6}\cos^3(x^2) + C$

31. $\frac{1}{3}\sin^3 x + C$

33. $\frac{1}{3}\tan^3 x + C$

35. $\frac{1}{4}\cosh^4 x + C$

SECTION 4

1. $\pi/6$

3. $-\pi/18$

5. $\frac{32}{3}$

7. $(2/\sqrt{5})\operatorname{arcsec}(x/\sqrt{5}) + C$

9. $\frac{1}{3}(9 - x^2)^{3/2} - 9\sqrt{9 - x^2} + C$

11. $\frac{1}{12}(2x^2 + 7)^{3/2} - \frac{7}{4}\sqrt{2x^2 + 7} + C$

13. $\dfrac{1}{5a^4}(a^2 u^2 + b^2)^{5/2} - \dfrac{b^2}{3a^4}(a^2 u^2 + b^2)^{3/2} + C$

15. $\sqrt{x^2 - a^2} - a\operatorname{arcsec}(x/a) + C$

17. $-(1/a^2 x)\sqrt{x^2 + a^2} + C$

19. $a^{-4}x^{-1}\left[\dfrac{(a^2 - x^2)^{3/2}}{3x^2} + \sqrt{a^2 - x^2}\right] + C$

21. $\sqrt{2}/32$

23. $3^{-1/2} - \pi/6$

25. $(\frac{2}{9})(1 - 3^{-1/2})$

27. $25\pi/16$

SECTION 5

1. $\arctan(x + 2) + C$

3. $x - \ln(x^2 + 2x + 5) - \dfrac{3}{2}\arctan\dfrac{x + 1}{2} + C$

5. $\operatorname{arcsec}(x + 2) + C$

7. $\operatorname{argsinh}\left(\dfrac{x - 1}{2}\right) + C$

9. $\frac{1}{2}\ln(x^2 + 2x + 5) + \arctan[(x + 1)/2] + C$

11. $\frac{1}{3}x^3 - \frac{3}{2}x^2 + 8x - (47/\sqrt{5})\operatorname{argtanh}[(2x + 3)/\sqrt{5}] - (21/2)\ln(x^2 + 3x + 1)$

13. $3\sqrt{x^2 + 2x} + \operatorname{argcosh}(x + 1) + C$

15. $\dfrac{11x - 19}{4(x^2 - 2x + 3)} + \dfrac{11\sqrt{2}}{8}\arctan\dfrac{x - 1}{\sqrt{2}} + C$

17. $16(23)^{-3/2}\arctan\dfrac{4x + 3}{\sqrt{23}} + \dfrac{8x - 17}{23(2x^2 + 3x + 4)} + C$

19. $\dfrac{9x - 13}{\sqrt{x^2 - 2x + 2}} + C$

21. $\dfrac{5x - 3}{4\sqrt{x^2 + 2x - 3}}$

SECTION 6

1. $(x^2/2)\ln x - \frac{1}{4}x^2 + C$

3. $-x^2\cos x + 2x\sin x + 2\cos x + C$

5. $x(\ln x)^2 - 2x\ln x + 2x + C$

7. $x\arctan x - \frac{1}{2}\ln(1 + x^2) + C$

9. $x\operatorname{arcsec} x - \operatorname{argcosh} x + C$

11. $\frac{1}{4}(2x^2 - 1)\arcsin x + \frac{1}{4}x\sqrt{1 - x^2} + C$

13. $-2x\cot(x/2) + 4\ln|\sin(x/2)| + C$

15. $3x\tan 3x - \frac{9}{2}x^2 + \ln|\cos 3x| + C$

17. $2x^3\arcsin 2x + \frac{1}{4}\sqrt{1 - 4x^2} - \frac{1}{12}(1 - 4x^2)^{3/2} + C$

19. $-\sqrt{2x}\cos\sqrt{2x} + \sin\sqrt{2x} + C$

21. $(x^2 - 1)e^{x^2} + C$ 23. $\frac{1}{5}e^x (\sin 2x - 2 \cos 2x) + C$

25. $\frac{1}{10}e^{-x}(3 \sin 3x - \cos 3x) + C$

27. $(a^2 + b^2)^{-1}(a \sin bx - b \cos bx)e^{ax} + C$

29. $\frac{1}{3} \sin^3 2x + C$

31. $\frac{1}{8}(\frac{5}{2}x - 2 \sin 2x + \frac{3}{8} \sin 4x + \frac{1}{6} \sin^3 2x) + C$

33. -2

35. $-\dfrac{\pi}{12} + \dfrac{1}{2}\left(\dfrac{\pi^2}{9} + \dfrac{1}{4}\right) \arctan \dfrac{2\pi}{3}$

37. $\frac{4}{25}(1 + e^{3\pi/4})$

SECTION 7

1. $\frac{1}{2}x^2 + 5x + 14 \ln |x - 2| + C$

3. $\frac{1}{2}x^2 - 4x + 13 \ln |x + 2| - \ln |x + 1| + C$

5. $x + 11 \ln |x - 2| - 6 \ln |x - 1| + C$

7. $x + (x - 2)^{-1} + 2 \ln |x - 2| + C$

9. $-\frac{8}{3} \ln |x + 2| + \frac{5}{2} \ln |x + 1| + \frac{1}{6} \ln |x - 1| + C$

11. $2 \ln |x + 3| - \frac{1}{3} \ln |x + 2| + \frac{1}{3} \ln |x - 1| + C$

13. $\frac{1}{2} \ln |x + 1| + \frac{1}{4} \ln (x^2 + 1) + \frac{5}{2} \arctan x + C$

15. $-\frac{4}{3}(x + 1)^{-1} + \frac{1}{9} \ln |x + 1| - \frac{1}{9} \ln |x - 2| + C$

17. $-\frac{1}{9} \ln |x + 2| - \frac{5}{3}(x - 1)^{-1} + \frac{1}{9} \ln |x - 1| + C$

19. $-\frac{3}{4} \ln |x + 1| + \frac{7}{4} \ln |x - 1| + \frac{1}{2}(x - 1)^{-1} - \frac{1}{2}(x - 1)^{-2} + C$

21. $\ln (x^2 + 4) - \frac{1}{2} \ln (x^2 + 1) + \frac{11}{6} \arctan (x/2) - \frac{2}{3} \arctan x + C$

23. $\frac{7}{8} \ln |x - 3| + \frac{1}{4} \ln |x - 1| - \frac{1}{8} \ln |x + 1| - \ln |x - 2| + C$

25. $-\frac{2}{5}(x - 1)^{-1} - \frac{4}{25} \ln |x - 1| + \frac{2}{25} \ln (x^2 + 4) + \frac{19}{50} \arctan (x/2) + C$

27. $\frac{1}{9}(x + 1)^{-1} - \frac{5}{27} \ln |x + 1| - \frac{5}{9}(x - 2)^{-1} + \frac{32}{27} \ln |x - 2| + C$

29. $\frac{1}{2}(16 - 11x)(x^2 + 4)^{-1} + 2 \ln (x^2 + 4) + \frac{5}{4} \arctan (x/2) + C$

31. $\frac{14}{27} \ln |x - 3| + \frac{13}{54} \ln (x^2 + 3x + 9) + \dfrac{14}{6\sqrt{27}} \arctan \dfrac{2x + 3}{\sqrt{27}}$

33. $\frac{51}{256} \arctan (x/2) - \dfrac{15x}{32(x^2 + 4)} + \dfrac{17x(4 - x^2)}{128(x^2 + 4)^2}$

SECTION 8

1. $\frac{4}{3}(x + 2)^{3/2} - 2(x + 2)^{1/2} + C$ 3. $\frac{2}{5}(x + 1)^{5/2} - \frac{2}{3}(x + 1)^{3/2} + C$

5. $\frac{1}{12}(3x - 1)^{4/3} - \frac{5}{3}(3x - 1)^{1/3} + C$

7. $\frac{3}{64}(2x + 1)^{8/3} - \frac{3}{20}(2x + 1)^{5/3} + \frac{3}{16}(2x + 1)^{2/3} + C$

9. $2\sqrt{x + 4} + 4 \ln |-2 + \sqrt{x + 4}| - 2 \ln |x| + C$

11. $x + 6\sqrt{x} + 6 \ln |\sqrt{x} - 1| + C$

13. $\frac{1}{3}(x^2 - 4)^{3/2} + 4(x^2 - 4)^{1/2} + C$

15. $\frac{1}{5}(x^2 + 4)^{5/2} - 2(x^2 + 4)^{3/2} + 8(x^2 + 4)^{1/2} + C$

17. $-5(16 - x^2)^{3/2} + \frac{1}{5}(16 - x^2)^{5/2} + C$

19. $(1/a) \ln |a - \sqrt{a^2 - x^2}| - (1/a) \ln |x| + C$

21. $\sqrt{a^2 - x^2} + a \ln |a - \sqrt{a^2 - x^2}| - a \ln |x| + C$

23. $\sqrt{x^2 - a^2} - a \arctan (\sqrt{x^2 - a^2}/a) + C$

25. $3x^{1/3} - 6x^{1/6} + 6 \ln |1 + x^{1/6}| + C$

27. $\frac{2}{3} \arctan \left[\frac{1}{3} \tan (\theta/2)\right] + C$

29. $(2/\sqrt{3}) \arctan [\sqrt{3} \tan (\theta/2)] + C$

31. $2 \arctan [\tan (\theta/2) + 2] + C$

33. $-\frac{1}{4} \cot^2 (x/2) - \frac{1}{2} \ln |\tan (x/2)| + C$

35. $\operatorname{argtanh} [\tan (\theta/2)] - \tan (\theta/2)[1 + \tan (\theta/2)]^{-2} + C$

37. $\frac{1}{4} \ln (2 + \sqrt{4 - x^2}) - \frac{1}{4} \ln |x| - \sqrt{4 - x^2}/(2x^2) + C$

CHAPTER 16

SECTION 1

1. $s = -16t^2 + 144t + 80$; highest point $= 404$ ft

3. $x = t^2 + 12t + 1$; $v = 2t + 12$

5. $x = \frac{1}{2}(5e^{2t} - 3)$; $v = 5e^{2t}$

7. $x = x_0 + (1/k) \ln (1 + kv_0t)$; $v = v_0/(1 + kv_0t)$

9. distance $= (187)^2\sqrt{3}$ ft; time $= 187\sqrt{3}/4$ sec

11. $t = \frac{1}{16}(275 + 5\sqrt{6865})$ 13. number $= 10,000e^{t/2}$

15. $t = -(3.5 \ln 0.1)/(\ln 2)$ 17. $400e^{-1/2}$ pounds

19. $T = 60 + 60(\frac{2}{3})^{t/10}$

SECTION 2

1. $y = -\dfrac{1}{x} + \dfrac{7}{2}$ 3. $y = \arcsin \dfrac{x}{2} + 3 + \dfrac{\pi}{6}$

5. $y = -\sqrt{x^2 + 9}$ 7. $y = (5 - 2x)^{-1}$

9. $y = x^3 - x^2 - 7x - 2$ 11. $y = \frac{1}{3}x^3 + \frac{8}{3}$ or $-\frac{1}{3}x^3 + \frac{10}{3}$

SECTION 3

1. 160π 3. $\pi/54$ 5. $4\pi a^3/3$

7. $512\pi/15$ 9. $\frac{1}{3}\pi(3\sqrt{3} - \pi)$ 11. $2\pi[(\ln 2)^2 - 2 \ln 2 + 1]$

13. 8π 15 $16\pi(2\sqrt{2} - 1)/3$ 17. 16π

19. $5\pi/14$ 21. $\frac{1}{2}\pi[4 + \sinh 4]$ 23. $45\pi/4$

25. $5\pi^2 a^3$ 27. $2\pi^2 a^2 b$

SECTION 4

1. $32\pi/5$ 3. $\pi/7$ 5. $2\pi[(\ln 2)^2 - 2 \ln 2 + 1]$

7. $2\pi^2$ 9. $256\pi/3$ 11. $2\pi/5$

13. $4\pi/3$ 15. $128\pi/3$ 17. $2\pi^2 + 4\pi$

SECTION 5

1. 1   3. 2   5. divergent   7. $1/(1 - p)$

9. divergent   11. 2   13. 1   15. 9

17. 0   19. $\frac{1}{2}$ 21. divergent   23. 4

25. $2(2\sqrt{2} - 1)$ 27. π 29. divergent   31. $2\sqrt{2}$

33. $4\pi\sqrt{3}/9$ 35. π

SECTION 6

1. $[\ln (2 + \sqrt{5}) + 2\sqrt{5}]/4$
5. $2 \ln (1 + \sqrt{2})$
9. $\frac{1}{4}(4\sqrt{17} - \sqrt{2}) + \ln \left(\dfrac{4 + \sqrt{17}}{1 + \sqrt{2}}\right)$
13. 4
17. $\frac{1}{2} \ln (1 + \sqrt{\frac{2}{3}}) - \frac{1}{2} \ln (1 - \sqrt{\frac{2}{3}})$

3. $3a$
7. $[(13)^{3/2} + (40)^{3/2} - 16]/27$
11. 8
15. $[\ln (2 + \sqrt{5}) + 2\sqrt{5}]/4$

SECTION 7

1. $\pi(17\sqrt{17} - 1)/9$
5. $26\pi/3$
9. $\pi a^2(2 + \sinh 2)/2$
13. $12\pi a^2/5$
17. $64\pi a^2/3$
19. $2\pi a^2 b$ $[\arcsin (c/a) + (c/a)\sqrt{1 - (c/a)^2}]/c$
21. $4\pi^2 ab$
25. $\pi[4\sqrt{17} + \ln (4 + \sqrt{17})]/2$

3. $8\pi(5\sqrt{5} - 2\sqrt{2})/3$
7. $1179\pi/256$
11. $\pi(15 + 4 \ln 2)/4$
15. $6\pi(\sqrt{2} + 1)/5$

23. $\pi(15 + 4 \ln 2)/4$

SECTION 8

1. $\frac{1}{3}$
7. $(3 \ln 3 - 2)/2$
13. (a) a; (b) $4a/3$

3. $(e^b - 1)/b$
9. $\frac{1}{2}$
15. (a) $2a/\pi$; (b) $4a/5$

5. $2/\pi$
11. $1/a$; limit is 0
17. (a) $\frac{16}{3}$; (b) $\frac{127}{20}$

SECTION 9

1. $(\frac{13}{4}, 0)$
3. $(\frac{2}{5}, 0)$
5. (a) $\bar{x} = \frac{11}{9}$
7. $(\frac{7}{8}, \frac{11}{8})$
9. $(\frac{23}{17}, \frac{35}{17})$
11. With axes along outer sides of figure, $\bar{x} = 2, \bar{y} = 1.5$.
13. With origin at point of tangency, x-axis through center of circle,

$$\bar{x} = \frac{4\pi - 5}{2\pi + 5}, \qquad \bar{y} = \frac{-5}{4\pi + 10}.$$

SECTION 10

1. $\bar{x} = \frac{18}{5}$; $\bar{y} = 3\sqrt{6}/4$
3. $\bar{x} = \pi/2, \bar{y} = \pi/8$
5. $\bar{x} = 0, \bar{y} = 4a/3\pi$
7. $\bar{x} = 67/18(8\sqrt{2} - 7)$; $\bar{y} = 2(72\sqrt{2} - 53)/15(8\sqrt{2} - 7)$
9. $\bar{x} = \dfrac{7 \ln 4 - 3}{3 \ln 4 - 2}$; $\bar{y} = \left[\dfrac{7 (\ln 4)^2}{4} - (3 \ln 4 - 2)\right]/(3 \ln 4 - 2)$
11. $\bar{x} = \frac{1}{4}; \bar{y} = \frac{1}{8}$

SECTION 11

1. $\bar{x} = 3h/4$
7. $\bar{x} = \pi/2$
13. $\bar{y} = \frac{9}{16}$
17. on axis $\dfrac{6h^2 + 8ah + 3a^2}{4(3h + 2a)}$

3. $\bar{x} = 3a/8$
9. $\bar{x} = \frac{5}{9}$
15. $\bar{y} = \dfrac{4 (\ln 4 - \frac{3}{4})}{3}$

5. $\bar{x} = \dfrac{256 \ln 2 - 150}{64 \ln 2 - 33}$
11. $\bar{x} = \frac{25}{32}$

SECTION 12

1. $\bar{x} = \frac{1179}{1056}$; $\bar{y} = \frac{268}{165}$

3. $\bar{x} = \bar{y} = 2a/5$

5. $\bar{x} = \dfrac{17\sqrt{17} - 1}{3(4\sqrt{17} + \operatorname{argsinh} 4)}$

7. $\bar{x} = \dfrac{27 - 16 \ln 2 - 4 (\ln 2)^2}{8(3 + 2 \ln 2)}$; $\bar{y} = \dfrac{20}{3(3 + 2 \ln 2)}$

9. $\bar{x} = \dfrac{2(25\sqrt{5} + 1)}{5(5\sqrt{5} - 1)}$

11. $\bar{x} = \dfrac{169\sqrt{13} - 31}{130\sqrt{13} - 10}$

13. 0

15. $\bar{y} = \dfrac{23(17)^{3/2} + 1}{10(17^{3/2} - 1)}$

17. $\bar{y} = \dfrac{a(3 + 2 \sinh 2 - \cosh 2)}{8(1 + \sinh 1 - \cosh 1)}$

SECTION 13

1. 2π 3. $\pi^2/2$ 5. $242\pi/5$ 7. $8\pi/105$ 9. $2\pi^2 a^2 b$

SECTION 14

1. approx. $= 21.1$; exact $= 21$

3. approx. $= 0.696$; exact $= \ln 2 \approx 0.693$

5. approx. $= 0.880$; exact $= \operatorname{argsinh} 1 \approx 0.8814$

7. $\frac{26}{3}$

9. $\frac{38}{3}$

11. approx. $= 0.6933$; exact $= \ln 2 \approx 0.69315$

13. approx. $= 0.8814$; exact $= \operatorname{argsinh} 1 \approx 0.8814$

15. approx. $= 0.6045$; exact $= (\pi\sqrt{3})/9 \approx 0.6046$

17. approx. $= 0.8358^{-}$ 19. approx. $= 1.0948^{+}$

21. approx. $= 0.4298^{+}$ 23. $-\epsilon_T = \frac{1}{8}$

25. $\frac{1}{2400} \leq -\epsilon_T \leq \sqrt{3}/1350$; $-\epsilon_T = \sqrt{3}/2700$, approx.

27. $\frac{1}{1200} \leq -\epsilon_T \leq \frac{1}{150}$; $\epsilon_T = -\frac{1}{400}$, approx.

$\dfrac{1}{150,000} \leq -\epsilon_S \leq \dfrac{32}{150,000}$; $\epsilon_S = -\dfrac{1}{20,000}$, approx.

CHAPTER 17

SECTION 1

1. $\overline{AB} = \sqrt{30}$, $\overline{AC} = \sqrt{21}$, $\overline{BC} = \sqrt{19}$

3. $\overline{AB} = \sqrt{17}$, $\overline{AC} = \sqrt{18}$, $\overline{BC} = \sqrt{35}$; right triangle

5. $\overline{AB} = \sqrt{21}$, $\overline{AC} = \sqrt{51}$, $\overline{BC} = \sqrt{126}$

7. $(3, \frac{5}{2}, 2)$ 9. $(-1, 2, -\frac{1}{2})$

11. $\frac{1}{2}\sqrt{61}, \frac{1}{2}\sqrt{61}, \frac{1}{2}\sqrt{10}$ 13. $\frac{1}{2}\sqrt{74}, \frac{1}{2}\sqrt{74}, \frac{1}{2}\sqrt{26}$

15. $P_2(4, 5, -6)$, $Q(1, 3, 0)$ 17. Not on line

19. Not on line

21. Straight line parallel to y-axis   27. $6x + 4y - 8z - 5 = 0$; plane

SECTION 2

1. $1, -5, 2; 1/\sqrt{30}, -5/\sqrt{30}, 2/\sqrt{30}$ 3. $7, 1, 2; 7/\sqrt{54}, 1/\sqrt{54}, 2/\sqrt{54}$

5. $P_2(5, 7, 6)$ 7. $P_2(0, 4, 2)$

9. Yes   11. No   13. Yes   15. No

17. Yes   19. $\sqrt{2}/3$ 21. $41/3\sqrt{190}$ 23. $4\sqrt{10}$

SECTION 3

1. $\dfrac{x-2}{3} = \dfrac{y-3}{6} = \dfrac{z-4}{2}$; $(5, 9, 6)$; $(-1, -3, 2)$

3. $\dfrac{x-1}{-2} = \dfrac{y-2}{3} = \dfrac{z+1}{-3}$; $(-1, 5, -4)$; $(5, -4, 5)$

5. $\dfrac{x-1}{2} = \dfrac{y}{1} = \dfrac{z+1}{-3}$ 7. $\dfrac{x-4}{2} = \dfrac{y}{-1} = \dfrac{z}{-3}$

9. $\dfrac{x-3}{2} = \dfrac{y+1}{0} - \dfrac{z+2}{0}$ 11. Perpendicular

13. Not perpendicular

15. $\dfrac{x-4}{1} = \dfrac{y}{-2} = \dfrac{z-2}{0}$; $\dfrac{x-3}{0} = \dfrac{y-1}{-1} = \dfrac{z-4}{2}$; $\dfrac{x-2}{1} = \dfrac{y-5}{-3} = \dfrac{z}{2}$

17. $(-\tfrac{3}{7}, -\tfrac{13}{7}, 0)$; $(-\tfrac{5}{3}, 0, \tfrac{13}{3})$; $(0, -\tfrac{5}{2}, -\tfrac{3}{2})$

19. $x = 3 - t, y = 1 + 3t, z = 5 + t$

21. $A'B'$: $\dfrac{x-2}{5} = \dfrac{y}{0} = \dfrac{z-6}{2}$; $A'C'$: $\dfrac{x-2}{3} = \dfrac{y}{0} = \dfrac{z-6}{1}$;

   $B'C'$: $\dfrac{x+3}{8} = \dfrac{y}{0} = \dfrac{z-4}{3}$

SECTION 4

1. $4x + 2y - z = 4$ 3. $4x - z = 7$

5. $2x - z = 1$ 7. $9x + y - 5z = 16$

9. $2x + 3y - 4z + 11 = 0$ 11. $3x - 2z = 10$

13. $\dfrac{x+2}{2} = \dfrac{y-3}{3} = \dfrac{z-1}{1}$ 15. $\dfrac{x+1}{1} = \dfrac{y}{0} = \dfrac{z+2}{2}$

17. $3x + 2y - z = 0$ 19. $x - 2y - 3z + 5 = 0$

21. $\dfrac{x-2}{3} = \dfrac{y+1}{-2} = \dfrac{z-3}{4}$ 23. $\dfrac{x-1}{2} = \dfrac{y+2}{-1} = \dfrac{z}{4}$

25. $2x - 2y - z = 4$ 27. $2x - 3y - 5z = 7$

29. $2x - 2y - z = 6$ 33. $aA + bB + cC = 0$

SECTION 5

1. $\tfrac{8}{21}$ 3. $\sqrt{14/17}$

5. $x = 11 + 5t, y = -19 - 8t, z = -t$

7. $x = -1 - 2t, y = t, z = 3$ 9. $(3, 2, -1)$

11. $(-\tfrac{3}{5}, 0, -\tfrac{6}{5})$ 13. 1

15. $8/\sqrt{29}$ 17. $10x - 17y + z + 25 = 0$

19. $14x + 8y - 13z + 15 = 0$ 21. $y + z = 1$

23. $\left(\frac{91}{57}, \frac{31}{57}, \frac{25}{57}\right)$ 25. No intersection
27. $x = 3 + 4t, y = -1 + 5t, z = 2 - t$
29. $x = 29t, y = 2 + t, z = 4 - 22t$

SECTION 6

1. $x^2 + y^2 + z^2 - 4x - 2z - 11 = 0$
3. $x^2 + y^2 + z^2 - 6x + 4y - 12z = 0$
5. Sphere; $C(-1, 0, 2), r = 2$
7. No locus
9. Sphere; $C(3, -2, -1), r = 2$
11. $x^2 + y^2 + z^2 + 5x + 7y - 12z + 41 = 0$
13. Plane   15. Plane
17. Parabolic cylinder   19. Elliptic cylinder
21. Circular cylinder   23. Circular cylinder
25. Circle   27. None

SECTION 7

1. Ellipsoid   3. Ellipsoid (oblate)
5. Elliptic hyperboloid of two sheets   7. Elliptic hyperboloid of one sheet
9. Elliptic paraboloid; axis: x-axis   11. Circular paraboloid; axis: y-axis
13. Circular cone about y-axis   15. Elliptic hyperboloid of one sheet
17. Hyperbolic paraboloid

SECTION 8

1. Sphere   3. Elliptic hyperboloid of one sheet
5. Elliptic paraboloid   7. Hyperbolic paraboloid
9. Circular cone   11. Hyperbolic paraboloid
13. Ellipsoid   15. Elliptic hyperboloid of one sheet

SECTION 9

1. (a) $\left(3\sqrt{2}, \frac{\pi}{4}, 7\right)$; (b) $(4\sqrt{5}, \tan^{-1} 2, 2)$; (c) $(\sqrt{13}, \pi - \arctan{(3/2)}, 1)$

3. (a) $\left(2\sqrt{3}, \frac{\pi}{4}, \cos^{-1}\left(\frac{1}{\sqrt{3}}\right)\right)$; (b) $\left(2\sqrt{3}, -\frac{\pi}{4}, \cos^{-1}\left(\frac{-1}{\sqrt{3}}\right)\right)$;

   (c) $\left(2\sqrt{2}, \frac{2\pi}{3}, \frac{\pi}{4}\right)$

5. (a) $\left(4, \frac{\pi}{3}, 0\right)$; (b) $\left(1, \frac{2\pi}{3}, -\sqrt{3}\right)$; (c) $\left(\frac{7}{2}, \frac{\pi}{2}, 7\sqrt{3}/2\right)$

7. $r^2 + z^2 = 9$ 9. $r^2 = 4z$ 11. $r^2 = z^2$
13. $r^2 \cos 2\theta = 4$ 15. $r = 4 \sin \theta$ 17. $\rho = 4 \cos \phi$
19. $\phi = \pi/4$ 21. $\rho = \pm 2/(1 \mp \cos \phi)$

SECTION 10

1. Vertices of region: $(0, 0, 0), (0, 0, 2), (0, 4, 0), (4, 0, 0)$
3. Vertices of region: $(0, 0, 0), (0, 0, -2), (0, 2, 0), (4, 0, 0)$
5. Infinite pentagonal prism bounded by $z \geq 0, (0, 0, 0), (2, 0, 0), (0, 2, 0), (2, \frac{3}{2}, 0),$
   $\left(\frac{5}{3}, 2, 0\right)$
7. Half infinite strip in the plane $y = 4$ satisfying the inequality $z \geq -2$ and situated
   above the segment joining $P(5, 4, -2)$ and $Q(3, 4, -2)$.

CHAPTER 18

SECTION 1

1. $-\mathbf{i} - 2\mathbf{j} + 4\mathbf{k}$

3. $-10\mathbf{j} - 7\mathbf{k}$

5. $4\mathbf{i} - 4\mathbf{k}$

7. $\dfrac{1}{\sqrt{29}}(3\mathbf{i} + 2\mathbf{j} - 4\mathbf{k})$

9. $\dfrac{1}{\sqrt{21}}(2\mathbf{i} - 4\mathbf{j} - \mathbf{k})$

11. $B = (3, 3, -4)$

13. $A = (-1, -2, 0)$

15. $A = (\frac{3}{2}, 0, 3),\ B = (\frac{5}{2}, -2, 5)$

17. $A = (\frac{7}{4}, -\frac{3}{4}, \frac{1}{2}),\ B = (\frac{3}{4}, \frac{1}{4}, \frac{5}{2})$

19. $4\mathbf{i} - 5\mathbf{j} + \mathbf{k}$

SECTION 2

1. $-7/2\sqrt{21}$

3. $-\sqrt{15/28}$

5. $2/\sqrt{574}$

7. $-\frac{2}{7}$

9. $-23/\sqrt{50}$

11. 96

13. 35

15. $\frac{1}{7}(2\mathbf{i} - 6\mathbf{j} + 3\mathbf{k})$

17. $\dfrac{1}{\sqrt{62}}(3\mathbf{i} - 2\mathbf{j} + 7\mathbf{k})$

19. $k = 2;\ h = \frac{2}{5}$

21. $k = 3;\ h = \frac{42}{145}$

25. $3g + 5h = 0$

27. $4g - 9h = 0$

29. $g = -1,\ h = 1$

SECTION 3

1. $\mathbf{i} - 7\mathbf{j} + 5\mathbf{k}$

3. $-15\mathbf{i} + 5\mathbf{j} - 6\mathbf{k}$

5. $\mathbf{0}$

7. $7\sqrt{3}/2;\ x - y - z = 0$

9. $3\sqrt{35}/2;\ 11x + 5y + 13z = 30$

11. $\sqrt{421}/2;\ 9x + 12y + 14z = 32$

13. $107/\sqrt{1038}$

15. $\dfrac{x + 1}{2} = \dfrac{y - 3}{-11} = \dfrac{z - 2}{-7}$

17. $\dfrac{x - 1}{1} = \dfrac{y + 2}{-1} = \dfrac{z - 3}{1}$

19. $\dfrac{x - 3}{-2} = \dfrac{y}{1} = \dfrac{z - 1}{3}$

21. $\dfrac{x + 2}{2} = \dfrac{y - 1}{11} = \dfrac{z + 1}{8}$

23. $8x + 14y + 13z + 37 = 0$

25. $2x - z + 1 = 0$

27. $5x - 3y - z = 6$

29. $4x - 3y - z + 9 = 0$

31. $x - y - z + 6 = 0$

33. $\dfrac{x - 3}{2} = \dfrac{y + 2}{1} = \dfrac{z}{2}$

SECTION 4

1. $\mathbf{f}'(t) = 2\mathbf{i} + 2t\mathbf{j} + 3\mathbf{k};\ \mathbf{f}''(t) = 2\mathbf{j}$

3. $\mathbf{f}'(t) = 2e^{2t}\mathbf{i} - 2e^{-2t}\mathbf{j};\ \mathbf{f}''(t) = 4e^{2t}\mathbf{i} + 4e^{-2t}\mathbf{j}$

5. $\mathbf{f}'(t) = -2(\sin 2t)\mathbf{i} - \dfrac{1}{t^2}\mathbf{j} + 2(\cos 2t)\mathbf{k};$

  $\mathbf{f}''(t) = -4(\cos 2t)\mathbf{i} + \dfrac{2}{t^3}\mathbf{j} - 4(\sin 2t)\mathbf{k}$

7. $f'(t) = 9t^2 + 2t + 2$

9. $f'(t) = 1$

11. 14

13. $\frac{1}{8}\pi\sqrt{\pi^2 + 8} + \ln(\pi + \sqrt{\pi^2 + 8}) - \frac{3}{2}\ln 2$

15. $\mathbf{r}'(t) = (\sin t + t \cos t)\mathbf{i} + (\cos t - t \sin t)\mathbf{j} + \mathbf{k}$; $|\mathbf{r}'(t)| = \sqrt{2 + t^2}$;
$\mathbf{r}''(t) = (2 \cos t - t \sin t)\mathbf{i} - (2 \sin t + t \cos t)\mathbf{j}$

SECTION 5

1. $(3t^2\mathbf{i} - \mathbf{j} + 2\mathbf{k})/\sqrt{9t^4 + 5}$ 3. $(-e^{-2t}\mathbf{i} + e^{2t}\mathbf{j} + t\mathbf{k})/\sqrt{e^{-4t} + e^{4t} + t^2}$

5. $\dfrac{[(\cos t + \sin t)\mathbf{i} + e^t(2 \cos t - \sin t)\mathbf{j} - e^{-2t}\mathbf{k}]}{[(1 + 2 \cos t \sin t) + e^{2t}(2 \cos t - \sin t)^2 + e^{-4t}]^{1/2}}$

7. $\mathbf{T} = \dfrac{1}{\sqrt{6}}(\mathbf{i} - \mathbf{j} + 2\mathbf{k})$; $\kappa = 0$; $\dfrac{x - 4}{1} = \dfrac{y}{-1} = \dfrac{z - 10}{2}$;

$\mathbf{B}$, $\mathbf{N}$ and osculating plane not defined.

9. $\mathbf{T} = \dfrac{1}{\sqrt{3}}(\mathbf{i} + \mathbf{j} + \mathbf{k})$; $\mathbf{N} = \dfrac{1}{\sqrt{2}}(-\mathbf{i} + \mathbf{j})$; $\mathbf{B} = \dfrac{1}{\sqrt{6}}(-\mathbf{i} - \mathbf{j} + 2\mathbf{k})$; $\kappa = \sqrt{2}/3$;

$\dfrac{x - 1}{1} = \dfrac{y}{1} = \dfrac{z - 1}{1}$; $x + y - 2z + 1 = 0$

11. $\mathbf{T} = \dfrac{1}{\sqrt{5}}(\mathbf{j} + 2\mathbf{k})$; $\mathbf{N} = \mathbf{i}$; $\mathbf{B} = \dfrac{1}{\sqrt{5}}(2\mathbf{j} - \mathbf{k})$; $\kappa = \frac{1}{10}$; $\dfrac{x - 2}{0} = \dfrac{y}{1} = \dfrac{z}{2}$;

$2y - z = 0$

13. $\mathbf{v} = \mathbf{i} + 6\mathbf{j} + 18\mathbf{k}$; $\mathbf{T} = \mathbf{v}/19$; $\mathbf{a} = 3\mathbf{j} + 18\mathbf{k}$; $\mathbf{N} = -\frac{1}{19}(6\mathbf{i} + 17\mathbf{j} - 6\mathbf{k})$;
$a_T = 18$; $a_N = 3$; $R = \frac{361}{3}$

15. $\mathbf{v} = \mathbf{i} + 2\mathbf{j} - 2\mathbf{k}$; $\mathbf{T} = \mathbf{v}/3$
$\mathbf{a} = 2\mathbf{i} + 4\mathbf{k}$; $\mathbf{N} = (2\mathbf{i} + \mathbf{j} + 2\mathbf{k})/3$
$a_T = -2$; $a_N = 36$; $R = \frac{1}{4}$

CHAPTER 19

SECTION 1

1. $\frac{3}{4}$	3. $\frac{3}{2}$	5. $\frac{2}{3}$	7. 0	9. 3
11. 4	13. ∞	15. 0	17. $\ln 3 - \ln 2$	
19. 0	21. 0	23. -1	25. 0	27. 0
29. 2	31. 1	33. 0	35. 0	37. 1
39. 1	41. 1	43. e		

SECTION 2

1. $\frac{53}{99}$ 3. $515,000/1111$ 5. $\frac{3718}{999}$ 7. $\frac{9}{4}$

9. $\frac{1}{4} + \frac{4}{11} + \frac{3}{7} + \frac{8}{17} + \frac{1}{2}$ 11. $e - \dfrac{e^2}{8} + \dfrac{e^3}{27} - \dfrac{e^4}{64} + \dfrac{e^5}{125}$

SECTION 3

1. Convergent	3. Convergent	5. Divergent
7. Convergent	9. Divergent	11. Divergent
13. Convergent	15. Convergent	17. Divergent
19. Convergent	21. Convergent	23. Convergent
25. Convergent	27. Convergent	29. Convergent

SECTION 4

1. Divergent
5. Absolutely convergent
9. Absolutely convergent
13. Divergent
17. Absolutely convergent
21. Absolutely convergent
25. Conditionally convergent

3. Divergent
7. Conditionally convergent
11. Absolutely convergent
15. Absolutely convergent
19. Conditionally convergent
23. Divergent
27. Conditionally convergent

SECTION 5

1. Converges for $-1 < x < 1$
5. Converges for $-1 < x < 1$
9. Converges for $-1 \le x + 2 < 1$
13. Converges for $-\frac{2}{3} < x \le \frac{2}{3}$
17. Converges for $-3 \le x + 4 \le 3$
21. Converges for $-\frac{4}{3} < x < \frac{4}{3}$
25. Converges for $-1 < x \le 1$
29. (a) converges for $|x| < 1$

3. Converges for $-\frac{1}{2} < x < \frac{1}{2}$
7. Converges for $-2 \le x - 1 \le 2$
11. Converges for $-\infty < x < \infty$
15. Converges for $-1 < x - 1 < 1$
19. Converges for $-8 < x - 2 < 8$
23. Converges for $-1 \le x < 1$
27. Converges for $-\frac{3}{2} \le x \le \frac{3}{2}$
31. Converges for $|x| < 1$

SECTION 6

1. $\displaystyle\sum_{n=0}^{\infty} \frac{x^n}{n!}$

3. $\displaystyle\sum_{n=1}^{\infty} \frac{(-1)^{n-1}x^n}{n}$

5. $\displaystyle\sum_{n=0}^{\infty} (n + 1)x^n$

7. $\displaystyle 1 + \sum_{n=1}^{\infty} \frac{(\frac{1}{2})(-\frac{1}{2})(-\frac{3}{2}) \cdots (-n + \frac{3}{2})x^n}{n!}$

9. $\displaystyle \ln 3 + \sum_{n=1}^{\infty} \frac{(-1)^{n-1}(x - 3)^n}{3^n \cdot n}$

11. $\displaystyle \frac{1}{2} - \frac{\sqrt{3}}{2}\left(x - \frac{\pi}{3}\right) - \frac{1}{2}\frac{\left(x - \frac{\pi}{3}\right)^2}{2!} + \frac{\sqrt{3}}{2}\frac{\left(x - \frac{\pi}{3}\right)^3}{3!} + \cdots$

13. $\displaystyle 2 + \frac{1}{4}(x - 4) + 2\sum_{n=2}^{\infty} (-1)^{n-1}\frac{1 \cdot 3 \cdots (2n - 3)(x - 4)^n}{2 \cdot 4 \cdots (2n) \cdot 4^n}$

15. $\displaystyle \cos\left(\frac{1}{2}\right) - x\sin\left(\frac{1}{2}\right) - \frac{x^2}{2!}\cos\left(\frac{1}{2}\right) + \frac{x^3}{3!}\sin\left(\frac{1}{2}\right) + \frac{x^4}{4!}\cos\left(\frac{1}{2}\right) + \cdots$

17. $\displaystyle 1 - x^2 + \frac{x^4}{2}$

19. $\displaystyle 1 - x^2 + x^4$

21. $\displaystyle 1 + x - \frac{x^3}{3} - \frac{x^4}{6}$

23. $\displaystyle x + \frac{x^3}{2 \cdot 3} + \frac{3x^5}{2 \cdot 4 \cdot 5}$

25. $\frac{1}{2}x^2 + \frac{1}{12}x^4 + \frac{1}{45}x^6$

27. $1 - \frac{1}{2}x^2 + \frac{5}{24}x^4$

29. $\displaystyle 2 + 2\sqrt{3}\left(x - \frac{\pi}{3}\right) + 7\left(x - \frac{\pi}{3}\right)^2 + \frac{23\sqrt{3}}{3}\left(x - \frac{\pi}{3}\right)^3$

SECTION 7

1. 0.81873
9. 0.36788
17. 0.95635

3. 1.22140
11. 1.01943
19. −0.22314

5. 0.87758
13. 0.96905
21. 0.017452

7. 0.1823
15. 1.97437
23. 0.99619

SECTION 8

1. $\displaystyle\sum_{n=0}^{\infty} \frac{(-1)^n x^{2n}}{(2n+1)!}$

3. $\displaystyle\sum_{n=1}^{\infty} \frac{(-1)^{n-1} x^{2n-1}}{(2n)!}$

5. $\displaystyle x + \sum_{n=1}^{\infty} \frac{1 \cdot 3 \cdot 5 \cdots (2n-1)}{2 \cdot 4 \cdot 6 \cdots (2n)} \cdot \frac{x^{2n+1}}{2n+1}$

7. $\displaystyle\sum_{n=0}^{\infty} \frac{x^{2n+1}}{2n+1}$

9. $\displaystyle 2\sum_{n=0}^{\infty} \frac{x^{2n+1}}{2n+1}$

11. $\displaystyle\sum_{n=0}^{\infty} (-1)^n (n+1) x^{2n+1}$

13. $\displaystyle\frac{1}{2} - \frac{1}{2}\sum_{n=0}^{\infty} \frac{(-1)^n (2x)^{2n}}{(2n)!}$

SECTION 9

1. $1 - \dfrac{3}{2}x + \dfrac{1 \cdot 3 \cdot 5}{2^2 \cdot 2!}x^2 - \dfrac{1 \cdot 3 \cdot 5 \cdot 7}{2^3 \cdot 3!}x^3 + \dfrac{1 \cdot 3 \cdot 5 \cdot 7 \cdot 9}{2^4 \cdot 4!}x^4$

3. $1 - \dfrac{2}{3}x^2 + \dfrac{2 \cdot 5}{3^2 \cdot 2!}x^4 - \dfrac{2 \cdot 5 \cdot 8}{3^3 \cdot 3!}x^6 + \dfrac{2 \cdot 5 \cdot 8 \cdot 11}{3^4 \cdot 4!}x^8$

5. $1 + 7x^3 + 21x^6 + 35x^9 + 35x^{12} + 21x^{15} + 7x^{18} + x^{21}$

7. $\dfrac{1}{3^3} - \dfrac{3}{3^4}x^{1/2} + \dfrac{3 \cdot 4}{3^5 \cdot 2!}x - \dfrac{3 \cdot 4 \cdot 5}{3^6 \cdot 3!}x^{3/2} + \dfrac{3 \cdot 4 \cdot 5 \cdot 6}{3^7 \cdot 4!}x^2$

9. 0.90452   11. 0.48540   13. 1.31790

15. 0.32939   17. 0.50826   19. 0.69315

SECTION 10

1. $x - x^2 + \dfrac{5}{6}x^3 - \dfrac{5}{6}x^4 + \dfrac{101}{120}x^5$

3. $1 - x + \dfrac{x^2}{2} - \dfrac{x^3}{2} + \dfrac{13}{24}x^4 - \dfrac{13}{24}x^5$

5. $x - \frac{1}{24}x^3 + \frac{1}{24}x^4 - \frac{71}{1920}x^5$

7. $x - x^2 + \frac{23}{24}x^3 - \frac{11}{12}x^4 + \frac{563}{640}x^5$

9. $1 + x + x^2 + \frac{2}{3}x^3 + \frac{1}{2}x^4 + \frac{3}{10}x^5$

11. $1 + x - \frac{1}{3}x^3 + \frac{1}{6}x^4 + \frac{3}{10}x^5$

13. $x - x^2 + \frac{2}{3}x^3 - \frac{2}{3}x^4 + \frac{13}{15}x^5$

15. $x - \frac{1}{3}x^3 + \frac{1}{5}x^5$

17. $1 + \frac{1}{3}x + \frac{11}{9}x^2 + \frac{41}{81}x^3 + \frac{8}{243}x^4$

19. $1 + \frac{3}{2}x^2 + \frac{1}{2}x^3 + \frac{3}{8}x^4$

CHAPTER 20

SECTION 1

1. $f_{,1} = 2x + 2y^2 - 2;\ f_{,2} = 4xy$

3. $f_{,1} = 3x^2 y - 6xy^2 + 2y;\ f_{,2} = x^3 - 6x^2 y + 2x$

5. $f_{,1} = x/\sqrt{x^2 + y^2};\ f_{,2} = y/\sqrt{x^2 + y^2}$

7. $f_{,1} = 2x/(x^2 + y^2);\ f_{,2} = 2y/(x^2 + y^2)$

9. $f_{,1} = -y/(x^2 + y^2);\ f_{,2} = x/(x^2 + y^2)$

11. $f_{,1} = ye^{x^2 + y^2}(2x^2 + 1);\ f_{,2} = xe^{x^2 + y^2}(2y^2 + 1)$

13. $f_{,1}(1, 2) = \infty;\ f_{,2}(1, 2) = \infty$

15. $f_{,1} = \dfrac{1}{2}e^{\sqrt{2}/2}(4 + \sqrt{2});\ f_{,2} = \dfrac{\pi}{2}e^{\sqrt{2}/2}$

17. $f_{,1} = 32\ln 2;\ f_{,2} = 32(1 + \ln 2)$

19. $f_{,1} = 2xy - 4xz + 3yz + 2z^2;\ f_{,2} = x^2 + 3xz - 2yz;$
$f_{,3} = -2x^2 + 3xy - y^2 + 4xz$

21. $f_{,1} = (yz + y \cot xy - 2z \tan 2xz)f(x, y, z)$
    $f_{,2} = (xz + x \cot xy)f(x, y, z)$
    $f_{,3} = (xy - 2x \tan 2xz)f(x, y, z)$

23. $\dfrac{\partial w}{\partial x} = \dfrac{y^2 - x^2}{x(x^2 + y^2)}; \dfrac{\partial w}{\partial y} = \dfrac{x^2 - y^2}{y(x^2 + y^2)}$

25. $\dfrac{\partial w}{\partial y} = \dfrac{1}{x} \cos\left(\dfrac{y}{x}\right) e^{\sin(y/x)}; \dfrac{\partial w}{\partial x} = -\dfrac{y}{x^2} \cos\left(\dfrac{y}{x}\right) e^{\sin(y/x)}$

SECTION 2

1. $\dfrac{\partial w}{\partial x} = \dfrac{1 - 6x}{12w}; \dfrac{\partial w}{\partial y} = -\dfrac{1 + 4y}{12w}$

3. $\dfrac{\partial w}{\partial x} = \dfrac{y - x - w}{x + w}; \dfrac{\partial w}{\partial y} = \dfrac{x - 3y}{w + x}$

5. $\dfrac{\partial w}{\partial r} = \dfrac{w(r^2 + s^2) + 2r \coth rw}{-r(r^2 + s^2) + \operatorname{csch} rw}; \dfrac{\partial w}{\partial s} = \dfrac{2s \cosh rw}{1 - r(r^2 + s^2) \sinh rw}$

7. $\dfrac{\partial w}{\partial x} = \dfrac{2w \tan 2xw - y \cot xy - yw}{x(y - 2 \tan 2xw)}; \dfrac{\partial w}{\partial y} = \dfrac{w + \cot xy}{2 \tan 2xw - y}$

9. $\dfrac{\partial w}{\partial x} = \dfrac{z(y + 2x + w)}{yz + 3w^2 - xz}; \dfrac{\partial w}{\partial y} = \dfrac{z(w - x - z)}{xz - yz - 3w^2}$

   $\dfrac{\partial w}{\partial z} = \dfrac{yw - xw - xy - 2yz - x^2}{xz - yz - 3w^2}$

11. $\dfrac{\partial w}{\partial x} = \dfrac{ye^{x(y-w)} + w^2}{y^2 e^{w(y-x)} - xw - 1}; \dfrac{\partial w}{\partial y} = \dfrac{xe^{y(x-w)} - yw - 1}{y^2 - (1 + xw)e^{w(x-y)}}$

SECTION 3

1. $\dfrac{\partial f}{\partial s} = 10s; \dfrac{\partial f}{\partial t} = 10t$

3. $\dfrac{\partial f}{\partial s} = 4s(s^2 + t^2); \dfrac{\partial f}{\partial t} = 4t(s^2 + t^2)$

5. $\dfrac{\partial f}{\partial s} = \dfrac{y(2y - x)}{(x^2 + y^2)^{3/2}}; \dfrac{\partial f}{\partial t} = \dfrac{-y(2x + y)}{(x^2 + y^2)^{3/2}}$

7. $\dfrac{\partial f}{\partial s} = 10x + 13y - 4z; \dfrac{\partial f}{\partial t} = -5x + y + 2z$

9. $\dfrac{df}{dr} = 4(2r^3 + 3r^2 - 6r + 1)$

11. $\dfrac{\partial f}{\partial r} = 2r(3u^2 + 4u - 3); \dfrac{\partial f}{\partial s} = -2s(3u^2 + 4u - 3); \dfrac{\partial f}{\partial t} = 2t(3u^2 + 4u - 3)$

13. $\dfrac{\partial z}{\partial r} = 0; \dfrac{\partial z}{\partial \theta} = -4$

15. $\dfrac{dw}{dt} = \dfrac{1}{8}\sqrt{2}\pi(4 + \sqrt{2})$

17. $\dfrac{\partial z}{\partial r} = 0; \dfrac{\partial z}{\partial \theta} = \dfrac{1}{2}$

19. $\dfrac{\partial w}{\partial s} = 0; \dfrac{\partial w}{\partial t} = -16$

SECTION 4

1. $\dfrac{290\pi}{\sqrt{13}}$

3. $\dfrac{25}{R} = \dfrac{T}{15}$

5. $\dfrac{40\pi\sqrt{3} - 63}{252}$

7. $-\dfrac{2\sqrt{10\pi} + 1}{15}$

11. (a) $\begin{cases} \dfrac{\partial z}{\partial r} = \dfrac{\partial z}{\partial x}\cos\theta + \dfrac{\partial z}{\partial y}\sin\theta; \\[4mm] \dfrac{\partial z}{\partial \theta} = r\left[-\dfrac{\partial z}{\partial x}\sin\theta + \dfrac{\partial z}{\partial y}\cos\theta\right] \end{cases}$

17. $1 + 2\sqrt{3} - \dfrac{14 + \sqrt{3}}{\sqrt{79} - 10\sqrt{3}}$

SECTION 5

1. $d_\theta f = 6\cos\theta + 8\sin\theta$

3. $d_\theta f = \dfrac{-3\cos\theta + 4\sin\theta}{25}$

5. $d_\theta f = \dfrac{\cos\theta - \sqrt{3}\sin\theta}{2}$

7. $d_\theta f = 2\cos\theta + \sin\theta$;   max if $\cos\theta = \dfrac{2}{\sqrt{5}}$, $\sin\theta = \dfrac{1}{\sqrt{5}}$

9. $d_\theta f = \frac{1}{2}\cos\theta + \frac{1}{2}\sqrt{3}\sin\theta$; max if $\theta = \pi/3$

11. $D_{\mathbf{a}}f = 7\lambda + 4\mu + 2\nu$ where $\mathbf{a} = \lambda\mathbf{i} + \mu\mathbf{j} + \nu\mathbf{k}$

13. $D_{\mathbf{a}}f = -\lambda$ where $\mathbf{a} = \lambda\mathbf{i} + \mu\mathbf{j} + \nu\mathbf{k}$

15. $\frac{11}{3}$

17. $2/\sqrt{6}$

19. $d_\theta T = 400\cos\theta - 300\sin\theta$; $\tan\theta = \frac{4}{3}$; slope of curve is $\frac{4}{3}$

21. $\nabla f = -4\mathbf{i} - \frac{4}{5}\mathbf{j}$

23. $(2e^2 + 2e^{-1} - e^{-2})\mathbf{i} + (-3e^2 + e^{-1} + e^{-2})\mathbf{j} - (4e^2 + e^{-2})\mathbf{k}$

25. $D_{\mathbf{a}}f = \dfrac{1}{\sqrt{14}}[-3e^2\cos 1 - e^2\sin 1 + 2e]$; $D_{\mathbf{a}}f = e\sqrt{1 + e^2}$ is maximum

27. $D_{\mathbf{a}}f = \dfrac{3 - \cos 1 - 6\sin 1 + 2\cos 2}{\sqrt{14}}$;

$D_{\mathbf{a}}f = \sqrt{\cos^2 1 + \cos^2 2 + (1 - 2\sin 1)^2}$ max

SECTION 6

1. $4x - 4y - z - 6 = 0$; $\dfrac{x - 2}{4} = \dfrac{y + 1}{-4} = \dfrac{z - 6}{-1}$

3. $x - 2y + z - 2 = 0$; $\dfrac{x - 2}{-1} = \dfrac{y + 1}{2} = \dfrac{z + 2}{-1}$

5. $ex - z = 0$; $\dfrac{x - 1}{e} = \dfrac{y - (\pi/2)}{0} = \dfrac{z - e}{-1}$

7. $3x - 4y + 25z = 25(\ln 5 - 1)$; $\dfrac{x + 3}{3} = \dfrac{y - 4}{-4} = \dfrac{z - \ln 5}{25}$

9. $2x + 2y + 3z = 3$; $\dfrac{x - 2}{2} = \dfrac{y - 1}{2} = \dfrac{z + 1}{3}$

11. $4x - 3z = 25$; $\dfrac{x-4}{4} = \dfrac{y+2}{0} = \dfrac{z+3}{-3}$

13. $3x + 6y + 2z = 36$; $\dfrac{x-4}{3} = \dfrac{y-1}{6} = \dfrac{z-9}{2}$

19. $\dfrac{x-4}{4} = \dfrac{y+2}{3} = \dfrac{z-20}{20}$ 21. $\dfrac{x-4}{3} = \dfrac{y+3}{4} = \dfrac{z-16}{24}$

SECTION 7

1. $df = -0.17$; $\Delta f = -0.1689$

3. $df = \dfrac{\pi}{2}(\pi - 5)$; $\Delta f = -\sqrt{3} + \sin\dfrac{13\pi^2}{2}$

5. $df = -0.45$; $\Delta f = -0.456035$ 7. $df = 0.05$; $\Delta f = 0.0499$

9. $df = -0.08$; $\Delta f = -0.080384$ 11. $300x^{-1}h + 700y^{-1}k + 400z^{-1}l$

13. $V \approx 4309.92$ 15. 1.4%

17. 3.3π 19. $1 + \dfrac{5\pi\sqrt{3}}{18}\% \approx 2.5\%$

21. 0.111427

23. $(12t^5 + 15t^4 + 48t^3 - 15t^2 + 12t - 35)\,dt$

25. $4r(3r^2 - s^2 + 6s^{-2})\,dr + 4s(3s^2 - r^2 - 6r^2 s^{-4})\,ds$

SECTION 8

1. $\dfrac{dy}{dx} = \dfrac{2x + 3y + 2}{-3x + 8y + 6}$ 3. $\dfrac{dy}{dx} = -\dfrac{2x + (1 + x^2 + y^2)ye^{xy}}{2y + (1 + x^2 + y^2)xe^{xy}}$

5. $\dfrac{dy}{dx} = -\dfrac{y}{x}$ 7. $\dfrac{dy}{dx} = -\dfrac{3x(x^2 + y^2)^{3/2} - y}{3y(x^2 + y^2)^{3/2} + x}$

9. $\dfrac{\partial w}{\partial x} = -\dfrac{3x^2 + 6xw + 2}{3x^2 - y^2 + 4yw - 3}$ 11. $\dfrac{\partial w}{\partial x} = -\dfrac{yw\cos(xyw) + 2x}{xy\cos(xyw) + 2w}$

13. $\dfrac{\partial w}{\partial y} = \dfrac{2y + 3x - 3}{2w - 4x + 3z}$ 15. $\dfrac{dy}{dx} = -\dfrac{2x + 2}{y}$; $\dfrac{dz}{dx} = -2(x + 2)$

17. $\dfrac{dy}{dx} = \dfrac{4z + 2xy}{4z^2 - 3y^2}$; $\dfrac{dz}{dx} = -\dfrac{3y + 2xz}{4z^2 - 3y^2}$

19. $\dfrac{\partial u}{\partial x} = \dfrac{u}{2(u^2 + v^2)}$; $\dfrac{\partial u}{\partial y} = \dfrac{v}{2(u^2 + v^2)}$

$\dfrac{\partial v}{\partial x} = -\dfrac{v}{2(u^2 + v^2)}$; $\dfrac{\partial v}{\partial y} = \dfrac{u}{2(u^2 + v^2)}$

21. $\dfrac{\partial u}{\partial x} = \dfrac{2xv}{u + v}$; $\dfrac{\partial u}{\partial y} = \dfrac{1}{2(u + v)}$; $\dfrac{\partial v}{\partial x} = \dfrac{2xu}{u + v}$; $\dfrac{\partial v}{\partial y} = -\dfrac{1}{2(u + v)}$

23. $\dfrac{\partial u}{\partial x} = 0$; $\dfrac{\partial u}{\partial y} = \dfrac{y}{u}$; $\dfrac{\partial v}{\partial x} = -\dfrac{x}{v}$; $\dfrac{\partial v}{\partial y} = 0$

25. $\dfrac{\partial u}{\partial x} = \dfrac{g_v}{f_u g_v - f_v g_u}$; $\dfrac{\partial u}{\partial y} = \dfrac{-f_v}{f_u g_v - f_v g_u}$; $\dfrac{\partial v}{\partial x} = \dfrac{-g_u}{f_u g_v - f_v g_u}$; $\dfrac{\partial v}{\partial y} = \dfrac{f_u}{f_u g_v - f_v g_u}$.

SECTION 9

1. $f_{,1,2} = f_{,2,1} = -2$ 3. $-2x + 4y$
5. $e^{rs}[(rs + 1) \sin r \cos s + r \cos r \cos s - s \sin r \sin s - \cos r \sin s]$
7. $(t^2 - s^2)/(s^2 + t^2)^2$ 9. $u_{xy} = u_{yx} = -2xy/(x^2 + y^2 + z^2)^2$;
$u_{xz} = u_{zz} = -2xz/(x^2 + y^2 + z^2)^2$

11. $u_{xy} = u_{yx} = -3z$; $u_{xz} = u_{zz} = -3y$
13. $u_{xy} = u_{yx} = e^{xy}[xy(x^2 + z^2) + z^2](x^2 + z^2)^{-3/2}$
$u_{xz} = u_{zz} = ze^{xy}[3x - y(x^2 + z^2)](x^2 + z^2)^{-5/2}$

17. $\dfrac{\partial^2 z}{\partial r^2} = 2 \cos 2s$ 19. $z_{rr} = 12r^2 - 24rs - 12s^2$

21. $F_{yy} + 2F_{yz}\dfrac{\partial z}{\partial y} + F_{zz}\left(\dfrac{\partial z}{\partial y}\right)^2 + F_z \dfrac{\partial^2 z}{\partial y^2}$

25. $\dfrac{\partial^2 u}{\partial r\, \partial s} = F_x \dfrac{\partial^2 x}{\partial r\, \partial s} + F_y \dfrac{\partial^2 y}{\partial r\, \partial s} + F_{xx} \dfrac{\partial x}{\partial r} \dfrac{\partial x}{\partial s}$

$+ F_{xy}\left(\dfrac{\partial x}{\partial r} \dfrac{\partial y}{\partial s} + \dfrac{\partial x}{\partial s} \dfrac{\partial y}{\partial r}\right) + F_{yy}\dfrac{\partial y}{\partial r} \dfrac{\partial y}{\partial s}$

SECTION 10

1. $10 + 13(x - 2) + 4(y - 1) + 6(x - 2)^2 + 2(x - 2)(y - 1) + 2(y - 1)^2$
$+ (x - 2)^3 + (x - 2)(y - 1)^2$
3. $x + y - \frac{1}{6}(x + y)^3$
5. $1 + (x + y) + \frac{1}{2}(x + y)^2 + \frac{1}{6}(x + y)^3$
7. $1 - \frac{1}{2}x^2 - \frac{1}{2}y^2 + \frac{1}{24}x^4 + \frac{1}{4}x^2y^2 + \frac{1}{24}y^4$
9. $3 + 4(x - 1) + 2(y - 1) + z + (x - 1)^2 + z^2$
$+ 2(x - 1)(y - 1) + (y - 1)z$
11. $\phi''(0) = 2\lambda^2 + 8\lambda\mu + 2\mu^2$. No.

13. $\displaystyle\sum_{i=0}^{k} \sum_{j=0}^{i} \dfrac{i!k!}{i!j!(k - i)!(i - j)!} A^i B^{i-j} C^{k-i}$

SECTION 11

1. Rel min at $(2, -1)$ 3. Rel min at $(1, -2)$
5. Rel min at $(\frac{27}{2}, 5)$; saddle point at $(\frac{3}{2}, 1)$
7. No rel max or min; $(1, \frac{2}{3})$, $(-1, -\frac{4}{3})$ saddle points.
9. Rel max at $\left(\dfrac{\pi}{3} \pm 2n\pi, \dfrac{\pi}{3} \pm 2m\pi\right)$ Rel min at $\left(-\dfrac{\pi}{3} \pm 2n\pi, -\dfrac{\pi}{3} \pm 2m\pi\right)$

Test fails at $(\pi \pm 2n\pi, \pi \pm 2m\pi)$
11. Rel max at $(0, 0)$
13. Test fails; critical points are along the lines $(x, n\pi)$
15. $(-\frac{3}{2}, -\frac{1}{2}, -\frac{1}{4})$ 17. $x = -\frac{9}{31}, y = \frac{55}{62}, z = \frac{18}{31}, t = -\frac{41}{31}$
19. $\dfrac{17}{\sqrt{10}}$ 21. $\frac{1}{2}\sqrt{10}$ 23. $\dfrac{6}{\sqrt{3}}, \dfrac{4}{\sqrt{3}}, \dfrac{8}{\sqrt{3}}$
25. Length = width = 4 times height
27. Take $S: 0 \le \alpha < \pi/2, 0 < x < P \cos \alpha/(1 + \cos \alpha)$. Max A is $P^2(2 - \sqrt{3})/4$ and occurs when $\alpha = \pi/6, x = P(2 - \sqrt{3})/2$. Max of A on the boundary is $P^2/16$, which is less than $P^2(2 - \sqrt{3})/4$.

SECTION 12

1. $\frac{8}{7}$

3. $d^2/(a^2 + b^2 + c^2)$

5. Min $= \frac{134}{75}$; occurs at $(\frac{16}{15}, \frac{1}{3}, -\frac{11}{15})$

7. $x = \pm\frac{1}{2}(1 - \sqrt{5})\sqrt{50 - 10\sqrt{5}}$, $y = \mp\sqrt{50 - 10\sqrt{5}}$

9. 2, 2, 1

11. $h = 2\sqrt{5}$; $H = \dfrac{V}{25\pi} - \frac{2}{3}\sqrt{5}$

13. $\frac{17}{23}$; occurs at $x = \frac{10}{23}$, $y = \frac{1}{23}$, $z = -\frac{1}{23}$, $t = \frac{17}{23}$

15. Closest: $(\pm\frac{1}{2}\sqrt{2}, \pm\frac{1}{2}\sqrt{2})$; farthest: $(\pm\sqrt{2}, \mp\sqrt{2})$

17. Max dimensions: length $\frac{100}{3}$, width $=$ height $= \frac{50}{3}$

19. If C is the cost (in dollars) per square ft of material, then length $=$ width $= \frac{1}{3}\sqrt{D/C}$; height $= \frac{1}{2}\sqrt{D/C}$

21. $x = aA/(a + b + c)$, $y = bA/(a + b + c)$, $z = cA/(a + b + c)$

SECTION 13

1. Exact; $(x^4/4) + x^3y + (y^4/4) + C$ 3. Exact; $2xy - \ln x + \ln y + C$

5. Not exact   7. Exact; $e^{x^2}\sin y + C$

9. Exact; $\arctan(y/x) + C$ 11. Not exact

13. Not exact   15. Not exact

17. Exact; $e^x \sin y \cos z + C$

19. (b) $f(x, y, z, t) = x^3 + z^3 - t^3 + y^2 + 2xz - yt + 3x - 2y + 4t + C$

SECTION 15

1. $\frac{7}{2}$ 3. $\frac{231}{64}$ 5. $\pi + 8$ 7. $4 + 2\ln(\frac{5}{4})$

9. $\arcsin(\frac{4}{5})$ 11. $508\sqrt{3}/11$ 13. $\frac{64}{105}$

15. $\dfrac{8}{9^4}\left\{(37)^{3/2}\left[\dfrac{1}{9}(37)^3 - \dfrac{3}{7}(37)^2 + \dfrac{3}{5}(37) - \dfrac{1}{3}\right]\right.$

$\left. - (10)^{3/2}\left[\dfrac{1}{9}(10)^3 - \dfrac{3}{7}(10)^2 + \dfrac{3}{5}(10) - \dfrac{1}{3}\right]\right\}$

17. $\frac{1}{2}(\sin 7 + \sin 1) + 2(\cos 3 - \cos 7)$

19. 24   21. $\frac{1}{2}\ln 17$ 23. 0

SECTION 16

1. $\frac{101}{3}$ 3. $-e + \cos 1$

5. $-\frac{7}{5}$ 7. $\sin 3 - \cos 2 + e^{-6}\cos 6$

9. -9 11. $e^{-6}\cos 1 + \sin 2 - \cos 3$

13. $\dfrac{1}{2}\ln\dfrac{a^2 + b^2}{c^2 + d^2}$ 15. $(d^2 + e^2 + f^2)^{-1/2} - (a^2 + b^2 + c^2)^{-1/2}$

CHAPTER 21

SECTION 1

1. 0.969   3. 3.5355   5. 3.8140   7. 3.2148   9. 3.4036

SECTION 2

1. Smallest $= 0$; largest $= 180$ 3. Smallest $= 48$; largest $= 1680$

5. Smallest $= -27\pi\sqrt{2}$; largest $= 27\pi\sqrt{2}$ 7. Smallest $= 9$; largest $= 9\sqrt{10}$

SECTION 3

1. $\frac{423}{4}$

3. $-\frac{20975}{14}$

5. $\frac{18}{7}\sqrt{3} - \frac{16}{21}\sqrt{2} - \frac{559}{8}$

7. 0

9. $\frac{1}{4}(2\cos 4 - \cos 8 - 1)$

11. $40\frac{88}{105}$

13. $\frac{\pi}{4}(\sqrt{3} - 1)$

15. $\dfrac{2\pi - 3\sqrt{3}}{48}$

17. $2e^{1/\sqrt{2}} - e\sqrt{2}$

19. 0

21. $(2\sqrt{2} - 1)/3$

23. $32\sqrt{2}/15$

25. $\frac{64}{3}$ 27. $\frac{8}{15}$

29. 8π 31. $\frac{16}{5}$

SECTION 4

1. $\frac{5}{12}$

3. $\frac{2}{3} + 4\ln\left(\frac{3}{2}\right)$

5. $\frac{9}{8}(3\pi + 2)$ 7. $\frac{9}{20}$

9. $\frac{2}{5}$

11. $\frac{207}{10}$

13. $2a^3$

SECTION 6

1. $4\pi/3$

3. 2π

5. $64(3\pi - 4)/9$ 7. $\sqrt{2} - 1$

9. $\frac{64}{3}$

11. 4π

13. $32\pi(8 - 3\sqrt{3})/3$

15. $\frac{64}{9}$

17. $9\pi/2$

19. $4\pi\sqrt{3}$ 21. $\pi/4$

23. $(3\pi - 4)a^3/9$

25. $[\sqrt{2} + \ln(1 + \sqrt{2})]a^3/3$

SECTION 7

1. $I = ma^2/3,\ R = a/\sqrt{3}$

3. $I = 9m/35;\ R = 3/\sqrt{35}$

5. $I = 2ma^2/5,\ R = a\sqrt{2/5}$

7. $I = m(\pi^2 - 4)/2;\ R = \sqrt{(\pi^2 - 4)/2}$

9. $47m/14$

11. $5m/14$

13. $3ma^2/10$

15. $\pi ma^2/8$

17. $I = \rho\left(\frac{\pi}{8} - \frac{1}{5}\right),\ m = \rho\left(\frac{\pi}{4} - \frac{1}{3}\right)$

19. $\bar{x} = \frac{235}{112},\ \bar{y} = \frac{25}{32}$

21. $\bar{x} = \frac{5}{9},\ \bar{y} = \frac{4}{7}$

23. $\bar{x} = \bar{y} = 5a/8$

25. $\bar{x} = \frac{5}{3},\ \bar{y} = 0$

27. $\bar{x} = -2/(8\sqrt{3} - 1),\ \bar{y} = 0$

SECTION 8

1. $(552 - 1600\sqrt{10})/1215$

3. $8a^2$

5. $2\pi\sqrt{2}$

7. $9\sqrt{2}$

9. $\pi\sqrt{2}/2$

11. $4(20 - 3\pi)/9$

13. $2a^2(\pi - 2)/3$

15. $2\pi\sqrt{2}$

17. $a^2(\pi + 6\sqrt{3} - 12)/3$

SECTION 9

1. $4\pi b^2 a/3$

3. $64\pi/15$

5. $2\pi a^3/21$ 7. $4\pi/9$

9. $269\pi/24$

11. $V = 256\pi\sqrt{2}/105;\ \bar{x} = 256\sqrt{2}/105\pi$

SECTION 10

1. $\frac{1}{8}$

3. $\frac{109}{1008}$

5. $(16 - 3\pi)/3$

7. $\frac{3}{2}$

9. $\frac{1}{3}$

11. $abc^2/24$

13. $a^4/840$

15. $243\pi/2$

17. $27a^5(2\pi + 3\sqrt{3})/2$

SECTION 11

1. $2\pi a^3 \delta(2 - \sqrt{2})/6$

3. $\pi k(b^4 - a^4)$

5. $12\pi ka^5\sqrt{3}/5$

7. $128ka^5(15\pi - 26)/225$

9. $7\pi ka^4/6$

11. $7\pi\delta a^3/6$

13. $2\delta a^3(3\pi + 20 - 16\sqrt{2})/9$

15. $k\pi a^4/4$

SECTION 12

1. $2\delta a^5/3$

3. $ka^6/90$

5. $32\delta\left(\dfrac{8}{27} - \dfrac{1}{5} + \dfrac{1}{21}\right) = \dfrac{4352\delta}{945}$

7. $\dfrac{5\pi\delta}{16}$

9. $4\pi k(b^6 - a^6)/9$

11. $4ka^6/9$

13. $4\pi abc\delta(a^2 + b^2)/15$

15. $4\pi\delta[(c^2 - a^2)^{3/2}(2c^2 + 3a^2) - (b^2 - a^2)^{3/2}(2b^2 + 3a^2)]/15$

17. $\bar{x} = \bar{z} = 2a/5; \bar{y} = a/5$

19. $\bar{y} = \bar{z} = 0; \bar{x} = \frac{8}{7}$

21. $\bar{x} = \bar{y} = 0; \bar{z} = \frac{1}{3}$

23. $\bar{y} = \bar{z} = 0; \bar{x} = 2a$

25. $\bar{x} = \bar{y} = 0; \bar{z} = 3(2 + \sqrt{2})a/16$

27. $\bar{x} = \bar{y} = 0; \bar{z} = 9a/7$

29. $\bar{x} = \bar{y} = 0; \bar{z} = \dfrac{4(1591 - 288\sqrt{3})a}{7(391 - 192\sqrt{3})}$

31. $\bar{y} = \bar{z} = 0; \bar{x} = a\sqrt{2}/2$

CHAPTER 22

SECTION 1

1. $(-1, 1, 0)$

3. $(1, -1, 2)$

5. $(2, 1, -1, -2)$

7. $(1, 1, -1, -1)$

9. $(1, 2, -1, 2)$

11. $(2, -1, 0, 3, -2)$

SECTION 2

1. $A = \begin{pmatrix} -4 & -7 \\ 7 & -6 \end{pmatrix}$

3. $A = \begin{pmatrix} 5 & 1 & 9 \\ 4 & 1 & 7 \end{pmatrix}$

5. $A = \begin{pmatrix} 0 & -2 & 1 \\ -2 & 2 & 0 \\ 0 & 2 & -1 \end{pmatrix}$

7. $A = \begin{pmatrix} 3 & 2 \\ 1 & 4 \end{pmatrix}$

11. $A = \begin{pmatrix} -4 & 1 & -2 \\ 1 & 3 & -4 \end{pmatrix}, \quad B = \begin{pmatrix} 3 & 0 & 1 \\ 0 & -2 & 3 \end{pmatrix}$

13. $A = \begin{pmatrix} 2 & -1 & 1 \\ 1 & 2 & 0 \end{pmatrix}, \quad B = \begin{pmatrix} 1 & 1 & 2 \\ -1 & 1 & -2 \end{pmatrix}$

15. $AB = \begin{pmatrix} 1 & -4 \\ 7 & 7 \end{pmatrix}, \quad BA = \begin{pmatrix} 0 & -5 \\ 7 & 8 \end{pmatrix}$

17. $AB = \begin{pmatrix} 0 & 1 \\ 0 & 1 \end{pmatrix}, \quad BA = \begin{pmatrix} 0 & 1 \\ 0 & 1 \end{pmatrix}$

19. $AB = \begin{pmatrix} 5 & 3 & -4 \\ -6 & 11 & -1 \end{pmatrix}$

21. $AB = \begin{pmatrix} 0 & 0 & 0 \\ 0 & 0 & 0 \\ 0 & 0 & 0 \end{pmatrix}, \quad BA = \begin{pmatrix} 0 & 0 & 0 \\ 0 & 0 & 0 \\ 1 & 1 & 0 \end{pmatrix}$

SECTION 3

17. 65   19. 6   21. 72   23. 45

25. $\displaystyle\sum_{j=0}^{4}\sum_{i=0}^{4-j}(3i + 2j)$

SECTION 4

1. -2 3. 24

SECTION 5

1. 14   3. 21   5. -21
7. -69 9. 297   11. -22

SECTION 6

1. $(1, -2, -1)$ 3. $(-\frac{73}{19}, \frac{21}{19}, -\frac{43}{19})$ 5. $(2, -1, 3)$
7. $(1, \frac{2}{3}, -\frac{1}{3})$ 9. $(2, -1, \frac{1}{2}, 1)$

SECTION 7

1. rank $= 2$ 3. rank $= 3$ 5. rank $= 3$ 7. rank $= 4$
9. rank $= 3$ 11. rank $= 4$ 13. rank $= 4$ 15. rank $= 4$

SECTION 8

1. $(-1, 1, 0)$ 3. $(2, -4, 7)$
5. $r = 2; r^* = 3$; inconsistent
7. $r = r^* = 3; (4 - 3x_3, 2 - x_3, x_3, 5x_3 - 4)$
9. $(0, 0, 0)$ 11. $(\frac{5}{3}x_4, -x_4, -\frac{2}{3}x_4, x_4)$
13. $(2x_3, x_3, x_3, 1)$; infinitely many solutions   15. $r = 3; r^* = 4$; inconsistent

SECTION 9

1. $(1, -2, 3)$ 3. $(3, \frac{1}{2}, -\frac{1}{3})$ 5. $(4, -2, 0, 1)$ 7. $(-1, -3, -2)$

TABLE 1

NATURAL TRIGONOMETRIC FUNCTIONS

Angle					Angle				
De-gree	Ra-dian	Sine	Co-sine	Tan-gent	De-gree	Ra-dian	Sine	Co-sine	Tan-gent
0°	0.000	0.000	1.000	0.000					
1°	0.017	0.017	1.000	0.017	46°	0.803	0.719	0.695	1.036
2°	0.035	0.035	0.999	0.035	47°	0.820	0.731	0.682	1.072
3°	0.052	0.052	0.999	0.052	48°	0.838	0.743	0.669	1.111
4°	0.070	0.070	0.998	0.070	49°	0.855	0.755	0.656	1.150
5°	0.087	0.087	0.996	0.087	50°	0.873	0.766	0.643	1.192
6°	0.105	0.105	0.995	0.105	51°	0.890	0.777	0.629	1.235
7°	0.122	0.122	0.993	0.123	52°	0.908	0.788	0.616	1.280
8°	0.140	0.139	0.990	0.141	53°	0.925	0.799	0.602	1.327
9°	0.157	0.156	0.988	0.158	54°	0.942	0.809	0.588	1.376
10°	0.175	0.174	0.985	0.176	55°	0.960	0.819	0.574	1.428
11°	0.192	0.191	0.982	0.194	56°	0.977	0.829	0.559	1.483
12°	0.209	0.208	0.978	0.213	57°	0.995	0.839	0.545	1.540
13°	0.227	0.225	0.974	0.231	58°	1.012	0.848	0.530	1.600
14°	0.244	0.242	0.970	0.249	59°	1.030	0.857	0.515	1.664
15°	0.262	0.259	0.966	0.268	60°	1.047	0.866	0.500	1.732
16°	0.279	0.276	0.961	0.287	61°	1.065	0.875	0.485	1.804
17°	0.297	0.292	0.956	0.306	62°	1.082	0.883	0.469	1.881
18°	0.314	0.309	0.951	0.325	63°	1.100	0.891	0.454	1.963
19°	0.332	0.326	0.946	0.344	64°	1.117	0.899	0.438	2.050
20°	0.349	0.342	0.940	0.364	65°	1.134	0.906	0.423	2.145
21°	0.367	0.358	0.934	0.384	66°	1.152	0.914	0.407	2.246
22°	0.384	0.375	0.927	0.404	67°	1.169	0.921	0.391	2.356
23°	0.401	0.391	0.921	0.424	68°	1.187	0.927	0.375	2.475
24°	0.419	0.407	0.914	0.445	69°	1.204	0.934	0.358	2.605
25°	0.436	0.423	0.906	0.466	70°	1.222	0.940	0.342	2.748
26°	0.454	0.438	0.899	0.488	71°	1.239	0.946	0.326	2.904
27°	0.471	0.454	0.891	0.510	72°	1.257	0.951	0.309	3.078
28°	0.489	0.469	0.883	0.532	73°	1.274	0.956	0.292	3.271
29°	0.506	0.485	0.875	0.554	74°	1.292	0.961	0.276	3.487
30°	0.524	0.500	0.866	0.577	75°	1.309	0.966	0.259	3.732
31°	0.541	0.515	0.857	0.601	76°	1.326	0.970	0.242	4.011
32°	0.559	0.530	0.848	0.625	77°	1.344	0.974	0.225	4.332
33°	0.576	0.545	0.839	0.649	78°	1.361	0.978	0.208	4.705
34°	0.593	0.559	0.829	0.675	79°	1.379	0.982	0.191	5.145
35°	0.611	0.574	0.819	0.700	80°	1.396	0.985	0.174	5.671
36°	0.628	0.588	0.809	0.727	81°	1.414	0.988	0.156	6.314
37°	0.646	0.602	0.799	0.754	82°	1.431	0.990	0.139	7.115
38°	0.663	0.616	0.788	0.781	83°	1.449	0.993	0.122	8.144
39°	0.681	0.629	0.777	0.810	84°	1.466	0.995	0.105	9.514
40°	0.698	0.643	0.766	0.839	85°	1.484	0.996	0.087	11.43
41°	0.716	0.656	0.755	0.869	86°	1.501	0.998	0.070	14.30
42°	0.733	0.669	0.743	0.900	87°	1.518	0.999	0.052	19.08
43°	0.750	0.682	0.731	0.933	88°	1.536	0.999	0.035	28.64
44°	0.768	0.695	0.719	0.966	89°	1.553	1.000	0.017	57.29
45°	0.785	0.707	0.707	1.000	90°	1.571	1.000	0.000	

TABLE 2

EXPONENTIAL FUNCTIONS

x	e^x	e^{-x}	x	e^x	e^{-x}
0.00	1.0000	1.0000	2.5	12.182	0.0821
0.05	1.0513	0.9512	2.6	13.464	0.0743
0.10	1.1052	0.9048	2.7	14.880	0.0672
0.15	1.1618	0.8607	2.8	16.445	0.0608
0.20	1.2214	0.8187	2.9	18.174	0.0550
0.25	1.2840	0.7788	3.0	20.086	0.0498
0.30	1.3499	0.7408	3.1	22.198	0.0450
0.35	1.4191	0.7047	3.2	24.533	0.0408
0.40	1.4918	0.6703	3.3	27.113	0.0369
0.45	1.5683	0.6376	3.4	29.964	0.0334
0.50	1.6487	0.6065	3.5	33.115	0.0302
0.55	1.7333	0.5769	3.6	36.598	0.0273
0.60	1.8221	0.5488	3.7	40.447	0.0247
0.65	1.9155	0.5220	3.8	44.701	0.0224
0.70	2.0138	0.4966	3.9	49.402	0.0202
0.75	2.1170	0.4724	4.0	54.598	0.0183
0.80	2.2255	0.4493	4.1	60.340	0.0166
0.85	2.3396	0.4274	4.2	66.686	0.0150
0.90	2.4596	0.4066	4.3	73.700	0.0136
0.95	2.5857	0.3867	4.4	81.451	0.0123
1.0	2.7183	0.3679	4.5	90.017	0.0111
1.1	3.0042	0.3329	4.6	99.484	0.0101
1.2	3.3201	0.3012	4.7	109.95	0.0091
1.3	3.6693	0.2725	4.8	121.51	0.0082
1.4	4.0552	0.2466	4.9	134.29	0.0074
1.5	4.4817	0.2231	5	148.41	0.0067
1.6	4.9530	0.2019	6	403.43	0.0025
1.7	5.4739	0.1827	7	1096.6	0.0009
1.8	6.0496	0.1653	8	2981.0	0.0003
1.9	6.6859	0.1496	9	8103.1	0.0001
2.0	7.3891	0.1353	10	22026	0.00005
2.1	8.1662	0.1225			
2.2	9.0250	0.1108			
2.3	9.9742	0.1003			
2.4	11.023	0.0907			

TABLE 3

NATURAL LOGARITHMS OF NUMBERS

n	$\log_e n$	n	$\log_e n$	n	$\log_e n$
0.0	*	4.5	1.5041	9.0	2.1972
0.1	7.6974	4.6	1.5261	9.1	2.2083
0.2	8.3906	4.7	1.5476	9.2	2.2192
0.3	8.7960	4.8	1.5686	9.3	2.2300
0.4	9.0837	4.9	1.5892	9.4	2.2407
0.5	9.3069	5.0	1.6094	9.5	2.2513
0.6	9.4892	5.1	1.6292	9.6	2.2618
0.7	9.6433	5.2	1.6487	9.7	2.2721
0.8	9.7769	5.3	1.6677	9.8	2.2824
0.9	9.8946	5.4	1.6864	9.9	2.2925
1.0	0.0000	5.5	1.7047	10	2.3026
1.1	0.0953	5.6	1.7228	11	2.3979
1.2	0.1823	5.7	1.7405	12	2.4849
1.3	0.2624	5.8	1.7579	13	2.5649
1.4	0.3365	5.9	1.7750	14	2.6391
1.5	0.4055	6.0	1.7918	15	2.7081
1.6	0.4700	6.1	1.8083	16	2.7726
1.7	0.5306	6.2	1.8245	17	2.8332
1.8	0.5878	6.3	1.8405	18	2.8904
1.9	0.6419	6.4	1.8563	19	2.9444
2.0	0.6931	6.5	1.8718	20	2.9957
2.1	0.7419	6.6	1.8871	25	3.2189
2.2	0.7885	6.7	1.9021	30	3.4012
2.3	0.8329	6.8	1.9169	35	3.5553
2.4	0.8755	6.9	1.9315	40	3.6889
2.5	0.9163	7.0	1.9459	45	3.8067
2.6	0.9555	7.1	1.9601	50	3.9120
2.7	0.9933	7.2	1.9741	55	4.0073
2.8	1.0296	7.3	1.9879	60	4.0943
2.9	1.0647	7.4	2.0015	65	4.1744
3.0	1.0986	7.5	2.0149	70	4.2485
3.1	1.1314	7.6	2.0281	75	4.3175
3.2	1.1632	7.7	2.0412	80	4.3820
3.3	1.1939	7.8	2.0541	85	4.4427
3.4	1.2238	7.9	2.0669	90	4.4998
3.5	1.2528	8.0	2.0794	95	4.5539
3.6	1.2809	8.1	2.0919	100	4.6052
3.7	1.3083	8.2	2.1041		
3.8	1.3350	8.3	2.1163		
3.9	1.3610	8.4	2.1282		
4.0	1.3863	8.5	2.1401		
4.1	1.4110	8.6	2.1518		
4.2	1.4351	8.7	2.1633		
4.3	1.4586	8.8	2.1748		
4.4	1.4816	8.9	2.1861		

Index

Index